PROSE *and* CRITICISM

PROSE
and
CRITICISM

John Hamilton McCallum
EDITOR

HARCOURT, BRACE & WORLD, INC.
New York   Chicago   Atlanta   Dallas   Burlingame

ABOUT THE EDITOR: John Hamilton McCallum, Editor of College and School English Programs, is a former Director and officer of Harcourt, Brace & World, Inc.

CONTENTS

FICTION: The Novel

NONFICTION

Part TWO:

CRITICAL COMMENT

CORRELATED CONTENTS

Those selections in *Part Two: Critical Comment* that deal with particular selections in *Part One* are listed below.

Part ONE

FICTION   NONFICTION

FICTION: The Novel

NONFICTION

INTRODUCTION

THE CRITERIA that determined the choice of selections in Part One of this volume were, simply, quality and completeness; that is, works of unquestioned literary stature—unabridged and, to the full extent the particular uses of this volume will allow, unadulterated and unbowdlerized. One might also add un-candy-coated. All of which is based on a few strong beliefs. First, the study of literature is a supreme intellectual discipline, the value of which increases in geometrical progression with the increase in the quality of the matter studied. Second, no one has the right to tamper with a work of literature, or with any work of art. Reject it if you will—but only after you have evaluated it whole. Third, the history of culture leads directly to the conclusion that quality counts, that a work of literature is both more pleasurable and more meaningful than a piece of hackwork. In many of our English classes we have at times—through indulgence—rejected this contention, and our students have suffered for it. Fourth, as the production of a work of literature is an act of creation, so too is the genuine study of a work of literature an act of creation, though of a different order. But such creation requires participation in depth. Accordingly, the student who reads this volume is given the opportunity to participate: The usual "helps" have been almost entirely eliminated. If a word—including proper names—in any of these selections is unknown to him, he is expected to look it up in one of the standard college dictionaries; words not in one of those volumes are footnoted—with occasional exceptions, e.g., when the word comes clear if carefully examined in the context, or when knowledge of the meaning of a word is not essential for a fair understanding of the passage: when the clutter of a footnote isn't worth the candle. In like manner, phrases (including foreign phrases) and passages not likely to be understood after proper study are explained; but the number of such explanations is few.

Because there are limits to the size of any volume; because, given the aims of this volume, representation in depth is better than representation in breadth; and because, most frequently, the study of poetry and drama better follows the study of fiction and the essay, the contents of Part One —indeed, of the whole volume—is restricted to works of prose. The desire for representation in depth led also to the selection of matter exclusively from the nineteenth and twentieth centuries; and the desire to present literature in so far as possible in its pure state led to the exclusion of all works in translation: a translation, no matter how excellent, is not the language of the original.

Other than its implicit argument that literature counts, Part One presents neither theme nor thesis. The individual selection is all. Accordingly, the ordering of selections is largely arbitrary. The sequence of sections—short stories, novel, nonfiction—might as usefully be reversed; and within sections, no attempt is made to teach "influences" or the history and development of the nineteenth- and twentieth-century short story and essay (though the raw materials for such analyses are of course there if one wants to dig them out). The stories are simply arranged chronologically by author's birth, while the essays tend to cluster about a few common subjects and forms, with the clusters tending to range from the less to the more complex. Teachers and students are free to pick and choose among the selections at will.

In his essay "The Archetypes of Literature," Northrop Frye, Principal of Victoria College in the University of Toronto, writes:

> Art, like nature, is the subject of a systematic study, and has to be distinguished from the study itself, which is criticism. It is therefore impossible to "learn literature": one learns about it in a certain way, but what one learns, transitively, is the criticism of literature. Similarly, the difficulty often felt in "teaching literature" arises from the fact that it cannot be done: the criticism of literature is all that can be directly taught.

Whether or not one wholly agrees with Professor Frye's statement, one is perhaps ready to agree that a work such as the present volume, devoted to the study of literature, ought to present critics as well as creators. For if the student is to give a work of literature more than a desultory reading, he must know something of the principles of literature—one might almost say the science of literature (". . . there is surely no reason," Professor Frye continues, "why criticism, as a systematic and organized study, should not be, at least partly, a science"); and if he is to study science, he had better do it in the laboratory, which is what, in effect, this volume becomes.

Part Two of *Prose and Criticism* contains a widely representative body of critical writing—about literature in general and in particular, about criticism itself, about the writer as artist and as man, about language, about literature as idea and literature as history. The body of material is of considerable intrinsic interest; but in the context of this volume, correlated, that is, with Part One, it provides the student with techniques and insights that will enable him to begin to understand what the study of literature, what literature itself, is all about.

Although writing about literature is here set off from literature itself, it does not follow that the matter in Part Two is without literary merit. "If" (to quote Professor Frye once again) criticism "is to be related to the sciences, it does not follow that it must be deprived of the graces of culture." The majority of the selections in Part Two are blessed with such graces, are in themselves literature. For obvious reasons, however, while the criterion of quality holds for Part Two as for Part One, the criterion of completeness does not. Here it was important to cover as much ground as possible, and excerpting accordingly proved a necessity.

"Un-candy-coated" was a term employed early in this Introduction. It would be false to contend that students are likely to find this volume easier to use than many more conventional anthologies. The reader of this book will have to work for what he gets out of it. But if the statements all of us make about the values of literature have any validity whatsoever, the rewards of that work will be commensurate.

J. H. M.

A NOTE ON SOME CONVENTIONS ADOPTED FOR THIS VOLUME

Ellipses. In Part One of this anthology, we have, as stated, aimed to reproduce the texts of the various selections whole and unchanged. There were, however, two or three occasions when it seemed wiser to let Mrs. Grundy in than to have her howl without. Each such decision (i.e., deletion) was most reluctantly made, but we believe each will be condoned by anyone who cares to check the originals. In addition, there were two or three instances where matter pertinent in the specific context in which the selection first appeared was not pertinent in the present context—indeed, was actually disruptive; in such instances we have felt justified in making a deletion (e.g., the De Voto selection, which stood originally as an introduction to a collection of Mark Twain's writings). Finally, there are, as noted above, cuts throughout Part Two, where, given the nature of that material and the reason for its inclusion in this volume, no attempt was made—could be made—to hold to the criterion of completeness. Accordingly, as there are, of course, occasional deletions made by the original authors themselves (see especially the William James selection), we have distinguished between authors' and editor's deletions by using the simple, conventional ellipsis (. . .) for the former and a bracketed ellipsis [. . .] for the latter.

Footnotes. In similar manner, footnotes supplied by the present editor are marked [1], [2], [3], etc., while those carried over from the original texts are marked *, †, ‡, etc. Occasionally (e.g., Holmes) a selection may have three types of footnotes, the author's, the original editor's, and the present editor's; in this event, the original editor's notes in each instance carry the editor's name.

Part
ONE

FICTION
NONFICTION

Fiction

THE SHORT STORY

Nathaniel Hawthorne

THE PROPHETIC PICTURES

"**B**UT this painter!" cried Walter Ludlow, with animation. "He not only excels in his peculiar art, but possesses vast acquirements in all other learning and science. He talks Hebrew with Doctor Mather, and gives lectures in anatomy to Doctor Boylston.[1] In a word, he will meet the best instructed man among us on his own ground. Moreover, he is a polished gentleman—a citizen of the world—yes, a true cosmopolite; for he will speak like a native of each clime and country on the globe, except our own forests, whither he is now going. Nor is this all what I most admire in him."

"Indeed!" said Elinor, who had listened with a woman's interest to the description of such a man. "Yet this is admirable enough."

"Surely it is," replied her lover, "but far less so than his natural gift of adapting himself to every variety of character, insomuch that all men—and all women too, Elinor—shall find a mirror of themselves in this wonderful painter. But the greatest wonder is yet to be told."

"Nay, if he have more wonderful attributes than these," said Elinor,

---

1. **Doctor Mather:** Cotton Mather (1663–1728), the learned scholar and divine of Boston; **Doctor Boylston:** Zabdiel Boylston (1679–1766), a famous physician of Boston.

3

laughing, "Boston is a perilous abode for the poor gentleman. Are you telling me of a painter, or a wizard?"

"In truth," answered he, "that question might be asked much more seriously than you suppose. They say that he paints not merely a man's features, but his mind and heart. He catches the secret sentiments and passions, and throws them upon the canvas, like sunshine—or perhaps, in the portraits of dark-souled men, like a gleam of infernal fire. It is an awful gift," added Walter, lowering his voice from its tone of enthusiasm. "I shall be almost afraid to sit to him."

"Walter, are you in earnest?" exclaimed Elinor.

"For heaven's sake, dearest Elinor, do not let him paint the look which you now wear," said her lover, smiling though rather perplexed. "There; it is passing away now, but when you spoke, you seemed frightened to death, and very sad besides. What were you thinking of?"

"Nothing, nothing," answered Elinor hastily. "You paint my face with your own fantasies. Well, come for me tomorrow, and we will visit this wonderful artist."

But when the young man had departed, it cannot be denied that a remarkable expression was again visible on the fair and youthful face of his mistress. It was a sad and anxious look, little in accordance with what should have been the feelings of a maiden on the eve of wedlock. Yet Walter Ludlow was the chosen of her heart.

"A look!" said Elinor to herself. "No wonder that it startled him, if it expressed what I sometimes feel. I know, by my own experience, how frightful a look may be. But it was all fancy. I thought nothing of it at the time—I have seen nothing of it since—I did but dream of it."

And she busied herself about the embroidery of a ruff, in which she meant that her portrait should be taken.

The painter of whom they had been speaking was not one of those native artists who, at a later period than this, borrowed their colors from the Indians, and manufactured their pencils of the furs of wild beasts. Perhaps, if he could have revoked his life and prearranged his destiny, he might have chosen to belong to that school without a master, in the hope of being at least original, since there were no works of art to imitate, nor rules to follow. But he had been born and educated in Europe. People said that he had studied the grandeur or beauty of conception, and every touch of the master hand, in all the most famous pictures, in cabinets and galleries, and on the walls of churches till there was nothing more for his powerful mind to learn. Art could add nothing to its lessons, but Nature might. He had therefore visited a world whither none of his professional brethren had preceded him, to feast his eyes on visible images that were noble and picturesque, yet had never been transferred to canvas. America was too poor to afford other temptations to an artist of eminence, though many of the colonial gentry, on the painter's arrival, had expressed a wish to transmit their lineaments to posterity, by means of his skill. Whenever such proposals were made, he fixed his piercing eyes on the applicant, and seemed to look him through and through. If he beheld only a sleek and comfortable visage, though there were a gold-laced coat to adorn the picture, and golden guineas to pay for it, he civilly rejected the task and the reward. But if the face were the index of anything uncommon, in thought, sentiment, or experience; or if he met a beggar in the street, with a white beard and a furrowed brow; or if sometimes a child happened to look up and smile; he would exhaust all the art on them that he denied to wealth.

Pictorial skill being so rare in the colonies, the painter became an object of general curiosity. If few or none could appreciate the technical merit of his productions, yet there were points in regard to which the opinion of the crowd was as valuable as the refined judgment of the amateur. He watched the effect that each picture produced on such untutored beholders, and derived profit from their remarks, while they would as soon have thought of instructing Nature herself, as him who seemed to rival her. Their admiration, it must be owned, was tinctured with the prejudices of the age and country. Some deemed it an offense against the Mosaic law, and even a presumptuous mockery of the Creator, to bring into existence such lively images of his creatures. Others, frightened at the art which could raise phantoms at will, and keep the form of the dead among the living, were inclined to consider the painter as a magician, or perhaps the famous Black Man,[2] of old witch times, plotting mischief in a new guise. These foolish fancies were more than half believed among the mob. Even in superior circles his character was invested with a vague awe, partly rising like smoke wreaths from the popular superstitions, but chiefly caused by the varied knowledge and talents which he made subservient to his profession.

Being on the eve of marriage, Walter Ludlow and Elinor were eager to obtain their portraits, as the first of what, they doubtless hoped, would be a long series of family pictures. The day after the conversation above recorded, they visited the painter's rooms. A servant ushered them into an apartment, where, though the artist himself was not visible, there were personages whom they could hardly forbear greeting with reverence. They knew, indeed, that the whole assembly were but pictures, yet felt it impossible to separate the idea of life and intellect from such striking counterfeits. Several of the portraits were known to them, either as distinguished characters of the day or their private acquaintances. There was

2. **Black Man:** Satan.

Governor Burnet,[3] looking as if he had just received an undutiful communication from the House of Representatives, and were inditing a most sharp response. Mr. Cooke [4] hung beside the ruler whom he opposed, sturdy, and somewhat puritanical, as befitted a popular leader. The ancient lady of Sir William Phipps [5] eyed them from the wall, in ruff and farthingale, an imperious old dame, not unsuspected of witchcraft. John Winslow,[6] then a very young man, wore the expression of warlike enterprise which long afterwards made him a distinguished general. Their personal friends were recognized at a glance. In most of the pictures, the whole mind and character were brought out on the countenance, and concentrated into a single look; so that, to speak paradoxically, the originals hardly resembled themselves so strikingly as the portraits did.

Among these modern worthies there were two old bearded saints, who had almost vanished into the darkening canvas. There was also a pale but unfaded Madonna, who had perhaps been worshiped in Rome, and now regarded the lovers with such a mild and holy look that they longed to worship too.

"How singular a thought," observed Walter Ludlow, "that this beautiful face has been beautiful for above two hundred years! Oh, if all beauty would endure so well! Do you not envy her, Elinor?"

"If earth were heaven, I might," she replied. "But where all things fade, how miserable to be the one that could not fade!"

"The dark old St. Peter has a fierce and ugly scowl, saint though he be," continued Walter. "He troubles me. But the Virgin looks kindly at us."

"Yes; but very sorrowfully, methinks," said Elinor.

The easel stood beneath these three old pictures, sustaining one that had been recently commenced. After a little inspection they began to recognize the features of their own minister, the Reverend Dr. Colman,[7] growing into shape and life, as it were, out of a cloud.

"Kind old man!" exclaimed Elinor. "He gazes at me as if he were about to utter a word of paternal advice."

"And at me," said Walter, "as if he were about to shake his head and rebuke me for some suspected iniquity. But so does the original. I shall never feel quite comfortable under his eye till we stand before him to be married."

---

3. **Governor Burnet:** William Burnet (1688–1729), a colonial governor of New York and New Jersey, and later of Massachusetts.
4. **Mr. Cooke:** Elisha Cooke (1638–1737), colonial physician and statesman.
5. **lady . . . Phipps:** Mary Spencer Hull Phips, wife of Sir William Phips, the first royal governor of Massachusetts.
6. **John Winslow:** (1703–1774), a distinguished colonial soldier.
7. **the Reverend Dr. Colman:** Benjamin Colman (1673–1747), the pastor of the Brattle Street Church in Boston.

They now heard a footstep on the floor, and, turning, beheld the painter, who had been some moments in the room, and had listened to a few of their remarks. He was a middle-aged man, with a countenance well worthy of his own pencil. Indeed, by the picturesque though careless arrangement of his rich dress, and, perhaps, because his soul dwelt always among painted shapes, he looked somewhat like a portrait himself. His visitors were sensible of a kindred between the artist and his work, and felt as if one of the pictures had stepped from the canvas to salute them.

Walter Ludlow, who was slightly known to the painter, explained the object of their visit. While he spoke, a sunbeam was falling athwart his figure and Elinor's, with so happy an effect that they also seemed living pictures of youth and beauty, gladdened by bright fortune. The artist was evidently struck.

"My easel is occupied for several ensuing days, and my stay in Boston must be brief," said he thoughtfully; then, after an observant glance, he added: "but your wishes shall be gratified, though I disappoint the Chief Justice and Madame Oliver.[8] I must not lose this opportunity for the sake of painting a few ells of broadcloth and brocade."

The painter expressed a desire to introduce both their portraits into one picture, and represent them engaged in some appropriate action. This plan would have delighted the lovers, but was necessarily rejected, because so large a space of canvas would have been unfit for the room which it was intended to decorate. Two half-length portraits were therefore fixed upon. After they had taken leave, Walter Ludlow asked Elinor, with a smile, whether she knew what an influence over their fates the painter was about to acquire.

"The old women of Boston affirm," continued he, "that after he has once got possession of a person's face and figure, he may paint him in any act or situation whatever—and the picture will be prophetic. Do you believe it?"

"Not quite," said Elinor, smiling. "Yet if he has such magic, there is something so gentle in his manner that I am sure he will use it well."

It was the painter's choice to proceed with both portraits at the same time, assigning as a reason, in the mystical language which he sometimes used, that the faces threw light upon each other. Accordingly, he gave now a touch to Walter, and now to Elinor, and the features of one and the other began to start forth so vividly that it appeared as if his triumphant art would actually disengage them from the canvas. Amid the rich light and deep shade, they beheld their phantom selves. But, though the likeness

---

8. **Chief . . . Oliver:** Peter Oliver (1713–1791), who became chief justice of Massachusetts in 1771, and his wife, Mary Clarke Oliver, who was a member of a prominent New England family.

promised to be perfect, they were not quite satisfied with the expression; it seemed more vague than in most of the painter's works. He, however, was satisfied with the prospect of success, and being much interested in the lovers, employed his leisure moments unknown to them, in making a crayon sketch of their two figures. During their sittings, he engaged them in conversation, and kindled up their faces with characteristic traits, which, though continually varying, it was his purpose to combine and fix. At length he announced that at their next visit both the portraits would be ready for delivery.

"If my pencil will but be true to my conception, in the few last touches which I meditate," observed he, "these two pictures will be my very best performances. Seldom, indeed, has an artist such subjects."

While speaking, he still bent his penetrative eye upon them, nor withdrew it till they had reached the bottom of the stairs.

Nothing in the whole circle of human vanities takes stronger hold of the imagination than this affair of having a portrait painted. Yet why should it be so? The looking glass, the polished globes of the andirons, the mirror-like water, and all other reflecting surfaces continually present us with portraits, or rather ghosts, of ourselves, which we glance at and straightway forget them. But we forget them only because they vanish. It is the idea of duration—of earthly immortality—that gives such a mysterious interest to our own portraits. Walter and Elinor were not insensible to this feeling, and hastened to the painter's room, punctually at the appointed hour, to meet those pictured shapes which were to be their representatives with posterity. The sunshine flashed after them into the apartment, but left it somewhat gloomy as they closed the door.

Their eyes were immediately attracted to their portraits, which rested against the farthest wall of the room. At the first glance, through the dim light and the distance, seeing themselves in precisely their natural attitudes, and with all the air that they recognized so well, they uttered a simultaneous exclamation of delight.

"There we stand," cried Walter, enthusiastically, "fixed in sunshine forever! No dark passions can gather on our faces!"

"No," said Elinor more calmly; "no dreary change can sadden us."

This was said while they were approaching, and had yet gained only an imperfect view of the pictures. The painter, after saluting them, busied himself at a table in completing a crayon sketch, leaving his visitors to form their own judgment as to his perfected labors. At intervals he sent a glance from beneath his deep eyebrows, watching their countenances in profile, with his pencil suspended over the sketch. They had now stood some moments, each in front of the other's picture, contemplating it with entranced attention, but without uttering a word. At length Walter stepped forward—then back—viewing Elinor's portrait in various lights, and finally spoke.

"Is there not a change?" said he in a doubtful and meditative tone. "Yes; the perception of it grows more vivid the longer I look. It is certainly the same picture that I saw yesterday; the dress—the features—all are the same, and yet something is altered."

"Is then the picture less like than it was yesterday?" inquired the painter, now drawing near with irrepressible interest.

"The features are perfect Elinor," answered Walter; "and at the first glance the expression seemed also hers. But I could fancy that the portrait has changed countenance while I have been looking at it. The eyes are fixed on mine with a strangely sad and anxious expression. Nay, it is grief and terror! Is this like Elinor?"

"Compare the living face with the pictured one," said the painter.

Walter glanced sidelong at his mistress and started. Motionless and absorbed—fascinated, as it were—in contemplation of Walter's portrait, Elinor's face had assumed precisely the expression of which he had just been complaining. Had she practiced for whole hours before a mirror, she could not have caught the look so successfully. Had the picture itself been a mirror, it could not have thrown back her present aspect with stronger and more melancholy truth. She appeared quite unconscious of the dialogue between the artist and her lover.

"Elinor," exclaimed Walter, in amazement, "what change has come over you?"

She did not hear him, nor desist from her fixed gaze, till he seized her hand, and thus attracted her notice; then, with a sudden tremor, she looked from the picture to the face of the original.

"Do you see no change in your portrait?" asked she.

"In mine? None!" replied Walter, examining it. "But let me see! Yes; there is a slight change—an improvement, I think, in the picture, though none in the likeness. It has a livelier expression than yesterday, as if some bright thought were flashing from the eyes, and about to be uttered from the lips. Now that I have caught the look, it becomes very decided."

While he was intent on these observations Elinor turned to the painter. She regarded him with grief and awe, and felt that he repaid her with sympathy and commiseration, though wherefore she could but vaguely guess.

"That look!" whispered she, and shuddered. "How came it there?"

"Madam," said the painter sadly, taking her hand and leading her apart, "in both these pictures I have painted what I saw. The artist—the true artist—must look beneath the exterior. It is his gift—his proudest, but often a melancholy one—to see the inmost soul, and, by a power indefinable even to himself, to make it glow or darken upon the canvas, in glances that express the thought and sentiment of years. Would that I might convince myself of error in the present instance!"

They had now approached the table, on which were heads in chalk, hands almost as expressive as ordinary faces, ivied church towers, thatched cottages, old thunder-stricken trees, oriental and antique costume, and all such picturesque vagaries of an artist's idle moments. Turning them over with seeming carelessness, a crayon sketch of two figures was disclosed.

"If I have failed," continued he—"if your heart does not see itself reflected in your own portrait—if you have no secret cause to trust my delineation of the other—it is not yet too late to alter them. I might change the action of these figures too. But would it influence the event?"

He directed her notice to the sketch. A thrill ran through Elinor's frame; a shriek was upon her lips; but she stifled it with the self-command that becomes habitual to all who hide thoughts of fear and anguish within their bosoms. Turning from the table, she perceived that Walter had advanced near enough to have seen the sketch, though she could not determine whether it had caught his eye.

"We will not have the pictures altered," said she hastily. "If mine is sad, I shall but look the gayer for the contrast."

"Be it so," answered the painter, bowing. "May your griefs be such fanciful ones that only your picture may mourn for them! For your joys—may they be true and deep, and paint themselves upon this lovely face, till it quite belie my art!"

After the marriage of Walter and Elinor, the pictures formed the two most splendid ornaments of their abode. They hung side by side, separated by a narrow panel, appearing to eye each other constantly, yet always returning the gaze of the spectator. Traveled gentlemen who professed a knowledge of such subjects reckoned these among the most admirable specimens of modern portraiture; while common observers compared them with the originals, feature by feature, and were rapturous in praise of the likeness. But it was on a third class—neither traveled connoisseurs nor common observers, but people of natural sensibility—that the pictures wrought their strongest effect. Such persons might gaze carelessly at first, but, becoming interested, would return day after day and study these painted faces like the pages of a mystic volume. Walter Ludlow's portrait attracted their earliest notice. In the absence of himself and his bride, they sometimes disputed as to the expression which the painter had intended to throw upon the features; all agreeing that there was a look of earnest import, though no two explained it alike. There was less diversity of opinion in regard to Elinor's picture. They differed, indeed, in their

attempts to estimate the nature and depth of the gloom that dwelt upon
her face, but agreed that it was gloom, and alien from the natural temperament of their youthful friend. A certain fanciful person announced, as
the result of much scrutiny, that both these pictures were parts of one
design, and that the melancholy strength of feeling in Elinor's countenance
bore reference to the more vivid emotion, or, as he termed it, the wild
passion, in that of Walter. Though unskilled in the art, he even began a
sketch, in which the action of the two figures was to correspond with
their mutual expression.

It was whispered among friends, that, day by day, Elinor's face was assuming a deeper shade of pensiveness, which threatened soon to render her
too true a counterpart of her melancholy picture. Walter, on the other
hand, instead of acquiring the vivid look which the painter had given him
on the canvas, became reserved and downcast, with no outward flashes of
emotion, however it might be smoldering within. In course of time Elinor
hung a gorgeous curtain of purple silk, wrought with flowers, and fringed
with heavy golden tassels, before the pictures, under pretense that the
dust would tarnish their hues, or the light dim them. It was enough. Her
visitors felt that the massive folds of the silk must never be withdrawn, nor
the portraits mentioned in her presence.

Time wore on; and the painter came again. He had been far enough to
the north to see the silver cascade of the Crystal Hills, and to look over
the vast round of cloud and forest from the summit of New England's
loftiest mountain. But he did not profane that scene by the mockery of his
art. He had also lain in a canoe on the bosom of Lake George, making his
soul the mirror of its loveliness and grandeur, till not a picture in the
Vatican was more vivid than his recollection. He had gone with the Indian hunters to Niagara, and there again had flung his hopeless pencil
down the precipice, feeling that he could as soon paint the roar as aught
else that goes to make up the wondrous cataract. In truth, it was seldom
his impulse to copy natural scenery, except as a framework for the delin-
eations of the human form and face, instinct with thought, passion, or suffering. With store of such, his adventurous ramble had enriched him: the
stern dignity of Indian chiefs; the dusky loveliness of Indian girls; the domestic life of wigwams; the stealthy march; the battle beneath gloomy
pine-trees; the frontier fortress with its garrison; the anomaly of the old
French partisan, bred in courts, but grown gray in shaggy deserts; such
were the scenes and portraits that he had sketched. The glow of perilous
moments; flashes of wild feeling; struggles of fierce power—love, hate,
grief, frenzy—in a word, all the worn-out heart of the old earth, had been
revealed to him under a new form. His portfolio was filled with graphic

illustrations of the volume of his memory, which genius would transmute
into its own substance, and imbue with immortality. He felt that the deep
wisdom in his art, which he had sought so far, was found.

But, amid stern or lovely nature, in the perils of the forest, or its overwhelming peacefulness, still there had been two phantoms, the companions
of his way. Like all other men around whom an engrossing purpose
wreathes itself, he was insulated from the mass of human kind. He had no
aim—no pleasure—no sympathies—but what were ultimately connected
with his art. Though gentle in manner, and upright in intent and action,
he did not possess kindly feelings; his heart was cold; no living creature
could be brought near enough to keep him warm. For these two beings,
however, he had felt, in its greatest intensity, the sort of interest which always allied him to the subjects of his pencil. He had pried into their souls
with his keenest insight, and pictured the result upon their features with
his utmost skill, so as barely to fall short of that standard which no genius
ever reached, his own severe conception. He had caught from the duski-
ness of the future—at least, so he fancied—a fearful secret; and had ob-
scurely revealed it on the portraits. So much of himself—of his imagination and all other powers—had been lavished on the study of Walter and
Elinor that he almost regarded them as creations of his own, like the thousands with which he had peopled the realms of Picture. Therefore did
they flit through the twilight of the woods, hover on the mist of water-
falls, look forth from the mirror of the lake, nor melt away in the noon-
tide sun. They haunted his pictorial fancy, not as mockeries of life, nor
pale goblins of the dead, but in the guise of portraits, each with the unalterable expression which his magic had evoked from the caverns of the
soul. He could not recross the Atlantic till he had again beheld the originals of those airy pictures.

"Oh, glorious Art!" thus mused the enthusiastic painter, as he trod the
street. "Thou art the image of the Creator's own. The innumerable forms
that wander in nothingness start into being at thy beck. The dead live
again. Thou recallest them to their old scenes, and givest their gray shadows the luster of a better life, at once earthly and immortal. Thou snatchest back the fleeting moments of History. With thee there is no Past; for,
at thy touch, all that is great becomes forever present; and illustrious men
live through long ages, in the visible performance of the very deeds which
made them what they are. Oh, potent Art! as thou bringest the faintly revealed Past to stand in that narrow strip of sunlight which we call Now,
canst thou summon the shrouded Future to meet her there? Have I not
achieved it? Am I not thy Prophet?"

Thus, with a proud yet melancholy fervor, did he almost cry aloud as
he passed through the toilsome street, among people that knew not of his

reveries, nor could understand nor care for them. It is not good for man to cherish a solitary ambition. Unless there be those around him by whose example he may regulate himself, his thoughts, desires, and hopes will become extravagant, and he the semblance, perhaps the reality, of a madman. Reading other bosoms with an acuteness almost preternatural, the painter failed to see the disorder of his own.

"And this should be the house," said he, looking up and down the front before he knocked. "Heaven help my brains! That picture! Methinks it will never vanish. Whether I look at the windows or the door, there it is framed within them, painted strongly, and glowing in the richest tints—the faces of the portraits—the figures and action of the sketch!"

He knocked.

"The portraits! Are they within?" inquired he of the domestic; then recollecting himself—"Your master and mistress? Are they at home?"

"They are, sir," said the servant, adding, as he noticed that picturesque aspect of which the painter could never divest himself—"and the portraits too!"

The guest was admitted into a parlor, communicating by a central door with an interior room of the same size. As the first apartment was empty he passed to the entrance of the second, within which his eyes were greeted by those living personages, as well as their pictured representatives, who had long been the objects of so singular an interest. He involuntarily paused on the threshold.

They had not perceived his approach. Walter and Elinor were standing before the portraits, whence the former had just flung back the rich and voluminous folds of the silken curtain, holding its golden tassel with one hand, while the other grasped that of his bride. The pictures, concealed for months, gleamed forth again in undiminished splendor, appearing to throw a somber light across the room, rather than to be disclosed by a borrowed radiance. That of Elinor had been almost prophetic. A pensiveness, and next a gentle sorrow, had successively dwelt upon her countenance, deepening with the lapse of time into a quiet anguish. A mixture of affright would now have made it the very expression of the portrait. Walter's face was moody and dull, or animated only by fitful flashes which left a heavier darkness for their momentary illumination. He looked from Elinor to her portrait and thence to his own, in the contemplation of which he finally stood absorbed.

The painter seemed to hear the step of Destiny approaching behind him on its progress towards its victims. A strange thought darted into his mind. Was not his own the form in which that Destiny had embodied itself, and he a chief agent of the coming evil which he had foreshadowed?

Still Walter remained silent before the picture, communing with it as with his own heart, and abandoning himself to the spell of evil influence that the painter had cast upon the features. Gradually his eyes kindled, while as Elinor watched the increasing wildness of his face her own assumed a look of terror; and when, at last, he turned upon her, the resemblance of both to their portraits was complete.

"Our fate is upon us!" howled Walter. "Die!"

Drawing a knife, he sustained her as she was sinking to the ground, and aimed it at her bosom. In the action and in the look and attitude of each, the painter beheld the figures of his sketch. The picture, with all its tremendous coloring, was finished.

"Hold, madman!" cried he, sternly.

He had advanced from the door, and interposed himself between the wretched beings with the same sense of power to regulate their destiny as to alter a scene upon the canvas. He stood like a magician controlling the phantoms which he had evoked.

"What!" muttered Walter Ludlow, as he relapsed from fierce excitement into sudden gloom. "Does fate impede its own decree?"

"Wretched lady!" said the painter. "Did I not warn you?"

"You did," replied Elinor, calmly, as her terror gave place to the quiet grief which it had disturbed. "But—I loved him!"

Is there not a deep moral in the tale? Could the result of one or of all our deeds be shadowed forth and set before us—some would call it Fate and hurry onward, others be swept along by their passionate desires, and none be turned aside by the PROPHETIC PICTURES.

Herman Melville

THE FIDDLER

So MY POEM is damned, and immortal fame is not for me! I am nobody forever and ever. Intolerable fate!

Snatching my hat, I dashed down the criticism, and rushed out into Broadway, where enthusiastic throngs were crowding to a circus in a side-street near by, very recently started, and famous for a capital clown.

Presently my old friend Standard rather boisterously accosted me.

"Well met, Helmstone, my boy! Ah! what's the matter? Haven't been committing murder? Ain't flying justice? You look wild!"

"You have seen it, then?" said I, of course referring to the criticism.

"Oh yes; I was there at the morning performance. Great clown, I assure you. But here comes Hautboy. Hautboy—Helmstone."

Without having time or inclination to resent so mortifying a mistake, I was instantly soothed as I gazed on the face of the new acquaintance so unceremoniously introduced. His person was short and full, with a juvenile, animated cast to it. His complexion rurally ruddy; his eye sincere, cheery, and gray. His hair alone betrayed that he was not an overgrown boy. From his hair I set him down as forty or more.

"Come, Standard," he gleefully cried to my friend, "are you not going to the circus? The clown is inimitable, they say. Come; Mr. Helmstone, too—come both; and circus over, we'll take a nice stew and punch at Taylor's."

The sterling content, good humor, and extraordinary ruddy, sincere expression of this most singular new acquaintance acted upon me like magic. It seemed mere loyalty to human nature to accept an invitation from so unmistakably kind and honest a heart.

During the circus performance I kept my eye more on Hautboy than on the celebrated clown. Hautboy was the sight for me. Such genuine enjoyment as his struck me to the soul with a sense of the reality of the thing called happiness. The jokes of the clown he seemed to roll under his tongue as ripe magnum-bonums.[1] Now the foot, now the hand, was employed to attest his grateful applause. At any hit more than ordinary, he turned upon Standard and me to see if his rare pleasure was shared. In a man of forty I saw a boy of twelve; and this too without the slightest abatement of my respect. Because all was so honest and natural, every expression and attitude so graceful with genuine good-nature, that the marvelous juvenility of Hautboy assumed a sort of divine and immortal air, like that of some forever youthful god of Greece.

But much as I gazed upon Hautboy, and much as I admired his air, yet that desperate mood in which I had first rushed from the house had not so entirely departed as not to molest me with momentary returns. But from these relapses I would rouse myself, and swiftly glance round the broad amphitheater of eagerly interested and all-applauding human faces. Hark! claps, thumps, deafening huzzas; the vast assembly seemed frantic with acclamation; and what, mused I, has caused all this? Why, the clown only comically grinned with one of his extra grins.

Then I repeated in my mind that sublime passage in my poem, in which

1. **magnum-bonums:** a large and excellent variety of things.

Cleothemes the Argive vindicates the justice of the war. Aye, aye, thought I to myself, did I now leap into the ring there, and repeat that identical passage, nay, enact the whole tragic poem before them, would they applaud the poet as they applaud the clown? No! They would hoot me, and call me doting or mad. Then what does this prove? Your infatuation or their insensibility? Perhaps both; but indubitably the first. But why wail? Do you seek admiration from the admirers of a buffoon? Call to mind the saying of the Athenian, who, when the people vociferously applauded in the forum, asked his friend in a whisper, what foolish thing had he said?

Again my eye swept the circus, and fell on the ruddy radiance of the countenance of Hautboy. But its clear, honest cheeriness disdained my disdain. My intolerant pride was rebuked. And yet Hautboy dreamed not what magic reproof to a soul like mine sat on his laughing brow. At the very instant I felt the dart of the censure, his eye twinkled, his hand waved, his voice was lifted in jubilant delight at another joke of the inexhaustible clown.

Circus over, we went to Taylor's. Among crowds of others, we sat down to our stews and punches at one of the small marble tables. Hautboy sat opposite to me. Though greatly subdued from its former hilarity, his face still shone with gladness. But added to this was a quality not so prominent before: a certain serene expression of leisurely, deep good sense. Good sense and good humor in him joined hands. As the conversation proceeded between the brisk Standard and him—for I said little or nothing —I was more and more struck with the excellent judgment he evinced. In most of his remarks upon a variety of topics Hautboy seemed intuitively to hit the exact line between enthusiasm and apathy. It was plain that while Hautboy saw the world pretty much as it was, yet he did not theoretically espouse its bright side nor its dark side. Rejecting all solutions, he but acknowledged facts. What was sad in the world he did not superficially gainsay; what was glad in it he did not cynically slur; and all which was to him personally enjoyable, he gratefully took to his heart. It was plain, then—so it seemed at that moment, at least—that his extraordinary cheerfulness did not arise either from deficiency of feeling or thought.

Suddenly remembering an engagement, he took up his hat, bowed pleasantly, and left us.

"Well, Helmstone," said Standard, inaudibly drumming on the slab, "what do you think of your new acquaintance?"

The two last words tingled with a peculiar and novel significance.

"New acquaintance indeed," echoed I. "Standard, I owe you a thousand thanks for introducing me to one of the most singular men I have ever seen. It needed the optical sight of such a man to believe in the possibility of his existence."

"You rather like him, then," said Standard, with ironical dryness.

"I hugely love and admire him, Standard. I wish I were Hautboy."

"Ah? That's a pity now. There's only one Hautboy in the world."

This last remark set me to pondering again, and somehow it revived my dark mood.

"His wonderful cheerfulness, I suppose," said I, sneering with spleen, "originates not less in a felicitous fortune than in a felicitous temper. His great good sense is apparent; but great good sense may exist without sublime endowments. Nay, I take it, in certain cases, that good sense is simply owing to the absence of those. Much more, cheerfulness. Unpossessed of genius, Hautboy is eternally blessed."

"Ah? You would not think him an extraordinary genius, then?"

"Genius? What! such a short, fat fellow a genius! Genius, like Cassius,[2] is lank."

"Ah? But could you not fancy that Hautboy might formerly have had genius, but luckily getting rid of it, at last fatted up?"

"For a genius to get rid of his genius is as impossible as for a man in the galloping consumption to get rid of that."

"Ah? You speak very decidedly."

"Yes, Standard," cried I, increasing in spleen, "your cheery Hautboy, after all, is no pattern, no lesson for you and me. With average abilities; opinions clear, because circumscribed; passions docile, because they are feeble; a temper hilarious, because he was born to it—how can your Hautboy be made a reasonable example to a heady fellow like you, or an ambitious dreamer like me? Nothing tempts him beyond common limit; in himself he has nothing to restrain. By constitution he is exempted from all moral harm. Could ambition but prick him; had he but once heard applause, or endured contempt, a very different man would your Hautboy be. Acquiescent and calm from the cradle to the grave, he obviously slides through the crowd."

"Ah?"

"Why do you say Ah to me so strangely whenever I speak?"

"Did you ever hear of Master Betty?"

"The great English prodigy, who long ago ousted the Siddons and the Kembles from Drury Lane, and made the whole town run mad with acclamation?"

"The same," said Standard, once more inaudibly drumming on the slab.

I looked at him perplexed. He seemed to be holding the master-key of our theme in mysterious reserve; seemed to be throwing out his Master Betty, too, to puzzle me only the more.

2. **Cassius:** in Shakespeare's *Julius Caesar:* CAESAR: "Yond Cassius has a lean and hungry look" (Act I, Scene 2, Line 194).

"What under heaven can Master Betty, the great genius and prodigy, an English boy twelve years old, have to do with the poor, commonplace plodder, Hautboy, an American of forty?"

"Oh, nothing in the least. I don't imagine that they ever saw each other. Besides, Master Betty must be dead and buried long ere this."

"Then why cross the ocean, and rifle the grave to drag his remains into this living discussion?"

"Absent-mindedness, I suppose. I humbly beg pardon. Proceed with your observations on Hautboy. You think he never had genius, quite too contented and happy and fat for that—ah? You think him no pattern for men in general? affording no lesson of value to neglected merit, genius ignored, or impotent presumption rebuked?—all of which three amount to much the same thing. You admire his cheerfulness, while scorning his commonplace soul. Poor Hautboy, how sad that your very cheerfulness should, by a by-blow, bring you despite!"

"I don't say I scorn him; you are unjust. I simply declare that he is no pattern for me."

A sudden noise at my side attracted my ear. Turning, I saw Hautboy again, who very blithely reseated himself on the chair he had left.

"I was behind time with my engagement," said Hautboy, "so thought I would run back and rejoin you. But come, you have sat long enough here. Let us go to my rooms. It is only a five-minutes' walk."

"If you will promise to fiddle for us, we will," said Standard.

Fiddle! thought I—he's a jiggumbob [3] *fiddler*, then? No wonder genius declines to measure its pace to a fiddler's bow. My spleen was very strong on me now.

"I will gladly fiddle you your fill," replied Hautboy to Standard. "Come on."

In a few minutes we found ourselves in the fifth story of a sort of storehouse, in a lateral street to Broadway. It was curiously furnished with all sorts of odd furniture which seemed to have been obtained, piece by piece, at auctions of old-fashioned household stuff. But all was charmingly clean and cozy.

Pressed by Standard, Hautboy forthwith got out his dented old fiddle, and sitting down on a tall, rickety stool, played away right merrily at Yankee Doodle and other off-handed, dashing, and disdainfully care-free airs. But common as were the tunes, I was transfixed by something miraculously superior in the style. Sitting there on the old stool, his rusty hat sideways cocked on his head, one foot dangling adrift, he plied the bow of an enchanter. All my moody discontent, every vestige of peevishness fled. My whole splenetic soul capitulated to the magical fiddle.

3. **jiggumbob:** thingumbob, something fanciful or ridiculous.

"Something of an Orpheus, ah?" said Standard, archly nudging me beneath the left rib.

"And I, the charmed Bruin," murmured I.

The fiddle ceased. Once more, with redoubled curiosity, I gazed upon the easy, indifferent Hautboy. But he entirely baffled inquisition.

When, leaving him, Standard and I were in the street once more, I earnestly conjured him to tell me who, in sober truth, this marvelous Hautboy was.

"Why, haven't you seen him? And didn't you yourself lay his whole anatomy open on the marble slab at Taylor's? What more can you possibly learn? Doutbless your own masterly insight has already put you in possession of all."

"You mock me, Standard. There is some mystery here. Tell me, I entreat you, who is Hautboy?"

"An extraordinary genius, Helmstone," said Standard, with sudden ardor, "who in boyhood drained the whole flagon of glory; whose going from city to city was a going from triumph to triumph. One who has been an object of wonder to the wisest, been caressed by the loveliest, received the open homage of thousands on thousands of the rabble. But today he walks Broadway and no man knows him. With you and me, the elbow of the hurrying clerk, and the pole of the remorseless omnibus, shove him. He who has a hundred times been crowned with laurels, now wears, as you see, a bunged beaver. Once fortune poured showers of gold into his lap, as showers of laurel leaves upon his brow. To-day, from house to house he hies, teaching fiddling for a living. Crammed once with fame, he is now hilarious without it. *With* genius and *without* fame, he is happier than a king. More prodigy now than ever."

"His true name?"

"Let me whisper it in your ear."

"What! Oh, Standard, myself, as a child, have shouted myself hoarse applauding that very name in the theater."

"I have heard your poem was not very handsomely received," said Standard, now suddenly shifting the subject.

"Not a word of that, for heaven's sake!" cried I. "If Cicero, traveling in the East, found sympathetic solace for his grief in beholding the arid overthrow of a once gorgeous city, shall not my petty affair be as nothing, when I behold in Hautboy the vine and the rose climbing the shattered shafts of his tumbled temple of Fame?"

Next day I tore all my manuscripts, bought me a fiddle, and went to take regular lessons of Hautboy.

Henry James

THE REAL THING

1

W HEN the porter's wife (she used to answer the house-bell), announced "A gentleman—with a lady, sir," I had, as I often had in
those days, for the wish was father to the thought, an immediate vision of
sitters. Sitters my visitors in this case proved to be; but not in the sense I
should have preferred. However, there was nothing at first to indicate that
they might not have come for a portrait. The gentleman, a man of fifty,
very high and very straight, with a moustache slightly grizzled and a dark
grey walking-coat admirably fitted, both of which I noted professionally
—I don't mean as a barber or yet as a tailor—would have struck me as a celebrity if celebrities often were striking. It was a truth of which I had for
some time been conscious that a figure with a good deal of frontage was,
as one might say, almost never a public institution. A glance at the lady
helped to remind me of this paradoxical law: she also looked too distinguished to be a "personality." Moreover one would scarcely come across
two variations together.

Neither of the pair spoke immediately—they only prolonged the preliminary gaze which suggested that each wished to give the other a chance.
They were visibly shy; they stood there letting me take them in—which,
as I afterwards perceived, was the most practical thing they could have
done. In this way their embarrassment served their cause. I had seen people painfully reluctant to mention that they desired anything so gross as
to be represented on canvas; but the scruples of my new friends appeared
almost insurmountable. Yet the gentleman might have said "I should like a
portrait of my wife," and the lady might have said "I should like a portrait of my husband." Perhaps they were not husband and wife—this naturally would make the matter more delicate. Perhaps they wished to be
done together—in which case they ought to have brought a third person
to break the news.

"We come from Mr. Rivet," the lady said at last, with a dim smile
which had the effect of a moist sponge passed over a "sunk" piece of painting, as well as of a vague allusion to vanished beauty. She was as tall and
straight, in her degree, as her companion, and with ten years less to carry.
She looked as sad as a woman could look whose face was not charged
with expression; that is, her tinted oval mask showed friction as an exposed surface shows it. The hand of time had played over her freely, but

only to simplify. She was slim and stiff, and so well-dressed, in dark blue cloth, with lappets and pockets and buttons, that it was clear she employed the same tailor as her husband. The couple had an indefinable air of prosperous thrift—they evidently got a good deal of luxury for their money. If I was to be one of their luxuries it would behove me to consider my terms.

"Ah, Claude Rivet recommended me?" I inquired; and I added that it was very kind of him, though I could reflect that, as he only painted landscape, this was not a sacrifice.

The lady looked very hard at the gentleman, and the gentleman looked round the room. Then staring at the floor a moment and stroking his moustache, he rested his pleasant eyes on me with the remark: "He said you were the right one."

"I try to be, when people want to sit."

"Yes, we should like to," said the lady anxiously.

"Do you mean together?"

My visitors exchanged a glance. "If you could do anything with *me*, I suppose it would be double," the gentleman stammered.

"Oh yes, there's naturally a higher charge for two figures than for one."

"We should like to make it pay," the husband confessed.

"That's very good of you," I returned, appreciating so unwonted a sympathy—for I supposed he meant pay the artist.

A sense of strangeness seemed to dawn on the lady. "We mean for the illustrations—Mr. Rivet said you might put one in."

"Put one in—an illustration?" I was equally confused.

"Sketch her off, you know," said the gentleman, colouring.

It was only then that I understood the service Claude Rivet had rendered me; he had told them that I worked in black and white, for magazines, for story-books, for sketches of contemporary life, and consequently had frequent employment for models. These things were true, but it was not less true (I may confess it now—whether because the aspiration was to lead to everything or to nothing I leave the reader to guess), that I couldn't get the honours, to say nothing of the emoluments, of a great painter of portraits out of my head. My "illustrations" were my potboilers; I looked to a different branch of art (far and away the most interesting it had always seemed to me), to perpetuate my fame. There was no shame in looking to it also to make my fortune; but that fortune was by so much further from being made from the moment my visitors wished to be "done" for nothing. I was disappointed; for in the pictorial sense I had immediately *seen* them. I had seized their type—I had already settled what I would do with it. Something that wouldn't absolutely have pleased them, I afterwards reflected.

"Ah, you're—you're—a—?" I began, as soon as I had mastered my surprise. I couldn't bring out the dingy word "models"; it seemed to fit the case so little.

"We haven't had much practice," said the lady.

"We've got to *do* something, and we've thought that an artist in your line might perhaps make something of us," her husband threw off. He further mentioned that they didn't know many artists and that they had gone first, on the off-chance (he painted views of course, but sometimes put in figures—perhaps I remembered), to Mr. Rivet, whom they had met a few years before at a place in Norfolk where he was sketching.

"We used to sketch a little ourselves," the lady hinted.

"It's very awkward, but we absolutely *must* do something," her husband went on.

"Of course, we're not so *very* young," she admitted, with a wan smile.

With the remark that I might as well know something more about them, the husband had handed me a card extracted from a neat new pocket-book (their appurtenances were all of the freshest) and inscribed with the words "Major Monarch." Impressive as these words were they didn't carry my knowledge much further; but my visitor presently added: "I've left the army, and we've had the misfortune to lose our money. In fact our means are dreadfully small."

"It's an awful bore," said Mrs. Monarch.

They evidently wished to be discreet—to take care not to swagger because they were gentlefolks. I perceived they would have been willing to recognise this as something of a drawback, at the same time that I guessed at an underlying sense—their consolation in adversity—that they *had* their points. They certainly had; but these advantages struck me as preponderantly social; such for instance as would help to make a drawing-room look well. However, a drawing-room was always, or ought to be, a picture.

In consequence of his wife's allusion to their age Major Monarch observed: "Naturally, it's more for the figure that we thought of going in. We can still hold ourselves up." On the instant I saw that the figure was indeed their strong point. His "naturally" didn't sound vain, but it lighted up the question. "*She* has got the best," he continued, nodding at his wife, with a pleasant after-dinner absence of circumlocution. I could only reply, as if we were in fact sitting over our wine, that this didn't prevent his own from being very good; which led him in turn to rejoin: "We thought that if you ever have to do people like us, we might be something like it. *She*, particularly—for a lady in a book, you know."

I was so amused by them that, to get more of it, I did my best to take their point of view; and though it was an embarrassment to find myself appraising physically, as if they were animals on hire or useful slaves, a pair whom I should have expected to meet only in one of the relations in which criticism is tacit, I looked at Mrs. Monarch judicially enough to be able to exclaim, after a moment, with conviction: "Oh yes, a lady in a book!" She was singularly like a bad illustration.

"We'll stand up, if you like," said the Major; and he raised himself before me with a really grand air.

I could take his measure at a glance—he was six feet two and a perfect gentleman. It would have paid any club in process of formation and in want of a stamp to engage him at a salary to stand in the principal window. What struck me immediately was that in coming to me they had rather missed their vocation; they could surely have been turned to better account for advertising purposes. I couldn't of course see the thing in detail, but I could see them make someone's fortune—I don't mean their own. There was something in them for a waistcoat-maker, an hotel-keeper or a soap-vendor. I could imagine "We always use it" pinned on their bosoms with the greatest effect; I had a vision of the promptitude with which they would launch a table d'hôte.

Mrs. Monarch sat still, not from pride but from shyness, and presently her husband said to her: "Get up my dear and show how smart you are." She obeyed, but she had no need to get up to show it. She walked to the end of the studio, and then she came back blushing, with her fluttered eyes on her husband. I was reminded of an incident I had accidentally had a glimpse of in Paris—being with a friend there, a dramatist about to produce a play—when an actress came to him to ask to be intrusted with a part. She went through her paces before him, walked up and down as Mrs. Monarch was doing. Mrs. Monarch did it quite as well, but I abstained from applauding It was very odd to see such people apply for such poor pay. She looked as if she had ten thousand a year.[1] Her husband had used the word that described her: she was, in the London current jargon, essentially and typically "smart." Her figure was, in the same order of ideas, conspicuously and irreproachably "good." For a woman of her age her waist was surprisingly small; her elbow moreover had the orthodox crook. She held her head at the conventional angle; but why did she come to *me?* She ought to have tried on jackets at a big shop. I feared my visitors were not only destitute, but "artistic"—which would be a great complication. When she sat down again I thanked her, observing that what a draughtsman most valued in his model was the faculty of keeping quiet.

"Oh, *she* can keep quiet," said Major Monarch. Then he added, jocosely: "I've always kept her quiet."

1. ten . . . year: ten thousand pounds a year. The English pound is now worth about $2.80; in short, Mrs. Monarch looked as if she had a substantial annual income.

"I'm not a nasty fidget, am I?" Mrs. Monarch appealed to her husband.

He addressed his answer to me. "Perhaps it isn't out of place to mention—because we ought to be quite business-like, oughtn't we?—that when I married her she was known as the Beautiful Statue."

"Oh dear!" said Mrs. Monarch, ruefully.

"Of course I should want a certain amount of expression," I rejoined.

"Of *course!*" they both exclaimed.

"And then I suppose you know that you'll get awfully tired."

"Oh, we *never* get tired!" they eagerly cried.

"Have you had any kind of practice?"

They hesitated—they looked at each other. "We've been photographed, *immensely*," said Mrs. Monarch.

"She means the fellows have asked us," added the Major.

"I see—because you're so good-looking."

"I don't know what they thought, but they were always after us."

"We always got our photographs for nothing," smiled Mrs. Monarch.

"We might have brought some, my dear," her husband remarked.

"I'm not sure we have any left. We've given quantities away," she explained to me.

"With our autographs and that sort of thing," said the Major.

"Are they to be got in the shops?" I inquired, as a harmless pleasantry.

"Oh, yes; *hers*—they used to be."

"Not now," said Mrs. Monarch, with her eyes on the floor.

2

I could fancy the "sort of thing" they put on the presentation-copies of their photographs, and I was sure they wrote a beautiful hand. It was odd how quickly I was sure of everything that concerned them. If they were now so poor as to have to earn shillings and pence, they never had had much of a margin. Their good looks had been their capital, and they had good-humouredly made the most of the career that this resource marked out for them. It was in their faces, the blankness, the deep intellectual repose of the twenty years of country-house visiting which had given them pleasant intonations. I could see the sunny drawing-rooms, sprinkled with periodicals she didn't read, in which Mrs. Monarch had continuously sat; I could see the wet shrubberies in which she had walked, equipped to admiration for either exercise. I could see the rich covers [2] the Major had helped to shoot and the wonderful garments in which, late at night, he repaired to the smoking-room to talk about them. I could imagine their leggings and waterproofs, their knowing tweeds and rugs, their rolls of

2. **covers:** woods sheltering game, i.e., in hunting.

sticks and cases of tackle and neat umbrellas; and I could evoke the exact appearance of their servants and the compact variety of their luggage on the platforms of country stations.

They gave small tips, but they were liked; they didn't do anything themselves, but they were welcome. They looked so well everywhere; they gratified the general relish for stature, complexion and "form." They knew it without fatuity or vulgarity, and they respected themselves in consequence. They were not superficial; they were thorough and kept themselves up—it had been their line. People with such a taste for activity had to have some line. I could feel how, even in a dull house, they could have been counted upon for cheerfulness. At present something had happened—it didn't matter what, their little income had grown less, it had grown least—and they had to do something for pocket-money. Their friends liked them, but didn't like to support them. There was something about them that represented credit—their clothes, their manners, their type; but if credit is a large empty pocket in which an occasional chink reverberates, the chink at least must be audible. What they wanted of me was to help to make it so. Fortunately they had no children—I soon divined that. They would also perhaps wish our relations to be kept secret: this was why it was "for the figure"—the reproduction of the face would betray them.

I liked them—they were so simple; and I had no objection to them if they would suit. But, somehow, with all their perfections I didn't easily believe in them. After all they were amateurs, and the ruling passion of my life was the detestation of the amateur. Combined with this was another perversity—an innate preference for the represented subject over the real one: the defect of the real one was so apt to be a lack of representation. I liked things that appeared; then one was sure. Whether they *were* or not was a subordinate and almost always a profitless question. There were other considerations, the first of which was that I already had two or three people in use, notably a young person with big feet, in alpaca, from Kilburn, who for a couple of years had come to me regularly for my illustrations and with whom I was still—perhaps ignobly—satisfied. I frankly explained to my visitors how the case stood; but they had taken more precautions than I supposed. They had reasoned out their opportunity, for Claude Rivet had told them of the projected *édition de luxe* of one of the writers of our day—the rarest of the novelists—who, long neglected by the multitudinous vulgar and dearly prized by the attentive (need I mention Philip Vincent?) had had the happy fortune of seeing, late in life, the dawn and then the full light of a higher criticism—an estimate in which, on the part of the public, there was something really of expiation. The edition in question, planned by a publisher of taste, was

practically an act of high reparation; the wood-cuts with which it was to
be enriched were the homage of English art to one of the most independent representatives of English letters. Major and Mrs. Monarch confessed to me that they had hoped I might be able to work *them* into my
share of the enterprise. They knew I was to do the first of the books,
"Rutland Ramsay," but I had to make clear to them that my participation
in the rest of the affair—this first book was to be a test—was to depend on
the satisfaction I should give. If this should be limited my employers
would drop me without a scruple. It was therefore a crisis for me, and
naturally I was making special preparations, looking about for new people,
if they should be necessary, and securing the best types. I admitted however that I should like to settle down to two or three good models who
would do for everything.

"Should we have often to—a—put on special clothes?" Mrs. Monarch
timidly demanded.

"Dear, yes—that's half the business."

"And should we be expected to supply our own costumes?"

"Oh, no; I've got a lot of things. A painter's models put on—or put off—
anything he likes."

"And do you mean—a—the same?"

"The same?"

Mrs. Monarch looked at her husband again.

"Oh, she was just wondering," he explained, "if the costumes are in
general use." I had to confess that they were, and I mentioned further that
some of them (I had a lot of genuine, greasy last-century things), had
served their time, a hundred years ago, on living, world-stained men and
women. "We'll put on anything that *fits*," said the Major.

"Oh, I arrange that—they fit in the pictures."

"I'm afraid I should do better for the modern books. I would come as
you like," said Mrs. Monarch.

"She has got a lot of clothes at home: they might do for contemporary
life," her husband continued.

"Oh, I can fancy scenes in which you'd be quite natural." And indeed
I could see the slipshod rearrangements of stale properties—the stories I
tried to produce pictures for without the exasperation of reading them—
whose sandy tracts the good lady might help to people. But I had to return
to the fact that for this sort of work—the daily mechanical grind—I was
already equipped; the people I was working with were fully adequate.

"We only thought we might be more like *some* characters," said Mrs.
Monarch mildly, getting up.

Her husband also rose; he stood looking at me with a dim wistfulness that was touching in so fine a man. "Wouldn't it be rather a pull sometimes to have—a—to have—?" He hung fire; he wanted me to help him by phrasing what he meant. But I couldn't—I didn't know. So he brought it out, awkwardly: "The *real* thing; a gentleman, you know, or a lady." I was quite ready to give a general assent—I admitted that there was a great deal in that. This encouraged Major Monarch to say, following up his appeal with an unacted gulp: "It's awfully hard—we've tried everything." The gulp was communicative; it proved too much for his wife. Before I knew it Mrs. Monarch had dropped again upon a divan and burst into tears. Her husband sat down beside her, holding one of her hands; whereupon she quickly dried her eyes with the other, while I felt embarrassed as she looked up at me. "There isn't a confounded job I haven't applied for—waited for—prayed for. You can fancy we'd be pretty bad first. Secretaryships and that sort of thing? You might as well ask for a peerage. I'd be *anything*—I'm strong; a messenger or a coal-heaver. I'd put on a gold-laced cap and open carriage-doors in front of the haberdasher's; I'd hang about a station, to carry portmanteaus; I'd be a postman. But they won't *look* at you; there are thousands, as good as yourself, already on the ground. *Gentlemen*, poor beggars, who have drunk their wine, who have kept their hunters!"

I was as reassuring as I knew how to be, and my visitors were presently on their feet again while, for the experiment, we agreed on an hour. We were discussing it when the door opened and Miss Churm came in with a wet umbrella. Miss Churm had to take the omnibus to Maida Vale [3] and then walk half-a-mile. She looked a trifle blowsy and slightly splashed. I scarcely ever saw her come in without thinking afresh how odd it was that, being so little in herself, she should yet be so much in others. She was a meagre little Miss Churm, but she was an ample heroine of romance. She was only a freckled cockney, but she could represent everything, from a fine lady to a shepherdess; she had the faculty, as she might have had a fine voice or long hair. She couldn't spell, and she loved beer, but she had two or three "points," and practice, and a knack, and mother-wit, and a kind of whimsical sensibility, and a love of the theatre, and seven sisters, and not an ounce of respect, especially for the *h*.[4] The first thing my visitors saw was that her umbrella was wet, and in their spotless perfection they visibly winced at it. The rain had come on since their arrival.

"I'm all in a soak; there *was* a mess of people in the 'bus. I wish you lived near a styion," said Miss Churm. I requested her to get ready as

3. **Maida Vale:** an unfashionable residential area of London.
4. The cockney commonly fails to pronounce *h* when it should be pronounced, and adds one when it doesn't belong.

quickly as possible, and she passed into the room in which she always changed her dress. But before going out she asked me what she was to get into this time.

"It's the Russian princess, don't you know?" I answered; "the one with the 'golden eyes,' in black velvet, for the long thing in the *Cheapside*."

"Golden eyes? I *say!*" cried Miss Churm, while my companions watched her with intensity as she withdrew. She always arranged herself, when she was late, before I could turn round; and I kept my visitors a little, on purpose, so that they might get an idea, from seeing her, what would be expected of themselves. I mentioned that she was quite my notion of an excellent model—she was really very clever.

"Do you think she looks like a Russian princess?" Major Monarch asked, with lurking alarm.

"When I make her, yes."

"Oh, if you have to *make* her—!" he reasoned, acutely.

"That's the most you can ask. There are so many that are not makeable."

"Well now, *here's* a lady"—and with a persuasive smile he passed his arm into his wife's—"who's already made!"

"Oh, I'm not a Russian princess," Mrs. Monarch protested, a little coldly. I could see that she had known some and didn't like them. There, immediately, was a complication of a kind that I never had to fear with Miss Churm.

This young lady came back in black velvet—the gown was rather rusty and very low on her lean shoulders—and with a Japanese fan in her red hands. I reminded her that in the scene I was doing she had to look over someone's head. "I forget whose it is; but it doesn't matter. Just look over a head."

"I'd rather look over a stove," said Miss Churm; and she took her station near the fire. She fell into position, settled herself into a tall attitude, gave a certain backward inclination to her head and a certain forward droop to her fan, and looked, at least to my prejudiced sense, distinguished and charming, foreign and dangerous. We left her looking so, while I went down-stairs with Major and Mrs. Monarch.

"I think I could come about as near it as that," said Mrs. Monarch.

"Oh, you think she's shabby, but you must allow for the alchemy of art."

However, they went off with an evident increase of comfort, founded on their demonstrable advantage in being the real thing. I could fancy them shuddering over Miss Churm. She was very droll about them when I went back, for I told her what they wanted.

"Well, if *she* can sit I'll tyke to bookkeeping," said my model.

"She's very lady-like," I replied, as an innocent form of aggravation.

"So much the worse for *you*. That means she can't turn round."

"She'll do for the fashionable novels."

"Oh yes, she'll *do* for them!" my model humorously declared. "Ain't they bad enough without her?" I had often sociably denounced them to Miss Churm.

3

It was for the elucidation of a mystery in one of these works that I first tried Mrs. Monarch. Her husband came with her, to be useful if necessary—it was sufficiently clear that as a general thing he would prefer to come with her. At first I wondered if this were for "propriety's" sake—if he were going to be jealous and meddling. The idea was too tiresome, and if it had been confirmed it would speedily have brought our acquaintance to a close. But I soon saw there was nothing in it and that if he accompanied Mrs. Monarch it was (in addition to the chance of being wanted), simply because he had nothing else to do. When she was away from him his occupation was gone—she never *had* been away from him. I judged, rightly, that in their awkward situation their close union was their main comfort and that this union had no weak spot. It was a real marriage, an encouragement to the hesitating, a nut for pessimists to crack. Their address was humble (I remember afterwards thinking it had been the only thing about them that was really professional), and I could fancy the lamentable lodgings in which the Major would have been left alone. He could bear them with his wife—he couldn't bear them without her.

He had too much tact to try and make himself agreeable when he couldn't be useful; so he simply sat and waited, when I was too absorbed in my work to talk. But I liked to make him talk—it made my work, when it didn't interrupt it, less sordid, less special. To listen to him was to combine the excitement of going out with the economy of staying at home. There was only one hindrance: that I seemed not to know any of the people he and his wife had known. I think he wondered extremely, during the term of our intercourse, whom the deuce I *did* know. He hadn't a stray sixpence of an idea to fumble for; so we didn't spin it very fine—we confined ourselves to questions of leather and even of liquor (saddlers and breeches-makers and how to get good claret cheap), and matters like "good trains" and the habits of small game. His lore on these last subjects was astonishing, he managed to interweave the station-master with the ornithologist. When he couldn't talk about greater things he could talk cheerfully about smaller, and since I couldn't accompany him into reminiscences of the fashionable world he could lower the conversation without a visible effort to my level.

So earnest a desire to please was touching in a man who could so easily have knocked one down. He looked after the fire and had an opinion on the draught of the stove, without my asking him, and I could see that he thought many of my arrangements not half clever enough. I remember telling him that if I were only rich I would offer him a salary to come and teach me how to live. Sometimes he gave a random sigh, of which the essence was: "Give me even such a bare old barrack as *this*, and I'd do something with it!" When I wanted to use him he came alone; which was an illustration of the superior courage of women. His wife could bear her solitary second floor, and she was in general more discreet; showing by various small reserves that she was alive to the propriety of keeping our relations markedly professional—not letting them slide into sociability. She wished it to remain clear that she and the Major were employed, not cultivated, and if she approved of me as a superior, who could be kept in his place, she never thought me quite good enough for an equal.

She sat with great intensity, giving the whole of her mind to it, and was capable of remaining for an hour almost as motionless as if she were before a photographer's lens. I could see she had been photographed often, but somehow the very habit that made her good for that purpose unfitted her for mine. At first I was extremely pleased with her lady-like air, and it was a satisfaction, on coming to follow her lines, to see how good they were and how far they could lead the pencil. But after a few times I began to find her too insurmountably stiff; do what I would with it my drawing looked like a photograph or a copy of a photograph. Her figure had no variety of expression—she herself had no sense of variety. You may say that this was my business, was only a question of placing her. I placed her in every conceivable position, but she managed to obliterate their differences. She was always a lady certainly, and into the bargain was always the same lady. She was the real thing, but always the same thing. There were moments when I was oppressed by the serenity of her confidence that she *was* the real thing. All her dealings with me and all her husband's were an implication that this was lucky for *me*. Meanwhile I found myself trying to invent types that approached her own, instead of making her own transform itself—in the clever way that was not impossible, for instance, to poor Miss Churm. Arrange as I would and take the precautions I would, she always, in my pictures, came out too tall—landing me in the dilemma of having represented a fascinating woman as seven feet high, which, out of respect perhaps to my own very much scantier inches, was far from my idea of such a personage.

The case was worse with the Major—nothing I could do would keep *him* down, so that he became useful only for the representation of brawny giants. I adored variety and range, I cherished human accidents, the illustrative note; I wanted to characterise closely, and the thing in the world I most hated was the danger of being ridden by a type. I had quarrelled with some of my friends about it—I had parted company with them for maintaining that one *had* to be, and that if the type was beautiful (witness Raphael and Leonardo), the servitude was only a gain. I was neither Leonardo nor Raphael; I might only be a presumptuous young modern searcher, but I held that everything was to be sacrificed sooner than character. When they averred that the haunting type in question could easily *be* character, I retorted, perhaps superficially: "Whose?" It couldn't be everybody's—it might end in being nobody's.

After I had drawn Mrs. Monarch a dozen times I perceived more clearly than before that the value of such a model as Miss Churm resided precisely in the fact that she had no positive stamp, combined of course with the other fact that what she did have was a curious and inexplicable talent for imitation. Her usual appearance was like a curtain which she could draw up at request for a capital performance. This performance was simply suggestive; but it was a word to the wise—it was vivid and pretty. Sometimes, even, I thought it, though she was plain herself, too insipidly pretty; I made it a reproach to her that the figures drawn from her were monotonously (*bêtement*,[5] as we used to say) graceful. Nothing made her more angry: it was so much her pride to feel that she could sit for characters that had nothing in common with each other. She would accuse me at such moments of taking away her "reputytion."

It suffered a certain shrinkage, this queer quantity, from the repeated visits of my new friends. Miss Churm was greatly in demand, never in want of employment, so I had no scruple in putting her off occasionally, to try them more at my ease. It was certainly amusing at first to do the real thing—it was amusing to do Major Monarch's trousers. They *were* the real thing, even if he did come out colossal. It was amusing to do his wife's back hair (it was so mathematically neat), and the particular "smart" tension of her tight stays. She lent herself especially to positions in which the face was somewhat averted or blurred; she abounded in lady-like back views and *profils perdus*.[6] When she stood erect she took naturally one of the attitudes in which court-painters represent queens and princesses; so that I found myself wondering whether, to draw out this accomplishment, I couldn't get the editor of the *Cheapside* to publish a really royal romance, "A Tale of Buckingham Palace." Sometimes, however, the real thing and the make-believe came into contact; by which I mean that Miss Churm, keeping an appointment or coming to make one on days when I had much work in hand, encountered her invidious rivals.

5. *bêtement:* beastly.
6. *profils perdus:* averted glances.

The encounter was not on their part, for they noticed her no more than if she had been the housemaid; not from intentional loftiness, but simply because, as yet, professionally, they didn't know how to fraternise, as I could guess that they would have liked—or at least that the Major would. They couldn't talk about the omnibus—they always walked; and they didn't know what else to try—she wasn't interested in good trains or cheap claret. Besides, they must have felt—in the air—that she was amused at them, secretly derisive of their ever knowing how. She was not a person to conceal her scepticism if she had had a chance to show it. On the other hand Mrs. Monarch didn't think her tidy; for why else did she take pains to say to me (it was going out of the way, for Mrs. Monarch), that she didn't like dirty women?

One day when my young lady happened to be present with my other sitters (she even dropped in, when it was convenient, for a chat), I asked her to be so good as to lend a hand in getting tea—a service with which she was familiar and which was one of a class that, living as I did in a small way, with slender domestic resources, I often appealed to my models to render. They liked to lay hands on my property, to break the sitting, and sometimes the china—I made them feel Bohemian. The next time I saw Miss Churm after this incident she surprised me greatly by making a scene about it—she accused me of having wished to humiliate her. She had not resented the outrage at the time, but had seemed obliging and amused, enjoying the comedy of asking Mrs. Monarch, who sat vague and silent, whether she would have cream and sugar, and putting an exaggerated simper into the question. She had tried intonations—as if she too wished to pass for the real thing; till I was afraid my other visitors would take offence.

Oh, *they* were determined not to do this; and their touching patience was the measure of their great need. They would sit by the hour, uncomplaining, till I was ready to use them; they would come back on the chance of being wanted and would walk away cheerfully if they were not. I used to go to the door with them to see in what magnificent order they retreated. I tried to find other employment for them—I introduced them to several artists. But they didn't "take," for reasons I could appreciate, and I became conscious, rather anxiously, that after such disappointments they fell back upon me with a heavier weight. They did me the honour to think that it was I who was most *their* form. They were not picturesque enough for the painters, and in those days there were not so many serious workers in black and white. Besides, they had an eye to the great job I had mentioned to them—they had secretly set their hearts on supplying the right essence for my pictorial vindication of our fine novelist. They knew that for this undertaking I should want no costume-effects, none of the frip-

pery of past ages—that it was a case in which everything would be contemporary and satirical and, presumably, genteel. If I could work them
into it their future would be assured, 'for the labour would of course be
long and the occupation steady.

One day Mrs. Monarch came without her husband—she explained his
absence by his having had to go to the City.[7] While she sat there in her
usual anxious stiffness there came, at the door, a knock which I immediately recognised as the subdued appeal of a model out of work. It was followed by the entrance of a young man whom I easily perceived to be a
foreigner and who proved in fact an Italian acquainted with no English
word but my name, which he uttered in a way that made it seem to include all others. I had not then visited his country, nor was I proficient in
his tongue; but as he was not so meanly constituted—what Italian is?—as
to depend only on that member for expression he conveyed to me, in
familiar but graceful mimicry, that he was in search of exactly the employment in which the lady before me was engaged. I was not struck with
him at first, and while I continued to draw I emitted rough sounds of dis-
couragement and dismissal. He stood his ground, however, not impor-
tunately, but with a dumb, dog-like fidelity in his eyes which amounted to
innocent impudence—the manner of a devoted servant (he might have
been in the house for years), unjustly suspected. Suddenly I saw that this
very attitude and expression made a picture, whereupon I told him to sit
down and wait till I should be free. There was another picture in the way
he obeyed me, and I observed as I worked that there were others still in
the way he looked wonderingly, with his head thrown back, about the
high studio. He might have been crossing himself in St. Peter's. Before I
finished I said to myself: "The fellow's a bankrupt orange-monger, but
he's a treasure."

When Mrs. Monarch withdrew he passed across the room like a flash to
open the door for her, standing there with the rapt, pure gaze of the
young Dante spellbound by the young Beatrice. As I never insisted, in
such situations, on the blankness of the British domestic, I reflected that he
had the making of a servant (and I needed one, but couldn't pay him to
be only that), as well as of a model; in short I made up my mind to adopt
my bright adventurer if he would agree to officiate in the double capacity.
He jumped at my offer, and in the event my rashness (for I had known
nothing about him), was not brought home to me. He proved a sympathetic though a desultory ministrant, and had in a wonderful degree the
sentiment de la pose.[8] It was uncultivated, instinctive; a part of the happy
instinct which had guided him to my door and helped him to spell out

7. the City: the business district of London.
8. *sentiment de la pose:* the instinct for striking poses.

my name on the card nailed to it. He had had no other introduction to me than a guess, from the shape of my high north window, seen outside, that my place was a studio and that as a studio it would contain an artist. He had wandered to England in search of fortune, like other itinerants, and had embarked, with a partner and a small green hand-cart, on the sale of penny ices. The ices had melted away and the partner had dissolved in their train. My young man wore tight yellow trousers with reddish stripes and his name was Oronte. He was sallow but fair, and when I put him into some old clothes of my own he looked like an Englishman. He was as good as Miss Churm, who could look, when required, like an Italian.

4

I thought Mrs. Monarch's face slightly convulsed when, on her coming back with her husband, she found Oronte installed. It was strange to have to recognise in a scrap of a *lazzarone* [9] a competitor to her magnificent Major. It was she who scented danger first, for the Major was anec-dotically unconscious. But Oronte gave us tea, with a hundred eager con-fusions (he had never seen such a queer process), and I think she thought better of me for having at last an "establishment." They saw a couple of drawings that I had made of the establishment, and Mrs. Monarch hinted that it never would have struck her that he had sat for them. "Now the drawings you make from *us*, they look exactly like us," she reminded me, smiling in triumph; and I recognised that this was indeed just their defect. When I drew the Monarchs I couldn't, somehow, get away from them—get into the character I wanted to represent; and I had not the least desire my model should be discoverable in my picture. Miss Churm never was, and Mrs. Monarch thought I hid her, very properly, because she was vul-gar; whereas if she was lost it was only as the dead who go to heaven are lost—in the gain of an angel the more.

By this time I had got a certain start with "Rutland Ramsay," the first novel in the great projected series; that is I had produced a dozen draw-ings, several with the help of the Major and his wife, and I had sent them in for approval. My understanding with the publishers, as I have already hinted, had been that I was to be left to do my work, in this particular case, as I liked, with the whole book committed to me; but my connection with the rest of the series was only contingent. There were moments when, frankly, it *was* a comfort to have the real thing under one's hand; for there were characters in "Rutland Ramsay" that were very much like it. There were people presumably as straight as the Major and women of as good a fashion as Mrs. Monarch. There was a great deal of country-

9. *lazzarone:* beggar.

house life—treated, it is true, in a fine, fanciful, ironical, generalised way—
and there was a considerable implication of knickerbockers and kilts.
There were certain things I had to settle at the outset; such things for instance as the exact appearance of the hero, the particular bloom of the
heroine. The author of course gave me a lead, but there was a margin for
interpretation. I took the Monarchs into my confidence, I told them
frankly what I was about, I mentioned my embarrassments and alterna-
tives. "Oh, take *him!*" Mrs. Monarch murmured sweetly, looking at her
husband; and "What could you want better than my wife?" the Major inquired, with the comfortable candour that now prevailed between us.

I was not obliged to answer these remarks—I was only obliged to place
my sitters. I was not easy in mind, and I postponed, a little timidly perhaps, the solution of the question. The book was a large canvas, the other
figures were numerous, and I worked off at first some of the episodes in
which the hero and the heroine were not concerned. When once I had set
them up I should have to stick to them—I couldn't make my young man
seven feet high in one place and five feet nine in another. I inclined on the
whole to the latter measurement, though the Major more than once reminded me that *he* looked about as young as anyone. It was indeed quite
possible to arrange him, for the figure, so that it would have been difficult
to detect his age. After the spontaneous Oronte had been with me a
month, and after I had given him to understand several different times that
his native exuberance would presently constitute an insurmountable barrier
to our further intercourse, I waked to a sense of his heroic capacity. He
was only five feet seven, but the remaining inches were latent. I tried him
almost secretly at first, for I was really rather afraid of the judgment my
other models would pass on such a choice. If they regarded Miss Churm as
little better than a snare, what would they think of the representation by
a person so little the real thing as an Italian street-vendor of a protagonist
formed by a public school?

If I went a little in fear of them it was not because they bullied me, because they had got an oppressive foothold, but because in their really
pathetic decorum and mysteriously permanent newness they counted on
me so intensely. I was therefore very glad when Jack Hawley came home:
he was always of such good counsel. He painted badly himself, but there
was no one like him for putting his finger on the place. He had been absent
from England for a year; he had been somewhere—I don't remember
where—to get a fresh eye. I was in a good deal of dread of any such organ,
but we were old friends; he had been away for months and a sense of
emptiness was creeping into my life. I hadn't dodged a missile for a year.

He came back with a fresh eye, but with the same old black velvet
blouse, and the first evening he spent in my studio we smoked cigarettes

till the small hours. He had done no work himself, he had only got the
eye; so the field was clear for the production of my little things. He
wanted to see what I had done for the *Cheapside*, but he was disappointed
in the exhibition. That at least seemed the meaning of two or three comprehensive groans which, as he lounged on my big divan, on a folded leg,
looking at my latest drawings, issued from his lips with the smoke of the
cigarette.

"What's the matter with you?" I asked.

"What's the matter with *you?*"

"Nothing save that I'm mystified."

"You are indeed. You're quite off the hinge. What's the meaning of this
new fad?" And he tossed me, with visible irreverence, a drawing in which
I happened to have depicted both my majestic models. I asked if he didn't
think it good, and he replied that it struck him as execrable, given the sort
of thing I had always represented myself to him as wishing to arrive at;
but I let that pass, I was so anxious to see exactly what he meant. The two
figures in the picture looked colossal, but I supposed this was *not* what he
meant, inasmuch as, for aught he knew to the contrary, I might have been
trying for that. I maintained that I was working exactly in the same way as
when he last had done me the honour to commend me. "Well, there's a
big hole somewhere," he answered; "wait a bit and I'll discover it." I depended upon him to do so: where else was the fresh eye? But he produced
at last nothing more luminous than "I don't know—I don't like your types."
This was lame, for a critic who had never consented to discuss with me
anything but the question of execution, the direction of strokes and the
mystery of values.

"In the drawings you've been looking at I think my types are very
handsome."

"Oh, they won't do!"

"I've had a couple of new models."

"I see you have. *They* won't do."

"Are you very sure of that?"

"Absolutely—they're stupid."

"You mean *I* am—for I ought to get round that."

"You *can't*—with such people. Who are they?"

I told him, as far as was necessary, and he declared, heartlessly: "*Ce sont
des gens qu'il faut mettre à la porte.*" [10]

"You've never seen them; they're awfully good," I compassionately
objected.

"Not seen them? Why, all this recent work of yours drops to pieces
with them. It's all I want to see of them."

10. *Ce . . . porte:* Such people should be shown the door.

"No one else has said anything against it—the *Cheapside* people are pleased."

"Everyone else is an ass, and the *Cheapside* people the biggest asses of all. Come, don't pretend, at this time of day, to have pretty illusions about the public, especially about publishers and editors. It's not for *such* animals you work—it's for those who know, *coloro che sanno;* so keep straight for *me* if you can't keep straight for yourself. There's a certain sort of thing you tried for from the first—and a very good thing it is. But this twaddle isn't *in* it." When I talked with Hawley later about "Rutland Ramsay" and its possible successors he declared that I must get back into my boat again or I would go to the bottom. His voice in short was the voice of warning.

I noted the warning, but I didn't turn my friends out of doors. They bored me a good deal; but the very fact that they bored me admonished me not to sacrifice them—if there was anything to be done with them—simply to irritation. As I look back at this phase they seem to me to have pervaded my life not a little. I have a vision of them as most of the time in my studio, seated, against the wall, on an old velvet bench to be out of the way, and looking like a pair of patient courtiers in a royal ante-chamber. I am convinced that during the coldest weeks of the winter they held their ground because it saved them fire. Their newness was losing its gloss, and it was impossible not to feel that they were objects of charity. Whenever Miss Churm arrived they went away, and after I was fairly launched in "Rutland Ramsay" Miss Churm arrived pretty often. They managed to express to me tacitly that they supposed I wanted her for the low life of the book, and I let them suppose it, since they had attempted to study the work—it was lying about the studio—without discovering that it dealt only with the highest circles. They had dipped into the most brilliant of our novelists without deciphering many passages. I still took an hour from them, now and again, in spite of Jack Hawley's warning: it would be time enough to dismiss them, if dismissal should be necessary, when the rigour of the season was over. Hawley had made their acquaintance—he had met them at my fireside—and thought them a ridiculous pair. Learning that he was a painter they tried to approach him, to show him too that they were the real thing; but he looked at them, across the big room, as if they were miles away: they were a compendium of everything that he most objected to in the social system of his country. Such people as that, all convention and patent-leather, with ejaculations that stopped conversation, had no business in a studio. A studio was a place to learn to see, and how could you see through a pair of feather beds?

The main inconvenience I suffered at their hands was that, at first, I was shy of letting them discover how my artful little servant had begun

to sit to me for "Rutland Ramsay." They knew that I had been odd
enough (they were prepared by this time to allow oddity to artists), to
pick a foreign vagabond out of the streets, when I might have had a person
with whiskers and credentials; but it was some time before they learned
how high I rated his accomplishments. They found him in an attitude more
than once, but they never doubted I was doing him as an organ-grinder.
There were several things they never guessed, and one of them was that
for a striking scene in the novel, in which a footman briefly figured, it occurred to me to make use of Major Monarch as the menial. I kept putting
this off, I didn't like to ask him to don the livery—besides the difficulty of
finding a livery to fit him. At last, one day late in the winter, when I was
at work on the despised Oronte (he caught one's idea in an instant), and
was in the glow of feeling that I was going very straight, they came in,
the Major and his wife, with their society laugh about nothing (there was
less and less to laugh at), like country-callers—they always reminded me
of that—who have walked across the park after church and are presently
persuaded to stay to luncheon. Luncheon was over, but they could stay
to tea—I knew they wanted it. The fit was on me, however, and I couldn't
let my ardour cool and my work wait, with the fading daylight, while my
model prepared it. So I asked Mrs. Monarch if she would mind laying it
out—a request which, for an instant, brought all the blood to her face. Her
eyes were on her husband's for a second, and some mute telegraphy
passed between them. Their folly was over the next instant; his cheerful
shrewdness put an end to it. So far from pitying their wounded pride, I
must add, I was moved to give it as complete a lesson as I could. They
bustled about together and got out the cups and saucers and made the
kettle boil. I know they felt as if they were waiting on my servant, and
when the tea was prepared I said: "He'll have a cup, please—he's tired."
Mrs. Monarch brought him one where he stood, and he took it from her
as if he had been a gentleman at a party, squeezing a crush-hat with an
elbow.

Then it came over me that she had made a great effort for me—made it
with a kind of nobleness—and that I owed her a compensation. Each time
I saw her after this I wondered what the compensation could be. I couldn't
go on doing the wrong thing to oblige them. Oh, it *was* the wrong thing,
the stamp of the work for which they sat—Hawley was not the only person to say it now. I sent in a large number of the drawings I had made for
"Rutland Ramsay," and I received a warning that was more to the point
than Hawley's. The artistic adviser of the house for which I was working
was of opinion that many of my illustrations were not what had been
looked for. Most of these illustrations were the subjects in which the
Monarchs had figured. Without going into the question of what *had* been

looked for, I saw at this rate I shouldn't get the other books to do. I hurled myself in despair upon Miss Churm, I put her through all her paces. I not only adopted Oronte publicly as my hero, but one morning when the Major looked in to see if I didn't require him to finish a figure for the *Cheapside,* for which he had begun to sit the week before, I told him that I had changed my mind—I would do the drawing from my man. At this my visitor turned pale and stood looking at me. "Is *he* your idea of an English gentleman?" he asked.

I was disappointed, I was nervous, I wanted to get on with my work; so I replied with irritation: "Oh, my dear Major—I can't be ruined for *you!*"

He stood another moment; then, without a word, he quitted the studio. I drew a long breath when he was gone, for I said to myself that I shouldn't see him again. I had not told him definitely that I was in danger of having my work rejected, but I was vexed at his not having felt the catastrophe in the air, read with me the moral of our fruitless collaboration, the lesson that, in the deceptive atmosphere of art, even the highest respectability may fail of being plastic.

I didn't owe my friends money, but I did see them again. They re-appeared together, three days later, and under the circumstances there was something tragic in the fact. It was a proof to me that they could find nothing else in life to do. They had threshed the matter out in a dismal conference—they had digested the bad news that they were not in for the series. If they were not useful to me even for the *Cheapside* their function seemed difficult to determine, and I could only judge at first that they had come, forgivingly, decorously, to take a last leave. This made me rejoice in secret that I had little leisure for a scene; for I had placed both my other models in position together and I was pegging away at a drawing from which I hoped to derive glory. It had been suggested by the passage in which Rutland Ramsay, drawing up a chair to Artemisia's piano-stool, says extraordinary things to her while she ostensibly fingers out a difficult piece of music. I had done Miss Churm at the piano before—it was an attitude in which she knew how to take on an absolutely poetic grace. I wished the two figures to "compose" together, intensely, and my little Italian had entered perfectly into my conception. The pair were vividly before me, the piano had been pulled out; it was a charming picture of blended youth and murmured love, which I had only to catch and keep. My visitors stood and looked at it, and I was friendly to them over my shoulder.

They made no response, but I was used to silent company and went on with my work, only a little disconcerted (even though exhilarated by the sense that *this* was at least the ideal thing), at not having got rid of them after all. Presently I heard Mrs. Monarch's sweet voice beside, or rather above me: "I wish her hair was a little better done." I looked up and she was staring with a strange fixedness at Miss Churm, whose back was turned to her. "Do you mind my just touching it?" she went on—a question which made me spring up for an instant, as with the instinctive fear that she might do the young lady a harm. But she quieted me with a glance I shall never forget—I confess I should like to have been able to paint *that*—and went for a moment to my model. She spoke to her softly, laying a hand upon her shoulder and bending over her; and as the girl, understanding, gratefully assented, she disposed her rough curls, with a few quick passes, in such a way as to make Miss Churm's head twice as charming. It was one of the most heroic personal services I have ever seen rendered. Then Mrs. Monarch turned away with a low sigh and, looking about her as if for something to do, stooped to the floor with a noble humility and picked up a dirty rag that had dropped out of my paint-box.

The Major meanwhile had also been looking for something to do and, wandering to the other end of the studio, saw before him my breakfast things, neglected, unremoved. "I say, can't I be useful *here?*" he called out to me with an irrepressible quaver. I assented with a laugh that I fear was awkward and for the next ten minutes, while I worked, I heard the light clatter of china and the tinkle of spoons and glass. Mrs. Monarch assisted her husband—they washed up my crockery, they put it away. They wandered off into my little scullery, and I afterwards found that they had cleaned my knives and that my slender stock of plate [11] had an unprecedented surface. When it came over me, the latent eloquence of what they were doing, I confess that my drawing was blurred for a moment—the picture swam. They had accepted their failure, but they couldn't accept their fate. They had bowed their heads in bewilderment to the perverse and cruel law in virtue of which the real thing could be so much less precious than the unreal; but they didn't want to starve. If my servants were my models, my models might be my servants. They would reverse the parts—the others would sit for the ladies and gentlemen, and *they* would do the work. They would still be in the studio—it was an intense dumb appeal to me not to turn them out. "Take us on," they wanted to say—"we'll do *anything*."

When all this hung before me the *afflatus* vanished—my pencil dropped from my hand. My sitting was spoiled and I got rid of my sitters, who were also evidently rather mystified and awestruck. Then, alone with the Major and his wife, I had a most uncomfortable moment. He put their prayer into a single sentence: "I say, you know—just let *us* do for you, can't you?" I couldn't—it was dreadful to see them emptying my slops; but I pretended I could, to oblige them, for about a week. Then I gave

11. **plate:** table utensils of gold, silver, or some other metal; here probably silver dishes.

them a sum of money to go away; and I never saw them again. I obtained the remaining books, but my friend Hawley repeats that Major and Mrs. Monarch did me a permanent harm, got me into a second-rate trick. If it be true I am content to have paid the price—for the memory.

Joseph Conrad

YOUTH

THIS *could have occurred nowhere but in England, where men and sea interpenetrate, so to speak—the sea entering into the life of most men, and the men knowing something, or everything about the sea, in the way of amusement, of travel, or of breadwinning.*

We were sitting around a mahogany table that reflected the bottle, the claret-glasses, and our faces as we leaned on our elbows. There was a director of companies, an accountant, a lawyer, Marlow, and myself. The director had been a Conway *boy, the accountant had served four years at sea, the lawyer—a fine crusted Tory, High Churchman, the best of old fellows, the soul of honour—had been chief officer in the* P. & O. *service in the good old days when mail-boats were square-rigged at least on two masts, and used to come down the China Sea before a fair monsoon with stun'sails set alow and aloft. We all began life in the merchant service. Between the five of us there was a strong bond of the sea, and also the fellowship of the craft, which no amount of enthusiasm for yachting, cruising, and so on can give, since one is only the amusement of life and the other is life itself.*

Marlow (at least I think that is how he spelled his name) told the story, or rather the chronicle, of a voyage:—

Yes, I have seen a little of the Eastern seas; but what I remember best is my first voyage there. You fellows know there are those voyages that seem ordered for the illustration of life, that might stand for a symbol of existence. You fight, work, sweat, nearly kill yourself, sometimes do kill yourself, trying to accomplish something—and you can't. Not from any fault of yours. You simply can do nothing, neither great nor little—not a thing in the world—not even marry an old maid, or get a wretched 600-ton cargo of coal to its port of destination.

It was altogether a memorable affair. It was my first voyage to the East, and my first voyage as second mate; it was also my skipper's first command. You'll admit it was time. He was sixty if a day; a little man, with a broad, not very straight back, with bowed shoulders and one leg more bandy than the other, he had that queer twisted-about appearance you see so often in men who work in the fields. He had a nut-cracker face—chin and nose trying to come together over a sunken mouth—and it was framed in iron-grey fluffy hair, that looked like a chin-strap of cotton-wool sprinkled with coal-dust. And he had blue eyes in that old face of his, which were amazingly like a boy's, with that candid expression some quite common men preserve to the end of their days by a rare internal gift of simplicity of heart and rectitude of soul. What induced him to accept me was a wonder. I had come out of a crack Australian clipper, where I had been third officer, and he seemed to have a prejudice against crack clippers as aristocratic and high-toned. He said to me, "You know, in this ship you will have to work." I said I had to work in every ship I had ever been in. "Ah, but this is different, and you gentlemen out of them big ships; . . . but there! I dare say you will do. Join tomorrow."

I joined tomorrow. It was twenty-two years ago; and I was just twenty. How time passes! It was one of the happiest days of my life. Fancy! Second mate for the first time—a really responsible officer! I wouldn't have thrown up my new billet for a fortune. The mate looked me over carefully. He was also an old chap, but of another stamp. He had a Roman nose, a snow-white, long beard, and his name was Mahon, but he insisted that it should be pronounced Mann. He was well connected; yet there was something wrong with his luck, and he had never got on.

As to the captain, he had been for years in coasters, then in the Mediterranean, and last in the West Indian trade. He had never been round the Capes.[1] He could just write a kind of sketchy hand, and didn't care for writing at all. Both were thorough good seamen of course, and between those two old chaps I felt like a small boy between two grandfathers.

The ship also was old. Her name was the *Judea*. Queer name, isn't it? She belonged to a man Wilmer, Wilcox—some name like that; but he has been bankrupt and dead these twenty years or more, and his name don't matter. She had been laid up in Shadwell[2] basin for ever so long. You may imagine her state. She was all rust, dust, grime—soot aloft, dirt on deck. To me it was like coming out of a palace into a ruined cottage. She was about 400 tons, had a primitive windlass, wooden latches to the doors, not a bit

---

1. **Capes:** Cape Horn and Cape of Good Hope.
2. **Shadwell:** a part of London in the area of the shipping docks on the Thames River.

of brass about her, and a big square stern. There was on it, below her name in big letters, a lot of scrollwork, with the gilt off, and some sort of a coat of arms, with the motto "Do or Die" underneath. I remember it took my fancy immensely. There was a touch of romance in it, something that made me love the old thing—something that appealed to my youth!

We left London in ballast—sand ballast—to load a cargo of coal in a northern port for Bankok. Bankok! I thrilled. I had been six years at sea, but had only seen Melbourne and Sydney, very good places, charming places in their way—but Bankok!

We worked out of the Thames under canvas, with a North Sea pilot on board. His name was Jermyn, and he dodged all day long about the galley drying his handkerchief before the stove. Apparently he never slept. He was a dismal man, with a perpetual tear sparkling at the end of his nose, who either had been in trouble, or was in trouble, or expected to be in trouble—couldn't be happy unless something went wrong. He mistrusted my youth, my common sense, and my seamanship, and made a point of showing it in a hundred little ways. I dare say he was right. It seems to me I knew very little then, and I know not much more now; but I cherish a hate for that Jermyn to this day.

We were a week working up as far as Yarmouth Roads, and then we got into a gale—the famous October gale of twenty-two years ago. It was wind, lightning, sleet, snow, and a terrific sea. We were flying light, and you may imagine how bad it was when I tell you we had smashed bulwarks and a flooded deck. On the second night she shifted her ballast into the lee bow, and by that time we had been blown off somewhere on the Dogger Bank. There was nothing for it but go below with shovels and try to right her, and there we were in that vast hold, gloomy like a cavern, the tallow dips stuck and flickering on the beams, the gale howling above, the ship tossing about like mad on her side; there we all were, Jermyn, the captain, everyone, hardly able to keep our feet, engaged on that gravedigger's work, and trying to toss shovelfuls of wet sand up to windward. At every tumble of the ship you could see vaguely in the dim light men falling down with a great flourish of shovels. One of the ship's boys (we had two), impressed by the weirdness of the scene, wept as if his heart would break. We could hear him blubbering somewhere in the shadows.

On the third day the gale died out, and by and by a north-country tug picked us up. We took sixteen days in all to get from London to the Tyne! When we got into dock we had lost our turn for loading, and they hauled us off to a tier [3] where we remained for a month. Mrs. Beard (the captain's name was Beard) came from Colchester to see the old man. She lived on board. The crew of runners had left, and there remained only the officers,

3. **tier:** a row of moored or anchored ships.

one boy and the steward, a mulatto who answered to the name of Abraham. Mrs. Beard was an old woman, with a face all wrinkled and ruddy like a winter apple, and the figure of a young girl. She caught sight of me once, sewing on a button, and insisted on having my shirts to repair. This was something different from the captains' wives I had known on board crack clippers. When I brought her the shirts, she said: "And the socks? They want mending, I am sure, and John's—Captain Beard's—things are all in order now. I would be glad of something to do." Bless the old woman. She overhauled my outfit for me, and meantime I read for the first time *Sartor Resartus* and Burnaby's *Ride to Khiva*.[4] I didn't understand much of the first then; but I remember I preferred the soldier to the philosopher at the time; a preference which life has only confirmed. One was a man, and the other was either more—or less. However, they are both dead and Mrs. Beard is dead, and youth, strength, genius, thoughts, achievements, simple hearts—all die. . . . No matter.

They loaded us at last. We shipped a crew. Eight able seamen and two boys. We hauled off one evening to the buoys at the dock-gates, ready to go out, and with a fair prospect of beginning the voyage next day. Mrs. Beard was to start for home by a late train. When the ship was fast we went to tea. We sat rather silent through the meal—Mahon, the old couple, and I. I finished first, and slipped away for a smoke, my cabin being in a deck-house just against the poop. It was high water, blowing fresh with a drizzle; the double dock-gates were opened, and the steam-colliers were going in and out in the darkness with their lights burning bright, a great plashing of propellers, rattling of winches, and a lot of hailing on the pierheads. I watched the procession of headlights gliding high and of green lights gliding low in the night, when suddenly a red gleam flashed at me, vanished, came into view again, and remained. The fore-end of a steamer loomed up close. I shouted down the cabin, "Come up, quick!" and then heard a startled voice saying afar in the dark, "Stop her, sir." A bell jingled. Another voice cried warningly, "We are going right into that barque, sir." The answer to this was a gruff "All right," and the next thing was a heavy crash as the steamer struck a glancing blow with the bluff of her bow about our fore-rigging. There was a moment of confusion, yelling, and running about. Steam roared. Then somebody was heard saying, "All clear, sir." . . . "Are you all right?" asked the gruff voice. I had jumped forward to see the damage, and hailed back, "I think so." "Easy astern," said the gruff voice. A bell jingled. "What steamer is that?" screamed Mahon. By that time she was no more to us than a bulky shadow maneuvering a little way off. They shouted at us some name—a woman's

---

4. *Sartor Resartus:* a discourse on the philosophy of clothes by Thomas Carlyle; Frederick Burnaby was a nineteenth-century English soldier and traveler.

name, Miranda or Melissa—or some such thing. "This means another month in this beastly hole," said Mahon to me, as we peered with lamps about the splintered bulwarks and broken braces. "But where's the captain?"

We had not heard or seen anything of him all that time. We went aft to look. A doleful voice arose hailing somewhere in the middle of the dock, "*Judea* ahoy!" . . . How the devil did he get there? . . . "Hallo!" we shouted. "I am adrift in our boat without oars," he cried. A belated waterman offered his services, and Mahon struck a bargain with him for half a crown to tow our skipper alongside; but it was Mrs. Beard that came up the ladder first. They had been floating about the dock in that mizzly cold rain for nearly an hour. I was never so surprised in my life.

It appears that when he heard my shout "Come up" he understood at once what was the matter, caught up his wife, ran on deck, and across, and down into our boat, which was fast to the ladder. Not bad for a sixty-year-old. Just imagine that old fellow saving heroically in his arms that old woman—the woman of his life. He set her down on a thwart, and was ready to climb back on board when the painter came adrift somehow, and away they went together. Of course in the confusion we did not hear him shouting. He looked abashed. She said cheerfully, "I suppose it does not matter my losing the train now?" "No, Jenny—you go below and get warm," he growled. Then to us: "A sailor has no business with a wife—I say. There I was, out of the ship. Well, no harm done this time. Let's go and look at what that fool of a steamer smashed."

It wasn't much, but it delayed us three weeks. At the end of that time, the captain being engaged with his agents, I carried Mrs. Beard's bag to the railway station and put her all comfy into a third-class carriage. She lowered the window to say, "You are a good young man. If you see John—Captain Beard—without his muffler at night, just remind him from me to keep his throat well wrapped up." "Certainly, Mrs. Beard," I said. "You are a good young man; I noticed how attentive you are to John—to Captain—" The train pulled out suddenly; I took my cap off to the old woman: I never saw her again. . . . Pass the bottle.

We went to sea next day. When we made that start for Bankok we had been already three months out of London. We had expected to be a fortnight or so—at the outside.

It was January, and the weather was beautiful—the beautiful sunny winter weather that has more charm than in the summertime, because it is unexpected, and crisp, and you know it won't, it can't, last long. It's like a windfall, like a godsend, like an unexpected piece of luck.

It lasted all down the North Sea, all down Channel; and it lasted till we were three hundred miles or so to the westward of the Lizards: then the wind went round to the sou'west and began to pipe up. In two days it blew a gale. The *Judea*, hove to, wallowed on the Atlantic like an old candlebox. It blew day after day: it blew with spite, without interval, without mercy, without rest. The world was nothing but an immensity of great foaming waves rushing at us, under a sky low enough to touch with the hand and dirty like a smoked ceiling. In the stormy space surrounding us there was as much flying spray as air. Day after day and night after night there was nothing round the ship but the howl of the wind, the tumult of the sea, the noise of water pouring over her deck. There was no rest for her and no rest for us. She tossed, she pitched, she stood on her head, she sat on her tail, she rolled, she groaned, and we had to hold on while on deck and cling to our bunks when below, in a constant effort of body and worry of mind.

One night Mahon spoke through the small window of my berth. It opened right into my very bed, and I was lying there sleepless, in my boots, feeling as though I had not slept for years, and could not if I tried. He said excitedly—

"You got the sounding-rod [5] in here, Marlow? I can't get the pumps to suck. By God! it's no child's play."

I gave him the sounding-rod and lay down again, trying to think of various things—but I thought only of the pumps. When I came on deck they were still at it, and my watch relieved at the pumps. By the light of the lantern brought on deck to examine the sounding-rod I caught a glimpse of their weary, serious faces. We pumped all the four hours. We pumped all night, all day, all the week—watch and watch. She was working herself loose, and leaked badly—not enough to drown us at once, but enough to kill us with the work at the pumps. And while we pumped the ship was going from us piecemeal: the bulwarks went, the stanchions were torn out, the ventilators smashed, the cabin-door burst in. There was not a dry spot in the ship. She was being gutted bit by bit. The long-boat changed, as if by magic, into matchwood where she stood in her gripes.[6] I had lashed her myself, and was rather proud of my handiwork, which had withstood so long the malice of the sea. And we pumped. And there was no break in the weather. The sea was white like a sheet of foam, like a caldron of boiling milk; there was not a break in the clouds, no—not the size of a man's hand—no, not for so much as ten seconds. There was for us no sky, there were for us no stars, no sun, no universe—nothing but angry clouds and an infuriated sea. We pumped watch and watch, for dear life; and it seemed to last for months, for years, for all eternity, as though

5. **sounding-rod:** an iron rod, marked in feet and inches, used to measure the depth of water.
6. **gripes:** bands of iron by which a boat is lashed to the deck.

we had been dead and gone to a hell for sailors. We forgot the day of the
week, the name of the month, what year it was, and whether we had ever
been ashore. The sails blew away, she lay broadside-on under a weather-
cloth,[7] the ocean poured over her, and we did not care. We turned those
handles, and had the eyes of idiots. As soon as we had crawled on deck I
used to take a round turn with a rope about the men, the pumps, and the
mainmast, and we turned, we turned incessantly, with the water to our
waists, to our necks, over our heads. It was all one. We had forgotten how
it felt to be dry.

And there was somewhere in me the thought: By Jove! this is the deuce
of an adventure—something you read about; and it is my first voyage as
second mate—and I am only twenty—and here I am lasting it out as well
as any of these men, and keeping my chaps up to the mark. I was pleased.
I would not have given up the experience for worlds. I had moments of
exultation. Whenever the old dismantled craft pitched heavily with her
counter high in the air, she seemed to me to throw up, like an appeal, like
a defiance, like a cry to the clouds without mercy, the words written on
her stern: "*Judea*, London. Do or Die."

O youth! The strength of it, the faith of it, the imagination of it! To
me she was not an old rattletrap carting about the world a lot of coal for
a freight—to me she was the endeavour, the test, the trial of life. I think
of her with pleasure, with affection, with regret—as you would think of
someone dead you have loved. I shall never forget her. . . . Pass the bottle.
One night when tied to the mast, as I explained, we were pumping on,
deafened with the wind, and without spirit enough in us to wish ourselves
dead, a heavy sea crashed aboard and swept clean over us. As soon as I
got my breath I shouted, as in duty bound, "Keep on, boys!" when suddenly I felt something hard floating on deck strike the calf of my leg. I
made a grab at it and missed. It was so dark we could not see each other's
faces within a foot—you understand.

After that thump the ship kept quiet for a while, and the thing, whatever it was, struck my leg again. This time I caught it—and it was a sauce-
pan. At first, being stupid with fatigue and thinking of nothing but the
pumps, I did not understand what I had in my hand. Suddenly it dawned
upon me, and I shouted, "Boys, the house on deck is gone. Leave this, and
let's look for the cook."

There was a deck-house forward, which contained the galley, the cook's
berth, and the quarters of the crew. As we had expected for days to see
it swept away, the hands had been ordered to sleep in the cabin—the only
safe place in the ship. The steward, Abraham, however, persisted in clinging to his berth, stupidly, like a mule—from sheer fright I believe, like an

7. **weather-cloth:** canvas cover.

animal that won't leave a stable falling in an earthquake. So we went to
look for him. It was chancing death, since once out of our lashings we
were as exposed as if on a raft. But we went. The house was shattered as
if a shell had exploded inside. Most of it had gone overboard—stove, men's
quarters, and their property, all was gone; but two posts, holding a portion
of the bulkhead to which Abraham's bunk was attached, remained as if by
a miracle. We groped in the ruins and came upon this, and there he was,
sitting in his bunk, surrounded by foam and wreckage, jabbering cheerfully to himself. He was out of his mind; completely and forever mad,
with this sudden shock coming upon the fag-end of his endurance. We
snatched him up, lugged him aft, and pitched him head-first down the
cabin companion. You understand there was no time to carry him down
with infinite precautions and wait to see how he got on. Those below
would pick him up at the bottom of the stairs all right. We were in a
hurry to go back to the pumps. That business could not wait. A bad leak
is an inhuman thing.

One would think that the sole purpose of that fiendish gale had been
to make a lunatic of that poor devil of a mulatto. It eased before morning,
and next day the sky cleared, and as the sea went down the leak took up.[8]
When it came to bending a fresh set of sails the crew demanded to put
back—and really there was nothing else to do. Boats gone, decks swept
clean, cabin gutted, men without a stitch but what they stood in, stores
spoiled, ship strained. We put her head for home, and—would you believe
it? The wind came east right in our teeth. It blew fresh, it blew continuously. We had to beat up every inch of the way, but she did not leak so
badly, the water keeping comparatively smooth. Two hours' pumping in
every four is no joke—but it kept her afloat as far as Falmouth.[9]

The good people there live on casualties of the sea, and no doubt were
glad to see us. A hungry crowd of shipwrights sharpened their chisels at
the sight of that carcass of a ship. And, by Jove! they had pretty pickings
off us before they were done. I fancy the owner was already in a tight
place. There were delays. Then it was decided to take part of the cargo
out and caulk her topsides. This was done, the repairs finished, cargo reshipped; a new crew came on board, and we went out—for Bankok. At
the end of a week we were back again. The crew said they weren't going
to Bankok—a hundred and fifty days' passage—in a something hooker that
wanted pumping eight hours out of the twenty-four; and the nautical
papers inserted again the little paragraph: "*Judea*. Barque. Tyne to Bankok; coals; put back to Falmouth leaky and with crew refusing duty."

8. **took up**: closed up of itself.
9. **Falmouth**: a seaport on the Channel in southwestern England.

There were more delays—more tinkering. The owner came down for a day, and said she was as right as a little fiddle. Poor old Captain Beard looked like the ghost of a Geordie [10] skipper—through the worry and humiliation of it. Remember he was sixty, and it was his first command. Mahon said it was a foolish business, and would end badly. I loved the ship more than ever, and wanted awfully to get to Bankok. To Bankok! Magic name, blessed name. Mesopotamia wasn't a patch on it. Remember I was twenty, and it was my first second-mate's billet, and the East was waiting for me.

We went out and anchored in the outer roads with a fresh crew—the third. She leaked worse than ever. It was as if those confounded shipwrights had actually made a hole in her. This time we did not even go outside. The crew simply refused to man the windlass.

They towed us back to the inner harbor, and we became a fixture, a feature, an institution of the place. People pointed us out to visitors as "That 'ere barque that's going to Bankok—has been here six months—put back three times." On holidays the small boys pulling about in boats would hail, "*Judea*, ahoy!" and if a head showed above the rail shouted, "Where you bound to?—Bankok?" and jeered. We were only three on board. The poor old skipper mooned in the cabin. Mahon undertook the cooking, and unexpectedly developed all a Frenchman's genius for preparing nice little messes. I looked languidly after the rigging. We became citizens of Falmouth. Every shopkeeper knew us. At the barber's or tobacconist's they asked familiarly, "Do you think you will ever get to Bankok?" Meantime the owner, the underwriters, and the charterers squabbled amongst themselves in London, and our pay went on. . . . Pass the bottle.

It was horrid. Morally it was worse than pumping for life. It seemed as though we had been forgotten by the world, belonged to nobody, would get nowhere; it seemed that, as if bewitched, we would have to live for ever and ever in that inner harbor, a derision and a byword to generations of longshore loafers and dishonest boatmen. I obtained three months' pay and a five days' leave, and made a rush for London. It took me a day to get there and pretty well another to come back—but three months' pay went all the same. I don't know what I did with it. I went to a music-hall, I believe, lunched, dined, and supped in a swell place in Regent Street, and was back to time, with nothing but a complete set of Byron's works and a new railway rug to show for three months' worth. The boatman who pulled me off to the ship said: "Hallo! I thought you had left the old thing. *She* will never get to Bankok." "That's all *you* know about it," I said scornfully—but I didn't like that prophecy at all.

10. **Geordie:** a coal-carrying vessel.

Suddenly a man, some kind of agent to somebody, appeared with full powers. He had grog-blossoms [11] all over his face, an indomitable energy, and was a jolly soul. We leaped into life again. A hulk came alongside, took our cargo, and then we went into dry dock to get our copper stripped.[12] No wonder she leaked. The poor thing, strained beyond endurance by the gale, had, as if in disgust, spat out all the oakum of her lower seams. She was recaulked, new coppered, and made as tight as a bottle. We went back to the hulk and reshipped our cargo.

Then, on a fine moonlight night, all the rats left the ship.

We had been infested with them. They had destroyed our sails, consumed more stores than the crew, affably shared our beds and our dangers, and now, when the ship was made seaworthy, concluded to clear out. I called Mahon to enjoy the spectacle. Rat after rat appeared on our rail, took a last look over his shoulder, and leaped with a hollow thud into the empty hulk. We tried to count them, but soon lost the tale. Mahon said: "Well, well! don't talk to me about the intelligence of rats. They ought to have left before, when we had that narrow squeak from foundering. There you have the proof how silly is the superstition about them. They leave a good ship for an old rotten hulk, where there is nothing to eat, too, the fools! . . . I don't believe they know what is safe or what is good for them, any more than you or I."

And after some more talk we agreed that the wisdom of rats had been grossly overrated, being in fact no greater than that of men.

The story of the ship was known, by this, all up the Channel from Land's End to the Forelands,[13] and we could get no crew on the south coast. They sent us one all complete from Liverpool, and we left once more—for Bankok.

We had fair breezes, smooth water right into the tropics, and the old *Judea* lumbered along in the sunshine. When she went eight knots everything cracked aloft, and we tied our caps to our heads; but mostly she strolled on at the rate of three miles an hour. What could you expect? She was tired—that old ship. Her youth was where mine is—where yours is—you fellows who listen to this yarn; and what friend would throw your years and your weariness in your face? We didn't grumble at her. To us aft, at least, it seemed as though we had been born in her, reared in her, had lived in her for ages, had never known any other ship. I would just as soon have abused the old village church at home for not being a cathedral.

And for me there was also my youth to make me patient. There was all

11. **grog-blossoms:** skin eruptions caused by excessive consumption of alcoholic liquors.
12. **copper stripped:** copper sheathing removed.
13. **Forelands:** two headlands in Kent on the southeast coast of England.

the East before me, and all life, and the thought that I had been tried in that ship and had come out pretty well. And I thought of men of old who, centuries ago, went that road in ships that sailed no better, to the land of palms, and spices, and yellow sands, and of brown nations ruled by kings more cruel than Nero the Roman, and more splendid than Solomon the Jew. The old bark lumbered on, heavy with her age and the burden of her cargo, while I lived the life of youth in ignorance and hope. She lumbered on through an interminable procession of days; and the fresh gilding flashed back at the setting sun, seemed to cry out over the darkening sea the words painted on her stern, "*Judea*, London. Do or Die."

Then we entered the Indian Ocean and steered northerly for Java Head. The winds were light. Weeks slipped by. She crawled on, do or die, and people at home began to think of posting us as overdue.

One Saturday evening, I being off duty, the men asked me to give them an extra bucket of water or so—for washing clothes. As I did not wish to screw on the fresh-water pump so late, I went forward whistling, and with a key in my hand to unlock the forepeak scuttle, intending to serve the water out of a spare tank we kept there.

The smell down below was as unexpected as it was frightful. One would have thought hundreds of paraffin-lamps had been flaring and smoking in that hole for days. I was glad to get out. The man with me coughed and said, "Funny smell, sir." I answered negligently, "It's good for the health they say," and walked aft.

The first thing I did was to put my head down the square of the midship ventilator. As I lifted the lid a visible breath, something like a thin fog, a puff of faint haze, rose from the opening. The ascending air was hot, and had a heavy, sooty, paraffiny smell. I gave one sniff, and put down the lid gently. It was no use choking myself. The cargo was on fire.

Next day she began to smoke in earnest. You see it was to be expected, for though the coal was of a safe kind, that cargo had been so handled, so broken up with handling, that it looked more like smithy coal [14] than anything else. Then it had been wetted—more than once. It rained all the time we were taking it back from the hulk, and now with this long passage it got heated, and there was another case of spontaneous combustion.

The captain called us into the cabin. He had a chart spread on the table, and looked unhappy. He said, "The coast of West Australia is near, but I mean to proceed to our destination. It is the hurricane month, too; but we will just keep her head for Bankok, and fight the fire. No more putting back anywhere, if we all get roasted. We will try first to stifle this 'ere damned combustion by want of air."

We tried. We battened down everything, and still she smoked. The

14. **smithy coal:** a grade of coal low in sulphur and ash, used by blacksmiths.

smoke kept coming out through imperceptible crevices; it forced itself through bulkheads and covers; it oozed here and there and everywhere in slender threads, in an invisible film, in an incomprehensible manner. It made its way into the cabin, into the forecastle; it poisoned the sheltered places on the deck, it could be sniffed as high as the mainyard. It was clear that if the smoke came out the air came in. This was disheartening. This combustion refused to be stifled.

We resolved to try water, and took the hatches off. Enormous volumes of smoke, whitish, yellowish, thick, greasy, misty, choking, ascended as high as the trucks. All hands cleared out aft. Then the poisonous cloud blew away, and we went back to work in a smoke that was no thicker now than that of an ordinary factory chimney.

We rigged the force-pump, got the hose along, and by-and-by it burst. Well, it was as old as the ship—a prehistoric hose, and past repair. Then we pumped with the feeble head-pump, drew water with buckets, and in this way managed in time to pour lots of Indian Ocean into the main hatch. The bright stream flashed in sunshine, fell into a layer of white crawling smoke, and vanished on the black surface of coal. Steam ascended mingling with the smoke. We poured salt water as into a barrel without a bottom. It was our fate to pump in that ship, to pump out of her, to pump into her; and after keeping water out of her to save ourselves from being drowned, we frantically poured water into her to save ourselves from being burned.

And she crawled on, do or die, in the serene weather. The sky was a miracle of purity, a miracle of azure. The sea was polished, was blue, was pellucid, was sparkling like a precious stone, extending on all sides, all round to the horizon—as if the whole terrestrial globe had been one jewel, one colossal sapphire, a single gem fashioned into a planet. And on the luster of the great calm waters the *Judea* glided imperceptibly, enveloped in languid and unclean vapors, in a lazy cloud that drifted to leeward, light and slow; a pestiferous cloud defiling the splendor of sea and sky.

All this time of course we saw no fire. The cargo smoldered at the bottom somewhere. Once Mahon, as we were working side by side, said to me with a queer smile: "Now, if she only would spring a tidy leak—like that time when we first left the Channel—it would put a stopper on this fire. Wouldn't it?" I remarked irrelevantly, "Do you remember the rats?"

We fought the fire and sailed the ship too as carefully as though nothing had been the matter. The steward cooked and attended on us. Of the other twelve men, eight worked while four rested. Everyone took his turn, captain included. There was equality, and if not exactly fraternity, then a deal of good feeling. Sometimes a man, as he dashed a bucketful of water down the hatchway, would yell out, "Hurrah for Bankok!" and the rest laughed. But generally we were taciturn and serious—and thirsty. Oh! how thirsty! And we had to be careful with the water. Strict allowance. The ship smoked, the sun blazed. . . . Pass the bottle.

We tried everything. We even made an attempt to dig down to the fire. No good, of course. No man could remain more than a minute below. Mahon, who went first, fainted there, and the man who went to fetch him out did likewise. We lugged them out on deck. Then I leaped down to show how easily it could be done. They had learned wisdom by that time, and contented themselves by fishing for me with a chain-hook [15] tied to a broom-handle, I believe. I did not offer to go and fetch up my shovel, which was left down below.

Things began to look bad. We put the long-boat into the water. The second boat was ready to swing out. We had also another, a 14-foot thing, on davits aft, where it was quite safe.

Then, behold, the smoke suddenly decreased. We redoubled our efforts to flood the bottom of the ship. In two days there was no smoke at all. Everybody was on the broad grin. This was on a Friday. On Saturday no work but sailing the ship, of course, was done. The men washed their clothes and their faces for the first time in a fortnight, and had a special dinner given them. They spoke of spontaneous combustion with contempt, and implied *they* were the boys to put out combustions. Somehow we all felt as though we each had inherited a large fortune. But a beastly smell of burning hung about the ship. Captain Beard had hollow eyes and sunken cheeks. I had never noticed so much before how twisted and bowed he was. He and Mahon prowled soberly about hatches and ventilators, sniffing. It struck me suddenly poor Mahon was a very, very old chap. As to me, I was as pleased and proud as though I had helped to win a great naval battle. O! Youth!

The night was fine. In the morning a homeward-bound ship passed us hull down—the first we had seen for months; but we were nearing the land at last, Java Head being about 190 miles off, and nearly due north.

Next day it was my watch on deck from eight to twelve. At breakfast the captain observed, "It's wonderful how that smell hangs about the cabin." About ten, the mate being on the poop, I stepped down on the main-deck for a moment. The carpenter's bench stood abaft the mainmast: I leaned against it sucking at my pipe, and the carpenter, a young chap, came to talk to me. He remarked, "I think we have done very well, haven't we?" and then I perceived with annoyance the fool was trying to tilt the bench. I said curtly, "Don't, Chips," and immediately became aware of a queer sensation, of an absurd delusion,—I seemed somehow to be in the

15. **chain-hook:** a hook used for dragging or lifting cables.

air. I heard all round me like a pent-up breath released—as if a thousand
giants simultaneously had said Phoo!—and felt a dull concussion which
made my ribs ache suddenly. No doubt about it—I was in the air, and my
body was describing a short parabola. But short as it was, I had the time
to think several thoughts in, as far as I can remember, the following order:
"This can't be the carpenter—What is it?—Some accident—Submarine vol-
cano?—Coals, gas!—By Jove! we are being blown up—Everybody's dead—
I am falling into the after-hatch—I see fire in it."

The coal-dust suspended in the air of the hold and glowed dull-red at
the moment of the explosion. In the twinkling of an eye, in an infinitesimal fraction of a second since the first tilt of the bench, I was sprawling
full length on the cargo. I picked myself up and scrambled out. It was
quick like a rebound. The deck was a wilderness of smashed timber, lying
crosswise like trees in a wood after a hurricane; an immense curtain of
soiled rags waved gently before me—it was the mainsail blown to strips.
I thought, The masts will be toppling over directly; and to get out of the
way bolted on all-fours towards the poop-ladder. The first person I saw
was Mahon, with eyes like saucers, his mouth open, and the long white
hair standing straight on end round his head like a silver halo. He was just
about to go down when the sight of the main-deck stirring, heaving up,
and changing into splinters before his eyes, petrified him on the top step.
I stared at him in unbelief, and he stared at me with a queer kind of
shocked curiosity. I did not know that I had no hair, no eyebrows, no eye-
lashes, that my young moustache was burned off, that my face was black,
one cheek laid open, my nose cut, and my chin bleeding. I had lost my
cap, one of my slippers, and my shirt was torn to rags. Of all this I was
not aware. I was amazed to see the ship still afloat, the poop-deck whole—
and, most of all, to see anybody alive. Also the peace of the sky and the
serenity of the sea were distinctly surprising. I suppose I expected to see
them convulsed with horror. . . . Pass the bottle.

There was a voice hailing the ship from somewhere—in the air, in the
sky—I couldn't tell. Presently I saw the captain—and he was mad. He asked
me eagerly, "Where's the cabin-table?" and to hear such a question was
a frightful shock. I had just been blown up, you understand, and vibrated
with that experience,—I wasn't quite sure whether I was alive. Mahon began to stamp with both feet and yelled at him, "Good God! don't you see
the deck's blown out of her?" I found my voice, and stammered out as if
conscious of some gross neglect of duty, "I don't know where the cabin-
table is." It was like an absurd dream.

Do you know what he wanted next? Well, he wanted to trim the yards.
Very placidly, and as if lost in thought, he insisted on having the foreyard
squared. "I don't know if there's anybody alive," said Mahon, almost tear-

fully. "Surely," he said, gently, "there will be enough left to square the foreyard."

The old chap, it seems, was in his own berth winding up the chronometers, when the shock sent him spinning. Immediately it occurred to him—as he said afterwards—that the ship had struck something, and he ran out into the cabin. There, he saw, the cabin-table had vanished somewhere. The deck being blown up, it had fallen down into the lazarette of course. Where we had our breakfast that morning he saw only a great hole in the floor. This appeared to him so awfully mysterious, and impressed him so immensely, that what he saw and heard after he got on deck were mere trifles in comparison. And, mark, he noticed directly the wheel deserted and his barque off her course—and his only thought was to get that miserable, stripped, undecked, smoldering shell of a ship back again with her head pointing at her port of destination. Bankok! That's what he was after. I tell you this quiet, bowed, bandy-legged, almost deformed little man was immense in the singleness of his idea and in his placid ignorance of our agitation. He motioned us forward with a commanding gesture, and went to take the wheel himself.

Yes; that was the first thing we did—trim the yards of that wreck! No one was killed, or even disabled, but everyone was more or less hurt. You should have seen them! Some were in rags, with black faces, like coal-heavers, like sweeps, and had bullet heads that seemed closely cropped, but were in fact singed to the skin. Others, of the watch below, awakened by being shot out from their collapsing bunks, shivered incessantly, and kept on groaning even as we went about our work. But they all worked. That crew of Liverpool hard cases had in them the right stuff. It's my experience they always have. It is the sea that gives it—the vastness, the loneliness surrounding their dark stolid souls. Ah! Well! we stumbled, we crept, we fell, we barked our shins on the wreckage, we hauled. The masts stood, but we did not know how much they might be charred down below. It was nearly calm, but a long swell ran from the west and made her roll. They might go at any moment. We looked at them with apprehension. One could not foresee which way they would fall.

Then we retreated aft and looked about us. The deck was a tangle of planks on edge, of planks on end, of splinters, of ruined woodwork. The masts rose from that chaos like big trees above a matted undergrowth. The interstices of that mass of wreckage were full of something whitish, sluggish, stirring—of something that was like a greasy fog. The smoke of the invisible fire was coming up again, was trailing, like a poisonous thick mist in some valley choked with dead wood. Already lazy wisps were beginning to curl upwards amongst the mass of splinters. Here and there a piece of timber, stuck upright, resembled a post. Half of a fife-rail had been shot through the foresail, and the sky made a patch of glorious blue in the ignobly soiled canvas. A portion of several boards holding together had fallen across the rail, and one end protruded overboard, like a gangway leading upon nothing, like a gangway leading over the deep sea, leading to death—as if inviting us to walk the plank at once and be done with our ridiculous troubles. And still the air, the sky—a ghost, something invisible was hailing the ship.

Someone had the sense to look over, and there was the helmsman, who had impulsively jumped overboard, anxious to come back. He yelled and swam lustily like a merman, keeping up with the ship. We threw him a rope, and presently he stood amongst us streaming with water and very crestfallen. The captain had surrendered the wheel, and apart, elbow on rail and chin in hand, gazed at the sea wistfully. We asked ourselves, What next? I thought, Now, this is something like. This is great. I wonder what will happen. O youth!

Suddenly Mahon sighted a steamer far astern. Captain Beard said, "We may do something with her yet." We hoisted two flags, which said in the international language of the sea, "On fire. Want immediate assistance." The steamer grew bigger rapidly, and by and by spoke with two flags on her foremast, "I am coming to your assistance."

In half an hour she was abreast, to windward, within hail, and rolling slightly, with her engines stopped. We lost our composure, and yelled all together with excitement, "We've been blown up." A man in a white helmet, on the bridge, cried, "Yes! All right! All right!" and he nodded his head, and smiled, and made soothing motions with his hand as though at a lot of frightened children. One of the boats dropped in the water, and walked towards us upon the sea with her long oars. Four Calashes pulled a swinging stroke. This was my first sight of Malay seamen. I've known them since, but what struck me then was their unconcern: they came alongside, and even the bowman standing up and holding to our mainchains with the boat-hook did not deign to lift his head for a glance. I thought people who had been blown up deserved more attention.

A little man, dry like a chip and agile like a monkey, clambered up. It was the mate of the steamer. He gave one look, and cried, "Oh, boys— you had better quit."

We were silent. He talked apart with the captain for a time,—seemed to argue with him. Then they went away together to the steamer.

When our skipper came back we learned that the steamer was the *Somerville*, Captain Nash, from West Australia to Singapore via Batavia with mails, and that the agreement was she should tow us to Anjer [16] or Batavia,

16. **Anjer:** a town on the west coast of India.

if possible, where we could extinguish the fire by scuttling, and then proceed on our voyage—to Bankok! The old man seemed excited. "We will do it yet," he said to Mahon, fiercely. He shook his fist at the sky. Nobody else said a word.

At noon the steamer began to tow. She went ahead slim and high, and what was left of the *Judea* followed at the end of seventy fathom of towrope,—followed her swiftly like a cloud of smoke with mast-heads protruding above. We went aloft to furl the sails. We coughed on the yards, and were careful about the bunts. Do you see the lot of us there, putting a neat furl on the sails of that ship doomed to arrive nowhere? There was not a man who didn't think that at any moment the masts would topple over. From aloft we could not see the ship for smoke, and they worked carefully, passing the gaskets with even turns. "Harbor furl—aloft there!" cried Mahon from below.

You understand this? I don't think one of those chaps expected to get down in the usual way. When we did I heard them saying to each other, "Well, I thought we would come down overboard, in a lump—sticks and all—blame me if I didn't." "That's what I was thinking to myself," would answer wearily another battered and bandaged scarecrow. And, mind, these were men without the drilled-in habit of obedience. To an onlooker they would be a lot of profane scallywags without a redeeming point. What made them do it—what made them obey me when I, thinking consciously how fine it was, made them drop the bunt of the foresail twice to try and do it better? What? They had no professional reputation—no examples, no praise. It wasn't a sense of duty; they all knew well enough how to shirk, and laze, and dodge—when they had a mind to it—and mostly they had. Was it the two pounds ten a month that sent them there? They didn't think their pay half good enough. No; it was something in them, something inborn and subtle and everlasting. I don't say positively that the crew of a French or German merchantman wouldn't have done it, but I doubt whether it would have been done in the same way. There was a completeness in it, something solid like a principle, and masterful like an instinct—a disclosure of something secret—of that hidden something, that gift of good or evil that makes racial difference, that shapes the fate of nations.

It was that night at ten that, for the first time since we had been fighting it, we saw the fire. The speed of the towing had fanned the smoldering destruction. A blue gleam appeared forward, shining below the wreck of the deck. It wavered in patches, it seemed to stir and creep like the light of a glowworm. I saw it first, and told Mahon. "Then the game's up," he said. "We had better stop this towing, or she will burst out suddenly fore

and aft before we can clear out." We set up a yell; rang bells to attract
their attention; they towed on. At last Mahon and I had to crawl forward
and cut the rope with an axe. There was no time to cast off the lashings.
Red tongues could be seen licking the wilderness of splinters under our
feet as we made our way back to the poop.

Of course they very soon found out in the steamer that the rope was
gone. She gave a loud blast of her whistle, her lights were seen sweeping
in a wide circle, she came up ranging close alongside, and stopped. We
were all in a tight group on the poop looking at her. Every man had saved
a little bundle or a bag. Suddenly a conical flame with a twisted top shot
up forward and threw upon the black sea a circle of light, with the two
vessels side by side and heaving gently in its centre. Captain Beard had
been sitting on the gratings still and mute for hours, but now he rose
slowly and advanced in front of us, to the mizzen-shrouds. Captain Nash
hailed: "Come along! Look sharp. I have mail-bags on board. I will take
you and your boats to Singapore."

"Thank you! No!" said our skipper. "We must see the last of the ship."

"I can't stand by any longer," shouted the other. "Mails—you know."

"Ay, ay! We are all right."

"Very well! I'll report you in Singapore. . . . Good-bye!"

He waved his hand. Our men dropped their bundles quietly. The
steamer moved ahead, and passing out of the circle of light, vanished at
once from our sight, dazzled by the fire which burned fiercely. And then
I knew that I would see the East first as commander of a small boat. I
thought it fine; and the fidelity to the old ship was fine. We should see the
last of her. Oh, the glamour of youth! Oh, the fire of it, more dazzling
than the flames of the burning ship, throwing a magic light on the wide
earth, leaping audaciously to the sky, presently to be quenched by time,
more cruel, more pitiless, more bitter than the sea—and like the flames of
the burning ship surrounded by an impenetrable night.

The old man warned us in his gentle and inflexible way that it was part
of our duty to save for the underwriters as much as we could of the ship's
gear. Accordingly we went to work aft, while she blazed forward to give
us plenty of light. We lugged out a lot of rubbish. What didn't we save?
An old barometer fixed with an absurd quantity of screws nearly cost me
my life: a sudden rush of smoke came upon me, and I just got away in
time. There were various stores, bolts of canvas, coils of rope; the poop
looked like a marine bazaar, and the boats were lumbered to the gunwales.
One would have thought the old man wanted to take as much as he could
of his first command with him. He was very, very quiet, but off his balance
evidently. Would you believe it? He wanted to take a length of old

stream-cable [17] and a kedge-anchor with him in the long-boat. We said, "Ay, ay, sir," deferentially, and on the quiet let the things slip overboard. The heavy medicine chest went that way, two bags of green coffee, tins of paint—fancy, paint!—a whole lot of things. Then I was ordered with two hands into the boats to make a stowage and get them ready against the time it would be proper for us to leave the ship.

We put everything straight, stepped the long-boat's mast for our skipper, who was to take charge of her, and I was not sorry to sit down for a moment. My face felt raw, every limb ached as if broken, I was aware of all my ribs, and would have sworn to a twist in the backbone. The boats, fast astern, lay in a deep shadow, and all around I could see the circle of the sea lighted by the fire. A gigantic flame arose forward straight and clear. It flared fierce, with noises like the whirr of wings, with rumbles as of thunder. There were cracks, detonations, and from the cone of flame the sparks flew upwards, as man is born to trouble, to leaky ships, and to ships that burn.

What bothered me was that the ship, lying broadside to the swell and to such wind as there was—a mere breath—the boats would not keep astern where they were safe, but persisted, in a pig-headed way boats have, in getting under the counter and then swinging alongside. They were knocking about dangerously and coming near the flame, while the ship rolled on them, and, of course, there was always the danger of the masts going over the side at any moment. I and my two boatkeepers kept them off as best we could, with oars and boat-hooks; but to be constantly at it became exasperating, since there was no reason why we should not leave at once. We could not see those on board, nor could we imagine what caused the delay. The boatkeepers were swearing feebly, and I had not only my share of the work but also had to keep at it two men who showed a constant inclination to lay themselves down and let things slide.

At last I hailed, "On deck there," and someone looked over. "We're ready here," I said. The head disappeared, and very soon popped up again. "The captain says, All right, sir, and to keep the boats well clear of the ship."

Half an hour passed. Suddenly there was a frightful racket, rattle, clanking of chain, hiss of water, and millions of sparks flew up into the shivering columns of smoke that stood leaning slightly above the ship. The cat-heads had burned away, and the two red-hot anchors had gone to the bottom, tearing out after them two hundred fathom of red-hot chain. The ship trembled, the mass of flame swayed as if ready to collapse, and the fore top-gallant-mast fell. It darted down like an arrow of fire, shot under, and

17. **stream-cable**: the relatively small-size cable for the stream anchor, which is smaller than the kedge anchor.

instantly leaping up within an oar's-length of the boats, floated quietly, very black on the luminous sea. I hailed the deck again. After some time a man in an unexpectedly cheerful but also muffled tone, as though he had been trying to speak with his mouth shut, informed me, "Coming directly, sir," and vanished. For a long time I heard nothing but the whirr and roar of the fire. There were also whistling sounds. The boats jumped, tugged at the painters, ran at each other playfully, knocked their sides together, or, do what we would, swung in a bunch against the ship's side. I couldn't stand it any longer, and swarming up a rope, clambered aboard over the stern.

It was as bright as day. Coming up like this, the sheet of fire facing me was a terrifying sight, and the heat seemed hardly bearable at first. On a settee cushion dragged out of the cabin Captain Beard, his legs drawn up and one arm under his head, slept with the light playing on him. Do you know what the rest were busy about? They were sitting on deck right aft, round an open case, eating bread and cheese and drinking bottled stout.

On the background of flames twisting in fierce tongues above their heads they seemed at home like salamanders, and looked like a band of desperate pirates. The fire sparkled in the whites of their eyes, gleamed on patches of white skin seen through the torn shirts. Each had the marks as of a battle about him—bandaged heads, tied-up arms, a strip of dirty rag round a knee—and each man had a bottle between his legs and a chunk of cheese in his hand. Mahon got up. With his handsome and disreputable head, his hooked profile, his long white beard, and with an uncorked bottle in his hand, he resembled one of those reckless sea-robbers of old making merry amidst violence and disaster. "The last meal on board," he explained solemnly. "We had nothing to eat all day, and it was no use leaving all this." He flourished the bottle and indicated the sleeping skipper. "He said he couldn't swallow anything, so I got him to lie down," he went on; and as I stared, "I don't know whether you are aware, young fellow, the man had no sleep to speak of for days—and there will be dam' little sleep in the boats." "There will be no boats by-and-by if you fool about much longer," I said, indignantly. I walked up to the skipper and shook him by the shoulder. At last he opened his eyes, but did not move. "Time to leave her, sir," I said quietly.

He got up painfully, looked at the flames, at the sea sparkling round the ship, and black, black as ink farther away; he looked at the stars shining dim through a thin veil of smoke in a sky black, black as Erebus.

"Youngest first," he said.

And the ordinary seaman, wiping his mouth with the back of his hand, got up, clambered over the taffrail, and vanished. Others followed. One, on the point of going over, stopped short to drain his bottle, and with a great swing of his arm flung it at the fire. "Take this!" he cried.

The skipper lingered disconsolately, and we left him to commune alone for a while with his first command. Then I went up again and brought him away at last. It was time. The ironwork on the poop was hot to the touch.

Then the painter of the long-boat was cut, and the three boats, tied together, drifted clear of the ship. It was just sixteen hours after the explosion when we abandoned her. Mahon had charge of the second boat, and I had the smallest—the 14-foot thing. The long-boat would have taken the lot of us; but the skipper said we must save as much property as we could —for the underwriters—and so I got my first command. I had two men with me, a bag of biscuits, a few tins of meat, and a breaker of water. I was ordered to keep close to the long-boat, that in case of bad weather we might be taken into her.

And do you know what I thought? I thought I would part company as soon as I could. I wanted to have my first command all to myself. I wasn't going to sail in a squadron if there were a chance for independent cruising. I would make land by myself. I would beat the other boats. Youth! All youth! The silly, charming, beautiful youth.

But we did not make a start at once. We must see the last of the ship. And so the boats drifted about that night, heaving and setting on the swell. The men dozed, waked, sighed, groaned. I looked at the burning ship.

Between the darkness of earth and heaven she was burning fiercely upon a disc of purple sea shot by the blood-red play of gleams; upon a disc of water glittering and sinister. A high, clear flame, an immense and lonely flame, ascended from the ocean, and from its summit the black smoke poured continuously at the sky. She burned furiously; mournful and imposing like a funeral pile kindled in the night, surrounded by the sea, watched over by the stars. A magnificent death had come like a grace, like a gift, like a reward to that old ship at the end of her laborious days. The surrender of her weary ghost to the keeping of stars and sea was stirring like the sight of a glorious triumph. The masts fell just before daybreak, and for a moment there was a burst and turmoil of sparks that seemed to fill with flying fire the night patient and watchful, the vast night lying silent upon the sea. At daylight she was only a charred shell, floating still under a cloud of smoke and bearing a glowing mass of coal within.

Then the oars were got out, and the boats forming in a line moved round her remains as if in procession—the long-boat leading. As we pulled across her stern a slim dart of fire shot out viciously at us, and suddenly she went down, head first, in a great hiss of steam. The unconsumed stern was the last to sink; but the paint had gone, had cracked, had peeled off, and there were no letters, there was no word, no stubborn device that was like her soul, to flash at the rising sun her creed and her name.

We made our way north. A breeze sprang up, and about noon all the boats came together for the last time. I had no mast or sail in mine, but I made a mast out of a spare oar and hoisted a boat-awning for a sail, with a boat-hook for a yard. She was certainly overmasted, but I had the satisfaction of knowing that with the wind aft I could beat the other two. I had to wait for them. Then we all had a look at the captain's chart, and, after a sociable meal of hard bread and water, got our last instructions. These were simple: steer north, and keep together as much as possible. "Be careful with that jury-rig, Marlow," said the captain; and Mahon, as I sailed proudly past his boat, wrinkled his curved nose and hailed, "You will sail that ship of yours under water, if you don't look out, young fellow." He was a malicious old man—and may the deep sea where he sleeps now rock him gently, rock him tenderly to the end of time!

Before sunset a thick rain-squall passed over the two boats, which were far astern, and that was the last I saw of them for a time. Next day I sat steering my cockle-shell—my first command—with nothing but water and sky around me. I did sight in the afternoon the upper sails of a ship far away, but said nothing, and my men did not notice her. You see I was afraid she might be homeward bound, and I had no mind to turn back from the portals of the East. I was steering for Java—another blessed name—like Bankok, you know. I steered many days.

I need not tell you what it is to be knocking about in an open boat. I remember nights and days of calm, and we pulled, we pulled, and the boat seemed to stand still, as if bewitched within the circle of the sea horizon. I remember the heat, the deluge of rain-squalls that kept us baling for dear life (but filled our water-cask), and I remember sixteen hours on end with a mouth dry as a cinder and a steering-oar over the stern to keep my first command head on to a breaking sea. I did not know how good a man I was till then. I remember the drawn faces, the dejected figures of my two men, and I remember my youth and the feeling that will never come back any more—the feeling that I could last forever, outlast the sea, the earth, and all men; the deceitful feeling that lures us on to joys, to perils, to love, to vain effort—to death; the triumphant conviction of strength, the heat of life in the handful of dust, the glow in the heart that with every year grows dim, grows cold, grows small, and expires—and expires, too soon, too soon—before life itself.

And this is how I see the East. I have seen its secret places and have looked into its very soul; but now I see it always from a small boat, a high outline of mountains, blue and afar in the morning; like faint mist at noon; a jagged wall of purple at sunset. I have the feel of the oar in my hand, the vision of a scorching blue sea in my eyes. And I see a bay, a wide bay, smooth as glass and polished like ice, shimmering in the dark. A red light burns far off upon the gloom of the land, and the night is soft and warm. We drag at the oars with aching arms, and suddenly a puff of wind, a puff faint and tepid and laden with strange odors of blossoms, of aromatic wood, comes out of the still night—the first sigh of the East on my face. That I can never forget. It was impalpable and enslaving, like a charm, like a whispered promise of mysterious delight.

We had been pulling this finishing spell for eleven hours. Two pulled, and he whose turn it was to rest sat at the tiller. We had made out the red light in that bay and steered for it, guessing it must mark some small coasting port. We passed two vessels, outlandish and high-sterned, sleeping at anchor, and, approaching the light, now very dim, ran the boat's nose against the end of a jutting wharf. We were blind with fatigue. My men dropped the oars and fell off the thwarts as if dead. I made fast to a pile. A current rippled softly. The scented obscurity of the shore was grouped into vast masses, a density of colossal clumps of vegetation, probably—mute and fantastic shapes. And at their foot the semicircle of a beach gleamed faintly, like an illusion. There was not a light, not a stir, not a sound. The mysterious East faced me, perfumed like a flower, silent like death, dark like a grave.

And I sat weary beyond expression, exulting like a conqueror, sleepless and entranced as if before a profound, a fateful enigma.

A splashing of oars, a measured dip reverberating on the level of water, intensified by the silence of the shore into loud claps, made me jump up. A boat, a European boat, was coming in. I invoked the name of the dead; I hailed: *Judea* ahoy! A thin shout answered.

It was the captain. I had beaten the flagship by three hours, and I was glad to hear the old man's voice again, tremulous and tired. "Is it you, Marlow?" "Mind the end of that jetty, sir," I cried.

He approached cautiously, and brought up with the deep-sea lead-line which we had saved—for the underwriters. I eased my painter and fell alongside. He sat, a broken figure at the stern, wet with dew, his hands clasped in his lap. His men were asleep already. "I had a terrible time of it," he murmured. "Mahon is behind—not very far." We conversed in whispers, in low whispers, as if afraid to wake up the land. Guns, thunder, earthquakes would not have awakened the men just then.

Looking round as we talked, I saw away at sea a bright light traveling in the night. "There's a steamer passing the bay," I said. She was not passing, she was entering, and she even came close and anchored. "I wish," said the old man, "you would find out whether she is English. Perhaps they could give us a passage somewhere." He seemed nervously anxious. So by dint of punching and kicking I started one of my men into a state of somnambulism, and giving him an oar, took another and pulled towards the lights of the steamer.

There was a murmur of voices in her, metallic hollow clangs of the engine-room, footsteps on the deck. Her ports shone, round like dilated eyes. Shapes moved about, and there was a shadowy man high up on the bridge. He heard my oars.

And then, before I could open my lips, the East spoke to me, but it was in a Western voice. A torrent of words was poured into the enigmatical, the fateful silence; outlandish, angry words, mixed with words and even whole sentences of good English, less strange but even more surprising. The voice swore and cursed violently; it riddled the solemn peace of the bay by a volley of abuse. It began by calling me Pig, and from that went crescendo into unmentionable adjectives—in English. The man up there raged aloud in two languages, and with a sincerity in his fury that almost convinced me I had, in some way, sinned against the harmony of the universe. I could hardly see him, but began to think he would work himself into a fit.

Suddenly he ceased, and I could hear him snorting and blowing like a porpoise. I said—

"What steamer is this, pray?"

"Eh? What's this? And who are you?"

"Castaway crew of an English barque burned at sea. We came here to-night. I am the second mate. The captain is in the long-boat, and wishes to know if you would give us a passage somewhere."

"Oh, my goodness! I say. . . . This is the *Celestial* from Singapore on her return trip. I'll arrange with your captain in the morning, . . . and, . . . I say, . . . did you hear me just now?"

"I should think the whole bay heard you."

"I thought you were a shore-boat. Now, look here—this infernal lazy scoundrel of a caretaker has gone to sleep again—curse him. The light is out, and I nearly ran foul of the end of this damned jetty. This is the third time he plays me this trick. Now, I ask you, can anybody stand this kind of thing? It's enough to drive a man out of his mind. I'll report him. . . . I'll get the Assistant Resident to give him the sack, by . . . ! See—there's no light. It's out, isn't it! I take you to witness the light's out. There should be a light, you know. A red light on the—"

"There was a light," I said, mildly.

"But it's out, man! What's the use of talking like this? You can see for yourself it's out—don't you? If you had to take a valuable steamer along this God-forsaken coast you would want a light, too. I'll kick him from end to end of his miserable wharf. You'll see if I don't. I will—"

"So I may tell my captain you'll take us?" I broke in.

"Yes, I'll take you. Good-night," he said, brusquely.

I pulled back, made fast again to the jetty, and then went to sleep at last. I had faced the silence of the East. I had heard some of its language. But when I opened my eyes again the silence was as complete as though it had never been broken. I was lying in a flood of light, and the sky had never looked so far, so high, before. I opened my eyes and lay without moving.

And then I saw the men of the East—they were looking at me. The whole length of the jetty was full of people. I saw brown, bronze, yellow faces, the black eyes, the glitter, the color of an Eastern crowd. And all these beings stared without a murmur, without a sigh, without a move-ment. They stared down at the boats, at the sleeping men who at night had come to them from the sea. Nothing moved. The fronds of palms stood still against the sky. Not a branch stirred along the shore, and the brown roofs of hidden houses peeped through the green foliage, through the big leaves that hung shining and still like leaves forged of heavy metal. This was the East of the ancient navigators, so old, so mysterious, resplendent and somber, living and unchanged, full of danger and prom-ise. And these were the men. I sat up suddenly. A wave of movement passed through the crowd from end to end, passed along the heads, swayed the bodies, ran along the jetty like a ripple on the water, like a breath of wind on a field—and all was still again. I see it now—the wide sweep of the bay, the glittering sands, the wealth of green infinite and varied, the sea blue like the sea of dream, the crowd of attentive faces, the blaze of vivid color—the water reflecting it all, the curve of the shore, the jetty, the high sterned outlandish craft floating still, and the three boats with the tired men from the West sleeping, unconscious of the land and the people and of the violence of sunshine. They slept thrown across the thwarts, curled on bottom-boards, in the careless attitudes of death. The head of the old skipper, leaning back in the stern of the long-boat, had fallen on his breast, and he looked as though he would never wake. Farther out old Mahon's face was upturned to the sky, with the long white beard spread out on his breast, as though he had been shot where he sat at the tiller; and a man, all in a heap in the bows of the boat, slept with both arms em-bracing the stem-head and with his cheek laid on the gunwale. The East looked at them without a sound.

I have known its fascination since; I have seen the mysterious shores, the still water, the lands of brown nations, where a stealthy Nemesis lies in wait, pursues, overtakes so many of the conquering race, who are proud of their wisdom, of their knowledge, of their strength. But for me all the

East is contained in that vision of my youth. It is all in that moment when I opened my young eyes on it. I came upon it from a tussle with the sea—and I was young—and I saw it looking at me. And this is all that is left of it! Only a moment; a moment of strength, of romance, of glamour—of youth! . . . A flick of sunshine upon a strange shore, the time to remember, the time for a sigh, and—good-bye!—Night—Good-bye . . . !

He drank.

Ah! The good old time—the good old time. Youth and the sea. Glamour and the sea! The good, strong sea, the salt, bitter sea, that could whisper to you and roar at you and knock your breath out of you.

He drank again.

By all that's wonderful it is the sea, I believe, the sea itself—or is it youth alone? Who can tell? But you here—you all had something out of life: money, love—whatever one gets on shore—and, tell me, wasn't that the best time, that time when we were young at sea; young and had nothing, on the sea that gives nothing, except hard knocks—and sometimes a chance to feel your strength—that only—what you all regret?

And we all nodded at him: the man of finance, the man of accounts, the man of law we all nodded at him over the polished table that like a still sheet of brown water reflected our faces, lined, wrinkled; our faces marked by toil, by deceptions, by success, by love; our weary eyes looking still, looking always, looking anxiously for something out of life, that while it is expected is already gone—has passed unseen, in a sigh, in a flash —together with the youth, with the strength, with the romance of illusions.

Stephen Crane

THE OPEN BOAT

A Tale Intended to be after the Fact: Being the Experience of Four Men from the Sun Steamer COMMODORE

1

NONE of them knew the color of the sky. Their eyes glanced level, and were fastened upon the waves that swept toward them. These waves were of the hue of slate, save for the tops, which were of foaming white, and all of the men knew the colors of the sea. The horizon narrowed and widened, and dipped and rose, and at all times its edge was jagged with waves that seemed thrust up in points like rocks.

Many a man ought to have a bathtub larger than the boat which here rode upon the sea. These waves were most wrongfully and barbarously abrupt and tall, and each froth-top was a problem in small-boat navigation.

The cook squatted in the bottom, and looked with both eyes at the six inches of gunwale which separated him from the ocean. His sleeves were rolled over his fat forearms, and the two flaps of his unbuttoned vest dangled as he bent to bail out the boat. Often he said, "Gawd! that was a narrow clip." As he remarked it he invariably gazed eastward over the broken sea.

The oiler, steering with one of the two oars in the boat, sometimes raised himself suddenly to keep clear of water that swirled in over the stern. It was a thin little oar, and it seemed often ready to snap.

The correspondent, pulling at the other oar, watched the waves and wondered why he was there.

The injured captain, lying in the bow, was at this time buried in that profound dejection and indifference which comes, temporarily at least, to even the bravest and most enduring when, willy-nilly, the firm fails, the army loses, the ship goes down. The mind of the master of a vessel is rooted deep in the timbers of her, though he command for a day or a decade; and this captain had on him the stern impression of a scene in the grays of dawn of seven turned faces, and later a stump of a topmast with a white ball on it, that slashed to and fro at the waves, went low and lower, and down. Thereafter there was something strange in his voice. Although steady, it was deep with mourning, and of a quality beyond oration or tears.

"Keep 'er a little more south, Billie," said he.

"A little more south, sir," said the oiler in the stern.

A seat in his boat was not unlike a seat upon a bucking broncho, and by the same token a broncho is not much smaller. The craft pranced and reared and plunged like an animal. As each wave came, and she rose for it, she seemed like a horse making at a fence outrageously high. The manner of her scramble over these walls of water is a mystic thing, and, moreover, at the top of them were ordinarily these problems in white water, the foam racing down from the summit of each wave requiring a new leap, and a leap from the air. Then, after scornfully bumping a crest, she would slide and race and splash down a long incline, and arrive bobbing and nodding in front of the next menace.

A singular disadvantage of the sea lies in the fact that after successfully surmounting one wave you discover that there is another behind it just as important and just as nervously anxious to do something effective in the way of swamping boats. In a ten-foot dinghy one can get an idea of the resources of the sea in the line of waves that is not probable to the average experience which is never at sea in a dinghy. As each slaty wall of water approached, it shut all else from the view of the men in the boat, and it was not difficult to imagine that this particular wave was the final outburst of the ocean, the last effort of the grim water. There was a terrible grace in the move of the waves, and they came in silence, save for the snarling of the crests.

In the wan light the faces of the men must have been gray. Their eyes must have glinted in strange ways as they gazed steadily astern. Viewed from a balcony, the whole thing would doubtless have been weirdly picturesque. But the men in the boat had no time to see it, and if they had had leisure, there were other things to occupy their minds. The sun swung steadily up the sky, and they knew it was broad day because the color of the sea changed from slate to emerald green streaked with amber lights, and the foam was like tumbling snow. The process of the breaking day was unknown to them. They were aware only of this effect upon the color of the waves that rolled toward them.

In disjointed sentences the cook and the correspondent argued as to the difference between a life-saving station and a house of refuge. The cook had said: "There's a house of refuge just north of the Mosquito Inlet Light, and as soon as they see us they'll come off in their boat and pick us up."

"As soon as who see us?" said the correspondent.

"The crew," said the cook.

"Houses of refuge don't have crews," said the correspondent. "As I understand them, they are only places where clothes and grub are stored for the benefit of shipwrecked people. They don't carry crews."

"Oh, yes, they do," said the cook.

"No, they don't," said the correspondent.

"Well, we're not there yet, anyhow," said the oiler, in the stern.

"Well," said the cook, "perhaps it's not a house of refuge that I'm thinking of as being near Mosquito Inlet Light; perhaps it's a life-saving station."

"We're not there yet," said the oiler in the stern.

2

As the boat bounced from the top of each wave the wind tore through the hair of the hatless men, and as the craft plopped her stern down again the spray slashed past them. The crest of each of these waves was a hill, from the top of which the men surveyed for a moment a broad tumultuous expanse, shining and wind-riven. It was probably splendid, it was probably glorious, this play of the free sea, wild with lights of emerald and white and amber.

"Bully good thing it's an on-shore wind," said the cook. "If not, where would we be? Wouldn't have a show."

"That's right," said the correspondent.

The busy oiler nodded his assent.

Then the captain, in the bow, chuckled in a way that expressed humor, contempt, tragedy, all in one. "Do you think we've got much of a show now, boys?" said he.

Whereupon the three were silent, save for a trifle of hemming and hawing. To express any particular optimism at this time they felt to be childish and stupid, but they all doubtless possessed this sense of the situation in their minds. A young man thinks doggedly at such times. On the other hand, the ethics of their condition was decidedly against any open suggestion of hopelessness. So they were silent.

"Oh, well," said the captain, soothing his children, "we'll get ashore all right."

But there was that in his tone which made them think; so the oiler quoth, "Yes! if this wind holds."

The cook was bailing. "Yes! if we don't catch hell in the surf."

Canton-flannel gulls flew near and far. Sometimes they sat down on the sea, near patches of brown seaweed that rolled over the waves with a movement like carpets on a line in a gale. The birds sat comfortably in groups, and they were envied by some in the dinghy, for the wrath of the sea was no more to them than it was to a covey of prairie chickens a thousand miles inland. Often they came very close and stared at the men with black bead-like eyes. At these times they were uncanny and sinister in their unblinking scrutiny, and the men hooted angrily at them, telling them to be gone. One came, and evidently decided to alight on the top of the captain's head. The bird flew parallel to the boat and did not circle, but made short sidelong jumps in the air in chicken-fashion. His black eyes were wistfully fixed upon the captain's head. "Ugly brute," said the oiler to the bird. "You look as if you were made with a jackknife." The cook and the correspondent swore darkly at the creature. The captain naturally wished to knock it away with the end of the heavy painter, but he did not dare do it, because anything resembling an emphatic gesture would have capsized this freighted boat; and so, with his open hand, the captain gently and carefully waved the gull away. After it had been discouraged from the pursuit the captain breathed easier on account of his hair, and others breathed easier because the bird struck their minds at this time as being somehow gruesome and ominous.

In the meantime the oiler and the correspondent rowed. And also they rowed. They sat together in the same seat, and each rowed an oar. Then the oiler took both oars; then the correspondent took both oars; then the oiler; then the correspondent. They rowed and they rowed. The very ticklish part of the business was when the time came for the reclining one in the stern to take his turn at the oars. By the very last star of truth, it is easier to steal eggs from under a hen than it was to change seats in the dinghy. First the man in the stern slid his hand along the thwart and moved with care, as if he were of Sèvres. Then the man in the rowing-seat slid his hand along the other thwart. It was all done with the most extraordinary care. As the two sidled past each other, the whole party kept watchful eyes on the coming wave, and the captain cried: "Look out, now! Steady, there!"

The brown mats of seaweed that appeared from time to time were like islands, bits of earth. They were traveling, apparently, neither one way nor the other. They were, to all intents, stationary. They informed the men in the boat that it was making progress slowly toward the land.

The captain, rearing cautiously in the bow after the dinghy soared on a great swell, said that he had seen the lighthouse at Mosquito Inlet. Presently the cook remarked that he had seen it. The correspondent was at the oars then, and for some reason he too wished to look at the lighthouse; but his back was toward the far shore, and the waves were important, and for some time he could not seize an opportunity to turn his head. But at last there came a wave more gentle than the others, and when at the crest of it he swiftly scoured the western horizon.

"See it?" said the captain.

"No," said the correspondent, slowly; "I didn't see anything."

"Look again," said the captain. He pointed. "It's exactly in that direction."

At the top of another wave the correspondent did as he was bid, and this time his eyes chanced on a small, still thing on the edge of the swaying horizon. It was precisely like the point of a pin. It took an anxious eye to find a lighthouse so tiny.

"Think we'll make it, Captain?"

"If this wind holds and the boat don't swamp, we can't do much else," said the captain.

The little boat, lifted by each towering sea and splashed viciously by the crests, made progress that in the absence of seaweed was not apparent to those in her. She seemed just a wee thing wallowing, miraculously top up, at the mercy of five oceans. Occasionally a great spread of water, like white flames, swarmed into her.

"Bail her, cook," said the captain, serenely.

"All right, Captain," said the cheerful cook.

3

It would be difficult to describe the subtle brotherhood of men that was here established on the seas. No one said that it was so. No one mentioned it. But it dwelt in the boat, and each man felt it warm him. They were a captain, an oiler, a cook, and a correspondent, and they were friends— friends in a more curiously iron-bound degree than may be common. The hurt captain, lying against the water-jar in the bow, spoke always in a low voice and calmly; but he could never command a more ready and swiftly obedient crew than the motley three of the dinghy. It was more than a mere recognition of what was best for the common safety. There was surely in it a quality that was personal and heart-felt. And after this devotion to the commander of the boat, there was this comradeship, that the correspondent, for instance, who had been taught to be cynical of men, knew even at the time was the best experience of his life. But no one said that it was so. No one mentioned it.

"I wish we had a sail," remarked the captain. "We might try my overcoat on the end of an oar, and give you two boys a chance to rest." So the cook and the correspondent held the mast and spread wide the overcoat; the oiler steered; and the little boat made good way with her new rig. Sometimes the oiler had to scull sharply to keep a sea from breaking into the boat, but otherwise sailing was a success.

Meanwhile the lighthouse had been growing slowly larger. It had now almost assumed color, and appeared like a little gray shadow on the sky. The man at the oars could not be prevented from turning his head rather often to try for a glimpse of this little gray shadow.

At last, from the top of each wave, the men in the tossing boat could see land. Even as the lighthouse was an upright shadow on the sky, this land seemed but a long black shadow on the sea. It certainly was thinner than paper. "We must be about opposite New Smyrna," said the cook, who had coasted this shore often in schooners. "Captain, by the way, I believe they abandoned that life-saving station there about a year ago."

"Did they?" said the captain.

The wind slowly died away. The cook and the correspondent were not now obliged to slave in order to hold high the oar. But the waves continued their old impetuous swooping at the dinghy, and the little craft, no longer under way, struggled woundily over them. The oiler or the correspondent took the oars again.

Shipwrecks are apropos of nothing. If men could only train for them and have them occur when the men had reached pink condition, there would be less drowning at sea. Of the four in the dinghy none had slept any time worth mentioning for two days and two nights previous to embarking in the dinghy, and in the excitement of clambering about the deck of a foundering ship they had also forgotten to eat heartily.

For these reasons, and for others, neither the oiler nor the correspondent was fond of rowing at this time. The correspondent wondered ingenuously how in the name of all that was sane could there be people who thought it amusing to row a boat. It was not an amusement; it was a diabolical punishment, and even a genius of mental aberrations could never conclude that it was anything but a horror to the muscles and a crime against the back. He mentioned to the boat in general how the amusement of rowing struck him, and the weary-faced oiler smiled in full sympathy. Previously to the foundering, by the way, the oiler had worked a double watch in the engine-room of the ship.

"Take her easy now, boys," said the captain. "Don't spend yourselves. If we have to run a surf you'll need all your strength, because we'll sure have to swim for it. Take your time."

Slowly the land arose from the sea. From a black line it became a line of black and a line of white—trees and sand. Finally the captain said that he could make out a house on the shore. "That's the house of refuge, sure," said the cook. "They'll see us before long, and come out after us."

The distant lighthouse reared high. "The keeper ought to be able to make us out now, if he's looking through a glass," said the captain. "He'll notify the life-saving people."

"None of those other boats could have got ashore to give word of this wreck," said the oiler, in a low voice, "else the life-boat would be out hunting us."

Slowly and beautifully the land loomed out of the sea. The wind came again. It had veered from the north-east to the south-east. Finally a new sound struck the ears of the men in the boat. It was the low thunder of the surf on the shore. "We'll never be able to make the lighthouse now," said the captain. "Swing her head a little more north, Billie."

"A little more north, sir," said the oiler.

Whereupon the little boat turned her nose once more down the wind, and all but the oarsman watched the shore grow. Under the influence of this expansion doubt and direful apprehension were leaving the minds of the men. The management of the boat was still most absorbing, but it could not prevent a quiet cheerfulness. In an hour, perhaps, they would be ashore.

Their backbones had become thoroughly used to balancing in the boat, and they now rode this wild colt of a dinghy like circus men. The correspondent thought that he had been drenched to the skin, but happening to feel in the top pocket of his coat, he found therein eight cigars. Four of them were soaked with sea-water; four were perfectly scatheless. After a search, somebody produced three dry matches; and thereupon the four waifs rode impudently in their little boat and, with an assurance of an impending rescue shining in their eyes, puffed at the big cigars, and judged well and ill of all men. Everybody took a drink of water.

4

"Cook," remarked the captain, "there don't seem to be any signs of life about your house of refuge."

"No," replied the cook. "Funny they don't see us!"

A broad stretch of lowly coast lay before the eyes of the men. It was of low dunes topped with dark vegetation. The roar of the surf was plain, and sometimes they could see the white lip of a wave as it spun up the beach. A tiny house was blocked out black upon the sky. Southward, the slim lighthouse lifted its little gray length.

Tide, wind, and waves were swinging the dinghy northward. "Funny they don't see us," said the men.

The surf's roar was here dulled, but its tone was nevertheless thunderous and mighty. As the boat swam over the great rollers the men sat listening to this roar. "We'll swamp sure," said everybody.

It is fair to say here that there was not a life-saving station within twenty miles in either direction; but the men did not know this fact, and in consequence they made dark and opprobrious remarks concerning the eyesight of the nation's lifesavers. Four scowling men sat in the dinghy and surpassed records in the invention of epithets.

"Funny they don't see us."

The light-heartedness of a former time had completely faded. To their sharpened minds it was easy to conjure pictures of all kinds of incompetency and blindness and, indeed, cowardice. There was the shore of the populous land, and it was bitter and bitter to them that from it came no sign.

"Well," said the captain, ultimately, "I suppose we'll have to make a try for ourselves. If we stay out here too long, we'll none of us have strength left to swim after the boat swamps."

And so the oiler, who was at the oars, turned the boat straight for the shore. There was a sudden tightening of muscles. There was some thinking.

"If we don't all get ashore," said the captain—"if we don't all get ashore, I suppose you fellows know where to send news of my finish?"

They then briefly exchanged some addresses and admonitions. As for the reflections of the men, there was a great deal of rage in them. Perchance they might be formulated thus: "If I am going to be drowned—if I am going to be drowned—if I am going to be drowned, why, in the name of the seven mad gods who rule the sea, was I allowed to come thus far and contemplate sand and trees? Was I brought here merely to have my nose dragged away as I was about to nibble the sacred cheese of life? It is preposterous. If this old ninny-woman, Fate, cannot do better than this, she should be deprived of the management of men's fortunes. She is an old hen who knows not her intention. If she has decided to drown me, why did she not do it in the beginning and save me all this trouble? The whole affair is absurd.—But no; she cannot mean to drown me. She dare not drown me. She cannot drown me. Not after all this work." Afterward the man might have had an impulse to shake his fist at the clouds. "Just you drown me, now, and then hear what I call you!"

The billows that came at this time were more formidable. They seemed always just about to break and roll over the little boat in a turmoil of foam. There was a preparatory and long growl in the speech of them. No mind unused to the sea would have concluded that the dinghy could ascend these sheer heights in time. The shore was still afar. The oiler was a wily surfman. "Boys," he said swiftly, "she won't live three minutes more, and we're too far out to swim. Shall I take her to sea again, Captain?"

"Yes; go ahead!" said the captain.

This oiler, by a series of quick miracles and fast and steady oarsmanship, turned the boat in the middle of the surf and took her safely to sea again.

There was a considerable silence as the boat bumped over the furrowed sea to deeper water. Then somebody in gloom spoke: "Well, anyhow, they must have seen us from the shore by now."

The gulls went in slanting flight up the wind toward the gray, desolate east. A squall, marked by dingy clouds and clouds brick-red like smoke from a burning building, appeared from the south-east.

"What do you think of those life-saving people? Ain't they peaches?"

"Funny they haven't seen us."

"Maybe they think we're out here for sport! Maybe they think we're fishin'. Maybe they think we're damned fools."

It was a long afternoon. A changed tide tried to force them southward, but wind and wave said northward. Far ahead, where coast-line, sea, and sky formed their mighty angle, there were little dots which seemed to indicate a city on the shore.

"St. Augustine?"

The captain shook his head. "Too near Mosquito Inlet."

And the oiler rowed, and then the correspondent rowed; then the oiler rowed. It was a weary business. The human back can become the seat of more aches and pains than are registered in books for the composite anatomy of a regiment. It is a limited area, but it can become the theater of innumerable muscular conflicts, tangles, wrenches, knots, and other comforts.

"Did you ever like to row, Billie?" asked the correspondent.

"No," said the oiler; "hang it!"

When one exchanged the rowing-seat for a place in the bottom of the boat, he suffered a bodily depression that caused him to be careless of everything save an obligation to wiggle one finger. There was cold sea-water swashing to and fro in the boat, and he lay in it. His head, pillowed on a thwart, was within an inch of the swirl of a wave-crest, and sometimes a particularly obstreperous sea came inboard and drenched him once more. But these matters did not annoy him. It is almost certain that if the boat had capsized he would have tumbled comfortably out upon the ocean as if he felt sure that it was a great soft mattress.

"Look! There's a man on the shore!"

"Where?"

"There! See 'im? See 'im?"

"Yes, sure! He's walking along."

"Now he's stopped. Look! He's facing us!"

"He's waving at us!"

"So he is! By thunder!"

"Ah, now we're all right! Now we're all right! There'll be a boat out here for us in half an hour."

"He's going on. He's running. He's going up to that house there."

The remote beach seemed lower than the sea, and it required a searching glance to discern the little black figure. The captain saw a floating stick, and they rowed to it. A bath towel was by some weird chance in the boat,

and, tying this on the stick, the captain waved it. The oarsman did not
dare turn his head, so he was obliged to ask questions.

"What's he doing now?"

"He's standing still again. He's looking, I think.—There he goes again—
toward the house.—Now he's stopped again."

"Is he waving at us?"

"No, not now; he was, though."

"Look! There comes another man!"

"He's running."

"Look at him go, would you!"

"Why, he's on a bicycle. Now he's met the other man. They're both
waving at us. Look!"

"There comes something up the beach."

"What the devil is that thing?"

"Why, it looks like a boat."

"Why, certainly, it's a boat."

"No; it's on wheels."

"Yes, so it is. Well, that must be the life-boat. They drag them along
shore on a wagon."

"That's the life-boat, sure."

"No, by God, it's—it's an omnibus."

"I tell you it's a life-boat."

"It is not! It's an omnibus. I can see it plain. See? One of these big
hotel omnibuses."

"By thunder, you're right. It's an omnibus, sure as fate. What do you
suppose they are doing with an omnibus? Maybe they are going around
collecting the life-crew, hey?"

"That's it, likely. Look! There's a fellow waving a little black flag. He's
standing on the steps of the omnibus. There come those other two fellows.
Now they're all talking together. Look at the fellow with the flag. Maybe
he ain't waving it!"

"That ain't a flag, is it? That's his coat. Why, certainly, that's his coat."

"So it is; it's his coat. He's taken it off and is waving it around his head.
But would you look at him swing it!"

"Oh, say, there isn't any life-saving station there. That's just a winter-
resort hotel omnibus that has brought over some of the boarders to see us
drown."

"What's that idiot with the coat mean? What's he signaling, anyhow?"

"It looks as if he were trying to tell us to go north. There must be a
life-saving station up there."

"No; he thinks we're fishing. Just giving us a merry hand. See? Ah,
there, Willie!"

"Well, I wish I could make something out of those signals. What do you suppose he means?"

"He don't mean anything; he's just playing."

"Well, if he'd just signal us to try the surf again, or to go to sea and wait, or go north, or go south, or go to hell, there would be some reason in it. But look at him! He just stands there and keeps his coat revolving like a wheel. The ass!"

"There come more people."

"Now there's quite a mob. Look! Isn't that a boat?"

"Where? Oh, I see where you mean. No, that's no boat."

"That fellow is still waving his coat."

"He must think we like to see him do that. Why don't he quit it? It don't mean anything."

"I don't know. I think he is trying to make us go north. It must be that there's a life-saving station there somewhere."

"Say, he ain't tired yet. Look at 'im wave!"

"Wonder how long he can keep that up. He's been revolving his coat ever since he caught sight of us. He's an idiot. Why aren't they getting men to bring a boat out? A fishing-boat—one of those big yawls—could come out here all right. Why don't he do something?"

"Oh, it's all right now."

"They'll have a boat out here for us in less than no time, now that they've seen us."

A faint yellow tone came into the sky over the low land. The shadows on the sea slowly deepened. The wind bore coldness with it, and the men began to shiver.

"Holy smoke!" said one, allowing his voice to express his impious mood, "if we keep on monkeying out here! If we've got to flounder out here all night!"

"Oh, we'll never have to stay here all night! Don't you worry. They've seen us now, and it won't be long before they'll come chasing out after us."

The shore grew dusky. The man waving a coat blended gradually into this gloom, and it swallowed in the same manner the omnibus and the group of people. The spray, when it dashed uproariously over the side, made the voyagers shrink and swear like men who were being branded.

"I'd like to catch the chump who waved the coat. I feel like socking him one, just for luck."

"Why? What did he do?"

"Oh, nothing, but then he seemed so damned cheerful."

In the meantime the oiler rowed, and then the correspondent rowed, and then the oiler rowed. Gray-faced and bowed forward, they mechanically, turn by turn, plied the leaden oars. The form of the lighthouse had vanished from the southern horizon, but finally a pale star appeared, just lifting from the sea. The streaked saffron in the west passed before the all-merging darkness, and the sea to the east was black. The land had vanished, and was expressed only by the low and drear thunder of the surf.

"If I am going to be drowned—if I am going to be drowned—if I am going to be drowned, why, in the name of the seven mad gods who rule the sea, was I allowed to come thus far and contemplate sand and trees? Was I brought here merely to have my nose dragged away as I was about to nibble the sacred cheese of life?"

The patient captain, drooped over the water-jar, was sometimes obliged to speak to the oarsman.

"Keep her head up! Keep her head up!"

"Keep her head up, sir." The voices were weary and low.

This was surely a quiet evening. All save the oarsman lay heavily and listlessly in the boat's bottom. As for him, his eyes were just capable of noting the tall black waves that swept forward in a most sinister silence, save for an occasional subdued growl of a crest.

The cook's head was on a thwart, and he looked without interest at the water under his nose. He was deep in other scenes. Finally he spoke. "Billie," he murmured dreamfully, "what kind of pie do you like best?"

5

"Pie!" said the oiler and the correspondent, agitatedly. "Don't talk about those things, blast you!"

"Well," said the cook, "I was just thinking about ham sandwiches and—"

A night on the sea in an open boat is a long night. As darkness settled finally, the shine of the light, lifting from the sea in the south, changed to full gold. On the northern horizon a new light appeared, a small bluish gleam on the edge of the waters. These two lights were the furniture of the world. Otherwise there was nothing but waves.

Two men huddled in the stern, and distances were so magnificent in the dinghy that the rower was enabled to keep his feet partly warm by thrusting them under his companions. Their legs indeed extended far under the rowing-seat until they touched the feet of the captain forward. Sometimes, despite the efforts of the tired oarsman, a wave came piling into the boat, an icy wave of the night, and the chilling water soaked them anew. They would twist their bodies for a moment and groan, and sleep the dead sleep once more, while the water in the boat gurgled about them as the craft rocked.

The plan of the oiler and the correspondent was for one to row until he lost the ability, and then arouse the other from his sea-water couch in the bottom of the boat.

The oiler plied the oars until his head drooped forward and the overpowering sleep blinded him; and he rowed yet afterward. Then he touched a man in the bottom of the boat, and called his name. "Will you spell me for a little while?" he said, meekly.

"Sure, Billie," said the correspondent, awaking and dragging himself to a sitting position. They exchanged places carefully, and the oiler, cuddling down in the sea-water at the cook's side, seemed to go to sleep instantly.

The particular violence of the sea had ceased. The waves came without snarling. The obligation of the man at the oars was to keep the boat headed so that the tilt of the rollers would not capsize her, and to preserve her from filling when the crests rushed past. The black waves were silent and hard to be seen in the darkness. Often one was almost upon the boat before the oarsman was aware.

In a low voice the correspondent addressed the captain. He was not sure that the captain was awake, although this iron man seemed to be always awake. "Captain, shall I keep her making for that light north, sir?"

The same steady voice answered him. "Yes. Keep it about two points off the port bow."

The cook had tied a life-belt around himself in order to get even the warmth which this clumsy cork contrivance could donate, and he seemed almost stove-like when a rower, whose teeth invariably chattered wildly as soon as he ceased his labor, dropped down to sleep.

The correspondent, as he rowed, looked down at the two men sleeping underfoot. The cook's arm was around the oiler's shoulders, and, with their fragmentary clothing and haggard faces, they were the babes of the sea—a grotesque rendering of the old babes in the wood.

Later he must have grown stupid at his work, for suddenly there was a growling of water, and a crest came with a roar and a swash into the boat, and it was a wonder that it did not set the cook afloat in his life-belt. The cook continued to sleep, but the oiler sat up, blinking his eyes and shaking with the new cold.

"Oh, I'm awful sorry, Billie," said the correspondent, contritely.

"That's all right, old boy," said the oiler, and lay down again and was asleep.

Presently it seemed that even the captain dozed, and the correspondent thought that he was the one man afloat on all the oceans. The wind had a voice as it came over the waves, and it was sadder than the end.

There was a long, loud swishing astern of the boat, and a gleaming trail of phosphorescence, like blue flame, was furrowed on the black waters. It might have been made by a monstrous knife.

Then there came a stillness, while the correspondent breathed with open mouth and looked at the sea.

Suddenly there was another swish and another long flash of bluish light, and this time it was alongside the boat, and might almost have been reached with an oar. The correspondent saw an enormous fin speed like a shadow through the water, hurling the crystalline spray and leaving the long glowing trail.

The correspondent looked over his shoulder at the captain. His face was hidden, and he seemed to be asleep. He looked at the babes of the sea. They certainly were asleep. So, being bereft of sympathy, he leaned a little way to one side and swore softly into the sea.

But the thing did not then leave the vicinity of the boat. Ahead or astern, on one side or the other, at intervals long or short, fled the long sparkling streak, and there was to be heard the *whirroo* of the dark fin. The speed and power of the thing was greatly to be admired. It cut the water like a gigantic and keen projectile.

The presence of this biding thing did not affect the man with the same horror that it would if he had been a picnicker. He simply looked at the sea dully and swore in an undertone.

Nevertheless, it is true that he did not wish to be alone with the thing. He wished one of his companions to awake by chance and keep him company with it. But the captain hung motionless over the water-jar, and the oiler and the cook in the bottom of the boat were plunged in slumber.

6

"If I am going to be drowned—if I am going to be drowned, why, in the name of the seven mad gods who rule the sea, was I allowed to come thus far and contemplate sand and trees?"

During this dismal night, it may be remarked that a man would conclude that it was really the intention of the seven mad gods to drown him, despite the abominable injustice of it. For it was certainly an abominable injustice to drown a man who had worked so hard, so hard. The man felt it would be a crime most unnatural. Other people had drowned at sea since galleys swarmed with painted sails, but still—

When it occurs to a man that nature does not regard him as important, and that she feels she would not maim the universe by disposing of him, he at first wishes to throw bricks at the temple, and he hates deeply the fact that there are no bricks and no temples. Any visible expression of nature would surely be pelleted with his jeers.

Then, if there be no tangible thing to hoot, he feels, perhaps, the desire to confront a personification and indulge in pleas, bowed to one knee, and with hands supplicant, saying, "Yes, but I love myself."

A high cold star on a winter's night is the word he feels that she says to him. Thereafter he knows the pathos of his situation.

The men in the dinghy had not discussed these matters, but each had, no doubt, reflected upon them in silence and according to his mind. There was seldom any expression upon their faces save the general one of complete weariness. Speech was devoted to the business of the boat.

To chime the notes of his emotion, a verse mysteriously entered the correspondent's head. He had even forgotten that he had forgotten this verse, but it suddenly was in his mind.

> A soldier of the Legion lay dying in Algiers;
> There was lack of woman's nursing, there was dearth of woman's tears;
> But a comrade stood beside him, and he took that comrade's hand,
> And he said, "I never more shall see my own, my native land."

In his childhood the correspondent had been made acquainted with the fact that a soldier of the Legion lay dying in Algiers, but he had never regarded the fact as important. Myriads of his school-fellows had informed him of the soldier's plight, but the dinning had naturally ended by making him perfectly indifferent. He had never considered it his affair that a soldier of the Legion lay dying in Algiers, nor had it appeared to him as a matter for sorrow. It was less to him than the breaking of a pencil's point.

Now, however, it quaintly came to him as a human, living thing. It was no longer merely a picture of a few throes in the breast of a poet, meanwhile drinking tea and warming his feet at the grate; it was an actuality—stern, mournful, and fine.

The correspondent plainly saw the soldier. He lay on the sand with his feet out straight and still. While his pale left hand was upon his chest in an attempt to thwart the going of his life, the blood came between his fingers. In the far Algerian distance, a city of low square forms was set against a sky that was faint with the last sunset hues. The correspondent, plying the oars and dreaming of the slow and slower movements of the lips of the soldier, was moved by a profound and perfectly impersonal comprehension. He was sorry for the soldier of the Legion who lay dying in Algiers.

The thing which had followed the boat and waited had evidently grown bored at the delay. There was no longer to be heard the slash of the cutwater, and there was no longer the flame of the long trail. The light in the north still glimmered, but it was apparently no nearer to the boat. Sometimes the boom of the surf rang in the correspondent's ears, and he turned the craft seaward then and rowed harder. Southward, some one had evidently built a watch-fire on the beach. It was too low and too far to be seen, but it made a shimmering, roseate reflection upon the bluff in back of it, and this could be discerned from the boat. The wind came stronger, and sometimes a wave suddenly raged out like a mountain cat, and there was to be seen the sheen and sparkle of a broken crest.

The captain, in the bow, moved on his water-jar and sat erect. "Pretty long night," he observed to the correspondent. He looked at the shore. "Those life-saving people take their time."

"Did you see that shark playing around?"

"Yes, I saw him. He was a big fellow, all right."

"Wish I had known you were awake."

Later the correspondent spoke into the bottom of the boat. "Billie!" There was a slow and gradual disentanglement. "Billie, will you spell me?"

"Sure," said the oiler.

As soon as the correspondent touched the cold, comfortable sea-water in the bottom of the boat and had huddled close to the cook's life-belt he was deep in sleep, despite the fact that his teeth played all the popular airs. This sleep was so good to him that it was but a moment before he heard a voice call his name in a tone that demonstrated the last stages of exhaustion. "Will you spell me?"

"Sure, Billie."

The light in the north had mysteriously vanished, but the correspondent took his course from the wide-awake captain.

Later in the night they took the boat farther out to sea, and the captain directed the cook to take one oar at the stern and keep the boat facing the seas. He was to call out if he should hear the thunder of the surf. This plan enabled the oiler and the correspondent to get respite together. "We'll give those boys a chance to get into shape again," said the captain. They curled down and, after a few preliminary chatterings and trembles, slept once more the dead sleep. Neither knew they had bequeathed to the cook the company of another shark, or perhaps the same shark.

As the boat caroused on the waves, spray occasionally bumped over the side and gave them a fresh soaking, but this had no power to break their repose. The ominous slash of the wind and the water affected them as it would have affected mummies.

"Boys," said the cook, with the notes of every reluctance in his voice, "she's drifted in pretty close. I guess one of you had better take her to sea again." The correspondent, aroused, heard the crash of the toppled crests.

As he was rowing, the captain gave him some whisky-and-water, and this steadied the chills out of him. "If I ever get ashore and anybody shows me even a photograph of an oar—"

At last there was a short conversation.

"—Billie!—Billie, will you spell me?"

"Sure," said the oiler.

7

When the correspondent again opened his eyes, the sea and the sky were each of the gray hue of the dawning. Later, carmine and gold was painted upon the waters. The morning appeared finally, in its splendor, with a sky of pure blue, and the sunlight flamed on the tips of the waves.

On the distant dunes were set many little black cottages, and a tall white windmill reared above them. No man, nor dog, nor bicycle appeared on the beach. The cottages might have formed a deserted village.

The voyagers scanned the shore. A conference was held in the boat. "Well," said the captain, "if no help is coming, we might better try a run through the surf right away. If we stay out here much longer we will be too weak to do anything for ourselves at all." The others silently acquiesced in this reasoning. The boat was headed for the beach. The correspondent wondered if none ever ascended the tall windtower, and if then they never looked seaward. This tower was a giant, standing with its back to the plight of the ants. It represented in a degree, to the correspondent, the serenity of nature amid the struggles of the individual—nature in the wind, and nature in the vision of men. She did not seem cruel to him then, nor beneficent, nor treacherous, nor wise. But she was indifferent, flatly indifferent. It is, perhaps, plausible that a man in this situation, impressed with the unconcern of the universe, should see the innumerable flaws of his life, and have them taste wickedly in his mind, and wish for another chance. A distinction between right and wrong seems absurdly clear to him, then, in this new ignorance of the grave-edge, and he understands that if he were given another opportunity he would mend his conduct and his words, and be better and brighter during an introduction or at a tea.

"Now, boys," said the captain, "she is going to swamp sure. All we can do is to work her in as far as possible, and then when she swamps, pile out and scramble for the beach. Keep cool now, and don't jump until she swamps sure."

The oiler took the oars. Over his shoulders he scanned the surf. "Captain," he said, "I think I'd better bring her about and keep her head-on to the seas and back her in."

"All right, Billie," said the captain. "Back her in." The oiler swung the boat then, and, seated in the stern, the cook and the correspondent were obliged to look over their shoulders to contemplate the lonely and indifferent shore.

The monstrous inshore rollers heaved the boat high until the men were again enabled to see the white sheets of water scudding up the slanted beach. "We won't get in very close," said the captain. Each time a man could wrest his attention from the rollers, he turned his glance toward the shore, and in the expression of the eyes during this contemplation there was a singular quality. The correspondent, observing the others, knew that they were not afraid, but the full meaning of their glances was shrouded.

As for himself, he was too tired to grapple fundamentally with the fact. He tried to coerce his mind into thinking of it, but the mind was dominated at this time by the muscles, and the muscles said they did not care. It merely occurred to him that if he should drown it would be a shame.

There were no hurried words, no pallor, no plain agitation. The men simply looked at the shore. "Now, remember to get well clear of the boat when you jump," said the captain.

Seaward the crest of a roller suddenly fell with a thunderous crash, and the long white comber came roaring down upon the boat.

"Steady now," said the captain. The men were silent. They turned their eyes from the shore to the comber and waited. The boat slid up the incline, leaped at the furious top, bounced over it, and swung down the long back of the wave. Some water had been shipped, and the cook bailed it out.

But the next crest crashed also. The tumbling, boiling flood of white water caught the boat and whirled it almost perpendicular. Water swarmed in from all sides. The correspondent had his hands on the gunwale at this time, and when the water entered at that place he swiftly withdrew his fingers, as if he objected to wetting them.

The little boat, drunken with this weight of water, reeled and snuggled deeper into the sea.

"Bail her out, cook! Bail her out!" said the captain.

"All right, Captain," said the cook.

"Now, boys, the next one will do for us sure," said the oiler. "Mind to jump clear of the boat."

The third wave moved forward, huge, furious, implacable. It fairly swallowed the dinghy, and almost simultaneously the men tumbled into the sea. A piece of life-belt had lain in the bottom of the boat, and as the correspondent went overboard he held this to his chest with his left hand.

The January water was icy, and he reflected immediately that it was colder than he had expected to find it off the coast of Florida. This appeared to his dazed mind as a fact important enough to be noted at the time. The coldness of the water was sad; it was tragic. This fact was somehow mixed and confused with his opinion of his own situation, so that it seemed almost a proper reason for tears. The water was cold.

When he came to the surface he was conscious of little but the noisy water. Afterward he saw his companions in the sea. The oiler was ahead in the race. He was swimming strongly and rapidly. Off to the correspondent's left, the cook's great white and corked back bulged out of the water; and in the rear the captain was hanging with his one good hand to the keel of the overturned dinghy.

There is a certain immovable quality to a shore, and the correspondent wondered at it amid the confusion of the sea.

It seemed also very attractive; but the correspondent knew that it was a long journey, and he paddled leisurely. The piece of life-preserver lay under him, and sometimes he whirled down the incline of a wave as if he were on a hand-sled.

But finally he arrived at a place in the sea where travel was beset with difficulty. He did not pause swimming to inquire what manner of current had caught him, but there his progress ceased. The shore was set before him like a bit of scenery on a stage, and he looked at it and understood with his eyes each detail of it.

As the cook passed, much farther to the left, the captain was calling to him, "Turn over on your back, cook! Turn over on your back and use the oar."

"All right, sir." The cook turned on his back, and, paddling with an oar, went ahead as if he were a canoe.

Presently the boat also passed to the left of the correspondent, with the captain clinging with one hand to the keel. He would have appeared like a man raising himself to look over a board fence if it were not for the extraordinary gymnastics of the boat. The correspondent marveled that the captain could still hold to it.

They passed on nearer to shore—the oiler, the cook, the captain—and following them went the water-jar, bouncing gaily over the seas.

The correspondent remained in the grip of this strange new enemy—a current. The shore, with its white slope of sand and its green bluff topped with little silent cottages, was spread like a picture before him. It was very near to him then, but he was impressed as one who, in a gallery, looks at a scene from Brittany or Algiers.

He thought: "I am going to drown? Can it be possible? Can it be possible? Can it be possible?" Perhaps an individual must consider his own death to be the final phenomenon of nature.

But later a wave perhaps whirled him out of this small deadly current, for he found suddenly that he could again make progress toward the shore. Later still he was aware that the captain, clinging with one hand to the keel of the dinghy, had his face turned away from the shore and toward him, and was calling his name. "Come to the boat! Come to the boat!"

In his struggle to reach the captain and the boat, he reflected that when one gets properly wearied drowning must really be a comfortable arrangement—a cessation of hostilities accompanied by a large degree of relief; and he was glad of it, for the main thing in his mind for some moments had been horror of the temporary agony. He did not wish to be hurt.

Presently he saw a man running along the shore. He was undressing with most remarkable speed. Coat, trousers, shirt, everything flew magically off him.

"Come to the boat!" called the captain.

"All right, Captain." As the correspondent paddled, he saw the captain let himself down to bottom and leave the boat. Then the correspondent performed his one little marvel of the voyage. A large wave caught him and flung him with ease and supreme speed completely over the boat and far beyond it. It struck him even then as an event in gymnastics and a true miracle of the sea. An overturned boat in the surf is not a plaything to a swimming man.

The correspondent arrived in water that reached only to his waist, but his condition did not enable him to stand for more than a moment. Each wave knocked him into a heap, and the undertow pulled at him.

Then he saw the man who had been running and undressing, and undressing and running, come bounding into the water. He dragged ashore the cook, and then waded toward the captain; but the captain waved him away and sent him to the correspondent. He was naked—naked as a tree in winter; but a halo was about his head, and he shone like a saint. He gave a strong pull, and a long drag, and a bully heave at the correspondent's hand. The correspondent, schooled in the minor formulæ, said, "Thanks, old man." But suddenly the man cried, "What's that?" He pointed a swift finger. The correspondent said, "Go."

In the shallows, face downward, lay the oiler. His forehead touched sand that was periodically, between each wave, clear of the sea.

The correspondent did not know all that transpired afterward. When he achieved safe ground he fell, striking the sand with each particular part of his body. It was as if he had dropped from a roof, but the thud was grateful to him.

It seemed that instantly the beach was populated with men with blankets, clothes, and flasks, and women with coffee-pots and all the remedies sacred to their minds. The welcome of the land to the men from the sea was warm and generous; but a still and dripping shape was carried slowly up the beach, and the land's welcome for it could only be the different and sinister hospitality of the grave.

When it came night, the white waves paced to and fro in the moonlight, and the wind brought the sound of the great sea's voice to the men on the shore, and they felt that they could then be interpreters.

James Joyce

ARABY

NORTH RICHMOND STREET, being blind, was a quiet street except at the hour when the Christian Brothers' School set the boys free. An uninhabited house of two storeys stood at the blind end, detached from its neighbours in a square ground. The other houses of the street, conscious of decent lives within them, gazed at one another with brown imperturbable faces.

The former tenant of our house, a priest, had died in the back drawing-room. Air, musty from having been long enclosed, hung in all the rooms, and the waste room behind the kitchen was littered with old useless papers. Among these I found a few paper-covered books, the pages of which were curled and damp: *The Abbot*, by Walter Scott, *The Devout Communicant* and *The Memoirs of Vidocq*.[1] I liked the last best because its leaves were yellow. The wild garden behind the house contained a central apple-tree and a few straggling bushes under one of which I found the late tenant's rusty bicycle-pump. He had been a very charitable priest; in his will he had left all his money to institutions and the furniture of his house to his sister.

When the short days of winter came dusk fell before we had well eaten our dinners. When we met in the street the houses had grown sombre. The space of sky above us was the colour of ever-changing violet and

1. *The Devout Communicant:* a religious tract by Rev. P. Baker; Vidocq (1775–1857) was a French detective, adventurer, and probable criminal.

towards it the lamps of the street lifted their feeble lanterns. The cold air stung us and we played till our bodies glowed. Our shouts echoed in the silent street. The career of our play brought us through the dark muddy lanes behind the houses where we ran the gauntlet of the rough tribes from the cottages, to the back doors of the dark dripping gardens where odours arose from the ashpits, to the dark odorous stables where a coachman smoothed and combed the horse or shook music from the buckled harness. When we returned to the street light from the kitchen windows had filled the areas. If my uncle was seen turning the corner we hid in the shadow until we had seen him safely housed. Or if Mangan's sister came out on the doorstep to call her brother in to his tea we watched her from our shadow peer up and down the street. We waited to see whether she would remain or go in and, if she remained, we left our shadow and walked up to Mangan's steps resignedly. She was waiting for us, her figure defined by the light from the half-opened door. Her brother always teased her before he obeyed and I stood by the railings looking at her. Her dress swung as she moved her body and the soft rope of her hair tossed from side to side.

Every morning I lay on the floor in the front parlour watching her door. The blind was pulled down to within an inch of the sash so that I could not be seen. When she came out on the doorstep my heart leaped. I ran to the hall, seized my books and followed her. I kept her brown figure always in my eye and, when we came near the point at which our ways diverged, I quickened my pace and passed her. This happened morning after morning. I had never spoken to her, except for a few casual words, and yet her name was like a summons to all my foolish blood.

Her image accompanied me even in places the most hostile to romance. On Saturday evenings when my aunt went marketing I had to go to carry some of the parcels. We walked through the flaring streets, jostled by drunken men and bargaining women, amid the curses of labourers, the shrill litanies of shop-boys who stood on guard by the barrels of pigs' cheeks, the nasal chanting of street-singers, who sang a *come-all-you* about O'Donovan Rossa,[2] or a ballad about the troubles in our native land. These noises converged in a single sensation of life for me: I imagined that I bore my chalice safely through a throng of foes. Her name sprang to my lips at moments in strange prayers and praises which I myself did not understand. My eyes were often full of tears (I could not tell why) and at times a flood from my heart seemed to pour itself out into my bosom. I thought little of the future. I did not know whether I would ever speak to her or not or, if I spoke to her, how I could tell her of my confused adora-

2. *come-all-you*: an Irish popular ballad; **O'Donovan Rossa**: Jeremiah O'Donovan Rossa, a contemporary Irish hero, member of an Irish-American revolutionary secret society, the Fenians. He died in 1915.

tion. But my body was like a harp and her words and gestures were like fingers running upon the wires.

One evening I went into the back drawing-room in which the priest had died. It was a dark rainy evening and there was no sound in the house. Through one of the broken panes I heard the rain impinge upon the earth, the fine incessant needles of water playing in the sodden beds. Some distant lamp or lighted window gleamed below me. I was thankful that I could see so little. All my senses seemed to desire to veil themselves and, feeling that I was about to slip from them, I pressed the palms of my hands together until they trembled, murmuring: *"O love! O love!"* many times.

At last she spoke to me. When she addressed the first words to me I was so confused that I did not know what to answer. She asked me was I going to *Araby*. I forgot whether I answered yes or no. It would be a splendid bazaar, she said she would love to go.

"And why can't you?" I asked.

While she spoke she turned a silver bracelet round and round her wrist. She could not go, she said, because there would be a retreat that week in her convent. Her brother and two other boys were fighting for their caps and I was alone at the railings. She held one of the spikes, bowing her head towards me. The light from the lamp opposite our door caught the white curve of her neck, lit up her hair that rested there and, falling, lit up the hand upon the railing. It fell over one side of her dress and caught the white border of a petticoat, just visible as she stood at ease.

"It's well for you," she said.

"If I go," I said, "I will bring you something."

What innumerable follies laid waste my waking and sleeping thoughts after that evening! I wished to annihilate the tedious intervening days. I chafed against the work of school. At night in my bedroom and by day in the classroom her image came between me and the page I strove to read. The syllables of the word *Araby* were called to me through the silence in which my soul luxuriated and cast an Eastern enchantment over me. I asked for leave to go to the bazaar on Saturday night. My aunt was surprised and hoped it was not some Freemason affair. I answered few questions in class. I watched my master's face pass from amiability to sternness; he hoped I was not beginning to idle. I could not call my wandering thoughts together. I had hardly any patience with the serious work of life which, now that it stood between me and my desire, seemed to me child's play, ugly monotonous child's play.

On Saturday morning I reminded my uncle that I wished to go to the bazaar in the evening. He was fussing at the hallstand, looking for the hat-brush, and answered me curtly:

"Yes, boy, I know."

As he was in the hall I could not go into the front parlour and lie at the window. I left the house in bad humour and walked slowly towards the school. The air was pitilessly raw and already my heart misgave me.

When I came home to dinner my uncle had not yet been home. Still it was early. I sat staring at the clock for some time and, when its ticking began to irritate me, I left the room. I mounted the staircase and gained the upper part of the house. The high cold empty gloomy rooms liberated me and I went from room to room singing. From the front window I saw my companions playing below in the street. Their cries reached me weakened and indistinct and, leaning my forehead against the cool glass, I looked over at the dark house where she lived. I may have stood there for an hour, seeing nothing but the brown-clad figure cast by my imagination, touched discreetly by the lamplight at the curved neck, at the hand upon the railings and at the border below the dress.

When I came downstairs again I found Mrs. Mercer sitting at the fire. She was an old garrulous woman, a pawnbroker's widow, who collected used stamps for some pious purpose. I had to endure the gossip of the tea-table. The meal was prolonged beyond an hour and still my uncle did not come. Mrs. Mercer stood up to go: she was sorry she couldn't wait any longer, but it was after eight o'clock and she did not like to be out late, as the night air was bad for her. When she had gone I began to walk up and down the room, clenching my fists. My aunt said:

"I'm afraid you may put off your bazaar for this night of Our Lord."

At nine o'clock I heard my uncle's latchkey in the halldoor. I heard him talking to himself and heard the hallstand rocking when it had received the weight of his overcoat. I could interpret these signs. When he was midway through his dinner I asked him to give me the money to go to the bazaar. He had forgotten.

"The people are in bed after their first sleep now," he said.

I did not smile. My aunt said to him energetically:

"Can't you give him the money and let him go? You've kept him late enough as it is."

My uncle said he was very sorry he had forgotten. He said he believed in the old saying: "All work and no play makes Jack a dull boy." He asked me where I was going and when I had told him a second time he asked me did I know *The Arab's Farewell to His Steed*.[3] When I left the kitchen he was about to recite the opening lines of the piece to my aunt.

---

3. *The . . . Steed:* a poem by the English poet Caroline Elizabeth Sarah Norton (1818–1877), variously entitled "The Arab's Farewell to His Horse" and "The Arab to His Favorite Steed."

I held a florin [4] tightly in my hand as I strode down Buckingham Street towards the station. The sight of the streets thronged with buyers and glaring with gas recalled to me the purpose of my journey. I took my seat in a third-class carriage of a deserted train. After an intolerable delay the train moved out of the station slowly. It crept onward among ruinous houses and over the twinkling river. At Westland Row Station a crowd of people pressed to the carriage doors; but the porters moved them back, saying that it was a special train for the bazaar. I remained alone in the bare carriage. In a few minutes the train drew up beside an improvised wooden platform. I passed out on to the road and saw by the lighted dial of a clock that it was ten minutes to ten. In front of me was a large building which displayed the magical name.

I could not find any sixpenny entrance and, fearing that the bazaar would be closed, I passed in quickly through a turnstile, handing a shilling to a weary-looking man. I found myself in a big hall girdled at half its height by a gallery. Nearly all the stalls were closed and the greater part of the hall was in darkness. I recognised a silence like that which pervades a church after a service. I walked into the centre of the bazaar timidly. A few people were gathered about the stalls which were still open. Before a curtain, over which the words *Café Chantant* [5] were written in coloured lamps, two men were counting money on a salver. I listened to the fall of the coins.

Remembering with difficulty why I had come I went over to one of the stalls and examined porcelain vases and flowered tea-sets. At the door of the stall a young lady was talking and laughing with two young gentlemen. I remarked their English accents and listened vaguely to their conversation.

"O, I never said such a thing!"

"O, but you did!"

"O, but I didn't!"

"Didn't she say that?"

"Yes. I heard her."

"O, there's a . . . fib!"

Observing me the young lady came over and asked me did I wish to buy anything. The tone of her voice was not encouraging; she seemed to have spoken to me out of a sense of duty. I looked humbly at the great jars that stood like eastern guards at either side of the dark entrance to the stall and murmured:

"No, thank you."

4. Today the florin is worth about 28 cents.
5. *Café Chantant:* a restaurant where concerts take place.

The young lady changed the position of one of the vases and went back to the two young men. They began to talk of the same subject. Once or twice the young lady glanced at me over her shoulder.

I lingered before her stall, though I knew my stay was useless, to make my interest in her wares seem the more real. Then I turned away slowly and walked down the middle of the bazaar. I allowed the two pennies to fall against the sixpence in my pocket. I heard a voice call from one end of the gallery that the light was out. The upper part of the hall was now completely dark.

Gazing up into the darkness I saw myself as a creature driven and derided by vanity; and my eyes burned with anguish and anger.

D. H. Lawrence

THE BLIND MAN

I SABEL PERVIN was listening for two sounds—for the sound of wheels on the drive outside and for the noise of her husband's footsteps in the hall. Her dearest and oldest friend, a man who seemed almost indispensable to her living, would drive up in the rainy dusk of the closing November day. The trap had gone to fetch him from the station. And her husband, who had been blinded in Flanders, and who had a disfiguring mark on his brow, would be coming in from the out-houses.

He had been home for a year now. He was totally blind. Yet they had been very happy. The Grange was Maurice's own place. The back was a farmstead, and the Wernhams, who occupied the rear premises, acted as farmers. Isabel lived with her husband in the handsome rooms in front. She and he had been almost entirely alone together since he was wounded. They talked and sang and read together in a wonderful and unspeakable intimacy. Then she reviewed books for a Scottish newspaper, carrying on her old interest, and he occupied himself a good deal with the farm. Sightless, he could still discuss everything with Wernham, and he could also do a good deal of work about the place—menial work, it is true, but it gave him satisfaction. He milked the cows, carried in the pails, turned the separator, attended to the pigs and horses. Life was still very full and strangely serene for the blind man, peaceful with the almost incomprehensible peace of immediate contact in darkness. With his wife he had a whole world, rich and real and invisible.

They were newly and remotely happy. He did not even regret the loss of his sight in these times of dark, palpable joy. A certain exultance swelled his soul.

But as time wore on, sometimes the rich glamour would leave them. Sometimes, after months of this intensity, a sense of burden overcame Isabel, a weariness, a terrible ennui, in that silent house approached between a colonnade of tall-shafted pines. Then she felt she would go mad, for she could not bear it. And sometimes he had devastating fits of depression, which seemed to lay waste his whole being. It was worse than depression—a black misery, when his own life was a torture to him, and when his presence was unbearable to his wife. The dread went down to the roots of her soul as these black days recurred. In a kind of panic she tried to wrap herself up still further in her husband. She forced the old spontaneous cheerfulness and joy to continue. But the effort it cost her was almost too much. She knew she could not keep it up. She felt she would scream with the strain, and would give anything, anything, to escape. She longed to possess her husband utterly; it gave her inordinate joy to have him entirely to herself. And yet, when again he was gone in a black and massive misery, she could not bear him, she could not bear herself; she wished she could be snatched away off the earth altogether, anything rather than live at this cost.

Dazed, she schemed for a way out. She invited friends, she tried to give him some further connection with the outer world. But it was no good. After all their joy and suffering, after their dark, great year of blindness and solitude and unspeakable nearness, other people seemed to them both shallow, prattling, rather impertinent. Shallow prattle seemed presumptuous. He became impatient and irritated, she was wearied. And so they lapsed into their solitude again. For they preferred it.

But now, in a few weeks' time, her second baby would be born. The first had died, an infant, when her husband first went out to France. She looked with joy and relief to the coming of the second. It would be her salvation. But also she felt some anxiety. She was thirty years old, her husband was a year younger. They both wanted the child very much. Yet she could not help feeling afraid. She had her husband on her hands, a terrible joy to her, and a terrifying burden. The child would occupy her love and attention. And then, what of Maurice? What would he do? If only she could feel that he, too, would be at peace and happy when the child came! She did so want to luxuriate in a rich, physical satisfaction of maternity. But the man, what would he do? How could she provide for him, how avert those shattering black moods of his, which destroyed them both?

She sighed with fear. But at this time Bertie Reid wrote to Isabel. He was her old friend, a second or third cousin, a Scotsman, as she was a Scotswoman. They had been brought up near to one another, and all her life he had been her friend, like a brother, but better than her own brothers. She loved him—though not in the marrying sense. There was a sort of kinship between them, an affinity. They understood one another instinctively. But Isabel would never have thought of marrying Bertie. It would have seemed like marrying in her own family.

Bertie was a barrister and a man of letters, a Scotsman of the intellectual type, quick, ironical, sentimental, and on his knees before the women he adored but did not want to marry. Maurice Pervin was different. He came of a good old country family—the Grange was not a very great distance from Oxford. He was passionate, sensitive, perhaps over-sensitive, wincing—a big fellow with heavy limbs and a forehead that flushed painfully. For his mind was slow, as if drugged by the strong provincial blood that beat in his veins. He was very sensitive to his own mental slowness, his feelings being quick and acute. So that he was just the opposite to Bertie, whose mind was much quicker than his emotions, which were not so very fine.

From the first the two men did not like each other. Isabel felt that they *ought* to get on together. But they did not. She felt that if only each could have the clue to the other there would be such a rare understanding between them. It did not come off, however. Bertie adopted a slightly ironical attitude, very offensive to Maurice, who returned the Scotch irony with English resentment, a resentment which deepened sometimes into stupid hatred.

This was a little puzzling to Isabel. However, she accepted it in the course of things. Men were made freakish and unreasonable. Therefore, when Maurice was going out to France for the second time, she felt that, for her husband's sake, she must discontinue her friendship with Bertie. She wrote to the barrister to this effect. Bertram Reid simply replied that in this, as in all other matters, he must obey her wishes, if these were indeed her wishes.

For nearly two years nothing had passed between the two friends. Isabel rather gloried in the fact; she had no compunction. She had one great article of faith, which was, that husband and wife should be so important to one another, that the rest of the world simply did not count. She and Maurice were husband and wife. They loved one another. They would have children. Then let everybody and everything else fade into insignificance outside this connubial felicity. She professed herself quite happy and ready to receive Maurice's friends. She was happy and ready: the happy wife, the ready woman in possession. Without knowing why, the friends retired abashed, and came no more. Maurice, of course, took as much satisfaction in this connubial absorption as Isabel did.

He shared in Isabel's literary activities, she cultivated a real interest in agriculture and cattle-raising. For she, being at heart perhaps an emotional enthusiast, always cultivated the practical side of life, and prided herself on her mastery of practical affairs. Thus the husband and wife had spent the five years of their married life. The last had been one of blindness and unspeakable intimacy. And now Isabel felt a great indifference coming over her, a sort of lethargy. She wanted to be allowed to bear her child in peace, to nod by the fire and drift vaguely, physically, from day to day. Maurice was like an ominous thunder-cloud. She had to keep waking up to remember him.

When a little note came from Bertie, asking if he were to put up a tombstone to their dead friendship, and speaking of the real pain he felt on account of her husband's loss of sight, she felt a pang, a fluttering agitation of re-awakening. And she read the letter to Maurice.

"Ask him to come down," he said.

"Ask Bertie to come here!" she re-echoed.

"Yes—if he wants to."

Isabel paused for a few moments.

"I know he wants to—he'd only be too glad," she replied. "But what about you, Maurice? How would you like it?"

"I should like it."

"Well—in that case—— But I thought you didn't care for him——"

"Oh, I don't know. I might think differently of him now," the blind man replied. It was rather abstruse to Isabel.

"Well, dear," she said, "if you're quite sure——"

"I'm sure enough. Let him come," said Maurice.

So Bertie was coming, coming this evening, in the November rain and darkness. Isabel was agitated, racked with her old restlessness and indecision. She had always suffered from this pain of doubt, just an agonising sense of uncertainty. It had begun to pass off, in the lethargy of maternity. Now it returned, and she resented it. She struggled as usual to maintain her calm, composed, friendly bearing, a sort of mask she wore over all her body.

A woman had lighted a tall lamp beside the table, and spread the cloth.

The long dining-room was dim, with its elegant but rather severe piece of old furniture. Only the round table glowed softly under the light. It had a rich, beautiful effect. The white cloth glistened and dropped its heavy, pointed lace corners almost to the carpet, the china was old and handsome, creamy-yellow, with a blotched pattern of harsh red and deep blue, the cups large and bell-shaped, the teapot gallant. Isabel looked at it with superficial appreciation.

Her nerves were hurting her. She looked automatically again at the high, uncurtained windows. In the last dusk she could just perceive outside a huge fir tree swaying its boughs: it was as if she thought it rather than saw it. The rain came flying on the window panes. Ah, why had she no peace? These two men, why did they tear at her? Why did they not come—why was there this suspense?

She sat in a lassitude that was really suspense and irritation. Maurice, at least, might come in—there was nothing to keep him out. She rose to her feet. Catching sight of her reflection in a mirror, she glanced at herself with a slight smile of recognition, as if she were an old friend to herself. Her face was oval and calm, her nose a little arched. Her neck made a beautiful line down to her shoulder. With hair knotted loosely behind, she had something of a warm, maternal look. Thinking this of herself, she arched her eyebrows and her rather heavy eyelids, with a little flicker of a smile, and for a moment her grey eyes looked amused and wicked, a little sardonic, out of her transfigured Madonna face.

Then, resuming her air of womanly patience—she was really fatally self-determined—she went with a little jerk towards the door. Her eyes were slightly reddened.

She passed down the wide hall, and through a door at the end. Then she was in the farm premises. The scent of dairy, and of farm-kitchen, and of farmyard and of leather almost overcame her: but particularly the scent of dairy. They had been scalding out the pans. The flagged passage in front of her was dark, puddled and wet. Light came out from the open kitchen door. She went forward and stood in the doorway. The farm-people were at tea, seated at a little distance from her, round a long, narrow table, in the centre of which stood a white lamp. Ruddy faces, ruddy hands holding food, red mouths working, heads bent over the tea-cups: men, land-girls, boys: it was tea-time, feeding-time. Some faces caught sight of her. Mrs. Wernham, going round behind the chairs with a large black teapot, halting slightly in her walk, was not aware of her for a moment. Then she turned suddenly.

"Oh, is it Madame!" she exclaimed. "Come in, then, come in! We're at tea." And she dragged forward a chair.

"No, I won't come in," said Isabel. "I'm afraid I interrupt your meal."

"No—no—not likely, Madame, not likely."

"Hasn't Mr. Pervin come in, do you know?"

"I'm sure I couldn't say! Missed him, have you, Madame?"

"No, I only wanted him to come in," laughed Isabel, as if shyly.

"Wanted him, did ye? Get up, boy—get up, now——"

Mrs. Wernham knocked one of the boys on the shoulder. He began to scrape to his feet, chewing largely.

"I believe he's in top stable," said another face from the table.

"Ah! No, don't get up. I'm going myself," said Isabel.

"Don't you go out of a dirty night like this. Let the lad go. Get along wi' ye, boy," said Mrs. Wernham.

"No, no," said Isabel, with a decision that was always obeyed. "Go on with your tea, Tom. I'd like to go across to the stable, Mrs. Wernham."

"Did ever you hear tell!" exclaimed the woman.

"Isn't the trap late?" asked Isabel.

"Why, no," said Mrs. Wernham, peering into the distace at the tall, dim clock. "No, Madame—we can give it another quarter or twenty minutes yet, good—yes, every bit of a quarter."

"Ah! It seems late when darkness falls so early," said Isabel.

"It do, that it do. Bother the days, that they draw in so," answered Mrs. Wernham. "Proper miserable!"

"They are," said Isabel, withdrawing.

She pulled on her over-shoes, wrapped a large tartan shawl around her, put on a man's felt hat, and ventured out along the causeways of the first yard. It was very dark. The wind was roaring in the great elms behind the out-houses. When she came to the second yard the darkness seemed deeper. She was unsure of her footing. She wished she had brought a lantern. Rain blew against her. Half she liked it, half she felt unwilling to battle.

She reached at last the just visible door of the stable. There was no sign of a light anywhere. Opening the upper half, she looked in: Into a simple well of darkness. The smell of horses, ammonia, and of warmth was startling to her, in that full night. She listened with all her ears, but could hear nothing save the night, and the stirring of a horse.

"Maurice!" she called, softly and musically, though she was afraid. "Maurice—are you there?"

Nothing came from the darkness. She knew the rain and wind blew in upon the horses, the hot animal life. Feeling it wrong, she entered the stable, and drew the lower half of the door shut, holding the upper part close. She did not stir, because she was aware of the presence of the dark hind-quarters of the horses, though she could not see them, and she was afraid. Something wild stirred in her heart.

She listened intensely. Then she heard a small noise in the distance—far away, it seemed—the chink of a pan, and a man's voice speaking a brief word. It would be Maurice, in the other part of the stable. She stood motionless, waiting for him to come through the partition door. The horses were so terrifyingly near to her, in the invisible.

The loud jarring of the inner door-latch made her start; the door was opened. She could hear and feel her husband entering and invisibly passing among the horses near to her, in darkness as they were, actively intermingled. The rather low sound of his voice as he spoke to the horses came velvety to her nerves. How near he was, and how invisible! The darkness seemed to be in a strange swirl of violent life, just upon her. She turned giddy.

Her presence of mind made her call, quietly and musically:

"Maurice! Maurice—dea-ar!"

"Yes," he answered. "Isabel?"

She saw nothing, and the sound of his voice seemed to touch her.

"Hello!" she answered cheerfully, straining her eyes to see him. He was still busy, attending to the horses near her, but she saw only darkness. It made her almost desperate.

"Won't you come in, dear?" she said.

"Yes, I'm coming. Just half a minute. *Stand over—now!* Trap's not come, has it?"

"Not yet," said Isabel.

His voice was pleasant and ordinary, but it had a slight suggestion of the stable to her. She wished he would come away. While he was so utterly invisible she was afraid of him.

"How's the time," he asked.

"Not yet six," she replied. She disliked to answer into the dark. Presently he came very near to her, and she retreated out of doors.

"The weather blows in here," he said, coming steadily forward, feeling for the doors. She shrank away. At last she could dimly see him.

"Bertie won't have much of a drive," he said, as he closed the doors.

"He won't indeed!" said Isabel calmly, watching the dark shape at the door.

"Give me your arm, dear," she said.

She pressed his arm close to her, as she went. But she longed to see him, to look at him. She was nervous. He walked erect, with face rather lifted, but with a curious tentative movement of his powerful, muscular legs. She could feel the clever, careful, strong contact of his feet with the earth, as she balanced against him. For a moment he was a tower of darkness to her, as if he rose out of the earth.

In the house-passage he wavered, and went cautiously, with a curious

look of silence about him as he felt for the bench. Then he sat down
heavily. He was a man with rather sloping shoulders, but with heavy
limbs, powerful legs that seemed to know the earth. His head was small,
usually carried high and light. As he bent down to unfasten his gaiters
and boots he did not look blind. His hair was brown and crisp, his hands
were large, reddish, intelligent, the veins stood out in the wrists; and his
thighs and knees seemed massive. When he stood up his face and neck
were surcharged with blood, the veins stood out on his temples. She did
not look at his blindness.

Isabel was always glad when they had passed through the dividing door
into their own regions of repose and beauty. She was a little afraid of him,
out there in the animal grossness of the back. His bearing also changed, as
he smelt the familiar, indefinable odour that pervaded his wife's surroundings, a delicate, defined scent, very faintly spicy. Perhaps it came from the
pot-pourri bowls.

He stood at the foot of the stairs, arrested, listening. She watched him,
and her heart sickened. He seemed to be listening to fate.

"He's not here yet," he said. "I'll go up and change."

"Maurice," she said, "you're not wishing he wouldn't come, are you?"

"I couldn't quite say," he answered. "I feel myself rather on the *qui
vive*."

"I can see you are," she answered. And she reached up and kissed his
cheek. She saw his mouth relax into a slow smile.

"What are you laughing at?" she said roguishly.

"You consoling me," he answered.

"Nay," she answered. "Why should I console you? You know we love
each other—you know *how* married we are! What does anything else
matter?"

"Nothing at all, my dear."

He felt for her face, and touched it, smiling.

"*You're* all right, aren't you?" he asked, anxiously.

"I'm wonderfully all right, love," she answered. "It's you I am a little
troubled about, at times."

"Why me?" he said, touching her cheeks delicately with the tips of his
fingers. The touch had an almost hypnotising effect on her.

He went away upstairs. She saw him mount into the darkness, unseeing
and unchanging. He did not know that the lamps on the upper corridor
were unlighted. He went on into the darkness with unchanging step. She
heard him in the bathroom.

Pervin moved about almost unconsciously in his familiar surroundings,
dark though everything was. He seemed to know the presence of objects
before he touched them. It was a pleasure to him to rock thus through a

world of things, carried on the flood in a sort of blood-prescience. He did
not think much or trouble much. So long as he kept this sheer immediacy
of blood-contact with the substantial world he was happy, he wanted no
intervention of visual consciousness. In this state there was a certain rich
positivity, bordering sometimes on rapture. Life seemed to move in him
like a tide lapping, lapping, and advancing, enveloping all things darkly. It
was a pleasure to stretch forth the hand and meet the unseen object, clasp
it, and possess it in pure contact. He did not try to remember, to visualise.
He did not want to. The new way of consciousness substituted itself in
him.

The rich suffusion of this state generally kept him happy, reaching its
culmination in the consuming passion for his wife. But at times the flow
would seem to be checked and thrown back. Then it would beat inside
him like a tangled sea, and he was tortured in the shattered chaos of his
own blood. He grew to dread this arrest, this throw-back, this chaos inside himself, when he seemed merely at the mercy of his own powerful
and conflicting elements. How to get some measure of control or surety,
this was the question. And when the question rose maddening in him, he
would clench his fists as if he would *compel* the whole universe to submit
to him. But it was in vain. He could not even compel himself.

To-night, however, he was still serene, though little tremors of unreasonable exasperation ran through him. He had to handle the razor very
carefully, as he shaved, for it was not at one with him, he was afraid of it.
His hearing also was too much sharpened. He heard the woman lighting
the lamps on the corridor, and attending to the fire in the visitor's room.
And then, as he went to his room he heard the trap arrive. Then came
Isabel's voice, lifted and calling, like a bell ringing:

"Is it you, Bertie? Have you come?"

And a man's voice answered out of the wind:

"Hello, Isabel! There you are."

"Have you had a miserable drive? I'm so sorry we couldn't send a closed
carriage. I can't see you at all, you know."

"I'm coming. No, I liked the drive—it was like Perthshire. Well, how
are you? You're looking fit as ever, as far as I can see."

"Oh, yes," said Isabel. "I'm wonderfully well. How are you? Rather
thin, I think——"

"Worked to death—everybody's old cry. But I'm all right, Ciss. How's
Pervin?—isn't he here?"

"Oh, yes, he's upstairs changing. Yes, he's awfully well. Take off your
wet things; I'll send them to be dried."

"And how are you both, in spirits? He doesn't fret?"

"No—no, not at all. No, on the contrary, really. We've been wonderfully happy, incredibly. It's more than I can understand—so wonderful: the nearness, and the peace——"

"Ah! Well, that's awfully good news——"

They moved away. Pervin heard no more. But a childish sense of desolation had come over him, as he heard their brisk voices. He seemed shut out—like a child that is left out. He was aimless and excluded, he did not know what to do with himself. The helpless desolation came over him. He fumbled nervously as he dressed himself, in a state almost of childishness. He disliked the Scotch accent in Bertie's speech, and the slight response it found on Isabel's tongue. He disliked the slight purr of complacency in the Scottish speech. He disliked intensely the glib way in which Isabel spoke of their happiness and nearness. It made him recoil. He was fretful and beside himself like a child, he had almost a childish nostalgia to be included in the life circle. And at the same time he was a man, dark and powerful and infuriated by his own weakness. By some fatal flaw, he could not be by himself, he had to depend on the support of another. And this very dependence enraged him. He hated Bertie Reid, and at the same time he knew the hatred was nonsense, he knew it was the outcome of his own weakness.

He went downstairs. Isabel was alone in the dining-room. She watched him enter, head erect, his feet tentative. He looked so strong-blooded and healthy, and, at the same time, cancelled. Cancelled—that was the word that flew across her mind. Perhaps it was his scars suggested it.

"You heard Bertie come, Maurice?" she said.

"Yes—isn't he here?"

"He's in his room. He looks very thin and worn."

"I suppose he works himself to death."

A woman came in with a tray—and after a few minutes Bertie came down. He was a little dark man, with a very big forehead, thin, wispy hair, and sad, large eyes. His expression was inordinately sad—almost funny. He had odd, short legs.

Isabel watched him hesitate under the door, and glance nervously at her husband. Pervin heard him and turned.

"Here you are, now," said Isabel. "Come, let us eat."

Bertie went across to Maurice.

"How are you, Pervin?" he said, as he advanced.

The blind man stuck his hand out into space, and Bertie took it.

"Very fit. Glad you've come," said Maurice.

Isabel glanced at them, and glanced away, as if she could not bear to see them.

"Come," she said. "Come to table. Aren't you both awfully hungry? I am, tremendously."

"I'm afraid you waited for me," said Bertie, as they sat down.

Maurice had a curious monolithic way of sitting in a chair, erect and distant. Isabel's heart always beat when she caught sight of him thus.

"No," she replied to Bertie. "We're very little later than usual. We're having a sort of high tea, not dinner. Do you mind? It gives us such a nice long evening uninterrupted."

"I like it," said Bertie.

Maurice was feeling, with curious little movements, almost like a cat kneading her bed, for his place, his knife and fork, his napkin. He was getting the whole geography of his cover into his consciousness. He sat erect and inscrutable, remote-seeming. Bertie watched the static figure of the blind man, the delicate tactile discernment of the large, ruddy hands, and the curious mindless silence of the brow, above the scar. With difficulty he looked away, and without knowing what he did, picked up a little crystal bowl of violets from the table, and held them to his nose.

"They are sweet-scented," he said. "Where do they come from?"

"From the garden—under the windows," said Isabel.

"So late in the year—and so fragrant! Do you remember the violets under Aunt Bell's south wall?"

The two friends looked at each other and exchanged a smile, Isabel's eyes lighting up.

"Don't I?" She replied. "*Wasn't* she queer!"

"A curious old girl," laughed Bertie. "There's a streak of freakishness in the family, Isabel."

"Ah—but not in you and me, Bertie," said Isabel. "Give them to Maurice, will you?" she added, as Bertie was putting down the flowers. "Have you smelled the violets, dear? Do!—they are so scented."

Maurice held out his hand, and Bertie placed the tiny bowl against his large, warm-looking fingers. Maurice's hand closed over the thin white fingers of the barrister. Bertie carefully extricated himself. Then the two watched the blind man smelling the violets. He bent his head and seemed to be thinking. Isabel waited.

"Aren't they sweet, Maurice?" she said at last, anxiously.

"Very," he said. And he held out the bowl. Bertie took it. Both he and Isabel were a little afraid, and deeply disturbed.

The meal continued. Isabel and Bertie chatted spasmodically. The blind man was silent. He touched his food repeatedly, with quick, delicate touches of his knife-point, then cut irregular bits. He could not bear to be helped. Both Isabel and Bertie suffered: Isabel wondered why. She did not suffer when she was alone with Maurice. Bertie made her conscious of a strangeness.

After the meal the three drew their chairs to the fire, and sat down to talk. The decanters were put on a table near at hand. Isabel knocked the logs on the fire, and clouds of brilliant sparks went up the chimney. Bertie noticed a slight weariness in her bearing.

"You will be glad when your child comes now, Isabel?" he said.

She looked up to him with a quick wan smile.

"Yes, I shall be glad," she answered. "It begins to seem long. Yes, I shall be very glad. So will you, Maurice, won't you?" she added.

"Yes, I shall," replied her husband.

"We are both looking forward so much to having it," she said.

"Yes, of course," said Bertie.

He was a bachelor, three or four years older than Isabel. He lived in beautiful rooms overlooking the river, guarded by a faithful Scottish man-servant. And he had his friends among the fair sex—not lovers, friends. So long as he could avoid any danger of courtship or marriage, he adored a few good women with constant and unfailing homage, and he was chiv-alrously fond of quite a number. But if they seemed to encroach on him, he withdrew and detested them.

Isabel knew him very well, knew his beautiful constancy, and kindness, also his incurable weakness, which made him unable ever to enter into close contact of any sort. He was ashamed of himself, because he could not marry, could not approach women physically. He wanted to do so. But he could not. At the centre of him he was afraid, helplessly and even brutally afraid. He had given up hope, had ceased to expect any more that he could escape his own weakness. Hence he was a brilliant and successful barrister, also *littérateur* of high repute, a rich man, and a great social success. At the centre he felt himself neuter, nothing.

Isabel knew him well. She despised him even while she admired him. She looked at his sad face, his little short legs, and felt contempt of him. She looked at his dark grey eyes, with their uncanny, almost child-like intuition, and she loved him. He understood amazingly—but she had no fear of his understanding. As a man she patronised him.

And she turned to the impassive, silent figure of her husband. He sat leaning back, with folded arms, and face a little uptilted. His knees were straight and massive. She sighed, picked up the poker, and again began to prod the fire, to rouse the clouds of soft, brilliant sparks.

"Isabel tells me," Bertie began suddenly, "that you have not suffered unbearably from the loss of sight."

Maurice straightened himself to attend, but kept his arms folded.

"No," he said, "not unbearably. Now and again one struggles against it, you know. But there are compensations."

"They say it is much worse to be stone deaf," said Isabel.

"I believe it is," said Bertie. "Are there compensations?" he added, to Maurice.

"Yes. You cease to bother about a great many things." Again Maurice stretched his figure, stretched the strong muscles of his back, and leaned backwards, with uplifted face.

"And that is a relief," said Bertie. "But what is there in place of the bothering? What replaces the activity?"

There was a pause. At length the blind man replied, as out of a negligent, unattentive thinking:

"Oh, I don't know. There's a good deal when you're not active."

"Is there?" said Bertie. "What, exactly? It always seems to me that when there is no thought and no action, there is nothing."

Again Maurice was slow in replying.

"There is something," he replied. "I couldn't tell you what it is."

And the talk lapsed once more, Isabel and Bertie chatting gossip and reminiscence, the blind man silent.

At length Maurice rose restlessly, a big, obtrusive figure. He felt tight and hampered. He wanted to go away.

"Do you mind," he said, "if I go and speak to Wernham?"

"No—go along, dear," said Isabel.

And he went out. A silence came over the two friends. At length Bertie said:

"Nevertheless, it is a great deprivation, Cissie."

"It is, Bertie. I know it is."

"Something lacking all the time," said Bertie.

"Yes, I know. And yet—and yet—Maurice is right. There is something else, something *there*, which you never knew was there, and which you can't express."

"What is there?" asked Bertie.

"I don't know—it's awfully hard to define it—but something strong and immediate. There's something strange in Maurice's presence—indefinable—but I couldn't do without it. I agree that it seems to put one's mind to sleep. But when we're alone I miss nothing; it seems awfully rich, almost splendid, you know."

"I'm afraid I don't follow," said Bertie.

They talked desultorily. The wind blew loudly outside, rain chattered on the window-panes, making a sharp drum-sound, because of the closed, mellow-golden shutters inside. The logs burned slowly, with hot, almost invisible small flames. Bertie seemed uneasy, there were dark circles round his eyes. Isabel, rich with her approaching maternity, leaned looking into the fire. Her hair curled in odd, loose strands, very pleasing to the man.

But she had a curious feeling of old woe in her heart, old, timeless night-woe.

"I suppose we're all deficient somewhere," said Bertie.

"I suppose so," said Isabel wearily.

"Damned, sooner or later."

"I don't know," she said, rousing herself. "I feel quite all right, you know. The child coming seems to make me indifferent to everything, just placid. I can't feel that there's anything to trouble about, you know."

"A good thing, I should say," he replied slowly.

"Well, there it is. I suppose it's just Nature. If only I felt I needn't trouble about Maurice, I should be perfectly content——"

"But you feel you must trouble about him?"

"Well—I don't know——" She even resented this much effort.

The evening passed slowly. Isabel looked at the clock. "I say," she said. "It's nearly ten o'clock. Where can Maurice be? I'm sure they're all in bed at the back. Excuse me a moment."

She went out, returning almost immediately.

"It's all shut up and in darkness," she said. "I wonder where he is. He must have gone out to the farm——"

Bertie looked at her.

"I suppose he'll come in," he said.

"I suppose so," she said. "But it's unusual for him to be out now."

"Would you like me to go out and see?"

"Well—if you wouldn't mind. I'd go, but——" She did not want to make the physical effort.

Bertie put on an old overcoat and took a lantern. He went out from the side door. He shrank from the wet and roaring night. Such weather had a nervous effect on him: too much moisture everywhere made him feel almost imbecile. Unwilling, he went through it all. A dog barked violently at him. He peered in all the buildings. At last, as he opened the upper door of a sort of intermediate barn, he heard a grinding noise, and looking in, holding up his lantern, saw Maurice, in his shirt-sleeves, standing listening, holding the handle of a turnip-pulper. He had been pulping sweet roots, a pile of which lay dimly heaped in a corner behind him.

"That you, Wernham?" said Maurice, listening.

"No, it's me," said Bertie.

A large, half-wild grey cat was rubbing at Maurice's leg. The blind man stooped to rub its sides. Bertie watched the scene, then unconsciously entered and shut the door behind him. He was in a high sort of barn-place, from which, right and left, ran off the corridors in front of the stalled cattle. He watched the slow, stooping motion of the other man, as he caressed the great cat.

Maurice straightened himself.

"You came to look for me?" he said.

"Isabel was a little uneasy," said Bertie.

"I'll come in. I like messing about doing these jobs."

The cat had reared her sinister, feline length against his leg, clawing at his thigh affectionately. He lifted her claws out of his flesh.

"I hope I'm not in your way at all at the Grange here," said Bertie, rather shy and stiff.

"My way? No, not a bit. I'm glad Isabel has somebody to talk to. I'm afraid it's I who am in the way. I know I'm not very lively company. Isabel's all right, don't you think? She's not unhappy, is she?"

"I don't think so."

"What does she say?"

"She says she's very content—only a little troubled about you."

"Why me?"

"Perhaps afraid that you might brood," said Bertie cautiously.

"She needn't be afraid of that." He continued to caress the flattened grey head of the cat with his fingers. "What I am a bit afraid of," he resumed, "is that she'll find me a dead weight, always alone with me down here."

"I don't think you need think that," said Bertie, though this was what he feared himself.

"I don't know," said Maurice. "Sometimes I feel it isn't fair that she's saddled with me." Then he dropped his voice curiously. "I say," he asked, secretly struggling, "is my face much disfigured? Do you mind telling me?"

"There is the scar," said Bertie, wondering. "Yes, it is a disfigurement. But more pitiable than shocking."

"A pretty bad scar, though," said Maurice.

"Oh yes."

There was a pause.

"Sometimes I feel I am horrible," said Maurice, in a low voice, talking as if to himself. And Bertie actually felt a quiver of horror.

"That's nonsense," he said.

Maurice again straightened himself, leaving the cat.

"There's no telling," he said. Then again, in an odd tone, he added: "I don't really know you, do I?"

"Probably not," said Bertie.

"Do you mind if I touch you?"

The lawyer shrank away instinctively. And yet, out of very philanthropy, he said, in a small voice: "Not at all."

But he suffered as the blind man stretched out a strong, naked hand to him. Maurice accidentally knocked off Bertie's hat.

"I thought you were taller," he said, starting. Then he laid his hand on Bertie Reid's head, closing the dome of the skull in a soft, firm grasp, gathering it, as it were; then, shifting his grasp and softly closing again, with a fine, close pressure, till he had covered the skull and the face of the smaller man, tracing the brows, and touching the full, closed eyes, touching the small nose and the nostrils, the rough, short moustache, the mouth, the rather strong chin. The hand of the blind man grasped the shoulder, the arm, the hand of the other man. He seemed to take him, in the soft, travelling grasp.

"You seem young," he said quietly, at last.

The lawyer stood almost annihilated, unable to answer.

"Your head seems tender, as if you were young," Maurice repeated. "So do your hands. Touch my eyes, will you?—touch my scar."

Now Bertie quivered with revulsion. Yet he was under the power of the blind man, as if hypnotised. He lifted his hand, and laid the fingers on the scar, on the scarred eyes. Maurice suddenly covered them with his own hand, pressed the fingers of the other man upon his disfigured eye-sockets, trembling in every fibre, and rocking slightly, slowly, from side to side. He remained thus for a minute or more, whilst Bertie stood as if in a swoon, unconscious, imprisoned.

Then suddenly Maurice removed the hand of the other man from his brow, and stood holding it in his own.

"Oh, my God," he said, "we shall know each other now, shan't we? We shall know each other now."

Bertie could not answer. He gazed mute and terror-struck, overcome by his own weakness. He knew he could not answer. He had an unreasonable fear, lest the other man should suddenly destroy him. Whereas Maurice was actually filled with hot, poignant love, the passion of friendship. Perhaps it was this very passion of friendship which Bertie shrank from most.

"We're all right together now, aren't we?" said Maurice. "It's all right now, as long as we live, so far as we're concerned."

"Yes," said Bertie, trying by any means to escape.

Maurice stood with head lifted, as if listening. The new delicate fulfilment of mortal friendship had come as a revelation and surprise to him, something exquisite and unhoped-for. He seemed to be listening to hear if it were real.

Then he turned for his coat.

"Come," he said, "we'll go to Isabel."

Bertie took the lantern and opened the door. The cat disappeared. The two men went in silence along the causeways. Isabel, as they came, thought their footsteps sounded strange. She looked up pathetically and anxiously for their entrance. There seemed a curious elation about Maurice. Bertie was haggard, with sunken eyes.

"What is it?" she asked.

"We've become friends," said Maurice, standing with his feet apart, like a strange colossus.

"Friends!" re-echoed Isabel. And she looked again at Bertie. He met her eyes with a furtive, haggard look; his eyes were as if glazed with misery.

"I'm so glad," she said, in sheer perplexity.

"Yes," said Maurice.

He was indeed so glad. Isabel took his hand with both hers, and held it fast.

"You'll be happier now, dear," she said.

But she was watching Bertie. She knew that he had one desire—to escape from this intimacy, this friendship, which had been thrust upon him. He could not bear it that he had been touched by the blind man, his insane reserve broken in. He was like a mollusc whose shell is broken.

Katherine Anne Porter

ROPE

O N THE third day after they moved to the country he came walking back from the village carrying a basket of groceries and a twenty-four-yard coil of rope. She came out to meet him, wiping her hands on her green smock. Her hair was tumbled, her nose was scarlet with sunburn; he told her that already she looked like a born country woman. His gray flannel shirt stuck to him, his heavy shoes were dusty. She assured him he looked like a rural character in a play.

Had he brought the coffee? She had been waiting all day long for coffee. They had forgot it when they ordered at the store the first day.

Gosh, no, he hadn't. Lord, now he'd have to go back. Yes, he would if it killed him. He thought, though, he had everything else. She reminded him it was only because he didn't drink coffee himself. If he did he would remember it quick enough. Suppose they ran out of cigarettes? Then she saw the rope. What was that for? Well, he thought it might do to hang clothes on, or something. Naturally she asked him if he thought they were going to run a laundry? They already had a fifty-foot line hanging right before his eyes? Why, hadn't he noticed it, really? It was a blot on the landscape to her.

He thought there were a lot of things a rope might come in handy for. She wanted to know what, for instance. He thought a few seconds, but nothing occurred. They could wait and see, couldn't they? You need all sorts of strange odds and ends around a place in the country. She said, yes, that was so; but she thought just at that time when every penny counted, it seemed funny to buy more rope. That was all. She hadn't meant anything else. She hadn't just seen, not at first, why he felt it was necessary.

Well, thunder, he had bought it because he wanted to, and that was all there was to it. She thought that was reason enough, and couldn't understand why he hadn't said so, at first. Undoubtedly it would be useful, twenty-four yards of rope, there were hundreds of things, she couldn't think of any at the moment, but it would come in. Of course. As he had said, things always did in the country.

But she was a little disappointed about the coffee, and oh, look, look, look at the eggs! Oh, my, they're all running! What had he put on top of them? Hadn't he known eggs mustn't be squeezed? Squeezed, who had squeezed them, he wanted to know. What a silly thing to say. He had simply brought them along in the basket with the other things. If they got broke it was the grocer's fault. He should know better than to put heavy things on top of eggs.

She believed it was the rope. That was the heaviest thing in the pack, she saw him plainly when he came in from the road, the rope was a big package on top of everything. He desired the whole wide world to witness that this was not a fact. He had carried the rope in one hand and the basket in the other, and what was the use of her having eyes if that was the best they could do for her?

Well, anyhow, she could see one thing plain: no eggs for breakfast. They'd have to scramble them now, for supper. It was too damned bad. She had planned to have steak for supper. No ice, meat wouldn't keep. He wanted to know why she couldn't finish breaking the eggs in a bowl and set them in a cool place.

Cool place! if he could find one for her, she'd be glad to set them there.

Well, then, it seemed to him they might very well cook the meat at the same time they cooked the eggs and then warm up the meat for tomorrow. The idea simply choked her. Warmed-over meat, when they might as well have had it fresh. Second best and scraps and makeshifts, even to the meat! He rubbed her shoulder a little. It doesn't really matter so much, does it, darling? Sometimes when they were playful, he would rub her shoulder and she would arch and purr. This time she hissed and almost clawed. He was getting ready to say that they could surely manage somehow when she turned on him and said, if he told her they could manage somehow she would certainly slap his face.

He swallowed the words red hot, his face burned. He picked up the rope and started to put it on the top shelf. She would not have it on the top shelf, the jars and tins belonged there; positively she would not have the top shelf cluttered up with a lot of rope. She had borne all the clutter she meant to bear in the flat in town, there was space here at least and she meant to keep things in order.

Well, in that case, he wanted to know what the hammer and nails were doing up there? And why had she put them there when she knew very well he needed that hammer and those nails upstairs to fix the window sashes? She simply slowed down everything and made double work on the place with her insane habit of changing things around and hiding them.

She was sure she begged his pardon, and if she had had any reason to believe he was going to fix the sashes this summer she would have left the hammer and nails right where he put them; in the middle of the bed-room floor where they could step on them in the dark. And now if he didn't clear the whole mess out of there she would throw them down the well.

Oh, all right, all right—could he put them in the closet? Naturally not, there were brooms and mops and dustpans in the closet, and why couldn't he find a place for his rope outside her kitchen? Had he stopped to consider there were seven God-forsaken rooms in the house, and only one kitchen?

He wanted to know what of it? And did she realize she was making a complete fool of herself? And what did she take him for, a three-year-old idiot? The whole trouble with her was she needed something weaker than she was to heckle and tyrannize over. He wished to God now they had a couple of children she could take it out on. Maybe he'd get some rest.

Her face changed at this, she reminded him he had forgot the coffee and had bought a worthless piece of rope. And when she thought of all the things they actually needed to make the place even decently fit to live in, well, she could cry, that was all. She looked so forlorn, so lost and despairing he couldn't believe it was only a piece of rope that was causing all the racket. What *was* the matter, for God's sake?

Oh, would he please hush and go away, and *stay* away, if he could, for five minutes? By all means, yes, he would. He'd stay away indefinitely if she wished. Lord, yes, there was nothing he'd like better than to clear out and never come back. She couldn't for the life of her see what was holding him, then. It was a swell time. Here she was, stuck, miles from a railroad, with a half-empty house on her hands, and not a penny in her pocket, and everything on earth to do; it seemed the God-sent moment for him to get out from under. She was surprised he hadn't stayed in town as it was until she had come out and done the work and got things straightened out. It was his usual trick.

It appeared to him that this was going a little far. Just a touch out of bounds, if she didn't mind his saying so. Why the hell had he stayed in town the summer before? To do a half-dozen extra jobs to get the money he had sent her. That was it. She knew perfectly well they couldn't have done it otherwise. She had agreed with him at the time. And that was the only time so help him he had ever left her to do anything by herself.

Oh, he could tell that to his great-grandmother. She had her notion of what had kept him in town. Considerably more than a notion, if he wanted to know. So, she was going to bring all that up again, was she? Well, she could just think what she pleased. He was tired of explaining. It may have looked funny but he had simply got hooked in, and what could he do? It was impossible to believe that she was going to take it seriously. Yes, yes, she knew how it was with a man: if he was left by himself a minute, some woman was certain to kidnap him. And naturally he couldn't hurt her feelings by refusing!

Well, what was she raving about? Did she forget she had told him those two weeks alone in the country were the happiest she had known for four years? And how long had they been married when she said that? All right, shut up! If she thought that hadn't stuck in his craw.

She hadn't meant she was happy because she was away from him. She meant she was happy getting the devilish house nice and ready for him. That was what she had meant, and now look! Bringing up something she had said a year ago simply to justify himself for forgetting her coffee and breaking the eggs and buying a wretched piece of rope they couldn't afford. She really thought it was time to drop the subject, and now she wanted only two things in the world. She wanted him to get that rope from underfoot, and go back to the village and get her coffee, and if he could remember it, he might bring a metal mitt for the skillets, and two more curtain rods, and if there were any rubber gloves in the village, her hands were simply raw, and a bottle of milk of magnesia from the drug-store.

He looked out at the dark blue afternoon sweltering on the slopes, and mopped his forehead and sighed heavily and said, if only she could wait a minute for *anything*, he was going back. He had said so, hadn't he, the very instant they found he had overlooked it?

Oh, yes, well . . . run along. She was going to wash windows. The country was so beautiful! She doubted they'd have a moment to enjoy it. He meant to go, but he could not until he had said that if she wasn't such a hopeless melancholiac she might see that this was only for a few days. Couldn't she remember anything pleasant about the other summers? Hadn't they ever had any fun? She hadn't time to talk about it, and now would he please not leave that rope lying around for her to trip on? He picked it up, somehow it had toppled off the table, and walked out with it under his arm.

Was he going this minute? He certainly was. She thought so. Some-times it seemed to her he had second sight about the precisely perfect mo-ment to leave her ditched. She had meant to put the mattresses out to sun, if they put them out this minute they would get at least three hours, he must have heard her say that morning she meant to put them out. So of course he would walk off and leave her to it. She supposed he thought the exercise would do her good.

Well, he was merely going to get her coffee. A four-mile walk for two pounds of coffee was ridiculous, but he was perfectly willing to do it. The habit was making a wreck of her, but if she wanted to wreck herself there was nothing he could do about it. If he thought it was coffee that was making a wreck of her, she congratulated him: he must have a damned easy conscience.

Conscience or no conscience, he didn't see why the mattresses couldn't very well wait until tomorrow. And anyhow, for God's sake, were they living *in* the house, or were they going to let the house ride them to death? She paled at this, her face grew livid about the mouth, she looked quite dangerous, and reminded him that housekeeping was no more her work than it was his: she had other work to do as well, and when did he think she was going to find time to do it at this rate?

Was she going to start on that again? She knew as well as he did that his work brought in the regular money, hers was only occasional, if they depended on what *she* made—and she might as well get straight on this question once for all!

That was positively not the point. The question was, when both of them were working on their own time, was there going to be a division of the housework, or wasn't there? She merely wanted to know, she had to make her plans. Why, he thought that was all arranged. It was understood that he was to help. Hadn't he always, in summers?

Hadn't he, though? Oh, just hadn't he? And when, and where, and doing what? Lord, what an uproarious joke!

It was such a very uproarious joke that her face turned slightly purple, and she screamed with laughter. She laughed so hard she had to sit down, and finally a rush of tears spurted from her eyes and poured down into the lifted corners of her mouth. He dashed towards her and dragged her up to her feet and tried to pour water on her head. The dipper hung by a string on a nail and he broke it loose. Then he tried to pump water with one hand while she struggled in the other. So he gave it up and shook her instead.

She wrenched away, crying out for him to take his rope and go to hell, she had simply given him up: and ran. He heard her high-heeled bedroom slippers clattering and stumbling on the stairs.

He went out around the house and into the lane; he suddenly realized he had a blister on his heel and his shirt felt as if it were on fire. Things broke so suddenly you didn't know where you were. She could work herself into a fury about simply nothing. She was terrible, damn it: not an ounce of reason. You might as well talk to a sieve as that woman when she got going. Damned if he'd spend his life humoring her! Well, what to do now? He would take back the rope and exchange it for something else. Things accumulated, things were mountainous, you couldn't move them or sort them out or get rid of them. They just lay and rotted around. He'd take it back. Hell, why should he? He wanted it. What was it anyhow? A piece of rope. Imagine anybody caring more about a piece of rope than about a man's feelings. What earthly right had she to say a word about it? He remembered all the useless, meaningless things she bought for herself: Why? because I wanted it, that's why! He stopped and selected a large stone by the road. He would put the rope behind it. He would put it in the tool-box when he got back. He'd heard enough about it to last him a life-time.

When he came back she was leaning against the post box beside the road waiting. It was pretty late, the smell of broiled steak floated nose high in the cooling air. Her face was young and smooth and fresh-looking. Her unmanageable funny black hair was all on end. She waved to him from a distance, and he speeded up. She called out that supper was ready and waiting, was he starved?

You bet he was starved. Here was the coffee. He waved it at her. She looked at his other hand. What was that he had there?

Well, it was the rope again. He stopped short. He had meant to exchange it but forgot. She wanted to know why he should exchange it, if it was something he really wanted. Wasn't the air sweet now, and wasn't it fine to be here?

She walked beside him with one hand hooked into his leather belt. She pulled and jostled him a little as he walked, and leaned against him. He put his arm clear around her and patted her stomach. They exchanged wary smiles. Coffee, coffee for the Ootsum-Wootsums! He felt as if he were bringing her a beautiful present.

He was a love, she firmly believed, and if she had had her coffee in the morning, she wouldn't have behaved so funny . . . There was a whippoorwill still coming back, imagine, clear out of season, sitting in the crab-apple tree calling all by himself. Maybe his girl stood him up. Maybe she did. She hoped to hear him once more, she loved whippoorwills . . . He knew how she was, didn't he?

Sure, he knew how she was.

F. Scott Fitzgerald

BASIL AND CLEOPATRA

WHEREVER she was became a beautiful and enchanted place to Basil, but he did not think of it that way. He thought the fascination was inherent in the locality, and long afterward a commonplace street or the mere name of a city would exude a peculiar glow, a sustained sound, that struck his soul alert with delight. In her presence he was too absorbed to notice his surroundings; so that her absence never made them empty, but, rather, sent him seeking for her through haunted rooms and gardens that he had never really seen before.

This time, as usual, he saw only the expression of her face, the mouth that gave an attractive interpretation of any emotion she felt or pretended to feel—oh, invaluable mouth—and the rest of her, new as a peach and old as sixteen. He was almost unconscious that they stood in a railroad station and entirely unconscious that she had just glanced over his shoulder and fallen in love with another young man. Turning to walk with the rest to the car, she was already acting for the stranger; no less so because her voice was pitched for Basil and she clung to him, squeezing his arm.

Had Basil noticed this other young man that the train discharged he would merely have been sorry for him—as he had been sorry for the wretched people in the villages along the railroad and for his fellow travelers—they were not entering Yale in a fortnight nor were they about to spend three days in the same town with Miss Erminie Gilbert Labouisse Bibble. There was something dense, hopeless and a little contemptible about them all.

Basil had come to visit here because Erminie Bibble was visiting here. On the sad eve of her departure from his native Western city a month before, she had said, with all the promise one could ask in her urgent voice:

"If you know a boy in Mobile, why don't you make him invite you down when I'll be there?"

He had followed this suggestion. And now with the soft, unfamiliar Southern city actually flowing around him, his excitement led him to believe that Fat Gaspar's car floated off immediately they entered it. A voice from the curb came as a surprise:

"Hi, Bessie Belle. Hi, William. How you all?"

The newcomer was tall and lean and a year or so older than Basil. He wore a white linen suit and a panama hat, under which burned fierce, undefeated Southern eyes.

"Why, Littleboy Le Moyne!" exclaimed Miss Cheever. "When did you get home?"

"Jus' now, Bessie Belle. Saw you lookin' so fine and pretty, had to come and see closer."

He was introduced to Minnie and Basil.

"Drop you somewhere, Littleboy?" asked Fat—on his native heath, William.

"Why—" Le Moyne hesitated. "You're very kind, but the man ought to be here with the car."

"Jump in."

Le Moyne swung his bag on top of Basil's and with courteous formality got in the back seat beside them. Basil caught Minnie's eye and she smiled quickly back, as if to say, "This is too bad, but it'll soon be over."

"Do you happen to come from New Orleans, Miss Bibble?" asked Le Moyne.

"Sure do."

" 'Cause I just came from there and they told me one of their mos' cele-

brated heartbreakers was visiting up here, and meanwhile her suitors were
shooting themselves all over the city. That's the truth. I used to help pick
'em up myself sometimes when they got littering the streets."

This must be Mobile Bay on the left, Basil thought; "Down Mobile,"
and the Dixie moonlight and stevedores singing. The houses on either
side of the street were gently faded behind proud, protecting vines;
there had been crinolines on these balconies, and guitars by night in these
broken gardens.

It was so warm; the voices were so sure they had time to say everything—even Minnie's voice, answering the banter of the youth with the
odd nickname, seemed slower and lazier—he had scarcely ever thought of
her as a Southern girl before. They stopped at a large gate where flickers
of a yellow house showed through luscious trees. Le Moyne got out.

"I certainly hope you both enjoy your visit here. If you'll permit me
I'll call around and see if there's anything I can do to add to your pleasure." He swooped his panama. "I bid you good day."

As they started off, Bessie Belle turned around and smiled at Minnie.

"Didn't I tell you?" she demanded.

"I guessed it in the station, before he came up to the car," said Minnie.
"Something told me that was him."

"Did you think he was good looking?"

"He was divine," Minnie said.

"Of course he's always gone with an older crowd."

To Basil, this prolonged discussion seemed a little out of place. After all,
the young man was simply a local Southerner who lived here; add to that,
that he went with an older crowd, and it seemed that his existence was
being unnecessarily insisted upon.

But now Minnie turned to him, said, "Basil," wriggled invitingly and
folded her hands in a humble, expectant way that invariably caused disturbances in his heart.

"I loved your letters," she said.

"You might have answered them."

"I haven't had a minute, Basil. I visited in Chicago and then in Nash-
ville. I haven't even been home." She lowered her voice. "Father and
mother are getting a divorce, Basil. Isn't that awful?"

He was startled; then, after a moment, he adjusted the idea to her and
she became doubly poignant; because of its romantic connection with her,
the thought of divorce would never shock him again.

"That's why I didn't write. But I've thought of you so much. You're
the best friend I have, Basil. You always understand."

This was decidedly not the note upon which they had parted in St. Paul.
A dreadful rumor that he hadn't intended to mention rose to his lips.

"Who is this fellow Bailey you met at Lake Forest?" he inquired lightly.

"Buzz Bailey!" Her big eyes opened in surprise. "He's very attractive and a divine dancer, but we're just friends." She frowned. "I bet Connie Davies has been telling tales in St. Paul. Honestly, I'm so sick of girls that, just out of jealousy or nothing better to do, sit around and criticize you if you have a good time."

He was convinced now that something had occurred in Lake Forest, but he concealed the momentary pang from Minnie.

"Anyhow, you're~a fine one to talk." She smiled suddenly. "I guess everybody knows how fickle you are, Mr. Basil Duke Lee."

Generally such an implication is considered flattering, but the lightness, almost the indifference, with which she spoke increased his alarm—and then suddenly the bomb exploded.

"You needn't worry about Buzz Bailey. At present I'm absolutely heart-whole and fancy free."

Before he could even comprehend the enormity of what she had said, they stopped at Bessie Belle Cheever's door and the two girls ran up the steps, calling back, "We'll see you this afternoon."

Mechanically Basil climbed into the front seat beside his host.

"Going out for freshman football, Basil?" William asked.

"What? Oh, sure. If I can get off my two conditions." There was no if in his heart; it was the greatest ambition of his life.

"You'll probably make the freshman team easy. That fellow Littleboy Le Moyne you just met is going to Princeton this fall. He played end at V. M. I."

"Where'd he get that crazy name?"

"Why, his family always called him that and everybody picked it up." After a moment he added, "He asked them to the country-club dance with him tonight."

"When did he?" Basil demanded in surprise.

"Right then. That's what they were talking about. I meant to ask them and I was just leading up to it gradually, but he stepped in before I could get a chance." He sighed, blaming himself. "Well, anyhow, we'll see them there."

"Sure; it doesn't matter," said Basil. But was it Fat's mistake? Couldn't Minnie have said right out: "But Basil came all this way to see me and I ought to go with him on his first night here."

What had happened? One month ago, in the dim, thunderous Union Station at St. Paul, they had gone behind a baggage truck and he had kissed her, and her eyes had said: Again. Up to the very end, when she disappeared in a swirl of vapor at the car window, she had been his—those

weren't things you thought; they were things you knew. He was bewildered. It wasn't like Minnie, who, for all her glittering popularity, was
invariably kind. He tried to think of something in his letters that might
have offended her, and searched himself for new shortcomings. Perhaps
she didn't like him the way he was in the morning. The joyous mood in
which he had arrived was vanishing into air.

She was her familiar self when they played tennis that afternoon; she
admired his strokes and once, when they were close at the net, she suddenly patted his hand. But later, as they drank lemonade on the Cheevers'
wide, shady porch, he couldn't seem to be alone with her even for a
minute. Was it by accident that, coming back from the courts, she had
sat in front with Fat? Last summer she had made opportunities to be alone
with him—made them out of nothing. It was in a state that seemed to
border on some terrible realization that he dressed for the country-club
dance.

The club lay in a little valley, almost roofed over by willows, and down
through their black silhouettes, in irregular blobs and patches, dripped the
light of a huge harvest moon. As they parked the car, Basil's tune of tunes,
Chinatown, drifted from the windows and dissolved into its notes which
thronged like elves through the glade. His heart quickened, suffocating
him; the throbbing tropical darkness held a promise of such romance as he
had dreamed of; but faced with it, he felt himself too small and impotent
to seize the felicity he desired. When he danced with Minnie he was
ashamed of inflicting his merely mortal presence on her in this fairyland
whose unfamiliar figures reached towering proportions of magnificence
and beauty. To make him king here, she would have to reach forth and
draw him close to her with soft words; but she only said, "Isn't it wonderful, Basil? Did you ever have a better time?"

Talking for a moment with Le Moyne in the stag line, Basil was
hesitantly jealous and oddly shy. He resented the tall form that stooped
down so fiercely over Minnie as they danced, but he found it impossible
to dislike him or not to be amused by the line of soberfaced banter he kept
up with passing girls. He and William Gaspar were the youngest boys
here, as Bessie Belle and Minnie were the youngest girls, and for the first
time in his life he wanted passionately to be older, less impressionable, less
impressed. Quivering at every scent, sigh or tune, he wanted to be blasé
and calm. Wretchedly he felt the whole world of beauty pour down upon
him like moonlight, pressing on him, making his breath now sighing, now
short, as he wallowed helplessly in a superabundance of youth for which a
hundred adults present would have given years of life.

Next day, meeting her in a world that had shrunk back to reality, things
were more natural, but something was gone and he could not bring him-

self to be amusing and gay. It would be like being brave after the battle. He should have been all that the night before. They went downtown in an unpaired foursome and called at a photographer's for some pictures of Minnie. Basil liked one proof that no one else liked—somehow, it reminded him of her as she had been in St. Paul—so he ordered two—one for her to keep and one to send after him to Yale. All afternoon she was distracted and vaguely singing, but back at the Cheevers' she sprang up the steps at the sound of the phone inside. Ten minutes later she appeared, sulky and lowering, and Basil heard a quick exchange between the two girls:

"He can't get out of it."

"—a pity."

"—back Friday."

It could only be Le Moyne who had gone away, and to Minnie it mattered. Presently, unable to endure her disappointment, he got up wretchedly and suggested to William that they go home. To his surprise, Minnie's hand on his arm arrested him.

"Don't go, Basil. It doesn't seem as if I've seen you a minute since you've been here."

He laughed unhappily.

"As if it mattered to you."

"Basil, don't be silly." She bit her lip as if she were hurt. "Let's go out to the swing."

He was suddenly radiant with hope and happiness. Her tender smile, which seemed to come from the heart of freshness, soothed him and he drank down her lies in grateful gulps like cool water. The last sunshine touched her cheeks with the unearthly radiance he had seen there before, as she told him how she hadn't wanted to accept Le Moyne's invitation, and how surprised and hurt she had been when he hadn't come near her last night.

"Then do one thing, Minnie," he pleaded: "Won't you let me kiss you just once?"

"But not here," she exclaimed, "you silly!"

"Let's go in the summerhouse, for just a minute."

"Basil, I can't. Bessie Belle and William are on the porch. Maybe some other time."

He looked at her distraught, unable to believe or disbelieve in her, and she changed the subject quickly:

"I'm going to Miss Beecher's school, Basil. It's only a few hours from New Haven. You can come up and see me this fall. The only thing is, they say you have to sit in glass parlors. Isn't that terrible?"

"Awful," he agreed fervently.

William and Bessie Belle had left the veranda and were out in front, talking to some people in a car.

"Minnie, come into the summerhouse now—for just a minute. They're so far away."

Her face set unwillingly.

"I can't, Basil. Don't you see I can't?"

"Why not? I've got to leave tomorrow."

"Oh, no."

"I have to. I only have four days to get ready for my exams. Minnie—"

He took her hand. It rested calmly enough in his, but when he tried to pull her to her feet she plucked it sharply away. The swing moved with the little struggle and Basil put out his foot and made it stop. It was terrible to swing when one was at a disadvantage.

She laid the recovered hand on his knee.

"I've stopped kissing people, Basil. Really. I'm too old; I'll be seventeen next May."

"I'll bet you kissed Le Moyne," he said bitterly.

"Well, you're pretty fresh—"

Basil got out of the swing.

"I think I'll go."

Looking up, she judged him dispassionately, as she never had before—his sturdy, graceful figure; the high, warm color through his tanned skin; his black, shining hair that she had once thought so romantic. She felt, too—as even those who disliked him felt—that there was something else in his face—a mark, a hint of destiny, a persistence that was more than will, that was rather a necessity of pressing its own pattern on the world, of having its way. That he would most probably succeed at Yale, that it would be nice to go there this year as his girl, meant nothing to her. She had never needed to be calculating. Hesitating, she alternatingly drew him toward her in her mind and let him go. There were so many men and they wanted her so much. If Le Moyne had been here at hand she wouldn't have hesitated, for nothing must interfere with the mysterious opening glory of that affair; but he was gone for three days and she couldn't decide quite yet to let Basil go.

"Stay over till Wednesday and I'll—I'll do what you want," she said.

"But I can't. I've got these exams to study for. I ought to have left this afternoon."

"Study on the train."

She wriggled, dropped her hands in her lap and smiled at him. Taking her hand suddenly, he pulled her to her feet and toward the summerhouse and the cool darkness behind its vines.

The following Friday Basil arrived in New Haven and set about crowding five days' work into two. He had done no studying on the train; instead he sat in a trance and concentrated upon Minnie, wondering what was happening now that Le Moyne was there. She had kept her promise to him, but only literally—kissed him once in the playhouse, once, grudgingly, the second evening; but the day of his departure there had been a telegram from Le Moyne, and in front of Bessie Belle she had not even dared to kiss him good-bye. As a sort of amend she had given him permission to call on the first day permitted by Miss Beecher's school.

The opening of college found him rooming with Brick Wales and George Dorsey in a suite of two bedrooms and a study in Wright Hall. Until the result of his trigonometry examination was published he was ineligible to play football, but watching the freshmen practice on Yale field, he saw that the quarterback position lay between Cullum, last year's Andover captain, and a man named Danziger from a New Bedford high school. There was a rumor that Cullum would be moved to halfback. The other quarterbacks did not appear formidable and Basil felt a great impatience to be out there with a team in his hands to move over the springy turf. He was sure he could at least get in some of the games.

Behind everything, as a light showing through, was the image of Minnie; he would see her in a week, three days, tomorrow. On the eve of the occasion he ran into Fat Gaspar, who was in Sheff, [1] in the oval by Haughton Hall. In the first busy weeks they had scarcely met; now they walked along for a little way together.

"We all came North together," Fat said. "You ought to have been along. We had some excitement. Minnie got in a jam with Littleboy Le Moyne."

Basil's blood ran cold.

"It was funny afterward, but she was pretty scared for a while," continued Fat. "She had a compartment with Bessie Belle, but she and Littleboy wanted to be alone; so in the afternoon Bessie Belle came and played cards in ours. Well, after about two hours Bessie Belle and I went back, and there were Minnie and Littleboy standing in the vestibule arguing with the conductor; Minnie white as a sheet. Seems they locked the door and pulled down the blinds, and I guess there was a little petting going on. When he came along after the tickets and knocked on the door, they thought it was us kidding them, and wouldn't let him in at first, and when they did, he was pretty upset. He asked Littleboy if that was his compartment, and whether he and Minnie were married that they locked the door, and Littleboy lost his temper trying to explain that there was nothing

1. **Sheff**: Sheffield Scientific School.

wrong. He said the conductor had insulted Minnie and he wanted him to fight. But that conductor could have made trouble, and believe me, I had an awful time smoothing it all over."

With every detail imagined, with every refinement of jealousy beating in his mind, including even envy for their community of misfortune as they stood together in the vestibule, Basil went up to Miss Beecher's next day. Radiant and glowing, more mysteriously desirable than ever, wearing her very sins like stars, she came down to him in her plain white uniform dress, and his heart turned over at the kindness of her eyes.

"You were wonderful to come up, Basil. I'm so excited having a beau so soon. Everybody's jealous of me."

The glass doors hinged like French windows, shutting them in on all sides. It was hot. Down through three more compartments he could see another couple—a girl and her brother, Minnie said—and from time to time they moved and gestured soundlessly, as unreal in these tiny human conservatories as the vase of paper flowers on the table. Basil walked up and down nervously.

"Minnie, I want to be a great man some day and I want to do everything for you. I understand you're tired of me now. I don't know how it happened, but somebody else came along—it doesn't matter. There isn't any hurry. But I just want you to—oh, remember me in some different way—try to think of me as you used to, not as if I was just another one you threw over. Maybe you'd better not see me for a while—I mean at the dance this fall. Wait till I've accomplished some big scene or deed, you know, and I can show it to you and say I did that all for you."

It was very futile and young and sad. Once, carried away by the tragedy of it all, he was on the verge of tears, but he controlled himself to that extent. There was sweat on his forehead. He sat across the room from her, and Minnie sat on the couch, looking at the floor, and said several times: "Can't we be friends, Basil? I always think of you as one of my best friends."

Toward the end she rose patiently.

"Don't you want to see the chapel?"

They walked upstairs and he glanced dismally into a small dark space, with her living, sweet-smelling presence half a yard from his shoulder. He was almost glad when the funereal business was over and he walked out of the school into the fresh autumn air.

Back in New Haven he found two pieces of mail on his desk. One was a notice from the registrar telling him that he had failed his trigonometry examination and would be ineligible for football. The second was a photograph of Minnie—the picture that he had liked and ordered two of in

Mobile. At first the inscription puzzled him: "L. L. from E. G. L. B. Trains are bad for the heart." Then suddenly he realized what had happened, and threw himself on his bed, shaken with wild laughter.

Three weeks later, having requested and passed a special examination in trigonometry, Basil began to look around him gloomily to see if there was anything left in life. Not since his miserable first year at school had he passed through such a period of misery; only now did he begin for the first time to be aware of Yale. The quality of romantic speculation reawoke, and, listlessly at first, then with growing determination, he set about merging himself into this spirit which had fed his dreams so long.

I want to be chairman of the *News* or the *Record*,[2] thought his old self one October morning, and I want to get my letter in football, and I want to be in Skull and Bones.[3]

Whenever the vision of Minnie and Le Moyne on the train occurred to him, he repeated this phrase like an incantation. Already he thought with shame of having stayed over in Mobile, and there began to be long strings of hours when he scarcely brooded about her at all.

He had missed half of the freshman football season, and it was with scant hope that he joined the squad on Yale field. Dressed in his black and white St. Regis jersey, amid the motley of forty schools, he looked enviously at the proud two dozen in Yale blue. At the end of four days he was reconciling himself to obscurity for the rest of the season when the voice of Carson, assistant coach, singled him suddenly out of a crowd of scrub backs.

"Who was throwing those passes just now?"

"I was, sir."

"I haven't seen you before, have I?"

"I just got eligible."

"Know the signals?"

"Yes, sir."

"Well, you take this team down the field—ends, Krutch and Bispam; tackles—"

A moment later he heard his own voice snapping out on the crisp air: "Thirty-two, sixty-five, sixty-seven, twenty-two—"

There was a ripple of laughter.

"Wait a minute! Where'd you learn to call signals like that?" said Carson.

2. **News:** *Yale Daily News;* **Record:** Yale's humorous magazine.
3. **Skull and Bones:** one of Yale's exclusive undergraduate societies.

"Why, we had a Harvard coach, sir."

"Well, just drop the Haughton [4] emphasis. You'll get everybody too excited."

After a few minutes they were called in and told to put on headgears.

"Where's Waite?" Carson asked. "Test, eh? Well, you then—what's your name?—in the black and white sweater?"

"Lee."

"You call signals. And let's see you get some life into this outfit. Some of you guards and tackles are big enough for the varsity. Keep them on their toes, you—what's your name?"

"Lee."

They lined up with possession of the ball on the freshmen's twenty-yard line. They were allowed unlimited downs, but when, after a dozen plays, they were in approximately that same place, the ball was given to the first team.

That's that! thought Basil. That finishes me.

But an hour later, as they got out of the bus, Carson spoke to him:

"Did you weigh this afternoon?"

"Yes. Hundred and fifty-eight."

"Let me give you a tip—you're still playing prep-school football. You're still satisfied with stopping them. The idea here is that if you lay them down hard enough you wear them out. Can you kick?"

"No, sir."

"Well, it's too bad you didn't get out sooner."

A week later his name was read out as one of those to go to Andover. Two quarterbacks ranked ahead of him, Danziger and a little hard rubber ball of a man, named Appleton, and Basil watched the game from the sidelines, but when, the following Tuesday, Danziger splintered his arm in practice, Basil was ordered to report to training table.

On the eve of the game with the Princeton freshmen, the egress of the student body to Princeton for the Varsity encounter left the campus almost deserted. Deep autumn had set in, with a crackling wind from the west, and walking back to his room after final skull practice, Basil felt the old lust for glory sweep over him. Le Moyne was playing end on the Princeton freshmen and it was probable that Minnie would be in the stands, but now, as he ran along the springy grass in front of Osborne, swaying to elude imaginary tacklers, the fact seemed of less importance than the game. Like most Americans, he was seldom able really to grasp the moment, to say: "This, for me, is the great equation by which everything else will be measured; this is the golden time," but for once the

4. **Haughton:** Percy Haughton (1876–1924), famous football coach at Harvard from 1908 to 1916.

present was sufficient. He was going to spend two hours in a country where life ran at the pace he demanded of it.

The day was fair and cool; an unimpassioned crowd, mostly townsmen, was scattered through the stands. The Princeton freshmen looked sturdy and solid in their diagonal stripes, and Basil picked out Le Moyne, noting coldly that he was exceptionally fast, and bigger than he had seemed in his clothes. On an impulse Basil turned and searched for Minnie in the crowd, but he could not find her. A minute later the whistle blew; sitting at the coach's side, he concentrated all his faculties on the play.

The first half was played between the thirty-yard lines. The main principles of Yale's offense seemed to Basil too simple; less effective than the fragments of the Haughton system he had learned at school, while the Princeton tactics, still evolved in Sam White's long shadow, were built around a punter and the hope of a break. When the break came, it was Yale's. At the start of the second half Princeton fumbled and Appleton sent over a drop kick from the thirty-yard line.

It was his last act of the day. He was hurt on the next kick-off and, to a burst of freshmen cheering, assisted from the game.

With his heart in a riot, Basil sprinted out on the field. He felt an overpowering strangeness, and it was someone else in his skin who called the first signals and sent an unsuccessful play through the line. As he forced his eyes to take the field slowly, they met Le Moyne's, and Le Moyne grinned at him. Basil called for a short pass over the line, throwing it himself for a gain of seven yards. He sent Cullum off tackle for three more and a first down. At the forty, with more latitude, his mind began to function smoothly and surely. His short passes worried the Princeton fullback, and, in consequence, the running gains through the line were averaging four yards instead of two.

At the Princeton forty he dropped back to kick formation and tried Le Moyne's end, but Le Moyne went under the interfering halfback and caught Basil by a foot. Savagely Basil tugged himself free, but too late—the halfback bowled him over. Again Le Moyne's face grinned at him, and Basil hated it. He called the same end and, with Cullum carrying the ball, they rolled over Le Moyne six yards, to Princeton's thirty-two. He was slowing down, was he? Then run him ragged! System counseled a pass, but he heard himself calling the end again. He ran parallel to the line, saw his interference melt away and Le Moyne, his jaw set, coming for him. Instead of cutting in, Basil turned full about and tried to reverse his field. When he was trapped he had lost fifteen yards.

A few minutes later the ball changed hands and he ran back to the safety position thinking: They'd yank me if they had anybody to put in my place.

The Princeton team suddenly woke up. A long pass gained thirty yards. A fast new back dazzled his way through the line for another first down. Yale was on the defensive, but even before they had realized the fact, the disaster had happened. Basil was drawn on an apparently developed play; too late he saw the ball shoot out of scrimmage to a loose end; saw, as he was neatly blocked, that the Princeton substitutes were jumping around wildly, waving their blankets. They had scored.

He got up with his heart black, but his brain cool. Blunders could be atoned for—if they only wouldn't take him out. The whistle blew for the quarter, and squatting on the turf with the exhausted team, he made himself believe that he hadn't lost their confidence, kept his face intent and rigid, refusing no man's eye. He had made his errors for today.

On the kick-off he ran the ball back to the thirty-five, and a steady rolling progress began. The short passes, a weak spot inside tackle, Le Moyne's end. Le Moyne was tired now. His face was drawn and dogged as he smashed blindly into the interference; the ball carrier eluded him— Basil or another.

Thirty more to go—twenty—over Le Moyne again. Disentangling himself from the pile, Basil met the Southerner's weary glance and insulted him in a crisp voice:

"You've quit, Littleboy. They better take you out."

He started the next play at him and, as Le Moyne charged in furiously, tossed a pass over his head for the score. Yale 10, Princeton 7. Up and down the field again, with Basil fresher every minute and another score in sight, and suddenly the game was over.

Trudging off the field, Basil's eye ranged over the stands, but he could not see her.

I wonder if she knows I was pretty bad, he thought, and then bitterly: If I don't, he'll tell her.

He could hear him telling her in that soft Southern voice—the voice that had wooed her so persuasively that afternoon on the train. As he emerged from the dressing room an hour later he ran into Le Moyne coming out of the visitors' quarters next door. He looked at Basil with an expression at once uncertain and angry.

"Hello, Lee." After a momentary hesitation he added: "Good work."

"Hello, Le Moyne," said Basil, clipping his words.

Le Moyne turned away, turned back again.

"What's the matter?" he demanded. "Do you want to carry this any further?"

Basil didn't answer. The bruised face and the bandaged hand assuaged his hatred a little, but he couldn't bring himself to speak. The game was over, and now Le Moyne would meet Minnie somewhere, make the defeat negligible in the victory of the night.

"If it's about Minnie, you're wasting your time being sore," Le Moyne exploded suddenly. "I asked her to the game, but she didn't come."

"Didn't she?" Basil was startled.

"That was it, eh? I wasn't sure. I thought you were just trying to get my goat in there." His eyes narrowed. "The young lady kicked me about a month ago."

"Kicked you?"

"Threw me over. Got a little weary of me. She runs through things quickly."

Basil perceived that his face was miserable.

"Who is it now?" he asked in more civil tone.

"It seems to be a classmate of yours named Jubal—and a mighty sad bird, if you ask me. She met him in New York the day before her school opened, and I hear it's pretty heavy. She'll be at the Lawn Club Dance tonight."

Basil had dinner at the Taft [5] with Jobena Dorsey and her brother George. The Varsity had won at Princeton and the college was jubilant and enthusiastic; as they came in, a table of freshmen by the door gave Basil a hand.

"You're getting very important," Jobena said.

A year ago Basil had thought for a few weeks that he was in love with Jobena; when they next met he knew immediately that he was not.

"And why was that?" he asked her now, as they danced. "Why did it all go so quick?"

"Do you really want to know?"

"Yes."

"Because I let it go."

"You let it go?" he repeated. "I like that!"

"I decided you were too young."

"Didn't I have anything to do with it?"

She shook her head.

"That's what Bernard Shaw says," Basil admitted thoughtfully. "But I thought it was just about older people. So you go after the men."

"Well, I should say not!" Her body stiffened indignantly in his arms. "The men are usually there, and the girl blinks at them or something. It's just instinct."

"Can't a man make a girl fall for him?"

"Some men can—the ones who really don't care."

He pondered this awful fact for a moment and stowed it away for fu-

5. **Taft:** the Taft Hotel in New Haven, near the Yale campus.

ture examination. On the way to the Lawn Club he brought forth more questions. If a girl who had been "crazy about a boy" became suddenly infatuated with another, what ought the first boy to do?

"Let her go," said Jobena.

"Supposing he wasn't willing to do that. What ought he to do?"

"There isn't anything to do."

"Well, what's the best thing?"

Laughing, Jobena laid her head on his shoulder.

"Poor Basil," she said, "I'll be Laura Jean Libbey [6] and you tell me the whole story."

He summarized the affair. "You see," he concluded, "if she was just anybody I could get over it, no matter how much I loved her. But she isn't— she's the most popular, most beautiful girl I've ever seen. I mean she's like Messalina and Cleopatra and Salome and all that."

"Louder," requested George from the front seat.

"She's sort of an immortal woman," continued Basil in a lower voice. "You know, like Madame du Barry and all that sort of thing. She's not just—"

"Not just like me."

"No. That is, you're sort of like her—all the girls I've cared about are sort of the same. Oh, Jobena, you know what I mean."

As the lights of the New Haven Lawn Club loomed up she became obligingly serious:

"There's nothing to do. I can see that. She's more sophisticated than you. She staged the whole thing from the beginning, even when you thought it was you. I don't know why she got tired, but evidently she is, and she couldn't create it again, even if she wanted to, and you couldn't because you're—"

"Go on. What?"

"You're too much in love. All that's left for you to do is to show her you don't care. Any girl hates to lose an old beau; so she may even smile at you—but don't go back. It's all over."

In the dressing room Basil stood thoughtfully brushing his hair. It was all over. Jobena's words had taken away his last faint hope, and after the strain of the afternoon the realization brought tears to his eyes. Hurriedly filling the bowl, he washed his face. Someone came in and slapped him on the back.

"You played a nice game, Lee."

"Thanks, but I was rotten."

"You were great. That last quarter—"

He went into the dance. Immediately he saw her, and in the same breath

6. **Laura Jean Libbey:** (1862–1924), a writer of popular romantic novels.

he was dizzy and confused with excitement. A little dribble of stags pursued her wherever she went, and she looked up at each one of them with the bright-eyed, passionate smile he knew so well. Presently he located her escort and indignantly discovered it was a flip, blatant boy from Hill School he had already noticed and set down as impossible. What quality lurked behind those watery eyes that drew her? How could that raw temperament appreciate that she was one of the immortal sirens of the world?

Having examined Mr. Jubal desperately and in vain for the answers to these questions, he cut in and danced all of twenty feet with her, smiling with cynical melancholy when she said:

"I'm so proud to know you, Basil. Everybody says you were wonderful this afternoon."

But the phrase was precious to him and he stood against the wall repeating it over to himself, separating it into its component parts and trying to suck out any lurking meaning. If enough people praised him it might influence her. "I'm proud to know you, Basil. Everybody says you were wonderful this afternoon."

There was a commotion near the door and someone said, "By golly, they got in after all!"

"Who?" another asked.

"Some Princeton freshmen. Their football season's over and three or four of them broke training at the Hofbrau." [7]

And now suddenly the curious specter of a young man burst out of the commotion, as a back breaks through a line, and neatly straight-arming a member of the dance committee, rushed unsteadily onto the floor. He wore no collar with his dinner coat, his shirt front had long expelled its studs, his hair and eyes were wild. For a moment he glanced around as if blinded by the lights; then his glance fell on Minnie Bibble and an unmistakable love light come into his face. Even before he reached her he began to call her name aloud in a strained, poignant Southern voice.

Basil sprang forward, but others were before him, and Littleboy Le Moyne, fighting hard, disappeared into the coatroom in a flurry of legs and arms, many of which were not his own. Standing in the doorway, Basil found his disgust tempered with a monstrous sympathy; for Le Moyne, each time his head emerged from under the faucet, spoke desperately of his rejected love.

But when Basil danced with Minnie again, he found her frightened and angry; so much so that she seemed to appeal to Basil for support, made him sit down.

"Wasn't he a fool?" she cried feelingly. "That sort of thing gives a girl a terrible reputation. They ought to have put him in jail."

7. **Hofbrau:** a New Haven restaurant, near the Yale campus.

"He didn't know what he was doing. He played a hard game and he's all in, that's all."

But her eyes filled with tears.

"Oh, Basil," she pleaded, "am I just perfectly terrible? I never want to be mean to anybody; things just happen."

He wanted to put his arm around her and tell her she was the most romantic person in the world, but he saw in her eyes that she scarcely perceived him; he was a lay figure—she might have been talking to another girl. He remembered what Jobena had said—there was nothing left except to escape with his pride.

"You've got more sense." Her soft voice flowed around him like an enchanted river. "You know that when two people aren't—aren't crazy about each other any more, the thing is to be sensible."

"Of course," he said, and forced himself to add lightly: "When a thing's over, it's over."

"Oh, Basil, you're so satisfactory. You always understand." And now suddenly, for the first time in months, she was actually thinking of him. He would be an invaluable person in any girl's life, she thought, if that brain of his, which was so annoying sometimes, was really used "to sort of understand."

He was watching Jobena dance, and Minnie followed his eyes.

"You brought a girl, didn't you? She's awfully pretty."

"Not as pretty as you."

"Basil."

Resolutely he refused to look at her, guessing that she had wriggled slightly and folded her hands in her lap. And as he held on to himself an extraordinary thing happened—the world around, outside of her, brightened a little. Presently more freshmen would approach him to congratulate him on the game, and he would like it—the words and the tribute in their eyes. There was a good chance he would start against Harvard next week.

"Basil!"

His heart made a dizzy tour of his chest. Around the corner of his eyes he felt her eyes waiting. Was she really sorry? Should he seize the opportunity to turn to her and say: "Minnie, tell this crazy nut to go jump in the river, and come back to me." He wavered, but a thought that had helped him this afternoon returned: He had made all his mistakes for this time. Deep inside of him the plea expired slowly.

Jubal the impossible came up with an air of possession, and Basil's heart went bobbing off around the ballroom in a pink silk dress. Lost again in a fog of indecision, he walked out on the veranda. There was a flurry of premature snow in the air and the stars looked cold. Staring up at them he saw that they were his stars as always—symbols of ambition, struggle and glory. The wind blew through them, trumpeting that high white note for which he always listened, and the thin-blown clouds, stripped for battle, passed in review. The scene was of an unparalleled brightness and magnificence, and only the practiced eye of the commander saw that one star was no longer there.

William Faulkner

THE BEAR

H E WAS TEN. But it had already begun, long before that day when at last he wrote his age in two figures and he saw for the first time the camp where his father and Major de Spain and old General Compson and the others spent two weeks each November and two weeks again each June. He had already inherited then, without ever having seen it, the tremendous bear with one trap-ruined foot which, in an area almost a hundred miles deep, had earned itself a name, a definite designation like a living man.

He had listened to it for years: the long legend of corncribs rifled, of shotes and grown pigs and even calves carried bodily into the woods and devoured, of traps and deadfalls overthrown and dogs mangled and slain, and shotgun and even rifle charges delivered at point-blank range and with no more effect than so many peas blown through a tube by a boy—a corridor of wreckage and destruction beginning back before he was born, through which sped, not fast but rather with the ruthless and irresistible deliberation of a locomotive, the shaggy tremendous shape.

It ran in his knowledge before he ever saw it. It looked and towered in his dreams before he even saw the unaxed woods where it left its crooked print, shaggy, huge, red-eyed, not malevolent but just big—too big for the dogs which tried to bay it, for the horses which tried to ride it down,

for the men and the bullets they fired into it, too big for the very country
which was its constricting scope. He seemed to see it entire with a child's
complete divination before he ever laid eyes on either—the doomed wilderness whose edges were being constantly and punily gnawed at by men
with axes and plows who feared it because it was wilderness, men myriad
and nameless even to one another in the land where the old bear had
earned a name, through which ran not even a mortal animal but an anachronism, indomitable and invincible, out of an old dead time, a phantom,
epitome and apotheosis of the old wild life at which the puny humans
swarmed and hacked in a fury of abhorrence and fear, like pygmies about
the ankles of a drowsing elephant: the old bear solitary, indomitable and
alone, widowered, childless, and absolved of mortality—old Priam reft of
his old wife and having outlived all his sons.

Until he was ten, each November he would watch the wagon containing
the dogs and the bedding and food and guns and his father and Tennie's
Jim, the Negro, and Sam Fathers, the Indian, son of a slave woman and a
Chickasaw chief, depart on the road to town, to Jefferson, where Major
de Spain and the others would join them. To the boy, at seven, eight, and
nine, they were not going into the Big Bottom to hunt bear and deer, but
to keep yearly rendezvous with the bear which they did not even intend
to kill. Two weeks later they would return, with no trophy, no head and
skin. He had not expected it. He had not even been afraid it would be in
the wagon. He believed that even after he was ten and his father would
let him go too, for those two weeks in November, he would merely make
another one, along with his father and Major de Spain and General Compson and the others, the dogs which feared to bay at it and the rifles and
shotguns which failed even to bleed it, in the yearly pageant of the old
bear's furious immortality.

Then he heard the dogs. It was in the second week of his first time in
the camp. He stood with Sam Fathers against a big oak beside the faint
crossing where they had stood each dawn for nine days now, hearing the
dogs. He had heard them once before, one morning last week—a murmur,
sourceless, echoing through the wet woods, swelling presently into separate voices which he could recognize and call by name. He had raised and
cocked his gun as Sam told him and stood motionless again while the uproar, the invisible course, swept up and past and faded; it seemed to him
that he could actually see the deer, the buck, blond, smoke-colored, elon-
gated with speed, fleeing, vanishing, the woods, the gray solitude, still
ringing even when the cries of the dogs had died away.

"Now let the hammers down," Sam said.

"You knew they were not coming here too," he said.

"Yes," Sam said. "I want you to learn how to do when you didn't shoot.

It's after the chance for the bear or the deer has done already come and gone that men and dogs get killed."

"Anyway," he said, "it was just a deer."

Then on the tenth morning he heard the dogs again. And he readied the too-long, too-heavy gun as Sam had taught him, before Sam even spoke. But this time is was no deer, no ringing chorus of dogs running strong on a free scent, but a moiling yapping an octave too high, with something more than indecision and even abjectness in it, not even moving very fast, taking a long time to pass completely out of hearing, leaving then some-where in the air that echo, thin, slightly hysterical, abject, almost grieving, with no sense of a fleeing, unseen, smoke-colored, grass-eating shape ahead of it, and Sam, who had taught him first of all to cock the gun and take position where he could see everywhere and then never move again, had himself moved up beside him; he could hear Sam breathing at his shoul-der, and he could see the arched curve of the old man's inhaling nostrils.

"Hah," Sam said. "Not even running. Walking."

"Old Ben!" the boy said. "But up here!" he cried. "Way up here!"

"He do it every year," Sam said. "Once. Maybe to see who in camp this time, if he can shoot or not. Whether we got the dog yet that can bay and hold him. He'll take them to the river, then he'll send them back home. We may as well go back too; see how they look when they come back to camp."

When they reached the camp the hounds were already there, ten of them crouching back under the kitchen, the boy and Sam squatting to peer back into the obscurity where they had huddled, quiet, the eyes luminous, glowing at them and vanishing, and no sound, only that effluvium of some-thing more than dog, stronger than dog and not just animal, just beast, because still there had been nothing in front of that abject and almost pain-ful yapping save the solitude, the wilderness, so that when the eleventh hound came in at noon and with all the others watching—even old Uncle Ash, who called himself first a cook—Sam daubed the tattered ear and the raked shoulder with turpentine and axle grease, to the boy it was still no living creature, but the wilderness which, leaning for the moment down, had patted lightly once the hound's temerity.

"Just like a man," Sam said. "Just like folks. Put off as long as she could having to be brave, knowing all the time that sooner or later she would have to be brave to keep on living with herself, and knowing all the time beforehand what was going to happen to her when she done it."

That afternoon, himself on the one-eyed wagon mule which did not mind the smell of blood nor, as they told him, of bear, and with Sam on the other one, they rode for more than three hours through the rapid, shortening winter day. They followed no path, no trail even that he could see; almost at once they were in a country which he had never seen before. Then he knew why Sam had made him ride the mule which would not spook.[1] The sound one stopped short and tried to whirl and bolt even as Sam got down, blowing its breath, jerking and wrenching at the rein, while Sam held it, coaxing it forward with his voice, since he could not risk tying it, drawing it forward while the boy got down from the marred one.

Then, standing beside Sam in the gloom of the dying afternoon, he looked down at the rotted over-turned log, gutted and scored with claw marks and, in the wet earth beside it, the print of the enormous warped two-toed foot. He knew now what he had smelled when he peered under the kitchen where the dogs huddled. He realized for the first time that the bear which had run in his listening and loomed in his dreams since before he could remember to the contrary, and which, therefore, must have existed in the listening and dreams of his father and Major de Spain and even old General Compson, too, before they began to remember in their turn, was a mortal animal, and that if they had departed for the camp each November without any actual hope of bringing its trophy back, it was not because it could not be slain, but because so far they had had no actual hope to.

"Tomorrow," he said.

"We'll try tomorrow," Sam said. "We ain't got the dog yet."

"We've got eleven. They ran him this morning."

"It won't need but one," Sam said. "He ain't here. Maybe he ain't nowhere. The only other way will be for him to run by accident over somebody that has a gun."

"That wouldn't be me," the boy said. "It will be Walter or Major or—"

"It might," Sam said. "You watch close in the morning. Because he's smart. That's how come he has lived this long. If he gets hemmed up and has to pick out somebody to run over, he will pick out you."

"How?" the boy said. "How will he know—" He ceased. "You mean he already knows me, that I ain't never been here before, ain't had time to find out yet whether I—" He ceased again, looking at Sam, the old man whose face revealed nothing until it smiled. He said humbly, not even amazed, "It was me he was watching. I don't reckon he did need to come but once."

The next morning they left the camp three hours before daylight. They rode this time because it was too far to walk, even the dogs in the wagon; again the first gray light found him in a place which he had never seen before, where Sam had placed him and told him to stay and then departed. With the gun which was too big for him, which did not even belong to

1. **spook:** take fright, as at a ghost.

him, but to Major de Spain, and which he had fired only once—at a stump on the first day, to learn the recoil and how to reload it—he stood against a gum tree beside a little bayou whose black still water crept without movement out of a canebrake and crossed a small clearing and into cane again, where, invisible, a bird—the big woodpecker called Lord-to-God by Negroes—clattered at a dead limb.

It was a stand like any other, dissimilar only in incidentals to the one where he had stood each morning for ten days; a territory new to him, yet no less familiar than that other one which, after almost two weeks, he had come to believe he knew a little—the same solitude, the same loneliness through which human beings had merely passed without altering it, leaving no mark, no scar, which looked exactly as it must have looked when the first ancestor of Sam Fathers' Chickasaw predecessors crept into it and looked about, club or stone ax or bone arrow drawn and poised; different only because, squatting at the edge of the kitchen, he smelled the hounds huddled and cringing beneath it and saw the raked ear and shoulder of the one who, Sam said, had had to be brave once in order to live with herself, and saw yesterday in the earth beside the gutted log the print of the living foot.

He heard no dogs at all. He never did hear them. He only heard the drumming of the woodpecker stop short off and knew that the bear was looking at him. He never saw it. He did not know whether it was in front of him or behind him. He did not move, holding the useless gun, which he had not even had warning to cock and which even now he did not cock, tasting in his saliva that taint as of brass which he knew now because he had smelled it when he peered under the kitchen at the huddled dogs.

Then it was gone. As abruptly as it had ceased, the woodpecker's dry, monotonous clatter set up again, and after a while he even believed he could hear the dogs—a murmur, scarce a sound even, which he had probably been hearing for some time before he even remarked it, drifting into hearing and then out again, dying away. They came nowhere near him. If it was a bear they ran, it was another bear. It was Sam himself who came out of the cane and crossed the bayou, followed by the injured bitch of yesterday. She was almost at heel, like a bird dog, making no sound. She came and crouched against his leg, trembling, staring off into the cane.

"I didn't see him," he said. "I didn't, Sam!"

"I know it," Sam said. "He done the looking. You didn't hear him neither, did you?"

"No," the boy said. "I—"

"He's smart," Sam said. "Too smart." He looked down at the hound, trembling faintly and steadily against the boy's knee. From the raked shoulder a few drops of fresh blood oozed and clung. "Too big. We ain't got the dog yet. But maybe someday. Maybe not next time. But someday."

So I must see him, he thought. *I must look at him.* Otherwise, it seemed to him that it would go on like this forever, as it had gone on with his father and Major de Spain, who was older than his father, and even with old General Compson, who had been old enough to be a brigade commander in 1865. Otherwise, it would go on so forever, next time and next time, after and after and after. It seemed to him that he could never see the two of them, himself and the bear, shadowy in the limbo from which time emerged, becoming time; the old bear absolved of mortality and himself partaking, sharing a little of it, enough of it. And he knew now what he had smelled in the huddled dogs and tasted in his saliva. He recognized fear. *So I will have to see him*, he thought, without dread or even hope. *I will have to look at him.*

It was in June of the next year. He was eleven. They were in camp again, celebrating Major de Spain's and General Compson's birthdays. Although the one had been born in September and the other in the depth of winter and in another decade, they had met for two weeks to fish and shoot squirrels and turkeys and run coons and wildcats with the dogs at night. That is, he and Boon Hoggenbeck and the Negroes fished and shot squirrels and ran the coons and cats, because the proved hunters, not only Major de Spain and old General Compson, who spent those two weeks sitting in a rocking chair before a tremendous iron pot of Brunswick stew, stirring and tasting, with old Ash to quarrel with about how he was making it and Tennie's Jim to pour whiskey from the demijohn into the tin dipper from which he drank it, but even the boy's father and Walter Ewell, who were still young enough, scorned such, other than shooting the wild gobblers with pistols for wagers on their marksmanship.

Or, that is, his father and the others believed he was hunting squirrels. Until the third day, he thought that Sam Fathers believed that too. Each morning he would leave the camp right after breakfast. He had his own gun now, a Christmas present. He went back to the tree beside the bayou where he had stood that morning. Using the compass which old General Compson had given him, he ranged from that point; he was teaching himself to be a better-than-fair woodsman without knowing he was doing it. On the second day he even found the gutted log where he had first seen the crooked print. It was almost completely crumbled now, healing with unbelievable speed, a passionate and almost visible relinquishment, back into the earth from which the tree had grown.

He ranged the summer woods now, green with gloom; if anything, actually dimmer than in November's gray dissolution, where, even at noon, the sun fell only in intermittent dappling upon the earth, which never completely dried out and which crawled with snakes—moccasins and water snakes and rattlers, themselves the color of the dappling gloom, so that he would not always see them until they moved, returning later and later, first day, second day, passing in the twilight of the third evening the little log pen enclosing the log stable where Sam was putting up the horses for the night.

"You ain't looked right yet," Sam said.

He stopped. For a moment he didn't answer. Then he said peacefully, in a peaceful rushing burst as when a boy's miniature dam in a little brook gives way, "All right. But how? I went to the bayou. I even found that log again. I—"

"I reckon that was all right. Likely he's been watching you. You never saw his foot?"

"I," the boy said—"I didn't—I never thought—"

"It's the gun," Sam said. He stood beside the fence motionless—the old man, the Indian, in the battered faded overalls and the five-cent straw hat which in the Negro's race had been the badge of his enslavement and was now the regalia of his freedom. The camp—the clearing, the house, the barn and its tiny lot with which Major de Spain in his turn had scratched punily and evanescently at the wilderness—faded in the dusk, back into the immemorial darkness of the woods. *The gun*, the boy thought. *The gun.*

"Be scared," Sam said. "You can't help that. But don't be afraid. Ain't nothing in the woods going to hurt you unless you corner it, or it smells that you are afraid. A bear or a deer, too, has got to be scared of a coward the same as a brave man has got to be."

The gun, the boy thought.

"You will have to choose," Sam said.

He left the camp before daylight, long before Uncle Ash would wake in his quilts on the kitchen floor and start the fire for breakfast. He had only the compass and a stick for snakes. He could go almost a mile before he would begin to need the compass. He sat on a log, the invisible compass in his invisible hand, while the secret night sounds, fallen still at his movements, scurried again and then ceased for good, and the owls ceased and gave over to the waking of day birds, and he could see the compass. Then he went fast yet still quietly; he was becoming better and better as a woodsman, still without having yet realized it.

He jumped a doe and a fawn at sunrise, walked them out of the bed, close enough to see them—the crash of undergrowth, the white scut, the fawn scudding behind her faster than he had believed it could run. He was hunting right, upwind, as Sam had taught him; not that it mattered now. He had left the gun; of his own will and relinquishment he had accepted not a gambit, not a choice, but a condition in which not only the bear's heretofore inviolable anonymity but all the old rules and balances of hunter and hunted had been abrogated. He would not even be afraid, not even in the moment when the fear would take him completely—blood, skin, bowels, bones, memory from the long time before it became his memory—all save that thin, clear, immortal lucidity which alone differed him from this bear and from all the other bear and deer he would ever kill in the humility and pride of his skill and endurance, to which Sam had spoken when he leaned in the twilight on the lot fence yesterday.

By noon he was far beyond the little bayou, farther into the new and alien country than he had ever been. He was traveling now not only by the old, heavy, biscuit-thick silver watch which had belonged to his grandfather. When he stopped at last, it was for the first time since he had risen from the log at dawn when he could see the compass. It was far enough. He had left the camp nine hours ago; nine hours from now, dark would have already been an hour old. But he didn't think that. He thought, *All right. Yes. But what?* and stood for a moment, alien and small in the green and topless solitude, answering his own question before it had formed and ceased. It was the watch, the compass, the stick—the three lifeless mechanicals with which for nine hours he had fended the wilderness off; he hung the watch and compass carefully on a bush and leaned the stick beside them and relinquished completely to it.

He had not been going very fast for the last two or three hours. He went no faster now, since distance would not matter even if he could have gone fast. And he was trying to keep a bearing on the tree where he had left the compass, trying to complete a circle which would bring him back to it or at least intersect itself, since direction would not matter now either. But the tree was not there, and he did as Sam had schooled him—made the next circle in the opposite direction, so that the two patterns would bisect somewhere, but crossing no print of his own feet, finding the tree at last, but in the wrong place—no bush, no compass, no watch—and the tree not even the tree, because there was a down log beside it and he did what Sam Fathers had told him was the next thing and the last.

As he sat down on the log he saw the crooked print—the warped, tremendous, two-toed indentation which, even as he watched it, filled with water. As he looked up, the wilderness coalesced, solidified—the glade, the tree he sought, the bush, the watch and the compass glinting where a ray of sunshine touched them. Then he saw the bear. It did not emerge, appear; it was just there, immobile, solid, fixed in the hot dappling of the green and windless noon, not as big as he had dreamed it, but as big as he had expected it, bigger, dimensionless, against the dappled obscurity, looking at him where he sat quietly on the log and looked back at it.

Then it moved. It made no sound. It did not hurry. It crossed the glade, walking for an instant into the full glare of the sun; when it reached the other side it stopped again and looked back at him across one shoulder while his quiet breathing inhaled and exhaled three times.

Then it was gone. It didn't walk into the woods, the undergrowth. It faded, sank back into the wilderness as he had watched a fish, a huge old bass, sink and vanish into the dark depths of its pool without even any movement of its fins.

He thought, *It will be next fall.* But it was not next fall, nor the next nor the next. He was fourteen then. He had killed his buck, and Sam Fathers had marked his face with the hot blood, and in the next year he killed a bear. But even before that accolade he had become as competent in the woods as many grown men with the same experience; by his fourteenth year he was a better woodsman than most grown men with more. There was no territory within thirty miles of the camp that he did not know— bayou, ridge, brake, landmark, tree and path. He could have led anyone to any point in it without deviation, and brought them out again. He knew the game trails that even Sam Fathers did not know; in his thirteenth year he found a buck's bedding place, and unbeknown to his father he borrowed Walter Ewell's rifle and lay in wait at dawn and killed the buck when it walked back to the bed, as Sam had told him how the old Chickasaw fathers did.

But not the old bear, although by now he knew its footprints better than he did his own, and not only the crooked one. He could see any one of the three sound ones and distinguish it from any other, and not only by its size. There were other bears within these thirty miles which left tracks almost as large, but this was more than that. If Sam Fathers had been his mentor and the back-yard rabbits and squirrels at home his kindergarten, then the wilderness the old bear ran was his college, the old male bear itself, so long unwifed and childless as to have become its own ungendered progenitor, was his alma mater. But he never saw it.

He could find the crooked print now almost whenever he liked, fifteen or ten or five miles, or sometimes nearer the camp than that. Twice while on stand during the three years he heard the dogs strike its trail by accident; on the second time they jumped it seemingly, the voices high, abject, almost human in hysteria, as on that first morning two years ago. But not the bear itself. He would remember that noon three years ago, the glade, himself and the bear fixed during that moment in the windless and dappled blaze, and it would seem to him that it had never happened, that he had dreamed that too. But it had happened. They had looked at each other, they had emerged from the wilderness old as earth, synchronized to the instant by something more than the blood that moved the flesh and bones which bore them, and touched, pledged something, affirmed, something more lasting than the frail web of bones and flesh which any accident could obliterate.

Then he saw it again. Because of the very fact that he thought of nothing else, he had forgotten to look for it. He was still hunting with Walter Ewell's rifle. He saw it cross the end of a long blow-down, a corridor where a tornado had swept, rushing through rather than over the tangle of trunks and branches as a locomotive would have, faster than he had ever believed it could move, almost as fast as a deer even, because a deer would have spent most of that time in the air, faster than he could bring the rifle sights up with it. And now he knew what had been wrong during all the three years. He sat on a log, shaking and trembling as if he had never seen the woods before nor anything that ran them, wondering with incredulous amazement how he could have forgotten the very thing which Sam Fathers had told him and which the bear itself had proved the next day and had now returned after three years to reaffirm.

And now he knew what Sam Fathers had meant about the right dog, a dog in which size would mean less than nothing. So when he returned alone in April—school was out then, so that the sons of farmers could help with the land's planting, and at last his father had granted him permission, on his promise to be back in four days—he had the dog. It was his own, a mongrel of the sort called by Negroes a fyce, a ratter, itself not much bigger than a rat and possessing that bravery which had long since stopped being courage and had become foolhardiness.

It did not take four days. Alone again, he found the trail on the first morning. It was not a stalk; it was an ambush. He timed the meeting almost as if it were an appointment with a human being. Himself holding the fyce muffled in a feed sack and Sam Fathers with two of the hounds on a piece of plowing rope, they lay down wind of the trail at dawn of the second morning. They were so close that the bear turned without even running, as if in surprised amazement at the shrill and frantic uproar of the released fyce, turning at bay against the trunk of a tree, on its hind feet; it seemed to the boy that it would never stop rising, taller and taller, and even the two hounds seemed to take a desperate and despairing courage from the fyce, following it as it went in.

Then he realized that the fyce was actually not going to stop. He flung, threw the gun away, and ran; when he overtook and grasped the frantically pin-wheeling little dog, it seemed to him that he was directly under the bear.

He could smell it, strong and hot and rank. Sprawling, he looked up to where it loomed and towered over him like a cloudburst and colored like a thunderclap, quite familiar, peacefully and even lucidly familiar, until he remembered: This was the way he had used to dream about it. Then it was gone. He didn't see it go. He knelt, holding the frantic fyce with both hands, hearing the abashed wailing of the hounds drawing farther and farther away, until Sam came up. He carried the gun. He laid it down quietly beside the boy and stood looking down at him.

"You've done seed him twice now with a gun in your hands," he said. "This time you couldn't have missed him."

The boy rose. He still held the fyce. Even in his arms and clear of the ground, it yapped frantically, straining and surging after the fading uproar of the two hounds like a tangle of wire springs. He was panting a little, but he was neither shaking nor trembling now.

"Neither could you!" he said. "You had the gun! Neither did you!"

"And you didn't shoot," his father said. "How close were you?"

"I don't know, sir," he said. "There was a big wood tick inside his right hind leg. I saw that. But I didn't have the gun then."

"But you didn't shoot when you had the gun," his father said. "Why?"

But he didn't answer, and his father didn't wait for him to, rising and crossing the room, across the pelt of the bear which the boy had killed two years ago and the larger one which his father had killed before he was born, to the bookcase beneath the mounted head of the boy's first buck. It was the room which his father called the office, from which all the plantation business was transacted; in it for the fourteen years of his life he had heard the best of all talking. Major de Spain would be there and sometimes old General Compson, and Walter Ewell and Boon Hoggenback and Sam Fathers and Tennie's Jim, too, were hunters, knew the woods and what ran them.

He would hear it, not talking himself but listening—the wilderness, the big woods, bigger and older than any recorded document of white man fatuous enough to believe he had bought any fragment of it or Indian ruthless enough to pretend that any fragment of it had been his to convey. It was of the men, not white nor black nor red, but men, hunters with the will and hardihood to endure and the humility and skill to survive, and the dogs and the bear and deer juxtaposed and reliefed against it, ordered and compelled by and within the wilderness in the ancient and unremitting contest by the ancient and immitigable rules which voided all regrets and brooked no quarter, the voices quiet and weighty and deliberate for retrospection and recollection and exact remembering, while he squatted in the blazing firelight as Tennie's Jim squatted, who stirred only to put more wood on the fire and to pass the bottle from one glass to another. Because the bottle was always present, so that after a while it seemed to him that those fierce instants of heart and brain and courage and wiliness and speed were concentrated and distilled into that brown liquor which not women, not boys and children, but only hunters drank, drinking not of the blood they had spilled but some condensation of the wild immortal spirit, drinking it moderately, humbly even, not with the pagan's base hope of acquiring the virtues of cunning and strength and speed, but in salute to them.

His father returned with the book and sat down again and opened it. "Listen," he said. He read the five stanzas aloud, his voice quiet and deliberate in the room where there was no fire now because it was already spring. Then he looked up. The boy watched him. "All right," his father said. "Listen." He read again, but only the second stanza this time, to the end of it, the last two lines, and closed the book and put it on the table beside him. "She cannot fade, though thou hast not thy bliss, forever wilt thou love, and she be fair," he said.

"He's talking about a girl," the boy said.

"He had to talk about something," his father said. Then he said, "He was talking about truth. Truth doesn't change. Truth is one thing. It covers all things which touch the heart—honor and pride and pity and justice and courage and love. Do you see now?"

He didn't know. Somehow it was simpler than that. There was an old bear, fierce and ruthless, not merely just to stay alive, but with the fierce pride of liberty and freedom, proud enough of the liberty and freedom to see it threatened without fear or even alarm; nay, who at times even seemed deliberately to put that freedom and liberty in jeopardy in order to savor them, to remind his old strong bones and flesh to keep supple and quick to defend and preserve them. There was an old man, son of a Negro slave and an Indian king, inheritor on the one side of the long chronicle of a people who had learned humility through suffering, and pride through the endurance which survived the suffering and injustice, and on the other side, the chronicle of a people even longer in the land than the first, yet who no longer existed in the land at all save in the solitary brotherhood of an old Negro's alien blood and the wild and invincible spirit of an old bear. There was a boy who wished to learn humility and pride in order to become skillful and worthy in the woods, who suddenly found himself becoming so skillful so rapidly that he feared he would never become worthy because he had not learned humility and pride, although he had tried to, until one day and as suddenly he discovered that an old man who could not have defined either had led him, as though by the hand, to that point where an old bear and a little mongrel of a dog showed him that, by possessing one thing other, he would possess them both.

And a little dog, nameless and mongrel and many-fathered, grown, yet weighing less than six pounds, saying as if to itself, "I can't be dangerous, because there's nothing much smaller than I am; I can't be fierce, because they would call it just a noise; I can't be humble, because I'm already too close to the ground to genuflect; I can't be proud, because I wouldn't be near enough to it for anyone to know who was casting the shadow, and I don't even know that I'm not going to heaven, because they have already decided that I don't possess an immortal soul. So all I can be is brave. But it's all right. I can be that, even if they still call it just noise."

That was all. It was simple, much simpler than somebody talking in a book about youth and a girl he would never need to grieve over, because he could never approach any nearer her and would never have to get any farther away. He had heard about a bear, and finally got big enough to trail it, and he trailed it four years and at last met it with a gun in his hands and he didn't shoot. Because a little dog— But he could have shot long before the little dog covered the twenty yards to where the bear waited, and Sam Fathers could have shot at any time during that interminable minute while Old Ben stood on his hind feet over them. He stopped. His father was watching him gravely across the spring-rife twilight of the room; when he spoke, his words were as quiet as the twilight, too, not loud, because they did not need to be because they would last. "Courage, and honor, and pride," his father said, "and pity, and love of justice and of liberty. They all touch the heart, and what the heart holds to becomes truth, as far as we know the truth. Do you see now?"

Sam, and Old Ben, and Nip, he thought. And himself too. He had been all right too. His father had said so. "Yes, sir," he said.

Ernest Hemingway

THE UNDEFEATED

MANUEL GARCIA climbed the stairs to Don Miguel Retana's office. He set down his suitcase and knocked on the door. There was no answer. Manuel, standing in the hallway, felt there was someone in the room. He felt it through the door.

"Retana," he said, listening.

There was no answer.

He's there, all right, Manuel thought.

"Retana," he said and banged the door.

"Who's there?" said someone in the office.

"Me, Manolo," Manuel said.

"What do you want?" asked the voice.

"I want to work," Manuel said.

Something in the door clicked several times and it swung open. Manuel went in, carrying his suitcase.

A little man sat behind a desk at the far side of the room. Over his head was a bull's head, stuffed by a Madrid taxidermist; on the walls were framed photographs and bullfight posters.

The little man sat looking at Manuel.

"I thought they'd kill you," he said.

Manuel knocked with his knuckles on the desk. The little man sat looking at him across the desk.

"How many corridas [1] you had this year?" Retana asked.

"One," he answered.

"Just that one?" the little man asked.

"That's all."

"I read about it in the papers," Retana said. He leaned back in the chair and looked at Manuel.

Manuel looked up at the stuffed bull. He had seen it often before. He felt a certain family interest in it. It had killed his brother, the promising one, about nine years ago. Manuel remembered the day. There was a brass plate on the oak shield the bull's head was mounted on. Manuel could not read it, but he imagined it was in memory of his brother. Well, he had been a good kid.

The plate said: "The Bull 'Mariposa' of the Duke of Veragua, which accepted 9 varas for 7 caballos, and caused the death of Antonio Garcia, Novillero,[2] April 27, 1909."

Retana saw him looking at the stuffed bull's head.

"The lot the Duke sent me for Sunday will make a scandal," he said. "They're all bad in the legs. What do they say about them at the Café?"

"I don't know," Manuel said. "I just got in."

"Yes," Retana said. "You still have your bag."

He looked at Manuel, leaning back behind the big desk.

"Sit down," he said. "Take off your cap."

---

1. **corridas:** bullfights.
2. **varas:** the spearlike pics used in bullfighting; **caballos:** horses, i.e., ridden by the picador, who wields the vara; **Novillero:** bullfighter.

Manuel sat down; his cap off, his face was changed. He looked pale, and his coleta [3] pinned forward on his head, so that it would not show under the cap, gave him a strange look.

"You don't look well,'" Retana said.

"I just got out of the hospital," Manuel said.

"I heard they'd cut your leg off," Retana said.

"No," said Manuel. "It got all right."

Retana leaned forward across the desk and pushed a wooden box of cigarettes toward Manuel.

"Have a cigarette," he said.

"Thanks."

Manuel lit it.

"Smoke?" he said, offering the match to Retana.

"No," Retana waved his hand, "I never smoke."

Retana watched him smoking.

"Why don't you get a job and go to work?" he said.

"I don't want to work," Manuel said. "I am a bullfighter."

"There aren't any bullfighters any more," Retana said.

"I'm a bullfighter," Manuel said.

"Yes, while you're in there," Retana said.

Manuel laughed.

Retana sat, saying nothing and looking at Manuel.

"I'll put you in a nocturnal if you want," Retana offered.

"When?" Manuel asked.

"Tomorrow night."

"I don't like to substitute for anybody," Manuel said. That was the way they all got killed. That was the way Salvator got killed. He tapped with his knuckles on the table.

"It's all I've got," Retana said.

"Why don't you put me on next week?" Manuel suggested.

"You wouldn't draw," Retana said. "All they want is Litri and Rubito and La Torre. Those kids are good."

"They'd come to see me get it," Manuel said, hopefully.

"No, they wouldn't. They don't know who you are any more."

"I've got a lot of stuff," Manuel said.

"I'm offering to put you on tomorrow night," Retana said. "You can work with young Hernandez and kill two novillos after the Charlots." [4]

"Whose novillos?" Manuel asked.

3. **coleta:** the bullfighter's pigtail, to which is attached a button that supports his hat.
4. **novillos:** bulls that are either overage or underage, used in other than the formal bullfights; **Charlots:** burlesque bullfights, usually held at night, in which the contestants dress in Charlie Chaplin and other comic costumes and the bulls are young, small, and relatively harmless. Also called "charlotada" and "Charlie Chaplins."

"I don't know. Whatever stuff they've got in the corrals. What the veterinaries won't pass in the daytime."

"I don't like to substitute," Manuel said.

"You can take it or leave it," Retana said. He leaned forward over the papers. He was no longer interested. The appeal that Manuel had made to him for a moment when he thought of the old days was gone. He would like to get him to substitute for Larita because he could get him cheaply. He could get others cheaply too. He would like to help him though. Still he had given him the chance. It was up to him.

"How much do I get?" Manuel asked. He was still playing with the idea of refusing. But he knew he could not refuse.

"Two hundred and fifty pesetas," Retana said. He had thought of five hundred, but when he opened his mouth it said two hundred and fifty.

"You pay Villalta seven thousand," Manuel said.

"You're not Villalta," Retana said.

"I know it," Manuel said.

"He draws it, Manolo," Retana said in explanation.

"Sure," said Manuel. He stood up. "Give me three hundred, Retana."

"All right," Retana agreed. He reached in the drawer for a paper.

"Can I have fifty now?" Manuel asked.

"Sure," said Retana. He took a fifty-peseta note out of his pocketbook and laid it, spread out flat, on the table.

Manuel picked it up and put it in his pocket.

"What about a cuadrilla?" [5] he asked.

"There's the boys that always work for me nights," Retana said. "They're all right."

"How about picadors?" Manuel asked.

"They're not much," Retana admitted.

"I've got to have one good pic," Manuel said.

"Get him then," Retana said. "Go and get him."

"Not out of this," Manuel said. "I'm not paying for any cuadrilla out of sixty duros."

Retana said nothing but looked at Manuel across the big desk.

"You know I've got to have one good pic," Manuel said.

Retana said nothing but looked at Manuel from a long way off.

"It isn't right," Manuel said.

Retana was still considering him, leaning back in his chair, considering him from a long way away.

"There're the regular pics," he offered.

"I know," Manuel said. "I know your regular pics."

5. **cuadrilla:** the troupe of bullfighters who assist the matador; it is the matador who actually kills the bull.

Retana did not smile. Manuel knew it was over.

"All I want is an even break," Manuel said reasoningly. "When I go out there I want to be able to call my shots on the bull. It only takes one good picador."

He was talking to a man who was no longer listening.

"If you want something extra," Retana said, "go and get it. There will be a regular cuadrilla out there. Bring as many of your own pics as you want. The charlotada is over by 10:30."

"All right," Manuel said. "If that's the way you feel about it."

"That's the way," Retana said.

"I'll see you tomorrow night," Manuel said.

"I'll be out there," Retana said.

Manuel picked up his suitcase and went out.

"Shut the door," Retana called.

Manuel looked back. Retana was sitting forward looking at some papers. Manuel pulled the door tight until it clicked.

He went down the stairs and out of the door into the hot brightness of the street. It was very hot in the street and the light on the white buildings was sudden and hard on his eyes. He walked down the shady side of the steep street toward the Puerta del Sol.[6] The shade felt solid and cool as running water. The heat came suddenly as he crossed the intersecting streets. Manuel saw no one he knew in all the people he passed.

Just before the Puerta del Sol he turned into a café.

It was quiet in the café. There were a few men sitting at tables against the wall. At one table four men played cards. Most of the men sat against the wall smoking, empty coffee-cups and liqueur-glasses before them on the tables. Manuel went through the long room to a small room in back. A man sat at a table in the corner asleep. Manuel sat down at one of the tables.

A waiter came in and stood beside Manuel's table.

"Have you seen Zurito?" Manuel asked him.

"He was in before lunch," the waiter answered. "He won't be back before five o'clock."

"Bring me some coffee and milk and a shot of the ordinary," Manuel said.

The waiter came back into the room carrying a tray with a big coffee-glass and a liqueur-glass on it. In his left hand he held a bottle of brandy. He swung these down to the table and a boy who had followed him poured coffee and milk into the glass from two shiny, spouted pots with long handles.

Manuel took off his cap and the waiter noticed his pigtail pinned for-

6. **Puerta del Sol:** literally, Gate of the Sun.

ward on his head. He winked at the coffee-boy as he poured out the brandy into the little glass beside Manuel's coffee. The coffee-boy looked at Manuel's pale face curiously.

"You fighting here?" asked the waiter, corking up the bottle.

"Yes," Manuel said. "Tomorrow."

The waiter stood there, holding the bottle on one hip.

"You in the Charlie Chaplins?" he asked.

The coffee-boy looked away, embarrassed.

"No. In the ordinary."

"I thought they were going to have Chaves and Hernandez," the waiter said.

"No. Me and another."

"Who? Chaves or Hernandez?"

"Hernandez, I think."

"What's the matter with Chaves?"

"He got hurt."

"Where did you hear that?"

"Retana."

"Hey, Looie," the waiter called to the next room, "Chaves got cogida." [7]

Manuel had taken the wrapper off the lumps of sugar and dropped them into his coffee. He stirred it and drank it down, sweet, hot, and warming in his empty stomach. He drank off the brandy.

"Give me another shot of that," he said to the waiter.

The waiter uncorked the bottle and poured the glass full, slopping another drink into the saucer. Another waiter had come up in front of the table. The coffee-boy was gone.

"Is Chaves hurt bad?" the second waiter asked Manuel.

"I don't know," Manuel said, "Retana didn't say."

"A hell of a lot he cares," the tall waiter said. Manuel had not seen him before. He must have just come up.

"If you stand in with Retana in this town, you're a made man," the tall waiter said. "If you aren't in with him, you might just as well go out and shoot yourself."

"You said it," the other waiter who had come in said. "You said it then."

"You're right I said it," said the tall waiter. "I know what I'm talking about when I talk about that bird."

"Look what he's done for Villalta," the first waiter said.

"And that ain't all," the tall waiter said. "Look what he's done for Marcial Lalanda. Look what he's done for Nacional."

"You said it, kid," agreed the short waiter.

7. **cogida**: tossed by the bull.

Manuel looked at them, standing talking in front of his table. He had drunk his second brandy. They had forgotten about him. They were not interested in him.

"Look at that bunch of camels," the tall waiter went on. "Did you ever see this Nacional II?"

"I seen him last Sunday, didn't I?" the original waiter said.

"He's a giraffe," the short waiter said.

"What did I tell you?" the tall waiter said. "Those are Retana's boys."

"Say, give me another shot of that," Manuel said. He had poured the brandy the waiter had slopped over in the saucer into his glass and drank it while they were talking.

The original waiter poured his glass full mechanically, and the three of them went out of the room talking.

In the far corner the man was still asleep, snoring slightly on the intaking breath, his head back against the wall.

Manuel drank his brandy. He felt sleepy himself. It was too hot to go out into the town. Besides there was nothing to do. He wanted to see Zurito. He would go to sleep while he waited. He kicked his suitcase under the table to be sure it was there. Perhaps it would be better to put it back under the seat, against the wall. He leaned down and shoved it under. Then he leaned forward on the table and went to sleep.

When he woke there was someone sitting across the table from him. It was a big man with a heavy brown face like an Indian. He had been sitting there some time. He had waved the waiter away and sat reading the paper and occasionally looking down at Manuel, asleep, his head on the table. He read the paper laboriously, forming the words with his lips as he read. When it tired him he looked at Manuel. He sat heavily in the chair, his black Cordoba hat tipped forward.

Manuel sat up and looked at him.

"Hello, Zurito," he said.

"Hello, kid," the big man said.

"I've been asleep." Manuel rubbed his forehead with the back of his fist.

"I thought maybe you were."

"How's everything?"

"Good. How is everything with you?"

"Not so good."

They were both silent. Zurito, the picador, looked at Manuel's white face. Manuel looked down at the picador's enormous hands folding the paper to put away in his pocket.

"I got a favor to ask you, Manos," Manuel said.

Manosduros [8] was Zurito's nickname. He never heard it without think-

8. **Manosduros:** hard, unmerciful hands.

ing of his huge hands. He put them forward on the table self-consciously.

"Let's have a drink," he said.

"Sure," said Manuel.

The waiter came and went and came again. He went out of the room looking back at the two men at the table.

"What's the matter, Manolo?" Zurito set down his glass.

"Would you pic two bulls for me tomorrow night?" Manuel asked, looking up at Zurito across the table.

"No," said Zurito. "I'm not pic-ing."

Manuel looked down at his glass. He had expected that answer; now he had it. Well, he had it.

"I'm sorry, Manolo, but I'm not pic-ing." Zurito looked at his hands.

"That's all right," Manuel said.

"I'm too old," Zurito said.

"I just asked you," Manuel said.

"Is it the nocturnal tomorrow?"

"That's it. I figured if I had just one good pic, I could get away with it."

"How much are you getting?"

"Three hundred pesetas."

"I get more than that for pic-ing."

"I know," said Manuel. "I didn't have any right to ask you."

"What do you keep on doing it for?" Zurito asked. "Why don't you cut off your coleta, Manolo?"

"I don't know," Manuel said.

"You're pretty near as old as I am," Zurito said.

"I don't know," Manuel said. "I got to do it. If I can fix it so that I get an even break, that's all I want. I got to stick with it, Manos."

"No, you don't."

"Yes, I do. I've tried keeping away from it."

"I know how you feel. But it isn't right. You ought to get out and stay out."

"I can't do it. Besides, I've been going good lately."

Zurito looked at his face.

"You've been in the hospital."

"But I was going great when I got hurt."

Zurito said nothing. He tipped the cognac out of his saucer into his glass.

"The papers said they never saw a better faena," [9] Manuel said.

Zurito looked at him.

"You know when I get going I'm good," Manuel said.

"You're too old," the picador said.

9. **faena:** the action of the matador with the cape in the latter part of the fight.

"No," said Manuel. "You're ten years older than I am."

"With me it's different."

"I'm not too old," Manuel said.

They sat silent, Manuel watching the picador's face.

"I was going great till I got hurt," Manuel offered.

"You ought to have seen me, Manos," Manuel said, reproachfully.

"I don't want to see you," Zurito said. "It makes me nervous."

"You haven't seen me lately."

"I've seen you plenty."

Zurito looked at Manuel, avoiding his eyes.

"You ought to quit it, Manolo."

"I can't," Manuel said. "I'm going good now, I tell you."

Zurito leaned forward, his hands on the table.

"Listen. I'll pic for you and if you don't go big tomorrow night, you'll quit. See? Will you do that?"

"Sure."

Zurito leaned back, relieved.

"You got to quit," he said. "No monkey business. You got to cut the coleta."

"I won't have to quit," Manuel said. "You watch me. I've got the stuff."

Zurito stood up. He felt tired from arguing.

"You got to quit," he said. "I'll cut your coleta myself."

"No, you won't," Manuel said. "You won't have a chance."

Zurito called the waiter.

"Come on," said Zurito. "Come on up to the house."

Manuel reached under the seat for his suitcase. He was happy. He knew Zurito would pic for him. He was the best picador living. It was all simple now.

"Come on up to the house and we'll eat," Zurito said.

Manuel stood in the patio de caballos waiting for the Charlie Chaplins to be over. Zurito stood beside him. Where they stood it was dark. The high door that led into the bull-ring was shut. Above them they heard a shout, then another shout of laughter. Then there was silence. Manuel liked the smell of the stables about the patio de caballos. It smelled good in the dark. There was another roar from the arena and then applause, prolonged applause, going on and on.

"You ever seen these fellows?" Zurito asked, big and looming beside Manuel in the dark.

"No," Manuel said.

"They're pretty funny," Zurito said. He smiled to himself in the dark. The high, double, tight-fitting door into the bull-ring swung open and

Manuel saw the ring in the hard light of the arc-lights, the plaza, dark all the way around, rising high; around the edge of the ring were running and bowing two men dressed like tramps, followed by a third in the uniform of a hotel bell-boy who stooped and picked up the hats and canes thrown down onto the sand and tossed them back up into the darkness.

The electric light went on in the patio.

"I'll climb onto one of those ponies while you collect the kids," Zurito said.

Behind them came the jingle of the mules, coming out to go into the arena and be hitched onto the dead bull.

The members of the cuadrilla, who had been watching the burlesque from the runway between the barrera [10] and the seats, came walking back and stood in a group talking, under the electric light in the patio. A good-looking lad in a silver-and-orange suit came up to Manuel and smiled.

"I'm Hernandez," he said and put out his hand.

Manuel shook it.

"They're regular elephants we've got tonight," the boy said cheerfully.

"They're big ones with horns," Manuel agreed.

"You drew the worst lot," the boy said.

"That's all right," Manuel said. "The bigger they are, the more meat for the poor."

"Where did you get that one?" Hernandez grinned.

"That's an old one," Manuel said. "You line up your cuadrilla, so I can see what I've got."

"You've got some good kids," Hernandez said. He was very cheerful. He had been on twice before in nocturnals and was beginning to get a following in Madrid. He was happy the fight would start in a few minutes.

"Where are the pics?" Manuel asked.

"They're back in the corrals fighting about who gets the beautiful horses," Hernandez grinned.

The mules came through the gate in a rush, the whips snapping, bells jangling and the young bull ploughing a furrow of sand.

They formed up for the paseo [11] as soon as the bull had gone through.

Manuel and Hernandez stood in front. The youths of the cuadrillas were behind, their heavy capes furled over their arms. In back, the four picadors, mounted, holding their steel-tipped push-poles erect in the half-dark of the corral.

"It's a wonder Retana wouldn't give us enough light to see the horses by," one picador said.

10. **barrera:** the red wooden fence surrounding a bullring.
11. **paseo:** the entry of the bullfighters into the ring and their parade across it.

"He knows we'll be happier if we don't get too good a look at these skins," another pic answered.

"This thing I'm on barely keeps me off the ground," the first picador said.

"Well, they're horses."

"Sure, they're horses."

They talked, sitting their gaunt horses in the dark.

Zurito said nothing. He had the only steady horse of the lot. He had tried him, wheeling him in the corrals and he responded to the bit and the spurs. He had taken the bandage off his right eye and cut the strings where they had tied his ears tight shut at the base. He was a good, solid horse, solid on his legs. That was all he needed. He intended to ride him all through the corrida. He had already, since he had mounted, sitting in the half-dark in the big, quilted saddle, waiting for the paseo, pic-ed through the whole corrida in his mind. The other picadors went on talking on both sides of him. He did not hear them.

The two matadors stood together in front of their three peones,[12] their capes furled over their left arms in the same fashion. Manuel was think-ing about the three lads in back of him. They were all three Madrilenos,[13] like Hernandez, boys about nineteen. One of them, a gypsy, serious, aloof, and dark-faced, he liked the look of. He turned.

"What's your name, kid?" he asked the gypsy.

"Fuentes," the gypsy said.

"That's a good name," Manuel said.

The gypsy smiled, showing his teeth.

"You take the bull and give him a little run when he comes out," Manuel said.

"All right," the gypsy said. His face was serious. He began to think about just what he would do.

"Here she goes," Manuel said to Hernandez.

"All right. We'll go."

Heads up, swinging with the music, their right arms swinging free, they stepped out, crossing the sanded arena under the arc-lights, the cuadrillas opening out behind, the picadors riding after; behind came the bull-ring servants and the jingling mules. The crowd applauded Hernan-dez as they marched across the arena. Arrogant, swinging, they looked straight ahead as they marched.

They bowed before the president, and the procession broke up into its component parts. The bullfighters went over to the barrera and changed

12. **peones:** the members of the cuadrilla who place the banderillos (darts with stream-
    ers attached) in the bull. Also called banderilleros.
13. **Madrilenos:** natives of Madrid.

their heavy mantles for the light fighting capes. The mules went out. The picadors galloped jerkily around the ring, and two rode out the gate they had come in by. The servants swept the sand smooth.

Manuel drank a glass of water poured for him by one of Retana's deputies, who was acting as his manager and sword-handler. Hernandez came over from speaking with his own manager.

"You got a good hand, kid," Manuel complimented him.

"They like me," Herandez said happily.

"How did the paseo go?" Manuel asked Retana's man.

"Like a wedding," said the handler. "Fine. You came out like Joselito and Belmonte."

Zurito rode by, a bulky equestrian statue. He wheeled his horse and faced him toward the toril[14] on the far side of the ring where the bull would come out. It was strange under the arc-light. He pic-ed in the hot afternoon sun for big money. He didn't like this arc-light business. He wished they would get started.

Manuel went up to him.

"Pic him, Manos," he said. "Cut him down to size for me."

"I'll pic him, kid." Zurito spat on the sand. "I'll make him jump out of the ring."

"Lean on him, Manos," Manuel said.

"I'll lean on him," Zurito said. "What's holding it up?"

"He's coming now," Manuel said.

Zurito sat there, his feet in the box-stirrups, his great legs in the buck-skin-covered armor gripping the horse, the reins in his left hand, the long pic held in his right hand, his broad hat well down over his eyes to shade them from the lights, watching the distant door of the toril. His horse's ears quivered. Zurito patted him with his left hand.

The red door of the toril swung back and for a moment Zurito looked into the empty passageway far across the arena. Then the bull came out in a rush, skidding on his four legs as he came out under the lights, then charging in a gallop, moving softly in a fast gallop, silent except as he woofed through wide nostrils as he charged, glad to be free after the dark pen.

In the first row of seats, slightly bored, leaning forward to write on the cement wall in front of his knees, the substitute bullfight critic of *El Heraldo* scribbled: "Campagnero, Negro,[15] 42, came out at 90 miles an hour with plenty of gas—"

Manuel, leaning against the barrera, watching the bull, waved his hand and the gypsy ran out, trailing his cape. The bull, in full gallop, pivoted

14. **toril:** the enclosure from which the bulls enter the ring.
15. **Negro:** jet black.

and charged the cape, his head down, his tail rising. The gypsy moved in a zigzag, and as he passed, the bull caught sight of him and abandoned the cape to charge the man. The gyp sprinted and vaulted the red fence of the barrera as the bull struck it with his horns. He tossed into it twice with his horns, banging into the wood blindly.

The critic of *El Heraldo* lit a cigarette and tossed the match at the bull, then wrote in his note-book, "large and with enough horns to satisfy the cash customers, Campagnero showed a tendency to cut into the terrain of the bullfighters."

Manuel stepped out on the hard sand as the bull banged into the fence. Out of the corner of his eye he saw Zurito sitting the white horse close to the barrera, about a quarter of the way around the ring to the left. Manuel held the cape close in front of him, a fold in each hand, and shouted at the bull. "Huh! Huh!" The bull turned, seemed to brace against the fence as he charged in a scramble, driving into the cape as Manuel side-stepped, pivoted on his heels with the charge of the bull, and swung the cape just ahead of the horns. At the end of the swing he was facing the bull again and held the cape in the same position close in front of his body, and pivoted again as the bull recharged. Each time, as he swung, the crowd shouted.

Four times he swung with the bull, lifting the cape so it billowed full, and each time bringing the bull around to charge again. Then, at the end of the fifth swing, he held the cape against his hip and pivoted, so the cape swung out like a ballet dancer's skirt and wound the bull around himself like a belt, to step clear, leaving the bull facing Zurito on the white horse, come up and planted firm, the horse facing the bull, its ears forward, its lips nervous, Zurito, his hat over his eyes, leaning forward, the long pole sticking out before and behind in a sharp angle under his right arm, held half-way down, the triangular iron point facing the bull.

El Heraldo's second-string critic, drawing on his cigarette, his eyes on the bull, wrote: "The veteran Manolo designed a series of acceptable veronicas, ending in a very Belmontistic recorte that earned applause from the regulars, and we entered the tercio [16] of the cavalry."

Zurito sat his horse, measuring the distance between the bull and the end of the pic. As he looked, the bull gathered himself together and charged, his eyes on the horse's chest. As he lowered his head to hook, Zurito sunk the point of the pic in the swelling hump of muscle above the bull's shoulder, leaned all his weight on the shaft, and with his left hand pulled the white horse into the air, front hoofs pawing, and swung him to

16. **recorte:** a swift movement of the cape that pulls the bull up short; **tercio:** third, i.e., the third and last part of the fight.

the right as he pushed the bull under and through so the horns passed safely under the horse's belly and the horse came down, quivering, the bull's tail brushing his chest as he charged the cape Hernandez offered him.

Hernandez ran sideways, taking the bull out and away with the cape, toward the other picador. He fixed him with a swing of the cape, squarely facing the horse and rider, and stepped back. As the bull saw the horse he charged. The picador's lance slid along his back, and as the shock of the charge lifted the horse, the picador was already halfway out of the saddle, lifting his right leg clear as he missed with the lance and falling to the left side to keep the horse between him and the bull. The horse, lifted and gored, crashed over with the bull driving into him, the picador gave a shove with his boots against the horse and lay clear, waiting to be lifted and hauled away and put on his feet.

Manuel let the bull drive into the fallen horse; he was in no hurry, the picador was safe; besides, it did a picador like that good to worry. He'd stay on longer next time. Lousy pics! He looked across the sand at Zurito a little way out from the barrera, his horse rigid, waiting.

"Huh!" he called to the bull, "Tomar!" [17] holding the cape in both hands so it would catch his eye. The bull detached himself from the horse and charged the cape, and Manuel, running sideways and holding the cape spread wide, stopped, swung on his heels, and brought the bull sharply around facing Zurito.

"Campagnero accepted a pair of varas for the death of one rosinante, with Hernandez and Manolo at the quites," [18] *El Heraldo's* critic wrote. "He pressed on the iron and clearly showed he was no horse-lover. The veteran Zurito resurrected some of his old stuff with the pike-pole, notably the suerte—" [19]

"Olé! [20] Olé!" the man sitting beside him shouted. The shout was lost in the roar of the crowd, and he slapped the critic on the back. The critic looked up to see Zurito, directly below him, leaning far out over his horse, the length of the pic rising in a sharp angle under his armpit, holding the pic almost by the point, bearing down with all his weight, holding the bull off, the bull pushing and driving to get at the horse, and Zurito, far out, on top of him, holding him, holding him, and slowly pivoting the horse against the pressure, so that at last he was clear. Zurito felt the moment when the horse was clear and the bull could come past, and relaxed the absolute steel lock of his resistance, and the triangular steel point of the

17. **Tomar:** to take, i.e., charge the cape.
18. **quites:** the taking away of the bull.
19. **suerte:** maneuver.
20. **Olé:** bravo.

pic ripped in the bull's hump of shoulder muscle as he tore loose to find Hernandez's cape before his muzzle. He charged blindly into the cape and the boy took him out into the open arena.

Zurito sat patting his horse and looking at the bull charging the cape that Hernandez swung for him out under the bright light while the crowd shouted.

"You see that one?" he said to Manuel.

"It was a wonder," Manuel said.

"I got him that time," Zurito said. "Look at him now."

At the conclusion of a closely turned pass of the cape the bull slid to his knees. He was up at once, but far out across the sand Manuel and Zurito saw the shine of the pumping flow of blood, smooth against the black of the bull's shoulder.

"I got him that time," Zurito said.

"He's a good bull," Manuel said.

"If they gave me another shot at him, I'd kill him," Zurito said.

"They'll change the thirds on us," Manuel said.

"Look at him now," Zurito said.

"I got to go over there," Manuel said, and started on a run for the other side of the ring, where the monos [21] were leading a horse out by the bridle toward the bull, whacking him on the legs with rods and all, in a procession, trying to get him toward the bull, who stood, dropping his head, pawing, unable to make up his mind to charge.

Zurito, sitting his horse, walking him toward the scene, not missing any detail, scowled.

Finally the bull charged, the horse leaders ran for the barrera, the picador hit too far back, and the bull got under the horse, lifted him, threw him onto his back.

Zurito watched. The monos, in their red shirts, running out to drag the picador clear. The picador, now on his feet, swearing and flopping his arms. Manuel and Herandez standing ready with their capes. And the bull, the great, black bull, with a horse on his back, hooves dangling, the bridle caught in the horns. Black bull with a horse on his back, staggering short-legged, then arching his neck and lifting, thrusting, charging to slide the horse off, horse sliding down. Then the bull into a lunging charge at the cape Manuel spread for him.

The bull was slower now, Manuel felt. He was bleeding badly. There was a sheen of blood all down his flank.

Manuel offered him the cape again. There he came, eyes open, ugly, watching the cape. Manuel stepped to the side and raised his arms, tightening the cape ahead of the bull for the veronica.

21. **monos:** horseboys.

Now he was facing the bull. Yes, his head was going down a little. He was carrying it lower. That was Zurito.

Manuel flopped the cape; there he comes; he side-stepped and swung in another veronica. He's shooting awfully accurately, he thought. He's had enough fight, so he's watching now. He's hunting now. Got his eye on me. But I always give him the cape.

He shook the cape at the bull; there he comes; he side-stepped. Awful close that time. I don't want to work that close to him.

The edge of the cape was wet with blood where it had swept along the bull's back as he went by.

All right, here's the last one.

Manuel, facing the bull, having turned with him each charge, offered the cape with his two hands. The bull looked at him. Eyes watching, horns straight forward, the bull looked at him, watching.

"Huh!" Manuel said, "Toro!" [22] and leaning back, swung the cape forward. Here he comes. He side-stepped, swung the cape in back of him, and pivoted, so the bull followed a swirl of cape and then was left with nothing, fixed by the pass, dominated by the cape. Manuel swung the cape under his muzzle with one hand, to show the bull was fixed, and walked away.

There was no applause.

Manuel walked across the sand toward the barrera, while Zurito rode out of the ring. The trumpet had blown to change the act to the planting of the banderillos while Manuel had been working with the bull. He had not consciously noticed it. The monos were spreading canvas over the two dead horses and sprinkling sawdust around them.

Manuel came up to the barrera for a drink of water. Retana's man handed him the heavy porous jug.

Fuentes, the tall gypsy, was standing holding a pair of banderillos, holding them together, slim, red sticks, fish-hook points out. He looked at Manuel.

"Go on out there," Manuel said.

The gypsy trotted out. Manuel set down the jug and watched. He wiped his face with his handkerchief.

The critic of *El Heraldo* reached for the bottle of warm champagne that stood between his feet, took a drink, and finished his paragraph.

"—the aged Manolo rated no applause for a vulgar series of lances [23] with the cape and we entered the third of the palings."

Alone in the center of the ring the bull stood, still fixed. Fuentes, tall, flat-backed, walking toward him arrogantly, his arms spread out, the two

22. **Toro:** the fighting bull.
23. **lances:** passes.

slim, red sticks, one in each hand, held by the fingers, points straight forward. Fuentes walked forward. Back of him and to one side was a peon with a cape. The bull looked at him and was no longer fixed.

His eyes watched Fuentes, now standing still. Now he leaned back, calling to him. Fuentes twitched the two banderillos and the light on the steel points caught the bull's eye.

His tail went up and he charged.

He came straight, his eyes on the man. Fuentes stood still, leaning back, the banderillos pointing forward. As the bull lowered his head to hook, Fuentes leaned backward, his arms came together and rose, his two hands touching, the banderillos two descending red lines, and leaning forward drove the points into the bull's shoulder, leaning far in over the bull's horns and pivoting on the two upright sticks, his legs tight together, his body curving to one side to let the bull pass.

"Olé!" from the crowd.

The bull was hooking wildly, jumping like a trout, all four feet off the ground. The red shafts of the banderillos tossed as he jumped.

Manuel, standing at the barrera, noticed that he looked always to the right.

"Tell him to drop the next pair on the right," he said to the kid who started to run out to Fuentes with the new banderillos.

A heavy hand fell on his shoulder. It was Zurito.

"How do you feel, kid?" he asked.

Manuel was watching the bull.

Zurito leaned forward on the barrera, leaning the weight of his body on his arms. Manuel turned to him.

"You're going good," Zurito said.

Manuel shook his head. He had nothing to do now until the next third. The gypsy was very good with the banderillos. The bull would come to him in the next third in good shape. He was a good bull. It had all been easy up to now. The final stuff with the sword was all he worried over. He did not really worry. He did not even think about it. But standing there he had a heavy sense of apprehension. He looked out at the bull, planning his faena, his work with the red cloth that was to reduce the bull, to make him manageable.

The gypsy was walking out toward the bull again, walking heel-and-toe, insultingly, like a ballroom dancer, the red shafts of the banderillos twitching with his walk. The bull watched him, not fixed now, hunting him, but waiting to get close enough so he could be sure of getting him, getting the horns into him.

As Fuentes walked forward the bull charged. Fuentes ran across the quarter of a circle as the bull charged and, as he passed running back-

ward, stopped, swung forward, rose on his toes, arm straight out, and
sunk the banderillos straight down into the tight of the big shoulder
muscles as the bull missed him.

The crowd were wild about it.

"That kid won't stay in this night stuff long," Retana's man said to
Zurito.

"He's good," Zurito said.

"Watch him now."

They watched.

Fuentes was standing with his back against the barrera. Two of the
cuadrilla were back of him, with their capes ready to flop over the
fence to distract the bull.

The bull, with his tongue out, his barrel heaving, was watching the
gypsy. He thought he had him now. Back against the red planks. Only a
short charge away. The bull watched him.

The gypsy bent back, drew back his arms, the banderillos pointing at
the bull. He called to the bull, stamped one foot. The bull was suspicious.
He wanted the man. No more barbs in the shoulder.

Fuentes walked a little closer to the bull. Bent back. Called again. Somebody in the crowd shouted a warning.

"He's too damn close," Zurito said.

"Watch him," Retana's man said.

Leaning back, inciting the bull with the banderillos, Fuentes jumped,
both feet off the ground. As he jumped the bull's tail rose and he charged.
Fuentes came down on his toes, arms straight out, whole body arching forward, and drove the shafts straight down as he swung his body clear of
the right horn.

The bull crashed into the barrera where the flopping capes had attracted
his eye as he lost the man.

The gypsy came running along the barrera toward Manuel, taking the
applause of the crowd. His vest was ripped where he had not quite cleared
the point of the horn. He was happy about it, showing it to the spectators.
He made the tour of the ring. Zurito saw him go by, smiling, pointing at
his vest. He smiled.

Somebody else was planting the last pair of banderillos. Nobody was
paying any attention.

Retana's man tucked a baton inside the red cloth of a muleta,[24] folded
the cloth over it, and handed it over the barrera to Manuel. He reached in
the leather sword-case, took out a sword, and holding it by its leather
scabbard, reached it over the fence to Manuel. Manuel pulled the blade
out by the red hilt and the scabbard fell limp.

24. **muleta:** the cape.

He looked at Zurito. The big man saw he was sweating.

"Now you get him, kid," Zurito said.

Manuel nodded.

"He's in good shape," Zurito said.

"Just like you want him," Retana's man assured him.

Manuel nodded.

The trumpeter, up under the roof, blew for the final act, and Manuel walked across the arena toward where, up in the dark boxes, the president must be.

In the front row of seats the substitute bullfight critic of *El Heraldo* took a long drink of the warm champagne. He had decided it was not worth while to write a running story and would write up the corrida back in the office. What the hell was it anyway? Only a nocturnal. If he missed anything he would get it out of the morning papers. He took another drink of the champagne. He had a date at Maxim's at twelve. Who were these bullfighters anyway? Kids and bums. A bunch of bums. He put his pad of paper in his pocket and looked over toward Manuel, standing very much alone in the ring, gesturing with his hat in a salute toward a box he could not see high up in the dark plaza. Out in the ring the bull stood quiet, looking at nothing.

"I dedicate this bull to you, Mr. President, and to the public of Madrid, the most intelligent and generous of the world," was what Manuel was saying. It was a formula. He said it all. It was a little long for nocturnal use.

He bowed at the dark, straightened, tossed his hat over his shoulder, and, carrying the muleta in his left hand and the sword in his right, walked out toward the bull.

Manuel walked toward the bull. The bull looked at him; his eyes were quick. Manuel noticed the way the banderillos hung down on his left shoulder and the steady sheen of blood from Zurito's pic-ing. He noticed the way the bull's feet were. As he walked forward, holding the muleta in his left hand and the sword in his right, he watched the bull's feet. The bull could not charge without gathering his feet together. Now he stood square on them, dully.

Manuel walked toward him, watching his feet. This was all right. He could do this. He must work to get the bull's head down, so he could go in past the horns and kill him. He did not think about the sword, not about killing the bull. He thought about one thing at a time. The coming things oppressed him, though. Walking forward, watching the bull's feet, he saw successively his eyes, his wet muzzle, and the wide, forward-pointing spread of his horns. The bull had light circles about his eyes. His eyes watched Manuel. He felt he was going to get this little one with the white face.

Standing still now and spreading the red cloth of the muleta with the sword, pricking the point into the cloth so that the sword, now held in his left hand, spread the red flannel like the jib of a boat, Manuel noticed the points of the bull's horns. One of them was splintered from banging against the barrera. The other was sharp as a porcupine quill. Manuel noticed while spreading the muleta that the white base of the horn was stained red. While he noticed these things he did not lose sight of the bull's feet. The bull watched Manuel steadily.

He's on the defensive now, Manuel thought. He's reserving himself. I've got to bring him out of that and get his head down. Always get his head down. Zurito had his head down once, but he's come back. He'll bleed when I start him going and that will bring it down.

Holding the muleta, with the sword in his left hand widening it in front of him, he called to the bull.

The bull looked at him.

He leaned back insultingly and shook the wide-spread flannel.

The bull saw the muleta. It was a bright scarlet under the arc-light. The bull's legs tightened.

Here he comes. Whoosh! Manuel turned as the bull came and raised the muleta so that it passed over the bull's horns and swept down his broad back from head to tail. The bull had gone clean up in the air with the charge. Manuel had not moved.

At the end of the pass the bull turned like a cat coming around a corner and faced Manuel.

He was on the offensive again. His heaviness was gone. Manuel noted the fresh blood shining down the black shoulder and dripping down the bull's leg. He drew the sword out of the muleta and held it in his right hand. The muleta held low down in his left hand, leaning toward the left, he called to the bull. The bull's legs tightened, his eyes on the muleta. Here he comes, Manuel thought. Yuh!

He swung with the charge, sweeping the muleta ahead of the bull, his feet firm, the sword following the curve, a point of light under the arcs.

The bull recharged as the pase natural finished and Manuel raised the muleta for a pase de pecho.[25] Firmly planted, the bull came by his chest under the raised muleta. Manuel leaned his head back to avoid the clattering banderillo shafts. The hot, black bull body touched his chest as it passed.

Too damn close, Manuel thought. Zurito, leaning on the barrera, spoke rapidly to the gypsy, who trotted out toward Manuel with a cape. Zurito pulled his hat down low and looked out across the arena at Manuel.

25. **pase natural**: a pass with the cape held low in the left hand; **pase de pecho**: a pass that brings the bull back, close to the matador's chest.

Manuel was facing the bull again, the muleta held low and to the left. The bull's head was down as he watched the muleta.

"If it was Belmonte doing that stuff, they'd go crazy," Retana's man said.

Zurito said nothing. He was watching Manuel out in the center of the arena.

"Where did the boss dig this fellow up?" Retana's man asked.

"Out of the hospital," Zurito said.

"That's where he's going damn quick," Retana's man said.

Zurito turned on him.

"Knock on that," he said, pointing to the barrera.

"I was just kidding, man," Retana's man said.

"Knock on the wood."

Retana's man leaned forward and knocked three times on the barrera.

"Watch the faena," Zurito said.

Out in the center of the ring, under the lights, Manuel was kneeling, facing the bull, and as he raised the muleta in both hands the bull charged, tail up.

Manuel swung his body clear and, as the bull recharged, brought around the muleta in a half-circle that pulled the bull to his knees.

"Why, that one's a great bullfighter," Retana's man said.

"No, he's not," said Zurito.

Manuel stood up and, the muleta in his left hand, the sword in his right, acknowledged the applause from the dark plaza.

The bull had humped himself up from his knees and stood waiting, his head hung low.

Zurito spoke to two of the other lads of the cuadrilla and they ran out to stand back of Manuel with their capes. There were four men back of him now. Hernandez had followed him since he first came out with the muleta. Fuentes stood watching, his cape held against his body, tall, in repose, watching lazy-eyed. Now the two came up. Hernandez motioned them to stand one at each side. Manuel stood alone, facing the bull.

Manuel waved back the men with the capes. Stepping back cautiously, they saw his face was white and sweating.

Didn't they know enough to keep back? Did they want to catch the bull's eye with the capes after he was fixed and ready? He had enough to worry about without that kind of thing.

The bull was standing, his four feet square, looking at the muleta. Manuel furled the muleta in his left hand. The bull's eyes watched it. His body was heavy on his feet. He carried his head low, but not too low.

Manuel lifted the muleta at him. The bull did not move. Only his eyes watched.

He's all lead, Manuel thought. He's all square. He's framed right. He'll take it.

He thought in bullfight terms. Sometimes he had a thought and the particular piece of slang would not come into his mind and he could not realize the thought. His instincts and his knowledge worked automatically, and his brain worked slowly and in words. He knew all about bulls. He did not have to think about them. He just did the right thing. His eyes noted things and his body performed the necessary measures without thought. If he thought about it, he would be gone.

Now, facing the bull, he was conscious of many things at the same time. There were the horns, the one splintered, the other smoothly sharp, the need to profile himself toward the left horn, lance himself short and straight, lower the muleta so the bull would follow it, and, going in over the horns, put the sword all the way into a little spot about as big as a five-peseta piece straight in back of the neck, between the sharp pitch of the bull's shoulders. He must do all this and must then come out from between the horns. He was conscious he must do all this, but his only thought was in words: "Corto y derecho."

"Corto y derecho," he thought, furling the multa. Short and straight. Corto y derecho, he drew the sword out of the muleta, profiled on the splintered left horn, dropped the muleta across his body, so his right hand with the sword on the level with his eye made the sign of the cross, and, rising on his toes, sighted along the dipping blade of the sword at the spot high up between the bull's shoulders.

Corto y derecho he launched himself on the bull.

There was a shock, and he felt himself go up in the air. He pushed on the sword as he went up and over, and it flew out of his hand. He hit the ground and the bull was on him. Manuel, lying on the ground, kicked at the bull's muzzle with his slippered feet. Kicking, kicking, the bull after him, missing him in his excitement, bumping him with his head, driving the horns into the sand. Kicking like a man keeping a ball in the air, Manuel kept the bull from getting a clean thrust at him.

Manuel felt the wind on his back from the capes flopping at the bull, and then the bull was gone, gone over him in a rush. Dark, as his belly went over. Not even stepped on.

Manuel stood up and picked up the muleta. Fuentes handed him the sword. It was bent where it had struck the shoulderblade. Manuel straightened it on his knee and ran toward the bull, standing now beside one of the dead horses. As he ran, his jacket flopped where it had been ripped under his arm pit.

"Get him out of there," Manuel shouted to the gypsy. The bull had smelled the blood of the dead horse and ripped into the canvas-cover with his horns. He charged Fuentes's cape, with the canvas hanging from his splintered horn, and the crowd laughed. Out in the ring, he tossed his head to rid himself of the canvas. Hernandez, running up from behind him, grabbed the end of the canvas and neatly lifted it off the horn.

The bull followed it in a half-charge and stopped still. He was on the defensive again. Manuel was walking toward him with the sword and muleta. Manuel swung the muleta before him. The bull would not charge.

Manuel profiled toward the bull, sighting along the dipping blade of the sword. The bull was motionless, seemingly dead on his feet, incapable of another charge.

Manuel rose to his toes, sighting along the steel, and charged.

Again there was the shock and he felt himself being borne back in a rush, to strike hard on the sand. There was no chance of kicking this time. The bull was on top of him. Manuel lay as though dead, his head on his arms, and the bull bumped him. Bumped his back, bumped his face in the sand. He felt the horn go into the sand between his folded arms. The bull hit him in the small of the back. His face drove into the sand. The horn drove through one of his sleeves and the bull ripped it off. Manuel was tossed clear and the bull followed the capes.

Manuel got up, found the sword and muleta, tried the point of the sword with his thumb, and then ran toward the barrera for a new sword.

Retana's man handed him the sword over the edge of the barrera.

"Wipe off your face," he said.

Manuel, running again toward the bull, wiped his bloody face with his handkerchief. He had not seen Zurito. Where was Zurito?

The cuadrilla had stepped away from the bull and waited with their capes. The bull stood, heavy and dull again after the action.

Manuel walked toward him with the muleta. He stopped and shook it. The bull did not respond. He passed it right and left, left and right before the bull's muzzle. The bull's eyes watched it and turned with the swing, but he would not charge. He was waiting for Manuel.

Manuel was worried. There was nothing to do but go in. Corto y dere-cho. He profiled close to the bull, crossed the muleta in front of his body and charged. As he pushed in the sword, he jerked his body to the left to clear the horn. The bull passed him and the sword shot up in the air, twinkling under the arc-lights, to fall red-hilted on the sand.

Manuel ran over and picked it up. It was bent and he straightened it over his knee.

As he came running toward the bull, fixed again now, he passed Hernandez standing with his cape.

"He's all bone," the boy said encouragingly.

Manuel nodded, wiping his face. He put the bloody handkerchief in his pocket.

There was the bull. He was close to the barrera now. Damn him. Maybe he was all bone. Maybe there was not any place for the sword to go in. The hell there wasn't! He'd show them.

He tried a pass with the muleta and the bull did not move. Manuel chopped the muleta back and forth in front of the bull. Nothing doing.

He furled the muleta, drew the sword out, profiled and drove in on the bull. He felt the sword buckle as he shoved it in, leaning his weight on it, and then it shot high in the air, end-over-ending into the crowd. Manuel had jerked clear as the sword jumped.

The first cushions thrown down out of the dark missed him. Then one hit him in the face, his bloody face looking toward the crowd. They were coming down fast. Spotting the sand. Somebody threw an empty champagne-bottle from close range. It hit Manuel on the foot. He stood there watching the dark, where the things were coming from. Then something whished through the air and struck by him. Manuel leaned over and picked it up. It was his sword. He straightened it over his knee and gestured with it to the crowd.

"Thank you," he said. "Thank you."

Oh, the dirty bastards! Dirty bastards! Oh, the lousy, dirty bastards! He kicked into a cushion as he ran.

There was the bull. The same as ever. All right, you dirty, lousy bastard!

Manuel passed the muleta in front of the bull's black muzzle.

Nothing doing.

You won't! All right. He stepped close and jammed the sharp peak of the muleta into the bull's damp muzzle.

The bull was on him as he jumped back and as he tripped on a cushion he felt the horn go into him, into his side. He grabbed the horn with his two hands and rode backward, holding tight onto the place. The bull tossed him and he was clear. He lay still. It was all right. The bull was gone.

He got up coughing and feeling broken and gone. The dirty bastards!

"Give me the sword," he shouted. "Give me the stuff."

Fuentes came up with the muleta and the sword.

Hernandez put his arm around him.

"Go on to the infirmary, man," he said. "Don't be a damn fool."

"Get away from me," Manuel said. "Get to hell away from me."

He twisted free. Hernandez shrugged his shoulders. Manuel ran toward the bull.

There was the bull standing, heavy, firmly planted.

All right, you bastard! Manuel drew the sword out of the muleta, sighted with the same movement, and flung himself onto the bull. He felt the sword go in all the way. Right up to the guard. Four fingers and his thumb into the bull. The blood was hot on his knuckles, and he was on top of the bull.

The bull lurched with him as he lay on, and seemed to sink; then he was standing clear. He looked at the bull going down slowly over on his side, then suddenly four feet in the air.

Then he gestured at the crowd, his hand warm from the bull blood.

All right, you bastards! He wanted to say something, but he started to cough. It was hot and choking. He looked down for the muleta. He must go over and salute the president. President, hell! He was sitting down looking at something. It was the bull. His four feet up. Thick tongue out. Things crawling around on his belly and under his legs. Crawling where the hair was thin. Dead bull. To hell with the bull! To hell with them all! He started to get to his feet and commenced to cough. He sat down again, coughing. Somebody came and pushed him up.

They carried him across the ring to the infirmary, running with him across the sand, standing blocked at the gate as the mules came in, then around under the dark passageway, men grunting as they took him up the stairway, and then laid him down.

The doctor and two men in white were waiting for him. They laid him out on the table. They were cutting away his shirt. Manuel felt tired. His whole chest felt scalding inside. He started to cough and they held something to his mouth. Everybody was very busy.

There was an electric light in his eyes. He shut his eyes.

He heard someone coming very heavily up the stairs. Then he did not hear it. Then he heard a noise far off. That was the crowd. Well, somebody would have to kill his other bull. They had cut away all his shirt. The doctor smiled at him. There was Retana.

"Hello, Retana!" Manuel said. He could not hear his voice.

Retana smiled at him and said something. Manuel could not hear it.

Zurito stood beside the table, bending over where the doctor was working. He was in his picador clothes, without his hat.

Zurito said something to him. Manuel could not hear it.

Zurito was speaking to Retana. One of the men in white smiled and handed Retana a pair of scissors. Retana gave them to Zurito. Zurito said something to Manuel. He could not hear it.

To hell with this operating-table. He'd been on plenty of operating-tables before. He was not going to die. There would be a priest if he was going to die.

Zurito was saying something to him. Holding up the scissors.

That was it. They were going to cut off his coleta. They were going to cut off his pigtail.

Manuel sat up on the operating-table. The doctor stepped back, angry. Someone grabbed him and held him.

"You couldn't do a thing like that, Manos," he said.

He heard suddenly, clearly, Zurito's voice.

"That's all right," Zurito said. "I won't do it. I was joking."

"I was going good," Manuel said. "I didn't have any luck. That was all."

Manuel lay back. They had put something over his face. It was all familiar. He inhaled deeply. He felt very tired. He was very, very tired. They took the thing away from his face.

"I was going good," Manuel said weakly. "I was going great."

Retana looked at Zurito and started for the door.

"I'll stay here with him," Zurito said.

Retana shrugged his shoulders.

Manuel opened his eyes and looked at Zurito.

"Wasn't I going good, Manos?" he asked, for confirmation.

"Sure," said Zurito. "You were going great."

The doctor's assistant put the cone over Manuel's face and he inhaled deeply. Zurito stood awkwardly, watching.

Eudora Welty

A WORN PATH

IT WAS December—a bright frozen day in the early morning. Far out in the country there was an old Negro woman with her head tied in a red rag, coming along a path through the pinewoods. Her name was Phoenix Jackson. She was very old and small and she walked slowly in the dark pine shadows, moving a little from side to side in her steps, with the balanced heaviness and lightness of a pendulum in a grandfather clock. She carried a thin, small cane made from an umbrella, and with this she kept tapping the frozen earth in front of her. This made a grave and persistent noise in the still air, that seemed meditative like the chirping of a solitary little bird.

She wore a dark striped dress reaching down to her shoe tops, and an equally long apron of bleached sugar sacks, with a full pocket: all neat and tidy, but every time she took a step she might have fallen over her shoelaces, which dragged from her unlaced shoes. She looked straight ahead. Her eyes were blue with age. Her skin had a pattern all its own of numberless branching wrinkles and as though a whole little tree stood in the middle of her forehead, but a golden color ran underneath, and the two knobs of her cheeks were illumined by a yellow burning under the dark. Under the red rag her hair came down on her neck in the frailest of ringlets, still black, and with an odor like copper.

Now and then there was a quivering in the thicket. Old Phoenix said, "Out of my way, all you foxes, owls, beetles, jack rabbits, coons and wild animals! . . . Keep out from under these feet, little bob-whites. . . . Keep the big wild hogs out of my path. Don't let none of those come running my direction. I got a long way." Under her small black-freckled hand her cane, limber as a buggy whip, would switch at the brush as if to rouse up any hiding things.

On she went. The woods were deep and still. The sun made the pine needles almost too bright to look at, up where the wind rocked. The cones dropped as light as feathers. Down in the hollow was the mourning dove—it was not too late for him.

The path ran up a hill. "Seem like there is chains about my feet, time I get this far," she said, in the voice of argument old people keep to use with themselves. "Something always take a hold of me on this hill—pleads I should stay."

After she got to the top she turned and gave a full, severe look behind her where she had come. "Up through pines," she said at length. "Now down through oaks."

Her eyes opened their widest, and she started down gently. But before she got to the bottom of the hill a bush caught her dress.

Her fingers were busy and intent, but her skirts were full and long, so that before she could pull them free in one place they were caught in another. It was not possible to allow the dress to tear. "I in the thorny bush," she said. "Thorns, you doing your appointed work. Never want to let folks pass, no sir. Old eyes thought you was a pretty little *green* bush."

Finally, trembling all over, she stood free, and after a moment dared to stoop for her cane.

"Sun so high!" she cried, leaning back and looking, while the thick tears went over her eyes. "The time getting all gone here."

At the foot of this hill was a place where a log was laid across the creek.

"Now comes the trial," said Phoenix.

Putting her right foot out, she mounted the log and shut her eyes. Lifting her skirt, leveling her cane fiercely before her, like a festival figure in some parade, she began to march across. Then she opened her eyes and she was safe on the other side.

"I wasn't as old as I thought," she said.

But she sat down to rest. She spread her skirts on the bank around her and folded her hands over her knees. Up above her was a tree in a pearly cloud of mistletoe. She did not dare to close her eyes, and when a little boy bought her a plate with a slice of marble-cake on it she spoke to him. "That would be acceptable," she said. But when she went to take it there was just her own hand in the air.

So she left that tree, and had to go through a barbed-wire fence. There she had to creep and crawl, spreading her knees and stretching her fingers like a baby trying to climb the steps. But she talked loudly to herself: she could not let her dress be torn now, so late in the day, and she could not pay for having her arm or her leg sawed off if she got caught fast where she was.

At last she was safe through the fence and risen up out in the clearing. Big dead trees, like black men with one arm, were standing in the purple stalks of the withered cotton field. There sat a buzzard.

"Who you watching?"

In the furrow she made her way along.

"Glad this not the season for bulls," she said, looking sideways, "and the good Lord made his snakes to curl up and sleep in the winter. A pleasure I don't see no two-headed snake coming around that tree, where it come once. It took a while to get by him, back in the summer."

She passed through the old cotton and went into a field of dead corn. It whispered and shook and was taller than her head. "Through the maze now," she said, for there was no path.

Then there was something tall, black, and skinny there, moving before her.

At first she took it for a man. It could have been a man dancing in the field. But she stood still and listened, and it did not make a sound. It was as silent as a ghost.

"Ghost," she said sharply, "who be you the ghost of? For I have heard of nary death close by."

But there was no answer—only the ragged dancing in the wind.

She shut her eyes, reached out her hand, and touched a sleeve. She found a coat and inside that an emptiness, cold as ice.

"You scarecrow," she said. Her face lighted. "I ought to be shut up for good," she said with laughter. "My senses is gone. I too old. I the oldest people I ever know. Dance, old scarecrow," she said, "while I dancing with you."

She kicked her foot over the furrow, and with mouth drawn down, shook her head once or twice in a little strutting way. Some husks blew down and whirled in streamers about her skirts.

Then she went on, parting her way from side to side with the cane, through the whispering field. At last she came to the end, to a wagon track where the silver grass blew between the red ruts. The quail were walking around like pullets, seeming all dainty and unseen.

"Walk pretty," she said. "This the easy place. This the easy going."

She followed the track, swaying through the quiet bare fields, through the little strings of trees silver in their dead leaves, past cabins silver from weather, with the doors and windows boarded shut, all like old women under a spell sitting there. "I walking in their sleep," she said, nodding her head vigorously.

In a ravine she went where a spring was silently flowing through a hollow log. Old Phoenix bent and drank. "Sweet-gum makes the water sweet," she said, and drank more. "Nobody know who made this well, for it was here when I was born."

The track crossed a swampy part where the moss hung as white as lace from every limb. "Sleep on, alligators, and blow your bubbles." Then the track went into the road.

Deep, deep the road went down between the high green-colored banks. Overhead the live-oaks met, and it was as dark as a cave.

A black dog with a lolling tongue came up out of the weeds by the ditch. She was meditating, and not ready, and when he came at her she only hit him a little with her cane. Over she went in the ditch, like a little puff of milkweed.

Down there, her senses drifted away. A dream visited her, and she reached her hand up, but nothing reached down and gave her a pull. So she lay there and presently went to talking. "Old woman," she said to herself, "that black dog come up out of the weeds to stall you off, and now there he sitting on his fine tail, smiling at you."

A white man finally came along and found her—a hunter, a young man, with his dog on a chain.

"Well, Granny!" he laughed. "What are you doing there?"

"Lying on my back like a June-bug waiting to be turned over, mister," she said, reaching up her hand.

He lifted her up, gave her a swing in the air, and set her down. "Anything broken, Granny?"

"No sir, them old dead weeds is springy enough," said Phoenix, when she had got her breath. "I thank you for your trouble."

"Where do you live, Granny?" he asked, while the two dogs were growling at each other.

"Away back yonder, sir, behind the ridge. You can't even see it from here."

"On your way home?"

"No sir, I going to town."

"Why, that's too far! That's as far as I walk when I come out myself, and I get something for my trouble." He patted the stuffed bag he carried, and there hung down a little closed claw. It was one of the bob-whites, with its beak hooked bitterly to show it was dead. "Now you go on home, Granny!"

"I bound to go to town, mister," said Phoenix. "The time come around."

He gave another laugh, filling the whole landscape. "I know you old colored people! Wouldn't miss going to town to see Santa Claus!"

But something held old Phoenix very still. The deep lines in her face went into a fierce and different radiation. Without warning, she had seen with her own eyes a flashing nickel fall out of the man's pocket onto the ground.

"How old are you, Granny?" he was saying.

"There is no telling, mister," she said, "no telling."

Then she gave a little cry and clapped her hands and said, "Git on away from here, dog! Look! Look at that dog!" She laughed as if in admiration. "He ain't scared of nobody. He a big black dog." She whispered, "Sic him!"

"Watch me get rid of that cur," said the man. "Sic him, Pete! Sic him!"

Phoenix heard the dogs fighting, and heard the man running and throwing sticks. She even heard a gunshot. But she was slowly bending forward by that time, further and further forward, the lids stretched down over her eyes, as if she were doing this in her sleep. Her chin was lowered almost to her knees. The yellow palm of her hand came out from the fold of her apron. Her fingers slid down and along the ground under the piece of money with the grace and care they would have in lifting an egg from under a setting hen. Then she slowly straightened up, she stood erect, and the nickel was in her apron pocket. A bird flew by. Her lips moved. "God watching me the whole time. I come to stealing."

The man came back, and his own dog panted about them. "Well, I scared him off that time," he said, and then he laughed and lifted his gun and pointed it at Phoenix.

She stood straight and faced him.

"Doesn't the gun scare you?" he said, still pointing it.

"No, sir, I seen plenty go off closer by, in my day, and for less than what I done," she said, holding utterly still.

He smiled, and shouldered the gun. "Well, Granny," he said, "you must be a hundred years old, and scared of nothing. I'd give you a dime if I had any money with me. But you take my advice and stay home, and nothing will happen to you."

"I bound to go on my way, mister," said Phoenix. She inclined her head in the red rag. Then they went in different directions, but she could hear the gun shooting again and again over the hill.

She walked on. The shadows hung from the oak trees to the road like curtains. Then she smelled wood-smoke, and smelled the river, and she saw a steeple and the cabins on their steep steps. Dozens of little black children whirled around her. There ahead was Natchez shining. Bells were ringing. She walked on.

In the paved city it was Christmas time. There were red and green electric lights strung and crisscrossed everywhere, and all turned on in the daytime. Old Phoenix would have been lost if she had not distrusted her eyesight and depended on her feet to know where to take her.

She paused quietly on the sidewalk where people were passing by. A lady came along in the crowd, carrying an armful of red-, green- and silver-wrapped presents; she gave off perfume like the red roses in hot summer, and Phoenix stopped her.

"Please, missy, will you lace up my shoe?" She held up her foot.

"What do you want, Grandma?"

"See my shoe," said Phoenix. "Do all right for out in the country, but wouldn't look right to go in a big building."

"Stand still then, Grandma," said the lady. She put her packages down on the sidewalk beside her and laced and tied both shoes tightly.

"Can't lace 'em with a cane," said Phoenix. "Thank you, missy. I doesn't mind asking a nice lady to tie up my shoe, when I gets out on the street."

Moving slowly and from side to side, she went into the big building, and into a tower of steps, where she walked up and around and around until her feet knew to stop.

She entered a door, and there she saw nailed up on the wall the document that had been stamped with the gold seal and framed in the gold frame, which matched the dream that was hung up in her head.

"Here I be," she said. There was a fixed and ceremonial stiffness over her body.

"A charity case, I suppose," said an attendant who sat at the desk before her.

But Phoenix only looked above her head. There was sweat on her face, the wrinkles in her skin shone like a bright net.

"Speak up, Grandma," the woman said. "What's your name? We must have your history, you know. Have you been here before? What seems to be the trouble with you?"

Old Phoenix only gave a twitch to her face as if a fly were bothering her.

"Are you deaf?" cried the attendant.

But then the nurse came in.

"Oh, that's just old Aunt Phoenix," she said. "She doesn't come for her-self—she has a little grandson. She makes these trips just as regular as clockwork. She lives away back off the Old Natchez Trace." She bent down. "Well, Aunt Phoenix, why don't you just take a seat? We won't keep you standing after your long trip." She pointed.

The old woman sat down, bolt upright in the chair.

"Now, how is the boy?" asked the nurse.

Old Phoenix did not speak.

"I said, how is the boy?"

But Phoenix only waited and stared straight ahead, her face very solemn and withdrawn into rigidity.

"Is his throat any better?" asked the nurse. "Aunt Phoenix, don't you hear me? Is your grandson's throat any better since the last time you came for the medicine?"

With her hands on her knees, the old woman waited, silent, erect and motionless, just as if she were in armor.

"You mustn't take up our time this way, Aunt Phoenix," the nurse said. "Tell us quickly about your grandson, and get it over. He isn't dead, is he?"

At last there came a flicker and then a flame of comprehension across her face, and she spoke.

"My grandson. It was my memory had left me. There I sat and forgot why I made my long trip."

"Forgot?" The nurse frowned. "After you came so far?"

Then Phoenix was like an old woman begging a dignified forgiveness for waking up frightened in the night. "I never did go to school, I was too old at the Surrender," she said in a soft voice. "I'm an old woman without an education. It was my memory fail me. My little grandson, he is just the same, and I forgot it in the coming."

"Throat never heals, does it?" said the nurse, speaking in a loud, sure voice to old Phoenix. By now she had a card with something written on it, a little list. "Yes. Swallowed lye. When was it?—January—two-three years ago—"

Phoenix spoke unasked now. "No, missy, he not dead, he just the same.

Every little while his throat begin to close up again, and he not able to swallow. He not get his breath. He not able to help himself. So the time come around, and I go on another trip for the soothing medicine."

"All right. The doctor said as long as you came to get it, you could have it," said the nurse. "But it's an obstinate case."

"My little grandson, he sit up there in the house all wrapped up, waiting by himself," Phoenix went on. "We is the only two left in the world. He suffer and it don't seem to put him back at all. He got a sweet look. He going to last. He wear a little patch quilt and peep out holding his mouth open like a little bird. I remembers so plain now. I not going to forget him again, no, the whole enduring time. I could tell him from all the others in creation."

"All right." The nurse was trying to hush her now. She brought her a bottle of medicine. "Charity," she said, making a check mark in a book.

Old Phoenix held the bottle close to her eyes, and then carefully put it into her pocket.

"I thank you," she said.

"It's Christmas time, Grandma," said the attendant. "Could I give you a few pennies out of my purse?"

"Five pennies is a nickel," said Phoenix stiffly.

"Here's a nickel," said the attendant.

Phoenix rose carefully and held out her hand. She received the nickel and then fished the other nickel out of her pocket and laid it beside the new one. She stared at her palm closely, with her head on one side.

Then she gave a tap with her cane on the floor.

"This is what come to me to do," she said. "I going to the store and buy my child a little windmill they sells, made out of paper. He going to find it hard to believe there such a thing in the world. I'll march myself back where he waiting, holding it straight up in this hand."

She lifted her free hand, gave a little nod, turned around, and walked out of the doctor's office. Then her slow step began on the stairs, going down.

William Golding

THE ANGLO–SAXON

Six hundred and fifty words were hung on hooks in George's dark cupboard; blunt words, broken and worn, clung to out of custom like a chipped cup.

"Bru-ah! Hu-ah!"

Six hundred and fifty words for dirty George, George small and warped, hot under his cap and army greatcoat and trousers coarse as sacking: one word only between the silken ears of each white heifer. This word was a single syllable he shared with them, dry smack of his ashplant on a twitching back. So as the herd lunged and sidled, blundered past each other between the high hedges, kicked clods from under the nettles that dripped on either side of the track, George brandished his word behind them and they understood.

"Bru-ah! Hu-ah!"

The hedges were high, the track straight and steep. One man could urge the herd up the track and over the downs to where the lorry was waiting, so no boy was cutting school. There was George and his collie and the heifers; and the hedges poking red berries up into the mist.

The collie crept and leapt. She made mock snappings between her barks, she was a good bitch. She shared five words and the word of the ashplant with George. So he shouted and lumbered, and she crept and snapped; and the herd more or less climbed the hill for all their panic. Nobody understood the heifers as well as George did; and he hardly understood them at all.

"What's up, then?"

Smack!

His greatcoat was swinging open, old khaki and dirty as George, but not as old as the scar that clung to his thigh out of an older war. It was a pink scar most times, but now it was tingling and red. Sweat was raising lumps on the scar and George could not stop to scratch. He swore therefore and shouted and laid about him and his boots pushed moonshaped lumps of mud out of the track that had known the feet of drovers for five thousand years.

Up front, a heifer bellowed and reared. She tried to shove herself at the hedge but turned among the branches and came stumbling down. A half

"The Anglo-Saxon" by William Golding. Reprinted by permission of the author.

hundredweight of earth fell with her. The collie raced forward so that the laggards started into clumsy curvets and snorted and erected tails and spattered dung.

Into the dark, angry cupboard came a sudden thought of the weak place in the hedge—there, where the heifer had tried to get up, there ahead in the mist. His own patch was on the other side of the hedge through that gap, and tended vegetables, a shed. But as if they shared this thought, the heifers turned suddenly and noisily, they shook themselves round and panicked at him so that he was jolted sideways into the nettles. They rushed down fifty yards and stopped. Their panic was soothed by the brutal movement. They stood, and cropped nettles, chewed gently, looking back at him out of ignorant, godlike eyes.

The collie crept to his feet, and whined. George lifted himself out of the nettles and opened his mouth.

He shut it again.

There was a figure standing further up the track, its outline dimmed by the mist. To its left was the weak place in the hedge and the figure cradled a stick. The weak place was weaker. Higher up than the heifer had reached a hoof, the hurdle slanted into the air. And as George stumbled forward, mouthing now, he saw that the figure stood impossibly in a shadow like indoors and that the stick was a strange sort of gun.

Room for anger.

"Thee daft fool!"

The American corporal did not move. As the mist cleared in front of him, he emerged, impassive, clean, uniformed, young and chewing. The automatic rifle in his arms was stiller than the ashplant.

"Hiya, Pop. No road."

The shadow like indoors was because of the roof. Out here, on the downs, a roof. It was metal with letters on, stretched away over the hedge, over the vegetable patch, away into mist.

The corporal shifted a lump across his face from one cheek to the other.

"Sorry, Pop. You gotta go back."

Room for nothing but anger. George shouted at the collie and she raced to round up the herd. They started loudly and clumsily up the track towards the corporal.

"Look. I'm real sorry——"

"You—out of my way——"

"Hey Sarge! Sarge!"

Gun butt against chest, heifers coming up, collie snapping . . .

"Sarge!"

Above them the gap crackled and the hurdle shifted. Another man in uniform looked down at George.

"Get those goddam animals out of here!"

The sergeant jumped down into the track. He and the corporal shoved at the heifers and George. The collie snapped round them.

"You gotta go back!"

There was shouts and animal noise and fierceness.

"Hey! Lootenant!"

And then the heifers were lumbering down the track again, the collie racing round them. George saw the stripes on the sergeant's arm. They were the wrong way up and they gave the wearer no real authority.

"I got to take they heifers up this track!"

"Lootenant!"

The sergeant leapt into the gap and made beckoning motions with his arm. George looked past him into the patch. The roof was a wing. A complication of pistons and pillars hung from it. They ended in a thing like a truck with four truck wheels. The truck was buried to the hubs. The curved trench that the truck had dug had destroyed the further hedge and then the shed, then mercilessly and finally raped everything from runner beans to carrots. So monstrous was the machine that the very earth thrown up by its passage had buried the rhubarb three feet deep.

The corporal spoke by his ear.

"Listen, Pop. We missed the runway. See?"

"I were going to show they carrots!"

Another man was picking his way across the place where the vegetables had grown. He was tall and young. There was authority about him, like Mr. Thomson. George flourished his ashplant.

"You come out of my patch!"

The lieutenant walked into the gap, pale, careful, treading a high wire, eyes unblinking as though the lids were locked back.

"What'll I do, sir? You said to use a gun—sir? Lootenant?"

The lieutenant looked down slowly at George. His eyes focused. He brought his hands up to his face and examined their shakes closely.

"Now look at my patch! And they heifers——"

The lieutenant put his hands slowly away in pockets as if they were precious and delicate.

"Lootenant——?"

The lieutenant looked round at each man in turn very slowly, like a tortoise. He looked at the track and the patch; looked at the wing, at the metal beast lying over the landscape, at the hidden belly that held whatever the beast needed for its trade.

He focused carefully on George.

"You'll get money."

"Forty year I been——"

The lieutenant stood in the gap. He stretched his arms out wide and shouted to someone in the sky. He sang, almost.

"For Christ's sake! Haven't we had enough?"

Then there was silence, except for the whining of the collie. The three men were hushed. The corporal moved the butt of his gun away from George's chest. He spoke in a confidential whisper like in church.

"You better get going, Pop."

The sergeant shifted a lump.

"Yes. You go. Take the way round."

"Way round?"

But the lieutenant was withdrawn again into his pallor. The sergeant and the corporal had moved a step or two, detached themselves. They ignored George so that their chewing faces were proof of determination and strength. He was settled, implied the face, settled as long as no one noticed him. So let him cease to exist. They watched the silken backs of the heifers with a stare that was mild and incurious. Above them, the metal wing roofed in and shadowed the track.

The floor of the bar parlour sloped up more and more and the walls wavered. Tobacco smoke bulged against them, recoiled, rolled in on itself and was gusted apart. Mrs. Williams at the bar was sweating into all her three chins. There were flashes from the beer engines and the lifted glasses, there were pin-ups grinning through the smoke. There was noise like a drumroll, like a circular saw. George's mouth was open. He saw the noises that came out, rather than heard them, they were shapes and eddies. The words jumping out were distorted as the walls and sloping floor. They jumped out from the backbone and jerked him as they passed through his mouth. He stood now where he had expected to stand when a day's wages and a tip were both spent; stood on a floor that tried to fool you so that the trick was to stay upright. There were other mouths wide open. Dan, from the car park, was singing. The two rivermen were holding each other up and laughing till the tears dripped through the stubble on their cheeks.

More words, distorted, dropping like shot sparrows.

"A bloody gun!"

There was a kind of fire burning in his belly that the wetness of drink did nothing to put out. The flames gave no light and licked through his neck and round his ears. Yet the words as they jumped out of his mouth had meaning and he knew they had meaning. All evening they had had meaning, but been received as if the bar parlour were a byre and the blank, drinking faces only acquainted with one word. Then the blank faces had lost interest in him and turned inward to each other like the smoke. That was when the smouldering fire began to burn. Now he stood, feeling the grip of his feet on the floor and the floor tried to fool him.

"Time gentlemen please. Time, gentlemen!"

The door connecting the bar parlour with the saloon slammed open against the stops and a storm of laughter crashed through. Beyond the door were more faces and smoke, more singing. A man in uniform backed into the room, his knees bent, his hands clapping. Another man followed him. He was in uniform too, a Negro, and he squatted on his hams, he beat his palms, his face was gleaming black and grinning. All the time he jerked his head backwards and forwards. The first man danced round to one side and George saw the stripes on his arm, the wrong way up. He lugged one foot out of the floor, took a step, and stumbled against the sergeant. The sergeant caught him by the shoulders, the Negro was dancing down there by his feet. A third face, laughing over uniform, swam into his.

"Hey, Pop! Have a drink!"

All laughing, all dancing. There was a glass now, thrust into his hand, faces, swirling.

"Time, gentlemen!"

"Dance, Pop!"

"A bloody gun!"

The fire blazed. A face flicked away from him on the end of his arm, so that for a moment he saw nothing there but his fist. He saw another face and jammed his glass into it. The bar parlour turned upside down and its drumroll broke up in shouts and screams. The floor jolted at George, feet, a glass, a mouth. He saw Mrs. Williams's face with the mouth like a black hole. Then there were legs like tree trunks, only weaving about. Two hands caught him by the lapels of his greatcoat, lifted him. Nothing of him but his toes touched the floor. His arms were gripped. His face was pressed against the silver buttons and dark blue cloth of the county police.

Mr. Brownlow had a baby face like a telly advert for shaving cream. He was without a stain or strain, businessman, churchwarden, magistrate, a round, baby face in a round hole. He frowned down, and his forehead did not line so much as pucker. When he spoke, his rosy mouth went putt, putt, putt.

"I'm asking you if you 'it this man?"

George peered through a sort of fuzz at the faces; Mr. Brownlow, Lady Watford, Colonel Proudie on the bench; the clerks and reporters below them; to one side, a row of uniforms and silent, ruminating faces.

"They carrots——"

"What *is* all this about vegetables? Carrots and runner beans . . . Did you hit this man? This . . . coloured soldier?"

"It were the sergeant I were trying to 'it, sir. 'Im with the stripes."

George gripped the edge of the dock. He leaned towards the clean faces. There was a clamp round his forehead and his brain hurt. When he tried to bring both eyes to see one face at a time, there were raw cords behind them that shortened and throbbed.

"I been driving cattle up that 'ill. Forty year I been driving——"

He turned his head painfully to one side, focused painfully on the ruminating figure with the stripes; and painfully the thought formed itself among the raw cords.

Not even the same sergeant.

Head bent together, nodding. Mr. Brownlow straightened up and sat back.

"George Smart. The bench finds you guilty. You're a local nuisance. Whenever you drive cattle in, you finish up disgustingly drunk. Do you think the police are paid to let the traffic get into a mess while they pull the likes of you out of the gutter? No indeed. What are you doing with yourself Smart? You've got a steady job and a good wage—and every day you come to the city you drink yourself into a hanimal stupor. Now you've started fighting. Half a crown won't do this time. You'll pay five pounds or go to prison for fourteen days."

A clerk glanced at George.

"Have you got the money, Smart?"

"No."

Papers rustled. A policeman beckoned George down.

The American stood up, fair, diffident, mild.

"Guess I'd like to pay Pop's fine."

He walked forward to the clerk's table.

"That right?"

He peeled one note off a thick roll and dropped it on the blotter. The court buzzed and was still. The chairman of the magistrates settled himself back to make a brief and gracious speech. Putt, putt, putt.

George's boss was waiting for him in the porch of the Guildhall. He stood waiting in prosperous tweed and heavy height and strength. His swarthy face was grim under his green trilby.

"George!"

George's fist knuckled his forehead.

"Mus' Thomson."

"I've just about had enough. Every dam' time I bring you to market you make a bloody fool of yourself. What's the matter with you? You've never fought before, have you?"

"No, Mus' Thomson."

"Well, I'm not going to spend the rest of my life telling the bench what a fine fellow you are. You're not the only drover in the county, George, or the best one. So from now on, watch out. That's all."

George let himself down the steps and his hobnails clattered on the stone. He wove giddily through the car park, went into the road, approximated to a white line that swept round to the left. There was The Cock in front of him again, ancient, lattice-window'd and tilted askew. He lowered one boot down to the threshold, leaned his elbow against the door for a moment and then went in.

Three faces regarded him silently from the bar, black, fair, saturnine, three pairs of eyes held his own, eyes alien, inscrutable, serene. Three pairs of jaws ruminated. He fumbled at the dirty neck of his shirt and moved to the counter.

The American sergeant lifted one arm from the elbow up.

"How, Pop."

Mrs. Williams waddled forward from the cellar stairs. She spread her hands on the bar counter and leaned on them. Her voice was shrill and all three chins quivered.

"Now get on home, George Smart. You been enough trouble to this 'ouse. We don't want you, see? There's the door. Good morning to you."

George pulled at his shirt again. Although the top was unbuttoned, it seemed to be clinging to his skin.

" 'An't this a pub, missus?"

"We never 'ad no trouble and we won't not if I can 'elp it. So go on with you. And keep out."

He felt in his empty pockets. Thought, slowly.

"A pint o' bitter——"

"Do you want me to call Mr. Williams? I won't 'ave these gentlemen disturbed by the likes of you. We got our custom to think of."

The mild sergeant stirred, stopped chewing.

"Aw, c'mon Mam. Let Pop have a drink. Here."

Without taking his elbow from the bar the sergeant peeled another note off the roll and dropped it among the beer rings. Mrs. Williams looked doubtfully at the note, then went to a beer engine, seized a tankard and pumped it full of beer.

"If you say so, sir. You're more than kind to 'im I must say. Now mind, George Smart. If I have any more trouble . . ."

"I jus' wanted . . ."

George stopped, confused by the hard, warm feeling in his throat. He avoided the sergeant's eye, and his hand on its way to the tankard, hovered uncertainly, as though it thought to knuckle his forehead. He saw without deduction of any sort that the Negro's face wore sticking plaster the same colour as his skin.

The sergeant raised his glass.

"That's fine. Down the hatch, Pop."

George understood that the twisted body inside his clothes was shaking with hangover. He did not understand the hot tides that seemed to be taking his chest and throat and eyes and filling them with water. He turned away, clutching the tankard, and blinked out of the warped window; saw, without deduction of any sort, the lights, the parking, the turn left, the signs of law and order on the Queen's Highway.

John Updike

SHOULD WIZARD HIT MOMMY?

IN THE evenings and for Saturday naps like today's, Jack told his daughter Jo a story out of his head. This custom, begun when she was two, was itself now nearly two years old, and his head felt empty. Each new story was a slight variation of a basic tale: a small creature, usually named Roger (Roger Fish, Roger Squirrel, Roger Chipmunk), had some problem and went with it to the wise old owl. The owl told him to go to the wizard, and the wizard performed a magic spell that solved the problem, demanding in payment a number of pennies greater than the number Roger Creature had but in the same breath directing the animal to a place where the extra pennies could be found. Then Roger was so happy he played many games with other creatures, and went home to his mother just in time to hear the train whistle that brought his daddy home from Boston. Jack described their supper, and the story was over. Working his way through this scheme was especially fatiguing on Saturday, because Jo never fell asleep in naps any more, and knowing this made the rite seem futile.

The little girl (not so little any more; the bumps her feet made under the covers were halfway down the bed, their big double bed that they let her be in for naps and when she was sick) had at last arranged herself, and from the way her fat face deep in the pillow shone in the sunlight sifting through the drawn shades, it did not seem fantastic that something magic would occur, and she would take her nap like an infant of two. Her brother, Bobby, was two, and already asleep with his bottle. Jack asked, "Who shall the story be about today?"

"Roger . . ." Jo squeezed her eyes shut and smiled to be thinking she was thinking. Her eyes opened, her mother's blue. "Skunk," she said firmly.

A new animal; they must talk about skunks at nursery school. Having a fresh hero momentarily stirred Jack to creative enthusiasm. "All right," he said. "Once upon a time, in the deep dark woods, there was a tiny little creature name of Roger Skunk. And he smelled very bad—"

"Yes," Jo said.

"He smelled so bad none of the other little woodland creatures would play with him." Jo looked at him solemnly; she hadn't foreseen this. "Whenever he would go out to play," Jack continued with zest, remembering certain humiliations of his own childhood, "all of the other tiny animals would cry, 'Uh-oh, here comes Roger Stinky Skunk,' and they would run away, and Roger Skunk would stand there all alone, and two little round tears would fall from his eyes." The corners of Jo's mouth drooped down and her lower lip bent forward as he traced with a forefinger along the side of her nose the course of one of Roger Skunk's tears.

"Won't he see the owl?" she asked in a high and faintly roughened voice.

Sitting on the bed beside her, Jack felt the covers tug as her legs switched tensely. He was pleased with this moment—he was telling her something true, something she must know—and had no wish to hurry on. But downstairs a chair scraped, and he realized he must get down to help Clare paint the living-room woodwork.

"Well, he walked along very sadly and came to a very big tree, and in the tiptop of the tree was an enormous wise old owl."

"Good."

" 'Mr. Owl,' Roger Skunk said, 'all the other little animals run away from me because I smell so bad.' 'So you do,' the owl said. 'Very, very bad.' 'What can I do?' Roger Skunk said, and he cried very hard."

"The wizard, the wizard," Jo shouted, and sat right up, and a Little Golden Book spilled from the bed.

"Now, Jo. Daddy's telling the story. Do you want to tell Daddy the story?"

"No. You tell me."

"Then lie down and be sleepy."

Her head relapsed onto the pillow and she said, "Out of your head."

"Well. The owl thought and thought. At last he said, 'Why don't you go see the wizard?' "

"Daddy?"

"What?"

"Are magic spells *real?*" This was a new phase, just this last month, a reality phase. When he told her spiders eat bugs, she turned to her mother and asked, "Do they *really?*" and when Clare told her God was in the sky and all around them, she turned to her father and insisted, with a sly yet eager smile, "Is He *really?*"

"They're real in stories," Jack answered curtly. She had made him miss a beat in the narrative. "The owl said, 'Go through the dark woods, under the apple trees, into the swamp, over the crick—' "

"What's a crick?"

"A little river. 'Over the crick, and there will be the wizard's house.' And that's the way Roger Skunk went, and pretty soon he came to a little white house, and he rapped on the door." Jack rapped on the window sill, and under the covers Jo's tall figure clenched in an infantile thrill. "And then a tiny little old man came out, with a long white beard and a pointed blue hat, and said, 'Eh? Whatzis? Whatcher want? You smell awful.' " The wizard's voice was one of Jack's own favorite effects; he did it by scrunching up his face and somehow whining through his eyes, which felt for the interval rheumy. He felt being an old man suited him.

" 'I know it,' Roger Skunk said, 'and all the little animals run away from me. The enormous wise owl said you could help me.'

" 'Eh? Well, maybe. Come on in. Don't git too close.' Now, inside, Jo, there were all these magic things, all jumbled together in a big dusty heap, because the wizard did not have any cleaning lady."

"Why?"

"Why? Because he was a wizard, and a very old man."

"Will he die?"

"No. Wizards don't die. Well, he rummaged around and found an old stick called a magic wand and asked Roger Skunk what he wanted to smell like. Roger thought and thought and said, 'Roses.' "

"Yes. Good," Jo said smugly.

Jack fixed her with a trancelike gaze and chanted in the wizard's elderly irritable voice:

> " 'Abracadabry, hocus-poo,
> Roger Skunk, how do you do,
> Roses, boses, pull an ear,
> Roger Skunk, you never fear:
> *Bingo!*' "

He paused as a rapt expression widened out from his daughter's nostrils, forcing her eyebrows up and her lower lip down in a wide noiseless grin, an expression in which Jack was startled to recognize his wife feigning pleasure at cocktail parties. "And all of a sudden," he whispered, "the whole inside of the wizard's house was full of the smell of—*roses!* 'Roses!' Roger Fish cried. And the wizard said, very cranky, 'That'll be seven pennies.' "

"Daddy."

"What?"

"Roger *Skunk*. You said Roger Fish."

"Yes. Skunk."

"You said Roger *Fish*. Wasn't that silly?"

"Very silly of your stupid old daddy. Where was I? Well, you know about the pennies."

"Say it."

"O.K. Roger Skunk said, 'But all I have is four pennies,' and he began to cry." Jo made the crying face again, but this time without a trace of sincerity. This annoyed Jack. Downstairs some more furniture rumbled. Clare shouldn't move heavy things; she was six months pregnant. It would be their third.

"So the wizard said, 'Oh, very well. Go to the end of the lane and turn around three times and look down the magic well and there you will find three pennies. Hurry up.' So Roger Skunk went to the end of the lane and turned around three times and there in the magic well were *three pennies!* So he took them back to the wizard and was very happy and ran out into the woods and all the other little animals gathered around him because he smelled so good. And they played tag, baseball, football, basketball, lacrosse, hockey, soccer, and pick-up-sticks."

"What's pick-up-sticks?"

"It's a game you play with sticks."

"Like the wizard's magic wand?"

"Kind of. And they played games and laughed all afternoon and then it began to get dark and they all ran home to their mommies."

Jo was starting to fuss with her hands and look out of the window, at the crack of day that showed under the shade. She thought the story was all over. Jack didn't like women when they took anything for granted; he liked them apprehensive, hanging on his words. "Now, Jo, are you listening?"

"Yes."

"Because this is very interesting. Roger Skunk's mommy said, 'What's that awful smell?' "

"Wha-at?"

"And Roger Skunk said, 'It's me, Mommy. I smell like roses.' And she said, 'Who made you smell like that?' And he said, 'The wizard,' and she said, 'Well, of all the nerve. You come with me and we're going right back to that very awful wizard.' "

Jo sat up, her hands dabbling in the air with genuine fright. "But Daddy, then he said about the other little aminals run *away!*" Her hands skittered off, into the underbrush.

"All right. He said, 'But Mommy, all the other little animals run away,' and she said, 'I don't care. You smelled the way a little skunk should have and I'm going to take you right back to that wizard,' and she took an umbrella and went back with Roger Skunk and hit that wizard right over the head."

"No," Jo said, and put her hand out to touch his lips, yet even in her agitation did not quite dare to stop the source of truth. Inspiration came to her. "Then the wizard hit *her* on the head and did not change that little skunk back."

"No," he said. "The wizard said 'O.K.' and Roger Skunk did not smell of roses any more. He smelled very bad again."

"But the other little amum—*oh!*—amum—"

"Joanne. It's Daddy's story. Shall Daddy not tell you any more stories?" Her broad face looked at him through sifted light, astounded. "This is what happened, then. Roger Skunk and his mommy went home and they heard *Woo-oo, woooo-oo* and it was the choo-choo train bringing Daddy Skunk home from Boston. And they had lima beans, pork chops, celery, liver, mashed potatoes, and Pie-Oh-My for dessert. And when Roger Skunk was in bed Mommy Skunk came up and hugged him and said he smelled like her little baby skunk again and she loved him very much. And that's the end of the story."

"But Daddy."

"What?"

"Then did the other little ani-mals run away?"

"No, because eventually they got used to the way he was and did not mind it at all."

"What's evenshiladee?"

"In a little while."

"That was a stupid mommy."

"It was *not*," he said with rare emphasis, and believed, from her expression, that she realized he was defending his own mother to her, or something as odd. "Now I want you to put your big heavy head in the pillow and have a good long nap." He adjusted the shade so not even a crack of day showed, and tiptoed to the door, in the pretense that she was already asleep. But when he turned, she was crouching on top of the covers and staring at him. "Hey. Get under the covers and fall faaast asleep. Bobby's asleep."

She stood up and bounced gingerly on the springs. "Daddy."

"What?"

"Tomorrow, I want you to tell me the story that that wizard took that magic wand and hit that mommy"—her plump arms chopped fiercely— "right over the head."

"No. That's not the story. The point is that the little skunk loved his mommy more than he loved aaalll the other animals and she knew what was right."

"No. Tomorrow you say he hit that mommy. Do it." She kicked her legs up and sat down on the bed with a great heave and complaint of springs, as she had done hundreds of times before, except that this time she did not laugh. "Say it, Daddy."

"Well, we'll see. Now at least have a rest. Stay on the bed. You're a good girl."

He closed the door and went downstairs. Clare had spread the newspapers and opened the paint can and, wearing an old shirt of his on top of her maternity smock, was stroking the chair rail with a dipped brush. Above him footsteps vibrated and he called, "*Joanne*. Shall I come up there and spank you?" The footsteps hesitated.

"That was a long story," Clare said.

"The poor kid," he answered, and with utter weariness watched his wife labor. The woodwork, a cage of moldings and rails and baseboards all around them, was half old tan and half new ivory and he felt caught in an ugly middle position, and though he as well felt his wife's presence in the cage with him, he did not want to speak with her, work with her, touch her, anything.

E. M. Forster

A PASSAGE TO INDIA

PART I

MOSQUE

CHAPTER 1

EXCEPT for the Marabar Caves—and they are twenty miles off—the city of Chandrapore presents nothing extraordinary. Edged rather than washed by the river Ganges, it trails for a couple of miles along the bank, scarcely distinguishable from the rubbish it deposits so freely. There are no bathing-steps on the river front, as the Ganges happens not to be holy here; indeed there is no river front, and bazaars shut out the wide and shifting panorama of the stream. The streets are mean, the temples ineffective, and though a few fine houses exist they are hidden away in gardens or down alleys whose filth deters all but the invited guest. Chandrapore was never large or beautiful, but two hundred years ago it lay on the road between Upper India, then imperial, and the sea, and the fine houses date from that period. The zest for decoration stopped in the eighteenth century, nor was it ever democratic. There is no painting and scarcely any carving in the bazaars. The very wood seems made of mud, the inhabitants of mud moving. So abased, so monotonous is everything that meets the eye, that when the Ganges comes down it might be expected to wash the excrescence back into the soil. Houses do fall, people are drowned and left rotting, but the general outline of the town persists, swelling here, shrinking there, like some low but indestructible form of life.

Inland, the prospect alters. There is an oval Maidan,[1] and a long sallow hospital. Houses belonging to Eurasians stand on the high ground by the railway station. Beyond the railway—which runs parallel to the river—the land sinks, then rises again rather steeply. On the second rise is laid out the little civil station,[2] and viewed hence Chandrapore appears to be a totally different place. It is a city of gardens. It is no city, but a forest sparsely scattered with huts. It is a tropical pleasaunce washed by a noble river. The toddy palms and neem trees[3] and mangoes and pepul that were hidden behind the bazaars now become visible and in their turn hide the bazaars. They rise from the gardens where ancient tanks nourish them, they burst out of stifling purlieus and unconsidered temples. Seeking light

1. **Maidan:** an esplanade.
2. **civil station:** the area where the British civil servants reside.
3. **neem trees:** large East Indian trees that have a bitter bark that is used as a tonic.

and air, and endowed with more strength than man or his works, they soar above the lower deposit to greet one another with branches and beckoning leaves, and to build a city for the birds. Especially after the rains do they screen what passes below, but at all times, even when scorched or leafless, they glorify the city to the English people who inhabit the rise, so that new-comers cannot believe it to be as meagre as it is described, and have to be driven down to acquire disillusionment. As for the civil station itself, it provokes no emotion. It charms not, neither does it repel. It is sensibly planned, with a red-brick club on its brow, and farther back a grocer's and a cemetery, and the bungalows are disposed along roads that intersect at right angles. It has nothing hideous in it, and only the view is beautiful; it shares nothing with the city except the overarching sky.

The sky too has its changes, but they are less marked than those of the vegetation and the river. Clouds map it up at times, but it is normally a dome of blending tints, and the main tint blue. By day the blue will pale down into white where it touches the white of the land, after sunset it has a new circumference—orange, melting upwards into tenderest purple. But the core of blue persists, and so it is by night. Then the stars hang like lamps from the immense vault. The distance between the vault and them is as nothing to the distance behind them, and that farther distance, though beyond colour, last freed itself from blue.

The sky settles everything—not only climates and seasons but when the earth shall be beautiful. By herself she can do little—only feeble outbursts of flowers. But when the sky chooses, glory can rain into the Chandrapore bazaars or a benediction pass from horizon to horizon. The sky can do this because it is so strong and so enormous. Strength comes from the sun, infused in it daily; size from the prostrate earth. No mountains infringe on the curve. League after league the earth lies flat, heaves a little, is flat again. Only in the south, where a group of fists and fingers are thrust up through the soil, is the endless expanse interrupted. These fists and fingers are the Marabar Hills, containing the extraordinary caves.

CHAPTER 2

Abandoning his bicycle, which fell before a servant could catch it, the young man sprang up on to the verandah. He was all animation. "Hamidullah, Hamidullah! am I late?" he cried.

"Do not apologize," said his host. "You are always late."

"Kindly answer my question. Am I late? Has Mahmoud Ali eaten all the food? If so I go elsewhere. Mr. Mahmoud Ali, how are you?"

"Thank you, Dr. Aziz, I am dying."

"Dying before your dinner? Oh, poor Mahmoud Ali!"

"Hamidullah here is actually dead. He passed away just as you rode up on your bike."

"Yes, that is so," said the other. "Imagine us both as addressing you from another and a happier world."

"Does there happen to be such a thing as a hookah in that happier world of yours?"

"Aziz, don't chatter. We are having a very sad talk."

The hookah had been packed too tight, as was usual in his friend's house, and bubbled sulkily. He coaxed it. Yielding at last, the tobacco jetted up into his lungs and nostrils, driving out the smoke of burning cow dung that had filled them as he rode through the bazaar. It was delicious. He lay in a trance, sensuous but healthy, through which the talk of the two others did not seem particularly sad—they were discussing as to whether or no it is possible to be friends with an Englishman. Mahmoud Ali argued that it was not, Hamidullah disagreed, but with so many reservations that there was no friction between them. Delicious indeed to lie on the broad verandah with the moon rising in front and the servants preparing dinner behind, and no trouble happening.

"Well, look at my own experience this morning."

"I only contend that it is possible in England," replied Hamidullah, who had been to that country long ago, before the big rush, and had received a cordial welcome at Cambridge.

"It is impossible here. Aziz! The red-nosed boy has again insulted me in Court. I do not blame him. He was told that he ought to insult me. Until lately he was quite a nice boy, but the others have got hold of him."

"Yes, they have no chance here, that is my point. They come out intending to be gentlemen, and are told it will not do. Look at Lesley, look at Blakiston, now it is your red-nosed boy, and Fielding will go next. Why, I remember when Turton came out first. It was in another part of the Province. You fellows will not believe me, but I have driven with Turton in his carriage—Turton! Oh yes, we were once quite intimate. He has shown me his stamp collection."

"He would expect you to steal it now. Turton! But red-nosed boy will be far worse than Turton!"

"I do not think so. They all become exactly the same, not worse, not better. I give any Englishman two years, be he Turton or Burton. It is only the difference of a letter. And I give any Englishwoman six months. All are exactly alike. Do you not agree with me?"

"I do not," replied Mahmoud Ali, entering into the bitter fun, and feeling both pain and amusement at each word that was uttered. "For my own part I find such profound differences among our rulers. Red-nose mumbles, Turton talks distinctly, Mrs. Turton takes bribes, Mrs. Red-nose does not and cannot, because so far there is no Mrs. Red-nose."

"Bribes?"

"Did you not know that when they were lent to Central India over a Canal Scheme, some Rajah or other gave her a sewing machine in solid gold so that the water should run through his state?"

"And does it?"

"No, that is where Mrs. Turton is so skillful. When we poor blacks take bribes, we perform what we are bribed to perform, and the law discovers us in consequence. The English take and do nothing. I admire them."

"We all admire them. Aziz, please pass me the hookah."

"Oh, not yet—hookah is so jolly now."

"You are a very selfish boy." He raised his voice suddenly, and shouted for dinner. Servants shouted back that it was ready. They meant that they wished it was ready, and were so understood, for nobody moved. Then Hamidullah continued, but with changed manner and evident emotion.

"But take my case—the case of young Hugh Bannister. Here is the son of my dear, my dead friends, the Reverend and Mrs. Bannister, whose goodness to me in England I shall never forget or describe. They were father and mother to me, I talked to them as I do now. In the vacations their Rectory became my home. They entrusted all their children to me —I often carried little Hugh about—I took him up to the Funeral of Queen Victoria, and held him in my arms above the crowd."

"Queen Victoria was different," murmured Mahmoud Ali.

"I learn now that this boy is in business as a leather merchant at Cawnpore. Imagine how I long to see him and to pay his fare that this house may be his home. But it is useless. The other Anglo-Indians will have got hold of him long ago. He will probably think that I want something, and I cannot face that from the son of my old friends. Oh, what in this country has gone wrong with everything, Vakil Sahib? I ask you."

Aziz joined in. "Why talk about the English? Brrrr . . . ! Why be either friends with the fellows or not friends? Let us shut them out and be jolly. Queen Victoria and Mrs. Bannister were the only exceptions, and they're dead."

"No, no, I do not admit that, I have met others."

"So have I," said Mahmoud Ali, unexpectedly veering. "All ladies are far from alike." Their mood was changed, and they recalled little kindnesses and courtesies. "She said 'Thank you so much' in the most natural way." "She offered me a lozenge when the dust irritated my throat." Hamidullah could remember more important examples of angelic ministration, but the other, who only knew Anglo-India, had to ransack his memory for scraps, and it was not surprising that he should return to

"But of course all this is exceptional. The exception does not prove the rule. The average woman is like Mrs. Turton, and, Aziz, you know what she is." Aziz did not know, but said he did. He too generalized from his disappointments—it is difficult for members of a subject race to do otherwise. Granted the exceptions, he agreed that all Englishwomen are haughty and venal. The gleam passed from the conversation, whose wintry surface unrolled and expanded interminably.

A servant announced dinner. They ignored him. The elder men had reached their eternal politics, Aziz drifted into the garden. The trees smelt sweet—green-blossomed champak—and scraps of Persian poetry came into his head. Dinner, dinner, dinner . . . but when he returned to the house for it, Mahmoud Ali had drifted away in his turn, to speak to his sais.[1] "Come and see my wife a little then," said Hamidullah, and they spent twenty minutes behind the purdah. Hamidullah Begum was a distant aunt of Aziz, and the only female relative he had in Chandrapore, and she had much to say to him on this occasion about a family circumcision that had been celebrated with imperfect pomp. It was difficult to get away, because until they had had their dinner she would not begin hers, and consequently prolonged her remarks in case they should suppose she was impatient. Having censured the circumcision, she bethought her of kindred topics, and asked Aziz when he was going to be married.

Respectful but irritated, he answered, "Once is enough."

"Yes, he has done his duty," said Hamidullah. "Do not tease him so. He carries on his family, two boys and their sister."

"Aunt, they live most comfortably with my wife's mother, where she was living when she died. I can see them whenever I like. They are such very, very small children."

"And he sends them the whole of his salary and lives like a low-grade clerk, and tells no one the reason. What more do you require him to do?"

But this was not Hamidullah Begum's point, and having courteously changed the conversation for a few moments she returned and made it. She said, "What is to become of all our daughters if men refuse to marry? They will marry beneath them, or——" And she began the oft-told tale of a lady of Imperial descent who could find no husband in the narrow circle where her pride permitted her to mate, and had lived on unwed, her age now thirty, and would die unwed, for no one would have her now. While the tale was in progress, it convinced the two men, the tragedy seemed a slur on the whole community; better polygamy almost, than that a woman should die without the joys God has intended her to receive. Wedlock, motherhood, power in the house—for what else is she born, and how can the man who has denied them to her stand up to face her

1. sais: groom.

creator and his own at the last day? Aziz took his leave saying "Perhaps
. . . but later . . ."—his invariable reply to such an appeal.

"You mustn't put off what you think right," said Hamidullah. "That
is why India is in such a plight, because we put off things." But seeing
that his young relative looked worried, he added a few soothing words,
and thus wiped out any impression that his wife might have made.

During their absence, Mahmoud Ali had gone off in his carriage leaving a message that he should be back in five minutes, but they were on no
account to wait. They sat down to meat with a distant cousin of the
house, Mohammed Latif, who lived on Hamidullah's bounty and who
occupied the position neither of a servant nor of an equal. He did not
speak unless spoken to, and since no one spoke kept unoffended silence.
Now and then he belched, in compliment to the richness of the food. A
gentle, happy and dishonest old man; all his life he had never done a stroke
of work. So long as some one of his relatives had a house he was sure of
a home, and it was unlikely that so large a family would all go bankrupt.
His wife led a similar existence some hundreds of miles away—he did not
visit her, owing to the expense of the railway ticket. Presently Aziz
chaffed him, also the servants, and then began quoting poetry, Persian,
Urdu, a little Arabic. His memory was good, and for so young a man
he had read largely; the themes he preferred were the decay of Islam and
the brevity of Love. They listened delighted, for they took the public
view of poetry, not the private which obtains in England. It never bored
them to hear words, words; they breathed them with the cool night air,
never stopping to analyse; the name of the poet, Hafiz, Hali, Iqbal,[2] was
sufficient guarantee. India—a hundred Indias—whispered outside beneath
the indifferent moon, but for the time India seemed one and their own,
and they regained their departed greatness by hearing its departure lamented, they felt young again because reminded that youth must fly.
A servant in scarlet interrupted him; he was the chuprassi [3] of the Civil
Surgeon, and he handed Aziz a note.

"Old Callendar wants to see me at his bungalow," he said, not rising.
"He might have the politeness to say why."

"Some case, I daresay."

"I daresay not, I daresay nothing. He has found out our dinner hour,
that's all, and chooses to interrupt us every time, in order to show his
power."

"On the one hand he always does this, on the other it may be a serious

---

2. **Hafiz:** a celebrated Persian poet who was born about 1300; **Hali:** a nineteenth-
century Hindu poet; **Iqbal:** Sir Muhammad Iqbal (1875–1938), a widely influential poet who wrote in the Urdu language.
3. **chuprassi:** a messenger who wears an official badge.

case, and you cannot know," said Hamidullah, considerately paving the way towards obedience. "Had you not better clean your teeth after pan?"

"If my teeth are to be cleaned, I don't go at all. I am an Indian, it is an Indian habit to take pan. The Civil Surgeon must put up with it. Mohammed Latif, my bike, please."

The poor relation got up. Slightly immersed in the realms of matter, he laid his hand on the bicycle's saddle, while a servant did the actual wheeling. Between them they took it over a tintack.[4] Aziz held his hands under the ewer, dried them, fitted on his green felt hat, and then with unexpected energy whizzed out of Hamidullah's compound.

"Aziz, Aziz, imprudent boy. . . ." But he was far down the bazaar, riding furiously. He had neither light nor bell nor had he a brake, but what use are such adjuncts in a land where the cyclist's only hope is to coast from face to face, and just before he collides with each it vanishes? And the city was fairly empty at this hour. When his tyre went flat, he leapt off and shouted for a tonga.

He did not at first find one, and he had also to dispose of his bicycle at a friend's house. He dallied furthermore to clean his teeth. But at last he was rattling towards the civil lines,[5] with a vivid sense of speed. As he entered their arid tidiness, depression suddenly seized him. The roads, named after victorious generals and intersecting at right angles, were symbolic of the net Great Britain had thrown over India. He felt caught in their meshes. When he turned into Major Callendar's compound he could with difficulty restrain himself from getting down from the tonga and approaching the bungalow on foot, and this not because his soul was servile but because his feelings—the sensitive edges of him—feared a gross snub. There had been a "case" last year—an Indian gentlman had driven up to an official's house and been turned back by the servants and been told to approach more suitably—only one case among thousands of visits to hundreds of officials, but its fame spread wide. The young man shrank from a repetition of it. He compromised, and stopped the driver just outside the flood of light that fell across the verandah.

The Civil Surgeon was out.

"But the sahib has left me some message?"

The servant returned an indifferent "No." Aziz was in despair. It was a servant whom he had forgotten to tip, and he could do nothing now because there were people in the hall. He was convinced that there was a message, and that the man was withholding it out of revenge. While they argued, the people came out. Both were ladies. Aziz lifted his hat.

4. **tintack:** a carpet tack.
5. **civil lines:** the boundaries of the civil station.

The first, who was in evening dress, glanced at the Indian and turned instinctively away.

"Mrs. Lesley, it *is* a tonga," she cried.

"Ours?" enquired the second, also seeing Aziz and doing likewise.

"Take the gifts the gods provide, anyhow," she screeched, and both jumped in. "O Tonga wallah, club, club. Why doesn't the fool go?"

"Go, I will pay you to-morrow," said Aziz to the driver, and as they went off he called courteously, "You are most welcome, ladies." They did not reply, being full of their own affairs.

So it had come, the usual thing—just as Mahmoud Ali said. The inevitable snub—his bow ignored, his carriage taken. It might have been worse, for it comforted him somehow that Mesdames Callendar and Lesley should both be fat and weigh the tonga down behind. Beautiful women would have pained him. He turned to the servant, gave him a couple of rupees, and asked again whether there was a message. The man, now very civil, returned the same answer. Major Callendar had driven away half an hour before.

"Saying nothing?"

He had as a matter of fact said, "Damn Aziz"—words that the servant understood, but was too polite to repeat. One can tip too much as well as too little, indeed the coin that buys the exact truth has not yet been minted.

"Then I will write him a letter."

He was offered the use of the house, but was too dignified to enter it. Paper and ink were brought on to the verandah. He began: "Dear Sir,— At your express command I have hastened as a subordinate should——" and then stopped. "Tell him I have called, that is sufficient," he said, tearing the protest up. "Here is my card. Call me a tonga."

"Huzoor,⁶ all are at the club."

"Then telephone for one down to the railway station." And since the man hastened to do this he said, "Enough, enough, I prefer to walk." He commandeered a match and lit a cigarette. These attentions, though purchased, soothed him. They would last as long as he had rupees, which is something. But to shake the dust of Anglo-India off his feet! To escape from the net and be back among manners and gestures that he knew! He began a walk, an unwonted exercise.

He was an athletic little man, daintily put together, but really very strong. Nevertheless walking fatigued him, as it fatigues everyone in India except the new-comer. There is something hostile in that soil. It either yields, and the foot sinks into a depression, or else it is unexpectedly rigid and sharp, pressing stones or crystals against the tread. A series of these

6. **Huzoor:** a respectful title of address used by Indian servants.

little surprises exhausts; and he was wearing pumps, a poor preparation for any country. At the edge of the civil station he turned into a mosque to rest.

He had always liked this mosque. It was gracious, and the arrangement pleased him. The courtyard—entered through a ruined gate—contained an ablution tank of fresh clear water, which was always in motion, being indeed part of a conduit that supplied the city. The courtyard was paved with broken slabs. The covered part of the mosque was deeper than is usual; its effect was that of an English parish church whose side has been taken out. Where he sat, he looked into three arcades whose darkness was illuminated by a small hanging lamp and by the moon. The front—in full moonlight—had the appearance of marble, and the ninety-nine names of God on the frieze stood out black, as the frieze stood out white against the sky. The contest between this dualism and the contention of shadows within pleased Aziz, and he tried to symbolize the whole into some truth of religion or love. A mosque by winning his approval let loose his imagination. The temple of another creed, Hindu, Christian, or Greek, would have bored him and failed to awaken his sense of beauty. Here was Islam, his own country, more than a Faith, more than a battle-cry, more, much more . . . Islam, an attitude towards life both exquisite and durable, where his body and his thoughts found their home.

His seat was the low wall that bounded the courtyard on the left. The ground fell away beneath him towards the city, visible as a blur of trees, and in the stillness he heard many small sounds. On the right, over in the club, the English community contributed an amateur orchestra. Elsewhere some Hindus were drumming—he knew they were Hindus, because the rhythm was uncongenial to him,—and others were bewailing a corpse —he knew whose, having certified it in the afternoon. There were owls, the Punjab mail . . . and flowers smelt deliciously in the station-master's garden. But the mosque—that alone signified, and he returned to it from the complex appeal of the night, and decked it with meanings the builder had never intended. Some day he too would build a mosque, smaller than this but in perfect taste, so that all who passed by should experience the happiness he felt now. And near it, under a low dome, should be his tomb, with a Persian inscription:

> Alas, without me for thousands of years
> The Rose will blossom and the Spring will bloom,
> But those who have secretly understood my heart—
> They will approach and visit the grave where I lie.

He had seen the quatrain on the tomb of a Deccan king, and regarded it as profound philosophy—he always held pathos to be profound. The secret understanding of the heart! He repeated the phrase with tears in his eyes, and as he did so one of the pillars of the mosque seemed to quiver. It swayed in the gloom and detached itself. Belief in ghosts ran in his blood, but he sat firm. Another pillar moved, a third, and then an Englishwoman stepped out into the moonlight. Suddenly he was furiously angry and shouted: "Madam! Madam! Madam!"

"Oh! Oh!" the woman gasped.

"Madam, this is a mosque, you have no right here at all; you should have taken off your shoes; this is a holy place for Moslems."

"I have taken them off."

"You have?"

"I left them at the entrance."

"Then I ask your pardon."

Still startled, the woman moved out, keeping the ablution-tank between them. He called after her, "I am truly sorry for speaking."

"Yes, I was right, was I not? If I remove my shoes, I am allowed?"

"Of course, but so few ladies take the trouble, especially if thinking no one is there to see."

"That makes no difference. God is here."

"Madam!"

"Please let me go."

"Oh, can I do you some service now or at any time?"

"No, thank you, really none—good night."

"May I know your name?"

She was now in the shadow of the gateway, so that he could not see her face, but she saw his, and she said with a change of voice, "Mrs. Moore."

"Mrs. ——" Advancing, he found that she was old. A fabric bigger than the mosque fell to pieces, and he did not know whether he was glad or sorry. She was older than Hamidullah Begum, with a red face and white hair. Her voice had deceived him.

"Mrs. Moore, I am afraid I startled you. I shall tell my community— our friends—about you. That God is here—very good, very fine indeed. I think you are newly arrived in India."

"Yes—how did you know?"

"By the way you address me. No, but can I call you a carriage?"

"I have only come from the club. They are doing a play that I have seen in London, and it was so hot."

"What was the name of the play?"

"*Cousin Kate*."

"I think you ought not to walk at night alone, Mrs. Moore. There are bad characters about and leopards may come across from the Marabar Hills. Snakes also."

She exclaimed; she had forgotten the snakes.

"For example, a six-spot beetle," he continued. "You pick it up, it bites, you die."

"But you walk about yourself."

"Oh, I am used to it."

"Used to snakes?"

They both laughed. "I'm a doctor," he said. "Snakes don't dare bite me." They sat down side by side in the entrance, and slipped on their evening shoes. "Please may I ask you a question now? Why do you come to India at this time of year, just as the cold weather is ending?"

"I intended to start earlier, but there was an unavoidable delay."

"It will soon be so unhealthy for you! And why ever do you come to Chandrapore?"

"To visit my son. He is the City Magistrate here."

"Oh, no, excuse me, that is quite impossible. Our City Magistrate's name is Mr. Heaslop. I know him intimately."

"He's my son all the same," she said, smiling.

"But, Mrs. Moore, how can he be?"

"I was married twice."

"Yes, now I see, and your first husband died."

"He did, and so did my second husband."

"Then we are in the same box," he said cryptically. "Then is the City Magistrate the entire of your family now?"

"No, there are the younger ones—Ralph and Stella in England."

"And the gentleman here, is he Ralph and Stella's half-brother?"

"Quite right."

"Mrs. Moore, this is all extremely strange, because like yourself I have also two sons and a daughter. Is not this the same box with a vengeance?"

"What are their names? Not also Ronny, Ralph, and Stella, surely?"

The suggestion delighted him. "No, indeed. How funny it sounds! Their names are quite different and will surprise you. Listen, please. I am about to tell you my children's names. The first is called Ahmed, the second is called Karim, the third—she is the eldest—Jamila. Three children are enough. Do not you agree with me?"

"I do."

They were both silent for a little, thinking of their respective families. She sighed and rose to go.

"Would you care to see over the Minto Hospital one morning?" he enquired. "I have nothing else to offer at Chandrapore."

"Thank you, I have seen it already, or I should have liked to come with you very much."

"I suppose the Civil Surgeon took you."

"Yes, and Mrs. Callendar."

His voice altered. "Ah! A very charming lady."

"Possibly, when one knows her better."

"What? What? You didn't like her?"

"She was certainly intending to be kind, but I did not find her exactly charming."

He burst out with: "She has just taken my tonga without my permission—do you call that being charming?—and Major Callendar interrupts me night after night from where I am dining with my friends and I go at once, breaking up a most pleasant entertainment, and he is not there and not even a message. Is this charming, pray? But what does it matter? I can do nothing and he knows it. I am just a subordinate, my time is of no value, the verandah is good enough for an Indian, yes, yes, let him stand, and Mrs. Callendar takes my carriage and cuts me dead . . ."

She listened.

He was excited partly by his wrongs, but much more by the knowledge that someone sympathized with them. It was this that led him to repeat, exaggerate, contradict. She had proved her sympathy by criticizing her fellow-countrywoman to him, but even earlier he had known. The flame that not even beauty can nourish was springing up, and though his words were querulous his heart began to glow secretly. Presently it burst into speech.

"You understand me, you know what others feel. Oh, if others resembled you!"

Rather surprised, she replied: "I don't think I understand people very well. I only know whether I like or dislike them."

"Then you are an Oriental."

She accepted his escort back to the club, and said at the gate that she wished she was a member, so that she could have asked him in.

"Indians are not allowed into the Chandrapore Club even as guests," he said simply. He did not expatiate on his wrongs now, being happy. As he strolled downhill beneath the lovely moon, and again saw the lovely mosque, he seemed to own the land as much as anyone owned it. What did it matter if a few flabby Hindus had preceded him there, and a few chilly English succeeded?

CHAPTER 3

The third act of *Cousin Kate* was well advanced by the time Mrs. Moore re-entered the club. Windows were barred, lest the servants should see their mem-sahibs acting, and the heat was consequently immense. One electric fan revolved like a wounded bird, another was out of order. Disinclined to return to the audience, she went into the billiard room, where she was greeted by "I want to see the *real* India," and her appropriate life came back with a rush. This was Adela Quested, the queer, cautious girl whom Ronny had commissioned her to bring from England, and Ronny was her son, also cautious, whom Miss Quested would probably though not certainly marry, and she herself was an elderly lady.

"I want to see it too, and I only wish we could. Apparently the Turtons will arrange something for next Tuesday."

"It'll end in an elephant ride, it always does. Look at this evening. *Cousin Kate!* Imagine, *Cousin Kate!* But where have you been off to? Did you succeed in catching the moon in the Ganges?"

The two ladies had happened, the night before, to see the moon's reflection in a distant channel of the stream. The water had drawn it out, so that it had seemed larger than the real moon, and brighter, which had pleased them.

"I went to the mosque, but I did not catch the moon."

"The angle would have altered—she rises later."

"Later and later," yawned Mrs. Moore, who was tired after her walk. "Let me think—we don't see the other side of the moon out here, no."

"Come, India's not as bad as all that," said a pleasant voice. "Other side of the earth, if you like, but we stick to the same old moon." Neither of them knew the speaker nor did they ever see him again. He passed with his friendly word through red-brick pillars into the darkness.

"We aren't even seeing the other side of the world; that's our complaint," said Adela. Mrs. Moore agreed; she too was disappointed at the dullness of their new life. They had made such a romantic voyage across the Mediterranean and through the sands of Egypt to the harbour of Bombay, to find only a gridiron of bungalows at the end of it. But she did not take the disappointment as seriously as Miss Quested, for the reason that she was forty years older, and had learnt that Life never gives us what we want at the moment that we consider appropriate. Adventures do occur, but not punctually. She said again that she hoped that something interesting would be arranged for next Tuesday.

"Have a drink," said another pleasant voice. "Mrs. Moore—Miss Quested —have a drink, have two drinks." They knew who it was this time—the Collector,[1] Mr. Turton, with whom they had dined. Like themselves, he had found the atmosphere of *Cousin Kate* too hot. Ronny, he told them, was stage-managing in place of Major Callendar, whom some native subordinate or other had let down, and doing it very well; then he turned to

1. the Collector: the administrative head of the district.

Ronny's other merits, and in quiet, decisive tones said much that was flattering. It wasn't that the young man was particularly good at the games or the lingo, or that he had much notion of the Law, but—apparently a large but—Ronny was dignified.

Mrs. Moore was surprised to learn this, dignity not being a quality with which any mother credits her son. Miss Quested learnt it with anxiety, for she had not decided whether she liked dignified men. She tried indeed to discuss this point with Mr. Turton, but he silenced her with a good-humoured motion of his hand, and continued what he had come to say. "The long and the short of it is Heaslop's a sahib; he's the type we want, he's one of us," and another civilian who was leaning over the billiard table said, "Hear, hear!" The matter was thus placed beyond doubt, and the Collector passed on, for other duties called him.

Meanwhile the performance ended, and the amateur orchestra played the National Anthem. Conversation and billiards stopped, faces stiffened. It was the Anthem of the Army of Occupation. It reminded every member of the club that he or she was British and in exile. It produced a little sentiment and a useful accession of willpower. The meagre tune, the curt series of demands on Jehovah, fused into a prayer unknown in England, and though they perceived neither Royalty nor Deity they did perceive something, they were strengthened to resist another day. Then they poured out, offering one another drinks.

"Adela, have a drink; mother, a drink."

They refused—they were weary of drinks—and Miss Quested, who always said exactly what was in her mind, announced anew that she was desirous of seeing the real India.

Ronny was in high spirits. The request struck him as comic, and he called out to another passer-by: "Fielding! how's one to see the real India?"

"Try seeing Indians," the man answered, and vanished.

"Who was that?"

"Our schoolmaster—Government College."

"As if one could avoid seeing him," sighed Mrs. Lesley.

"I've avoided," said Miss Quested. "Excepting my own servant, I've scarcely spoken to an Indian since landing."

"Oh, lucky you."

"But I want to see them."

She became the centre of an amused group of ladies. One said, "Wanting to see Indians! How new that sounds!" Another, "Natives! why, fancy!" A third, more serious, said, "Let me explain. Natives don't respect one any the more after meeting one, you see."

"That occurs after so many meetings."

But the lady, entirely stupid and friendly, continued: "What I mean is, I was a nurse before my marriage, and came across them a great deal, so I know. I really do know the truth about Indians. A most unsuitable position for any Englishwoman—I was a nurse in a Native State. One's only hope was to hold sternly aloof."

"Even from one's patients?"

"Why, the kindest thing one can do to a native is to let him die," said Mrs. Callendar.

"How if he went to heaven?" asked Mrs. Moore, with a gentle but crooked smile.

"He can go where he likes as long as he doesn't come near me. They give me the creeps."

"As a matter of fact I have thought what you were saying about heaven, and that is why I am against Missionaries," said the lady who had been a nurse. "I am all for Chaplains, but all against Missionaries. Let me explain."

But before she could do so, the Collector intervened.

"Do you really want to meet the Aryan Brother, Miss Quested? That can be easily fixed up. I didn't realize he'd amuse you." He thought a moment. "You can practically see any type you like. Take your choice. I know the Government people and the landowners, Heaslop here can get hold of the barrister crew, while if you want to specialize on education, we can come down on Fielding."

"I'm tired of seeing picturesque figures pass before me as a frieze," the girl explained. "It was wonderful when we landed, but that superficial glamour soon goes."

Her impressions were of no interest to the Collector; he was only concerned to give her a good time. Would she like a Bridge Party? He explained to her what that was—not the game, but a party to bridge the gulf between East and West; the expression was his own invention, and amused all who heard it.

"I only want those Indians whom you come across socially—as your friends."

"Well, we don't come across them socially," he said, laughing. "They're full of all the virtues, but we don't, and it's now eleven-thirty, and too late to go into the reasons."

"Miss Quested, what a name!" remarked Mrs. Turton to her husband as they drove away. She had not taken to the new young lady, thinking her ungracious and cranky. She trusted that she hadn't been brought out to marry nice little Heaslop, though it looked like it. Her husband agreed with her in his heart, but he never spoke against an Englishwoman if he could avoid doing so, and he only said that Miss Quested naturally made mistakes. He added: "India does wonders for the judgment, especially during the hot weather; it has even done wonders for Fielding." Mrs. Turton closed her eyes at this name and remarked that Mr. Fielding wasn't pukka, and had better marry Miss Quested, for she wasn't pukka. Then they reached their bungalow, low and enormous, the oldest and most uncomfortable bungalow in the civil station, with a sunk soup plate of a lawn, and they had one drink more, this time of barley water, and went to bed. Their withdrawal from the club had broken up the evening, which, like all gatherings, had an official tinge. A community that bows the knee to a Viceroy and believes that the divinity that hedges a king can be transplanted, must feel some reverence for any viceregal substitute. At Chandrapore the Turtons were little gods; soon they would retire to some suburban villa, and die exiled from glory.

"It's decent of the Burra Sahib," chattered Ronny, much gratified at the civility that had been shown to his guests. "Do you know he's never given a Bridge Party before? Coming on top of the dinner too! I wish I could have arranged something myself, but when you know the natives better you'll realize it's easier for the Burra Sahib than for me. They know him—they know he can't be fooled—I'm still fresh comparatively. No one can even begin to think of knowing this country until he has been in it twenty years.—Hullo, the mater! Here's your cloak.—Well: for an example of the mistakes one makes. Soon after I came out I asked one of the Pleaders to have a smoke with me—only a cigarette, mind. I found afterwards that he had sent touts all over the bazaar to announce the fact—told all the litigants, 'Oh, you'd better come to my Vakil Mahmoud Ali—he's in with the City Magistrate.' Ever since then I've dropped on him in Court as hard as I could. It's taught me a lesson, and I hope him."

"Isn't the lesson that you should invite all the Pleaders to have a smoke with you?"

"Perhaps, but time's limited and the flesh weak. I prefer my smoke at the club amongst my own sort, I'm afraid."

"Why not ask the Pleaders to the club?" Miss Quested presisted.

"Not allowed." He was pleasant and patient, and evidently understood why she did not understand. He implied that he had once been as she, though not for long. Going to the verandah, he called firmly to the moon. His sais answered, and without lowering his head, he ordered his trap to be brought round.

Mrs. Moore, whom the club had stupefied, woke up outside. She watched the moon, whose radiance stained with primrose the purple of the surrounding sky. In England the moon had seemed dead and alien; here she was caught in the shawl of night together with earth and all the other stars. A sudden sense of unity, of kinship with the heavenly bodies, passed into the old woman and out, like water through a tank, leaving a strange freshness behind. She did not dislike *Cousin Kate* or the National Anthem, but their note had died into a new one, just as cocktails and cigars had died into invisible flowers. When the mosque, long and domeless, gleamed at the turn of the road, she exclaimed, "Oh, yes—that's where I got to—that's where I've been."

"Been there when?" asked her son.

"Between the acts."

"But, mother, you can't do that sort of thing."

"Can't mother?" she replied.

"No, really not in this country. It's not done. There's the danger from snakes for one thing. They are apt to lie out in the evening."

"Ah yes, so the young man there said."

"This sounds very romantic," said Miss Quested, who was exceedingly fond of Mrs. Moore, and was glad she should have had this little escapade. "You meet a young man in a mosque, and then never let me know!"

"I was going to tell you, Adela, but something changed the conversation and I forgot. My memory grows deplorable."

"Was he nice?"

She paused, then said emphatically: "Very nice."

"Who was he?" Ronny enquired.

"A doctor. I don't know his name."

"A doctor? I know of no young doctor in Chandrapore. How odd! What was he like?"

"Rather small, with a little moustache and quick eyes. He called out to me when I was in the dark part of the mosque—about my shoes. That was how we began talking. He was afraid I had them on, but I remembered luckily. He told me about his children, and then we walked back to the club. He knows you well."

"I wish you had pointed him out to me. I can't make out who he is."

"He didn't come into the club. He said he wasn't allowed to."

Thereupon the truth struck him, and he cried, "Oh, good gracious! Not a Mohammedan? Why ever didn't you tell me you'd been talking to a native? I was going all wrong."

"A Mohammedan! How perfectly magnificent!" exclaimed Miss Quested. "Ronny, isn't that like your mother? While we talk about seeing the real India, she goes and sees it, and then forgets she's seen it."

But Ronny was ruffled. From his mother's description he had thought the doctor might be young Muggins from over the Ganges, and had brought out all the comradely emotions. What a mix-up! Why hadn't she indicated by the tone of her voice that she was talking about an Indian?

Scratchy and dictatorial, he began to question her. "He called to you in
the mosque, did he? How? Impudently? What was he doing there himself at that time of night?—No, it's not their prayer time."—This in answer
to a suggestion of Miss Quested's, who showed the keenest interest. "So
he called to you over your shoes. Then it was impudence. It's an old
trick. I wish you had had them on."

"I think it was impudence, but I don't know about a trick," said Mrs.
Moore. "His nerves were all on edge—I could tell from his voice. As soon
as I answered he altered."

"You oughtn't to have answered."

"Now look here," said the logical girl, "wouldn't you expect a Mohammedan to answer if you asked him to take off his hat in church?"

"It's different, it's different; you don't understand."

"I know I don't, and I want to. What is the difference, please?"

He wished she wouldn't interfere. His mother did not signify—she was
just a globe-trotter, a temporary escort, who could retire to England
with what impressions she chose. But Adela, who meditated spending her
life in the country, was a more serious matter; it would be tiresome if she
started crooked over the native question. Pulling up the mare, he said,
"There's your Ganges."

Their attention was diverted. Below them a radiance had suddenly appeared. It belonged neither to water nor moonlight, but stood like a luminous sheaf upon the fields of darkness. He told them that it was where
the new sand-bank was forming, and that the dark ravelled bit at the top
was the sand, and that the dead bodies floated down that way from Benares, or would if the crocodiles let them. "It's not much of a dead body
that gets down to Chandrapore."

"Crocodiles down in it too, how terrible!" his mother murmured. The
young people glanced at each other and smiled; it amused them when the
old lady got these gentle creeps, and harmony was restored between them
consequently. She continued: "What a terrible river! what a wonderful
river!" and sighed. The radiance was already altering, whether through
shifting of the moon or of the sand; soon the bright sheaf would be gone,
and a circlet, itself to alter, be burnished upon the streaming void. The
women discussed whether they would wait for the change or not, while
the silence broke into patches of unquietness and the mare shivered. On
her account they did not wait, but drove on to the City Magistrate's
bungalow, where Miss Quested went to bed, and Mrs. Moore had a short
interview with her son.

He wanted to enquire about the Mohammedan doctor in the mosque.
It was his duty to report suspicious characters and conceivably it was
some disreputable hakim who had prowled up from the bazaar. When she

told him that it was someone connected with the Minto Hospital, he was relieved, and said that the fellow's name must be Aziz, and that he was quite all right, nothing against him at all.

"Aziz! what a charming name!"

"So you and he had a talk. Did you gather he was well disposed?"

Ignorant of the force of this question, she replied, "Yes, quite, after the first moment."

"I meant, generally. Did he seem to tolerate us—the brutal conqueror, the sundried bureaucrat, that sort of thing?"

"Oh, yes, I think so, except the Callendars—he doesn't care for the Callendars at all."

"Oh. So he told you that, did he? The Major will be interested. I wonder what was the aim of the remark."

"Ronny, Ronny! you're never going to pass it on to Major Callendar?"

"Yes, rather. I must, in fact!"

"But, my dear boy——"

"If the Major heard I was disliked by any native subordinate of mine, I should expect him to pass it on to me."

"But, my dear boy—a private conversation!"

"Nothing's private in India. Aziz knew that when he spoke out, so don't you worry. He had some motive in what he said. My personal belief is that the remark wasn't true."

"How not true?"

"He abused the Major in order to impress you."

"I don't know what you mean, dear."

"It's the educated native's latest dodge. They used to cringe, but the younger generation believe in a show of manly independence. They think it will pay better with the itinerant M.P. But whether the native swaggers or cringes, there's always something behind every remark he makes, always something, and if nothing else he's trying to increase his izzat—in plain Anglo-Saxon, to score. Of course there are exceptions."

"You never used to judge people like this at home."

"India isn't home," he retorted, rather rudely, but in order to silence her he had been using phrases and arguments that he had picked up from older officials, and he did not feel quite sure of himself. When he said "of course there are exceptions" he was quoting Mr. Turton, while "increasing the izzat" was Major Callendar's own. The phrases worked and were in current use at the club, but she was rather clever at detecting the first from the second hand, and might press him for definite examples.

She only said, "I can't deny that what you say sounds very sensible, but you really must not hand on to Major Callendar anything I have told you about Doctor Aziz."

He felt disloyal to his caste, but he promised, adding, "In return please don't talk about Aziz to Adela."

"Not talk about him? Why?"

"There you go again, mother—I really can't explain every thing. I don't want Adela to be worried, that's the fact; she'll begin wondering whether we treat the natives properly, and all that sort of nonsense."

"But she came out to be worried—that's exactly why she's here. She discussed it all on the boat. We had a long talk when we went on shore at Aden. She knows you in play, as she put it, but not in work, and she felt she must come and look round, before she decided—and before you decided. She is very, very fair-minded."

"I know," he said dejectedly.

The note of anxiety in his voice made her feel that he was still a little boy, who must have what he liked, so she promised to do as he wished, and they kissed good night. He had not forbidden her to think about Aziz, however, and she did this when she retired to her room. In the light of her son's comment she reconsidered the scene at the mosque, to see whose impression was correct. Yes, it could be worked into quite an unpleasant scene. The doctor had begun by bullying her, had said Mrs. Callendar was nice, and then—finding the ground safe—had changed; he had alternately whined over his grievances and patronized her, had run a dozen ways in a single sentence, had been unreliable, inquisitive, vain. Yes, it was all true, but how false as a summary of the man; the essential life of him had been slain.

Going to hang up her cloak, she found that the tip of the peg was occupied by a small wasp. She had known this wasp or his relatives by day; they were not as English wasps, but had long yellow legs which hung down behind when they flew. Perhaps he mistook the peg for a branch —no Indian animal has any sense of an interior. Bats, rats, birds, insects will as soon nest inside a house as out; it is to them a normal growth of the eternal jungle, which alternately produces houses trees, houses trees. There he clung, asleep, while jackals in the plain bayed their desires and mingled with the percussion of drums.

"Pretty dear," said Mrs. Moore to the wasp. He did not wake, but her voice floated out, to swell the night's uneasiness.

CHAPTER 4

The Collector kept his word. Next day he issued invitation cards to numerous Indian gentlemen in the neighbourhood, stating that he would be at home in the garden of the club between the hours of five and seven on the following Tuesday, also that Mrs. Turton would be glad to receive any ladies of their families who were out of purdah. His action caused much excitement and was discussed in several worlds.

"It is owing to orders from the L.G.," was Mahmoud Ali's explanation. "Turton would never do this unless compelled. Those high officials are different—they sympathize, the Viceroy sympathizes, they would have us treated properly. But they come too seldom and live too far away. Meanwhile——"

"It is easy to sympathize at a distance," said an old gentleman with a beard. "I value more the kind word that is spoken close to my ear. Mr. Turton has spoken it, from whatever cause. He speaks, we hear. I do not see why we need discuss it further." Quotations followed from the Koran.

"We have not all your sweet nature, Nawab Bahadur, nor your learning."

"The Lieutenant-Governor may be my very good friend, but I give him no trouble.—How do you do, Nawab Bahadur?—Quite well, thank you, Sir Gilbert; how are you?—And all is over. But I can be a thorn in Mr. Turton's flesh, and if he asks me I accept the invitation. I shall come in from Dilkusha specially, though I have to postpone other business."

"You will make yourself chip," suddenly said a little black man.

There was a stir of disapproval. Who was this ill-bred upstart, that he could criticize the leading Mohammedan landowner of the district? Mahmoud Ali, though sharing his opinion, felt bound to oppose it. "Mr. Ram Chand!" he said, swaying forward stiffly with his hands on his hips.

"Mr. Mahmoud Ali!"

"Mr. Ram Chand, the Nawab Bahadur can decide what is cheap without our valuation, I think."

"I do not expect I shall make myself cheap," said the Nawab Bahadur to Mr. Ram Chand, speaking very pleasantly, for he was aware that the man had been impolite and he desired to shield him from the consequences. It had passed through his mind to reply, "I expect I shall make myself cheap," but he rejected this as the less courteous alternative. "I do not see why we should make ourselves cheap. I do not see why we should. The invitation is worded very graciously." Feeling that he could not further decr ase the social gulf between himself and his auditors, he sent his elegant grandson, who was in attendance on him, to fetch his car. When it came, he repeated all that he had said before, though at greater length, ending up with "Till Tuesday, then, gentlemen all, when I hope we may meet in the flower gardens of the club."

This opinion carried great weight. The Nawab Bahadur was a big proprietor and a philanthropist, a man of benevolence and decision. His character among all the communities in the province stood high. He was a straightforward enemy and a staunch friend, and his hospitality was proverbial. "Give, do not lend; after death who will thank you?" was his favourite remark. He held it a disgrace to die rich. When such a man was prepared to motor twenty-five miles to shake the Collector's hand, the entertainment took another aspect. For he was not like some eminent men, who give out that they will come, and then fail at the last moment, leaving the small fry floundering. If he said he would come, he would come, he would never deceive his supporters. The gentlemen whom he had lectured now urged one another to attend the party, although convinced at heart that his advice was unsound.

He had spoken in the little room near the Courts where the pleaders waited for clients; clients, waiting for pleaders, sat in the dust outside. These had not received a card from Mr. Turton. And there were circles even beyond these—people who wore nothing but a loincloth, people who wore not even that, and spent their lives in knocking two sticks together before a scarlet doll—humanity grading and drifting beyond the educated vision, until no earthly invitation can embrace it.

All invitations must proceed from heaven perhaps; perhaps it is futile for men to initiate their own unity, they do but widen the gulfs between them by the attempt. So at all events thought old Mr. Graysford and young Mr. Sorley, the devoted missionaries who lived out beyond the slaughterhouses, always travelled third on the railways, and never came up to the club. In our Father's house are many mansions, they taught, and there alone will the incompatible multitudes of mankind be welcomed and soothed. Not one shall be turned away by the servants on that verandah, be he black or white, not one shall be kept standing who approaches with a loving heart. And why should the divine hospitality cease here? Consider, with all reverence, the monkeys. May there not be a mansion for the monkeys also? Old Mr. Graysford said No, but young Mr. Sorley, who was advanced, said Yes; he saw no reason why monkeys should not have their collateral share of bliss, and he had sympathetic discussions about them with his Hindu friends. And the jackals? Jackals were indeed less to Mr. Sorley's mind, but he admitted that the mercy of God, being infinite, may well embrace all mammals. And the wasps? He became uneasy during the descent to wasps, and was apt to change the conversation. And oranges, cactuses, crystals and mud? and the bacteria inside Mr. Sorley? No, no, this is going too far. We must exclude someone from our gathering, or we shall be left with nothing.

CHAPTER 5

The Bridge Party was not a success—at least it was not what Mrs. Moore and Miss Quested were accustomed to consider a successful party.

They arrived early, since it was given in their honour, but most of the Indian guests had arrived even earlier, and stood massed at the farther side of the tennis lawns, doing nothing.

"It is only just five," said Mrs. Turton. "My husband will be up from his office in a moment and start the thing. I have no idea what we have to do. It's the first time we've ever given a party like this at the club. Mr. Heaslop, when I'm dead and gone will you give parties like this? It's enough to make the old type of Burra Sahib turn in his grave."

Ronny laughed deferentially. "You wanted something not picturesque and we've provided it," he remarked to Miss Quested. "What do you think of the Aryan Brother in a topi and spats?"

Neither she nor his mother answered. They were gazing rather sadly over the tennis lawn. No, it was not picturesque; the East, abandoning its secular magnificence, was descending into a valley whose farther side no man can see.

"The great point to remember is that no one who's here matters; those who matter don't come. Isn't that so, Mrs. Turton?"

"Absolutely true," said the great lady, leaning back. She was "saving herself up," as she called it—not for anything that would happen that afternoon or even that week, but for some vague future occasion when a high official might come along and tax her social strength. Most of her public appearances were marked by this air of reserve.

Assured of her approbation, Ronny continued: "The educated Indians will be no good to us if there's a row, it's simply not worth while conciliating them, that's why they don't matter. Most of the people you see are seditious at heart, and the rest 'ld run squealing. The cultivator—he's another story. The Pathan—he's a man if you like. But these people—don't imagine they're India." He pointed to the dusky line beyond the court, and here and there it flashed a pince-nez or shuffled a shoe, as if aware that he was despising it. European costume had lighted like a leprosy. Few had yielded entirely, but none were untouched. There was a silence when he had finished speaking, on both sides of the court; at last, more ladies joined the English group, but their words seemed to die as soon as uttered. Some kites hovered overhead, impartial, over the kites passed the mass of a vulture, and with an impartiality exceeding all, the sky, not deeply coloured but translucent, poured light from its whole circumference. It seemed unlikely that the series stopped here. Beyond the sky must not there be something that overarches all the skies, more impartial even than they? Beyond which again . . .

They spoke of *Cousin Kate*.

They had tried to reproduce their own attitude to life upon the stage, and to dress up as the middle-class English people they actually were. Next year they would do *Quality Street* or *The Yeomen of the Guard*. Save for this annual incursion, they left literature alone. The men had no time for it, the women did nothing that they could not share with the men. Their ignorance of the Arts was notable, and they lost no opportunity of proclaiming it to one another; it was the Public School attitude; flourishing more vigorously than it can yet hope to do in England. If Indians were shop, the Arts were bad form, and Ronny had repressed his mother when she enquired after his viola; a viola was almost a demerit, and certainly not the sort of instrument one mentioned in public. She noticed now how tolerant and conventional his judgments had become; when they had seen *Cousin Kate* in London together in the past, he had scorned it; now he pretended that it was a good play, in order to hurt nobody's feelings. An "unkind notice" had appeared in the local paper, "the sort of thing no white man could have written," as Mrs. Lesley said. The play was praised, to be sure, and so were the stage management and the performance as a whole, but the notice contained the following sentence: "Miss Derek, though she charmingly looked her part, lacked the necessary experience, and occasionally forgot her words." This tiny breath of genuine criticism had given deep offence, not indeed to Miss Derek, who was as hard as nails, but to her friends. Miss Derek did not belong to Chandrapore. She was stopping for a fortnight with the McBrydes, the police people, and she had been so good as to fill up a gap in the cast at the last moment. A nice impression of local hospitality she would carry away with her.

"To work, Mary, to work," cried the Collector, touching his wife on the shoulder with a switch.

Mrs. Turton got up awkwardly. "What do you want me to do? Oh, those purdah women! I never thought any would come. Oh dear!"

A little group of Indian ladies had been gathering in a third quarter of the grounds, near a rustic summer-house in which the more timid of them had already taken refuge. The rest stood with their backs to the company and their faces pressed into a bank of shrubs. At a little distance stood their male relatives, watching the venture. The sight was significant: an island bared by the turning tide, and bound to grow.

"I consider they ought to come over to me."

"Come along, Mary, get it over."

"I refuse to shake hands with any of the men, unless it has to be the Nawab Bahadur."

"Whom have we so far?" He glanced along the line. "H'm! h'm! much as one expected. We know why he's here, I think—over that contract, and

he wants to get the right side of me for Mohurram,[1] and he's the astrol-
oger who wants to dodge the municipal building regulations, and he's
that Parsi, and he's—Hullo! there he goes—smash into our hollyhocks.
Pulled the left rein when he meant the right. All as usual."

"They ought never to have been allowed to drive in; it's so bad for
them," said Mrs. Turton, who had at last begun her progress to the summer-house, accompanied by Mrs. Moore, Miss Quested, and a terrier.
"Why they come at all I don't know. They hate it as much as we do. Talk
to Mrs. McBryde. Her husband made her give purdah parties until she
struck."

"This isn't a purdah party," corrected Miss Quested.

"Oh, really," was the haughty rejoinder.

"Do kindly tell us who these ladies are," asked Mrs. Moore.

"You're superior to them, anyway. Don't forget that. You're superior
to everyone in India except one or two of the Ranis, and they're on an
equality."

Advancing, she shook hands with the group and said a few words of
welcome in Urdu. She had learnt the lingo, but only to speak to her
servants, so she knew none of the politer forms and of the verbs only
the imperative mood. As soon as her speech was over, she enquired of her
companions, "Is that what you wanted?"

"Please tell these ladies that I wish we could speak their language, but
we have only just come to their country."

"Perhaps we speak yours a little," one of the ladies said.

"Why, fancy, she understands!" said Mrs. Turton.

"Eastbourne, Piccadilly, High Park Corner," said another of the ladies.

"Oh yes, they're English-speaking."

"But now we can talk: how delightful!" cried Adela, her face lighting up.

"She knows Paris also," called one of the onlookers.

"They pass Paris on the way, no doubt," said Mrs. Turton, as if she
was describing the movements of migratory birds. Her manner had
grown more distant since she had discovered that some of the group was
Westernized, and might apply her own standards to her.

"The shorter lady, she is my wife, she is Mrs. Bhattacharya," the onlooker explained. "The taller lady, she is my sister, she is Mrs. Das."

The shorter and the taller ladies both adjusted their saris, and smiled.
There was a curious uncertainty about their gestures, as if they sought
for a new formula which neither East nor West could provide. When

1. **Mohurram:** a Mohammedan festival celebrated during the first ten days of the
   first month of the Mohammedan year.

Mrs. Bhattacharya's husband spoke, she turned away from him, but she did not mind seeing the other men. Indeed all the ladies were uncertain, cowering, recovering, giggling, making tiny gestures of atonement or despair at all that was said, and alternately fondling the terrier or shrinking from him. Miss Quested now had her desired opportunity; friendly Indians were before her, and she tried to make them talk, but she failed, she strove in vain against the echoing walls of their civility. Whatever she said produced a murmur of deprecation, varying into a murmur of concern when she dropped her pocket-handkerchief. She tried doing nothing, to see what that produced, and they too did nothing. Mrs. Moore was equally unsuccessful. Mrs. Turton waited for them with a detached expression; she had known what nonsense it all was from the first.

When they took their leave, Mrs. Moore had an impulse, and said to Mrs. Bhattacharya, whose face she liked, "I wonder whether you would allow us to call on you some day."

"When?" she replied, inclining charmingly.

"Whenever is convenient."

"All days are convenient."

"Thursday . . ."

"Most certainly."

"We shall enjoy it greatly, it would be a real pleasure. What about the time?"

"All hours."

"Tell us which you would prefer. We're quite strangers to your country; we don't know when you have visitors," said Miss Quested.

Mrs. Bhattacharya seemed not to know either. Her gesture implied that she had known, since Thursdays began, that English ladies would come to see her on one of them, and so always stayed in. Everything pleased her, nothing surprised her. She added, "We leave for Calcutta to-day."

"Oh, do you?" said Adela, not at first seeing the implication. Then she cried, "Oh, but if you do we shall find you gone."

Mrs. Bhattacharya did not dispute it. But her husband called from the distance, "Yes, yes, you come to us Thursday."

"But you'll be in Calcutta."

"No, no, we shall not." He said something swiftly to his wife in Bengali. "We expect you Thursday."

"Thursday . . ." the woman echoed.

"You can't have done such a dreadful thing as to put off going for our sake?" exclaimed Mrs. Moore.

"No, of course not, we are not such people." He was laughing.

"I believe that you have. Oh, please—it distresses me beyond words."

Everyone was laughing now, but with no suggestion that they had blundered. A shapeless discussion occurred, during which Mrs. Turton retired, smiling to herself. The upshot was that they were to come Thursday, but early in the morning, so as to wreck the Bhattacharya plans as little as possible, and Mr. Bhattacharya would send his carriage to fetch them, with servants to point out the way. Did he know where they lived? Yes, of course he knew, he knew everything; and he laughed again. They left among a flutter of compliments and smiles, and three ladies, who had hitherto taken no part in the reception, suddenly shot out of the summerhouse like exquisitely coloured swallows, and salaamed them.

Meanwhile the Collector had been going his rounds. He made pleasant remarks and a few jokes, which were applauded lustily, but he knew something to the discredit of nearly every one of his guests, and was consequently perfunctory. When they had not cheated, it was bhang, women, or worse, and even the desirables wanted to get something out of him. He believed that a "Bridge Party" did good rather than harm, or he would not have given one, but he was under no illusions, and at the proper moment he retired to the English side of the lawn. The impressions he left behind him were various. Many of the guests, especially the humbler and less Anglicized, were genuinely grateful. To be addressed by so high an official was a permanent asset. They did not mind how long they stood, or how little happened, and when seven o'clock struck, they had to be turned out. Others were grateful with more intelligence. The Nawab Bahadur, indifferent for himself and for the distinction with which he was greeted, was moved by the mere kindness that must have prompted the invitation. He knew the difficulties. Hamidullah also thought that the Collector had played up well. But others, such as Mahmoud Ali, were cynical; they were firmly convinced that Turton had been made to give the party by his official superiors and was all the time consumed with impotent rage, and they infected some who were inclined to a healthier view. Yet even Mahmoud Ali was glad he had come. Shrines are fascinating, especially when rarely opened, and it amused him to note the ritual of the English club, and to caricature it afterwards to his friends.

After Mr. Turton, the official who did his duty best was Mr. Fielding, the Principal of the little Government College. He knew little of the district and less against the inhabitants, so he was in a less cynical state of mind. Athletic and cheerful, he romped about, making numerous mistakes which the parents of his pupils tried to cover up, for he was popular among them. When the moment for refreshments came, he did not move back to the English side, but burnt his mouth with gram. He talked to anyone and he ate anything. Amid much that was alien, he learnt that the two new ladies from England had been a great success, and that their politeness in wishing to be Mrs. Bhattacharya's guests had pleased not only her but all Indians who heard of it. It pleased Mr. Fielding also. He scarcely knew the two new ladies, still he decided to tell them what pleasure they had given by their friendliness.

He found the younger of them alone. She was looking through a nick in the cactus hedge at the distant Marabar Hills, which had crept near, as was their custom at sunset; if the sunset had lasted long enough, they would have reached the town, but it was swift, being tropical. He gave her his information, and she was so much pleased and thanked him so heartily that he asked her and the other lady to tea.

"I'd like to come very much indeed, and so would Mrs. Moore, I know."

"I'm rather a hermit, you know."

"Much the best thing to be in this place."

"Owing to my work and so on, I don't get up much to the club."

"I know, I know, and we never get down from it. I envy you being with Indians."

"Do you care to meet one or two?"

"Very, very much indeed; it's what I long for. This party to-day makes me so angry and miserable. I think my countrymen out here must be mad. Fancy inviting guests and not treating them properly! You and Mr. Turton and perhaps Mr. McBryde are the only people who showed any common politeness. The rest make me perfectly ashamed, and it's got worse and worse."

It had. The Englishmen had intended to play up better, but had been prevented from doing so by their women folk, whom they had to attend, provide with tea, advise about dogs, etc. When tennis began, the barrier grew impenetrable. It had been hoped to have some sets between East and West, but this was forgotten, and the courts were monopolized by the usual club couples. Fielding resented it too, but did not say so to the girl, for he found something theoretical in her outburst. Did she care about Indian music? he enquired; there was an old professor down at the College, who sang.

"Oh, just what we wanted to hear. And do you know Doctor Aziz?"

"I know all about him. I don't know him. Would you like him asked too?"

"Mrs. Moore says he is so nice."

"Very well, Miss Quested. Will Thursday suit you?"

"Indeed it will, and that morning we go to this Indian lady's. All the nice things are coming Thursday."

"I won't ask the City Magistrate to bring you. I know he'll be busy at that time."

"Yes, Ronny is always hard-worked," she replied, contemplating the hills. How lovely they suddenly were! But she couldn't touch them. In front, like a shutter, fell a vision of her married life. She and Ronny would look into the club like this every evening, then drive home to dress; they would see the Lesleys and the Callendars and the Turtons and the Burtons, and invite them and be invited by them, while the true India slid by unnoticed. Colour would remain—the pageant of birds in the early morning, brown bodies, white turbans, idols whose flesh was scarlet or blue—and movement would remain as long as there were crowds in the bazaar and bathers in the tanks. Perched up on the seat of a dogcart, she would see them. But the force that lies behind colour and movement would escape her even more effectually than it did now. She would see India always as a frieze, never as a spirit, and she assumed that it was a spirit of which Mrs. Moore had had a glimpse.

And sure enough they did drive away from the club in a few minutes, and they did dress, and to dinner came Miss Derek and the McBrydes, and the menu was: Julienne soup full of bullety bottled peas, pseudo-cottage bread, fish full of branching bones, pretending to be plaice, more bottled peas with the cutlets, trifle, sardines on toast: the menu of Anglo-India. A dish might be added or subtracted as one rose or fell in the official scale, the peas might rattle less or more, the sardines and the vermouth be imported by a different firm, but the tradition remained; the food of exiles, cooked by servants who did not understand it. Adela thought of the young men and women who had come out before her, P. & O.[2] full after P. & O. full, and had been set down to the same food and the same ideas, and been snubbed in the same good-humoured way until they kept to the accredited themes and began to snub others. "I should never get like that," she thought, for she was young herself; all the same she knew that she had come up against something that was both insidious and tough, and against which she needed allies. She must gather around her at Chandrapore a few people who felt as she did, and she was glad to have met Mr. Fielding and the Indian lady with the unpronounceable name. Here at all events was a nucleus; she should know much better where she stood in the course of the next two days.

Miss Derek—she companioned a Maharani in a remote Native State. She was genial and gay and made them all laugh about her leave, which she had taken because she felt she deserved it, not because the Maharani said she might go. Now she wanted to take the Maharajah's motor-car as well; it had gone to a Chiefs' Conference at Delhi, and she had a great scheme for burgling it at the junction as it came back in the train. She was also very funny about the Bridge Party—indeed she regarded the entire peninsula as a comic opera. "If one couldn't see the laughable side of these people one 'ld be done for," said Miss Derek. Mrs. McBryde—it was she who

2. **P. & O.**: Peninsular and Oriental Steamship Company.

had been the nurse—ceased not to exclaim, "Oh, Nancy, how topping! Oh, Nancy, how killing! I wish I could look at things like that." Mr. Mc-Bryde did not speak much; he seemed nice.

When the guests had gone, and Adela gone to bed, there was another interview between mother and son. He wanted her advice and support—while resenting interference. "Does Adela talk to you much?" he began. "I'm so driven with work, I don't see her as much as I hoped, but I hope she finds things comfortable."

"Adela and I talk mostly about India. Dear, since you mention it, you're quite right—you ought to be more alone with her than you are."

"Yes, perhaps, but then people 'ld gossip."

"Well, they must gossip sometime! Let them gossip."

"People are so odd out here, and it's not like home—one's always facing the footlights, as the Burra Sahib said. Take a silly little example: when Adela went out to the boundary of the club compound, and Fielding followed her. I saw Mrs. Callendar notice it. They notice everything, until they're perfectly sure you're their sort."

"I don't think Adela'll ever be quite their sort—she's much too individual."

"I know, that's so remarkable about her," he said thoughtfully. Mrs. Moore thought him rather absurd. Accustomed to the privacy of London, she could not realize that India, seemingly so mysterious, contains none, and that consequently the conventions have greater force. "I suppose nothing's on her mind," he continued.

"Ask her, ask her yourself, my dear boy."

"Probably she's heard tales of the heat, but of course, I should pack her off to the Hills every April—I'm not one to keep a wife grilling in the Plains."

"Oh, it wouldn't be the weather."

"There's nothing in India but the weather, my dear mother; it's the Alpha and Omega of the whole affair."

"Yes, as Mrs. McBryde was saying, but it's much more the Anglo-Indians themselves who are likely to get on Adela's nerves. She doesn't think they behave pleasantly to Indians, you see."

"What did I tell you?" he exclaimed, losing his gentle manner. "I knew it last week. Oh, how like a woman to worry over a side-issue!"

She forgot about Adela in her surprise. "A side-issue, a side-issue?" she repeated. "How can it be that?"

"We're not out here for the purpose of behaving pleasantly!"

"What do you mean?"

"What I say. We're out here to do justice and keep the peace. Them's my sentiments. India isn't a drawing-room."

"Your sentiments are those of a god," she said quietly, but it was his manner rather than his sentiments that annoyed her.

Trying to recover his temper, he said, "India likes gods."

"And Englishmen like posing as gods."

"There's no point in all this. Here we are, and we're going to stop, and the country's got to put up with us, gods or no gods. Oh, look here," he broke out, rather pathetically, "what do you and Adela want me to do? Go against my class, against all the people I respect and admire out here? Lose such power as I have for doing good in this country because my behaviour isn't pleasant? You neither of you understand what work is, or you 'ld never talk such eyewash. I hate talking like this, but one must occasionally. It's morbidly sensitive to go on as Adela and you do. I noticed you both at the club to-day—after the Burra Sahib had been at all that trouble to amuse you. I am out here to work, mind, to hold this wretched country by force. I'm not a missionary or a Labour Member or a vague sentimental sympathetic literary man. I'm just a servant of the Government; it's the profession you wanted me to choose myself, and that's that. We're not pleasant in India, and we don't intend to be pleasant. We've something more important to do."

He spoke sincerely. Every day he worked hard in the court trying to decide which of two untrue accounts was the less untrue, trying to dispense justice fearlessly, to protect the weak against the less weak, the incoherent against the plausible, surrounded by lies and flattery. That morning he had convicted a railway clerk of overcharging pilgrims for their tickets, and a Pathan of attempted rape. He expected no gratitude, no recognition for this, and both clerk and Pathan might appeal, bribe their witnesses more effectually in the interval, and get their sentences reversed. It was his duty. But he did expect sympathy from his own people, and except from new-comers he obtained it. He did think he ought not to be worried about "Bridge Parties" when the day's work was over and he wanted to play tennis with his equals or rest his legs upon a long chair.

He spoke sincerely, but she could have wished with less gusto. How Ronny revelled in the drawbacks of his situation! How he did rub it in that he was not in India to behave pleasantly, and derived positive satisfaction therefrom! He reminded her of his public-schooldays. The traces of young-man humanitarianism had sloughed off, and he talked like an intelligent and embittered boy. His words without his voice might have impressed her, but when she heard the self-satisfied lilt of them, when she saw the mouth moving so complacently and competently beneath the little red nose, she felt, quite illogically, that this was not the last word on India. One touch of regret—not the canny substitute but the true regret from the heart—would have made him a different man, and the British Empire a different institution.

"I'm going to argue, and indeed dictate," she said clinking her rings. "The English *are* out here to be pleasant."

"How do you make that out, mother?" he asked, speaking gently again, for he was ashamed of his irritability.

"Because India is part of the earth. And God had put us on the earth in order to be pleasant to each other. God . . . is . . . love." She hesitated, seeing how much he disliked the argument, but something made her go on. "God has put us on earth to love our neighbours and to show it, and He is omnipresent, even in India, to see how we are succeeding."

He looked gloomy, and a little anxious. He knew this religious strain in her, and that it was a symptom of bad health; there had been much of it when his stepfather died. He thought, "She is certainly ageing, and I ought not to be vexed with anything she says."

"The desire to behave pleasantly satisfies God. . . . The sincere if impotent desire wins His blessing. I think everyone fails, but there are so many kinds of failure. Good will and more good will and more good will. Though I speak with the tongues of . . ."

He waited until she had done, and then said gently, "I quite see that. I suppose I ought to get off to my files now, and you'll be going to bed."

"I suppose so, I suppose so." They did not part for a few minutes, but the conversation had become unreal since Christianity had entered it. Ronny approved of religion as long as it endorsed the National Anthem, but he objected when it attempted to influence his life. Then he would say in respectful yet decided tones, "I don't think it does to talk about these things, every fellow has to work out his own religion," and any fellow who heard him muttered, "Hear!"

Mrs. Moore felt that she had made a mistake in mentioning God, but she found Him increasingly difficult to avoid as she grew older, and He had been constantly in her thoughts since she entered India, though oddly enough He satisfied her less. She must needs pronounce His name frequently, as the greatest she knew, yet she had never found it less efficacious. Outside the arch there seemed always an arch, beyond the remotest echo a silence. And she regretted afterwards that she had not kept to the real serious subject that had caused her to visit India—namely, the relationship between Ronny and Adela. Would they, or would they not, succeed in becoming engaged to be married?

CHAPTER 6

Aziz had not gone to the Bridge Party. Immediately after his meeting with Mrs. Moore he was diverted to other matters. Several surgical cases came in, and kept him busy. He ceased to be either outcaste or poet, and became the medical student, very gay, and full of details of operations which he poured into the shrinking ears of his friends. His profession fascinated him at times, but he required it to be exciting, and it was his hand, not his mind, that was scientific. The knife he loved and used skilfully, and he also liked pumping in the latest serums. But the boredom of régime and hygiene repelled him, and after inoculating a man for enteric, he would go away and drink unfiltered water himself. "What can you expect from the fellow?" said dour Major Callendar. "No grits, no guts." But in his heart he knew that if Aziz and not he had operated last year on Mrs. Graysford's appendix, the old lady would probably have lived. And this did not dispose him any better towards his subordinate.

There was a row the morning after the mosque—they were always having rows. The Major, who had been up half the night, wanted damn well to know why Aziz had not come promptly when summoned.

"Sir, excuse me, I did. I mounted my bike, and it bust in front of the Cow Hospital. So I had to find a tonga."

"Bust in front of the Cow Hospital, did it? And how did you come to be there?"

"I beg your pardon?"

"Oh Lord, oh Lord! When I live here"—he kicked the gravel—"and you live there—not ten minutes from me—and the Cow Hospital is right ever so far away the other side of you—*there*—then how did you come to be passing the Cow Hospital on the way to me? Now do some work for a change."

He strode away in a temper, without waiting for the excuse, which as far as it went was a sound one: the Cow Hospital was in a straight line between Hamidullah's house and his own, so Aziz had naturally passed it. He never realized that the educated Indians visited one another constantly, and were weaving, however painfully, a new social fabric. Caste "or something of the sort" would prevent them. He only knew that no one ever told him the truth, although he had been in the country for twenty years.

Aziz watched him go with amusement. When his spirits were up he felt that the English are a comic institution, and he enjoyed being misunderstood by them. But it was an amusement of the emotions and nerves, which an accident or the passage of time might destroy; it was apart from the fundamental gaiety that he reached when he was with those whom he trusted. A disobliging simile involving Mrs. Callendar occurred to his fancy. "I must tell that to Mahmoud Ali, it'll make him laugh," he thought. Then he got to work. He was competent and indispensable, and he knew it. The simile passed from his mind while he exercised his professional skill.

During these pleasant and busy days, he heard vaguely that the Collector was giving a party, and that the Nawab Bahadur said everyone ought to go to it. His fellow-assistant, Doctor Panna Lal, was in ecstasies at the prospect, and was urgent that they should attend it together in his new tum-tum. The arrangement suited them both. Aziz was spared the indignity of a bicycle or the expense of hiring, while Dr. Panna Lal, who was timid and elderly, secured someone who could manage his horse. He could manage it himself, but only just, and he was afraid of the motors and of the unknown turn into the club grounds. "Disaster may come," he said politely, "but we shall at all events get there safe, even if we do not get back." And with more logic: "It will, I think, create a good impression should two doctors arrive at the same time."

But when the time came, Aziz was seized with a revulsion, and determined not to go. For one thing his spell of work, lately concluded, left him independent and healthy. For another, the day chanced to fall on the anniversary of his wife's death. She had died soon after he had fallen in love with her; he had not loved her at first. Touched by Western feeling, he disliked union with a woman whom he had never seen; moreover, when he did see her, she disappointed him, and he begat his first child in mere animality. The change began after its birth. He was won by her love for him, by a loyalty that implied something more than submission, and by her efforts to educate herself against that lifting of the purdah that would come in the next generation if not in theirs. She was intelligent, yet had old-fashioned grace. Gradually he lost the feeling that his relatives had chosen wrongly for him. Sensuous enjoyment—well, even if he had had it, it would have dulled in a year, and he had gained something instead, which seemed to increase the longer they lived together. She became the mother of a son . . . and in giving him a second son she died. Then he realized what he had lost, and that no woman could ever take her place; a friend would come nearer to her than another woman. She had gone, there was no one like her, and what is that uniqueness but love? He amused himself, he forgot her at times: but at other times he felt that she had sent all the beauty and joy of the world into Paradise, and he meditated suicide. Would he meet her beyond the tomb? Is there such a meetingplace? Though orthodox, he did not know. God's unity was indubitable and indubitably announced, but on all other points he wavered like the average Christian; his belief in the life to come would pale to a hope, vanish, reappear, all in a single sentence or a dozen heart-beats, so that the corpuscles of his blood rather than he seemed to decide which opinion he should hold, and for how long. It was so with all his opinions. Nothing stayed, nothing passed that did not return; the circulation was ceaseless and kept him young, and he mourned his wife the more sincerely because he mourned her seldom.

It would have been simpler to tell Dr. Lal that he had changed his mind about the party, but until the last minute he did not know that he had changed it; indeed, he didn't change it, it changed itself. Unconquerable aversion welled. Mrs. Callendar, Mrs. Lesley—no, he couldn't stand them in his sorrow: they would guess it—for he dowered the British matron with strange insight—and would delight in torturing him, they would mock him to their husbands. When he should have been ready, he stood at the Post Office, writing a telegram to his children, and found on his return that Dr. Lal had called for him, and gone on. Well, let him go on, as befitted the coarseness of his nature. For his own part, he would commune with the dead.

And unlocking a drawer, he took out his wife's photograph. He gazed at it, and tears spouted from his eyes. He thought, "How unhappy I am!" But because he really was unhappy, another emotion soon mingled with his self-pity: he desired to remember his wife and could not. Why could he remember people whom he did not love? They were always so vivid to him, whereas the more he looked at this photograph, the less he saw. She had eluded him thus, ever since they had carried her to her tomb. He had known that she would pass from his hands and eyes, but had thought she could live in his mind, not realizing that the very fact that we have loved the dead increases their unreality, and that the more passionately we invoke them the further they recede. A piece of brown cardboard and three children—that was all that was left of his wife. It was unbearable, and he thought again, "How unhappy I am!" and became happier. He had breathed for an instant the mortal air that surrounds Orientals and all men, and he drew back from it with a gasp, for he was young. "Never, never shall I get over this," he told himself. "Most certainly my career is a failure, and my sons will be badly brought up." Since it was certain, he strove to avert it, and looked at some notes he had made on a case at the hospital. Perhaps some day a rich person might require this particular operation, and he gain a large sum. The notes interesting him on their own account, he locked the photograph up again. Its moment was over, and he did not think about his wife any more.

After tea his spirits improved, and he went round to see Hamidullah. Hamidullah had gone to the party, but his pony had not, so Aziz borrowed it, also his friend's riding breeches and polo mallet. He repaired to the Maidan. It was deserted except at its rim, where some bazaar youths were training. Training for what? They would have found it hard to say, but the word had got into the air. Round they ran, weedy and knock-kneed—the local physique was wretched—with an expression on their faces not so much of determination as of a determination to be determined. "Maharajah, salaam," he called for a joke. The youths stopped and laughed. He advised them not to exert themselves. They promised they would not, and ran on.

Riding into the middle, he began to knock the ball about. He could not play, but his pony could, and he set himself to learn, free from all human tension. He forgot the whole damned business of living as he scurried over the brown platter of the Maidan, with the evening wind on his forehead, and the encircling trees soothing his eyes. The ball shot away towards a stray subaltern who was also practising; he hit it back to Aziz and called, "Send it along again."

"All right."

The new-comer had some notion of what to do, but his horse had none, and forces were equal. Concentrated on the ball, they somehow became fond of one another, and smiled when they drew rein to rest. Aziz liked soldiers—they either accepted you or swore at you, which was preferable to the civilian's hauteur—and the subaltern liked anyone who could ride.

"Often play?" he asked.

"Never."

"Let's have another chukker."

As he hit, his horse bucked and off he went, cried, "Oh God!" and jumped on again. "Don't you ever fall off?"

"Plenty."

"Not you."

They reined up again, the fire of good fellowship in their eyes. But it cooled with their bodies, for athletics can only raise a temporary glow. Nationality was returning, but before it could exert its poison they parted, saluting each oth. "If only they were all like that," each thought.

Now it was sunset. A few of his co-religionists had come to the Maidan, and were praying with their faces towards Mecca. A Brahminy Bull walked towards them, and Aziz, though disinclined to pray himself, did not see why they should be bothered with the clumsy and idolatrous animal. He gave it a tap with his polo mallet. As he did so, a voice from the road hailed him: it was Dr. Panna Lal, returning in high distress from the Collector's party.

"Dr. Aziz, Dr. Aziz, where you been? I waited ten full minutes' time at your house, then I went."

"I am so awfully sorry—I was compelled to go to the Post Office."

One of his own circle would have accepted this as meaning that he had changed his mind, an event too common to merit censure. But Dr. Lal, being of low extraction, was not sure whether an insult had not been intended, and he was further annoyed because Aziz had buffeted the Brahminy Bull. "Post Office? Do you not send your servants?" he said.

"I have so few—my scale is very small."

"Your servant spoke to me. I saw your servant."

"But, Dr. Lal, consider. How could I send my servant when you were coming: you come, we go, my house is left alone, my servant comes back perhaps, and all my portable property has been carried away by bad characters in the meantime. Would you have that? The cook is deaf—I can never count on my cook—and the boy is only a little boy. Never, never do I and Hassan leave the house at the same time together. It is my fixed rule." He said all this and much more out of civility, to save Dr. Lal's face. It was not offered as truth and should not have been criticized as such. But the other demolished it—an easy and ignoble task. "Even if this so, what prevents leaving a chit saying where you go?" and so on. Aziz detested ill breeding, and made his pony caper. "Farther away, or mine will start out of sympathy," he wailed, revealing the true source of his irritation. "It has been so rough and wild this afternoon. It spoiled some most valuable blossoms in the club garden, and had to be dragged back by four men. English ladies and gentlemen looking on, and the Collector Sahib himself taking a note. But, Dr. Aziz, I'll not take up your valuable time. This will not interest you, who have so many engagements and telegrams. I am just a poor old doctor who thought right to pay my respects when I was asked and where I was asked. Your absence, I may remark, drew commentaries."

"They can damn well comment."

"It is fine to be young. Damn well! Oh, very fine. Damn whom?"

"I go or not as I please."

"Yet you promise me, and then fabricate this tale of a telegram. Go forward, Dapple."

They went, and Aziz had a wild desire to make an enemy for life. He could do it so easily by galloping near them. He did it. Dapple bolted. He thundered back on to the Maidan. The glory of his play with the subaltern remained for a little, he galloped and swooped till he poured with sweat, and until he returned the pony to Hamidullah's stable he felt the equal of any man. Once on his feet, he had creeping fears. Was he in bad odour with the powers that be? Had he offended the Collector by absenting himself? Dr. Panna Lal was a person of no importance, yet was it wise to have quarrelled even with him? The complexion of his mind turned from human to political. He thought no longer, "Can I get on with people?" but "Are they stronger than I?" breathing the prevalent miasma.

At his home a chit was awaiting him, bearing the Government stamp. It lay on his table like a high explosive, which at a touch might blow his flimsy bungalow to bits. He was going to be cashiered because he had not turned up at the party. When he opened the note, it proved to be quite different; an invitation from Mr. Fielding, the Principal of Government College, asking him to come to tea the day after to-morrow. His spirits revived with violence. They would have revived in any case, for he possessed a soul that could suffer but not stifle, and led a steady life beneath his mutability. But this invitation gave him particular joy, because Fielding had asked him to tea a month ago, and he had forgotten about it —never answered, never gone, just forgotten. And here came a second invitation, without a rebuke or even an allusion to his slip. Here was true courtesy—the civil deed that shows the good heart—and snatching up his pen he wrote an affectionate reply, and hurried back for news to Hamidullah's. For he had never met the Principal, and believed that the one serious gap in his life was going to be filled. He longed to know everything about the splendid fellow—his salary, preferences, antecedents, how best one might please him. But Hamidullah was still out, and Mahmoud Ali, who was in, would only make silly rude jokes about the party.

CHAPTER 7

This Mr. Fielding had been caught by India late. He was over forty when he entered that oddest portal, the Victoria Terminus at Bombay, and—having bribed a European ticket inspector—took his luggage into the compartment of his first tropical train. The journey remained in his mind as significant. Of his two carriage companions one was a youth, fresh to the East like himself, the other a seasoned Anglo-Indian of his own age. A gulf divided him from either; he had seen too many cities and men to be the first or to become the second. New impressions crowded on him, but they were not the orthodox new impressions; the past conditioned them, and so it was with his mistakes. To regard an Indian as if he were an Italian is not, for instance, a common error, nor perhaps a fatal one, and Fielding often attempted analogies between this peninsula and that other, smaller and more exquisitely shaped, that stretches into the classic waters of the Mediterranean.

His career, though scholastic, was varied, and had included going to the bad and repenting thereafter. By now he was a hard-bitten, good-tempered, intelligent fellow on the verge of middle age, with a belief in education. He did not mind whom he taught; public schoolboys, mental de-

fectives and policemen, had all come his way, and he had no objection to
adding Indians. Through the influence of friends, he was nominated Principal of the little college at Chandrapore, liked it, and assumed he was a
success. He did succeed with his pupils, but the gulf between himself and
his countrymen, which he had noticed in the train, widened distressingly.
He could not at first see what was wrong. He was not unpatriotic, he always got on with Englishmen in England, all his best friends were English, so why was it not the same out here? Outwardly of the large shaggy
type, with sprawling limbs and blue eyes, he appeared to inspire confidence until he spoke. Then something in his manner puzzled people and
failed to allay the distrust which his profession naturally inspired. There
needs must be this evil of brains in India, but woe to him through whom
they are increased! The feeling grew that Mr. Fielding was a disruptive
force, and rightly, for ideas are fatal to caste, and he used ideas by that
most potent method—interchange. Neither a missionary nor a student,
he was happiest in the give-and-take of a private conversation. The world,
he believed, is a globe of men who are trying to reach one another and
can best do so by the help of good will plus culture and intelligence—
a creed ill suited to Chandrapore, but he had come out too late to lose it.
He had no racial feeling—not because he was superior to his brother
civilians, but because he had matured in a different atmosphere, where
the herd-instinct does not flourish. The remark that did him most harm
at the club was a silly aside to the effect that the so-called white races
are really pinko-grey. He only said this to be cheery, he did not realize
that "white" has no more to do with a colour than "God save the King"
with a god, and that it is the height of impropriety to consider what it
does connote. The pinko-grey male whom he addressed was subtly scandalized; his sense of insecurity was awoken, and he communicated it to
the rest of the herd.

Still, the men tolerated him for the sake of his good heart and strong
body; it was their wives who decided that he was not a sahib really. They
disliked him. He took no notice of them, and this, which would have
passed without comment in feminist England, did him harm in a community where the male is expected to be lively and helpful. Mr. Fielding
never advised one about dogs or horses, or dined, or paid his midday calls,
or decorated trees for one's children at Christmas, and though he came to
the club, it was only to get his tennis or billiards, and to go. This was
true. He had discovered that it is possible to keep in with Indians and
Englishmen, but that he who would also keep in with Englishwomen
must drop the Indians. The two wouldn't combine. Useless to blame
either party, useless to blame them for blaming one another. It just was
so, and one had to choose. Most Englishmen preferred their own kins-

women, who, coming out in increasing numbers, made life on the home pattern yearly more possible. He had found it convenient and pleasant to associate with Indians and he must pay the price. As a rule no English-woman entered the College except for official functions, and if he invited Mrs. Moore and Miss Quested to tea, it was because they were new-comers who would view everything with an equal if superficial eye, and would not turn on a special voice when speaking to his other guests.

The College itself had been slapped down by the Public Works De-partment, but its grounds included an ancient garden and a garden-house, and here he lived for much of the year. He was dressing after a bath when Dr. Aziz was announced. Lifting up his voice, he shouted from the bedroom, "Please make yourself at home." The remark was unpremedi-tated, like most of his actions; it was what he felt inclined to say.

To Aziz it had a very definite meaning. "May I really, Mr. Fielding? It's very good of you," he called back; "I like unconventional behaviour so extremely." His spirits flared up, he glanced round the living-room. Some luxury in it, but no order—nothing to intimidate poor Indians. It was also a very beautiful room, opening into the garden through three high arches of wood. "The fact is I have long wanted to meet you," he continued. "I have heard so much about your warm heart from the Nawab Bahadur. But where is one to meet in a wretched hole like Chan-drapore?" He came close up to the door. "When I was greener here, I'll tell you what. I used to wish you to fall ill so that we could meet that way." They laughed, and encouraged by his success he began to improvise. "I said to myself, How does Mr. Fielding look this morning? Perhaps pale. And the Civil Surgeon is pale too, he will not be able to attend upon him when the shivering commences. I should have been sent for instead. Then we would have had jolly talks, for you are a celebrated student of Persian poetry."

"You know me by sight, then."

"Of course, of course. You know me?"

"I know you very well by name."

"I have been here such a short time, and always in the bazaar. No wonder you have never seen me, and I wonder you know my name. I say, Mr. Fielding?"

"Yes?"

"Guess what I look like before you come out. That will be a kind of game."

"You're five feet nine inches high," said Fielding, surmising this much through the ground glass of the bedroom door.

"Jolly good. What next? Have I not a venerable white beard?"

"Blast!"

"Anything wrong?"

"I've stamped on my last collar stud."

"Take mine, take mine."

"Have you a spare one?"

"Yes, yes, one minute."

"Not if you're wearing it yourself."

"No, no, one in my pocket." Stepping aside, so that his outline might vanish, he wrenched off his collar, and pulled out of his shirt the back stud, a gold stud, which was part of a set that his brother-in-law had brought him from Europe. "Here it is," he cried.

"Come in with it if you don't mind the unconventionality."

"One minute again." Replacing his collar, he prayed that it would not spring up at the back during tea. Fielding's bearer, who was helping him to dress, opened the door for him.

"Many thanks." They shook hands smiling. He began to look round, as he would have with any old friend. Fielding was not surprised at the rapidity of their intimacy. With so emotional a people it was apt to come at once or never, and he and Aziz, having heard only good of each other, could afford to dispense with preliminaries.

"But I always thought that Englishmen kept their rooms so tidy. It seems that this is not so. I need not be so ashamed." He sat down gaily on the bed; then, forgetting himself entirely, drew up his legs and folded them under him. "Everything ranged coldly on shelves was what *I* thought.—I say, Mr. Fielding, is the stud going to go in?"

"I hae ma doots."

"What's that last sentence, please? Will you teach me some new words and so improve my English?"

Fielding doubted whether "everything ranged coldly on shelves" could be improved. He was often struck with the liveliness with which the younger generation handled a foreign tongue. They altered the idiom, but they could say whatever they wanted to say quickly; there were none of the babuisms [1] ascribed to them up at the club. But then the club moved slowly; it still declared that few Mohammedans and no Hindus would eat at an Englishman's table, and that all Indian ladies were in impenetrable purdah. Individually it knew better; as a club it declined to change.

"Let me put in your stud. I see . . . the shirt back's hole is rather small and to rip it wider a pity."

"Why in hell does one wear collars at all?" grumbled Fielding as he bent his neck.

"We wear them to pass the Police."

"What's that?"

1. **babuisms:** mistakes made by natives who have a smattering of English.

"If I'm biking in English dress—starch collar, hat with ditch—they take no notice. When I wear a fez, they cry, 'Your lamp's out!' Lord Curzon did not consider this when he urged natives of India to retain their picturesque costumes.—Hooray! Stud's gone in.—Sometimes I shut my eyes and dream I have splendid clothes again and am riding into battle behind Alamgir.[2] Mr. Fielding, must not India have been beautiful then, with the Mogul Empire at its height and Alamgir reigning at Delhi upon the Peacock Throne?"

"Two ladies are coming to tea to meet you—I think you know them."

"Meet me? I know no ladies."

"Not Mrs. Moore and Miss Quested?"

"Oh yes—I remember." The romance at the mosque had sunk out of his consciousness as soon as it was over. "An excessively aged lady; but will you please repeat the name of her companion?"

"Miss Quested."

"Just as you wish." He was disappointed that other guests were coming, for he preferred to be alone with his new friend.

"You can talk to Miss Quested about the Peacock Throne if you like—she's artistic, they say."

"Is she a Post Impressionist?"

"Post Impressionism, indeed! Come along to tea. This world is getting too much for me altogether."

Aziz was offended. The remark suggested that he, an obscure Indian, had no right to have heard of Post Impressionism—a privilege reserved for the Ruling Race, that. He said stiffly, "I do not consider Mrs. Moore my friend, I only met her accidentally in my mosque," and was adding "a single meeting is too short to make a friend," but before he could finish the sentence the stiffness vanished from it, because he felt Fielding's fundamental good will. His own went out to it, and grappled beneath the shifting tides of emotion which can alone bear the voyager to an anchorage but may also carry him across it on to the rocks. He was safe really—as safe as the shore-dweller who can only understand stability and supposes that every ship must be wrecked, and he had sensations the shore-dweller cannot know. Indeed, he was sensitive rather than responsive. In every remark he found a meaning, but not always the true meaning, and his life though vivid was largely a dream. Fielding, for instance, had not meant that Indians are obscure, but that Post Impressionism is; a gulf divided his remark from Mrs. Turton's "Why, they speak English," but to Aziz the two sounded alike. Fielding saw that something had gone wrong, and equally that it had come right, but he didn't fidget, being an optimist

2. Alamgir: (1618–1707), the Emperor of Hindustan. He is regarded by the Moslems of India as one of their greatest monarchs.

where personal relations were concerned, and their talk rattled on as before.

"Besides the ladies I am expecting one of my assistants—Narayan Godbole."

"Oho, the Deccani Brahman!"

"He wants the past back too, but not precisely Alamgir."

"I should think not. Do you know what Deccani Brahmans say? That England conquered India from them—from them, mind, and not from the Moguls. Is not that like their cheek? They have even bribed it to appear in text-books, for they are so subtle and immensely rich. Professor Godbole must be quite unlike all other Deccani Brahmans from all I can hear say. A most sincere chap."

"Why don't you fellows run a club in Chandrapore, Aziz?"

"Perhaps—some day . . . just now I see Mrs. Moore and—what's her name—coming."

How fortunate that it was an "unconventional" party, where formalities are ruled out! On this basis Aziz found the English ladies easy to talk to, he treated them like men. Beauty would have troubled him, for it entails rules of its own, but Mrs. Moore was so old and Miss Quested so plain that he was spared this anxiety. Adela's angular body and the freckles on her face were terrible defects in his eyes, and he wondered how God could have been so unkind to any female form. His attitude towards her remained entirely straightforward in consequence.

"I want to ask you something, Dr. Aziz," she began. "I heard from Mrs. Moore how helpful you were to her in the mosque, and how interesting. She learnt more about India in those few minutes' talk with you than in the three weeks since we landed."

"Oh, please do not mention a little thing like that. Is there anything else I may tell you about my country?"

"I want you to explain a disappointment we had this morning; it must be some point of Indian etiquette."

"There honestly is none," he replied. "We are by nature a most informal people."

"I am afraid we must have made some blunder and given offence," said Mrs. Moore.

"That is even more impossible. But may I know the facts?"

"An Indian lady and gentleman were to send their carriage for us this morning at nine. It has never come. We waited and waited and waited; we can't think what happened."

"Some misunderstanding," said Fielding, seeing at once that it was the type of incident that had better not be cleared up.

"Oh no, it wasn't that," Miss Quested persisted. "They even gave up going to Calcutta to entertain us. We must have made some stupid blunder, we both feel sure."

"I wouldn't worry about that."

"Exactly what Mr. Heaslop tells me," she retorted, reddening a little. "If one doesn't worry, how's one to understand?"

The host was inclined to change the subject, but Aziz took it up warmly, and on learning fragments of the delinquents' name pronounced that they were Hindus.

"Slack Hindus—they have no idea of society; I know them very well because of a doctor at the hospital. Such a slack, unpunctual fellow! It is as well you did not go to their house, for it would give you a wrong idea of India. Nothing sanitary. I think for my own part they grew ashamed of their house and that is why they did not send."

"That's a notion," said the other man.

"I do so hate mysteries," Adela announced.

"We English do."

"I dislike them not because I'm English, but from my own personal point of view," she corrected.

"I like mysteries but I rather dislike muddles," said Mrs. Moore.

"A mystery is a muddle."

"Oh, do you think so, Mr. Fielding?"

"A mystery is only a high-sounding term for a muddle. No advantage in stirring it up, in either case. Aziz and I know well that India's a muddle."

"India's—— Oh, what an alarming idea!"

"There'll be no muddle when you come to see me," said Aziz, rather out of his depth. "Mrs. Moore and everyone—I invite you all—oh, please."

The old lady accepted: she still thought the young doctor excessively nice; moreover, a new feeling, half languor, half excitement, bade her turn down any fresh path. Miss Quested accepted out of adventure. She also liked Aziz, and believed that when she knew him better he would unlock his country for her. His invitation gratified her, and she asked him for his address.

Aziz thought of his bungalow with horror. It was a detestable shanty near a low bazaar. There was practically only one room in it, and that infested with small black flies. "Oh, but we will talk of something else now," he exclaimed. "I wish I lived here. See this beautiful room! Let us admire it together for a little. See those curves at the bottom of the arches. What delicacy! It is the architecture of Question and Answer. Mrs. Moore, you are in India; I am not joking." The room inspired him. It was an audience hall built in the eighteenth century for some high of-ficial, and though of wood had reminded Fielding of the Loggia de' Lanzi at Florence. Little rooms, now Europeanized, clung to it on either side, but the central hall was unpapered and unglassed, and the air of the garden poured in freely. One sat in public—on exhibition, as it were—in full view of the gardeners who were screaming at the birds and of the man who rented the tank for the cultivation of water chestnut. Fielding let the mango trees too—there was no knowing who might not come in—and his servants sat on his steps night and day to discourage thieves. Beautiful certainly, and the Englishman had not spoilt it, whereas Aziz in an occidental moment would have hung Maude Goodmans on the walls. Yet there was no doubt to whom the room really belonged. . . .

"I am doing justice here. A poor widow who has been robbed comes along and I give her fifty rupees, to another a hundred, and so on and so on. I should like that."

Mrs. Moore smiled, thinking of the modern method as exemplified in her son. "Rupees don't last for ever, I'm afraid," she said.

"Mine would. God would give me more when He saw I gave. Always be giving, like the Nawab Bahadur. My father was the same, that is why he died poor." And pointing about the room he peopled it with clerks and officials, all benevolent because they lived long ago. "So we would sit giving for ever—on a carpet instead of chairs, that is the chief change between now and then, but I think we would never punish anyone."

The ladies agreed.

"Poor criminal, give him another chance. It only makes a man worse to go to prison and be corrupted." His face grew very tender—the tenderness of one incapable of administration, and unable to grasp that if the poor criminal is let off he will again rob the poor widow. He was tender to everyone except a few family enemies whom he did not consider human: on these he desired revenge. He was even tender to the English; he knew at the bottom of his heart that they could not help being so cold and odd and circulating like an ice stream through his land. "We punish no one, no one," he repeated, "and in the evening we will give a great banquet with a nautch and lovely girls shall shine on every side of the tank with fireworks in their hands, and all shall be feasting and happiness until the next day, when there shall be justice as before—fifty rupees, a hundred, a thousand—till peace comes. Ah, why didn't we live in that time?—But are you admiring Mr. Fielding's house? Do look how the pillars are painted blue, and the verandah's pavilions—what do you call them?—that are above us inside are blue also. Look at the carving on the pavilions. Think of the hours it took. Their little roofs are curved to imitate bamboo. So pretty—and the bamboos waving by the tank outside. Mrs. Moore! Mrs. Moore!"

"Well?" she said, laughing.

"You remember the water by our mosque? It comes down and fills this tank—a skilful arrangement of the Emperors. They stopped here going down into Bengal. They loved water. Wherever they went they created fountains, gardens, hammams.[3] I was telling Mr. Fielding I would give anything to serve them."

He was wrong about the water, which no Emperor, however skilful, can cause to gravitate uphill; a depression of some depth together with the whole of Chandrapore lay between the mosque and Fielding's house. Ronny would have pulled him up, Turton would have wanted to pull him up, but restrained himself. Fielding did not even want to pull him up; he had dulled his craving for verbal truth and cared chiefly for truth of mood. As for Miss Quested, she accepted everything Aziz said as true verbally. In her ignorance, she regarded him as "India," and never surmised that his outlook was limited and his method inaccurate, and that no one is India.

He was now much excited, chattering away hard, and even saying damn when he got mixed up in his sentences. He told them of his profession, and of the operations he had witnessed and performed, and he went into details that scared Mrs. Moore, though Miss Quested mistook them for proofs of his broad-mindedness; she had heard such talk at home in advanced academic circles, deliberately free. She supposed him to be emancipated as well as reliable, and placed him on a pinnacle which he could not retain. He was high enough for the moment, to be sure, but not on any pinnacle. Wings bore him up, and flagging would deposit him.

The arrival of Professor Godbole quieted him somewhat, but it remained his afternoon. The Brahman, polite and enigmatic, did not impede his eloquence, and even applauded it. He took his tea at a little distance from the outcasts, from a low table placed slightly behind him, to which he stretched back, and as it were encountered food by accident; all feigned indifference to Professor Godbole's tea. He was elderly and wizen with a grey moustache and grey-blue eyes, and his complexion was as fair as a European's. He wore a turban that looked like pale purple macaroni, coat, waistcoat, dhoti, socks with clocks. The clocks matched the turban, and his whole appearance suggested harmony—as if he had reconciled the products of East and West, mental as well as physical, and could never be discomposed. The ladies were interested in him, and hoped that he would supplement Dr. Aziz by saying something about religion. But he only ate—ate and ate, smiling, never letting his eyes catch sight of his hand.

Leaving the Mogul Emperors, Aziz turned to topics that could distress no one. He described the ripening of the mangoes, and how in his boyhood

3. **hammams**: bathhouses.

he used to run out in the Rains to a big mango grove belonging to an uncle and gorge there. "Then back with water streaming over you and perhaps rather a pain inside. But I did not mind. All my friends were paining with me. We have a proverb in Urdu: 'What does unhappiness matter when we are all unhappy together?' which comes in conveniently after mangoes. Miss Quested, do wait for mangoes. Why not settle altogether in India?"

"I'm afraid I can't do that," said Adela. She made the remark without thinking what it meant. To her, as to the three men, it seemed in key with the rest of the conversation, and not for several minutes—indeed, not for half an hour—did she realize that it was an important remark, and ought to have been made in the first place to Ronny.

"Visitors like you are too rare."

"They are indeed," said Professor Godbole. "Such affability is seldom seen. But what can we offer to detain them?"

"Mangoes, mangoes."

They laughed. "Even mangoes can be got in England now," put in Fielding. "They ship them in ice-cold rooms. You can make India in England apparently, just as you can make England in India."

"Frightfully expensive in both cases," said the girl.

"I suppose so."

"And nasty."

But the host wouldn't allow the conversation to take this heavy turn. He turned to the old lady, who looked flustered and put out—he could not imagine why—and asked about her own plans. She replied that she should like to see over the College. Everyone immediately rose, with the exception of Professor Godbole, who was finishing a banana.

"Don't you come too, Adela; you dislike institutions."

"Yes, that is so," said Miss Quested, and sat down again.

Aziz hesitated. His audience was splitting up. The more familiar half was going, but the more attentive remained. Reflecting that it was an "unconventional" afternoon, he stopped.

Talk went on as before. Could one offer the visitors unripe mangoes in a fool? "I speak now as a doctor: no." Then the old man said, "But I will send you up a few healthy sweets. I will give myself that pleasure."

"Miss Quested, Professor Godbole's sweets are delicious," said Aziz sadly, for he wanted to send sweets too and had no wife to cook them. "They will give you a real Indian treat. Ah, in my poor position I can give you nothing."

"I don't know why you say that, when you have so kindly asked us to your house."

He thought again of his bungalow with horror. Good heavens, the stupid girl had taken him at his word! What was he to do? "Yes, all that is settled," he cried. "I invite you all to see me in the Marabar Caves."

"I shall be delighted."

"Oh, that is a most magnificent entertainment compared to my poor sweets. But has not Miss Quested visited our caves already?"

"No. I've not even heard of them."

"Not heard of them?" both cried. "The Marabar Caves in the Marabar Hills?"

"We hear nothing interesting up at the club. Only tennis and ridiculous gossip."

The old man was silent, perhaps feeling that it was unseemly of her to criticize her race, perhaps fearing that if he agreed she would report him for disloyalty. But the young man uttered a rapid "I know."

"Then tell me everything you will, or I shall never understand India. Are they the hills I sometimes see in the evening? What are these caves?"

Aziz undertook to explain, but it presently appeared that he had never visited the caves himself—had always been "meaning" to go, but work or private business had prevented him, and they were so far. Professor Godbole chaffed him pleasantly. "My dear young sir, the pot and the kettle! Have you ever heard of that useful proverb?"

"Are they large caves?" she asked.

"No, not large."

"Do describe them, Professor Godbole."

"It will be a great honour." He drew up his chair and an expression of tension came over his face. Taking the cigarette box, she offered to him and to Aziz, and lit up herself. After an impressive pause he said: "There is an entrance in the rock which you enter, and through the entrance is the cave."

"Something like the caves at Elephanta?"

"Oh no, not at all; at Elephanta there are sculptures of Siva and Parvati. There are no sculptures at Marabar."

"They are immensely holy, no doubt," said Aziz, to help on the narrative.

"Oh no, oh no."

"Still, they are ornamented in some way."

"Oh no."

"Well, why are they so famous? We all talk of the famous Marabar Caves. Perhaps that is our empty brag."

"No, I should not quite say that."

"Describe them to this lady, then."

"It will be a great pleasure." He forewent the pleasure, and Aziz realized that he was keeping back something about the caves. He realized because he often suffered from similar inhibitions himself. Sometimes, to the exasperation of Major Callendar, he would pass over the one relevant fact in a position, to dwell on the hundred irrelevant. The Major accused him of disingenuousness, and was roughly right, but only roughly. It was rather that a power he couldn't control capriciously silenced his mind. Godbole had been silenced now; no doubt not willingly, he was concealing something. Handled subtly, he might regain control and announce that the Marabar Caves were —full of stalactites, perhaps; Aziz led up to this, but they weren't.

The dialogue remained light and friendly, and Adela had no conception of its underdrift. She did not know that the comparatively simple mind of the Mohammedan was encountering Ancient Night. Aziz played a thrilling game. He was handling a human toy that refused to work—he knew that much. If it worked, neither he nor Professor Godbole would be the least advantaged, but the attempt enthralled him and was akin to abstract thought. On he chattered, defeated at every move by an opponent who would not even admit that a move had been made, and further than ever from discovering what, if anything, was extraordinary about the Marabar Caves.

Into this Ronny dropped.

With an annoyance he took no trouble to conceal, he called from the garden: "What's happened to Fielding? Where's my mother?"

"Good evening!" she replied coolly.

"I want you and mother at once. There's to be polo."

"I thought there was to be no polo."

"Everything's altered. Some soldier men have come in. Come along and I'll tell you about it."

"Your mother will return shortly, sir," said Professor Godbole, who had risen with deference. "There is but little to see at our poor college."

Ronny took no notice, but continued to address his remarks to Adela; he had hurried away from his work to take her to see the polo, because he thought it would give her pleasure. He did not mean to be rude to the two men, but the only link he could be conscious of with an Indian was the official, and neither happened to be his subordinate. As private individuals he forgot them.

Unfortunately Aziz was in no mood to be forgotten. He would not give up the secure and intimate note of the last hour. He had not risen with Godbole, and now, offensively friendly, called from his seat, "Come along up and join us, Mr. Heaslop; sit down till your mother turns up."

Ronny replied by ordering one of Fielding's servants to fetch his master at once.

"He may not understand that. Allow me——" Aziz repeated the order idiomatically.

Ronny was tempted to retort; he knew the type; he knew all the types, and this was the spoilt Westernized. But he was a servant of the Government, it was his job to avoid "incidents," so he said nothing, and ignored the provocation that Aziz continued to offer. Aziz was provocative. Everything he said had an impertinent flavour or jarred. His wings were failing, but he refused to fall without a struggle. He did not mean to be impertinent to Mr. Heaslop, who had never done him harm, but here was an Anglo-Indian who must become a man before comfort could be regained. He did not mean to be greasily confidential to Miss Quested, only to enlist her support; nor to be loud and jolly towards Professor Godbole. A strange quartette—he fluttering to the ground, she puzzled by the sudden ugliness, Ronny fuming, the Brahman observing all three, but with downcast eyes and hands folded, as if nothing was noticeable. A scene from a play, thought Fielding, who now saw them from the distance across the garden grouped among the blue pillars of his beautiful hall.

"Don't trouble to come, mother," Ronny called; "we're just starting." Then he hurried to Fielding, drew him aside and said with pseudo-heartiness, "I say, old man, do excuse me, but I think perhaps you oughtn't to have left Miss Quested alone."

"I'm sorry, what's up?" replied Fielding, also trying to be genial.

"Well . . . I'm the sun-dried bureaucrat, no doubt; still, I don't like to see an English girl left smoking with two Indians."

"She stopped, as she smokes, by her own wish, old man."

"Yes, that's all right in England."

"I really can't see the harm."

"If you can't see, you can't see. . . . Can't you see that fellow's a bounder?"

Aziz flamboyant, was patronizing Mrs. Moore.

"He isn't a bounder," protested Fielding. "His nerves are on edge, that's all."

"What should have upset his precious nerves?"

"I don't know. He was all right when I left."

"Well, it's nothing I've said," said Ronny reassuringly. "I never even spoke to him."

"Oh well, come along now, and take your ladies away; the catastrophe is over."

"Fielding . . . don't think I'm taking it badly, or anything of that sort. . . . I suppose you won't come on to the polo with us? We should all be delighted."

"I'm afraid I can't, thanks all the same. I'm awfully sorry you feel I've been remiss. I didn't mean to be."

So the leave-taking began. Every one was cross or wretched. It was as if irritation exuded from the very soil. Could one have been so petty on a Scotch moor or an Italian alp? Fielding wondered afterwards. There seemed no reserve of tranquillity to draw upon in India. Either none, or else tranquillity swallowed up everything, as it appeared to do for Professor Godbole. Here was Aziz all shoddy and odious, Mrs. Moore and Miss Quested both silly, and he himself and Heaslop both decorous on the surface, but detestable really, and detesting each other.

"Good-bye, Mr. Fielding, and thank you so much. . . . What lovely College buildings!"

"Good-bye, Mrs. Moore."

"Good-bye, Mr. Fielding. Such an interesting afternoon. . . ."

"Good-bye, Miss Quested."

"Good-bye, Dr. Aziz."

"Good-bye, Mrs. Moore."

"Good-bye, Dr. Aziz."

"Good-bye, Miss Quested." He pumped her hand up and down to show that he felt at ease. "You'll jolly jolly well not forget those caves, won't you? I'll fix the whole show up in a jiffy."

"Thank you. . . ."

Inspired by the devil to a final effort, he added, "What a shame you leave India so soon! Oh, do reconsider your decision, do stay."

"Good-bye, Professor Godbole," she continued, suddenly agitated. "It's a shame we never heard you sing."

"I may sing now," he replied, and did.

His thin voice rose, and gave out one sound after another. At times there seemed rhythm, at times there was the illusion of a Western melody. But the ear, baffled repeatedly, soon lost any clue, and wandered in a maze of noises, none harsh or unpleasant, none intelligible. It was the song of an unknown bird. Only the servants understood it. They began to whisper to one another. The man who was gathering water chestnut came naked out of the tank, his lips parted with delight, disclosing his scarlet tongue. The sounds continued and ceased after a few moments as casually as they had begun—apparently half through a bar, and upon the subdominant.

"Thanks so much: what was that?" asked Fielding.

"I will explain in detail. It was a religious song. I place myself in the position of a milkmaiden. I say to Shri [4] Krishna, 'Come! come to me only.' The god refuses to come. I grow humble and say: 'Do not come to me only. Multiply yourself into a hundred Krishnas, and let one go to

4. **Shri**: Holy.

each of my hundred companions, but one, O Lord of the Universe, come to me.' He refuses to come. This is repeated several times. The song is composed in a raga [5] appropriate to the present hour, which is the evening."

"But He comes in some other song, I hope?" said Mrs. Moore gently.

"Oh no, He refuses to come," repeated Godbole, perhaps not understanding her question. "I say to Him, 'Come, come, come, come, come, come.' He neglects to come."

Ronny's steps had died away, and there was a moment of absolute silence. No ripple disturbed the water, no leaf stirred.

CHAPTER 8

Although Miss Quested had known Ronny well in England, she felt well advised to visit him before deciding to be his wife. India had developed sides of his character that she had never admired. His self-complacency, his censoriousness, his lack of subtlety, all grew vivid beneath a tropic sky; he seemed more indifferent than of old to what was passing in the minds of his fellows, more certain that he was right about them or that if he was wrong it didn't matter. When proved wrong, he was particularly exasperating; he always managed to suggest that she needn't have bothered to prove it. The point she made was never the relevant point, her arguments conclusive but barren, she was reminded that he had expert knowledge and she none, and that experience would not help her because she could not interpret it. A Public School, London University, a year at a crammer's, a particular sequence of posts in a particular province, a fall from a horse and a touch of fever were presented to her as the only training by which Indians and all who reside in their country can be understood; the only training she could comprehend, that is to say, for of course above Ronny there stretched the higher realms of knowledge, inhabited by Callendars and Turtons, who had been not one year in the country but twenty and whose instincts were superhuman. For himself he made no extravagant claims; she wished he would. It was the qualified bray of the callow official, the "I am not perfect, but——" that got on her nerves.

How gross he had been at Mr. Fielding's—spoiling the talk and walking off in the middle of the haunting song! As he drove them away in the tum-tum, her irritation became unbearable, and she did not realize that much of it was directed against herself. She longed for an opportunity to fly out at him, and since he felt cross too, and they were both in India, an opportunity soon occurred. They had scarcely left the College grounds

5. **raga:** a musical term; a mode or scale on which a composition is based.

before she heard him say to his mother, who was with him on the front
seat, "What was that about caves?" and she promptly opened fire.

"Mrs. Moore, your delightful doctor has decided on a picnic, instead of
a party in his house; we are to meet him out there—you, myself, Mr.
Fielding, Professor Godbole—exactly the same party."

"Out where?" asked Ronny.

"The Marabar Caves."

"Well, I'm blessed," he murmured after a pause. "Did he descend to any
details?"

"He did not. If you had spoken to him, we could have arranged them."

He shook his head, laughing.

"Have I said anything funny?"

"I was only thinking how the worthy doctor's collar climbed up his
neck."

"I thought you were discussing the caves."

"So I am. Aziz was exquisitely dressed, from tie-pin to spats, but he
had forgotten his back collar-stud, and there you have the Indian all over:
inattention to detail; the fundamental slackness that reveals the race. Similarly, to 'meet' in the caves as if they were the clock at Charing Cross,
when they're miles from a station and each other."

"Have you been to them?"

"No, but I know all about them, naturally."

"Oh, naturally!"

"Are you too pledged to this expedition, mother?"

"Mother is pledged to nothing," said Mrs. Moore, rather unexpectedly.
"Certainly not to this polo. Will you drive up to the bungalow first, and
drop me there, please? I prefer to rest."

"Drop me too," said Adela. "I don't want to watch polo either, I'm
sure."

"Simpler to drop the polo," said Ronny. Tired and disappointed, he
quite lost self-control, and added in a loud lecturing voice, "I won't have
you messing about with Indians any more! If you want to go to the
Marabar Caves, you'll go under British auspices."

"I've never heard of these caves, I don't know what or where they
are," said Mrs. Moore, "but I really can't have"—she tapped the cushion
beside her—"so much quarrelling and tiresomeness!"

The young people were ashamed. They dropped her at the bungalow
and drove on together to the polo, feeling it was the least they could do.
Their crackling bad humour left them, but the heaviness of their spirit
remained; thunderstorms seldom clear the air. Miss Quested was thinking
over her own behaviour, and didn't like it at all. Instead of weighing
Ronny and herself, and coming to a reasoned conclusion about marriage,

she had incidentally, in the course of a talk about mangoes, remarked to mixed company that she didn't mean to stop in India. Which meant that she wouldn't marry Ronny: but what a way to announce it, what a way for a civilized girl to behave! She owed him an explanation, but unfortunately there was nothing to explain. The "thorough talk" so dear to her principles and temperament had been postponed until too late. There seemed no point in being disagreeable to him and formulating her complaints against his character at this hour of the day, which was the evening. . . . The polo took place on the Maidan near the entrance of Chandrapore city. The sun was already declining and each of the trees held a premonition of night. They walked away from the governing group to a distant seat, and there, feeling that it was his due and her own, she forced out of herself the undigested remark: "We must have a thorough talk, Ronny, I'm afraid."

"My temper's rotten, I must apologize," was his reply. "I didn't mean to order you and mother about, but of course the way those Bengalis let you down this morning annoyed me, and I don't want that sort of thing to keep happening."

"It's nothing to do with them that I . . ."

"No, but Aziz would make some similar muddle over the caves. He meant nothing by the invitation, I could tell by his voice; it's just their way of being pleasant."

"It's something very different, nothing to do with caves, that I wanted to talk over with you." She gazed at the colourless grass. "I've finally decided we are not going to be married, my dear boy."

The news hurt Ronny very much. He had heard Aziz announce that she would not return to the country, but had paid no attention to the remark, for he never dreamt that an Indian could be a channel of communication between two English people. He controlled himself and said gently, "You never said we should marry, my dear girl; you never bound either yourself or me—don't let this upset you."

She felt ashamed. How decent he was! He might force his opinions down her throat, but did not press her to an "engagement," because he believed, like herself, in the sanctity of personal relationships: it was this that had drawn them together at their first meeting, which had occurred among the grand scenery of the English Lakes. Her ordeal was over, but she felt it should have been more painful and longer. Adela will not marry Ronny. It seemed slipping away like a dream. She said, "But let us discuss things; it's all so frightfully important, we mustn't make false steps. I want next to hear your point of view about me—it might help us both."

His manner was unhappy and reserved. "I don't much believe in this discussing—besides, I'm so dead with all this extra work Mohurram's bring-ing, if you'll excuse me."

"I only want everything to be absolutely clear between us, and to an-swer any questions you care to put to me on my conduct."

"But I haven't got any questions. You've acted within your rights, you were quite right to come out and have a look at me doing my work, it was an excellent plan, and anyhow it's no use talking further—we should only get up steam." He felt angry and bruised; he was too proud to tempt her back, but he did not consider that she had behaved badly, because where his compatriots were concerned he had a generous mind.

"I suppose that there is nothing else; it's unpardonable of me to have given you and your mother all this bother," said Miss Quested heavily, and frowned up at the tree beneath which they were sitting. A little green bird was observing her, so brilliant and neat that it might have hopped straight out of a shop. On catching her eye it closed its own, gave a small skip and prepared to go to bed. Some Indian wild bird. "Yes, nothing else," she repeated, feeling that a profound and passionate speech ought to have been delivered by one or both of them. "We've been awfully British over it, but I suppose that's all right."

"As we are British, I suppose it is."

"Anyhow we've not quarrelled, Ronny."

"Oh, that would have been too absurd. Why should we quarrel?"

"I think we shall keep friends."

"I know we shall."

"Quite so."

As soon as they had exchanged this admission, a wave of relief passed through them both, and then transformed itself into a wave of tenderness, and passed back. They were softened by their own honesty, and began to feel lonely and unwise. Experiences, not character, divided them; they were not dissimilar, as humans go; indeed, when compared with the peo-ple who stood nearest to them in point of space they became practically identical. The Bhil [1] who was holding an officer's polo pony, the Eura-sian who drove the Nawab Bahadur's car, the Nawab Bahadur himself, the Nawab Bahadur's debauched grandson—none would have examined a difficulty so frankly and coolly. The mere fact of examination caused it to diminish. Of course they were friends, and for ever. "Do you know what the name of that green bird up above us is?" she asked, putting her shoulder rather nearer to his.

"Bee-cater."

"Oh no, Ronny, it has red bars on its wings."

1. **Bhil**: a low-caste native.

"Parrot," he hazarded.

"Good gracious no."

The bird in question dived into the dome of the tree. It was of no importance, yet they would have liked to identify it, it would somehow have solaced their hearts. But nothing in India is identifiable, the mere asking of a question causes it to disappear or to merge in something else.

"McBryde has an illustrated bird book," he said dejectedly. "I'm no good at all at birds, in fact I'm useless at any information outside my own job. It's a great pity."

"So am I. I'm useless at everything."

"What do I hear?" shouted the Nawab Bahadur at the top of his voice, causing both of them to start. "What most improbable statement have I heard? An English lady useless? No, no, no, no, no." He laughed genially, sure, within limits, of his welcome.

"Hallo, Nawab Bahadur! Been watching the polo again?" said Ronny tepidly.

"I have, sahib, I have."

"How do you do?" said Adela, likewise pulling herself together. She held out her hand. The old gentleman judged from so wanton a gesture that she was new to his country, but he paid little heed. Women who exposed their face became by that one act so mysterious to him that he took that at the valuation of their men folk rather than at his own. Perhaps they were not immoral, and anyhow they were not his affair. On seeing the City Magistrate alone with a maiden at twilight, he had borne down on them with hospitable intent. He had a new little car, and wished to place it at their disposal; the City Magistrate would decide whether the offer was acceptable.

Ronny was by this time rather ashamed of his curtness to Aziz and Godbole, and here was an opportunity of showing that he could treat Indians with consideration when they deserved it. So he said to Adela, with the same sad friendliness that he had employed when discussing the bird, "Would half an hour's spin entertain you at all?"

"Oughtn't we to get back to the bungalow?"

"Why?" He gazed at her.

"I think perhaps I ought to see your mother and discuss future plans."

"That's as you like, but there's no hurry, is there?"

"Let me take you to the bungalow, and first the little spin," cried the old man, and hastened to the car.

"He may show you some aspect of the country I can't, and he's a real loyalist. I thought you might care for a bit of a change."

Determined to give him no more trouble, she agreed, but her desire to

see India had suddenly decreased. There had been a factitious element
in it.

How should they seat themselves in the car? The elegant grandson had
to be left behind. The Nawab Bahadur got up in front, for he had no intention of neighbouring an English girl. "Despite my advanced years, I
am learning to drive," he said. "Man can learn everything if he will but
try." And foreseeing a further difficulty, he added, "I do not do the actual
steering. I sit and ask my chauffeur questions, and thus learn the reason for
everything that is done before I do it myself. By this method serious and I
may say ludicrous accidents, such as befell one of my compatriots during
that delightful reception at the English Club, are avoided. Our good Panna
Lal! I hope, sahib, that great damage was not done to your flowers. Let us
have our little spin down the Gangavati road. Half one league onwards!"
He fell asleep.

Ronny instructed the chauffeur to take the Marabar road rather than
the Gangavati, since the latter was under repair, and settled himself down
beside the lady he had lost. The car made a burring noise and rushed
along a chaussée [2] that ran upon an embankment above melancholy fields.
Trees of a poor quality bordered the road, indeed the whole scene was
inferior, and suggested that the countryside was too vast to admit of excellence. In vain did each item in it call out, "Come, come." There was
not enough god to go round. The two young people conversed feebly
and felt unimportant. When the darkness began, it seemed to well out
of the meagre vegetation, entirely covering the fields each side of them
before it brimmed over the road. Ronny's face grew dim—an event that
always increased her esteem for his character. Her hand touched his, owing to a jolt, and one of the thrills so frequent in the animal kingdom
passed between them, and announced that all their difficulties were only
a lovers' quarrel. Each was too proud to increase the pressure, but neither
withdrew it, and a spurious unity descended on them, as local and temporary as the gleam that inhabits a firefly. It would vanish in a moment, perhaps to reappear, but the darkness is alone durable. And the night that
encircled them, absolute as it seemed, was itself only a spurious unity, being modified by the gleams of day that leaked up round the edges of the
earth, and by the stars.

They gripped . . . bump, jump, a swerve, two wheels lifted in the air,
brakes on, bump with tree at edge of embankment, standstill. An accident. A slight one. Nobody hurt. The Nawab Bahadur awoke. He cried
out in Arabic, and violently tugged his beard.

"What's the damage?" enquired Ronny, after the moment's pause that

2. chaussée: a causeway.

he permitted himself before taking charge of a situation. The Eurasian, inclined to be flustered, rallied to the sound of his voice, and, every inch an Englishman, replied, "You give me five minutes' time, I'll take you any dam anywhere."

"Frightened, Adela?" He released her hand.

"Not a bit."

"I consider not to be frightened the height of folly," cried the Nawab Bahadur quite rudely.

"Well, it's all over now, tears are useless," said Ronny, dismounting. "We had some luck butting that tree."

"All over . . . oh yes, the danger is past, let us smoke cigarettes, let us do anything we please. Oh yes . . . enjoy ourselves—oh my merciful God . . ." His words died into Arabic again.

"Wasn't the bridge. We skidded."

"We didn't skid," said Adela, who had seen the cause of the accident, and thought everyone must have seen it too. "We ran into an animal."

A loud cry broke from the old man: his terror was disproportionate and ridiculous.

"An animal?"

"A large animal rushed up out of the dark on the right and hit us."

"By jove, she's right," Ronny exclaimed. "The paint's gone."

"By jove, sir, your lady is right," echoed the Eurasian. Just by the hinges of the door was a dent, and the door opened with difficulty.

"Of course I'm right. I saw its hairy back quite plainly."

"I say, Adela, what was it?"

"I don't know the animals any better than the birds here—too big for a goat."

"Exactly, too big for a goat . . ." said the old man.

Ronny said, "Let's go into this; let's look for its tracks."

"Exactly; you wish to borrow this electric torch."

The English people walked a few steps back into the darkness, united and happy. Thanks to their youth and upbringing, they were not upset by the accident. They traced back the writhing of the tyres to the source of their disturbance. It was just after the exit from a bridge; the animal had probably come up out of the nullah. Steady and smooth ran the marks of the car, ribbons neatly nicked with lozenges, then all went mad. Certainly some external force had impinged, but the road had been used by too many objects for any one track to be legible, and the torch created such high lights and black shadows that they could not interpret what it revealed. Moreover, Adela in her excitement knelt and swept her skirts about, until it was she if anyone who appeared to have attacked the car. The incident was a great relief to them both. They forgot their abortive personal relationship, and felt adventurous as they muddled about in the dust.

"I believe it was a buffalo," she called to their host, who had not accompanied them.

"Exactly."

"Unless it was a hyena."

Ronny approved this last conjecture. Hyenas prowl in nullahs and headlights dazzle them.

"Excellent, a hyena," said the Indian with an angry irony and a gesture at the night. "Mr. Harris!"

"Half a mo-ment. Give me ten minutes' time."

"Sahib says hyena."

"Don't worry Mr. Harris. He saved us from a nasty smash. Harris, well done!"

"A smash, sahib, that would not have taken place had he obeyed and taken us Gangavati side, instead of Marabar."

"My fault that. I told him to come this way because the road's better. Mr. Lesley has made it pukka right up to the hills."

"Ah, now I begin to understand." Seeming to pull himself together, he apologized slowly and elaborately for the accident. Ronny murmured, "Not at all," but apologies were his due, and should have started sooner: because English people are so calm at a crisis, it is not to be assumed that they are unimportant. The Nawab Bahadur had not come out very well.

At that moment a large car approached from the opposite direction. Ronny advanced a few steps down the road, and with authority in his voice and gesture stopped it. It bore the inscription "Mudkul State" across its bonnet. All friskiness and friendliness, Miss Derek sat inside.

"Mr. Heaslop, Miss Quested, what are you holding up an innocent female for?"

"We've had a breakdown."

"But how putrid!"

"We ran into a hyena!"

"How absolutely rotten!"

"Can you give us a lift?"

"Yes, indeed."

"Take me too," said the Nawab Bahadur.

"Heh, what about me?" cried Mr. Harris.

"Now what's all this? I'm not an omnibus," said Miss Derek with decision. "I've a harmonium and two dogs in here with me as it is. I'll take three of you if one'll sit in front and nurse a pug. No more."

"I will sit in front," said the Nawab Bahadur.

"Then hop in: I've no notion who you are."

"Heh no, what about my dinner? I can't be left alone all the night."
Trying to look and feel like a European, the chauffeur interposed aggressively. He still wore a topi, despite the darkness, and his face, to which
the Ruling Race had contributed little beyond bad teeth, peered out of it
pathetically, and seemed to say, "What's it all about? Don't worry me so,
you blacks and whites. Here I am, stuck in dam India same as you, and
you got to fit me in better than this."

"Nussu will bring you out some suitable dinner upon a bicycle," said
the Nawab Bahadur, who had regained his usual dignity. "I shall despatch
him with all possible speed. Meanwhile, repair my car."

They sped off, and Mr. Harris, after a reproachful glance, squatted
down upon his hams. When English and Indians were both present, he
grew self-conscious, because he did not know to whom he belonged. For
a little he was vexed by opposite currents in his blood, then they blended,
and he belonged to one one but himself.

But Miss Derek was in tearing spirits. She had succeeded in stealing the
Mudkul car. Her Maharajah would be awfully sick, but she didn't mind,
he could sack her if he liked. "I don't believe in these people letting you
down," she said. "If I didn't snatch like the devil, I should be nowhere.
He doesn't want the car, silly fool! Surely it's to the credit of his State
I should be seen about in it at Chandrapore during my leave. He ought
to look at it that way. Anyhow he's got to look at it that way. My Maharani's different—my Maharani's a dear. That's her fox terrier, poor little
devil. I fished them out both with the driver. Imagine taking dogs to a
Chiefs' Conference! As sensible as taking Chiefs, perhaps." She shrieked
with laughter. "The harmonium—the harmonium's my little mistake, I
own. They rather had me over the harmonium. I meant it to stop on the
train. Oh lor'!"

Ronny laughed with restraint. He did not approve of English people
taking service under the Native States, where they obtain a certain amount
of influence, but at the expense of the general prestige. The humorous
triumphs of a free lance are of no assistance to an administrator, and he
told the young lady that she would outdo Indians at their own game
if she went on much longer.

"They always sack me before that happens, and then I get another job.
The whole of India seethes with Maharanis and Ranis and Begums who
clamour for such as me."

"Really. I had no idea."

"How could you have any idea, Mr. Heaslop? What should he know
about Maharanis, Miss Quested? Nothing. At least I should hope not."

"I understand those big people are not particularly interesting," said

Adela, quietly, disliking the young woman's tone. Her hand touched Ronny's again in the darkness, and to the animal thrill there was now added a coincidence of opinion.

"Ah, there you're wrong. They're priceless."

"I would scarcely call her wrong," broke out the Nawab Bahadur, from his isolation on the front seat, whither they had relegated him. "A Native State, a Hindu State, the wife of a ruler of a Hindu State, may beyond doubt be a most excellent lady, and let it not be for a moment supposed that I suggest anything against the character of Her Highness the Maharani of Mudkul. But I fear she will be uneducated, I fear she will be superstitious. Indeed, how could she be otherwise? What opportunity of education has such a lady had? Oh, superstition is terrible, terrible! oh, it is the great defect in our Indian character!"—and as if to point his criticism, the lights of the civil station appeared on a rise to the right. He grew more and more voluble. "Oh, it is the duty of each and every citizen to shake superstition off, and though I have little experience of Hindu States, and none of this particular one, namely Mudkul (the Ruler, I fancy, has a salute of but eleven guns)—yet I cannot imagine that they have been as successful as British India, where we see reason and order-liness spreading in every direction, like a most health-giving flood!"

Miss Derek said "Golly!"

Undeterred by the expletive, the old man swept on. His tongue had been loosed and his mind had several points to make. He wanted to endorse Miss Quested's remark that big people are not interesting, be-cause he was bigger himself than many an independent chief; at the same time, he must neither remind nor inform her that he was big, lest she felt she had committed a discourtesy. This was the groundwork of his ora-tion; worked in with it was his gratitude to Miss Derek for the lift, his willingness to hold a repulsive dog in his arms, and his general regret for the trouble he had caused the human race during the evening. Also he wanted to be dropped near the city to get hold of his cleaner, and to see what mischief his grandson was up to. As he wove all these anxieties into a single rope, he suspected that his audience felt no interest, and that the City Magistrate fondled either maiden behind the cover of the harmonium, but good breeding compelled him to continue; it was nothing to him if they were bored, because he did not know what boredom is, and it was nothing to him if they were licentious, because God has created all races to be different. The accident was over, and his life, equally useful, dis-tinguished, happy, ran on as before and expressed itself in streams of well-chosen words.

When this old geyser left them, Ronny made no comment, but talked lightly about polo; Turton had taught him that it is sounder not to discuss a man at once, and he reserved what he had to say on the Nawab's character until later in the evening. His hand, which he had removed to say good-bye, touched Adela's again; she caressed it definitely, he responded, and their firm and mutual pressure surely meant something. They looked at each other when they reached the bungalow, for Mrs. Moore was inside it. It was for Miss Quested to speak, and she said nervously, "Ronny, I should like to take back what I said on the Maidan." He assented, and they became engaged to be married in consequence.

Neither had foreseen such a consequence. She had meant to revert to her former condition of important and cultivated uncertainty, but it had passed out of her reach at its appropriate hour. Unlike the green bird or the hairy animal, she was labelled now. She felt humiliated again, for she deprecated labels, and she felt too that there should have been another scene between her lover and herself at this point, something dramatic and lengthy. He was pleased instead of distressed, he was surprised, but he had really nothing to say. What indeed is there to say? To be or not to be married, that was the question, and they had decided it in the affirmative.

"Come along and let's tell the mater all this"—opening the perforated zinc door that protected the bungalow from the swarms of winged creatures. The noise woke the mater up. She had been dreaming of the absent children who were so seldom mentioned, Ralph and Stella, and did not at first grasp what was required of her. She too had become used to thoughtful procrastination, and felt alarmed when it came to an end.

When the announcement was over, he made a gracious and honest remark. "Look here, both of you, see India if you like and as you like—I know I made myself rather ridiculous at Fielding's, but . . . it's different now. I wasn't quite sure of myself."

"My duties here are evidently finished, I don't want to see India now; now for my passage back," was Mrs. Moore's thought. She reminded herself of all that a happy marriage means, and of her own happy marriages, one of which had produced Ronny. Adela's parents had also been happily married, and excellent it was to see the incident repeated by the younger generation. On and on! the number of such unions would certainly increase as education spread and ideals grew loftier, and characters firmer. But she was tired by her visit to Government College, her feet ached, Mr. Fielding had walked too fast and far, the young people had annoyed her in the tum-tum, and given her to suppose they were breaking with each other, and though it was all right now she could not speak as enthusiastically of wedlock or of anything as she should have done. Ronny was suited, now she must go home and help the others, if they wished. She was past marrying herself, even unhappily; her function was to help others, her reward to be informed that she was sympathetic. Elderly ladies must not expect more than this.

They dined alone. There was much pleasant and affectionate talk about the future. Later on they spoke of passing events, and Ronny reviewed and recounted the day from his own point of view. It was a different day from the women's because while they had enjoyed themselves or thought, he had worked. Mohurram was approaching, and as usual the Chandrapore Mohammedans were building paper towers of a size too large to pass under the branches of a certain pepul tree.[3] One knew what happened next; the tower stuck, a Mohammedan climbed up the pepul and cut the branch off, the Hindus protested, there was a religious riot, and Heaven knew what, with perhaps the troops sent for. There had been deputations and conciliation committees under the auspices of Turton, and all the normal work of Chandrapore had been hung up. Should the procession take another route, or should the towers be shorter? The Mohammedans offered the former, the Hindus insisted on the latter. The Collector had favoured the Hindus, until he suspected that they had artificially bent the tree nearer the ground. They said it sagged naturally. Measurements, plans, an official visit to the spot. But Ronny had not disliked his day, for it proved that the British were necessary to India; there would certainly have been bloodshed without them. His voice grew complacent again; he was here not to be pleasant but to keep the peace, and now that Adela had promised to be his wife, she was sure to understand.

"What does our old gentleman of the car think?" she asked, and her negligent tone was exactly what he desired.

"Our old gentleman is helpful and sound, as he always is over public affairs. You've seen in him our show Indian."

"Have I really?"

"I'm afraid so. Incredible, aren't they, even the best of them? They're all—they all forget their back collar studs sooner or later. You've had to do with three sets of Indians to-day, the Bhattacharyas, Aziz, and this chap, and it really isn't a coincidence that they've all let you down."

"I like Aziz, Aziz is my real friend," Mrs. Moore interposed.

"When the animal runs into us the Nawab loses his head, deserts his unfortunate chauffeur, intrudes upon Miss Derek . . . no great crimes, no great crimes, but no white man would have done it."

"What animal?"

"Oh, we had a small accident on the Marabar Road. Adela thinks it was a hyena."

"An accident?" she cried.

"Nothing; no one hurt. Our excellent host awoke much rattled from

3. **pepul tree:** the Indian bo tree (see footnote 1 on page 273).

his dreams, appeared to think it was our fault, and chanted exactly, exactly."

Mrs. Moore shivered, "A ghost!" But the idea of a ghost scarcely passed her lips. The young people did not take it up, being occupied with their own outlooks, and deprived of support it perished, or was reabsorbed into the part of the mind that seldom speaks.

"Yes, nothing criminal," Ronny summed up, "but there's the native, and there's one of the reasons why we don't admit him to our clubs, and how a decent girl like Miss Derek can take service under natives puzzles me. . . . But I must get on with my work. Krishna!" Krishna was the peon who should have brought the files from his office. He had not turned up, and a terrific row ensued. Ronny stormed, shouted, howled, and only the experienced observer could tell that he was not angry, did not much want the files, and only made a row because it was the custom. Servants, quite understanding, ran slowly in circles, carrying hurricane lamps. Krishna the earth, Krishna the stars replied, until the Englishman was appeased by their echoes, fined the absent peon eight annas, and sat down to his arrears in the next room.

"Will you play Patience with your future mother-in-law, dear Adela, or does it seem too tame?"

"I should like to—I don't feel a bit excited—I'm just glad it's settled up at last, but I'm not conscious of vast changes. We are all three the same people still."

"That's much the best feeling to have." She dealt out the first row of "demon." [4]

"I suppose so," said the girl thoughtfully.

"I feared at Mr. Fielding's that it might be settled the other way . . . black knave on a red queen. . . ." They chatted gently about the game. Presently Adela said: "You heard me tell Aziz and Godbole I wasn't stopping in their country. I didn't mean it, so why did I say it? I feel I haven't been—frank enough, attentive enough, or something. It's as if I got everything out of proportion. You have been so very good to me, and I meant to be good when I sailed, but somehow I haven't been. . . . Mrs. Moore, if one isn't absolutely honest, what is the use of existing?"

She continued to lay out her cards. The words were obscure, but she understood the uneasiness that produced them. She had experienced it twice herself, during her own engagements—this vague contrition and doubt. All had come right enough afterwards and doubtless would this time—marriage makes most things right enough. "I wouldn't worry," she said. "It's partly the odd surroundings; you and I keep on attending to

4. **demon:** another name for Canfield solitaire.

trifles instead of what's important; we are what the people here call 'new.' "

"You mean that my bothers are mixed up with India?"

"India's——" She stopped.

"What made you call it a ghost?"

"Call what a ghost?"

"The animal thing that hit us. Didn't you say 'Oh, a ghost,' in passing."

"I couldn't have been thinking of what I was saying."

"It was probably a hyena, as a matter of fact."

"Ah, very likely."

And they went on with their Patience. Down in Chandrapore the Nawab Bahadur waited for his car. He sat behind his town house (a small unfurnished building which he rarely entered) in the midst of the little court that always improvises itself round Indians of position. As if turbans were the natural product of darkness a fresh one would occasionally froth to the front, incline itself towards him, and retire. He was preoccupied, his diction was appropriate to a religious subject. Nine years previously, when first he had had a car, he had driven it over a drunken man and killed him, and the man had been waiting for him ever since. The Nawab Bahadur was innocent before God and the Law, he had paid double the compensation necessary; but it was no use, the man continued to wait in an unspeakable form, close to the scene of his death. None of the English people knew of this, nor did the chauffeur; it was a racial secret communicable more by blood than speech. He spoke now in horror of the particular circumstances; he had led others into danger, he had risked the lives of two innocent and honoured guests. He repeated, "If I had been killed, what matter? it must happen sometimes; but they who trusted me——" The company shuddered and invoked the mercy of God. Only Aziz held aloof, because a personal experience restrained him: was it not by despising ghosts that he had come to know Mrs. Moore? "You know, Nureddin," he whispered to the grandson—an effeminate youth whom he seldom met, always liked, and invariably forgot—"you know, my dear fellow, we Moslems simply must get rid of these superstitions, or India will never advance. How long must I hear of the savage pig upon the Marabar Road?" Nureddin looked down. Aziz continued: "Your grandfather belongs to another generation, and I respect and love the old gentleman, as you know. I say nothing against him, only that it is wrong for us, because we are young. I want you to promise me—Nureddin, are you listening?—not to believe in Evil Spirits, and if I die (for my health grows very weak) to bring up my three children to disbelieve in them too." Nureddin smiled, and a suitable answer rose to his pretty lips, but before he could make it the car arrived, and his grandfather took him away.

The game of Patience up in the civil lines went on longer than this. Mrs. Moore continued to murmur "Red ten on a black knave," Miss Quested to assist her, and to intersperse among the intricacies of the play details about the hyena, the engagement, the Maharani of Mudkul, the Bhattacharyas, and the day generally, whose rough desiccated surface acquired as it receded a definite outline, as India itself might, could it be viewed from the moon. Presently the players went to bed, but not before other people had woken up elsewhere, people whose emotions they could not share, and whose existence they ignored. Never tranquil, never perfectly dark, the night wore itself away, distinguished from other nights by two or three blasts of wind, which seemed to fall perpendicularly out of the sky and to bounce back into it, hard and compact, leaving no freshness behind them: the hot weather was approaching.

CHAPTER 9

Aziz fell as he foretold—slightly ill. Three days later he lay abed in his bungalow, pretending to be very ill. It was a touch of fever, which he would have neglected if there was anything important at the hospital. Now and then he groaned and thought he should die, but did not think so for long, and a very little diverted him. It was Sunday, always an equivocal day in the East, and an excuse for slacking. He could hear church bells as he drowsed, both from the civil station and from the missionaries out beyond the slaughter house—different bells and rung with different intent, for one set was calling firmly to the Anglo-India, and the other feebly to mankind. He did not object to the first set; the other he ignored, knowing their inefficiency. Old Mr. Graysford and young Mr. Sorley made converts during a famine, because they distributed food; but when times improved they were naturally left alone again, and though surprised and aggrieved each time this happened, they never learnt wisdom. "No Englishman understands us except Mr. Fielding," he thought; "but how shall I see him again? If he entered this room the disgrace of it would kill me." He called to Hassan to clear up, but Hassan, who was testing his wages by ringing them on the step of the verandah, found it possible not to hear him; heard and didn't hear, just as Aziz had called and hadn't called. "That's India all over . . . how like us . . . there we are . . ." He dozed again, and his thoughts wandered over the varied surface of life.

Gradually they steadied upon a certain spot—the Bottomless Pit according to missionaries, but he had never regarded it as more than a dimple. Yes, he did want to spend an evening with some girls, singing and all that, the vague jollity that would culminate in voluptuousness. Yes, that was what he did want. How could it be managed? If Major Callendar had been an Indian, he would have remembered what young men are, and granted two or three days' leave to Calcutta without asking questions. But the Major assumed either that his subordinates were made of ice, or that they repaired to the Chandrapore bazaars—disgusting ideas both. It was only Mr. Fielding who——

"Hassan!"

The servant came running.

"Look at those flies, brother"; and he pointed to the horrible mass that hung from the ceiling. The nucleus was a wire which had been inserted as a homage to electricity. Electricity had paid no attention, and a colony of eye-flies had come instead and blackened the coils with their bodies.

"Huzoor, those are flies."

"Good, good, they are, excellent, but why have I called you?"

"To drive them elsewhere," said Hassan, after painful thought.

"Driven elsewhere, they always return."

"Huzoor."

"You must make some arrangement against flies; that is why you are my servant," said Aziz gently.

Hassan would call the little boy to borrow the stepladder from Mahmoud Ali's house; he would order the cook to light the Primus stove and heat water; he would personally ascend the steps with a bucket in his arms, and dip the end of the coil into it.

"Good, very good. Now what have you to do?"

"Kill flies."

"Good. Do it."

Hassan withdrew, the plan almost lodged in his head, and began to look for the little boy. Not finding him, his steps grew slower, and he stole back to his post on the verandah, but did not go on testing his rupees, in case his master heard them clink. On twittered the Sunday bells; the East had returned to the East via the suburbs of England, and had become ridiculous during the detour.

Aziz continued to think about beautiful women.

His mind here was hard and direct, though not brutal. He had learnt all he needed concerning his own constitution many years ago, thanks to the social order into which he had been born, and when he came to study medicine he was repelled by the pedantry and fuss with which Europe tabulates the facts of sex. Science seemed to discuss everything from the

wrong end. It didn't interpret his experiences when he found them in a
German manual, because by being there they ceased to be his experiences.
What he had been told by his father or mother or had picked up from
servants—it was information of that sort that he found useful, and handed
on as occasion offered to others.

But he must not bring any disgrace on his children by some silly escapade. Imagine if it got about that he was not respectable! His professional position too must be considered, whatever Major Callendar thought.
Aziz upheld the proprieties, though he did not invest them with any moral
halo, and it was here that he chiefly differed from an Englishman. His
conventions were social. There is no harm in deceiving society as long as
she does not find you out, because it is only when she finds you out that
you have harmed her; she is not like a friend or God, who are injured by
the mere existence of unfaithfulness. Quite clear about this, he meditated
what type of lie he should tell to get away to Calcutta, and had thought
of a man there who could be trusted to send him a wire and a letter that
he could show to Major Callendar, when the noise of wheels was heard in
his compound. Someone had called to enquire. The thought of sympathy
increased his fever, and with a sincere groan he wrapped himself in his
quilt.

"Aziz, my dear fellow, we are greatly concerned," said Hamidullah's
voice. One, two, three, four bumps, as people sat down upon his bed.

"When a doctor falls ill it is a serious matter," said the voice of Mr.
Syed Mohammed, the assistant engineer.

"When an engineer falls ill, it is equally important," said the voice of
Mr. Haq, a police inspector.

"Oh yes, we are all jolly important, our salaries prove it."

"Dr. Aziz took tea with our Principal last Thursday afternoon," piped
Rafi, the engineer's nephew. "Professor Godbole, who also attended, has
sickened too, which seems rather a curious thing, sir, does it not?"

Flames of suspicion leapt up in the breast of each man. "Humbug!" exclaimed Hamidullah, in authoritative tones, quenching them.

"Humbug, most certainly," echoed the others, ashamed of themselves.
The wicked schoolboy, having failed to start a scandal, lost confidence
and stood up with his back to the wall.

"Is Professor Godbole ill?" enquired Aziz, penetrated by the news. "I
am sincerely sorry." Intelligent and compassionate, his face peeped out of
the bright crimson folds of the quilt. "How do you do, Mr. Syed Mohammed, Mr. Haq? How very kind of you to enquire after my health!
How do you do, Hamidullah? But you bring me bad news. What is wrong
with him, the excellent fellow?"

"Why don't you answer, Rafi? You're the great authority," said his uncle.

"Yes, Rafi's the great man," said Hamidullah, rubbing it in. "Rafi is the Sherlock Holmes of Chandrapore. Speak up, Rafi."

Less than the dust, the schoolboy murmured the word "Diarrhœa," but took courage as soon as it had been uttered, for it improved his position. Flames of suspicion shot up again in the breasts of his elders, though in a different direction. Could what was called diarrhœa really be an early case of cholera?

"If this is so, this is a very serious thing: this is scarcely the end of March. Why have I not been informed?" cried Aziz.

"Dr. Panna Lal attended him, sir."

"Oh yes, both Hindus; there we have it; they hang together like flies and keep everything dark. Rafi, come here. Sit down. Tell me all the details. Is there vomiting also?"

"Oh yes indeed, sir, and the serious pains."

"That settles it. In twenty-four hours he will be dead."

Everybody looked and felt shocked, but Professor Godbole had diminished his appeal by linking himself with a co-religionist. He moved them less than when he had appeared as a suffering individual. Before long they began to condemn him as a source of infection. "All illness proceeds from Hindus," Mr. Haq said. Mr. Syed Mohammed had visited religious fairs, at Allahabad and at Ujjain, and described them with biting scorn. At Allahabad there was flowing water, which carried impurities away, but at Ujjain the little river Sipra was banked up, and thousands of bathers deposited their germs in the pool. He spoke with disgust of the hot sun, the cowdung and marigold flowers, and the encampment of saddhus,[1] some of whom strode stark naked through the streets. Asked what was the name of the chief idol at Ujjain, he replied that he did not know, he had disdained to enquire, he really could not waste his time over such trivialities. His outburst took some time, and in his excitement he fell into Punjabi (he came from that side) and was unintelligible.

Aziz liked to hear his religion praised. It soothed the surface of his mind, and allowed beautiful images to form beneath. When the engineer's noisy tirade was finished, he said, "That is exactly my own view." He held up his hand, palm outward, his eyes began to glow, his heart to fill with tenderness. Issuing still farther from his quilt, he recited a poem by Ghalib.[2] It had no connection with anything that had gone before, but

1. saddhus: Hindu ascetics.
2. Ghalib: an eighteenth-century Turkish poet.

it came from his heart and spoke to theirs. They were overwhelmed by its pathos; pathos, they agreed, is the highest quality in art; a poem should touch the hearer with a sense of his own weakness, and should institute some comparison between mankind and flowers. The squalid bedroom grew quiet; the silly intrigues, the gossip, the shallow discontent were stilled, while words accepted as immortal filled the indifferent air. Not as a call to battle, but as a calm assurance came the feeling that India was one; Moslem; always had been; an assurance that lasted until they looked out of the door. Whatever Ghalib had felt, he had anyhow lived in India, and this consolidated it for them: he had gone with his own tulips and roses, but tulips and roses do not go. And the sister kingdoms of the north —Arabia, Persia, Ferghana, Turkestan—stretched out their hands as he sang, sadly, because all beauty is sad, and greeted ridiculous Chandrapore, where every street and house was divided against itself, and told her that she was a continent and a unity.

Of the company, only Hamidullah had any comprehension of poetry. The minds of the others were inferior and rough. Yet they listened with pleasure, because literature had not been divorced from their civilization. The police inspector, for instance, did not feel that Aziz had degraded himself by reciting, nor break into the cheery guffaw with which an Englishman averts the infection of beauty. He just sat with his mind empty, and when his thoughts, which were mainly ignoble, flowed back into it they had a pleasant freshness. The poem had done no "good" to anyone, but it was a passing reminder, a breath from the divine lips of beauty, a nightingale between two worlds of dust. Less explicit, than the call to Krishna, it voiced our loneliness nevertheless, our isolation, our need for the Friend who never comes yet is not entirely disproved. Aziz it left thinking about women again, but in a different way: less definite, more intense. Sometimes poetry had this effect on him, sometimes it only increased his local desires, and he never knew beforehand which effect would ensue: he could discover no rule for this or for anything else in life.

Hamidullah had called in on his way to a worrying committee of notables, nationalist in tendency, where Hindus, Moslems, two Sikhs, two Parsis, a Jain, and a Native Christian tried to like one another more than came natural to them. As long as someone abused the English, all went well, but nothing constructive had been achieved, and if the English were to leave India, the committee would vanish also. He was glad that Aziz, whom he loved and whose family was connected with his own, took no interest in politics, which ruin the character and career, yet nothing can be achieved without them. He thought of Cambridge—sadly, as of another poem that had ended. How happy he had been there, twenty years ago!

Politics had not mattered in Mr. and Mrs. Bannister's rectory. There, games, work, and pleasant society had interwoven, and appeared to be sufficient substructure for a national life. Here all was wire-pulling and fear. Messrs. Syed Mohammed and Haq—he couldn't even trust them, although they had come in his carriage, and the schoolboy was a scorpion. Bending down, he said, "Aziz, Aziz, my dear boy, we must be going, we are already late. Get well quickly, for I do not know what our little circle would do without you."

"I shall not forget those affectionate words," replied Aziz.

"Add mine to them," said the engineer.

"Thank you, Mr. Syed Mohammed, I will."

"And mine." "And, sir, accept mine," cried the others, stirred each according to his capacity towards goodwill. Little ineffectual unquenchable flames! The company continued to sit on the bed and to chew sugar-cane, which Hassan had run for into the bazaar, and Aziz drank a cup of spiced milk. Presently there was the sound of another carriage. Dr. Panna Lal had arrived, driven by horrid Mr. Ram Chand. The atmosphere of a sick-room was at once re-established, and the invalid retired under his quilt.

"Gentlemen, you will excuse, I have come to enquire by Major Callendar's orders," said the Hindu, nervous of the den of fanatics into which his curiosity had called him.

"Here he lies," said Hamidullah, indicating the prostrate form.

"Dr. Aziz, Dr. Aziz, I come to enquire."

Aziz presented an expressionless face to the thermometer.

"Your hand also, please." He took it, gazed at the flies on the ceiling, and finally announced, "Some temperature."

"I think not much," said Ram Chand, desirous of fomenting trouble.

"Some; he should remain in bed," repeated Dr. Panna Lal, and shook the thermometer down, so that its altitude remained for ever unknown. He loathed his young colleague since the disasters with Dapple, and he would have liked to do him a bad turn and report to Major Callendar that he was shamming. But he might want a day in bed himself soon,—besides, though Major Callendar always believed the worst of natives, he never believed them when they carried tales about one another. Sympathy seemed the safer course. "How is stomach?" he enquired, "how head?" And catching sight of the empty cup, he recommended a milk diet.

"This is a great relief to us, it is very good of you to call, Doctor Sahib," said Hamidullah, buttering him up a bit.

"It is only my duty."

"We know how busy you are."

"Yes, that is true."

"And how much illness there is in the city."

The doctor suspected a trap in this remark; if he admitted that there was or was not illness, either statement might be used against him. "There is always illness," he replied, "and I am always busy—it is a doctor's nature."

"He has not a minute, he is due double sharp at Government College now," said Ram Chand.

"You attend Professor Godbole there perhaps?"

The doctor looked professional and was silent.

"We hope his diarrhœa is ceasing."

"He progresses, but not from diarrhœa."

"We are in some anxiety over him—he and Dr. Aziz are great friends. If you could tell us the name of his complaint we should be grateful to you."

After a cautious pause he said, "Hæmorrhoids."

"And so much, my dear Rafi, for your cholera," hooted Aziz, unable to restrain himself.

"Cholera, cholera, what next, what now?" cried the doctor, greatly fussed. "Who spreads such untrue reports about my patients?"

Hamidullah pointed to the culprit.

"I hear cholera, I hear bubonic plague, I hear every species of lie. Where will it end, I ask myself sometimes. This city is full of misstatements, and the originators of them ought to be discovered and punished authoritatively."

"Rafi, do you hear that? Now why do you stuff us up with all this humbug?"

The schoolboy murmured that another boy had told him, also that the bad English grammar the Government obliged them to use often gave the wrong meaning for words, and so led scholars into mistakes.

"That is no reason you should bring a charge against a doctor," said Ram Chand.

"Exactly, exactly," agreed Hamidullah, anxious to avoid an unpleasantness. Quarrels spread so quickly and so far, and Messrs. Syed Mohammed and Haq looked cross, and ready to fly out. "You must apologize properly, Rafi, I can see your uncle wishes it," he said. "You have not yet said that you are sorry for the trouble you have caused this gentleman by your carelessness."

"It is only a boy," said Dr. Panna Lal, appeased.

"Even boys must learn," said Ram Chand.

"Your own son failing to pass the lowest standard, I think," said Syed Mohammed suddenly.

"Oh, indeed? Oh yes, perhaps. He has not the advantage of a relative in the Prosperity Printing Press."

"Nor you the advantage of conducting their cases in the Courts any longer."

Their voices rose. They attacked one another with obscure allusions and had a silly quarrel. Hamidullah and the doctor tried to make peace between them. In the midst of the din someone said, "I say! Is he ill or isn't he ill?" Mr. Fielding had entered unobserved. All rose to their feet, and Hassan, to do an Englishman honour, struck up with a sugar-cane at the coil of flies.

Aziz said, "Sit down," coldly. What a room! What a meeting! Squalor and ugly talk, the floor strewn with fragments of cane and nuts, and spotted with ink, the pictures crooked upon the dirty walls, no punkah! He hadn't meant to live like this or among these third-rate people. And in his confusion he thought only of the insignificant Rafi, whom he had laughed at, and allowed to be teased. The boy must be sent away happy, or hospitality would have failed, along the whole line.

"It is good of Mr. Fielding to condescend to visit our friend," said the police inspector. "We are touched by this great kindness."

"Don't talk to him like that, he doesn't want it, and he doesn't want three chairs; he's not three Englishmen," he flashed. "Rafi, come here. Sit down again. I'm delighted you could come with Mr. Hamidullah, my dear boy; it will help me to recover, seeing you."

"Forgive my mistakes," said Rafi, to consolidate himself.

"Well, are you ill, Aziz, or aren't you?" Fielding repeated.

"No doubt Major Callendar has told you that I am shamming."

"Well, are you?" The company laughed, friendly and pleased. "An Englishman at his best," they thought; "so genial."

"Enquire from Dr. Panna Lal."

"You're sure I don't tire you by stopping?"

"Why, no! There are six people present in my small room already. Please remain seated, if you will excuse the informality." He turned away and continued to address Rafi, who was terrified at the arrival of his Principal, remembered that he had tried to spread slander about him, and yearned to get away.

"He is ill and he is not ill," said Hamidullah, offering a cigarette. "And I suppose that most of us are in that same case."

Fielding agreed; he and the pleasant sensitive barrister got on well. They were fairly intimate and beginning to trust each other.

"The whole world looks to be dying, still it doesn't die, so we must assume the existence of a beneficent Providence."

"Oh, that is true, how true!" said the policeman, thinking religion had been praised.

"Does Mr. Fielding think it's true?"

"Think which true? The world isn't dying. I'm certain of that!"

"No, no—the existence of Providence."

"Well, I don't believe in Providence."

"But how then can you believe in God?" asked Syed Mohammed.

"I don't believe in God."

A tiny movement as of "I told you so!" passed round the company, and Aziz looked up for an instant, scandalized. "Is it correct that most are atheists in England now?" Hamidullah enquired.

"The educated thoughtful people? I should say so, though they don't like the name. The truth is that the West doesn't bother much over belief and disbelief in these days. Fifty years ago, or even when you and I were young, much more fuss was made."

"And does not morality also decline?"

"It depends what you call—yes, yes, I suppose morality does decline."

"Excuse the question, but if this is the case, how is England justified in holding India?"

There they were! Politics again. "It's a question I can't get my mind on to," he replied. "I'm out here personally because I needed a job. I cannot tell you why England is here or whether she ought to be here. It's beyond me."

"Well-qualified Indians also need jobs in the educational."

"I guess they do; I got in first," said Fielding, smiling.

"Then excuse me again—is it fair an Englishman should occupy one when Indians are available? Of course I mean nothing personally. Personally we are delighted you should be here, and we benefit greatly by this frank talk."

There is only one answer to a conversation of this type: "England holds India for her good." Yet Fielding was disinclined to give it. The zeal for honesty had eaten him up. He said, "I'm delighted to be here too—that's my answer, there's my only excuse. I can't tell you anything about fairness. It mayn't have been fair I should have been born. I take up some other fellow's air, don't I, whenever I breathe? Still, I'm glad it's happened, and I'm glad I'm out here. However big a badmash [3] one is—if one's happy in consequence, that is some justification."

The Indians were bewildered. The line of thought was not alien to them, but the words were too definite and bleak. Unless a sentence paid a few compliments to Justice and Morality in passing, its grammar wounded

3. **badmash:** rascal.

their ears and paralysed their minds. What they said and what they felt
were (except in the case of affection) seldom the same. They had numerous mental conventions and when these were flouted they found it
very difficult to function. Hamidullah bore up best. "And those Englishmen who are not delighted to be in India—have they no excuse?" he asked.

"None. Chuck 'em out."

"It may be difficult to separate them from the rest," he laughed.

"Worse than difficult, wrong," said Mr. Ram Chand. "No Indian gentleman approves chucking out as a proper thing. Here we differ from
those other nations. We are so spiritual."

"Oh, that is true, how true!" said the police inspector.

"Is it true, Mr. Haq? I don't consider us spiritual. We can't co-ordinate,
it only comes to that. We can't keep engagements, we can't catch trains.
What more than this is the so-called spirituality of India? You and I
ought to be at the Committee of Notables, we're not; our friend Dr. Lal
ought to be with his patients, he isn't. So we go on, and so we shall continue to go, I think, until the end of time."

"It is not the end of time, it is scarcely ten-thirty, ha, ha!" cried Dr.
Panna Lal, who was again in confident mood. "Gentlemen, if I may be allowed to say a few words, what an interesting talk, also thankfulness and
gratitude to Mr. Fielding in the first place teaches our sons and gives them
all the great benefits of his experience and judgment——"

"Dr. Lal!"

"Dr. Aziz?"

"You sit on my leg."

"I beg pardon, but some might say your leg kicks."

"Come along, we tire the invalid in either case," said Fielding, and they
filed out—four Mohammedans, two Hindus and the Englishman. They
stood on the verandah while their conveyances were summoned out of
various patches of shade.

"Aziz has a high opinion of you, he only did not speak because of his
illness."

"I quite understand," said Fielding, who was rather disappointed with
his call. The Club comment, "making himself cheap as usual," passed
through his mind. He couldn't even get his horse brought up. He had
liked Aziz so much at their first meeting, and had hoped for developments.

CHAPTER 10

The heat had leapt forward in the last hour, the street was deserted as if
a catastrophe had cleaned off humanity during the inconclusive talk. Op-

posite Aziz' bungalow stood a large unfinished house belonging to two brothers, astrologers, and a squirrel hung head-downwards on it, pressing its belly against burning scaffolding and twitching a mangy tail. It seemed the only occupant of the house, and the squeals it gave were in tune with the infinite, no doubt, but not attractive except to other squirrels. More noises came from a dusty tree, where brown birds creaked and floundered about looking for insects; another bird, the invisible coppersmith, had started his "ponk ponk." It matters so little to the majority of living beings what the minority, that calls itself human, desires or decides. Most of the inhabitants of India do not mind how India is governed. Nor are the lower animals of England concerned about England, but in the tropics the indifference is more prominent, the inarticulate world is closer at hand and readier to resume control as soon as men are tired. When the seven gentlemen who had held such various opinions inside the bungalow came out of it, they were aware of a common burden, a vague threat which they called "the bad weather coming." They felt that they could not do their work, or would not be paid enough for doing it. The space between them and their carriage, instead of being empty, was clogged with a medium that pressed against their flesh, the carriage cushions scalded their trousers, their eyes pricked, domes of hot water accumulated under their head-gear and poured down their cheeks. Salaaming feebly, they dispersed for the interior of other bungalows, to recover their self-esteem and the qualities that distinguished them from each other.

All over the city and over much of India the same retreat on the part of humanity was beginning, into cellars, up hills, under trees. April, herald of horrors, is at hand. The sun was returning to his kingdom with power but without beauty—that was the sinister feature. If only there had been beauty! His cruelty would have been tolerable then. Through excess of light, he failed to triumph, he also; in his yellowy-white overflow not only matter, but brightness itself lay drowned. He was not the unattainable friend, either of men or birds or other suns, he was not the eternal promise, the never-withdrawn suggestion that haunts our consciousness; he was merely a creature, like the rest, and so debarred from glory.

CHAPTER 11

Although the Indians had driven off, and Fielding could see his horse standing in a small shed in the corner of the compound, no one troubled to bring it to him. He started to get it himself, but was stopped by a call from the house. Aziz was sitting up in bed, looking dishevelled and sad. "Here's your home," he said sardonically. "Here's the celebrated hospi-

tality of the East. Look at the flies. Look at the chunam [1] coming off the
walls. Isn't it jolly? Now I suppose you want to be off, having seen an
Oriental interior."

"Anyhow, you want to rest."

"I can rest the whole day, thanks to worthy Dr. Lal. Major Callendar's
spy, I suppose you know, but this time it didn't work. I am allowed to
have a slight temperature."

"Callendar doesn't trust anyone, English or Indian: that's his character,
and I wish you weren't under him; but you are, and that's that."

"Before you go, for you are evidently in a great hurry, will you please
unlock that drawer? Do you see a piece of brown paper at the top?"

"Yes."

"Open it."

"Who is this?"

"She was my wife. You are the first Englishman she has ever come before. Now put her photograph away."

He was astonished, as a traveller who suddenly sees, between the stones
of the desert, flowers. The flowers have been there all the time, but suddenly he sees them. He tried to look at the photograph, but in itself it was
just a woman in a sari, facing the world. He muttered, "Really, I don't
know why you pay me this great compliment, Aziz, but I do appreciate
it."

"Oh, it's nothing, she was not a highly educated woman or even beautiful, but put it away. You would have seen her, so why should you not see
her photograph?"

"You would have allowed me to see her?"

"Why not? I believe in the purdah, but I should have told her you were
my brother, and she would have seen you. Hamidullah saw her, and several others."

"Did she think they were your brothers?"

"Of course not, but the word exists and is convenient. All men are my
brothers, and as soon as one behaves as such he may see my wife."

"And when the whole world behaves as such, there will be no more
purdah?"

"It is because you can say and feel such a remark as that, that I show
you the photograph," said Aziz gravely. "It is beyond the power of most
men. It is because you behave well while I behave badly that I show it
you. I never expected you to come back just now when I called you. I
thought, 'He has certainly done with me; I have insulted him.' Mr. Fielding, no one can ever realize how much kindness we Indians need, we do

1. chunam: Indian cement or plaster.

not even realize it ourselves. But we know when it has been given. We do not forget, though we may seem to. Kindness, more kindness, and even after that more kindness. I assure you it is the only hope." His voice seemed to arise from a dream. Altering it, yet still deep below his normal surface, he said, "We can't build up India except on what we feel. What is the use of all these reforms, and Conciliation Committees for Mohurram, and shall we cut the tazia [2] short or shall we carry it another route, and Councils of Notables and official parties where the English sneer at our skins?"

"It's beginning at the wrong end, isn't it? I know, but institutions and the governments don't." He looked again at the photograph. The lady faced the world at her husband's wish and her own, but how bewildering she found it, the echoing contradictory world!

"Put her away, she is of no importance, she is dead," said Aziz gently. "I showed her to you because I have nothing else to show. You may look round the whole of my bungalow now, and empty everything. I have no other secrets, my three children live away with their grandmamma, and that is all."

Fielding sat down by the bed, flattered at the trust reposed in him, yet rather sad. He felt old. He wished that he too could be carried away on waves of emotion. The next time they met, Aziz might be cautious and standoffish. He realized this, and it made him sad that he should realize it. Kindness, kindness, and more kindness—yes, that he might supply, but was that really all that the queer nation needed? Did it not also demand an occasional intoxication of the blood? What had he done to deserve this outburst of confidence, and what hostage could he give in exchange? He looked back at his own life. What a poor crop of secrets it had produced! There were things in it that he had shown to no one, but they were so uninteresting, it wasn't worth while lifting a purdah on their account. He'd been in love, engaged to be married, lady broke it off, memories of her and thoughts about her had kept him from other women for a time; then indulgence, followed by repentance and equilibrium. Meagre really except the equilibrium, and Aziz didn't want to have that confided to him —he would have called it "everything ranged coldly on shelves."

"I shall not really be intimate with this fellow," Fielding thought, and then "nor with anyone." That was the corollary. And he had to confess that he really didn't mind, that he was content to help people, and like them as long as they didn't object, and if they objected pass on serenely. Experience can do much, and all that he had learnt in England and Eu-

---

2. **tazia:** a crude representation of the shrine of Husain carried in procession during the Mohurram.

rope was an assistance to him, and helped him towards clarity, but clarity prevented him from experiencing something else.

"How did you like the two ladies you met last Thursday?" he asked.

Aziz shook his head distastefully. The question reminded him of his rash remark about the Marabar Caves.

"How do you like Englishwomen generally?"

"Hamidullah liked them in England. Here we never look at them. Oh no, much too careful. Let's talk of something else."

"Hamidullah's right: they are much nicer in England. There's something that doesn't suit them out here."

Aziz after another silence said, "Why are you not married?"

Fielding was pleased that he had asked. "Because I have more or less come through without it," he replied. "I was thinking of telling you a little about myself some day if I can make it interesting enough. The lady I liked wouldn't marry me—that is the main point, but that's fifteen years ago and now means nothing."

"But you haven't children."

"None."

"Excuse the following question: have you any illegitimate children?"

"No. I'd willingly tell you if I had."

"Then your name will entirely die out."

"It must."

"Well." He shook his head. "This indifference is what the Oriental will never understand."

"I don't care for children."

"Caring has nothing to do with it," he said impatiently.

"I don't feel their absence, I don't want them weeping around my deathbed and being polite about me afterwards, which I believe is the general notion. I'd far rather leave a thought behind me than a child. Other people can have children. No obligation, with England getting so chock-a-block and overrunning India for jobs."

"Why don't you marry Miss Quested?"

"Good God! why, the girl's a prig."

"Prig, prig? Kindly explain. Isn't that a bad word?"

"Oh, I don't know her, but she struck me as one of the more pathetic products of Western education. She depresses me."

"But prig, Mr. Fielding? How's that?"

"She goes on and on as if she's at a lecture—trying ever so hard to understand India and life, and occasionally taking a note."

"I thought her so nice and sincere."

"So she probably is," said Fielding, ashamed of his roughness: any suggestion that he should marry always does produce overstatements on the part of the bachelor, and a mental breeze. "But I can't marry her if I wanted to, for she has just become engaged to the City Magistrate."

"Has she indeed? I am so glad!" he exclaimed with relief, for this exempted him from the Marabar expedition: he would scarcely be expected to entertain regular Anglo-Indians.

"It's the old mother's doing. She was afraid her dear boy would choose for himself, so she brought out the girl on purpose, and flung them together until it happened."

"Mrs. Moore did not mention that to me among her plans."

"I may have got it wrong—I'm out of club gossip. But anyhow they're engaged to be married."

"Yes, you're out of it, my poor chap," he smiled. "No Miss Quested for Mr. Fielding. However, she was not beautiful. She has practically no breasts, if you come to think of it."

He smiled too, but found a touch of bad taste in the reference to a lady's breasts.

"For the City Magistrate they shall be sufficient perhaps, and he for her. For you I shall arrange a lady with breasts like mangoes. . . ."

"No, you won't."

"I will not really, and besides your position makes it dangerous for you." His mind had slipped from matrimony to Calcutta. His face grew grave. Fancy if he had persuaded the Principal to accompany him there, and then got him into trouble! And abruptly he took up a new attitude towards his friend, the attitude of the protector who knows the dangers of India and is admonitory. "You can't be too careful in every way, Mr. Fielding; whatever you say or do in this damned country there is always some envious fellow on the lookout. You may be surprised to know that there were at least three spies sitting here when you came to enquire. I was really a good deal upset that you talked in that fashion about God. They will certainly report it."

"To whom?"

"That's all very well, but you spoke against morality also, and you said you had come to take other people's jobs. All that was very unwise. This is an awful place for scandal. Why, actually one of your own pupils was listening."

"Thanks for telling me that; yes, I must try and be more careful. If I'm interested, I'm apt to forget myself. Still, it doesn't do real harm."

"But speaking out may get you into trouble."

"It's often done so in the past."

"There, listen to that! But the end of it might be that you lost your job."

"If I do, I do. I shall survive it. I travel light."

"Travel light! You are a most extraordinary race," said Aziz, turning away as if he were going to sleep, and immediately turning back again. "Is it your climate, or what?"

"Plenty of Indians travel light too—saddhus and such. It's one of the things I admire about your country. Any man can travel light until he has a wife or children. That's part of my case against marriage. I'm a holy man minus the holiness. Hand that on to your three spies, and tell them to put it in their pipes."

Aziz was charmed and interested, and turned the new idea over in his mind. So this was why Mr. Fielding and a few others were so fearless! They had nothing to lose. But he himself was rooted in society and Islam. He belonged to a tradition which bound him, and he had brought children into the world, the society of the future. Though he lived so vaguely in this flimsy bungalow, nevertheless he was placed, placed.

"I can't be sacked from my job, because my job's Education. I believe in teaching people to be individuals, and to understand other individuals. It's the only thing I do believe in. At Government College, I mix it up with trigonometry, and so on. When I'm a saddhu, I shall mix it up with something else."

He concluded his manifesto, and both were silent. The eye-flies[3] became worse than ever and danced close up to their pupils, or crawled into their ears. Fielding hit about wildly. The exercise made him hot, and he got up to go.

"You might tell your servant to bring my horse. He doesn't seem to appreciate my Urdu."

"I know. I gave him orders not to. Such are the tricks we play on unfortunate Englishmen. Poor Mr. Fielding! But I will release you now. Oh dear! With the exception of yourself and Hamidullah, I have no one to talk to in this place. You like Hamidullah, don't you?"

"Very much."

"Do you promise to come at once to us when you are in trouble?"

"I never can be in trouble."

"There goes a queer chap, I trust he won't come to grief," thought Aziz, left alone. His period of admiration was over, and he reacted towards patronage. It was difficult for him to remain in awe of anyone who played with all his cards on the table. Fielding, he discovered on closer acquaintance, was truly warm-hearted and unconventional, but not what he called wise. That frankness of speech in the presence of Ram Chand Rafi and Co. was dangerous and inelegant. It served no useful end.

But they were friends, brothers. That part was settled, their compact

3. eye-flies: gnats that attack one's eyes.

had been subscribed by the photograph, they trusted one another, affection had triumphed for once in a way. He dropped off to sleep amid the happier memories of the last two hours—poetry of Ghalib, female grace, good old Hamidullah, good Fielding, his honoured wife and dear boys. He passed into a region where these joys had no enemies but bloomed harmoniously in an eternal garden, or ran down watershoots of ribbed marble, or rose into domes whereunder were inscribed, black against white, the ninety-nine attributes of God.

PART II

CAVES

CHAPTER 12

THE GANGES, though flowing from the foot of Vishnu and through Siva's hair, is not an ancient stream. Geology, looking further than religion, knows of a time when neither the river nor the Himalayas that nourished it existed, and an ocean flowed over the holy places of Hindustan. The mountains rose, their debris silted up the ocean, the gods took their seats on them and contrived the river, and the India we call immemorial came into being. But India is really far older. In the days of the prehistoric ocean the southern part of the peninsula already existed, and the high places of Dravidia have been land since land began, and have seen on the one side the sinking of a continent that joined them to Africa, and on the other the upheaval of the Himalayas from a sea. They are older than anything in the world. No water has ever covered them, and the sun who has watched them for countless æons may still discern in their outlines forms that were his before our globe was torn from his bosom. If flesh of the sun's flesh is to be touched anywhere, it is here, among the incredible antiquity of these hills.

Yet even they are altering. As Himalayan India rose, this India, the primal, has been depressed, and is slowly re-entering the curve of the earth. It may be that in æons to come an ocean will flow here too, and cover the sun-born rocks with slime. Meanwhile the plain of the Ganges encroaches on them with something of the sea's action. They are sinking beneath the newer lands. Their main mass is untouched, but at the edge their outposts have been cut off and stand knee-deep, throat-deep, in the advancing soil. There is something unspeakable in these outposts. They are like nothing else in the world, and a glimpse of them makes the breath catch. They rise abruptly, insanely, without the proportion that is kept by the wildest hills elsewhere, they bear no relation to anything dreamt or seen. To call them "uncanny" suggests ghosts, and they are older than all spirit. Hinduism has scratched and plastered a few rocks, but the shrines are unfrequented, as if pilgrims, who generally seek the extraordinary, had here found too much of it. Some saddhus did once settle in a cave, but they were smoked out, and even Buddha, who must have passed this way down to the Bo Tree of Gya,[1] shunned a renunciation more complete than his own, and has left no legend of struggle or victory in the Marabar.

1. Buddha acquired his name, which means the "Enlightened," under the famous Bo Tree in the village of Gya in northeast India.

273

The caves are readily described. A tunnel eight feet long, five feet high, three feet wide, leads to a circular chamber about twenty feet in diameter. This arrangement occurs again and again throughout the group of hills, and this is all, this is a Marabar Cave. Having seen one such cave, having seen two, having seen three, four, fourteen, twenty-four, the visitor returns to Chandrapore uncertain whether he has had an interesting experience or a dull one or any experience at all. He finds it difficult to discuss the caves, or to keep them apart in his mind, for the pattern never varies, and no carving, not even a bees'-nest or a bat distinguishes one from another. Nothing, nothing attaches to them, and their reputation—for they have one—does not depend upon human speech. It is as if the surrounding plain or the passing birds have taken upon themselves to exclaim "extraordinary," and the word has taken root in the air, and been inhaled by mankind.

They are dark caves. Even when they open towards the sun, very little light penetrates down the entrance tunnel into the circular chamber. There is little to see, and no eye to see it, until the visitor arrives for his five minutes, and strikes a match. Immediately another flame rises in the depths of the rock and moves towards the surface like an imprisoned spirit: the walls of the circular chamber have been most marvellously polished. The two flames approach and strive to unite, but cannot, because one of them breathes air, the other stone. A mirror inlaid with lovely colours divides the lovers, delicate stars of pink and grey interpose, exquisite nebulæ, shadings fainter than the tail of a comet or the midday moon, all the evanescent life of the granite, only here visible. Fists and fingers thrust above the advancing soil—here at last is their skin, finer than any covering acquired by the animals, smoother than windless water, more voluptuous than love. The radiance increases, the flames touch one another, kiss, expire. The cave is dark again, like all the caves.

Only the wall of the circular chamber has been polished thus. The sides of the tunnel are left rough, they impinge as an afterthought upon the internal perfection. An entrance was necessary, so mankind made one. But elsewhere, deeper in the granite, are there certain chambers that have no entrances? Chambers never unsealed since the arrival of the gods. Local report declares that these exceed in number those that can be visited, as the dead exceed the living—four hundred of them, four thousand or million. Nothing is inside them, they were sealed up before the creation of pestilence or treasure; if mankind grew curious and excavated, nothing, nothing would be added to the sum of good or evil. One of them is rumoured within the boulder that swings on the summit of the highest of the hills; a bubble-shaped cave that has neither ceiling nor floor, and mirrors its own darkness in every direction infinitely. If the boulder falls and smashes,

the cave will smash too—empty as an Easter egg. The boulder because of
its hollowness sways in the wind, and even moves when a crow perches
upon it: hence its name and the name of its stupendous pedestal: the
Kawa Dol.[2]

CHAPTER 13

These hills look romantic in certain lights and at suitable distances, and
seen of an evening from the upper verandah of the club they caused Miss
Quested to say conversationally to Miss Derek that she should like to have
gone, that Dr. Aziz at Mr. Fielding's had said he would arrange something, and that Indians seem rather forgetful. She was overheard by the
servant who offered them vermouths. This servant understood English.
And he was not exactly a spy, but he kept his ears open, and Mahmoud
Ali did not exactly bribe him, but did encourage him to come and squat
with his own servants, and would happen to stroll their way when he was
there. As the story travelled, it accreted emotion and Aziz learnt with horror that the ladies were deeply offended with him, and had expected an
invitation daily. He thought his facile remark had been forgotten. Endowed with two memories, a temporary and a permanent, he had hitherto
relegated the caves to the former. Now he transferred them once for all,
and pushed the matter through. They were to be a stupendous replica of
the tea party. He began by securing Fielding and old Godbole, and then
commissioned Fielding to approach Mrs. Moore and Miss Quested when
they were alone—by this device Ronny, their official protector, could be
circumvented. Fielding didn't like the job much; he was busy, caves bored
him, he foresaw friction and expense, but he would not refuse the first
favour his friend had asked from him, and did as required. The ladies
accepted. It was a little inconvenient in the present press of their engagements, still, they hoped to manage it after consulting Mr. Heaslop. Consulted, Ronny raised no objection, provided Fielding undertook full responsibility for their comfort. He was not enthusiastic about the picnic,
but, then, no more were the ladies—no one was enthusiastic, yet it took
place.

Aziz was terribly worried. It was not a long expedition—a train left
Chandrapore just before dawn, another would bring them back for tiffin
—but he was only a little official still, and feared to acquit himself dishon-
ourably. He had to ask Major Callendar for half a day's leave, and be refused because of his recent malingering; despair; renewed approach of
Major Callendar through Fielding, and contemptuous snarling permission.
He had to borrow cutlery from Mahmoud Ali without inviting him. Then

2. **Kawa Dol**: literally, the stone (*dol*) on which the crow (*kawa*) perches; so,
"Crow Peak."

there was the question of alcohol; Mr. Fielding, and perhaps the ladies, were drinkers, so must he provide whisky-sodas and ports? There was the problem of transport from the wayside station of Marabar to the caves. There was the problem of Professor Godbole and his food, and of Professor Godbole and other people's food—two problems, not one problem. The Professor was not a very strict Hindu—he would take tea, fruit, soda-water and sweets, whoever cooked them, and vegetables and rice if cooked by a Brahman; but not meat, not cakes lest they contained eggs, and he would not allow anyone else to eat beef: a slice of beef upon a distant plate would wreck his happiness. Other people might eat mutton, they might eat ham. But over ham Aziz' own religion raised its voice: he did not fancy other people eating ham. Trouble after trouble encountered him, because he had challenged the spirit of the Indian earth, which tries to keep men in compartments.

At last the moment arrived.

His friends thought him most unwise to mix himself up with English ladies, and warned him to take every precaution against unpunctuality. Consequently he spent the previous night at the station. The servants were huddled on the platform, enjoined not to stray. He himself walked up and down with old Mohammed Latif, who was to act as major-domo. He felt insecure and also unreal. A car drove up, and he hoped Fielding would get out of it, to lend him solidity. But it contained Mrs. Moore, Miss Quested, and their Goanese servant. He rushed to meet them, suddenly happy. "But you've come, after all. Oh, how very very kind of you!" he cried. "This is the happiest moment in all my life."

The ladies were civil. It was not the happiest moment in their lives, still, they looked forward to enjoying themselves as soon as the bother of the early start was over. They had not seen him since the expedition was arranged, and they thanked him adequately.

"You don't require tickets—please stop your servant. There are no tickets on the Marabar branch line; it is its peculiarity. You come to the carriage and rest till Mr. Fielding joins us. Did you know you are to travel purdah? Will you like that?"

They replied that they should like it. The train had come in, and a crowd of dependents were swarming over the seats of the carriage like monkeys. Aziz had borrowed servants from his friends, as well as bringing his own three, and quarrels over precedence were resulting. The ladies' servant stood apart, with a sneering expression on his face. They had hired him while they were still globe-trotters, at Bombay. In a hotel or among smart people he was excellent, but as soon as they consorted with anyone whom he thought second-rate he left them to their disgrace.

The night was still dark, but had acquired the temporary look that indicates its end. Perched on the roof of a shed, the station-master's hens began to dream of kites instead of owls. Lamps were put out, in order to save the trouble of putting them out later; the smell of tobacco and the sound of spitting arose from third-class passengers in dark corners; heads were enshrouded, teeth cleaned on the twigs of a tree. So convinced was a junior official that another sun would rise, that he rang a bell with enthusiasm. This upset the servants. They shrieked that the train was starting, and ran to both ends of it to intercede. Much had still to enter the purdah carriage—a box bound with brass, a melon wearing a fez, a towel containing guavas, a step-ladder and a gun. The guests played up all right. They had no race-consciousness—Mrs. Moore was too old, Miss Quested too new —and they behaved to Aziz as to any young man who had been kind to them in the country. This moved him deeply. He had expected them to arrive with Mr. Fielding, instead of which they trusted themselves to be with him a few moments alone.

"Send back your servant," he suggested. "He is unnecessary. Then we shall all be Moslems together."

"And he is such a horrible servant. Antony, you can go; we don't want you," said the girl impatiently.

"Master told me to come."

"Mistress tells you to go."

"Master says, keep near the ladies all the morning."

"Well, your ladies won't have you." She turned to the host. "Do get rid of him, Dr. Aziz!"

"Mohammed Latif!" he yelled.

The poor relative exchanged fezzes with the melon, and peeped out of the window of the railway carriage, whose confusion he was superintending.

"Here is my cousin, Mr. Mohammed Latif. Oh no, don't shake hands. He is an Indian of the old-fashioned sort, he prefers to salaam. There, I told you so. Mohammed Latif, how beautifully you salaam. See, he hasn't understood; he knows no English."

"You spick lie," said the old man gently.

"I spick a lie! Oh, jolly good. Isn't he a funny old man? We will have great jokes with him later. He does all sorts of little things. He is not nearly as stupid as you think, and awfully poor. It's lucky ours is a large family." He flung an arm round the grubby neck. "But you get inside, make yourselves at home; yes, you lie down." The celebrated Oriental confusion appeared at last to be at an end. "Excuse me, now I must meet our other two guests!"

He was getting nervous again, for it was ten minutes to the time. Still, Fielding was an Englishman, and they never do miss trains, and Godbole was a Hindu and did not count, and, soothed by this logic, he grew calmer as the hour of departure approached. Mohammed Latif had bribed Antony not to come. They walked up and down the platform, talking usefully. They agreed that they had overdone the servants, and must leave two or three behind at Marabar station. And Aziz explained that he might be playing one or two practical jokes at the caves—not out of unkindness, but to make the guests laugh. The old man assented with slight sideway motions of the head: he was always willing to be ridiculed, and he bade Aziz not spare him. Elated by his importance, he began an indecent anecdote.

"Tell me another time, brother, when I have more leisure, for now, as I have already explained, we have to give pleasure to non-Moslems. Three will be Europeans, one a Hindu, which must not be forgotten. Every attention must be paid to Professor Godbole, lest he feel that he is inferior to my other guests."

"I will discuss philosophy with him."

"That will be kind of you; but the servants are even more important. We must not convey an impression of disorganization. It can be done, and I expect you to do it . . ."

A shriek from the purdah carriage. The train had started.

"Merciful God!" cried Mohammed Latif. He flung himself at the train, and leapt on to the footboard of a carriage. Aziz did likewise. It was an easy feat, for a branch-line train is slow to assume special airs. "We're monkeys, don't worry," he called, hanging on to a bar and laughing. Then he howled, "Mr. Fielding! Mr. Fielding!"

There were Fielding and old Godbole, held up at the level-crossing. Appalling catastrophe! The gates had been closed earlier than usual. They leapt from their tonga; they gesticulated, but what was the good. So near and yet so far! As the train joggled past over the points, there was time for agonized words.

"Bad, bad, you have destroyed me."

"Godbole's pujah [1] did it," cried the Englishman.

The Brahman lowered his eyes, ashamed of religion. For it was so: he had miscalculated the length of a prayer.

"Jump on, I must have you," screamed Aziz, beside himself.

"Right, give me a hand."

"He's not to, he'll kill himself," Mrs. Moore protested. He jumped, he failed, missed his friend's hand, and fell back on to the line. The train rumbled past. He scrambled on to his feet, and bawled after them, "I'm all right, you're all right, don't worry," and then they passed beyond range of his voice.

1. **pujah**: devotional service.

"Mrs. Moore, Miss Quested, our expedition is a ruin." He swung himself along the footboard, almost in tears.

"Get in, get in; you'll kill yourself as well as Mr. Fielding. I see no ruin."

"How is that? Oh, explain to me!" he said piteously, like a child.

"We shall be all Moslems together now, as you promised."

She was perfect as always, his dear Mrs. Moore. All the love for her he had felt at the mosque welled up again, the fresher for forgetfulness. There was nothing he would not do for her. He would die to make her happy.

"Get in, Dr. Aziz, you make us giddy," the other lady called. "If they're so foolish as to miss the train, that's their loss, not ours."

"I am to blame. I am the host."

"Nonsense, go to your carriage. We're going to have a delightful time without them."

Not perfect like Mrs. Moore, but very sincere and kind. Wonderful ladies, both of them, and for one precious morning his guests. He felt important and competent. Fielding was a loss personally, being a friend, increasingly dear, yet if Fielding had come, he himself would have remained in leading-strings. "Indians are incapable of responsibility," said the officials, and Hamidullah sometimes said so too. He would show those pessimists that they were wrong. Smiling proudly, he glanced outward at the country, which was still invisible except as a dark movement in the darkness; then upwards at the sky, where the stars of sprawling Scorpion had begun to pale. Then he dived through a window into a second-class carriage.

"Mohammed Latif, by the way, what is in these caves, brother? Why are we all going to see them?"

Such a question was beyond the poor relative's scope. He could only reply that God and the local villagers knew, and that the latter would gladly act as guides.

CHAPTER 14

Most of life is so dull there is nothing to be said about it, and the books and talk that would describe it as interesting are obliged to exaggerate, in the hope of justifying their own existence. Inside its cocoon of work or social obligation, the human spirit slumbers for the most part, registering the distinction between pleasure and pain, but not nearly as alert as we pretend. There are periods in the most thrilling day during which nothing happens, and though we continue to exclaim, "I do enjoy myself," or, "I am horrified," we are insincere. "As far as I feel anything, it

is enjoyment, horror"—it's no more than that really, and a perfectly adjusted organism would be silent.

It so happened that Mrs. Moore and Miss Quested had felt nothing
acutely for a fortnight. Ever since Professor Godbole had sung his queer
little song, they had lived more or less inside cocoons, and the difference
between them was that the elder lady accepted her own apathy, while the
younger resented hers. It was Adela's faith that the whole stream of events
is important and interesting, and if she grew bored she blamed herself severely and compelled her lips to utter enthusiasms. This was the only insincerity in a character otherwise sincere, and it was indeed the intellectual protest of her youth. She was particularly vexed now because she
was both in India and engaged to be married, which double event should
have made every instant sublime.

India was certainly dim this morning, though seen under the auspices of
Indians. Her wish had been granted, but too late. She could not get excited over Aziz and his arrangements. She was not the least unhappy or
depressed, and the various odd objects that surrounded her—the comic
"purdah" carriage, the piles of rugs and bolsters, the rolling melons, the
scent of sweet oils, the ladder, the brass-bound box, the sudden irruption
of Mahmoud Ali's butler from the lavatory with tea and poached eggs
upon a tray—they were all new and amusing, and led her to comment ap-
propriately, but they wouldn't bite into her mind. So she tried to find
comfort by reflecting that her main interest would henceforward be
Ronny.

"What a nice cheerful servant! What a relief after Antony!"

"They startle one rather. A strange place to make tea in," said Mrs.
Moore, who had hoped for a nap.

"I want to sack Antony. His behaviour on the platform has decided
me."

Mrs. Moore thought that Antony's better self would come to the front
at Simla. Miss Quested was to be married at Simla; some cousins, with a
house looking straight on to Thibet, had invited her.

"Anyhow, we must get a second servant, because at Simla you will be
at the hotel, and I don't think Ronny's Boldeo . . ." She loved plans.

"Very well, you get another servant, and I'll keep Antony with me. I
am used to his unappetizing ways. He will see me through the Hot
Weather."

"I don't believe in the Hot Weather. People like Major Callendar who
always talk about it—it's in the hope of making one feel inexperienced and
small, like their everlasting, 'I've been twenty years in this country.'"

"I believe in the Hot Weather, but never did I suppose it would bottle
me up as it will." For owing to the sage leisureliness of Ronny and

Adela, they could not be married till May, and consequently Mrs. Moore could not return to England immediately after the wedding, which was what she had hoped to do. By May a barrier of fire would have fallen across India and the adjoining sea, and she would have to remain perched up in the Himalayas waiting for the world to get cooler.

"I won't be bottled up," announced the girl. "I've no patience with these women here who leave their husbands grilling in the plains. Mrs. Mc-Bryde hasn't stopped down once since she married; she leaves her quite intelligent husband alone half the year, and then's surprised she's out of touch with him."

"She has children, you see."

"Oh, yes, that's true," said Miss Quested, disconcerted.

"It is the children who are the first consideration. Until they are grown up, and married off. When that happens one has again the right to live for oneself—in the plains or the hills, as suits."

"Oh yes, you're perfectly right. I never thought it out."

"If one has not become too stupid and old." She handed her empty cup to the servant.

"My idea now is that my cousins shall find me a servant in Simla, at all events to see me through the wedding, after which Ronny means to reorganize his staff entirely. He does it very well for a bachelor, still, when he is married no doubt various changes will have to be made—his old servants won't want to take their orders from me, and I don't blame them."

Mrs. Moore pushed up the shutters and looked out. She had brought Ronny and Adela together by their mutual wish, but really she could not advise them further. She felt increasingly (vision or nightmare?) that, though people are important, the relations between them are not, and that in particular too much fuss has been made over marriage; centuries of carnal embracement, yet man is no nearer to understanding man. And to-day she felt this with such force that it seemed itself a relationship, itself a person who was trying to take hold of her hand.

"Anything to be seen of the hills?"

"Only various shades of the dark."

"We can't be far from the place where my hyena was." She peered into the timeless twilight. The train crossed a nullah. "Pomper, pomper, pomper," was the sound that the wheels made as they trundled over the bridge, moving very slowly. A hundred yards on came a second nullah, then a third, suggesting the neighbourhood of higher ground. "Perhaps this is mine; anyhow, the road runs parallel with the railway." Her accident was a pleasant memory; she felt in her dry, honest way that it had given her a good shake up, and taught her Ronny's true worth. Then she went back to her plans; plans had been a passion with her from girlhood.

Now and then she paid tribute to the present, said how friendly and intelligent Aziz was, ate a guava, couldn't eat a fried sweet, practised her Urdu on the servant; but her thoughts ever veered to the manageable future, and to the Anglo-Indian life she had decided to endure. And as she appraised it with its adjuncts of Turtons and Burtons, the train accompanied her sentences, "pomper, pomper," the train half asleep, going nowhere in particular and with no passenger of importance in any of its carriages, the branch-line train, lost on a low embankment between dull fields. Its message—for it had one—avoided her well-equipped mind. Far away behind her, with a shriek that meant business, rushed the Mail, connecting up important towns such as Calcutta and Lahore, where interesting events occur and personalities are developed. She understood that. Unfortunately, India has few important towns. India is the country, fields, fields, then hills, jungle, hills, and more fields. The branch line stops, the road is only practicable for cars to a point, the bullock-carts lumber down the side tracks, paths fray out into the cultivation, and disappear near a spalsh of red paint. How can the mind take hold of such a country? Generations of invaders have tried, but they remain in exile. The important towns they build are only retreats, their quarrels the malaise of men who cannot find their way home. India knows of their trouble. She knows of the whole world's trouble, to its uttermost depth. She calls "Come" through her hundred mouths, through objects ridiculous and august. But come to what? She has never defined. She is not a promise, only an appeal.

"I will fetch you from Simla when it's cool enough. I will unbottle you in fact," continued the reliable girl. "We then see some of the Mogul stuff —how appalling if we let you miss the Taj!—and then I will see you off at Bombay. Your last glimpse of this country really shall be interesting." But Mrs. Moore had fallen asleep, exhausted by the early start. She was in rather low health, and ought not to have attempted the expedition, but had pulled herself together in case the pleasure of the others should suffer. Her dreams were of the same texture, but there it was her other children who were wanting something, Stella and Ralph, and she was explaining to them that she could not be in two families at once. When she awoke, Adela had ceased to plan, and leant out of a window, saying, "They're rather wonderful."

Astonishing even from the rise of the civil station, here the Marabar were gods to whom earth is a ghost. Kawa Dol was nearest. It shot up in a single slab, on whose summit one rock was poised—if a mass so great can be called one rock. Behind it, recumbent, were the hills that contained the other caves, isolated each from his neighbour by broad channels of the plain. The assemblage, ten in all, shifted a little as the train crept past them, as if observing its arrival.

"I 'ld not have missed this for anything," said the girl, exaggerating her enthusiasm. "Look, the sun's rising—this'll be absolutely magnificent—come quickly—look. I wouldn't have missed this for anything. We should never have seen it if we'd stuck to the Turtons and their eternal elephants."

As she spoke, the sky to the left turned angry orange. Colour throbbed and mounted behind a pattern of trees, grew in intensity, was yet brighter, incredibly brighter, strained from without against the globe of the air. They awaited the miracle. But at the supreme moment, when night should have died and day lived, nothing occurred. It was as if virtue had failed in the celestial fount. The hues in the east decayed, the hills seemed dimmer though in fact better lit, and a profound disappointment entered with the morning breeze. Why, when the chamber was prepared, did the bridegroom not enter with trumpets and shawms, as humanity expects? The sun rose without splendour. He was presently observed trailing yellowish behind the trees, or aganist insipid sky, and touching the bodies already at work in the fields.

"Ah, that must be the false dawn—isn't it caused by dust in the upper layers of the atmosphere that couldn't fall down during the night? I think Mr. McBryde said so. Well, I must admit that England has it as regards sunrises. Do you remember Grasmere?"

"Ah, dearest Grasmere!" Its little lakes and mountains were beloved by them all. Romantic yet manageable, it sprang from a kindlier planet. Here an untidy plain stretched to the knees of the Marabar.

"Good morning, good morning, put on your topis," shouted Aziz from farther down the train. "Put on your topis at once, the early sun is highly dangerous for heads. I speak as a doctor."

"Good morning, good morning, put on your own."

"Not for my thick head," he laughed, banging it and holding up pads of hair.

"Nice creature he is," murmured Adela.

"Listen—Mohammed Latif says 'Good morning' next." Various pointless jests.

"Dr. Aziz, what's happened to your hills? The train has forgotten to stop."

"Perhaps it is a circular train and goes back to Chandrapore without a break. Who knows!"

Having wandered off into the plain for a mile, the train slowed up against an elephant. There was a platform too, but it shrivelled into insignificance. An elephant, waving her painted forehead at the morn! "Oh, what a surprise!" called the ladies politely. Aziz said nothing, but he nearly burst with pride and relief. The elephant was the one grand feature of the picnic, and God alone knew what he had gone through to obtain her.

Semi-official, she was best approached through the Nawab Bahadur, who was best approached through Nureddin, but he never answered letters, but his mother had great influence with him and was a friend of Hamidullah Begum's, who had been excessively kind and had promised to call on her provided the broken shutter of the purdah carriage came back soon enough from Calcutta. That an elephant should depend from so long and so slender a string filled Aziz with content, and with humorous appreciation of the East, where the friends of friends are a reality, where everything gets done sometime, and sooner or later every one gets his share of happiness. And Mohammed Latif was likewise content, because two of the guests had missed the train, and consequently he could ride on the howdah instead of following in a cart, and the servants were content because an elephant increased their self-esteem, and they tumbled out the luggage into the dust with shouts and bangs, issuing orders to one another, and convulsed with goodwill.

"It takes an hour to get there, an hour to get back, and two hours for the caves, which we will call three," said Aziz, smiling charmingly. There was suddenly something regal about him. "The train back is at eleven-thirty, and you will be sitting down to your tiffin in Chandrapore with Mr. Heaslop at exactly your usual hour, namely, one-fifteen. I know everything about you. Four hours—quite a small expedition—and an hour extra for misfortunes, which occur somewhat frequently among my people. My idea is to plan everything without consulting you; but you, Mrs. Moore, or Miss Quested, you are at any moment to make alterations if you wish, even if it means giving up the caves. Do you agree? Then mount this wild animal."

The elephant had knelt, grey and isolated, like another hill. They climbed up the ladder, and he mounted shikar fashion, treading first on the sharp edge of the heel and then into the looped-up tail. When Mohammed Latif followed him, the servant who held the end of the tail let go of it according to previous instructions, so that the poor relative slipped and had to cling to the netting over the buttocks. It was a little piece of Court buffoonery, and distressed only the ladies, whom it was intended to divert. Both of them disliked practical jokes. Then the beast rose in two shattering movements, and poised them ten feet above the plain. Immediately below was the scurf of life that an elephant always collects round its feet—villagers, naked babies. The servants flung crockery into togas. Hassan annexed the stallion intended for Aziz, and defied Mahmoud Ali's man from its altitude. The Brahman who had been hired to cook for Professor Godbole was planted under an acacia tree, to await their return. The train, also hoping to return, wobbled away through the fields, turning its head this way and that like a centipede. And the only other movement to be seen was a movement as of antennæ, really the counterpoises of the wells which rose and fell on their pivots of mud all over the plain and dispersed a feeble flow of water. The scene was agreeable rather than not in the mild morning air, but there was little colour in it, and no vitality.

As the elephant moved towards the hills (the pale sun had by this time saluted them to the base, and pencilled shadows down their creases) a new quality occurred, a spiritual silence which invaded more senses than the ear. Life went on as usual, but had no consequences, that is to say, sounds did not echo or thoughts develop. Everything seemed cut off at its root, and therefore infected with illusion. For instance, there were some mounds by the edge of the track, low, serrated, and touched with whitewash. What were these mounds—graves, breasts of the goddess Parvati? The villagers beneath gave both replies. Again, there was a confusion about a snake which was never cleared up. Miss Quested saw a thin, dark object reared on end at the farther side of a watercourse, and said, "A snake!" The villagers agreed, and Aziz explained: yes, a black cobra, very venomous, who had reared himself up to watch the passing of the elephant. But when she looked through Ronny's field-glasses, she found it wasn't a snake, but the withered and twisted stump of a toddy-palm. So she said, "It isn't a snake." The villagers contradicted her. She had put the word into their minds, and they refused to abandon it. Aziz admitted that it looked like a tree through the glasses, but insisted that it was a black cobra really, and improvised some rubbish about protective mimicry. Nothing was explained, and yet there was no romance. Films of heat, radiated from the Kawa Dol precipices, increased the confusion. They came at irregular intervals and moved capriciously. A patch of field would jump as if it was being fried, and then lie quiet. As they drew closer the radiation stopped.

The elephant walked straight at the Kawa Dol as if she would knock for admission with her forehead, then swerved, and followed a path round its base. The stones plunged straight into the earth, like cliffs into the sea, and while Miss Quested was remarking on this, and saying that it was striking, the plain quietly disappeared, peeled off, so to speak, and nothing was to be seen on either side but the granite, very dead and quiet. The sky dominated as usual, but seemed unhealthily near, adhering like a ceiling to the summits of the precipices. It was as if the contents of the corridor had never been changed. Occupied by his own munificence, Aziz noticed nothing. His guests noticed a little. They did not feel that it was an attractive place or quite worth visiting, and wished it could have turned into some Mohammedan object, such as a mosque, which their host would have appreciated and explained. His ignorance became evident, and was really rather a drawback. In spite of his gay, confident talk, he had no notion how to treat this particular aspect of India; he was lost in it without Professor Godbole, like themselves.

The corridor narrowed, then widened into a sort of tray. Here, more or less, was their goal. A ruined tank held a little water which would do for the animals, and close above the mud was punched a black hole—the first of the caves. Three hills encircled the tray. Two of them pumped out heat busily, but the third was in shadow, and here they camped.

"A horrid, stuffy place really," murmured Mrs. Moore to herself.

"How quick your servants are!" Miss Quested exclaimed. For a cloth had already been laid, with a vase of artificial flowers in its centre, and Mahmoud Ali's butler offered them poached eggs and tea for the second time.

"I thought we would eat this before our caves, and breakfast after."

"Isn't this breakfast?"

"This breakfast? Did you think I should treat you so strangely?" He had been warned that English people never stop eating, and that he had better nourish them every two hours until a solid meal was ready.

"How very well it is all arranged."

"That you shall tell me when I return to Chandrapore. Whatever disgraces I bring upon myself, you remain my guests." He spoke gravely now. They were dependent on him for a few hours, and he felt grateful to them for placing themselves in such a position. All was well so far; the elephant held a fresh cut bough to her lips, the tonga shafts stuck up into the air, the kitchen-boy peeled potatoes, Hassan shouted, and Mohammed Latif stood as he ought, with a peeled switch in his hand. The expedition was a success, and it was Indian; an obscure young man had been allowed to show courtesy to visitors from another country, which is what all Indians long to do—even cynics like Mahmoud Ali—but they never have the chance. Hospitality had been achieved, they were "his" guests; his honour was involved in their happiness, and any discomfort they endured would tear his own soul.

Like most Orientals, Aziz overrated hospitality, mistaking it for intimacy, and not seeing that it is tainted with the sense of possession. It was only when Mrs. Moore or Fielding was near him that he saw further, and knew that it is more blessed to receive than to give. These two had strange and beautiful effects on him—they were his friends, his for ever, and he theirs for ever; he loved them so much that giving and receiving became one. He loved them even better than the Hamidullah's because he had surmounted obstacles to meet them, and this stimulates a generous mind. Their images remained somewhere in his soul up to his dying day, permanent additions. He looked at her now as she sat on a deck-chair, sipping his tea, and had for a moment a joy that held the seeds of its own decay, for it would lead him to think, "Oh, what more can I do for her?" and so back to the dull round of hospitality. The black bullets of his eyes filled with soft expressive light, and he said, "Do you ever remember our mosque, Mrs. Moore?"

"I do. I do," she said, suddenly vital and young.

"And how rough and rude I was, and how good you were."

"And how happy we both were."

"Friendships last longest that begin like that, I think. Shall I ever entertain your other children?"

"Do you know about the others? She will never talk about them to me," said Miss Quested, unintentionally breaking a spell.

"Ralph and Stella, yes, I know everything about them. But we must not forget to visit our caves. One of the dreams of my life is accomplished in having you both here as my guests. You cannot imagine how you have honoured me. I feel like the Emperor Babur."

"Why like him?" she enquired, rising.

"Because my ancestors came down with him from Afghanistan. They joined him at Herat. He also had often no more elephants than one, none sometimes, but he never ceased showing hospitality. When he fought or hunted or ran away, he would always stop for a time among hills, just like us; he would never let go of hospitality and pleasure, and if there was only a little food, he would have it arranged nicely, and if only one musical instrument, he would compel it to play a beautiful tune. I take him as my ideal. He is the poor gentleman, and he became a great king."

"I thought another Emperor is your favourite—I forget the name—you mentioned him at Mr. Fielding's: what my book calls Aurangzebe."

"Alamgir? Oh yes, he was of course the more pious. But Babur—never in his whole life did he betray a friend, so I can only think of him this morning. And you know how he died? He laid down his life for his son. A death far more difficult than battle. They were caught in the heat. They should have gone back to Kabul for the bad weather, but could not for reasons of state, and at Agra Humayun fell sick. Babur walked round the bed three times, and said, 'I have borne it away,' and he did bear it away; the fever left his son and came to him instead, and he died. That is why I prefer Babur to Alamgir. I ought not to do so, but I do. However, I mustn't delay you. I see you are ready to start."

"Not at all," she said, sitting down by Mrs. Moore again. "We enjoy talk like this very much." For at last he was talking about what he knew and felt, talking as he had in Fielding's garden-house; he was again the Oriental guide whom they appreciated.

"I always enjoy conversing about the Moguls. It is the chief pleasure I know. You see, those first six emperors were all most wonderful men, and as soon as one of them is mentioned, no matter which, I forget everything else in the world except the other five. You could not find six such kings in all the countries of the earth, not, I mean, coming one after the other—father, son."

"Tell us something about Akbar."

"Ah you have heard the name of Akbar. Good. Hamidullah—whom you shall meet—will tell you that Akbar is the greatest of all. I say, 'Yes, Akbar is very wonderful, but half a Hindu; he was not a true Moslem,' which makes Hamidullah cry, 'No more was Babur, he drank wine.' But Babur always repented afterwards, which makes the entire difference, and Akbar never repented of the new religion he invented instead of the Holy Koran."

"But wasn't Akbar's new religion very fine? It was to embrace the whole of India."

"Miss Quested, fine but foolish. You keep your religion, I mine. That is the best. Nothing embraces the whole of India, nothing, nothing, and that was Akbar's mistake."

"Oh, do you feel that, Dr. Aziz?" she said thoughtfully. "I hope you're not right. There will have to be something universal in this country—I don't say religion, for I'm not religious, but something, or how else are barriers to be broken down?"

She was only recommending the universal brotherhood he sometimes dreamed of, but as soon as it was put into prose it became untrue.

"Take my own case," she continued—it was indeed her own case that had animated her. "I don't know whether you happen to have heard, but I'm going to marry Mr. Heaslop."

"On which my heartiest congratulations."

"Mrs. Moore, may I put our difficulty to Dr. Aziz—I mean our Anglo-Indian one?"

"It is your difficulty, not mine, my dear."

"Ah, that's true. Well, by marrying Mr. Heaslop, I shall become what is known as an Anglo-Indian."

He held up his hand in protest. "Impossible. Take back such a terrible remark."

"But I shall! it's inevitable. I can't avoid the label. What I do hope to avoid is the mentality. Women like——" She stopped, not quite liking to mention names; she would boldly have said "Mrs. Turton and Mrs. Callendar" a fortnight ago. "Some women are so—well, ungenerous and snobby about Indians, and I should feel too ashamed for words if I turned like them, but—and here's my difficulty—there's nothing special about me, nothing specially good or strong, which will help me to resist my environ-

ment and avoid becoming like them. I've most lamentable defects. That's
why I want Akbar's 'universal religion' or the equivalent to keep me decent and sensible. Do you see what I mean?"

Her remarks pleased him, but his mind shut up tight because she had al-
luded to her marriage. He was not going to be mixed up in that side of
things. "You are certain to be happy with any relative of Mrs. Moore's,"
he said with a formal bow.

"Oh, my happiness—that's quite another problem. I want to consult you
about this Anglo-Indian difficulty. Can you give me any advice?"

"You are absolutely unlike the others, I assure you. You will never be
rude to my people."

"I am told we all get rude after a year."

"Then you are told a lie," he flashed, for she had spoken the truth and
it touched him on the raw; it was itself an insult in these particular circumstances. He recovered himself at once and laughed, but her error
broke up their conversation—their civilization it had almost been—which
scattered like the petals of a desert flower, and left them in the middle of
the hills. "Come along," he said, holding out a hand to each. They got up
a little reluctantly, and addressed themselves to sightseeing.

The first cave was tolerably convenient. They skirted the puddle of water, and then climbed up over some unattractive stones, the sun crashing
on their backs. Bending their heads, they disappeared one by one into the
interior of the hills. The small black hole gaped where their varied forms
and colours had momentarily functioned. They were sucked in like water
down a drain. Bland and bald rose the precipices; bland and glutinous the
sky that connected the precipices; solid and white, a Brahminy kite
flapped between the rocks with a clumsiness that seemed intentional. Before man, with his itch for the seemly, had been born, the planet must have
looked thus. The kite flapped away. . . . Before birds, perhaps. . . . And
then the hole belched and humanity returned.

A Marabar cave had been horrid as far as Mrs. Moore was concerned,
for she had nearly fainted in it, and had some difficulty in preventing herself from saying so as soon as she got into the air again. It was natural
enough: she had always suffered from faintness, and the cave had become
too full, because all their retinue followed them. Crammed with villagers
and servants, the circular chamber began to smell. She lost Aziz and Adela
in the dark, didn't know who touched her, couldn't breathe, and some
vile naked thing struck her face and settled on her mouth like a pad. She
tried to regain the entrance tunnel, but an influx of villagers swept her
back. She hit her head. For an instant she went mad, hitting and gasping
like a fanatic. For not only did the crush and stench alarm her; there was
also a terrifying echo.

Professor Godbole had never mentioned an echo; it never impressed him, perhaps. There are some exquisite echoes in India; there is the whisper round the dome at Bijapur [1]; there are the long, solid sentences that voyage through the air at Mandu,[2] and return unbroken to their creator. The echo in a Marabar cave is not like these, it is entirely devoid of distinction. Whatever is said, the same monotonous noise replies, and quivers up and down the walls until it is absorbed into the roof. "Boum" is the sound as far as the human alphabet can express it, or "bou-oum," or "ou-boum,"—utterly dull. Hope, politeness, the blowing of a nose, the squeak of a boot, all produce "boum." Even the striking of a match starts a little worm coiling, which is too small to complete a circle but is eternally watchful. And if several people talk at once, an overlapping howling noise begins, echoes generate echoes, and the cave is stuffed with a snake composed of small snakes, which writhe independently.

After Mrs. Moore all the others poured out. She had given the signal for the reflux. Aziz and Adela both emerged smiling and she did not want him to think his treat was a failure, so smiled too. As each person emerged she looked for a villain, but none was there, and she realized that she had been among the mildest individuals, whose only desire was to honour her, and that the naked pad was a poor little baby, astride its mother's hip. Nothing evil had been in the cave, but she had not enjoyed herself; no, she had not enjoyed herself, and she decided not to visit a second one.

"Did you see the reflection of his match—rather pretty?" asked Adela.

"I forget . . ."

"But he says this isn't a good cave, the best are on the Kawa Dol."

"I don't think I shall go on to there. I dislike climbing."

"Very well, let's sit down again in the shade until breakfast's ready."

"Ah, but that'll disappoint him so; he has taken such trouble. You should go on; you don't mind."

"Perhaps I ought to," said the girl, indifferent to what she did, but desirous of being amiable.

The servants, etc., were scrambling back to the camp, pursued by grave censures from Mohammed Latif. Aziz came to help the guests over the rocks. He was at the summit of his powers, vigorous and humble, too sure of himself to resent criticism, and he was sincerely pleased when he heard they were altering his plans. "Certainly, Miss Quested, so you and I will go together, and leave Mrs. Moore here, and we will not be long, yet we will not hurry, because we know that will be her wish."

"Quite right. I'm sorry not to come too, but I'm a poor walker."

1. **Bijapur:** a district in the southern division of Bombay.
2. **Mandu:** the site of a historic fort in west central India, famous for the remains of the fourteenth- and fifteenth-century tanks, palaces, and mosques.

"Dear Mrs. Moore, what does anything matter so long as you are my guests? I am very glad you are *not* coming, which sounds strange, but you are treating me with true frankness, as a friend."

"Yes, I am your friend," she said, laying her hand on his sleeve, and thinking, despite her fatigue, how very charming, how very good, he was, and how deeply she desired his happiness. "So may I make another suggestion? Don't let so many people come with you this time. I think you may find it more convenient."

"Exactly, exactly," he cried, and, rushing to the other extreme, forbade all except one guide to accompany Miss Quested and him to the Kawa Dol. "Is that all right?" he enquired.

"Quite right, now enjoy yourselves, and when you come back tell me all about it." And she sank into the deck-chair.

If they reached the big pocket of caves, they would be away nearly an hour. She took out her writing-pad, and began, "Dear Stella, Dear Ralph," then stopped, and looked at the queer valley and their feeble invasion of it. Even the elephant had become a nobody. Her eye rose from it to the entrance tunnel. So, she did not wish to repeat that experience. The more she thought over it, the more disagreeable and frightening it became. She minded it much more now than at the time. The crush and the smells she could forget, but the echo began in some indescribable way to undermine her hold on life. Coming at a moment when she chanced to be fatigued, it had managed to murmur, "Pathos, piety, courage—they exist, but are identical, and so is filth. Everything exists, nothing has value." If one had spoken vileness in that place, or quoted lofty poetry, the comment would have been the same—"ou-boum." If one had spoken with the tongues of angels and pleaded for all the unhappiness and misunderstanding in the world, past, present, and to come, for all the misery men must undergo whatever their opinion and position, and however much they dodge or bluff—it would amount to the same, the serpent would descend and return to the ceiling. Devils are of the North, and poems can be written about them, but no one could romanticize the Marabar because it robbed infinity and eternity of their vastness, the only quality that accommodates them to mankind.

She tried to go on with her letter, reminding herself that she was only an elderly woman who had got up too early in the morning and journeyed too far, that the despair creeping over her was merely her despair, her personal weakness, and that even if she got a sunstroke and went mad the rest of the world would go on. But suddenly, at the edge of her mind, Religion appeared, poor little talkative Christianity, and she knew that all its divine words from "Let there be Light" to "It is finished" only amounted to "boum." Then she was terrified over an area larger than usual; the universe, never comprehensible to her intellect, offered no repose to her soul, the mood of the last two months took definite form at last, and she realized that she didn't want to write to her children, didn't want to communicate with anyone, not even with God. She sat motionless with horror, and, when old Mohammed Latif came up to her, thought he would notice a difference. For a time she thought, "I am going to be ill," to comfort herself, then she surrendered to the vision. She lost all interest, even in Aziz, and the affectionate and sincere words that she had spoken to him seemed no longer hers but the air's.

CHAPTER 15

Miss Quested and Aziz and a guide continued the slightly tedious expedition. They did not talk much, for the sun was getting high. The air felt like a warm bath into which hotter water is trickling constantly, the temperature rose and rose, the boulders said, "I am alive," the small stones answered, "I am almost alive." Between the chinks lay the ashes of little plants. They meant to climb to the rocking-stone on the summit, but it was too far, and they contented themselves with the big group of caves. *En route* for these, they encountered several isolated caves, which the guide persuaded them to visit, but really there was nothing to see; they lit a match, admired its reflection in the polish, tested the echo and came out again. Aziz was "pretty sure they should come on some interesting old carvings soon," but only meant he wished there were some carvings. His deeper thoughts were about the breakfast. Symptoms of disorganization had appeared as he left the camp. He ran over the menu: an English breakfast, porridge and mutton chops, but some Indian dishes to cause conversation, and pan afterwards. He had never liked Miss Quested as much as Mrs. Moore, and had little to say to her, less than ever now that she would marry a British official.

Nor had Adela much to say to him. If his mind was with the breakfast, hers was mainly with her marriage. Simla next week, get rid of Antony, a view of Thibet, tiresome wedding bells, Agra in October, see Mrs. Moore comfortably off from Bombay—the procession passed before her again, blurred by the heat, and then she turned to the more serious business of her life at Chandrapore. There were real difficulties here—Ronny's limitations and her own—but she enjoyed facing difficulties, and decided that if she could control her peevishness (always her weak point), and neither rail against Anglo-India nor succumb to it, their married life ought to be happy and profitable. She mustn't be too theoretical; she would deal with each problem as it came up, and trust to Ronny's common sense and her own. Luckily, each had abundance of common sense and good will.

But as she toiled over a rock that resembled an inverted saucer, she thought, "What about love?" The rock was nicked by a double row of footholds, and somehow the question was suggested by them. Where had she seen footholds before? Oh, yes, they were the pattern traced in the dust by the wheels of the Nawab Bahadur's car. She and Ronny—no, they did not love each other.

"Do I take you too fast?" enquired Aziz, for she had paused, a doubtful expression on her face. The discovery had come so suddenly that she felt like a mountaineer whose rope had broken. Not to love the man one's going to marry! Not to find it out till this moment! Not even to have asked oneself the question until now! Something else to think about. Vexed rather than appalled, she stood still, her eyes on the sparkling rock. There was esteem and animal contact at dusk, but the emotion that links them was absent. Ought she to break her engagement off? She was inclined to think not—it would cause so much trouble to others; besides, she wasn't convinced that love is necessary to a successful union. If love is everything, few marriages would survive the honeymoon. "No, I'm all right, thanks," she said, and, her emotions well under control, resumed the climb, though she felt a bit dashed. Aziz held her hand, the guide adhered to the surface like a lizard and scampered about as if governed by a personal centre of gravity.

"Are you married, Dr. Aziz?" she asked, stopping again, and frowning.

"Yes, indeed, do come and see my wife"—for he felt it more artistic to have his wife alive for a moment.

"Thank you," she said absently.

"She is not in Chandrapore just now."

"And have you children?"

"Yes, indeed, three," he replied in firmer tones.

"Are they a great pleasure to you?"

"Why, naturally, I adore them," he laughed.

"I suppose so." What a handsome little Oriental he was, and no doubt his wife and children were beautiful too, for people usually get what they already possess. She did not admire him with any personal warmth, for there was nothing of the vagrant in her blood, but she guessed he might attract women of his own race and rank, and she regretted that neither she nor Ronny had physical charm. It does make a difference in a relationship—beauty, thick hair, a fine skin. Probably this man had several wives—Mohammedans always insist on their full four, according to Mrs. Turton. And having no one else to speak to on that eternal rock, she gave rein to the subject of marriage and said in her honest, decent, inquisitive way: "Have you one wife or more than one?"

The question shocked the young man very much. It challenged a new conviction of his community, and new convictions are more sensitive than old. If she had said, "Do you worship one god or several?" he would not have objected. But to ask an educated Indian Moslem how many wives he has—appalling, hideous! He was in trouble how to conceal his confusion. "One, one in my own particular case," he sputtered, and let go of her hand. Quite a number of caves were at the top of the track, and thinking, "Damn the English even at their best," he plunged into one of them to recover his balance. She followed at her leisure, quite unconscious that she had said the wrong thing, and not seeing him, she also went into a cave, thinking with half her mind "sight-seeing bores me," and wondering with the other half about marriage.

CHAPTER 16

He waited in his cave a minute, and lit a cigarette, so that he could remark on rejoining her, "I bolted in to get out of the draught," or something of the sort. When he returned, he found the guide, alone, with his head on one side. He had heard a noise, he said, and then Aziz heard it too: the noise of a motor-car. They were now on the outer shoulder of the Kawa Dol, and by scrambling twenty yards they got a glimpse of the plain. A car was coming toward the hills down the Chandrapore road. But they could not get a good view of it, because the precipitous bastion curved at the top, so that the base was not easily seen and the car disappeared as it came nearer. No doubt it would stop almost exactly beneath them, at the place where the pukka road degenerated into a path, and the elephant had turned to sidle into the hills.

He ran back to tell the strange news to his guest.

The guide explained that she had gone into a cave.

"Which cave?"

He indicated the group vaguely.

"You should have kept her in sight, it was your duty," said Aziz severely. "Here are twelve caves at least. How am I to know which contains my guest? Which is the cave I was in myself?"

The same vague gesture. And Aziz, looking again, could not even be sure he had returned to the same group. Caves appeared in every direction —it seemed their original spawning place—and the orifices were always the same size. He thought, "Merciful Heavens, Miss Quested is lost," then pulled himself together, and began to look for her calmly.

"Shout!" he commanded.

When they had done this for awhile, the guide explained that to shout is useless, because a Marabar cave can hear no sound but its own. Aziz wiped his head, and sweat began to stream inside his clothes. The place was so confusing; it was partly a terrace, partly a zigzag, and full of grooves that led this way and that like snake-tracks. He tried to go into every one, but he never knew where he had started. Caves got behind caves or confabulated in pairs, and some were at the entrance of a gully.

"Come here!" he called gently, and when the guide was in reach, he struck him in the face for a punishment. The man fled, and he was left alone. He thought, "This is the end of my career, my guest is lost." And then he discovered the simple and sufficient explanation of the mystery.

Miss Quested wasn't lost. She had joined the people in the car—friends of hers, no doubt, Mr. Heaslop perhaps. He had a sudden glimpse of her, far down the gully—only a glimpse, but there she was quite plain, framed between rocks, and speaking to another lady. He was so relieved that he did not think her conduct odd. Accustomed to sudden changes of plan, he supposed that she had run down the Kawa Dol impulsively, in the hope of a little drive. He started back alone towards his camp, and almost at once caught sight of something which would have disquieted him very much a moment before: Miss Quested's field glasses. They were lying at the verge of a cave, half-way down an entrance tunnel. He tried to hang them over his shoulder, but the leather strap had broken, so he put them into his pocket instead. When he had gone a few steps, he thought she might have dropped something else, so he went back to look. But the previous difficulty recurred: he couldn't identify the cave. Down in the plain he heard the car starting; however, he couldn't catch a second glimpse of that. So he scrambled down the valley-face of the hill towards Mrs. Moore, and here he was more successful: the colour and confusion of his little camp soon appeared, and in the midst of it he saw an Englishman's topi, and beneath it—oh, joy!—smiled not Mr. Heaslop, but Fielding.

"Fielding! Oh, I have so wanted you!" he cried, dropping the "Mr." for the first time.

And his friend ran to meet him, all so pleasant and jolly, no dignity, shouting explanations and apologies about the train. Fielding had come in the newly arrived car—Miss Derek's car—that other lady was Miss Derek. Chatter, chatter, all the servants leaving their cooking to listen. Excellent Miss Derek! She had met Fielding by chance at the post office, said, "Why haven't you gone to the Marabar?" heard how he missed the train, offered to run him there and then. Another nice English lady. Where was she? Left with car and chauffeur while Fielding found camp. Car couldn't get up—no, of course not—hundreds of people must go down to escort Miss Derek and show her the way. The elephant in person. . . .

"Aziz, can I have a drink?"

"Certainly not." He flew to get one.

"Mr. Fielding!" called Mrs. Moore, from her patch of shade; they had not spoken yet, because his arrival had coincided with the torrent from the hill.

"Good morning again!" he cried, relieved to find all well.

"Mr. Fielding, have you seen Miss Quested?"

"But I've only just arrived. Where is she?"

"I do not know."

"Aziz! Where have you put Miss Quested to?"

Aziz, who was returning with a drink in his hand, had to think for a moment. His heart was full of new happiness. The picnic, after a nasty shock or two, had developed into something beyond his dreams, for Fielding had not only come, but brought an uninvited guest. "Oh, she's all right," he said; "she went down to see Miss Derek. Well, here's luck! Chin-chin!" [1]

"Here's luck, but chin-chin I do refuse," laughed Fielding, who detested the phrase. "Here's to India!"

"Here's luck, and here's to England!"

Miss Derek's chauffeur stopped the cavalcade which was starting to escort his mistress up, and informed it that she had gone back with the other young lady to Chandrapore; she had sent him to say so. She was driving herself.

"Oh yes, that's quite likely," said Aziz. "I knew they'd gone for a spin."

"Chandrapore? The man's made a mistake," Fielding exclaimed.

"Oh no, why?" He was disappointed, but made light of it; no doubt the two young ladies were great friends. He would prefer to give breakfast to all four; still, guests must do as they wish, or they become prisoners. He went away cheerfully to inspect the porridge and the ice.

"What's happened?" asked Fielding, who felt at once that something had gone queer. All the way out Miss Derek had chattered about the picnic, called it an unexpected treat, and said that she preferred Indians who didn't invite her to their entertainments to those who did it. Mrs. Moore sat swinging her foot, and appeared sulky and stupid. She said: "Miss Derek is most unsatisfactory and restless, always in a hurry, always wanting something new; she will do anything in the world except go back to the Indan lady who pays her."

Fielding, who didn't dislike Miss Derek, replied: "She wasn't in a hurry when I left her. There was no question of returning to Chandrapore. It looks to me as if Miss Quested's in the hurry."

1. **Chin-chin:** a salutation, commonly used when giving a toast.

"Adela?—she's never been in a hurry in her life," said the old lady sharply.

"I say it'll prove to be Miss Quested's wish, in fact I know it is," persisted the schoolmaster. He was annoyed—chiefly with himself. He had begun by missing a train—a sin he was never guilty of—and now that he did arrive it was to upset Aziz' arrangements for the second time. He wanted someone to share the blame, and frowned at Mrs. Moore rather magisterially. "Aziz is a charming fellow," he announced.

"I know," she answered, with a yawn.

"He has taken endless trouble to make a success of our picnic."

They knew one another very little, and felt rather awkward at being drawn together by an Indian. The racial problem can take subtle forms. In their case it had induced a sort of jealousy, a mutual suspicion. He tried to goad her enthusiasm; she scarcely spoke. Aziz fetched them to breakfast.

"It is quite natural about Miss Quested," he remarked, for he had been working the incident a little in his mind, to get rid of its roughnesses. "We were having an interesting talk with our guide, then the car was seen, so she decided to go down to her friend." Incurably inaccurate, he already thought that this was what had occurred. He was inaccurate because he was sensitive. He did not like to remember Miss Quested's remark about polygamy, because it was unworthy of a guest, so he put it from his mind, and with it the knowledge that he had bolted into a cave to get away from her. He was inaccurate because he desired to honour her, and—facts being entangled—he had to arrange them in her vicinity, as one tidies the ground after extracting a weed. Before breakfast was over, he had told a good many lies. "She ran to her friend, I to mine," he went on, smiling. "And now I am with my friends and they are with me and each other, which is happiness."

Loving them both, he expected them to love each other. They didn't want to. Fielding thought with hostility, "I knew these women would make trouble," and Mrs. Moore thought, "This man, having missed the train, tries to blame us"; but her thoughts were feeble; since her faintness in the cave she was sunk in apathy and cynicism. The wonderful India of her opening weeks, with its cool nights and acceptable hints of infinity, had vanished.

Fielding ran up to see one cave. He wasn't impressed. Then they got on the elephant and the picnic began to unwind out of the corridor and escaped under the precipice towards the railway station, pursued by stabs of hot air. They came to the place where he had quitted the car. A disagreeable thought now struck him, and he said: "Aziz, exactly where and how did you leave Miss Quested?"

"Up there." He indicated the Kawa Dol cheerfully.

"But how——" A gully, or rather a crease, showed among the rocks at this place; it was scurfy with cactuses. "I suppose the guide helped her."

"Oh, rather, most helpful."

"Is there a path off the top?"

"Millions of paths, my dear fellow."

Fielding could see nothing but the crease. Everywhere else the glaring granite plunged into the earth.

"But you saw them get down safe?"

"Yes, yes, she and Miss Derek, and go off in the car."

"Then the guide came back to you?"

"Exactly. Got a cigarette?"

"I hope she wasn't ill," purused the Englishman. The crease continued as a nullah across the plain, the water draining off this way towards the Ganges.

"She would have wanted me, if she was ill, to attend her."

"Yes, that sounds sense."

"I see you're worrying, let's talk of other things," he said kindly. "Miss Quested was always to do what she wished, it was our arrangement. I see you are worrying on my account, but really I don't mind, I never notice trifles."

"I do worry on your account. I consider they have been impolite!" said Fielding, lowering his voice. "She had no right to dash away from your party, and Miss Derek had no right to abet her."

So touchy as a rule, Aziz was unassailable. The wings that uplifted him did not falter, because he was a Mogul emperor who had done his duty. Perched on his elephant, he watched the Marabar Hills recede, and saw again, as provinces of his kingdom, the grim untidy plain, the frantic and feeble movements of the buckets, the white shrines, the shallow graves, the suave sky, the snake that looked like a tree. He had given his guests as good a time as he could, and if they came late or left early that was not his affair. Mrs. Moore slept, swaying against the rods of the howdah, Mohammed Latif embraced her with efficiency and respect, and by his own side Fielding, whom he began to think of as "Cyril."

"Aziz, have you figured out what this picnic will cost you?"

"Sh! my dear chap, don't mention that part. Hundreds and hundreds of rupees. The completed account will be too awful; my friends' servants have robbed me right and left, and as for an elephant, she apparently eats gold. I can trust you not to repeat this. And M.L.—please employ initials, he listens—is far the worst of all."

"I told you he's no good."

"He is plenty of good for himself; his dishonesty will ruin me."

"Aziz, how monstrous!"

"I am delighted with him really, he has made my guests comfortable; besides, it is my duty to employ him, he is my cousin. If money goes, money comes. If money stays, death comes. Did you ever hear that useful Urdu proverb? Probably not, for I have just invented it."

"My proverbs are: A penny saved is a penny earned; A stitch in time saves nine; Look before you leap; and the British Empire rests on them. You will never kick us out, you know, until you cease employing M.L.'s and such."

"Oh, kick you out? Why should I trouble over that dirty job? Leave it to the politicians. . . . No, when I was a student I got excited over your damned countrymen, certainly; but if they'll let me get on with my profession and not be too rude to me officially, I really don't ask for more."

"But you do; you take them to a picnic."

"This picnic is nothing to do with English or Indian; it is an expedition of friends."

So the cavalcade ended partly pleasant, partly not; the Brahman cook was picked up, the train arrived, pushing its burning throat over the plain, and the twentieth century took over from the sixteenth. Mrs. Moore entered her carriage, the three men went to theirs, adjusted the shutters, turned on the electric fan and tried to get some sleep. In the twilight, all resembled corpses, and the train itself seemed dead though it moved—a coffin from the scientific north which troubled the scenery four times a day. As it left the Marabars, their nasty little cosmos disappeared, and gave place to the Marabars seen from a distance, finite and rather romantic. The train halted once under a pump, to drench the stock of coal in its tender. Then it caught sight of the main line in the distance, took courage, and bumped forward, rounded the civil station, surmounted the level-crossing (the rails were scorching now), and clanked to a standstill. Chandrapore, Chandrapore! The expedition was over.

And as it ended, as they sat up in the gloom and prepared to enter ordinary life, suddenly the long drawn strangeness of the morning snapped. Mr. Haq, the Inspector of Police, flung open the door of their carriage and said in shrill tones: "Dr. Aziz, it is my highly painful duty to arrest you."

"Hullo, some mistake," said Fielding, at once taking charge of the situation.

"Sir, they are my instructions. I know nothing."

"On what charge do you arrest him?"

"I am under instructions not to say."

"Don't answer me like that. Produce your warrant."

"Sir, excuse me, no warrant is required under these particular circumstances. Refer to Mr. McBryde."

"Very well, so we will. Come along, Aziz, old man; nothing to fuss about, some blunder."

"Dr. Aziz, will you kindly come?—a closed conveyance stands in readiness."

The young man sobbed—his first sound—and tried to escape out of the opposite door on to the line.

"That will compel me to use force," Mr. Haq wailed.

"Oh, for God's sake——" cried Fielding, his own nerves breaking under the contagion, and pulled him back before a scandal started, and shook him like a baby. A second later, and he would have been out, whistles blowing, a man-hunt. . . . "Dear fellow, we're coming to McBryde together, and enquire what's gone wrong—he's a decent fellow, it's all unintentional . . . he'll appologize. Never, never act the criminal."

"My children and my name!" he gasped, his wings broken.

"Nothing of the sort. Put your hat straight and take my arm. I'll see you through."

"Ah, thank God, he comes," the Inspector exclaimed.

They emerged into the midday heat, arm in arm. The station was seething. Passengers and porters rushed out of every recess, many Government servants, more police. Ronny escorted Mrs. Moore. Mohammed Latif began wailing. And before they could make their way through the chaos, Fielding was called off by the authoritative tones of Mr. Turton, and Aziz went on to prison alone.

CHAPTER 17

The Collector had watched the arrest from the interior of the waiting-room, and throwing open its perforated doors of zinc, he was now revealed like a god in a shrine. When Fielding entered the doors clapped to, and were guarded by a servant, while a punkah, to mark the importance of the moment, flapped dirty petticoats over their heads. The Collector could not speak at first. His face was white, fanatical, and rather beautiful—the expression that all English faces were to wear at Chandrapore for many days. Always brave and unselfish, he was now fused by some white and generous heat; he would have killed himself, obviously, if he had thought it right to do so. He spoke at last. "The worst thing in my whole career has happened," he said. "Miss Quested has been insulted in one of the Marabar caves."

"Oh no, oh no, no," gasped the other, feeling sickish.

"She escaped—by God's grace."

"Oh no, no, but not Aziz . . . not Aziz . . ."

He nodded.

"Absolutely impossible, grotesque."

"I called you to preserve you from the odium that would attach to you if you were seen accompanying him to the Police Station," said Turton, paying no attention to his protest, indeed scarcely hearing it.

He repeated "Oh no," like a fool. He couldn't frame other words. He felt that a mass of madness had arisen and tried to overwhelm them all; it had to be shoved back into its pit somehow, and he didn't know how to do it, because he did not understand madness: he had always gone about sensibly and quietly until a difficulty came right. "Who lodges this infamous charge?" he asked, pulling himself together.

"Miss Derek and—the victim herself. . . ." He nearly broke down, unable to repeat the girl's name.

"Miss Quested herself definitely accuses him of——"

He nodded and turned his face away.

"Then she's mad."

"I cannot pass that last remark," said the Collector, waking up to the knowledge that they differed, and trembling with fury. "You will withdraw it instantly. It is the type of remark you have permitted yourself to make ever since you came to Chandrapore."

"I'm excessively sorry, sir; I certainly withdraw it unconditionally." For the man was half mad himself.

"Pray, Mr. Fielding, what induced you to speak to me in such a tone?"

"The news gave me a very great shock, so I must ask you to forgive me. I cannot believe that Dr. Aziz is guilty."

He slammed his hand on the table. "That—that is a repetition of your insult in an aggravated form."

"If I may venture to say so, no," said Fielding, also going white, but sticking to his point. "I make no reflection on the good faith of the two ladies, but the charge they are bringing against Aziz rests upon some mistake, and five minutes will clear it up. The man's manner is perfectly natural; besides, I know him to be incapable of infamy."

"It does indeed rest upon a mistake," came the thin, biting voice of the other. "It does indeed. I have had twenty-five years' experience of this country"—he paused, and "twenty-five years" seemed to fill the waiting-room with their staleness and ungenerosity—"and during those twenty-five years I have never known anything but disaster result when English people and Indians attempt to be intimate socially. Intercourse, yes. Courtesy, by all means. Intimacy—never, never. The whole weight of my authority is against it. I have been in charge at Chandrapore for six years, and if everything has gone smoothly, if there has been mutual respect and esteem, it is because both peoples kept to this simple rule. New-comers set our traditions aside, and in an instant what you see happens, the work of years is undone and the good name of my District ruined for a generation. I—I—can't see the end of this day's work, Mr. Fielding. You, who are imbued with modern ideas—no doubt you can. I wish I had never lived to see its beginning, I know that. It is the end of me. That a lady, that a young lady engaged to my most valued subordinate—that she—an English girl fresh from England—that I should have lived——"

Involved in his own emotions, he broke down. What he had said was both dignified and pathetic, but had it anything to do with Aziz? Nothing at all, if Fielding was right. It is impossible to regard a tragedy from two points of view, and whereas Turton had decided to avenge the girl, he hoped to save the man. He wanted to get away and talk to McBryde, who had always been friendly to him, was on the whole sensible, and could, anyhow, be trusted to keep cool.

"I came down particularly on your account—while poor Heaslop got his mother away. I regarded it as the most friendly thing I could do. I meant to tell you that there will be an informal meeting at the club this evening to discuss the situation, but I am doubtful whether you will care to come. Your visits there are always infrequent."

"I shall certainly come, sir, and I am most grateful to you for all the trouble you have taken over me. May I venture to ask—where Miss Quested is."

He replied with a gesture; she was ill.

"Worse and worse, appalling," he said feelingly.

But the Collector looked at him sternly, because he was keeping his head. He had not gone mad at the phrase "an English girl fresh from England," he had not rallied to the banner of race. He was still after facts, though the herd had decided on emotion. Nothing enrages Anglo-India more than the lantern of reason if it is exhibited for one moment after its extinction is decreed. All over Chandrapore that day the Europeans were putting aside their normal personalities and sinking themselves in their community. Pity, wrath, heroism, filled them, but the power of putting two and two together was annihilated.

Terminating the interview, the Collector walked on to the platform. The confusion there was revolting. A chuprassi of Ronny's had been told to bring up some trifles belonging to the ladies, and was appropriating for himself various articles to which he had no right; he was a camp follower of the angry English. Mohammed Latif made no attempt to resist him. Hassan flung off his turban, and wept. All the comforts that had been provided so liberally were rolled about and wasted in the sun. The Collector took in the situation at a glance, and his sense of justice functioned though he was insane with rage. He spoke the necessary word, and the looting stopped. Then he drove off to his bungalow and gave rein to his passions again. When he saw the coolies asleep in the ditches or the shopkeepers rising to salute him on their little platforms, he said to himself: "I know what you're like at last; you shall pay for this, you shall squeal."

CHAPTER 18

Mr. McBryde, the District Superintendent of Police, was the most reflective and best educated of the Chandrapore officials. He had read and thought a good deal, and, owing to a somewhat unhappy marriage, had evolved a complete philosophy of life. There was much of the cynic about him, but nothing of the bully; he never lost his temper or grew rough, and he received Aziz with courtesy, was almost reassuring. "I have to detain you until you get bail," he said, "but no doubt your friends will be applying for it, and of course they will be allowed to visit you, under regulations. I am given certain information, and have to act on it—I'm not your judge." Aziz was led off weeping. Mr. McBryde was shocked at his downfall, but no Indian ever surprised him, because he had a theory about climatic zones. The theory ran: "All unfortunate natives are criminals at heart, for the simple reason that they live south of latitude 30. They are not to blame, they have not a dog's chance—we should be like them if we settled here." Born at Karachi, he seemed to contradict his theory, and would sometimes admit as much with a sad, quiet smile.

"Another of them found out," he thought, as he set to work to draft his statement to the Magistrate.

He was interrupted by the arrival of Fielding.

He imparted all he knew without reservations. Miss Derek had herself driven in the Mudkul car about an hour ago, she and Miss Quested both in a terrible state. They had gone straight to his bungalow where he happened to be, and there and then he had taken down the charge and arranged for the arrest at the railway station.

"What is the charge, precisely?"

"That he followed her into the cave and made insulting advances. She hit at him with her field-glasses; he pulled at them and the strap broke, and that is how she got away. When we searched him just now, they were in his pocket."

"Oh no, oh no, no; it'll be cleared up in five minutes," he cried again.

"Have a look at them."

The strap had been newly broken, the eye-piece was jammed. The logic of evidence said "Guilty."

"Did she say any more?"

"There was an echo that appears to have frightened her. Did you go into those caves?"

"I saw one of them. There was an echo. Did it get on her nerves?"

"I couldn't worry her overmuch with questions. She'll have plenty to go through in the witness-box. They don't bear thinking about, these next weeks. I wish the Marabar Hills and all they contain were at the bottom of the sea. Evening after evening one saw them from the club, and they were just a harmless name. . . . Yes, we start already." For a visiting card was brought; Vakil Mahmoud Ali, legal adviser to the prisoner, asked to be allowed to see him. McBryde signed, gave permission, and continued: "I heard some more from Miss Derek—she is an old friend of us both and talks freely; well—her account is that you went off to locate the camp, and almost at once she heard stones falling on the Kawa Dol and saw Miss Quested running straight down the face of a precipice. Well. She climbed up a sort of gully to her, and found her practically done for—her helmet off——"

"Was a guide not with her?" interrupted Fielding.

"No. She had got among some cactuses. Miss Derek saved her life coming just then—she was beginning to fling herself about. She helped her down to the car. Miss Quested couldn't stand the Indian driver, cried, 'Keep him away'—and it was that that put our friend on the track of what had happened. They made straight for our bungalow, and are there now. That's the story as far as I know it yet. She sent the driver to join you. I think she behaved with great sense."

"I suppose there's no possibility of my seeing Miss Quested?" he asked suddenly.

"I hardly think that would do. Surely."

"I was afraid you 'ld say that. I should very much like to."

"She is in no state to see anyone. Besides, you don't know her well."

"Hardly at all. . . . But you see I believe she's under some hideous delusion, and that that wretched boy is innocent."

The policeman started in surprise, and a shadow passed over his face, for he could not bear his dispositions to be upset. "I had no idea that was in your mind," he said, and looked for support at the signed deposition, which lay before him.

"Those field-glasses upset me for a minute, but I've thought since: it's impossible that, having attempted to assault her, he would put her glasses into his pocket."

"Quite possible, I'm afraid; when an Indian goes bad, he goes not only very bad, but very queer."

"I don't follow."

"How should you? When you think of crime you think of English crime. The psychology here is different. I dare say you'll tell me next that he was quite normal when he came down from the hill to greet you. No reason he should not be. Read any of the Mutiny records; which, rather than the Bhagavad Gita, should be your Bible in this country. Though I'm not sure that the one and the other are not closely connected. Am I not being beastly? But, you see, Fielding, as I've said to you once before, you're a schoolmaster, and consequently you come across these people at their best. That's what puts you wrong. They can be charming as boys. But I know them as they really are, after they have developed into men. Look at this, for instance." He held up Aziz' pocket-case. "I am going through the contents. They are not edifying. Here is a letter from a friend who apparently keeps a brothel."

"I don't want to hear his private letters."

"It'll have to be quoted in Court, as bearing on his morals. He was fixing up to see women at Calcutta."

"Oh, that'll do, that'll do."

McBryde stopped, naïvely puzzled. It was obvious to him that any two sahibs ought to pool all they knew about any Indian, and he could not think where the objection came in.

"I dare say you have the right to throw stones at a young man for doing that, but I haven't. I did the same at his age."

So had the Superintendent of Police, but he considered that the conversation had taken a turn that was undesirable. He did not like Fielding's next remark either.

"Miss Quested really cannot be seen? You do know that for a certainty?"

"You have never explained to me what's in your mind here. Why on earth do you want to see her?"

"On the off chance of her recanting before you send in that report and he's committed for trial, and the whole thing goes to blazes. Old man, don't argue about this, but do of your goodness just ring up your wife or Miss Derek and enquire. It'll cost you nothing."

"It's no use ringing up them," he replied, stretching out for the telephone. "Callendar settles a question like that, of course. You haven't grasped that she's seriously ill."

"He's sure to refuse, it's all he exists for," said the other desperately.

The expected answer came back: the Major would not hear of the patient being troubled.

"I only wanted to ask her whether she is certain, dead certain, that it was Aziz who followed her into the cave."

"Possibly my wife might ask her that much."

"But *I* wanted to ask her. I want someone who believes in him to ask her."

"What difference does that make?"

"She is among people who disbelieve in Indians."

"Well, she tells her own story, doesn't she?"

"I know, but she tells it to you."

McBryde raised his eyebrows, murmuring: "A bit too finespun. Anyhow, Callendar won't hear of you seeing her. I'm sorry to say he gave a bad account just now. He says that she is by no means out of danger."

They were silent. Another card was brought into the office—Hamidullah's. The opposite army was gathering.

"I must put this report through now, Fielding."

"I wish you wouldn't."

"How can I not?"

"I feel that things are rather unsatisfactory as well as most disastrous. We are heading for a most awful smash. I can see your prisoner, I suppose."

He hesitated. "His own people seem in touch with him all right."

"Well, when he's done with them."

"I wouldn't keep you waiting; good heavens, you take precedence of any Indian visitor, of course. I meant what's the good. Why mix yourself up with pitch?"

"I say he's innocent——"

"Innocence or guilt, why mix yourself up? What's the good?"

"Oh, good, good," he cried, feeling that every earth was being stopped. "One's got to breathe occasionally, at least I have. I mayn't see her, and now I mayn't see him. I promised him to come up here with him to you, but Turton called me off before I could get two steps."

"Sort of all-white thing the Burra Sahib would do," he muttered sentimentally. And trying not to sound patronizing, he stretched his hand over the table, and said: "We shall all have to hang together, old man, I'm afraid. I'm your junior in years, I know, but very much your senior in service; you don't happen to know this poisonous country as well as I do, and you must take it from me that the general situation is going to be nasty at Chandrapore during the next few weeks, very nasty indeed."

"So I have just told you."

"But at a time like this there's no room for—well—personal views. The man who doesn't toe the line is lost."

"I see what you mean."

"No, you don't see entirely. He not only loses himself, he weakens his friends. If you leave the line, you leave a gap in the line. These jackals"—he pointed at the lawyers' cards—"are looking with all their eyes for a gap."

"Can I visit Aziz?" was his answer.

"No." Now that he knew of Turton's attitude, the policeman had no doubts. "You may see him on a magistrate's order, but on my own responsibility I don't feel justified. It might lead to more complications."

Fielding paused, reflecting that if he had been either ten years younger or ten years longer in India, he would have responded to McBryde's appeal. The bit between his teeth, he then said, "To whom do I apply for an order?"

"City Magistrate."

"That sounds comfortable!"

"Yes, one can't very well worry poor Heaslop."

More "evidence" appeared at this moment—the table-drawer from Aziz' bungalow, borne with triumph in a corporal's arms.

"Photographs of women. Ah!"

"That's his wife," said Fielding, wincing.

"How do you know that?"

"He told me."

McBryde gave a faint, incredulous smile, and started rummaging in the drawer. His face became inquisitive and slightly bestial. "Wife indeed, I know those wives!" he was thinking. Aloud he said: "Well, you must trot off now, old man, and the Lord help us, the Lord help us all. . . ."

As if his prayer had been heard, there was a sudden rackety-dacket on a temple bell.

CHAPTER 19

Hamidullah was the next stage. He was waiting outside the Superintendent's office, and sprang up respectfully when he saw Fielding. To the Englishman's passionate "It's all a mistake," he answered, "Ah, ah, has some evidence come?"

"It will come," said Fielding, holding his hand.

"Ah, yes, Mr. Fielding; but when once an Indian has been arrested, we do not know where it will stop." His manner was deferential. "You are very good to greet me in this public fashion, I appreciate it; but, Mr. Fielding, nothing convinces a magistrate except evidence. Did Mr. McBryde make any remark when my card came in? Do you think my application annoyed him, will prejudice him against my friend at all? If so, I will gladly retire."

"He's not annoyed, and if he was, what does it matter?"

"Ah, it's all very well for you to speak like that, but we have to live in this country."

The leading barrister of Chandrapore, with the dignified manner and Cambridge degree, had been rattled. He too loved Aziz, and knew he was calumniated; but faith did not rule his heart, and he prated of "policy" and "evidence" in a way that saddened the Englishman. Fielding, too, had his anxieties—he didn't like the field-glasses or the discrepancy over the guide—but he relegated them to the edge of his mind, and forbade them to infect its core. Aziz *was* innocent, and all action must be based on that, and the people who said he was guilty were wrong, and it was hopeless to try to propitiate them. At the moment when he was throwing in his lot with Indians, he realized the profundity of the gulf that divided him from them. They always do something disappointing. Aziz had tried to run away from the police, Mohammed Latif had not checked the pilfering. And now Hamidullah!—instead of raging and denouncing, he temporized. Are Indians cowards? No, but they are bad starters and occasionally jib. Fear is everywhere; the British Raj rests on it; the respect and courtesy Fielding himself enjoyed were unconscious acts of propitiation. He told Hamidullah to cheer up, all would end well; and Hamidullah did cheer up, and became pugnacious and sensible. McBryde's remark, "If you leave the line, you leave a gap in the line," was being illustrated.

"First and foremost, the question of bail . . ."

Application must be made this afternoon. Fielding wanted to stand surety. Hamidullah thought the Nawab Bahadur should be approached.

"Why drag in him, though?"

To drag in everyone was precisely the barrister's aim. He then suggested that the lawyer in charge of the case would be a Hindu; the defence would then make a wider appeal. He mentioned one or two names—men from a distance who would not be intimidated by local conditions—and said he should prefer Amritrao, a Calcutta barrister, who had a high reputation professionally and personally, but who was notoriously anti-British.

Fielding demurred; this seemed to him going to the other extreme. Aziz must be cleared, but with a minimum of racial hatred. Amritrao was loathed at the club. His retention would be regarded as a political challenge.

"Oh no, we must hit with all our strength. When I saw my friend's private papers carried in just now in the arms of a dirty policeman, I said to myself, 'Amritrao is the man to clear up this.'"

There was a lugubrious pause. The temple bell continued to jangle harshly. The interminable and disastrous day had scarcely reached its afternoon. Continuing their work, the wheels of Dominion now propelled a messenger on a horse from the Superintendent to the Magistrate with an official report of arrest. "Don't complicate, let the cards play themselves," entreated Fielding, as he watched the man disappear into dust. "We're bound to win, there's nothing else we can do. She will never be able to substantiate the charge."

This comforted Hamidullah, who remarked with complete sincerity, "At a crisis, the English are really unequalled."

"Good-bye, then, my dear Hamidullah (we must drop the 'Mr.' now). Give Aziz my love when you see him, and tell him to keep calm, calm, calm. I shall go back to the College now. If you want me, ring me up; if you don't, don't, for I shall be very busy."

"Good-bye, my dear Fielding, and you actually are on our side against your own people?"

"Yes. Definitely."

He regretted taking sides. To slink through India unlabelled was his aim. Henceforward he would be called "anti-British," "seditious"—terms that bored him, and diminished his utility. He foresaw that besides being a tragedy, there would be a muddle; already he saw several tiresome little knots, and each time his eye returned to them, they were larger. Born in freedom, he was not afraid of the muddle, but he recognized its existence.

This section of the day concluded in a queer vague talk with Professor Godbole. The interminable affair of the Russell's Viper was again in question. Some weeks before, one of the masters at the College, an unpopular Parsi, had found a Russell's Viper nosing round his classroom. Perhaps it had crawled in of itself, but perhaps it had not, and the staff still continued to interview their Principal about it, and to take up his time with their theories. The reptile is so poisonous that he did not like to cut them short, and this they knew. Thus when his mind was bursting with other troubles and he was debating whether he should compose a letter of appeal to Miss Quested, he was obliged to listen to a speech which lacked both basis and conclusion, and floated through air. At the end of it Godbole said, "May I now take my leave?"—always an indication that he had not come to his point yet. "Now I take my leave, I must tell you how glad I am to hear that after all you succeeded in reaching the Marabar. I feared my unpunctuality had prevented you, but you went (a far pleasanter method) in Miss Derek's car. I hope the expedition was a successful one."

"The news has not reached you yet, I can see."

"Oh yes."

"No; there has been a terrible catastrophe about Aziz."

"Oh yes. That is all round the College."

"Well, the expedition where that occurs can scarcely be called a successful one," said Fielding, with an amazed stare.

"I cannot say. I was not present."

He stared again—a most useless operation, for no eye could see what lay at the bottom of the Brahman's mind, and yet he had a mind and a heart too, and all his friends trusted him, without knowing why. "I am most frightfully cut up," he said.

"So I saw at once on entering your office. I must not detain you, but I have a small private difficulty on which I want your help; I am leaving your service shortly, as you know."

"Yes, alas!"

"And am returning to my birthplace in Central India to take charge of education there. I want to start a High School there on sound English lines, that shall be as like Government College as possible."

"Well?" he sighed, trying to take an interest.

"At present there is only vernacular education at Mau. I shall feel it my duty to change all that. I shall advise His Highness to sanction at least a High School in the Capital, and if possible another in each pargana." [1]

Fielding sunk his head on his arms; really, Indians were sometimes unbearable.

"The point—the point on which I desire your help is this: what name should be given to the school?"

"A name? A name for a school?" he said, feeling sickish suddenly, as he had done in the waiting-room.

"Yes, a name, a suitable title, by which it can be called, by which it may be generally known."

"Really—I have no names for schools in my head. I can think of nothing but our poor Aziz. Have you grasped that at the present moment he is in prison?"

"Oh yes. Oh no, I do not expect an answer to my question now. I only meant that when you are at leisure, you might think the matter over, and suggest two or three alternative titles for schools. I had thought of the 'Mr. Fielding High School,' but failing that, the 'King-Emperor George the Fifth.' "

"Godbole!"

The old fellow put his hands together, and looked sly and charming.

"Is Aziz innocent or guilty?"

"That is for the Court to decide. The verdict will be in strict accordance with the evidence, I make no doubt."

"Yes, yes, but your personal opinion. Here's a man we both like, generally esteemed; he lives here quietly doing his work. Well, what's one to make of it? Would he or would he not do such a thing?"

"Ah, that is rather a different question from your previous one, and also more difficult: I mean difficult in our philosophy. Dr. Aziz is a most worthy young man, I have a great regard for him; but I think you are asking me whether the individual can commit good actions or evil actions, and that is rather difficult for us." He spoke without emotion and in short tripping syllables.

"I ask you: did he do it or not? Is that plain? I know he didn't, and

1. **pargana**: a territorial division; i.e., like a county.

from that I start. I mean to get at the true explanation in a couple of days. My last notion is that it's the guide who went round with them. Malice on Miss Quested's part—it couldn't be that, though Hamidullah thinks so. She has certainly had some appalling experience. But you tell me, oh no— because good and evil are the same."

"No, not exactly, please, according to our philosophy. Because nothing can be performed in isolation. All perform a good action, when one is performed, and when an evil action is performed, all perform it. To illustrate my meaning, let me take the case in point as an example.

"I am informed that an evil action was performed in the Marabar Hills, and that a highly esteemed English lady is now seriously ill in consequence. My answer to that is this: that action was performed by Dr. Aziz." He stopped and sucked in his thin cheeks. "It was performed by the guide." He stopped again. "It was performed by you." Now he had an air of daring and of coyness. "It was performed by me." He looked shyly down the sleeve of his own coat. "And by my students. It was even performed by the lady herself. When evil occurs, it expresses the whole of the universe. Similarly when good occurs."

"And similarly when suffering occurs, and so on and so forth, and everything is anything and nothing something," he muttered in his irritation, for he needed the solid ground.

"Excuse me, you are now again changing the basis of our discussion. We were discussing good and evil. Suffering is merely a matter for the individual. If a young lady has sunstroke, that is a matter of no significance to the universe. Oh no, not at all. Oh no, not the least. It is an isolated matter, it only concerns herself. If she thought her head did not ache, she would not be ill, and that would end it. But it is far otherwise in the case of good and evil. They are not what we think them, they are what they are, and each of us has contributed to both."

"You're preaching that evil and good are the same."

"Oh no, excuse me once again. Good and evil are different, as their names imply. But, in my own humble opinion, they are both of them aspects of my Lord. He is present in the one, absent in the other, and the difference between presence and absence is great, as great as my feeble mind can grasp. Yet absence implies presence, absence is not non-existence, and we are therefore entitled to repeat, 'Come, come, come, come.'" And in the same breath, as if to cancel any beauty his words might have contained, he added, "But did you have time to visit any of the interesting Marabar antiquities?"

Fielding was silent, trying to meditate and rest his brain.

"Did you not even see the tank by the usual camping ground?" he nagged.

"Yes, yes," he answered distractedly, wandering over half a dozen things at once.

"That is good, then you saw the Tank of the Dagger." And he related a legend which might have been acceptable if he had told it at the tea-party a fortnight ago. It concerned a Hindu Rajah who had slain his own sister's son, and the dagger with which he performed the deed remained clamped to his hand until in the course of years he came to the Marabar Hills, where he was thirsty and wanted to drink but saw a thirsty cow and ordered the water to be offered to her first, which, when done, "dagger fell from his hand, and to commemorate miracle he built Tank." Professor Godbole's conversations frequently culminated in a cow. Fielding received this one in gloomy silence.

In the afternoon he obtained a permit and saw Aziz, but found him un-approachable through misery. "You deserted me," was the only coherent remark. He went away to write his letter to Miss Quested. Even if it reached her, it would do no good, and probably the McBrydes would withhold it. Miss Quested did pull him up short. She was such a dry, sensible girl, and quite without malice: the last person in Chandrapore wrongfully to accuse an Indian.

CHAPTER 20

Although Miss Quested had not made herself popular with the English, she brought out all that was fine in their character. For a few hours an exalted emotion gushed forth, which the women felt even more keenly than the men, if not for so long. "What can we do for our sister?" was the only thought of Mesdames Callendar and Lesley, as they drove through the pelting heat to enquire. Mrs. Turton was the only visitor admitted to the sick-room. She came out ennobled by an unselfish sorrow. "She is my own darling girl," were the words she spoke, and then, remembering that she had called her "not pukka" and resented her engagement to young Heaslop, she began to cry. No one had ever seen the Collector's wife cry. Capable of tears—yes, but always reserving them for some adequate occasion, and now it had come. Ah, why had they not all been kinder to the stranger, more patient, given her not only hospitality but their hearts? The tender core of the heart that is so seldom used—they employed it for a little, under the stimulus of remorse. If all is over (as Major Callendar implied), well, all is over, and nothing can be done, but they retained some responsibility in her grievous wrong that they couldn't define. If she wasn't one of them, they ought to have made her one, and they could never do that now, she had passed beyond their invitation. "Why don't one think more of other people?" sighed pleasure-loving Miss Derek.

These regrets only lasted in their pure form for a few hours. Before sunset, other considerations adulterated them, and the sense of guilt (so strangely connected with our first sight of any suffering) had begun to wear away.

People drove into the club with studious calm—the jogtrot of country gentlefolk between green hedgerows, for the natives must not suspect that they were agitated. They exchanged the usual drinks, but everything tasted different, and then they looked out at the palisade of cactuses stabbing the purple throat of the sky; they realized that they were thousands of miles from any scenery that they understood. The club was fuller than usual, and several parents had brought their children into the rooms reserved for adults, which gave the air of the Residency at Lucknow. One young mother—a brainless but most beautiful girl—sat on a low ottoman in the smoking-room with her baby in her arms; her husband was away in the district, and she dared not return to her bungalow in case the "niggers attacked." The wife of a small railway official, she was generally snubbed; but this evening, with her abundant figure and masses of corn-gold hair, she symbolized all that is worth fighting and dying for; more permanent a symbol, perhaps, than poor Adela. "Don't worry, Mrs. Blakiston, those drums are only Mohurram," the men would tell her. "Then they've started," she moaned, clasping the infant and rather wishing he would not blow bubbles down his chin at such a moment as this. "No, of course not, and anyhow, they're not coming to the club." "And they're not coming to the Burra Sahib's bungalow either, my dear, and that's where you and your baby'll sleep to-night," answered Mrs. Turton, towering by her side like Pallas Athene, and determining in the future not to be such a snob.

The Collector clapped his hands for silence. He was much calmer than when he had flown out at Fielding. He was indeed always calmer when he addressed several people than in a *tête-à-tête*. "I want to talk specially to the ladies," he said. "Not the least cause for alarm. Keep cool, keep cool. Don't go out more than you can help, don't go into the city, don't talk before your servants. That's all."

"Harry, is there any news from the city?" asked his wife, standing at some distance from him, and also assuming her public safety voice. The rest were silent during the august colloquy.

"Everything absolutely normal."

"I had gathered as much. Those drums are merely Mohurram, of course."

"Merely the preparation for it—the Procession is not till next week."

"Quite so, not till Monday."

"Mr. McBryde's down there disguised as a Holy Man," said Mrs. Callendar.

"That's exactly the sort of thing that must not be said," he remarked, pointing at her. "Mrs. Callendar, be more careful than that, please, in these times."

"I . . . well, I . . ." She was not offended, his severity made her feel safe.

"Any more questions? Necessary questions."

"Is the—where is he——" Mrs. Lesley quavered.

"Jail. Bail has been refused."

Fielding spoke next. He wanted to know whether there was an official bulletin about Miss Quested's health, or whether the grave reports were due to gossip. His question produced a bad effect, partly because he had pronounced her name; she like Aziz, was always referred to by a periphrasis.

"I hope Callendar may be able to let us know how things are going before long."

"I fail to see how that last question can be termed a necessary question," said Mrs. Turton.

"Will all ladies leave the smoking-room now, please?" he cried, clapping his hands again. "And remember what I have said. We look to you to help us through a difficult time, and you can help us by behaving as if everything is normal. It is all I ask. Can I rely on you?"

"Yes, indeed, Burra Sahib," they chorused out of peaked, anxious faces. They moved out, subdued yet elated, Mrs. Blakiston in their midst like a sacred flame. His simple words had reminded them that they were an outpost of Empire. By the side of their compassionate love for Adela another sentiment sprang up which was to strangle it in the long run. Its first signs were prosaic and small. Mrs. Turton made her loud, hard jokes at bridge, Mrs. Lesley began to knit a comforter.

When the smoking-room was clear, the Collector sat on the edge of a table, so that he could dominate without formality. His mind whirled with contradictory impulses. He wanted to avenge Miss Quested and punish Fielding, while remaining scrupulously fair. He wanted to flog every native that he saw, but to do nothing that would lead to a riot or to the necessity for military intervention. The dread of having to call in the troops was vivid to him; soldiers put one thing straight, but leave a dozen others crooked, and they love to humiliate the civilian administration. One soldier was in the room this evening—a stray subaltern from a Gurkha regiment; he was a little drunk, and regarded his presence as providential. The Collector sighed. There seemed nothing for it but the old weary business of compromise and moderation. He longed for the good old days when an Englishman could satisfy his own honour and no questions asked afterwards. Poor young Heaslop had taken a step in this direction, by refusing bail, but the Collector couldn't feel this was wise of poor young Heaslop. Not only would the Nawab Bahadur and others be angry, but the Government of India itself also watches—and behind it is that caucus of cranks and cravens, the British Parliament. He had constantly to remind himself that, in the eyes of the law, Aziz was not yet guilty, and the effort fatigued him.

The others, less responsible, could behave naturally. They had started speaking of "women and children"—that phrase that exempts the male from sanity when it has been repeated a few times. Each felt that all he loved best in the world was at stake, demanded revenge, and was filled with a not unpleasing glow, in which the chilly and half-known features of Miss Quested vanished, and were replaced by all that is sweetest and warmest in the private life. "But it's the women and children," they repeated, and the Collector knew he ought to stop them intoxicating themselves, but he hadn't the heart. "They ought to be compelled to give hostages," etc. Many of the said women and children were leaving for the Hill Station in a few days, and the suggestion was made that they should be packed off at once in a special train.

"*And* a jolly suggestion," the subaltern cried. "The army's got to come in sooner or later. (A special train was in his mind inseparable from troops.) This would never have happened if Barabas Hill was under military control. Station a bunch of Gurkhas at the entrance of the cave was all that was wanted."

"Mrs. Blakiston was saying if only there were a few Tommies," remarked someone.

"English no good," he cried, getting his loyalties mixed. "Native troops for this country. Give me the sporting type of native, give me Gurkhas, give me Rajputs, give me Jats, give me the Punjabi, give me Sikhs, give me Marathas, Bhils, Afridis and Pathans, and really if it comes to that, I don't mind if you give me the scums of the bazaars. Properly led, mind. I'd lead them anywhere——"

The Collector nodded at him pleasantly, and said to his own people: "Don't start carrying arms about. I want everything to go on precisely as usual, until there's cause for the contrary. Get the womenfolk off to the hills, but do it quietly, and for Heaven's sake no more talk of special trains. Never mind what you think or feel. Possibly I have feelings too. One isolated Indian has attempted—is charged with an attempted crime." He flipped his forehead hard with his finger-nail, and they all realized that he felt as deeply as they did, and they loved him, and determined not to increase his difficulties. "Act upon that fact until there are more facts," he concluded. "Assume every Indian is an angel."

They murmured, "Right you are, Burra Sahib. . . . Angels. . . . Exactly. . . ." From the subaltern: "Exactly what I said. The native's all

right if you get him alone. Lesley! Lesley! You remember the one I had a
knock with on your Maidan last month. Well, he was all right. Any native
who plays polo is all right. What you've got to stamp on is these educated
classes, and, mind, I do know what I'm talking about this time."

The smoking-room door opened, and let in a feminine buzz. Mrs.
Turton called out, "She's better," and from both sections of the community a sigh of joy and relief rose. The Civil Surgeon, who had brought
the good news, came in. His cumbrous, pasty face looked ill-tempered. He
surveyed the company, saw Fielding crouched below him on an ottoman,
and said, "H'm!" Everyone began pressing him for details. "No one's out
of danger in this country as long as they have a temperature," was his answer. He appeared to resent his patient's recovery, and no one who knew
the old Major and his ways was surprised at this.

"Squat down, Callendar; tell us all about it."

"Take me some time to do that."

"How's the old lady?"

"Temperature."

"My wife heard she was sinking."

"So she may be. I guarantee nothing. I really can't be plagued with questions, Lesley."

"Sorry, old man."

"Heaslop's just behind me."

At the name of Heaslop a fine and beautiful expression was renewed on
every face. Miss Quested was only a victim, but young Heaslop was a
martyr; he was the recipient of all the evil intended against them by the
country they had tried to serve; he was bearing the sahib's cross. And
they fretted because they could do nothing for him in return; they felt
so craven sitting on softness and attending the course of the law.

"I wish to God I hadn't given my jewel of an assistant leave. I 'ld cut
my tongue out first. To feel I'm responsible, that's what hits me. To refuse, and then give in under pressure. That is what I did, my sons, that is
what I did."

Fielding took his pipe from his mouth and looked at it thoughtfully.
Thinking him afraid, the other went on: "I understood an Englishman was
to accompany the expedition. That is why I gave in."

"No one blames you, my dear Callendar," said the Collector, looking
down. "We are all to blame in the sense that we ought to have seen the
expedition was insufficiently guaranteed, and stopped it. I knew about it
myself; we lent our car this morning to take the ladies to the station. We
are all implicated in that sense, but not an atom of blame attaches to you
personally."

"I don't feel that. I wish I could. Responsibility is a very awful thing, and I've no use for the man who shirks it." His eyes were directed on Fielding. Those who knew that Fielding had undertaken to accompany and missed the early train were sorry for him; it was what is to be expected when a man mixes himself up with natives; always ends in some indignity. The Collector, who knew more, kept silent, for the official in him still hoped that Fielding would toe the line. The conversation turned to women and children again, and under its cover Major Callendar got hold of the subaltern, and set him on to bait the schoolmaster. Pretending to be more drunk than he really was, he began to make semi-offensive remarks.

"Heard about Miss Quested's servant?" reinforced the Major.

"No, what about him?"

"Heaslop warned Miss Quested's servant last night never to lose sight of her. Prisoner got hold of this and managed to leave him behind. Bribed him. Heaslop has just found out the whole story, with names and sums—a well-known pimp to those people gave the money, Mohammed Latif by name. So much for the servant. What about the Englishman—our friend here? How did they get rid of him? Money again."

Fielding rose to his feet, supported by murmurs and exclamations, for no one yet suspected his integrity.

"Oh, I'm being misunderstood, apologies," said the Major offensively. "I didn't mean they bribed Mr. Fielding."

"Then what do you mean?"

"They paid the other Indian to make you late—Godbole. He was saying his prayers. I know those prayers!"

"That's ridiculous . . ." He sat down again, trembling with rage; person after person was being dragged into the mud.

Having shot this bolt, the Major prepared the next. "Heaslop also found out something from his mother. Aziz paid a herd of natives to suffocate her in a cave. That was the end of her, or would have been only she got out. Nicely planned, wasn't it? Neat. Then he could go on with the girl. He and she and a guide, provided by the same Mohammed Latif. Guide now can't be found. Pretty." His voice broke into a roar. "It's not the time for sitting down. It's the time for action. Call in the troops and clear the bazaars."

The Major's outbursts were always discounted, but he made everyone uneasy on this occasion. The crime was even worse than they had supposed—the unspeakable limit of cynicism, untouched since 1857.[1] Fielding forgot his anger on poor old Godbole's behalf, and became thoughtful; the evil was propagating in every direction, it seemed to have an existence of its own, apart from anything that was done or said by individuals, and

1. 1857 was the year of the famous Sepoy Rebellion at Lucknow.

he understood better why both Aziz and Hamidullah had been inclined to
lie down and die. His adversary saw that he was in trouble, and now ventured to say, "I suppose nothing that's said inside the club will go outside
the club?" winking the while at Lesley.

"Why should it?" responded Lesley.

"Oh, nothing. I only heard a rumour that a certain member here present
has been seeing the prisoner this afternoon. You can't run with the hare
and hunt with the hounds, at least not in this country."

"Does anyone here present want to?"

Fielding was determined not to be drawn again. He had something to
say, but it should be at his own moment. The attack failed to mature, because the Collector did not support it. Attention shifted from him for a
time. Then the buzz of women broke out again. The door had been
opened by Ronny.

The young man looked exhausted and tragic, also gentler than usual.
He always showed deference to his superiors, but now it came straight
from his heart. He seemed to appeal for their protection in the insult that
had befallen him, and they, in instinctive homage, rose to their feet. But
every human act in the East is tainted with officialism, and while honour-
ing him they condemned Aziz and India. Fielding realized this, and he
remained seated. It was an ungracious, a caddish thing to do, perhaps an
unsound thing to do, but he felt he had been passive long enough, and that
he might be drawn into the wrong current if he did not make a stand.
Ronny, who had not seen him, said in husky tones, "Oh, please—please all
sit down, I only want to listen what has been decided."

"Heaslop, I'm telling them I'm against any show of force," said the Collector apologetically. "I don't know whether you will feel as I do, but
that is how I am situated. When the verdict is obtained, it will be another
matter."

"You are sure to know best; I have no experience, Burra Sahib."

"How is your mother, old boy?"

"Better, thank you. I wish everyone would sit down."

"Some have never got up," the young soldier said.

"And the Major brings us an excellent report of Miss Quested," Turton
went on.

"I do, I do, I'm satisfied."

"You thought badly of her earlier, did you not, Major? That's why I
refused bail."

Callendar laughed with friendly inwardness, and said, "Heaslop, Heaslop, next time bail's wanted, ring up the old doctor before giving it; his
shoulders are broad, and, speaking in the strictest confidence, don't take
the old doctor's opinion too seriously. He's a blithering idiot, we can

always leave it at that, but he'll do the little he can towards keeping in quod the——" He broke off with affected politeness. "Oh, but he has one of his friends here."

The subaltern called, "Stand up, you swine."

"Mr. Fielding, what has prevented you from standing up?" said the Collector, entering the fray at last. It was the attack for which Fielding had waited, and to which he must reply.

"May I make a statement, sir?"

"Certainly."

Seasoned and self-contained, devoid of the fervours of nationality or youth, the schoolmaster did what was for him a comparatively easy thing. He stood up and said. "I believe Dr. Aziz to be innocent."

"You have a right to hold that opinion if you choose, but pray is that any reason why you should insult Mr. Heaslop?"

"May I conclude my statement?"

"Certainly."

"I am waiting for the verdict of the courts. If he is guilty I resign from my service, and leave India. I resign from the club now."

"Hear, hear!" said voices, not entirely hostile, for they liked the fellow for speaking out.

"You have not answered my question. Why did you not stand when Mr. Heaslop entered?"

"With all deference, sir, I am not here to answer questions, but to make a personal statement, and I have concluded it."

"May I ask whether you have taken over charge of this District?"

Fielding moved towards the door.

"One moment, Mr. Fielding. You are not to go yet, please. Before you leave the club, from which you do very well to resign, you will express some detestation of the crime, and you will apologize to Mr. Heaslop."

"Are you speaking to me officially, sir?"

The Collector, who never spoke otherwise, was so infuriated that he lost his head. He cried, "Leave this room at once, and I deeply regret that I demeaned myself to meet you at the station. You have sunk to the level of your associates; you are weak, weak, that is what is wrong with you——"

"I want to leave the room, but cannot while this gentleman prevents me," said Fielding lightly; the subaltern had got across his path.

"Let him go," said Ronny, almost in tears.

It was the only appeal that could have saved the situation. Whatever Heaslop wished must be done. There was a slight scuffle at the door, from which Fielding was propelled, a little more quickly than is natural, into the room where the ladies were playing cards. "Fancy if I'd fallen or got angry," he thought. Of course he was a little angry. His peers had never offered him violence or called him weak before, besides Heaslop had heaped coals of fire on his head. He wished he had not picked the quarrel over poor suffering Heaslop, when there were cleaner issues at hand.

However, there it was, done, muddled through, and to cool himself and regain mental balance he went on to the upper verandah for a moment, where the first object he saw was the Marabar Hills. At this distance and hour they leapt into beauty; they were Monsalvat, Walhalla,[2] the towers of a cathedral, peopled with saints and heroes, and covered with flowers. What miscreant lurked in them, presently to be detected by the activities of the law? Who was the guide, and had he been found yet? What was the "echo" of which the girl complained? He did not know, but presently he would know. Great is information, and she shall prevail. It was the last moment of the light, and as he gazed at the Marabar Hills they seemed to move graciously towards him like a queen, and their charm became the sky's. At the moment they vanished they were everywhere, the cool benediction of the night descended, the stars sparkled, and the whole universe was a hill. Lovely, exquisite moment—but passing the Englishman with averted face and on swift wings. He experienced nothing himself; it was as if someone had told him there was such a moment, and he was obliged to believe. And he felt dubious and discontented suddenly, and wondered whether he was really and truly successful as a human being. After forty years' experience, he had learnt to manage his life and make the best of it on advanced European lines, had developed his personality, explored his limitations, controlled his passions—and he had done it all without becoming either pedantic or worldly. A creditable achievement, but as the moment passed, he felt he ought to have been working at something else the whole time,—he didn't know at what, never would know, never could know, and that was why he felt sad.

CHAPTER 21

Dismissing his regrets, as inappropriate to the matter in hand, he accomplished the last section of the day by riding off to his new allies. He was glad that he had broken with the club, for he would have picked up scraps of gossip there, and reported them down in the city, and he was glad to be denied this opportunity. He would miss his billiards, and occasional tennis, and cracks with McBryde, but really that was all, so light did he travel. At the entrance of the bazaars, a tiger made his horse shy—a youth

---

2. **Monsalvat:** the castle of the Holy Grail in Richard Wagner's opera *Parsifal;* **Walhalla:** in Norse mythology, the great hall into which the souls of fallen heroes were borne.

dressed up as a tiger, the body striped brown and yellow, a mask over the face. Mohurram was working up. The city beat a good many drums, but seemed good-tempered. He was invited to inspect a small tazia—a flimsy and frivolous erection, more like a crinoline than the tomb of the grandson of the Prophet, done to death at Kerbela. Excited children were pasting coloured paper over its ribs. The rest of the evening he spent with the Nawab Bahadur, Hamidullah, Mahmoud Ali, and others of the confederacy. The campaign was also working up. A telegram had been sent to the famous Amritrao, and his acceptance received. Application for bail was to be renewed—it could not well be withheld now that Miss Quested was out of danger. The conference was serious and sensible, but marred by a group of itinerant musicians, who were allowed to play in the compound. Each held a large earthenware jar, containing pebbles, and jerked it up and down in time to a doleful chant. Distracted by the noise, he suggested their dismissal, but the Nawab Bahadur vetoed it; he said that musicians, who had walked many miles, might bring good luck.

Late at night, he had an inclination to tell Professor Godbole of the tactical and moral error he had made in being rude to Heaslop, and to hear what he would say. But the old fellow had gone to bed and slipped off unmolested to his new job in a day or two: he always did possess the knack of slipping off.

CHAPTER 22

Adela lay for several days in the McBryde's bungalow. She had been touched by the sun, also hundreds of cactus spines had to be picked out of her flesh. Hour after hour Miss Derek and Mrs. McBryde examined her through magnifying glasses, always coming on fresh colonies, tiny hairs that might snap off and be drawn into the blood if they were neglected. She lay passive beneath their fingers, which developed the shock that had begun in the cave. Hitherto she had not much minded whether she was touched or not: her senses were abnormally inert and the only contact she anticipated was that of mind. Everything now was transferred to the surface of her body, which began to avenge itself, and feed unhealthily. People seemed very much alike, except that some would come close while others kept away. "In space things touch, in time things part," she repeated to herself while the thorns were being extracted—her brain so weak that she could not decide whether the phrase was a philosophy or a pun.

They were kind to her, indeed over-kind, the men too respectful, the women too sympathetic; whereas Mrs. Moore, the only visitor she wanted, kept away. No one understood her trouble, or knew why she vibrated between hard commonsense and hysteria. She would begin a speech as if nothing particular had happened. "I went into this detestable cave," she would say dryly, "and I remember scratching the wall with my finger-nail, to start the usual echo, and then as I was saying there was this shadow, or sort of shadow, down the entrance tunnel, bottling me up. It seemed like an age, but I suppose the whole thing can't have lasted thirty seconds really. I hit at him with the glasses, he pulled me round the cave by the strap, it broke, I escaped, that's all. He never actually touched me once. It all seems such nonsense." Then her eyes would fill with tears. "Naturally I'm upset, but I shall get over it." And then she would break down entirely, and the women would feel she was one of themselves and cry too, and men in the next room murmur: "Good God, good God!" No one realized that she thought tears vile, a degradation more subtle than anything endured in the Marabar, a negation of her advanced outlook and the natural honesty of her mind. Adela was always trying to "think the incident out," always reminding herself that no harm had been done. There was "the shock," but what is that? For a time her own logic would convince her, then she would hear the echo again, weep, declare she was unworthy of Ronny, and hope her assailant would get the maximum pen-alty. After one of these bouts, she longed to go out into the bazaars and ask pardon from everyone she met, for she felt in some vague way that she was leaving the world worse than she found it. She felt that it was her crime, until the intellect, reawakening, pointed out to her that she was in-accurate here, and set her again upon her sterile round.

If only she could have seen Mrs. Moore! The old lady had not been well either, and was disinclined to come out, Ronny reported. And conse-quently the echo flourished, raging up and down like a nerve in the faculty of her hearing, and the noise in the cave, so unimportant intellectually, was prolonged over the surface of her life. She had struck the polished wall—for no reason—and before the comment had died away, he followed her, and the climax was the falling of her field-glasses. The sound had spouted after her when she escaped, and was going on still like a river that gradu-ally floods the plain. Only Mrs. Moore could drive it back to its source and seal the broken reservoir. Evil was loose . . . she could even hear it entering the lives of others. . . . And Adela spent days in this atmosphere of grief and depression. Her friends kept up their spirits by demanding holocausts of natives, but she was too worried and weak to do that.

When the cactus thorns had all been extracted, and her temperature fallen to normal, Ronny came to fetch her away. He was worn with in-dignation and suffering, and she wished she could comfort him; but inti-macy seemed to caricature itself, and the more they spoke the more wretched and self-conscious they became. Practical talk was the least painful, and he and McBryde now told her one or two things which they had concealed from her during the crisis, by the doctor's orders. She learnt for the first time of the Mohurram troubles. There had nearly been a riot. The last day of the festival, the great procession left its official route, and tried to enter the civil station, and a telephone had been cut because it interrupted the advance of one of the larger paper towers. McBryde and his police had pulled the thing straight—a fine piece of work. They passed on to another and very painful subject: the trial. She would have to appear in court, identify the prisoner, and submit to cross-examination by an Indian lawyer.

"Can Mrs. Moore be with me?" was all she said.

"Certainly, and I shall be there myself," Ronny replied. "The case won't come before me; they've objected to me on personal grounds. It will be at Chandrapore—we thought at one time it would be transferred elsewhere."

"Miss Quested realizes what all that means, though," said McBryde sadly. "The case will come before Das."

Das was Ronny's assistant—own brother to the Mrs. Bhattacharya whose carriage had played them false last month. He was courteous and intelligent, and with the evidence before him could only come to one conclusion; but that he should be judge over an English girl had convulsed the station with wrath, and some of the women had sent a telegram about it to Lady Mellanby, the wife of the Lieutenant-Governor.

"I must come before someone."

"That's—that's the way to face it. You have the pluck, Miss Quested." He grew very bitter over the arrangements, and called them "the fruits of democracy." In the old days an Englishwoman would not have had to appear, nor would any Indian have dared to discuss her private affairs. She would have made her deposition, and judgment would have followed. He apologized to her for the condition of the country, with the result that she gave one of her sudden little shoots of tears. Ronny wandered miserably about the room while she cried, treading upon the flowers of the Kashmir carpet that so inevitably covered it or drumming on the brass Benares bowls. "I do this less every day, I shall soon be quite well," she said, blowing her nose and feeling hideous. "What I need is something to do. That is why I keep on with this ridiculous crying."

"It's not ridiculous, we think you wonderful," said the policeman very sincerely. "It only bothers us that we can't help you more. Your stopping here—at such a time—is the greatest honour this house——" He too was overcome with emotion. "By the way, a letter came here for you while you were ill," he continued. "I opened it, which is a strange confession to make. Will you forgive me? The circumstances are peculiar. It is from Fielding."

"Why should he write to me?"

"A most lamentable thing has happened. The defence got hold of him."

"He's a crank, a crank," said Ronny lightly.

"That's your way of putting it, but a man can be a crank without being a cad. Miss Quested had better know how he behaved to you. If you don't tell her, somebody else will." He told her. "He is now the mainstay of the defence, I needn't add. He is the one righteous Englishman in a horde of tyrants. He receives deputations from the bazaar, and they all chew betel nut and smear one another's hands with scent. It is not easy to enter into the mind of such a man. His students are on strike—out of enthusiasm for him they won't learn their lessons. If it weren't for Fielding one would never have had the Mohurram trouble. He has done a very grave disservice to the whole community. The letter lay here a day or two, waiting till you were well enough, then the situation got so grave that I decided to open it in case it was useful to us."

"Is it?" she said feebly.

"Not at all. He only has the impertinence to suggest you have made a mistake."

"Would that I had!" She glanced through the letter, which was careful and formal in its wording. "Dr. Aziz is innocent," she read. Then her voice began to tremble again. "But think of his behaviour to you, Ronny. When you had already to bear so much for my sake! It was shocking of him. My dear, how can I repay you? How can one repay when one has nothing to give? What is the use of personal relationships when everyone brings less and less to them? I feel we ought all to go back into the desert for centuries and try and get good. I want to begin at the beginning. All the things I thought I'd learnt are just a hindrance, they're not knowledge at all. I'm not fit for personal relationships. Well, let's go, let's go. Of course Mr. Fielding's letter doesn't count; he can think and write what he likes, only he shouldn't have been rude to you when you had so much to bear. That's what matters. . . . I don't want your arm, I'm a magnificent walker, so don't touch me, please."

Mrs. McBryde wished her an affectionate good-bye—a woman with whom she had nothing in common and whose intimacy oppressed her. They would have to meet now, year after year, until one of their husbands was superannuated. Truly Anglo-India had caught her with a vengeance and perhaps it served her right for having tried to take up a line of her own. Humbled yet repelled, she gave thanks. "Oh, we must help one another, we must take the rough with the smooth," said Mrs. McBryde. Miss Derek was there too, still making jokes about her comic Maharajah and Rani. Required as a witness at the trial, she had refused to send back the Mudkul car; they would be frightfully sick. Both Mrs. McBryde and

Miss Derek kissed her, and called her by her Christian name. Then Ronny drove her back. It was early in the morning, for the day, as the hot weather advanced, swelled like a monster at both ends, and left less and less room for the movements of mortals.

As they neared his bungalow, he said: "Mother's looking forward to seeing you, but of course she's old, one mustn't forget that. Old people never take things as one expects, in my opinion." He seemed warning her against approaching disappointment, but she took no notice. Her friendship with Mrs. Moore was so deep and real that she felt sure it would last, whatever else happened. "What can I do to make things easier for you? It's you who matter," she sighed.

"Dear old girl to say so."

"Dear old boy." Then she cried: "Ronny, she isn't ill too?"

He reassured her; Major Callendar was not dissatisfied.

"But you'll find her—irritable. We are an irritable family. Well, you'll see for yourself. No doubt my own nerves are out of order, and I expected more from mother when I came in from the office than she felt able to give. She is sure to make a special effort for you; still, I don't want your home-coming to be a disappointing one. Don't expect too much."

The house came in sight. It was a replica of the bungalow she had left. Puffy, red, and curiously severe, Mrs. Moore was revealed upon a sofa. She didn't get up when they entered, and the surprise of this roused Adela from her own troubles.

"Here you are both back," was the only greeting.

Adela sat down and took her hand. It withdrew, and she felt that just as others repelled her, so did she repel Mrs. Moore.

"Are you all right? You appeared all right when I left," said Ronny, trying not to speak crossly, but he had instructed her to give the girl a pleasant welcome, and he could not but feel annoyed.

"I am all right," she said heavily. "As a matter of fact I have been looking at my return ticket. It is interchangeable, so I have a much larger choice of boats home than I thought."

"We can go into that later, can't we?"

"Ralph and Stella may be wanting to know when I arrive."

"There is plenty of time for all such plans. How do you think our Adela looks?"

"I am counting on you to help me through; it is such a blessing to be with you again, everyone else is a stranger," said the girl rapidly.

But Mrs. Moore showed no inclination to be helpful. A sort of resentment emanated from her. She seemed to say: "Am I to be bothered for ever?" Her Christian tenderness had gone, or had developed into a hardness, a just irritation against the human race; she had taken no interest at the arrest, asked scarcely any questions, and had refused to leave her bed on the awful last night of Mohurram, when an attack was expected on the bungalow.

"I know it's all nothing; I must be sensible, I do try——" Adela continued, working again towards tears. "I shouldn't mind if it had happened anywhere else; at least I really don't know where it did happen."

Ronny supposed that he understood what she meant: she could not identify or describe the particular cave, indeed almost refused to have her mind cleared up about it, and it was recognized that the defence would try to make capital out of this during the trial. He reassured her: the Marabar caves were notoriously like one another; indeed, in the future they were to be numbered in sequence with white paint.

"Yes, I mean that, at least not exactly; but there is this echo that I keep on hearing."

"Oh, what of the echo?" asked Mrs. Moore, paying attention to her for the first time.

"I can't get rid of it."

"I don't suppose you ever will."

Ronny had emphasized to his mother that Adela would arrive in a morbid state, yet she was being positively malicious.

"Mrs. Moore, what is this echo?"

"Don't you know?"

"No—what is it? oh, do say! I felt you would be able to explain it . . . this will comfort me so. . . ."

"If you don't know, you don't know; I can't tell you."

"I think you're rather unkind not to say."

"Say, say, say," said the old lady bitterly. "As if anything can be said! I have spent my life in saying or in listening to sayings; I have listened too much. It is time I was left in peace. Not to die," she added sourly. "No doubt you expect me to die, but when I have seen you and Ronny married, and seen the other two and whether they want to be married—I'll retire then into a cave of my own." She smiled, to bring down her remark into ordinary life and thus add to its bitterness. "Somewhere where no young people will come asking questions and expecting answers. Some shelf."

"Quite so, but meantime a trial is coming on," said her son hotly, "and the notion of most of us is that we'd better pull together and help one another through, instead of being disagreeable. Are you going to talk like that in the witness-box?"

"Why should I be in the witness-box?"

"To confirm certain points in our evidence."

"I have nothing to do with your ludicrous law courts," she said, angry. "I will not be dragged in at all."

"I won't have her dragged in, either! I won't have any more trouble on my account," cried Adela, and again took the hand, which was again withdrawn. "Her evidence is not the least essential."

"I thought she would want to give it. No one blames you, mother, but the fact remains that you dropped off at the first cave, and encouraged Adela to go on with him alone, whereas if you'd been well enough to keep on too nothing would have happened. He planned it, I know. Still, you fell into his trap just like Fielding and Antony before you. . . . Forgive me for speaking so plainly, but you've no right to take up this high and mighty attitude about law courts. If you're ill, that's different; but you say you're all right and you seem so, in which case I thought you'ld want to take your part, I did really."

"I'll not have you worry her whether she's well or ill," said Adela, leaving the sofa and taking his arm; then dropped it with a sigh and sat down again. But he was pleased she had rallied to him and surveyed his mother patronizingly. He had never felt easy with her. She was by no means the dear old lady outsiders supposed, and India had brought her into the open.

"I shall attend your marriage, but not your trial," she informed them, tapping her knee; she had become very restless, and rather ungraceful. "Then I shall go to England."

"You can't go to England in May, as you agreed."

"I have changed my mind."

"Well, we'd better end this unexpected wrangle," said the young man, striding about. "You appear to want to be left out of everything, and that's enough."

"My body, my miserable body," she sighed. "Why isn't it strong? Oh, why can't I walk away and be gone? Why can't I finish my duties and be gone? Why do I get headaches and puff when I walk? And all the time this to do and that to do and this to do in your way and that to do in her way, and everything sympathy and confusion and bearing one another's burdens. Why can't this be done and that be done in my way and they be done and I at peace? Why has anything to be done, I cannot see. Why all this marriage, marriage? . . . The human race would have become a single person centuries ago if marriage was any use. And all this rubbish about love, love in a church, love in a cave, as if there is the least difference, and I held up from my business over such trifles!"

"What do you want?" he said, exasperated. "Can you state it in simple language? If so, do."

"I want my pack of patience cards."

"Very well, get them."

He found, as he expected, that the poor girl was crying. And, as always, an Indian close outside the window, a mali [1] in this case, picking up sounds. Much upset, he sat silent for a moment, thinking over his mother and her senile intrusions. He wished he had never asked her to visit India, or become under any obligation to her.

"Well, my dear girl, this isn't much of a home-coming," he said at last. "I had no idea she had this up her sleeve."

Adela had stopped crying. An extraordinary expression was on her face, half relief, half horror. She repeated, "Aziz, Aziz."

They all avoided mentioning that name. It had become synonymous with the power of evil. He was "the defence," and the sound of it now rang out like the first note of a new symphony.

"Aziz . . . have I made a mistake?"

"You're over-tired," he cried, not much surprised.

"Ronny, he's innocent; I made an awful mistake."

"Well, sit down anyhow." He looked round the room, but only two sparrows were chasing one another. She obeyed and took hold of his hand. He stroked it and she smiled, and gasped as if she had risen to the surface of the water, then touched her ear.

"My echo's better."

"That's good. You'll be perfectly well in a few days, but you must save yourself up for the trial. Das is a very good fellow, we shall all be with you."

"But Ronny, dear Ronny, perhaps there oughtn't to be any trial."

"I don't quite know what you're saying, and I don't think you do."

"If Dr. Aziz never did it he ought to be let out."

A shiver like impending death passed over Ronny. He said hurriedly, "He was let out—until the Mohurram riot, when he had to be put in again." To divert her, he told her the story, which was held to be amusing. Nureddin had stolen the Nawab Bahadur's car and driven Aziz into a ditch in the dark. Both of them had fallen out, and Nureddin had cut his face open. Their wailing had been drowned by the cries of the faithful, and it was quite a time before they were rescued by the police. Nureddin was taken to the Minto Hospital, Aziz restored to prison, with an additional charge against him of disturbing the public peace. "Half a minute," he remarked when the anecdote was over, and went to the telephone to ask Callendar to look in as soon as he found it convenient, because she hadn't borne the journey well.

When he returned, she was in a nervous crisis, but it took a different

1. **mali:** a member of a gardener caste.

form—she clung to him, and sobbed, "Help me to do what I ought. Aziz is good. You heard your mother say so."

"Heard what?"

"He's good; I've been so wrong to accuse him."

"Mother never said so."

"Didn't she?" she asked, quite reasonable, open to every suggestion anyway.

"She never mentioned that name once."

"But, Ronny, I heard her."

"Pure illusion. You can't be quite well, can you, to make up a thing like that."

"I suppose I can't. How amazing of me!"

"I was listening to all she said, as far as it could be listened to; she gets very incoherent."

"When her voice dropped she said it—towards the end, when she talked above love—love—I couldn't follow, but just then she said: 'Doctor Aziz never did it.' "

"Those words?"

"The idea more than the words."

"Never, never, my dear girl. Complete illusion. His name was not mentioned by anyone. Look here—you are confusing this with Fielding's letter."

"That's it, that's it," she cried, greatly relieved. "I knew I'd heard his name somewhere. I am so grateful to you for clearing this up—it's the sort of mistake that worries me, and proves I'm neurotic."

"So you won't go saying he's innocent again, will you? for every servant I've got is a spy." He went to the window. The mali had gone, or rather had turned into two small children—impossible they should know English, but he sent them packing. "They all hate us," he explained. "It'll be all right after the verdict, for I will say this for them, they do accept the accomplished fact; but at present they're pouring out money like water to catch us tripping, and a remark like yours is the very thing they look out for. It would enable them to say it was a put-up job on the part of us officials. You see what I mean."

Mrs. Moore came back, with the same air of ill-temper, and sat down with a flump by the card-table. To clear the confusion up, Ronny asked her point-blank whether she had mentioned the prisoner. She could not understand the question and the reason of it had to be explained. She replied: "I never said his name," and began to play patience.

"I thought you said, 'Aziz is an innocent man,' but it was in Mr. Fielding's letter."

"Of course he is innocent," she answered indifferently: it was the first time she had expressed an opinion on the point.

"You see, Ronny, I was right," said the girl.

"You were not right, she never said it."

"But she thinks it."

"Who cares what she thinks?"

"Red nine on black ten——" from the card-table.

"She can think, and Fielding too, but there's such a thing as evidence, I suppose."

"I know, but——"

"Is it again my duty to talk?" asked Mrs. Moore, looking up. "Apparently, as you keep interrupting me."

"Only if you have anything sensible to say."

"Oh, how tedious . . . trivial . . ." and as when she had scoffed at love, love, love, her mind seemed to move towards them from a great distance and out of darkness. "Oh, why is everything still my duty? when shall I be free from your fuss? Was he in the cave and were you in the cave and on and on . . . and Unto us a Son is born, unto us a Child is given . . . and am I good and is he bad and are we saved? . . . and ending everything the echo."

"I don't hear it so much," said Adela, moving towards her. "You send it away, you do nothing but good, you are so good."

"I am not good, no, bad." She spoke more calmly and resumed her cards, saying as she turned them up, "A bad old woman, bad, bad, detestable. I used to be good with the children growing up, also I meet this young man in his mosque, I wanted him to be happy. Good, happy, small people. They do not exist, they were a dream. . . . But I will not help you to torture him for what he never did. There are different ways of evil and I prefer mine to yours."

"Have you any evidence in the prisoner's favour?" said Ronny in the tones of the just official. "If so, it is your bounden duty to go into the witness-box for him instead of for us. No one will stop you."

"One knows people's characters, as you call them," she retorted disdainfully, as if she really knew more than character but could not impart it. "I have heard both English and Indians speak well of him, and I felt it isn't the sort of thing he would do."

"Feeble, mother, feeble."

"Most feeble."

"And most inconsiderate to Adela."

Adela said: "It would be so appalling if I was wrong. I should take my own life."

He turned on her with: "What was I warning you just now? You know you're right, and the whole station knows it."

"Yes, he . . . This is very, very awful. I'm as certain as ever he followed me . . . only, wouldn't it be possible to withdraw the case? I dread the idea of giving evidence more and more, and you are all so good to women here and you have so much more power than in England—look at Miss Derek's motor-car. Oh, of course it's out of the question, I'm ashamed to have mentioned it; please forgive me."

"That's all right," he said inadequately. "Of course I forgive you, as you call it. But the case has to come before a magistrate now; it really must, the machinery has started."

"She has started the machinery; it will work to its end."

Adela inclined towards tears in consequence of this unkind remark, and Ronny picked up the list of steamship sailings with an excellent notion in his head. His mother ought to leave India at once: she was doing no good to herself or to anyone else there.

CHAPTER 23

Lady Mellanby, wife to the Lieutenant-Governor of the Province, had been gratified by the appeal addressed to her by the ladies of Chandrapore. She could not do anything—besides, she was sailing for England; but she desired to be informed if she could show sympathy in any other way. Mrs. Turton replied that Mr. Heaslop's mother was trying to get a passage, but had delayed too long, and all the boats were full; could Lady Mellanby use her influence? Not even Lady Mellanby could expand the dimensions of a P. and O., but she was a very, very nice woman, and she actually wired offering the unknown and obscure old lady accommodation in her own reserved cabin. It was like a gift from heaven; humble and grateful, Ronny could not but reflect that there are compensations for every woe. His name was familiar at Government House owing to poor Adela, and now Mrs. Moore would stamp it on Lady Mellanby's imagination, as they journeyed across the Indian Ocean and up the Red Sea. He had a return of tenderness for his mother—as we do for our relatives when they receive conspicuous and unexpected honour. She was not negligible, she could still arrest the attention of a high official's wife.

So Mrs. Moore had all she wished; she escaped the trial, the marriage, and the hot weather; she would return to England in comfort and distinction, and see her other children. At her son's suggestion, and by her own desire, she departed. But she accepted her good luck without enthusiasm. She had come to that state where the horror of the universe and its smallness are both visible at the same time—the twilight of the double vision in which so many elderly people are involved. If this world is not to our taste, well, at all events there is Heaven, Hell, Annihilation—one or other of those large things, that huge scenic background of stars, fires, blue or black air. All heroic endeavour, and all that is known as art, assumes that there is such a background, just as all practical endeavour, when the world is to our taste, assumes that the world is all. But in the twilight of the double vision, a spiritual muddledom is set up for which no high-sounding words can be found; we can neither act nor refrain from action, we can neither ignore nor respect Infinity. Mrs. Moore had always inclined to resignation. As soon as she landed in India it seemed to her good, and when she saw the water flowing through the mosque-tank, or the Ganges, or the moon, caught in the shawl of night with all the other stars, it seemed a beautiful goal and an easy one. To be one with the universe! So dignified and simple. But there was always some little duty to be performed first, some new card to be turned up from the diminishing pack and placed, and while she was pottering about, the Marabar struck its gong.

What had spoken to her in that scoured-out cavity of the granite? What dwelt in the first of the caves? Something very old and very small. Before time, it was before space also. Something snub-nosed, incapable of generosity—the undying worm [1] itself. Since hearing its voice, she had not entertained one large thought, she was actually envious of Adela. All this fuss over a frightened girl! Nothing had happened, "and if it had," she found herself thinking with the cynicism of a withered priestess, "if it had, there are worse evils than love." The unspeakable attempt presented itself to her as love: in a cave, in a church—Boum, it amounts to the same. Visions are supposed to entail profundity, but—— Wait till you get one, dear reader! The abyss also may be petty, the serpent of eternity made of maggots; her constant thought was: "Less attention should be paid to my future daughter-in-law and more to me, there is no sorrow like my sorrow," although when the attention was paid she rejected it irritably.

Her son couldn't escort her to Bombay, for the local situation continued acute, and all officials had to remain at their posts. Antony couldn't come either, in case he never returned to give his evidence. So she travelled with no one who could remind her of the past. This was a relief. The heat had drawn back a little before its next advance, and the journey was not unpleasant. As she left Chandrapore the moon, full again, shone over the Ganges and touched the shrinking channels into threads of silver, then veered and looked into her window. The swift and comfortable mail-train

1. **worm**: serpent; i.e., evil.

slid with her through the night, and all the next day she was rushing through Central India, through landscapes that were baked and bleached but had not the hopeless melancholy of the plain. She watched the indestructible life of man and his changing faces, and the houses he has built for himself and God, and they appeared to her not in terms of her own trouble but as things to see. There was, for instance, a place called Asirgarh which she passed at sunset and identified on a map—an enormous fortress among wooded hills. No one had ever mentioned Asirgarh to her, but it had huge and noble bastions and to the right of them was a mosque. She forgot it. Ten minutes later, Asirgarh reappeared. The mosque was to the left of the bastions now. The train in its descent through the Vindyas had described a semicircle round Asirgarh. What could she connect it with except its own name? Nothing; she knew no one who lived there. But it had looked at her twice and seemed to say: "I do not vanish." She woke in the middle of the night with a start, for the train was falling over the western cliff. Moonlit pinnacles rushed up at her like the fringes of a sea; then a brief episode of plain, the real sea, and the soupy dawn of Bombay. "I have not seen the right places," she thought, as she saw embayed in the platforms of the Victoria Terminus the end of the rails that had carried her over a continent and could never carry her back. She would never visit Asirgarh or the other untouched places; neither Delhi nor Agra nor the Rajputana cities nor Kashmir, nor the obscurer marvels that had sometimes shone through men's speech: the bilingual rock of Girnar, the statue of Shri Belgola, the ruins of Mandu and Hampi, temples of Khajraha, gardens of Shalimar.[2] As she drove through the huge city which the West has built and abandoned with a gesture of despair, she longed to stop, though it was only Bombay, and disentangle the hundred Indias that passed each other in its streets. The feet of the horses moved her on, and presently the boat sailed and thousands of coconut palms appeared all round the anchorage and climbed the hills to wave her farewell. "So you thought an echo was India; you took the Marabar caves as final?" they laughed. "What have we in common with them, or they with Asirgarh? Good-bye!" Then the steamer rounded Colaba, the continent swung about, the cliff of the Ghats[3] melted into the haze of a tropic sea. Lady Mellanby turned up and advised her not to stand in the heat: "We are

2. **Girnar:** a sacred hill in western India that has at its foot a rock that bears various ancient inscriptions; at Sravana Belgola, in Mysore, is found an enormous statue, about 70 feet high, sculptured out of one piece of solid rock; **Mandu:** see footnote 2 on page 290; **Hampi:** the site of a famous Hindu city that flourished in the fourteenth, fifteenth, and sixteenth centuries; **Khajraha:** a village famous for its tenth- and eleventh-century temples; the Shalimar gardens, laid out in 1637, are near the ancient city of Lahore.

3. **Colaba:** a district of Bombay, located on a promontory south of the city; **the Ghats:** the coastal mountain range.

safely out of the frying-pan," said Lady Mellanby, "it will never do to fall into the fire."

CHAPTER 24

Making sudden changes of gear, the heat accelerated its advance after Mrs. Moore's departure until existence had to be endured and crime punished with the thermometer at a hundred and twelve. Electric fans hummed and spat, water splashed on to screens, ice clinked, and outside these defences, between a greyish sky and a yellowish earth, clouds of dust moved hesitatingly. In Europe life retreats out of the cold, and exquisite fireside myths have resulted—Balder, Persephone—but here the retreat is from the source of life, the treacherous sun, and no poetry adorns it because disillusionment cannot be beautiful. Men yearn for poetry though they may not confess it; they desire that joy shall be graceful and sorrow august and infinity have a form, and India fails to accommodate them. The annual helter-skelter of April, when irritability and lust spread like a canker, is one of her comments on the orderly hopes of humanity. Fish manage better; fish, as the tanks dry, wriggle into the mud and wait for the rains to uncake them. But men try to be harmonious all the year round, and the results are occasionally disastrous. The triumphant machine of civilization may suddenly hitch and be immobilized into a car of stone, and at such moments the destiny of the English seems to resemble their predecessors', who also entered the country with intent to refashion it, but were in the end worked into its pattern and covered with its dust.

Adela, after years of intellectualism, had resumed her morning kneel to Christianity. There seemed no harm in it, it was the shortest and easiest cut to the unseen, and she could tack her troubles on to it. Just as the Hindu clerks asked Lakshmi [1] for an increase in pay, so did she implore Jehovah for a favourable verdict. God who saves the King will surely support the police. Her deity returned a consoling reply, but the touch of her hands on her face started prickly heat, and she seemed to swallow and expectorate the same insipid clot of air that had weighed on her lungs all the night. Also the voice of Mrs. Turton disturbed her. "Are you ready, young lady?" it pealed from the next room.

"Half a minute," she murmured. The Turtons had received her after Mrs. Moore left. Their kindness was incredible, but it was her position not her character that moved them; she was the English girl who had had the terrible experience, and for whom too much could not be done. No one, except Ronny, had any idea of what passed in her mind, and he only dimly, for where there is officialism every human relationship suffers. In

1. **Lakshmi:** the goddess of beauty and wealth.

her sadness she said to him, "I bring you nothing but trouble; I was right
on the Maidan, we had better just be friends," but he protested, for the
more she suffered the more highly he valued her. Did she love him? This
question was somehow draggled up with the Marabar, it had been in her
mind as she entered the fatal cave. Was she capable of loving anyone?

"Miss Quested, Adela, what d'ye call yourself, it's half-past seven; we
ought to think of starting for that Court when you feel inclined."

"She's saying her prayers," came the Collector's voice.

"Sorry, my dear; take your time. . . . Was your chota hazri [2] all
right?"

"I can't eat; might I have a little brandy?" she asked, deserting Jehovah.

When it was brought, she shuddered, and said she was ready to go.

"Drink it up; not a bad notion, a peg."

"I don't think it'll really help me, Burra Sahib."

"You sent brandy down to the Court, didn't you, Mary?"

"I should think I did, champagne too."

"I'll thank you this evening, I'm all to pieces now," said the girl, forming each syllable carefully as if her trouble would diminish if it were
accurately defined. She was afraid of reticence, in case something that she
herself did not perceive took shape beneath it, and she had rehearsed with
Mr. McBryde in an odd, mincing way her terrible adventure in the cave,
how the man had never actually touched her but dragged her about, and
so on. Her aim this morning was to announce, meticulously, that the
strain was appalling, and she would probably break down under Mr.
Amritrao's cross-examination and disgrace her friends. "My echo has come
back again badly," she told them.

"How about aspirin?"

"It is not a headache, it is an echo."

Unable to dispel the buzzing in her ears, Major Callendar had diagnosed it as a fancy, which must not be encouraged. So the Turtons
changed the subject. The cool little lick of the breeze was passing over
the earth, dividing night from day; it would fail in ten minutes, but they
might profit by it for their drive down into the city.

"I am sure to break down," she repeated.

"You won't," said the Collector, his voice full of tenderness.

"Of course she won't, she's a real sport."

"But, Mrs. Turton . . ."

"Yes, my dear child?"

"If I do break down, it is of no consequence. It would matter in some
trials, not in this. I put it to myself in the following way: I can really be-

2. chota hazri: a light meal, taken early in the morning.

have as I like, cry, be absurd, I am sure to get my verdict, unless Mr. Das is most frightfully unjust."

"You're bound to win," he said calmly, and did not remind her that there was bound to be an appeal. The Nawab Bahadur had financed the defence, and would ruin himself sooner than let an "innocent Moslem perish," and other interests, less reputable, were in the background too. The case might go up from court to court, with consequences that no official could foresee. Under his very eyes, the temper of Chandrapore was altering. As his car turned out of the compound, there was a tap of silly anger on its paint—a pebble thrown by a child. Some larger stones were dropped near the mosque. In the Maidan, a squad of native police on motor cycles waited to escort them through the bazaars. The Collector was irritated and muttered, "McBryde's an old woman"; but Mrs. Turton said, "Really, after Mohurram a show of force will do no harm; it's ridiculous to pretend they don't hate us; do give up that farce." He replied in an odd, sad voice, "I don't hate them, I don't know why," and he didn't hate them; for if he did, he would have had to condemn his own career as a bad investment. He retained a contemptuous affection for the pawns he had moved about for so many years, they must be worth his pains. "After all, it's our women who make everything more difficult out here," was his inmost thought, as he caught sight of some obscenities upon a long blank wall, and beneath his chivalry to Miss Quested resentment lurked, waiting its day—perhaps there is a grain of resentment in all chivalry. Some students had gathered in front of the City Magistrate's Court—hysterical boys whom he would have faced if alone, but he told the driver to work round to the rear of the building. The students jeered, and Rafi (hiding behind a comrade that he might not be identified) called out the English were cowards.

They gained Ronny's private room, where a group of their own sort had collected. None were cowardly, all nervy, for queer reports kept coming in. The Sweepers had just struck, and half the commodes of Chandrapore remained desolate in consequence—only half, and Sweepers from the District, who felt less strongly about the innocence of Dr. Aziz, would arrive in the afternoon, and break the strike, but why should the grotesque incident occur? And a number of Mohammedan ladies had sworn to take no food until the prisoner was acquitted; their death would make little difference, indeed, being invisible, they seemed dead already, nevertheless it was disquieting. A new spirit seemed abroad, a rearrangement, which no one in the stern little band of whites could explain. There was a tendency to see Fielding at the back of it: the idea that he was weak and cranky had been dropped. They abused Fielding vigorously: he had been seen driving up with the two counsels, Amritrao and Mahmoud Ali; he encouraged the Boy Scout movement for seditious reasons; he received letters with foreign stamps on them, and was probably a Japanese spy. This morning's verdict would break the renegade, but he had done his country and the Empire incalculable disservice. While they denounced him, Miss Quested lay back with her hands on the arms of her chair and her eyes closed, reserving her strength. They noticed her after a time, and felt ashamed of making so much noise.

"Can we do nothing for you?" Miss Derek said.

"I don't think so, Nancy, and I seem able to do nothing for myself."

"But you're strictly forbidden to talk like that; you're wonderful."

"Yes, indeed," came the reverent chorus.

"My old Das is all right," said Ronny, starting a new subject in low tones.

"Not one of them's all right," contradicted Major Callendar.

"Das is, really."

"You mean he's more frightened of acquitting than convicting, because if he acquits he'll lose his job," said Lesley with a clever little laugh.

Ronny did mean that, but he cherished "illusions" about his own subordinates (following the finer traditions of his service here), and he liked to maintain that his old Das really did possess moral courage of the Public School brand. He pointed out that—from one point of view—it was good that an Indian was taking the case. Conviction was inevitable; so better let an Indian pronounce it, there would be less fuss in the long run. Interested in the argument, he let Adela become dim in his mind.

"In fact, you disapprove of the appeal I forwarded to Lady Mellanby," said Mrs. Turton with considerable heat. "Pray don't apologize, Mr. Heaslop; I am accustomed to being in the wrong."

"I didn't mean that . . ."

"All right. I said don't apologize."

"Those swine are always on the lookout for a grievance," said Lesley, to propitiate her.

"Swine, I should think so," the Major echoed. "And what's more, I'll tell you what. What's happened is a damn good thing really, barring of course its application to present company. It'll make them squeal and it's time they did squeal. I've put the fear of God into them at the hospital anyhow. You should see the grandson of our so-called leading loyalist." He tittered brutally as he described poor Nureddin's present appearance. "His beauty's gone, five upper teeth, two lower and a nostril. . . . Old Panna Lal brought him the looking-glass yesterday and he blubbered. . . . I laughed; I laughed, I tell you, and so would you; that used to be one of these buck niggers, I thought, now he's all septic; damn him, blast his soul—er—I believe he was unspeakably immoral—er——" He subsided, nudged in the ribs, but added, "I wish I'd had the cutting up of my late assistant too; nothing's too bad for these people."

"At last some sense is being talked," Mrs. Turton cried, much to her husband's discomfort.

"That's what I say; I say there's not such a thing as cruelty after a thing like this."

"Exactly, and remember it afterwards, you men. You're weak, weak, weak. Why, they ought to crawl from here to the caves on their hands and knees whenever an Englishwoman's in sight, they oughtn't to be spoken to, they ought to be spat at, they ought to be ground into the dust, we've been far too kind with our Bridge Parties and the rest."

She paused. Profiting by her wrath, the heat had invaded her. She subsided into a lemon squash, and continued between the sips to murmur, "Weak, weak." And the process was repeated. The issues Miss Quested had raised were so much more important than she was herself that people inevitably forgot her.

Presently the case was called.

Their chairs preceded them into the Court, for it was important that they should look dignified. And when the chuprassies had made all ready, they filed into the ramshackly room with a condescending air, as if it was a booth at a fair. The Collector made a small official joke as he sat down, at which his entourage smiled, and the Indians, who could not hear what he said, felt that some new cruelty was afoot, otherwise the sahibs would not chuckle.

The Court was crowded and of course very hot, and the first person Adela noticed in it was the humblest of all who were present, a person who had no bearing officially upon the trial: the man who pulled the punkah. Almost naked, and splendidly formed, he sat on a raised platform near the back, in the middle of the central gangway, and he caught her attention as she came in, and he seemed to control the proceedings. He had the strength and beauty that sometimes come to flower in Indians of low birth. When that strange race nears the dust and is condemned as untouchable, then nature remembers the physical perfection that she accomplished elsewhere, and throws out a god—not many, but one here and there, to prove to society how little its categories impress her. This man would have been notable anywhere: among the thin-hammed, flat-chested mediocrities of Chandrapore he stood out as divine, yet he was of the city, its garbage had nourished him, he would end on its rubbish heaps. Pulling the rope towards him, relaxing it rhythmically, sending swirls of air over others, receiving none himself, he seemed apart from human destinies, a male fate, a winnower of souls. Opposite him, also on a platform, sat the little assistant magistrate, cultivated, self-conscious, and conscientious. The punkah wallah was none of these things: he scarcely knew that he existed and did not understand why the Court was fuller than usual, indeed he did not know that it was fuller than usual, didn't even know he worked a fan, though he thought he pulled a rope. Something in his aloofness impressed the girl from middle-class England, and rebuked the narrowness of her sufferings. In virtue of what had she collected this roomful of people together? Her particular brand of opinions, and the suburban Jehovah who sanctified them—by what right did they claim so much importance in the world, and assume the title of civilization? Mrs. Moore—she looked round, but Mrs. Moore was far away on the sea; it was the kind of question they might have discussed on the voyage out before the old lady had turned disagreeable and queer.

While thinking of Mrs. Moore she heard sounds, which gradually grew more distinct. The epoch-making trial had started, and the Superintendent of Police was opening the case for the prosecution.

Mr. McBryde was not at pains to be an interesting speaker; he left eloquence to the defence, who would require it. His attitude was, "Everyone knows the man's guilty, and I am obliged to say so in public before he goes to the Andamans." [3] He made no moral or emotional appeal, and it was only by degrees that the studied negligence of his manner made itself felt, and lashed part of the audience to fury. Laboriously did he describe the genesis of the picnic. The prisoner had met Miss Quested at an entertainment given by the Principal of Government College, and had there conceived his intentions concerning her: prisoner was a man of loose life, as documents found upon him at his arrest would testify, also his fellow-assistant, Dr. Panna Lal, was in a position to throw light on his character, and Major Callendar himself would speak. Here Mr. McBryde paused. He wanted to keep the proceedings as clean as possible, but Oriental Pathology, his favourite theme, lay around him, and he could not resist it. Taking off his spectacles, as was his habit before enunciating a general truth, he looked into them sadly, and remarked that the darker races are physically attracted by the fairer, but not *vice versa*—not a matter for bitterness this, not a matter for abuse, but just a fact which any scientific observer will confirm.

"Even when the lady is so uglier than the gentleman?"

The comment fell from nowhere, from the ceiling perhaps. It was the first interruption, and the Magistrate felt bound to censure it. "Turn that man out," he said. One of the native policemen took hold of a man who had said nothing, and turned him out roughly. Mr. McBryde resumed his spectacles and proceeded. But the comment had upset Miss Quested. Her body resented being called ugly, and trembled.

3. There was a prison colony on the Andaman Islands, located in the Bay of Bengal.

"Do you feel faint, Adela?" asked Miss Derek, who tended her with loving indignation.

"I never feel anything else, Nancy. I shall get through, but it's awful, awful."

This led to the first of a series of scenes. Her friends began to fuss around her, and the Major called out, "I must have better arrangements than this made for my patient; why isn't she given a seat on the platform? She gets no air."

Mr. Das looked annoyed and said: "I shall be happy to accommodate Miss Quested with a chair up here in view of the particular circumstances of her health." The chuprassies passed up not one chair but several, and the entire party followed Adela on to the platform, Mr. Fielding being the only European who remained in the body of the hall.

"That's better," remarked Mrs. Turton, as she settled herself.

"Thoroughly desirable change for several reasons," replied the Major.

The Magistrate knew that he ought to censure this remark, but did not dare to. Callendar saw that he was afraid, and called out authoritatively, "Right, McBryde, go ahead now; sorry to have interrupted you."

"Are you all right yourselves?" asked the Superintendent.

"We shall do, we shall do."

"Go on, Mr. Das, we are not here to disturb you," said the Collector patronizingly. Indeed, they had not so much disturbed the trial as taken charge of it.

While the prosecution continued, Miss Quested examined the hall—timidly at first, as though it would scorch her eyes. She observed to left and right of the punkah man many a half-known face. Beneath her were gathered all the wreckage of her silly attempt to see India—the people she had met at the Bridge Party, the man and his wife who hadn't sent their carriage, the old man who would lend his car, various servants, villagers, officials, and the prisoner himself. There he sat—strong, neat little Indian with very black hair, and pliant hands. She viewed him without special emotion. Since they last met, she had elevated him into a principle of evil, but now he seemed to be what he had always been—a slight acquaintance. He was negligible, devoid of significance, dry like a bone, and though he was "guilty" no atmosphere of sin surrounded him. "I suppose he *is* guilty. Can I possibly have made a mistake?" she thought. For this question still occurred to her intellect, though since Mrs. Moore's departure it had ceased to trouble her conscience.

Pleader Mahmoud Ali now arose, and asked with ponderous and ill-judged irony whether his client could be accommodated on the platform too: even Indians felt unwell sometimes, though naturally Major Callendar did not think so, being in charge of a Government Hospital. "Another

example of their exquisite sense of humour," sang Miss Derek. Ronny
looked at Mr. Das to see how he would handle the difficulty, and Mr.
Das became agitated, and snubbed Pleader Mahmoud Ali severely.

"Excuse me——" It was the turn of the eminent barrister from Calcutta.
He was a fine-looking man, large and bony, with grey closely cropped
hair. "We object to the presence of so many European ladies and gentlemen upon the platform," he said in an Oxford voice. "They will have the
effect of intimidating our witnesses. Their place is with the rest of the
public in the body of the hall. We have no objection to Miss Quested remaining on the platform, since she has been unwell; we shall extend every
courtesy to her throughout, despite the scientific truths revealed to us by
the District Superintendent of Police; but we do object to the others."

"Oh, cut the cackle and let's have the verdict," the Major growled.

The distinguished visitor gazed at the Magistrate respectfully.

"I agree to that," said Mr. Das, hiding his face desperately in some papers. "It was only to Miss Quested that I gave permission to sit up here.
Her friends should be so excessively kind as to climb down."

"Well done, Das, quite sound," said Ronny with devastating honesty.

"Climb down, indeed, what incredible impertinence!" Mrs. Turton
cried.

"Do come quietly, Mary," murmured her husband.

"Hi! my patient can't be left unattended."

"Do you object to the Civil Surgeon remaining, Mr. Amritrao?"

"I should object. A platform confers authority."

"Even when it's one foot high; so come along all," said the Collector,
trying to laugh.

"Thank you very much, sir," said Mr. Das, greatly relieved. "Thank
you, Mr. Heaslop; thank you, ladies all."

And the party, including Miss Quested, descended from its rash eminence. The news of their humiliation spread quickly, and people jeered
outside. Their special chairs followed them. Mahmoud Ali (who was quite
silly and useless with hatred) objected even to these; by whose authority
had special chairs been introduced, why had the Nawab Bahadur not been
given one? etc. People began to talk all over the room, about chairs ordinary and special, strips of carpet, platforms one foot high.

But the little excursion had a good effect on Miss Quested's nerves. She
felt easier now that she had seen all the people who were in the room. It
was like knowing the worst. She was sure now that she should come
through "all right"—that is to say, without spiritual disgrace, and she
passed the good news on to Ronny and Mrs. Turton. They were too much
agitated with the defeat to British prestige to be interested. From where
she sat, she could see the renegade Mr. Fielding. She had had a better view

of him from the platform, and knew that an Indian child perched on his knee. He was watching the proceedings, watching her. When their eyes met, he turned his away, as if direct intercourse was of no interest to him.

The Magistrate was also happier. He had won the battle of the platform, and gained confidence. Intelligent and impartial, he continued to listen to the evidence, and tried to forget that later on he should have to pronounce a verdict in accordance with it. The Superintendent trundled steadily forward: he had expected these outbursts of insolence—they are the natural gestures of an inferior race, and he betrayed no hatred of Aziz, merely an abysmal contempt.

The speech dealt at length with the "prisoner's dupes," as they were called—Fielding, the servant Antony, the Nawab Bahadur. This aspect of the case had always seemed dubious to Miss Quested, and she had asked the police not to develop it. But they were playing for a heavy sentence, and wanted to prove that the assault was premeditated. And in order to illustrate the strategy, they produced a plan of the Marabar Hills, showing the route that the party had taken, and the "Tank of the Dagger" where they had camped.

The Magistrate displayed interest in archæology.

An elevation of a specimen cave was produced; it was lettered "Buddhist Cave."

"Not Buddhist, I think, Jain. . . ."

"In which cave is the offence alleged, the Buddhist or the Jain?" asked Mahmoud Ali, with the air of unmasking a conspiracy.

"All the Marabar caves are Jain."

"Yes, sir; then in which Jain cave?"

"You will have an opportunity of putting such questions later."

Mr. McBryde smiled faintly at their fatuity. Indians invariably collapse over some such point as this. He knew that the defence had some wild hope of establishing an alibi, that they had tried (unsuccessfully) to identify the guide, and that Fielding and Hamidullah had gone out to the Kawa Dol and paced and measured all one moonlit night. "Mr. Lesley says they're Buddhist, and he ought to know if anyone does. But may I call attention to the shape?" And he described what had occurred there. Then he spoke of Miss Derek's arrival, of the scramble down the gully, of the return of the two ladies to Chandrapore, and of the document Miss Quested signed on her arrival, in which mention was made of the field-glasses. And then came the culminating evidence: the discovery of the field-glasses on the prisoner. "I have nothing to add at present," he concluded, removing his spectacles. "I will now call my witnesses. The facts will speak for themselves. The prisoner is one of those individuals who have led a double life. I dare say his degeneracy gained upon him gradually. He has been very cunning at concealing, as is usual with the type, and pretending to be a respectable member of society, getting a Government position even. He is now entirely vicious and beyond redemption, I am afraid. He behaved most cruelly, most brutally, to another of his guests, another English lady. In order to get rid of her, and leave him free for his crime, he crushed her into a cave among his servants. However, that is by the way."

But his last words brought on another storm, and suddenly a new name, Mrs. Moore, burst on the court like a whirlwind. Mahmoud Ali had been enraged, his nerves snapped; he shrieked like a maniac, and asked whether his client was charged with murder as well as rape, and who was this second English lady.

"I don't propose to call her."

"You don't because you can't, you have smuggled her out of the country; she is Mrs. Moore, she would have proved his innocence, she was on our side, she was poor Indians' friend."

"You could have called her yourself," cried the Magistrate. "Neither side called her, neither must quote her as evidence."

"She was kept from us until too late—I learn too late—this is English justice, here is your British Raj. Give us back Mrs. Moore for five minutes only, and she will save my friend, she will save the name of his sons; don't rule her out, Mr. Das; take back those words as you yourself are a father; tell me where they have put her; oh, Mrs. Moore. . . ."

"If the point is of any interest, my mother should have reached Aden," said Ronny dryly; he ought not to have intervened, but the onslaught had startled him.

"Imprisoned by you there because she knew the truth." He was almost out of his mind, and could be heard saying above the tumult: "I ruin my career, no matter; we are all to be ruined one by one."

"This is no way to defend your case," counselled the Magistrate.

"I am not defending a case, nor are you trying one. We are both of us slaves."

"Mr. Mahmoud Ali, I have already warned you, and unless you sit down I shall exercise my authority."

"Do so; this trial is a farce, I am going." And he handed his papers to Amritrao and left, calling from the door histrionically yet with intense passion, "Aziz, Aziz—farewell for ever." The tumult increased, the invocation of Mrs. Moore continued, and people who did not know what the syllables meant repeated them like a charm. They became Indianized into Esmiss Esmoor, they were taken up in the street outside. In vain the Magistrate threatened and expelled. Until the magic exhausted itself, he was powerless.

"Unexpected," remarked Mr. Turton.

Ronny furnished the explanation. Before she sailed, his mother had taken to talk about the Marabar in her sleep, especially in the afternoon when servants were on the veranda, and her disjointed remarks on Aziz had doubtless been sold to Mahmoud Ali for a few annas: that kind of thing never ceases in the East.

"I thought they'd try something of the sort. Ingenious." He looked into their wide-open mouths. "They get just like that over their religion," he added calmly. "Start and can't stop. I'm sorry for your old Das, he's not getting much of a show."

"Mr. Heaslop, how disgraceful dragging in your dear mother," said Miss Derek, bending forward.

"It's just a trick, and they happened to pull it off. Now one sees why they had Mahmoud Ali—just to make a scene on the chance. It is his specialty." But he disliked it more than he showed. It was revolting to hear his mother travestied into Esmiss Esmoor, a Hindu goddess.

> "Esmiss Esmoor
> Esmiss Esmoor
> Esmiss Esmoor
> Esmiss Esmoor. . . ."

"Ronny——"

"Yes, old girl?"

"Isn't it all queer."

"I'm afraid it's very upsetting for you."

"Not the least. I don't mind it."

"Well, that's good."

She had spoken more naturally and healthily than usual. Bending into the middle of her friends, she said: "Don't worry about me, I'm much better than I was; I don't feel the least faint; I shall be all right, and thank you all, thank you, thank you for your kindness." She had to shout her gratitude, for the chant, Esmiss Esmoor, went on.

Suddenly it stopped. It was as if the prayer had been heard, and the relics exhibited. "I apologize for my colleague," said Mr. Amritrao, rather to everyone's surprise. "He is an intimate friend of our client, and his feelings have carried him away."

"Mr. Mahmoud Ali will have to apologize in person," the Magistrate said.

"Exactly, sir, he must. But we had just learned that Mrs. Moore had important evidence which she desired to give. She was hurried out of the country by her son before she could give it; and this unhinged Mr. Mahmoud Ali—coming as it does upon an attempt to intimidate our only other

European witness, Mr. Fielding. Mr. Mahmoud Ali would have said nothing had not Mrs. Moore been claimed as a witness by the police." He sat down.

"An extraneous element is being introduced into the case," said the Magistrate. "I must repeat that as a witness Mrs. Moore does not exist. Neither you, Mr. Amritrao, nor, Mr. McBryde, you, have any right to surmise what that lady would have said. She is not here, and consequently she can say nothing."

"Well, I withdraw my reference," said the Superintendent wearily. "I would have done so fifteen minutes ago if I had been given the chance. She is not of the least importance to me."

"I have already withdrawn it for the defence." He added with forensic humour: "Perhaps you can persuade the gentlemen outside to withdraw it too," for the refrain in the street continued.

"I am afraid my powers do not extend so far," said Das, smiling.

So peace was restored, and when Adela came to give her evidence the atmosphere was quieter than it had been since the beginning of the trial. Experts were not surprised. There is no stay in your native. He blazes up over a minor point, and has nothing left for the crisis. What he seeks is a grievance, and this he had found in the supposed abduction of an old lady. He would now be less aggrieved when Aziz was deported.

But the crisis was still to come.

Adela had always meant to tell the truth and nothing but the truth, and she had rehearsed this as a difficult task—difficult, because her disaster in the cave was connected, though by a thread, with another part of her life, her engagement to Ronny. She had thought of love just before she went in, and had innocently asked Aziz what marriage was like, and she supposed that her question had roused evil in him. To recount this would have been incredibly painful, it was the one point she wanted to keep obscure; she was willing to give details that would have distressed other girls, but this story of her private failure she dared not allude to, and she dreaded being examined in public in case something came out. But as soon as she rose to reply, and heard the sound of her own voice, she feared not even that. A new and unknown sensation protected her, like magnificent armour. She didn't think what had happened or even remember in the ordinary way of memory, but she returned to the Marabar Hills, and spoke from them across a sort of darkness to Mr. McBryde. The fatal day recurred, in every detail, but now she was of it and not of it at the same time, and this double relation gave it indescribable splendour. Why had she thought the expedition "dull"? Now the sun rose again, the elephant waited, the pale masses of the rock flowed round her and presented the first cave; she entered, and a match was reflected in the polished walls—all beautiful and significant, though she had been blind to it at the time. Questions were asked, and to each she found the exact reply; yes, she had noticed the "Tank of the Dagger," but not known its name; yes, Mrs. Moore had been tired after the first cave and sat in the shadow of a great rock, near the dried-up mud. Smoothly the voice in the distance proceeded, leading along the paths of truth, and the airs from the punkah behind her wafted her on. . . .

". . . the prisoner and the guide took you on to the Kawa Dol, no one else being present?"

"The most wonderfully shaped of those hills. Yes." As she spoke, she created the Kawa Dol, saw the niches up the curve of the stone, and felt the heat strike her face. And something caused her to add: "No one else was present to my knowledge. We appeared to be alone."

"Very well, there is a ledge half-way up the hill, or broken ground rather, with caves scattered near the beginning of a nullah."

"I know where you mean."

"You went alone into one of those caves?"

"That is quite correct."

"And the prisoner followed you."

"Now we've got 'im," from the Major.

She was silent. The court, the place of question, awaited her reply. But she could not give it until Aziz entered the place of answer.

"The prisoner followed you, didn't he?" he repeated in the monotonous tones that they both used; they were employing agreed words throughout, so that this part of the proceedings held no surprises.

"May I have half a minute before I reply to that, Mr. McBryde?"

"Certainly."

Her vision was of several caves. She saw herself in one, and she was also outside it, watching its entrance, for Aziz to pass in. She failed to locate him. It was the doubt that had often visited her, but solid and attractive, like the hills, "I am not——" Speech was more difficult than vision. "I am not quite sure."

"I beg your pardon?" said the Superintendent of Police.

"I cannot be sure . . ."

"I didn't catch that answer." He looked scared, his mouth shut with a snap. "You are on that landing, or whatever we term it, and you have entered a cave. I suggest to you that the prisoner followed you."

She shook her head.

"What do you mean, please?"

"No," she said in a flat, unattractive voice. Slight noises began in various parts of the room, but no one yet understood what was occurring except

Fielding. He saw that she was going to have a nervous breakdown and that his friend was saved.

"What is that, what are you saying? Speak up, please." The Magistrate bent forward.

"I'm afraid I have made a mistake."

"What nature of mistake?"

"Dr. Aziz never followed me into the cave."

The Superintendent slammed down his papers, then picked them up and said calmly: "Now, Miss Quested, let us go on. I will read you the words of the deposition which you signed two hours later in my bungalow."

"Excuse me, Mr. McBryde, you cannot go on. I am speaking to the witness myself. And the public will be silent. If it continues to talk, I have the court cleared. Miss Quested, address your remarks to me, who am the Magistrate in charge of the case, and realize their extreme gravity. Remember you speak on oath, Miss Quested."

"Dr. Aziz never——"

"I stop these proceedings on medical grounds," cried the Major on a word from Turton, and all the English rose from their chairs at once, large white figures behind which the little magistrate was hidden. The Indians rose too, hundreds of things went on at once, so that afterwards each person gave a different account of the catastrophe.

"You withdraw the charge? Answer me," shrieked the representative of Justice.

Something that she did not understand took hold of the girl and pulled her through. Though the vision was over, and she had returned to the insipidity of the world, she remembered what she had learnt. Atonement and confession—they could wait. It was in hard prosaic tones that she said, "I withdraw everything."

"Enough—sit down. Mr. McBryde, do you wish to continue in the face of this?"

The Superintendent gazed at his witness as if she was a broken machine, and said, "Are you mad?"

"Don't question her, sir; you have no longer the right."

"Give me time to consider——"

"Sahib, you will have to withdraw; this becomes a scandal," boomed the Nawab Bahadur suddenly from the back of the court.

"He shall not," shouted Mrs. Turton against the gathering tumult. "Call the other witnesses; we're none of us safe——" Ronny tried to check her, and she gave him an irritable blow, then screamed insults at Adela.

The Superintendent moved to the support of his friends, saying nonchalantly to the Magistrate as he did so, "Right, I withdraw."

Mr. Das rose, nearly dead with the strain. He had controlled the case, just controlled it. He had shown that an Indian can preside. To those who could hear him he said, "The prisoner is released without one stain on his character; the question of costs will be decided elsewhere."

And then the flimsy framework of the court broke up, the shouts of derision and rage culminated, people screamed and cursed, kissed one another, wept passionately. Here were the English, whom their servants protected, there Aziz fainted in Hamidullah's arms. Victory on this side, defeat on that—complete for one moment was the antithesis. Then life returned to its complexities, person after person struggled out of the room to their various purposes, and before long no one remained on the scene of the fantasy but the beautiful naked god. Unaware that anything unusual had occurred, he continued to pull the cord of his punkah, to gaze at the empty dais and the overturned special chairs, and rhythmically to agitate the clouds of descending dust.

CHAPTER 25

Miss Quested had renounced her own people. Turning from them, she was drawn into a mass of Indians of the shopkeeping class, and carried by them towards the public exit of the court. The faint, indescribable smell of the bazaars invaded her, sweeter than a London slum, yet more disquieting: a tuft of scented cotton wool, wedged in an old man's ear, fragments of pan between his black teeth, odorous powders, oils—the Scented East of tradition, but blended with human sweat as if a great king had been entangled in ignominy and could not free himself, or as if the heat of the sun had boiled and fried all the glories of the earth into a single mess. They paid no attention to her. They shook hands over her shoulder, shouted through her body—for when the Indian does ignore his rulers, he becomes genuinely unaware of their existence. Without part in the universe she had created, she was flung against Mr. Fielding.

"What do you want here?"

Knowing him for her enemy, she passed on into the sunlight without speaking.

He called after her, "Where are you going, Miss Quested?"

"I don't know."

"You can't wander about like that. Where's the car you came in?"

"I shall walk."

"What madness . . . there's supposed to be a riot on . . . the police have struck, no one knows what'll happen next. Why don't you keep to your own people?"

"Ought I to join them?" she said, without emotion. She felt emptied, valueless; there was no more virtue in her.

"You can't, it's too late. How are you to get round to the private entrance now? Come this way with me—quick—I'll put you into my carriage."

"Cyril, Cyril, don't leave me," called the shattered voice of Aziz.

"I'm coming back. . . . This way, and don't argue." He gripped her
arm. "Excuse manners, but I don't know anyone's position. Send my carriage back any time to-morrow, if you please."

"But where am I to go in it?"

"Where you like. How should I know your arrangements?"

The victoria was safe in a quiet side lane, but there were no horses, for
the sais, not expecting the trial would end so abruptly, had led them away
to visit a friend. She got into it obediently. The man could not leave her,
for the confusion increased, and spots of it sounded fanatical. The main
road through the bazaars was blocked, and the English were gaining the
civil station by by-ways; they were caught like caterpillars, and could
have been killed off easily.

"What—what have you been doing?" he cried suddenly. "Playing a
game, studying life, or what?"

"Sir, I intend these for you, sir," interrupted a student, running down
the lane with a garland of jasmine on his arm.

"I don't want the rubbish; get out."

"Sir, I am a horse, we shall be your horses," another cried as he lifted
the shafts of the victoria into the air.

"Fetch my sais, Rafi; there's a good chap."

"No, sir, this is an honour for us."

Fielding wearied of his students. The more they honoured him the less
they obeyed. They lassoed him with jasmine and roses, scratched the
splash-board against a wall, and recited a poem, the noise of which filled
the lane with a crowd.

"Hurry up, sir; we pull you in a procession." And, half affectionate, half
impudent, they bundled him in.

"I don't know whether this suits you, but anyhow you're safe," he remarked. The carriage jerked into the main bazaar, where it created some
sensation. Miss Quested was so loathed in Chandrapore that her recanta-
tion was discredited, and the rumour ran that she had been stricken by
the Deity in the middle of her lies. But they cheered when they saw her
sitting by the heroic Principal (some addressed her as Mrs. Moore!), and
they garlanded her to match him. Half gods, half guys, with sausages of
flowers round their necks, the pair were dragged in the wake of Aziz's victorious landau. In the applause that greeted them some derision mingled.
The English always stick together! That was the criticism. Nor was it unjust. Fielding shared it himself, and knew that if some misunderstanding

occurred, and an attack was made on the girl by his allies, he would be obliged to die in her defence. He didn't want to die for her, he wanted to be rejoicing with Aziz.

Where was the procession going? To friends, to enemies, to Aziz' bungalow, to the Collector's bungalow, to the Minto Hospital where the Civil Surgeon would eat dust and the patients (confused with prisoners) be released, to Delhi, Simla. The students thought it was going to Government College. When they reached a turning, they twisted the victoria to the right, ran it by side lanes down a hill and through a garden gate into the mango plantation, and, as far as Fielding and Miss Quested were concerned, all was peace and quiet. The trees were full of glossy foliage and slim green fruit, the tank slumbered; and beyond it rose the exquisite blue arches of the garden-house. "Sir, we fetch the others; sir, it is a somewhat heavy load for our arms," were heard. Fielding took the refugee to his office, and tried to telephone to McBryde. But this he could not do; the wires had been cut. All his servants had decamped. Once more he was unable to desert her. He assigned her a couple of rooms, provided her with ice and drinks and biscuits, advised her to lie down, and lay down himself —there was nothing else to do. He felt restless and thwarted as he listened to the retreating sounds of the procession, and his joy was rather spoilt by bewilderment. It was a victory, but such a queer one.

At that moment Aziz was crying, "Cyril, Cyril . . ." Crammed into a carriage with the Nawab Bahadur, Hamidullah, Mahmoud Ali, his own little boys, and a heap of flowers, he was not content; he wanted to be surrounded by all who loved him. Victory gave no pleasure, he had suffered too much. From the moment of his arrest he was done for, he had dropped like a wounded animal; he had despaired, not through cowardice, but because he knew that an Englishwoman's one word would always outweigh his own. "It is fate," he said; and, "It is fate," when he was imprisoned anew after Mohurram. All that existed, in that terrible time, was affection, and affection was all that he felt in the first painful moments of his freedom. "Why isn't Cyril following? Let us turn back." But the procession could not turn back. Like a snake in a drain, it advanced down the narrow bazaar towards the basin of the Maidan, where it would turn about itself, and decide on its prey.

"Forward, forward," shrieked Mahmoud Ali, whose every utterance had become a yell. "Down with the Collector, down with the Superintendent of Police."

"Mr. Mahmoud Ali, this is not wise," implored the Nawab Bahadur: he knew that nothing was gained by attacking the English, who had fallen into their own pit and had better be left there; moreover, he had great possessions and deprecated anarchy.

"Cyril, again you desert," cried Aziz.

"Yet some orderly demonstration is necessary," said Hamidullah, "otherwise they will still think we are afraid."

"Down with the Civil Surgeon . . . rescue Nureddin."

"Nureddin?"

"They are torturing him."

"Oh, my God . . ."—for this, too, was a friend.

"They are not. I will not have my grandson made an excuse for an attack on the hospital," the old man protested.

"They are. Callendar boasted so before the trial. I heard through the tatties; [1] he said, 'I have tortured that nigger.'"

"Oh, my God, my God. . . . He called him a nigger, did he?"

"They put pepper instead of antiseptic on the wounds."

"Mr. Mahmoud Ali, impossible; a little roughness will not hurt the boy, he needs discipline."

"Pepper. Civil Surgeon said so. They hope to destroy us one by one; they shall fail."

The new injury lashed the crowd to fury. It had been aimless hitherto, and had lacked a grievance. When they reached the Maidan and saw the sallow arcades of the Minto they shambled towards it howling. It was near midday. The earth and sky were insanely ugly, the spirit of evil again strode abroad. The Nawab Bahadur alone struggled against it, and told himself that the rumour must be untrue. He had seen his grandson in the ward only last week. But he too was carried forward over the new precipice. To rescue, to maltreat Major Callendar in revenge, and then was to come the turn of the civil station generally.

But disaster was averted, and averted by Dr. Panna Lal.

Dr. Panna Lal had offered to give witness for the prosecution in the hope of pleasing the English, also because he hated Aziz. When the case broke down, he was in a very painful position. He saw the crash coming sooner than most people, slipped from the court before Mr. Das had finished, and drove Dapple off through the bazaars, in flight from the wrath to come. In the hospital he should be safe, for Major Callendar would protect him. But the Major had not come, and now things were worse than ever, for here was a mob, entirely desirous of his blood, and the orderlies were mutinous and would not help him over the back wall, or rather hoisted him and let him drop back, to the satisfaction of the patients. In agony he cried, "Man can but die the once," and waddled across the compound to meet the invasion, salaaming with one hand and holding up a pale yellow umbrella in the other. "Oh, forgive me," he whined

1. **tatties:** screens or mats placed over windows and kept wet in order to cool the air.

as he approached the victorious landau. "Oh, Dr. Aziz, forgive the wicked lies I told." Aziz was silent, the others thickened their throats and threw up their chins in token of scorn. "I was afraid, I was mislaid," the suppliant continued. "I was mislaid here, there, and everywhere as regards your character. Oh, forgive the poor old hakim who gave you milk when ill! Oh, Nawab Bahadur, whoever merciful, is it my poor little dispensary you require? Take every cursed bottle." Agitated, but alert, he saw them smile at his indifferent English, and suddenly he started playing the buffoon, flung down his umbrella, trod through it, and struck himself upon the nose. He knew what he was doing, and so did they. There was nothing pathetic or eternal in the degradation of such a man. Of ignoble origin, Dr. Panna Lal possessed nothing that could be disgraced, and he wisely decided to make the other Indians feel like kings, because it would put them into better tempers. When he found they wanted Nureddin, he skipped like a goat, he scuttled like a hen to do their bidding, the hospital was saved, and to the end of his life he could not understand why he had not obtained promotion on the morning's work. "Promptness, sir, promptness similar to you," was the argument he employed to Major Callendar when claiming it.

When Nureddin emerged, his face all bandaged, there was a roar of relief as though the Bastille had fallen. It was the crisis of the march, and the Nawab Bahadur managed to get the situation into hand. Embracing the young man publicly, he began a speech about Justice, Courage, Liberty, and Prudence, ranged under heads, which cooled the passion of the crowd. He further announced that he should give up his British-conferred title, and live as a private gentleman, plain Mr. Zulfiqar, for which reason he was instantly proceeding to his country seat. The landau turned, the crowd accompanied it, the crisis was over. The Marabar caves had been a terrible strain on the local administration; they altered a good many lives and wrecked several careers, but they did not break up a continent or even dislocate a district.

"We will have rejoicings to-night," the old man said. "Mr. Hamidullah, I depute you to bring out our friends Fielding and Amritrao, and to discover whether the latter will require special food. The others will keep with me. We shall not go out to Dilkusha until the cool of the evening, of course. I do not know the feelings of other gentlemen; for my own part, I have a slight headache, and I wish I had thought to ask our good Panna Lal for aspirin."

For the heat was claiming its own. Unable to madden, it stupefied, and before long most of the Chandrapore combatants were asleep. Those in the civil station kept watch a little, fearing an attack, but presently they too entered the world of dreams—that world in which a third of each man's life is spent, and which is thought by some pessimists to be a premonition of eternity.

CHAPTER 26

Evening approached by the time Fielding and Miss Quested met and had the first of their numerous curious conversations. He had hoped, when he woke up, to find someone had fetched her away, but the College remained isolated from the rest of the universe. She asked whether she could have "a sort of interview," and, when he made no reply, said, "Have you any explanation of my extraordinary behaviour?"

"None," he said curtly. "Why make such a charge if you were going to withdraw it?"

"Why, indeed."

"I ought to feel grateful to you, I suppose, but——"

"I don't expect gratitude. I only thought you might care to hear what I have to say."

"Oh, well," he grumbled, feeling rather schoolboyish, "I don't think a discussion between us is desirable. To put it frankly, I belong to the other side in this ghastly affair."

"Would it not interest you to hear my side?"

"Not much."

"I shouldn't tell you in confidence, of course. So you can hand on all my remarks to your side, for there is one great mercy that has come out of all to-day's misery: I have no longer any secrets. My echo has gone—I call the buzzing sound in my ears an echo. You see, I have been unwell ever since that expedition to the caves, and possibly before it."

The remark interested him rather; it was what he had sometimes suspected himself. "What kind of illness?" he enquired.

She touched her head at the side, then shook it.

"That was my first thought, the day of the arrest: hallucination."

"Do you think that would be so?" she asked with great humility. "What should have given me an hallucination?"

"One of three things certainly happened in the Marabar," he said, getting drawn into a discussion against his will. "One of four things. Either Aziz is guilty, which is what your friends think; or you invented the charge out of malice, which is what my friends think; or you have had an hallucination. I'm very much inclined"—getting up and striding about— "now that you tell me that you felt unwell before the expedition—it's an important piece of evidence—I believe that you yourself broke the strap of the field-glasses; you were alone in that cave the whole time."

"Perhaps. . . ."

"Can you remember when you first felt out of sorts?"

"When I came to tea with you there, in that garden-house."

"A somewhat unlucky party. Aziz and old Godbole were both ill after it too."

"I was not ill—it is far too vague to mention: it is all mixed up with my private affairs. I enjoyed the singing . . . but just about then a sort of sadness began that I couldn't detect at the time . . . no, nothing as solid as sadness: living at half pressure expresses it best. Half pressure. I remember going on to polo with Mr. Heaslop at the Maidan. Various other things happened—it doesn't matter what, but I was under par for all of them. I was certainly in that state when I saw the caves, and you suggest (nothing shocks or hurts me)—you suggest that I had an hallucination there, the sort of thing—though in an awful form—that makes some women think they've had an offer of marriage when none was made."

"You put it honestly, anyhow."

"I was brought up to be honest; the trouble is it gets me nowhere."

Liking her better, he smiled and said, "It'll get us to heaven."

"Will it?"

"If heaven existed."

"Do you not believe in heaven, Mr. Fielding, may I ask?" she said, looking at him shyly.

"I do not. Yet I believe that honesty gets us there."

"How can that be?"

"Let us go back to hallucinations. I was watching you carefully through your evidence this morning, and if I'm right, the hallucination (what you call half pressure—quite as good a word) disappeared suddenly."

She tried to remember what she had felt in court, but could not; the vision disappeared whenever she wished to interpret it. "Events presented themselves to me in their logical sequence," was what she said, but it hadn't been that at all.

"My belief—and of course I was listening carefully, in hope you would make some slip—my belief is that poor McBryde exorcised you. As soon as he asked you a straightforward question, you gave a straightforward answer, and broke down."

"Exorcise in that sense. I thought you meant I'd seen a ghost."

"I don't go to that length!"

"People whom I respect very much believe in ghosts," she said rather sharply. "My friend Mrs. Moore does."

"She's an old lady."

"I think you need not be impolite to her, as well as to her son."

"I did not intend to be rude. I only meant it is difficult, as we get on in life, to resist the supernatural. I've felt it coming on me myself. I still jog on without it, but what a temptation, at forty-five, to pretend that the dead live again; one's own dead; no one else's matter."

"Because the dead don't live again."

"I fear not."

"So do I."

There was a moment's silence, such as often follows the triumph of rationalism. Then he apologized handsomely enough for his behaviour to Heaslop at the club.

"What does Dr. Aziz say of me?" she asked, after another pause.

"He—he has not been capable of thought in his misery, naturally he's very bitter," said Fielding, a little awkward, because such remarks as Aziz had made were not merely bitter, they were foul. The underlying notion was, "It disgraces me to have been mentioned in connection with such a hag." It enraged him that he had been accused by a woman who had no personal beauty; sexually, he was a snob. This had puzzled and worried Fielding. Sensuality, as long as it is straightforward, did not repel him, but this derived sensuality—the sort that classes a mistress among motor-cars if she is beautiful, and among eye-flies if she isn't—was alien to his own emotions, and he felt a barrier between himself and Aziz whenever it arose. It was, in a new form, the old, old trouble that eats the heart out of every civilization: snobbery, the desire for possessions, creditable appendages; and it is to escape this rather than the lusts of the flesh that saints retreat into the Himalayas. To change the subject, he said, "But let me conclude my analysis. We are agreed that he is not a villain and that you are not one, and we aren't really sure that it was an hallucination. There's a fourth possibility which we must touch on: was it somebody else?"

"The guide."

"Exactly, the guide. I often think so. Unluckily Aziz hit him on the face, and he got a fright and disappeared. It is most unsatisfactory, and we hadn't the police to help us, the guide was of no interest to them."

"Perhaps it was the guide," she said quietly; the question had lost interest for her suddenly.

"Or could it have been one of that gang of Pathans who have been drifting through the district?"

"Someone who was in another cave, and followed me when the guide was looking away? Possibly."

At that moment Hamidullah joined them, and seemed not too pleased to find them closeted together. Like everyone else in Chandrapore, he could make nothing of Miss Quested's conduct. He had overheard their last remark. "Hullo, my dear Fielding," he said. "So I run you down at last. Can you come out at once to Dilkusha?"

"At once?"

"I hope to leave in a moment, don't let me interrupt," said Adela.

"The telephone has been broken; Miss Quested can't ring up her friends," he explained.

"A great deal has been broken, more than will ever be mended," said the other. "Still, there should be some way of transporting this lady back to the civil lines. The resources of civilization are numerous." He spoke without looking at Miss Quested, and he ignored the slight movement she made towards him with her hand.

Fielding, who thought the meeting might as well be friendly, said, "Miss Quested has been explaining a little about her conduct of this morning."

"Perhaps the age of miracles has returned. One must be prepared for everything, our philosophers say."

"It must have seemed a miracle to the onlookers," said Adela, addressing him nervously. "The fact is that I realized before it was too late that I had made a mistake, and had just enough presence of mind to say so. That is all my extraordinary conduct amounts to."

"All it amounts to, indeed," he retorted, quivering with rage but keeping himself in hand, for he felt she might be setting another trap. "Speaking as a private individual, in a purely informal conversation, I admired your conduct, and I was delighted when our warmhearted students garlanded you. But, like Mr. Fielding, I am surprised; indeed, surprise is too weak a word. I see you drag my best friend into the dirt, damage his health and ruin his prospects in a way you cannot conceive owing to your ignorance of our society and religion, and then suddenly you get up in the witness-box: 'Oh no, Mr. McBryde, after all I am not quite sure, you may as well let him go.' Am I mad? I keep asking myself. Is it a dream, and if so, when did it start? And without doubt it is a dream that has not yet finished. For I gather you have not done with us yet, and it is now the turn of the poor old guide who conducted you round the caves."

"Not at all, we were only discussing possibilities," interposed Fielding.

"An interesting pastime, but a lengthy one. There are one hundred and seventy million Indians in this notable peninsula, and of course one or other of them entered the cave. Of course some Indian is the culprit, we must never doubt that. And since, my dear Fielding, these possibilities will take you some time"—here he put his arm over the Englishman's shoulder and swayed him to and fro gently—"don't you think you had better come out to the Nawab Bahadur's—or I should say to Mr. Zulfiqar's, for that is the name he now requires us to call him by."

"Gladly, in a minute . . ."

"I have just settled my movements," said Miss Quested. "I shall go to the Dak Bungalow."

"Not the Turtons'?" said Hamidullah, goggle-eyed. "I thought you were their guest."

The Dak Bungalow of Chandrapore was below the average, and certainly servantless. Fielding, though he continued to sway with Hamidullah, was thinking on independent lines, and said in a moment: "I have a better idea than that, Miss Quested. You must stop here at the College. I shall be away at least two days, and you can have the place entirely to yourself, and make your plans at your convenience."

"I don't agree at all," said Hamidullah, with every symptom of dismay. "The idea is a thoroughly bad one. There may quite well be another demonstration to-night, and suppose an attack is made on the College. You would be held responsible for this lady's safety, my dear fellow."

"They might equally attack the Dak Bungalow."

"Exactly, but the responsibility there ceases to be yours."

"Quite so. I have given trouble enough."

"Do you hear? The lady admits it herself. It's not an attack from our people I fear—you should see their orderly conduct at the hospital; what we must guard against is an attack secretly arranged by the police for the purpose of discrediting you. McBryde keeps plenty of roughs for this purpose, and this would be the very opportunity for him."

"Never mind. She is not going to the Dak Bungalow," said Fielding. He had a natural sympathy for the down-trodden—that was partly why he rallied from Aziz—and had become determined not to leave the poor girl in the lurch. Also, he had a new-born respect for her, consequent on their talk. Although her hard school-mistressy manner remained, she was no longer examining life, but being examined by it; she had become a real person.

"Then where is she to go? We shall never have done with her!" For Miss Quested had not appealed to Hamidullah. If she had shown emotion in court, broke down, beat her breast, and invoked the name of God, she would have summoned forth his imagination and generosity—he had plenty of both. But while relieving the Oriental mind, she had chilled it, with the result that he could scarcely believe she was sincere, and indeed from his standpoint she was not. For her behaviour rested on cold justice and honesty; she had felt, while she recanted, no passion of love for those whom she had wronged. Truth is not truth in that exacting land unless there go with it kindness and more kindness and kindness again, unless the Word that was with God also is God. And the girl's sacrifice—so creditable according to Western notions—was rightly rejected, because, though it came from her heart, it did not include her heart. A few garlands from students was all that India ever gave her in return.

"But where is she to have her dinner, where is she to sleep? I say here, here, and if she is hit on the head by roughs, she is hit on the head. That is my contribution. Well, Miss Quested?"

"You are very kind. I should have said yes, I think, but I agree with Mr. Hamidullah, I must give no more trouble to you. I believe my best plan is to return to the Turtons, and see if they will allow me to sleep, and if they turn me away I must go to the Dak. The Collector would take me in, I know, but Mrs. Turton said this morning that she would never see me again." She spoke without bitterness, or, as Hamidullah thought, without proper pride. Her aim was to cause the minimum of annoyance.

"Far better stop here than expose yourself to insults from that preposterous woman."

"Do you find her preposterous? I used to. I don't now."

"Well, here's our solution," said the barrister, who had terminated his slightly minatory caress and strolled to the window. "Here comes the City Magistrate. He comes in a third-class band-ghari [1] for purposes of disguise, he comes unattended, but here comes the City Magistrate."

"At last," said Adela sharply, which caused Fielding to glance at her.

"He comes, he comes, he comes. I cringe. I tremble."

"Will you ask him what he wants, Mr. Fielding?"

"He wants you, of course."

"He may not even know I'm here."

"I'll see him first, if you prefer."

When he had gone, Hamidullah said to her bitingly: "Really, really. Need you have exposed Mr. Fielding to this further discomfort? He is far too considerate." She made no reply, and there was complete silence between them until their host returned.

"He has some news for you," he said. "You'll find him on the verandah. He prefers not to come in."

"Does he tell me to come out to him?"

"Whether he tells you or not, you will go, I think," said Hamidullah.

She paused, then said, "Perfectly right," and then said a few words of thanks to the Principal for his kindness to her during the day.

"Thank goodness, that's over," he remarked, not escorting her to the verandah, for he held it unnecessary to see Ronny again.

"It was insulting of him not to come in."

"He couldn't very well after my behaviour to him at the Club. Heaslop doesn't come out badly. Besides, Fate has treated him pretty roughly

1. **band-ghari:** a closed (*band*) carriage (*ghari*), like an English hansom cab.

to-day. He has had a cable to the effect that his mother's dead, poor old soul."

"Oh, really. Mrs. Moore. I'm sorry," said Hamidullah rather indifferently.

"She died at sea."

"The heat, I suppose."

"Presumably."

"May is no month to allow an old lady to travel in."

"Quite so. Heaslop ought never to have let her go, and he knows it. Shall we be off?"

"Let us wait until the happy couple leave the compound clear . . . they really are intolerable dawdling there. Ah well, Fielding, you don't believe in Providence, I remember. I do. This is Heaslop's punishment for abducting our witness in order to stop us establishing our alibi."

"You go rather too far there. The poor old lady's evidence could have had no value, shout and shriek Mahmoud Ali as he will. She couldn't see through the Kawa Dol even if she had wanted to. Only Miss Quested could have saved him."

"She loved Aziz, he says, also India, and he loved her."

"Love is of no value in a witness, as a barrister ought to know. But I see there is about to be an Esmiss Esmoor legend at Chandrapore, my dear Hamidullah, and I will not impede its growth."

The other smiled, and looked at his watch. They both regretted the death, but they were middle-aged men, who had invested their emotions elsewhere, and outbursts of grief could not be expected from them over a slight acquaintance. It's only one's own dead who matter. If for a moment the sense of communion in sorrow came to them, it passed. How indeed is it possible for one human being to be sorry for all the sadness that meets him on the face of the earth, for the pain that is endured not only by men, but by animals and plants, and perhaps by the stones? The soul is tired in a moment, and in fear of losing the little she does understand, she retreats to the permanent lines which habit or chance have dictated, and suffers there. Fielding had met the dead woman only two or three times, Hamidullah had seen her in the distance once, and they were far more occupied with the coming gathering at Dilkusha, the "victory" dinner, for which they would be most victoriously late. They agreed not to tell Aziz about Mrs. Moore till the morrow, because he was fond of her, and the bad news might spoil his fun.

"Oh, this is unbearable!" muttered Hamidullah. For Miss Quested was back again.

"Mr. Fielding, has Ronny told you of this new misfortune?"

He bowed.

"Ah me!" She sat down, and seemed to stiffen into a monument.

"Heaslop is waiting for you, I think."

"I do so long to be alone. She was my best friend, far more to me than to him. I can't bear to be with Ronny . . . I can't explain . . . Could you do me the very great kindness of letting me stop after all?"

Hamidullah swore violently in the vernacular.

"I should be pleased, but does Mr. Heaslop wish it?"

"I didn't ask him, we are too much upset—it's so complex, not like what unhappiness is supposed to be. Each of us ought to be alone, and think. Do come and see Ronny again."

"I think he should come in this time," said Fielding, feeling that this much was due to his own dignity. "Do ask him to come."

She returned with him. He was half miserable, half arrogant—indeed, a strange mix-up—and broke at once into uneven speech. "I came to bring Miss Quested away, but her visit to the Turtons has ended, and there is no other arrangement so far, mine are bachelor quarters now——"

Fielding stopped him courteously. "Say no more, Miss Quested stops here. I only wanted to be assured of your approval. Miss Quested, you had better send for your own servant if he can be found, but I will leave orders with mine to do all they can for you, also I'll let the Scouts know. They have guarded the College ever since it was closed, and may as well go on. I really think you'll be as safe here as anywhere. I shall be back Thursday."

Meanwhile Hamidullah, determined to spare the enemy no incidental pain, had said to Ronny: "We hear, sir, that your mother has died. May we ask where the cable came from?"

"Aden."

"Ah, you were boasting she had reached Aden, in court."

"But she died on leaving Bombay," broke in Adela. "She was dead when they called her name this morning. She must have been buried at sea."

Somehow this stopped Hamidullah, and he desisted from his brutality, which had shocked Fielding more than anyone else. He remained silent while the details of Miss Quested's occupation of the College were arranged, merely remarking to Ronny, "It is clearly to be understood, sir, that neither Mr. Fielding nor any of us are responsible for this lady's safety at Government College," to which Ronny agreed. After that, he watched the semi-chivalrous behavings of the three English with quiet amusement; he thought Fielding had been incredibly silly and weak, and he was amazed by the younger people's want of proper pride. When they were driving out to Dilkusha, hours late, he said to Amritrao, who accompanied them: "Mr. Amritrao, have you considered what sum Miss Quested ought to pay as compensation?"

"Twenty thousand rupees."

No more was then said, but the remark horrified Fielding. He couldn't bear to think of the queer honest girl losing her money and possibly her young man too. She advanced into his consciousness suddenly. And, fatigued by the merciless and enormous day, he lost his usual sane view of human intercourse, and felt that we exist not in ourselves, but in terms of each others' minds—a notion for which logic offers no support and which had attacked him only once before, the evening after the catastrophe, when from the verandah of the club he saw the fists and fingers of the Marabar swell until they included the whole night sky.

CHAPTER 27

"Aziz, are you awake?"

"No, so let us have a talk; let us dream plans for the future."

"I am useless at dreaming."

"Good night then, dear fellow."

The Victory Banquet was over, and the revellers lay on the roof of plain Mr. Zulfiqar's mansion, asleep, or gazing through mosquito nets at the stars. Exactly above their heads hung the constellation of the Lion, the disc of Regulus so large and bright that it resembled a tunnel, and when this fancy was accepted all the other stars seemed tunnels too.

"Are you content with our day's work, Cyril?" the voice on his left continued.

"Are you?"

"Except that I ate too much. 'How is stomach, how head?'—I say, Panna Lal and Callendar'll get the sack."

"There'll be a general move at Chandrapore."

"And you'll get promotion."

"They can't well move me down, whatever their feelings."

"In any case we spend our holidays together, and visit Kashmir, possibly Persia, for I shall have plenty of money. Paid to me on account of the injury sustained by my character," he explained with cynical calm. "While with me you shall never spend a single pie. This is what I have always wished, and as the result of my misfortunes it has come."

"You have won a great victory . . ." began Fielding.

"I know, my dear chap, I know; your voice need not become so solemn and anxious. I know what you are going to say next: Let, oh let Miss Quested off paying, so that the English may say, 'Here is a native who has actually behaved like a gentleman; if it was not for his black face we would almost allow him to join our club.' The approval of your compatriots no longer interests me, I have become anti-British, and ought to have done so sooner, it would have saved me numerous misfortunes."

"Including knowing me."

"I say, shall we go and pour water on to Mohammed Latif's face? He is so funny when this is done to him asleep."

The remark was not a question but a full-stop. Fielding accepted it as such and there was a pause, pleasantly filled by a little wind which managed to brush the top of the house. The banquet, though riotous, had been agreeable, and now the blessings of leisure—unknown to the West, which either works or idles—descended on the motley company. Civilization strays about like a ghost here, revisiting the ruins of empire, and is to be found not in great works of art or mighty deeds, but in the gestures well-bred Indians make when they sit or lie down. Fielding, who had dressed up in native costume, learnt from his excessive awkwardness in it that all his motions were makeshifts, whereas when the Nawab Bahadur stretched out his hand for food or Nureddin applauded a song, something beautiful had been accomplished which needed no development. This restfulness of gesture—it is the Peace that passeth Understanding, after all, it is the social equivalent of Yoga. When the whirring of action ceases, it becomes visible, and reveals a civilization which the West can disturb but will never acquire. The hand stretches out for ever, the lifted knee has the eternity though not the sadness of the grave. Aziz was full of civilization this evening, complete, dignified, rather hard, and it was with diffidence that the other said: "Yes, certainly you must let off Miss Quested easily. She must pay all your costs, that is only fair, but do not treat her like a conquered enemy."

"Is she wealthy! I depute you to find out."

"The sums mentioned at dinner when you all got so excited—they would ruin her, they are perfectly preposterous. Look here . . ."

"I am looking, though it gets a bit dark. I see Cyril Fielding to be a very nice chap indeed and my best friend, but in some ways a fool. You think that by letting Miss Quested off easily I shall make a better reputation for myself and Indians generally. No, no. It will be put down to weakness and the attempt to gain promotion officially. I have decided to have nothing more to do with British India, as a matter of fact. I shall seek service in some Moslem State, such as Hyderabad, Bhopal, where Englishmen cannot insult me any more. Don't counsel me otherwise."

"In the course of a long talk with Miss Quested . . ."

"I don't want to hear your long talks."

"Be quiet. In the course of a long talk with Miss Quested I have begun to understand her character. It's not an easy one, she being a prig. But she is perfectly genuine and very brave. When she saw she was wrong, she pulled herself up with a jerk and said so. I want you to realize what that means. All her friends around her, the entire British Raj pushing her forward. She stops, sends the whole thing to smithereens. In her place I should have funked it. But she stopped, and almost did she become a national heroine, but my students ran us down a side street before the crowd caught flame. Do treat her considerately. She really mustn't get the worst of both worlds. I know what all these"—he indicated the shrouded forms on the roof—"will want, but you mustn't listen to them. Be merciful. Act like one of your six Mogul Emperors, or all the six rolled into one."

"Not even Mogul Emperors showed mercy until they received an apology."

"She'll apologize if that's the trouble," he cried, sitting up. "Look, I'll make you an offer. Dictate to me whatever form of words you like, and this time to-morrow I'll bring it back signed. This is not instead of any public apology she may make you in law. It's an addition."

"'Dear Dr. Aziz, I wish you had come into the cave; I am an awful old hag, and it is my last chance.' Will she sign that?"

"Well good night, good night, it's time to go to sleep, after that."

"Good night, I suppose it is."

"Oh, I wish you wouldn't make that kind of remark," he continued after a pause. "It is the one thing in you I can't put up with."

"I put up with all things in you, so what is to be done?"

"Well, you hurt me by saying it; good night."

There was silence, then dreamily but with deep feeling the voice said: "Cyril, I have had an idea which will satisfy your tender mind: I shall consult Mrs. Moore."

Opening his eyes, and beholding thousands of stars, he could not reply, they silenced him.

"Her opinion will solve everything; I can trust her so absolutely. If she advises me to pardon this girl, I shall do so. She will counsel me nothing against my real and true honour, as you might."

"Let us discuss that to-morrow morning."

"Is it not strange? I keep on forgetting she has left India. During the shouting of her name in court I fancied she was present. I had shut my eyes, I confused myself on purpose to deaden the pain. Now this very instant I forgot again. I shall be obliged to write. She is now far away, well on her way towards Ralph and Stella."

"To whom?"

"To those other children."

"I have not heard of other children."

"Just as I have two boys and a girl, so has Mrs. Moore. She told me in the mosque."

"I knew her so slightly."

"I have seen her but three times, but I know she is an Oriental."

"You are so fantastic. . . . Miss Quested, you won't treat her generously; while over Mrs. Moore there is this elaborate chivalry. Miss Quested anyhow behaved decently this morning, whereas the old lady never did anything for you at all, and it's pure conjecture that she would have come forward in your favour, it only rests on servants' gossip. Your emotions never seem in proportion to their objects, Aziz."

"Is emotion a sack of potatoes, so much the pound, to be measured out? Am I a machine? I shall be told I can use up my emotions by using them, next."

"I should have thought you would. It sounds common sense. You can't eat your cake and have it, even in the world of the spirit."

"If you are right, there is no point in any friendship; it all comes down to give and take, or give and return, which is disgusting, and we had better all leap over this parapet and kill ourselves. Is anything wrong with you this evening that you grow so materialistic?"

"Your unfairness is worse than my materialism."

"I see. Anything further to complain of?" He was good-tempered and affectionate but a little formidable. Imprisonment had made channels for his character, which would never fluctuate as widely now as in the past. "Because it is far better you put all your difficulties before me, if we are to be friends for ever. You do not like Mrs. Moore, and are annoyed because I do; however, you will like her in time."

When a person, really dead, is supposed to be alive, an unhealthiness infects the conversation. Fielding could not stand the tension any longer and blurted out: "I'm sorry to say Mrs. Moore's dead."

But Hamidullah, who had been listening to all their talk, and did not want the festive evening spoilt, cried from the adjoining bed: "Aziz, he is trying to pull your leg; don't believe him, the villain."

"I do not believe him," said Aziz; he was inured to practical jokes, even of this type.

Fielding said no more. Facts are facts, and everyone would learn of Mrs. Moore's death in the morning. But it struck him that people are not really dead until they are felt to be dead. As long as there is some misunderstanding about them, they possess a sort of immortality. An experience of his own confirmed this. Many years ago he had lost a great friend, a woman, who believed in the Christian heaven and assured him that after the changes and chances of this mortal life they would meet in it again. Fielding was a blank, frank atheist, but he respected every opinion his friend held: to do this is essential in friendship. And it seemed to him for a time that the dead awaited him, and when the illusion faded it left behind it an emptiness that was almost guilt: "This really is the end," he thought, "and I gave her the final blow." He had tried to kill Mrs. Moore this evening, on the roof of the Nawab Bahadur's house; but she still eluded him, and the atmosphere remained tranquil. Presently the moon rose—the exhausted crescent that precedes the sun—and shortly after men and oxen began their interminable labour, and the gracious interlude, which he had tried to curtail, came to its natural conclusion.

CHAPTER 28

Dead she was—committed to the deep while still on the southward track, for the boats from Bombay cannot point towards Europe until Arabia has been rounded; she was further in the tropics than ever achieved while on shore, when the sun touched her for the last time and her body was lowered into yet another India—the Indian Ocean. She left behind her sore discomfort, for a death gives a ship a bad name. Who was this Mrs. Moore? When Aden was reached, Lady Mellanby cabled, wrote, did all that was kind, but the wife of a Lieutenant-Governor does not bargain for such an experience; and she repeated: "I had only seen the poor creature for a few hours when she was taken ill; really this has been needlessly distressing, it spoils one's home-coming." A ghost followed the ship up the Red Sea, but failed to enter the Mediterranean. Somewhere about Suez there is always a social change: the arrangements of Asia weaken and those of Europe begin to be felt, and during the transition Mrs. Moore was shaken off. At Port Said the grey blustery north began. The weather was so cold and bracing that the passengers felt it must have broken in the land they had left, but it became hotter steadily there in accordance with its usual law.

The death took subtler and more lasting shapes in Chandrapore. A legend sprang up that an Englishman had killed his mother for trying to save an Indian's life—and there was just enough truth in this to cause annoyance to the authorities. Sometimes it was a cow that had been killed—or a crocodile with the tusks of a boar had crawled out of the Ganges. Nonsense of this type is more difficult to combat than a solid lie. It hides in rubbish heaps and moves when no one is looking. At one period two distinct tombs containing Esmiss Esmoor's remains were reported: one by the tannery, the other up near the goods station. Mr. McBryde visited them both and saw signs of the beginning of a cult—earthenware saucers and so on. Being an experienced official, he did nothing to irritate it, and after a week or so, the rash died down. "There's propaganda behind all this," he said, forgetting that a hundred years ago, when Europeans still made their home in the country-side and appealed to its imagination, they occasionally became local demons after death—not a whole god, perhaps, but part of one, adding an epithet or gesture to what already existed, just as the gods contribute to the great gods, and they to the philosophic Brahm.[1]

Ronny reminded himself that his mother had left India at her own wish, but his conscience was not clear. He had behaved badly to her, and he had either to repent (which involved a mental overturn), or to persist in unkindness towards her. He chose the latter course. How tiresome she had been with her patronage of Aziz! What a bad influence upon Adela! And now she still gave trouble with ridiculous "tombs," mixing herself up with natives. She could not help it, of course, but she had attempted similar exasperating expeditions in her lifetime, and he reckoned it against her. The young man had much to worry him—the heat, the local tension, the approaching visit of the Lieutenant-Governor, the problems of Adela—and threading them all together into a grotesque garland were these Indianizations of Mrs. Moore. What does happen to one's mother when she dies? Presumably she goes to heaven, anyhow she clears out. Ronny's religion was of the sterilized Public School brand, which never goes bad, even in the tropics. Wherever he entered, mosque, cave, or temple, he retained the spiritual outlook of the Fifth Form, and condemned as "weakening" any attempt to understand them. Pulling himself together, he dismissed the matter from his mind. In due time he and his half-brother and sister would put up a tablet to her in the Northamptonshire church where she had worshipped, recording the dates of her birth and death and the fact that she had been buried at sea. This would be sufficient.

And Adela—she would have to depart too; he hoped she would have made the suggestion herself ere now. He really could not marry her—it would mean the end of his career. Poor lamentable Adela. . . . She remained at Government College, by Fielding's courtesy—unsuitable and humiliating, but no one would receive her at the civil station. He postponed all private talk until the award against her was decided. Aziz was suing her for damages in the sub-judge's court. Then he would ask her to release him. She had killed his love, and it had never been very robust; they would never have achieved betrothal but for the accident to the Nawab Bahadur's car. She belonged to the callow academic period of his life which he had outgrown—Grasmere, serious talks and walks, that sort of thing.

CHAPTER 29

The visit of the Lieutenant-Governor of the Province formed the next stage in the decomposition of the Marabar. Sir Gilbert, though not an en-

1. **Brahm:** God in the Hindu religion.

lightened man, held enlightened opinions. Exempted by a long career in the Secretariate from personal contact with the peoples of India, he was able to speak of them urbanely, and to deplore racial prejudice. He applauded the outcome of the trial, and congratulated Fielding on having taken "the broad, the sensible, the only possible charitable view from the first. Speaking confidentially . . ." he proceeded. Fielding deprecated confidences, but Sir Gilbert insisted on imparting them; the affair had been "mishandled by certain of our friends up the hill" who did not realize that "the hands of the clock move forward, not back," etc., etc. One thing he could guarantee: the Principal would receive a most cordial invitation to rejoin the club, and he begged, nay commanded him, to accept. He returned to his Himalayan altitudes well satisfied; the amount of money Miss Quested would have to pay, the precise nature of what had happened in the caves—these were local details, and did not concern him.

Fielding found himself drawn more and more into Miss Quested's affairs. The College remained closed and he ate and slept at Hamidullah's, so there was no reason she should not stop on if she wished. In her place he would have cleared out, sooner than submit to Ronny's half-hearted and distracted civilities, but she was waiting for the hour-glass of her sojourn to run through. A house to live in, a garden to walk in during the brief moment of the cool—that was all she asked, and he was able to provide them. Disaster had shown her her limitations, and he realized now what a fine loyal character she was. Her humility was touching. She never repined at getting the worst of both worlds; she regarded it as the due punishment of her stupidity. When he hinted to her that a personal apology to Aziz might be seemly, she said sadly: "Of course. I ought to have thought of it myself, my instincts never help me. Why didn't I rush up to him after the trial? Yes, of course I will write him an apology, but please will you dictate it?" Between them they concocted a letter, sincere, and full of moving phrases, but it was not moving as a letter. "Shall I write another?" she enquired. "Nothing matters if I can undo the harm I have caused. I can do this right, and that right; but when the two are put together they come wrong. That's the defect of my character. I have never realized it until now. I thought that if I was just and asked questions I would come through every difficulty." He replied: "Our letter is a failure for a simple reason which we had better face: you have no real affection for Aziz, or Indians generally." She assented. "The first time I saw you, you were wanting to see India, not Indians, and it occurred to me: Ah, that won't take us far. Indians know whether they are liked or not—they cannot be fooled here. Justice never satisfies them, and that is why the British Empire rests on sand." Then she said: "Do I like anyone, though?" Presumably she liked

Heaslop, and he changed the subject, for this side of her life did not concern him.

His Indian friends were, on the other hand, a bit above themselves. Victory, which would have made the English sanctimonious, made them aggressive. They wanted to develop an offensive, and tried to do so by discovering new grievances and wrongs, many of which had no existence. They suffered from the usual disillusion that attends warfare. The aims of battle and the fruits of conquest are never the same; the latter have their value and only the saint rejects them, but their hint of immortality vanishes as soon as they are held in the hand. Although Sir Gilbert had been courteous, almost obsequious, the fabric he represented had in no wise bowed its head. British officialism remained, as all-pervading and as unpleasant as the sun; and what was next to be done against it was not very obvious, even to Mahmoud Ali. Loud talk and trivial lawlessness were attempted, and behind them continued a genuine but vague desire for education. "Mr. Fielding, we must all be educated promptly."

Aziz was friendly and domineering. He wanted Fielding to "give in to the East," as he called it, and live in a condition of affectionate dependence upon it. "You can trust me, Cyril." No question of that, and Fielding had no roots among his own people. Yet he really couldn't become a sort of Mohammed Latif. When they argued about it something racial intruded—not bitterly, but inevitably, like the colour of their skins: coffee-colour versus pinko-grey. And Aziz would conclude: "Can't you see that I'm grateful to you for your help and want to reward you?" And the other would retort: "If you want to reward me, let Miss Quested off paying."

The insensitiveness about Adela displeased him. It would, from every point of view, be right to treat her generously, and one day he had the notion of appealing to the memory of Mrs. Moore. Aziz had this high and fantastic estimate of Mrs. Moore. Her death had been a real grief to his warm heart; he wept like a child and ordered his three children to weep also. There was no doubt that he respected and loved her. Fielding's first attempt was a failure. The reply was: "I see your trick. I want revenge on them. Why should I be insulted and suffer the contents of my pockets read and my wife's photograph taken to the police station? Also I want the money—to educate my little boys, as I explained to her." But he began to weaken, and Fielding was not ashamed to practise a little necromancy. Whenever the question of compensation came up, he introduced the dead woman's name. Just as other propagandists invented her a tomb, so did he raise a questionable image of her in the heart of Aziz, saying nothing that he believed to be untrue, but producing something that was probably far from the truth. Aziz yielded suddenly. He felt it was Mrs. Moore's wish that he should spare the woman who was about to marry her son, that it was the only honour he could pay her, and he renounced with a passionate and beautiful outburst the whole of the compensation money, claiming only costs. It was fine of him, and, as he foresaw, it won him no credit with the English. They still believed he was guilty, they believed it to the end of their careers, and retired Anglo-Indians in Tunbridge Wells or Cheltenham still murmur to each other: "That Marabar case which broke down because the poor girl couldn't face giving her evidence—that was another bad case."

When the affair was thus officially ended, Ronny, who was about to be transferred to another part of the Province, approached Fielding with his usual constraint and said: "I wish to thank you for the help you have given Miss Quested. She will not of course trespass on your hospitality further; she has as a matter of fact decided to return to England. I have just arranged about her passage for her. I understand she would like to see you."

"I shall go round at once."

On reaching the College, he found her in some upset. He learnt that the engagement had been broken by Ronny. "Far wiser of him," she said pathetically. "I ought to have spoken myself, but I drifted on wondering what would happen. I would willingly have gone on spoiling his life through inertia—one has nothing to do, one belongs nowhere and becomes a public nuisance without realizing it." In order to reassure him, she added: "I speak only of India. I am not astray in England. I fit in there—no, don't think I shall do harm in England. When I am forced back there, I shall settle down to some career. I have sufficient money left to start myself, and heaps of friends of my own type. I shall be quite all right." Then sighing: "But oh, the trouble I've brought on everyone here. . . . I can never get over it. My carefulness as to whether we should marry or not . . . and in the end Ronny and I part and aren't even sorry. We ought never to have thought of marriage. Weren't you amazed when our engagement was originally announced?"

"Not much. At my age one's seldom amazed," he said, smiling. "Marriage is too absurd in any case. It begins and continues for such very slight reasons. The social business props it up on one side, and the theological business on the other, but neither of them are marriage, are they? I've friends who can't remember why they married, no more can their wives. I suspect that it mostly happens haphazard, though afterwards various noble reasons are invented. About marriage I am cynical."

"I am not. This false start has been all my own fault. I was bringing to Ronny nothing that ought to be brought, that was why he rejected me really. I entered that cave thinking: Am I fond of him? I have not yet told you that, Mr. Fielding. I didn't feel justified. Tenderness, respect, personal intercourse—I tried to make them take the place—of——"

"I no longer want love," he said, supplying the word.

"No more do I. My experiences here have cured me. But I want others to want it."

"But to go back to our first talk (for I suppose this is our last one)— when you entered that cave, who did follow you, or did no one follow you? Can you now say? I don't like it left in air."

"Let us call it the guide," she said indifferently. "It will never be known. It's as if I ran my finger along that polished wall in the dark, and cannot get further. I am up against something, and so are you. Mrs. Moore—she did know."

"How could she have known what we don't?"

"Telepathy, possibly."

The pert, meagre word fell to the ground. Telepathy? What an explanation! Better withdraw it, and Adela did so. She was at the end of her spiritual tether, and so was he. Were there worlds beyond which they could never touch, or did all that is possible enter their consciousness? They could not tell. They only realized that their outlook was more or less similar, and found in this a satisfaction. Perhaps life is a mystery, not a muddle; they could not tell. Perhaps the hundred Indias which fuss and squabble so tiresomely are one, and the universe they mirror is one. They had not the apparatus for judging.

"Write to me when you get to England."

"I shall, often. You have been excessively kind. Now that I'm going, I realize it. I wish I could do something for you in return, but I see you've all you want."

"I think so," he replied after a pause. "I have never felt more happy and secure out here. I really do get on with Indians, and they do trust me. It's pleasant that I haven't had to resign my job. It's pleasant to be praised by an L.-G. Until the next earthquake I remain as I am."

"Of course this death has been troubling me."

"Aziz was so fond of her too."

"But it has made me remember that we must all die: all these personal relations we try to live by are temporary. I used to feel death selected people, it is a notion one gets from novels, because some of the characters are usually left talking at the end. Now 'death spares no one' begins to be real."

"Don't let it become too real, or you'll die yourself. That is the objection to meditating upon death. We are subdued to what we work in. I have felt the same temptation, and had to sheer off. I want to go on living a bit."

"So do I."

A friendliness, as of dwarfs shaking hands, was in the air. Both man and woman were at the height of their powers—sensible, honest, even subtle. They spoke the same language, and held the same opinions, and the variety of age and sex did not divide them. Yet they were dissatisfied. When they agreed, "I want to go on living a bit," or, "I don't believe in God," the words were followed by a curious backwash as though the universe had displaced itself to fill up a tiny void, or as though they had seen their own gestures from an immense height—dwarfs talking, shaking hands and assuring each other that they stood on the same footing of insight. They did not think they were wrong, because as soon as honest people think they are wrong instability sets up. Not for them was an infinite goal behind the stars, and they never sought it. But wistfulness descended on them now, as on other occasions; the shadow of the shadow of a dream fell over their clear-cut interests, and objects never seen again seemed messages from another world.

"And I do like you so very much, if I may say so," he affirmed.

"I'm glad, for I like you. Let's meet again."

"We will, in England, if I ever take home leave."

"But I suppose you're not likely to do that yet."

"Quite a chance. I have a scheme on now as a matter of fact."

"Oh, that would be very nice."

So it petered out. Ten days later Adela went off, by the same route as her dead friend. The final beat up before the monsoon had come. The country was stricken and blurred. Its houses, trees and fields were all modelled out of the same brown paste, and the sea at Bombay slid about like broth against the quays. Her last Indian adventure was with Antony, who followed her on to the boat and tried to blackmail her. She had been Mr. Fielding's mistress, Antony said. Perhaps Antony was discontented with his tip. She rang the cabin bell and had him turned out, but his statement created rather a scandal, and people did not speak to her much during the first part of the voyage. Through the Indian Ocean and the Red Sea she was left to herself, and to the dregs of Chandrapore.

With Egypt the atmosphere altered. The clean sands, heaped on each side of the canal, seemed to wipe off everything that was difficult and equivocal, and even Port Said looked pure and charming in the light of a rose-grey morning. She went on shore there with an American missionary, they walked out to the Lesseps statue, they drank the tonic air of the Levant. "To what duties Miss Quested, are you returning in your own country after your taste of the tropics?" the missionary asked. "Observe, I don't say to what do you turn, but to what do you *return*. Every life ought to contain both a turn and a return. This celebrated pioneer (he pointed to the statue) will make my question clear. He turns to the East, he *re*turns to the West. You can see it from the cute position of his hands, one of which holds a string of sausages." The missionary looked at her humorously, in order to cover the emptiness of his mind. He had no idea what he meant by "turn" and "return," but he often used words in pairs, for the sake of moral brightness. "I see," she replied. Suddenly, in the Mediterranean clarity, she had seen. Her first duty on returning to England was to look up those other children of Mrs. Moore's, Ralph and Stella, then she would turn to her profession. Mrs. Moore had tended to keep the products of her two marriages apart, and Adela had not come across the younger branch so far.

CHAPTER 30

Another local consequence of the trial was a Hindu-Moslem entente. Loud protestations of amity were exchanged by prominent citizens, and there went with them a genuine desire for a good understanding. Aziz, when he was at the hospital one day, received a visit from rather a sympathetic figure: Mr. Das. The magistrate sought two favours from him: a remedy for shingles and a poem for his brother-in-law's new monthly magazine. He accorded both.

"My dear Das, why, when you tried to send me to prison, should I try to send Mr. Bhattacharya a poem? Eh? That is naturally entirely a joke. I will write him the best I can, but I thought your magazine was for Hindus."

"It is not for Hindus, but Indians generally," he said timidly.

"There is no such person in existence as the general Indian."

"There was not, but there may be when you have written a poem. You are our hero; the whole city is behind you, irrespective of creed."

"I know, but will it last?"

"I fear not," said Das, who had much mental clearness. "And for that reason, if I may say so, do not introduce too many Persian expressions into the poem, and not too much about the bulbul."

"Half a sec," said Aziz, biting his pencil. He was writing out a prescription. "Here you are. . . . Is not this better than a poem?"

"Happy the man who can compose both."

"You are full of compliments to-day."

"I know you bear me a grudge for trying that case," said the other, stretching out his hand impulsively. "You are so kind and friendly, but always I detect irony beneath your manner."

"No, no, what nonsense!" protested Aziz. They shook hands, in a half-embrace that typified the entente. Between people of distant climes there is always the possibility of romance, but the various branches of Indians know too much about each other to surmount the unknowable easily. The approach is prosaic. "Excellent," said Aziz, patting a stout shoulder and thinking, "I wish they did not remind me of cow-dung"; Das thought, "Some Moslems are very violent." They smiled wistfully, each spying the thought in the other's heart, and Das, the more articulate, said: "Excuse my mistakes, realize my limitations. Life is not easy as we know it on the earth."

"Oh, well, about this poem—how did you hear I sometimes scribbled?" he asked, much pleased, and a good deal moved—for literature had always been a solace to him, something that the ugliness of facts could not spoil.

"Professor Godbole often mentioned it, before his departure for Mau."

"How did he hear?"

"He too was a poet; do you not divine each other?"

Flattered by the invitation, he got to work that evening. The feel of the pen between his fingers generated bulbuls at once. His poem was again about the decay of Islam and the brevity of love; as sad and sweet as he could contrive, but not nourished by personal experience, and of no interest to these excellent Hindus. Feeling dissatisfied, he rushed to the other extreme, and wrote a satire, which was too libellous to print. He could only express pathos or venom, though most of his life had no concern with either. He loved poetry—science was merely an acquisition, which he laid aside when unobserved like his European dress—and this evening he longed to compose a new song which should be acclaimed by multitudes and even sung in the fields. In what language shall it be written? And what shall it announce? He vowed to see more of Indians who were not Mohammedans, and never to look backward. It is the only healthy course. Of what help, in this latitude and hour, are the glories of Cordova and Samarcand? [1] They have gone, and while we lament them the English occupy Delhi and exclude us from East Africa. Islam itself, though true, throws cross-lights over the path to freedom. The song of the future must transcend creed.

The poem for Mr. Bhattacharya never got written, but it had an effect. It led him towards the vague and bulky figure of a mother-land. He was without natural affection for the land of his birth, but the Marabar Hills drove him to it. Half closing his eyes, he attempted to love India. She must imitate Japan. Not until she is a nation will her sons be treated with respect. He grew harder and less approachable. The English, whom he had laughed at or ignored, persecuted him everywhere; they had even thrown nets over his dreams. "My great mistake has been taking our rulers as a joke," he said to Hamidullah next day; who replied with a sigh: "It is far the wisest way to take them, but not possible in the long run. Sooner

1. **Cordova and Samarcand:** respectively, the westernmost and easternmost outposts of the Moslem conquest in the eighth to tenth centuries.

or later a disaster such as yours occurs, and reveals their secret thoughts about our character. If God himself descended from heaven into their club and said you were innocent, they would disbelieve him. Now you see why Mahmoud Ali and self waste so much time over intrigues and associate with creatures like Ram Chand."

"I cannot endure committees. I shall go right away."

"Where to? Turtons and Burtons, all are the same."

"But not in an Indian state."

"I believe the Politicals are obliged to have better manners. It amounts to no more."

"I do want to get away from British India, even to a poor job. I think I could write poetry there. I wish I had lived in Babur's time and fought and written for him. Gone, gone, and not even any use to say 'Gone, gone,' for it weakens us while we say it. We need a king, Hamidullah; it would make our lives easier. As it is, we must try to appreciate these quaint Hindus. My notion now is to try for some post as doctor in one of their states."

"Oh, that is going much too far."

"It is not going as far as Mr. Ram Chand."

"But the money, the money—they will never pay an adequate salary, those savage Rajas."

"I shall never be rich anywhere, it is outside my character."

"If you had been sensible and made Miss Quested pay——"

"I chose not to. Discussion of the past is useless," he said, with sudden sharpness of tone. "I have allowed her to keep her fortune and buy herself a husband in England, for which it will be very necessary. Don't mention the matter again."

"Very well, but your life must continue a poor man's; no holidays in Kashmir for you yet, you must stick to your profession and rise to a highly paid post, not retire to a jungle-state and write poems. Educate your children, read the latest scientific periodicals, compel European doctors to respect you. Accept the consequences of your own actions like a man."

Aziz winked at him slowly and said: "We are not in the law courts. There are many ways of being a man; mine is to express what is deepest in my heart."

"To such a remark there is certainly no reply," said Hamidullah, moved. Recovering himself and smiling, he said: "Have you heard this naughty rumour that Mohammed Latif has got hold of?"

"Which?"

"When Miss Quested stopped in the College, Fielding used to visit her . . . rather too late in the evening, the servants say."

"A pleasant change for her if he did," said Aziz, making a curious face. "But you understand my meaning!"

The young man winked again and said: "Just! Still, your meaning doesn't help me out of my difficulties. I am determined to leave Chandrapore. The problem is, for where? I am determined to write poetry. The problem is, about what? You give me no assistance." Then, surprising both Hamidullah and himself, he had an explosion of nerves. "But who does give me assistance? No one is my friend. All are traitors, even my own children. I have had enough of friends."

"I was going to suggest we go behind the purdah, but your three treacherous children are there, so you will not want to."

"I am sorry, it is ever since I was in prison my temper is strange; take me, forgive me."

"Nureddin's mother is visiting my wife now. That is all right, I think."

"They come before me separately, but not so far together. You had better prepare them for the united shock of my face."

"No, let us surprise them without warning, far too much nonsense still goes on among our ladies. They pretended at the time of your trial they would give up purdah! indeed, those of them who can write composed a document to that effect, and now it ends in humbug. You know how deeply they all respect Fielding, but not one of them has seen him. My wife says she will, but always when he calls there is some excuse—she is not feeling well, she is ashamed of the room, she has no nice sweets to offer him, only Elephants' Ears,[2] and if I say Elephants' Ears are Mr. Fielding's favourite sweet, she replies that he will know how badly hers are made, so she cannot see him on their account. For fifteen years, my dear boy, have I argued with my begum, for fifteen years, and never gained a point, yet the missionaries inform us our women are down-trodden. If you want a subject for a poem, take this: The Indian lady as she is and not as she is supposed to be."

CHAPTER 31

Aziz had no sense of evidence. The sequence of his emotions decided his beliefs, and led to the tragic coolness between himself and his English friend. They had conquered but were not to be crowned. Fielding was away at a conference, and after the rumour about Miss Quested had been with him undisturbed for a few days, he assumed it was true. He had no objection on moral grounds to his friends amusing themselves, and Cyril, being middle-aged, could no longer expect the pick of the female market,

2. **Elephants' Ears:** a variety of the Indian *puris*, which is like a pancake.

and must take his amusement where he could find it. But he resented him
making up to this particular woman, whom he still regarded as his enemy;
also, why had he not been told? What is friendship without confidences?
He himself had told things sometimes regarded as shocking, and the
Englishman had listened, tolerant, but surrendering nothing in return.

He met Fielding at the railway station on his return, agreed to dine with
him, and then started taxing him by the oblique method, outwardly merry.
An avowed European scandal there was—Mr. McBryde and Miss Derek.
Miss Derek's faithful attachment to Chandrapore was now explained: Mr.
McBryde had been caught in her room, and his wife was divorcing him.
"That pure-minded fellow. However, he will blame the Indian climate.
Everything is our fault really. Now, have I not discovered an important
piece of news for you, Cyril?"

"Not very," said Fielding, who took little interest in distant sins. "Listen
to mine." Aziz's face lit up. "At the conference, it was settled."

"This evening will do for schoolmastery. I should go straight to the
Minto now, the cholera looks bad. We begin to have local cases as well as
imported. In fact, the whole of life is somewhat sad. The new Civil Surgeon is the same as the last, but does not yet dare to be. That is all any administrative change amounts to. All my suffering has won nothing for us.
But look here, Cyril, while I remember it. There's gossip about you as
well as McBryde. They say that you and Miss Quested became also rather
too intimate friends. To speak perfectly frankly, they say you and she
have been guilty of impropriety."

"They would say that."

"It's all over the town, and may injure your reputation. You know,
every one is by no means your supporter. I have tried all I could to silence
such a story."

"Don't bother. Miss Quested has cleared out at last."

"It is those who stop in the country, not those who leave it, whom such
a story injures. Imagine my dismay and anxiety. I could scarcely get a
wink of sleep. First my name was coupled with her and now it is yours."

"Don't use such exaggerated phrases."

"As what?"

"As dismay and anxiety."

"Have I not lived all my life in India? Do I not know what produces a
bad impression here?" His voice shot up rather crossly.

"Yes, but the scale, the scale. You always get the scale wrong, my dear
fellow. A pity there is this rumour, but such a very small pity—so small
that we may as well talk of something else."

"You mind for Miss Quested's sake, though. I can see from your face."

"As far as I do mind. I travel light."

"Cyril, that boastfulness about travelling light will be your ruin. It is raising up enemies against you on all sides, and makes me feel excessively uneasy."

"What enemies?"

Since Aziz had only himself in mind, he could not reply. Feeling a fool, he became angrier. "I have given you list after list of the people who cannot be trusted in this city. In your position I should have the sense to know I was surrounded by enemies. You observe I speak in a low voice. It is because I see your sais is new. How do I know he isn't a spy?" He lowered his voice: "Every third servant is a spy."

"Now, what is the matter?" he asked, smiling.

"Do you contradict my last remark?"

"It simply doesn't affect me. Spies are as thick as mosquitoes, but it's years before I shall meet the one that kills me. You've something else in your mind."

"I've not; don't be ridiculous."

"You have. You're cross with me about something or other."

Any direct attack threw him out of action. Presently he said: "So you and Madamsell Adela used to amuse one another in the evening, naughty boy."

Those drab and high-minded talks had scarcely made for dalliance. Fielding was so startled at the story being taken seriously, and so disliked being called a naughty boy, that he lost his head and cried: "You little rotter! Well, I'm damned. Amusement indeed. Is it likely at such a time?"

"Oh, I beg your pardon, I'm sure. The licentious Oriental imagination was at work," he replied, speaking gaily, but cut to the heart; for hours after his mistake he bled inwardly.

"You see, Aziz, the circumstances . . . also the girl was still engaged to Heaslop, also I never felt . . ."

"Yes, yes; but you didn't contradict what I said, so I thought it was true. Oh dear, East and West. Most misleading. Will you please put your little rotter down at his hospital?"

"You're not offended?"

"Most certainly I am not."

"If you are, this must be cleared up later on."

"It has been," he answered, dignified. "I believe absolutely what you say, and of that there need be no further question."

"But the way I said it must be cleared up. I was unintentionally rude. Unreserved regrets."

"The fault is entirely mine."

Tangles like this still interrupted their intercourse. A pause in the wrong place, an intonation misunderstood, and a whole conversation went awry.

Fielding had been startled, not shocked, but how convey the difference? There is always trouble when two people do not think of sex at the same moment, always mutual resentment and surprise, even when the two people are of the same race. He began to recapitulate his feelings about Miss Quested. Aziz cut him short with: "But I believe you, I believe. Mohammed Latif shall be severely punished for inventing this."

"Oh, leave it alone, like all gossip—it's merely one of those half-alive things that try to crowd out real life. Take no notice, it'll vanish, like poor old Mrs. Moore's tombs."

"Mohammed Latif has taken to intriguing. We are already much displeased with him. Will it satisfy you if we send him back to his family without a present?"

"We'll discuss M.L. at dinner."

His eyes went clotted and hard. "Dinner. This is most unlucky—I forgot. I have promised to dine with Das."

"Bring Das to me."

"He will have invited other friends."

"You are coming to dinner with me as arranged," said Fielding, looking away. "I don't stand this. You are coming to dinner with me. You come."

They had reached the hospital now. Fielding continued round the Maidan alone. He was annoyed with himself, but counted on dinner to pull things straight. At the post office he saw the Collector. Their vehicles were parked side by side while their servants competed in the interior of the building. "Good morning; so you are back," said Turton icily. "I should be glad if you will put in your appearance at the club this evening."

"I have accepted re-election, sir. Do you regard it as necessary I should come? I should be glad to be excused; indeed, I have a dinner engagement this evening."

"It is not a question of your feelings, but of the wish of the Lieutenant-Governor. Perhaps you will ask me whether I speak officially. I do. I shall expect you this evening at six. We shall not interfere with your subsequent plans."

He attended the grim little function in due course. The skeletons of hospitality rattled—"Have a peg, have a drink." He talked for five minutes to Mrs. Blakiston, who was the only surviving female. He talked to McBryde, who was defiant about his divorce, conscious that he had sinned as a sahib. He talked to Major Roberts, the new Civil Surgeon; and to young Milner, the new City Magistrate; but the more the club changed, the more it promised to be the same thing. "It is no good," he thought, as he returned past the mosque, "we all build upon sand; and the more modern the country gets, the worse'll be the crash. In the old eighteenth century, when cruelty and injustice raged, an invisible power repaired their ravages. Everything echoes now; there's no stopping the echo. The original sound may be harmless, but the echo is always evil." This reflection about an echo lay at the verge of Fielding's mind. He could never develop it. It belonged to the universe that he had missed or rejected. And the mosque missed it too. Like himself, those shallow arcades provided but a limited asylum. "There is no God but God" doesn't carry us far through the complexities of matter and spirit; it is only a game with words, really, a religious pun, not a religious truth.

He found Aziz overtired and dispirited, and he determined not to allude to their misunderstanding until the end of the evening; it would be more acceptable then. He made a clean breast about the club—said he had only gone under compulsion, and should never attend again unless the order was renewed. "In other words, probably never; for I am going quite soon to England."

"I thought you might end in England," he said very quietly, then changed the conversation. Rather awkwardly they ate their dinner, then went out to sit in the Mogul garden-house.

"I am only going for a little time. On official business. My service is anxious to get me away from Chandrapore for a bit. It is obliged to value me highly, but does not care for me. The situation is somewhat humorous."

"What is the nature of the business? Will it leave you much spare time?"

"Enough to see my friends."

"I expected you to make such a reply. You are a faithful friend. Shall we now talk about something else?"

"Willingly. What subject?"

"Poetry," he said, with tears in his eyes. "Let us discuss why poetry has lost the power of making men brave. My mother's father was also a poet, and fought against you in the Mutiny. I might equal him if there was another mutiny. As it is, I am a doctor, who has won a case and has three children to support, and whose chief subject of conversation is official plans."

"Let us talk about poetry." He turned his mind to the innocuous subject. "You people are sadly circumstanced. Whatever are you to write about? You cannot say, 'The rose is faded,' for evermore. We know it's faded. Yet you can't have patriotic poetry of the 'India, my India' type, when it's nobody's India."

"I like this conversation. It may lead to something interesting."

"You are quite right in thinking that poetry must touch life. When I knew you first, you used it as an incantation."

"I was a child when you knew me first. Everyone was my friend then.

The Friend: a Persian expression for God. But I do not want to be a religious poet either."

"I hoped you would be."

"Why, when you yourself are an atheist?"

"There is something in religion that may not be true, but has not yet been sung."

"Explain in detail."

"Something that the Hindus have perhaps found."

"Let them sing it."

"Hindus are unable to sing."

"Cyril, you sometimes make a sensible remark. That will do for poetry for the present. Let us now return to your English visit."

"We haven't discussed poetry for two seconds," said the other, smiling.

But Aziz was addicted to cameos. He held the tiny conversation in his hand, and felt it epitomized his problem. For an instant he recalled his wife, and, as happens when a memory is intense, the past became the future, and he saw her with him in a quiet Hindu jungle native state, far away from foreigners. He said: "I suppose you will visit Miss Quested."

"If I have time. It will be strange seeing her in Hampstead."

"What is Hampstead?"

"An artistic and thoughtful little suburb of London——"

"And there she lives in comfort: you will enjoy seeing her. . . . Dear me, I've got a headache this evening. Perhaps I am going to have cholera. With your permission, I'll leave early."

"When would you like the carriage?"

"Don't trouble—I'll bike."

"But you haven't got your bicycle. My carriage fetched you—let it take you away."

"Sound reasoning," he said, trying to be gay. "I have not got my bicycle. But I am seen too often in your carriage. I am thought to take advantage of your generosity by Mr. Ram Chand." He was out of sorts and uneasy. The conversation jumped from topic to topic in a broken-backed fashion. They were affectionate and intimate, but nothing clicked tight.

"Aziz, you have forgiven me the stupid remark I made this morning?"

"When you called me a little rotter?"

"Yes, to my eternal confusion. You know how fond I am of you."

"That is nothing, of course; we all of us make mistakes. In a friendship such as ours a few slips are of no consequence."

But as he drove off, something depressed him—a dull pain of body or mind, waiting to rise to the surface. When he reached the bungalow he wanted to return and say something very affectionate; instead, he gave the sais a heavy tip, and sat down gloomily on the bed, and Hassan massaged him incompetently. The eye-flies had colonized the top of an almeira; the red stains on the durry [1] were thicker, for Mohammed Latif had slept here during his imprisonment and spat a good deal; the table drawer was scarred where the police had forced it open; everything in Chandrapore was used up, including the air. The trouble rose to the surface now: he was suspicious; he suspected his friend of intending to marry Miss Quested for the sake of her money, and of going to England for that purpose.

"Huzoor?"—for he had muttered.

"Look at those flies on the ceiling. Why have you not drowned them?"

"Huzoor, they return."

"Like all evil things."

To divert the conversation, Hassan related how the kitchen-boy had killed a snake, good, but killed it by cutting it in two, bad, because it becomes two snakes.

"When he breaks a plate, does it become two plates?"

"Glasses and a new teapot will similarly be required, also for myself a coat."

Aziz sighed. Each for himself. One man needs a coat, another a rich wife; each approaches his goal by a clever detour. Fielding had saved the girl a fine of twenty thousand rupees, and now followed her to England. If he desired to marry her, all was explained; she would bring him a larger dowry. Aziz did not believe his own suspicions—better if he had, for then he would have denounced and cleared the situation up. Suspicion and belief could in his mind exist side by side. They sprang from different sources, and need never intermingle. Suspicion in the Oriental is a sort of malignant tumour, a mental malady, that makes him self-conscious and unfriendly suddenly; he trusts and mistrusts at the same time in a way the Westerner cannot comprehend. It is his demon, as the Westerner's is hypocrisy. Aziz was seized by it, and his fancy built a satanic castle of which the foundation had been laid when he talked at Dilkusha under the stars. The girl had surely been Cyril's mistress when she stopped in the College—Mohammed Latif was right. But was that all? Perhaps it was Cyril who followed her into the cave. . . . No; impossible. Cyril hadn't been on the Kawa Dol at all. Impossible. Ridiculous. Yet the fancy left him trembling with misery. Such treachery—if true—would have been the worst in Indian history; nothing so vile, not even the murder of Afzul Khan by Sivaji.[2] He was shaken, as though by a truth, and told Hassan to leave him.

Next day he decided to take his children back to Mussoorie. They had

---

1. **almeira:** cupboard; **durry:** carpet.
2. **Sivaji:** (1627–1680), a national hero of the Mahrattas in India. He treacherously murdered Afzul Kahn, a general who opposed him.

come down for the trial, that he might bid them farewell, and had stayed on at Hamidullah's for the rejoicings. Major Roberts would give him leave, and during his absence Fielding would go off to England. The idea suited both his beliefs and his suspicions. Events would prove which was right, and preserve, in either case, his dignity.

Fielding was conscious of something hostile, and because he was really fond of Aziz his optimism failed him. Travelling light is less easy as soon as affection is involved. Unable to jog forward in the serene hope that all would come right, he wrote an elaborate letter in the rather modern style: "It is on my mind that you think me a prude about women. I had rather you thought anything else of me. If I live impeccably now, it is only because I am well on the forties—a period of revision. In the eighties I shall revise again. And before the nineties come—I shall be revised! But, alive or dead, I am absolutely devoid of morals. Do kindly grasp this about me." Aziz did not care for the letter at all. It hurt his delicacy. He liked confidences, however gross, but generalizations and comparisons always repelled him. Life is not a scientific manual. He replied coldly, regretting his inability to return from Mussoorie before his friend sailed: "But I must take my poor little holiday while I can. All must be economy henceforward, all hopes of Kashmir have vanished for ever and ever. When you return I shall be slaving far away in some new post."

And Fielding went, and in the last gutterings of Chandrapore—heaven and earth both looking like toffee—the Indian's bad fancies were confirmed. His friends encouraged them, for though they had like the Principal, they felt uneasy at his getting to know so much about their private affairs. Mahmoud Ali soon declared that treachery was afoot. Hamidullah murmured, "Certainly of late he no longer addressed us with his former frankness," and warned Aziz "not to expect too much—he and she are, after all, both members of another race." "Where are my twenty thousand rupees?" he thought. He was absolutely indifferent to money—not merely generous with it, but promptly paying his debts when he could remember to do so—yet these rupees haunted his mind, because he had been tricked about them, and allowed them to escape overseas, like so much of the wealth of India. Cyril would marry Miss Quested—he grew certain of it, all the unexplained residue of the Marabar contributing. It was the natural conclusion of the horrible senseless picnic, and before long he persuaded himself that the wedding had actually taken place.

CHAPTER 32

Egypt was charming—a green strip of carpet and walking up and down it four sorts of animals and one sort of man. Fielding's business took him there for a few days. He re-embarked at Alexandria—bright blue sky, constant wind, clean low coast-line, as against the intricacies of Bombay. Crete welcomed him next with the long snowy ridge of its mountains, and then came Venice. As he landed on the piazzetta [1] a cup of beauty was lifted to his lips, and he drank with a sense of disloyalty. The buildings of Venice, like the mountains of Crete and the fields of Egypt, stood in the right place, whereas in poor India everything was placed wrong. He had forgotten the beauty of form among idol temples and lumpy hills; indeed, without form, how can there be beauty? Form stammered here and there in a mosque, became rigid through nervousness even, but oh these Italian churches! San Giorgio standing on the island which could scarcely have risen from the waves without it, the Salute holding the entrance of a canal which, but for it, would not be the Grand Canal! In the old undergraduate days he had wrapped himself up in the many-coloured blanket of St. Mark's, but something more precious than mosaics and marbles was offered to him now: the harmony between the works of man and the earth that upholds them, the civilization that has escaped muddle, the spirit in a reasonable form, with flesh and blood subsisting. Writing picture postcards to his Indian friends, he felt that all of them would miss the joys he experienced now, the joys of form, and that this constituted a serious barrier. They would see the sumptuousness of Venice, not its shape, and though Venice was not Europe, it was part of the Mediterranean harmony. The Mediterranean is the human norm. When men leave that exquisite lake, whether through the Bosphorus or the Pillars of Hercules, they approach the monstrous and extraordinary; and the southern exit leads to the strangest experience of all. Turning his back on it yet again, he took the train northward, and tender romantic fancies that he thought were dead for ever, flowered when he saw the buttercups and daisies of June.

1. **piazzetta**: small square.

PART III

TEMPLE

CHAPTER 33

SOME hundreds of miles westward of the Marabar Hills, and two years later in time, Professor Narayan Godbole stands in the presence of God. God is not born yet—that will occur at midnight—but He has also been born centuries ago, nor can He ever be born, because He is the Lord of the Universe, who transcends human processes. He is, was not, is not, was. He and Professor Godbole stood at opposite ends of the same strip of carpet.

> "Tukaram,[1] Tukaram,
> Thou art my father and mother and everybody.
> Tukaram, Tukaram,
> Thou art my father and mother and everybody.
> Tukaram, Tukaram,
> Thou art my father and mother and everybody.
> Tukaram, Tukaram,
> Thou art my father and mother and everybody.
> Tukaram. . . ."

This corridor in the palace at Mau opened through other corridors into a courtyard. It was of beautiful hard white stucco, but its pillars and vaulting could scarcely be seen behind coloured rags, iridescent balls, chandeliers of opaque pink glass, and murky photographs framed crookedly. At the end was the small but famous shrine of the dynastic cult, and the God to be born was largely a silver image the size of a teaspoon. Hindus sat on either side of the carpet where they could find room, or overflowed into the adjoining corridors and the courtyard—Hindus, Hindus only, mild-featured men, mostly villagers, for whom anything outside their villages passed in a dream. They were the toiling ryot, whom some call the real India. Mixed with them sat a few tradesmen out of the little town, officials, courtiers, scions of the ruling house. Schoolboys kept inefficient order. The assembly was in a tender, happy state unknown to an English crowd, it seethed like a beneficent potion. When the villagers broke cordon for a glimpse of the silver image, a most beautiful and radiant expression came into their faces, a beauty in which there was nothing personal, for it caused them all to resemble one another during the moment of its indwelling, and only when it was withdrawn did they revert to individual clods. And so with the music. Music there was, but from so many sources that the

---

1. **Tukaram:** (1608–1649), a contemporary of Sivaji (see footnote 2 on page 381). He was the greatest writer in the Mahratta language.

sum-total was untrammelled. The braying banging crooning melted into a single mass which trailed round the palace before joining the thunder. Rain fell at intervals throughout the night.

It was the turn of Professor Godbole's choir. As Minister of Education, he gained this special honour. When the previous group of singers dispersed into the crowd, he pressed forward from the back, already in full voice, that the chain of sacred sounds might be uninterrupted. He was barefoot and in white, he wore a pale blue turban; his old pince-nez had caught in a jasmine garland, and lay sideways down his nose. He and the six colleagues who supported him clashed their cymbals, hit small drums, droned upon a portable harmonium, and sang:

> "Tukaram, Tukaram,
> Thou art my father and mother and everybody.
> Tukaram, Tukaram,
> Thou art my father and mother and everybody.
> Tukaram, Tukaram. . . ."

They sang not even to the God who confronted them, but to a saint; they did not one thing which the non-Hindu would feel dramatically correct; this approaching triumph of India was a muddle (as we call it), a frustration of reason and form. Where was the God Himself, in whose honour the congregation had gathered? Indistinguishable in the jumble of His own altar, huddled out of sight amid images of inferior descent, smothered under rose-leaves, overhung by oleographs, outblazed by golden tablets representing the Rajah's ancestors, and entirely obscured, when the wind blew, by the tattered foliage of a banana. Hundreds of electric lights had been lit in His honour (worked by an engine whose thumps destroyed the rhythm of the hymn). Yet His face could not be seen. Hundreds of His silver dishes were piled around Him with the minimum of effect. The inscriptions which the poets of the State had composed were hung where they could not be read, or had twitched their drawing-pins out of the stucco, and one of them (composed in English to indicate His universality) consisted, by an unfortunate slip of the draughtsman, of the words, "God si Love."

God si Love. Is this the final message of India?

> "Tukaram, Tukaram . . . ,"

continued the choir, reinforced by a squabble behind the purdah curtain, where two mothers tried to push their children at the same moment to the front. A little girl's leg shot out like an eel. In the courtyard, drenched by the rain, the small Europeanized band stumbled off into a waltz. "Nights of Gladness" they were playing. The singers were not perturbed by this rival, they lived beyond competition. It was long before the tiny fragment of Professor Godbole that attended to outside things decided that his pince-nez was in trouble, and that until it was adjusted he could not choose a new hymn. He laid down one cymbal, with the other he clashed the air, with his free hand he fumbled at the flowers round his neck. A colleague assisted him. Singing into one another's grey moustaches, they disentangled the chain from the tinsel into which it had sunk. Godbole consulted the music-book, said a word to the drummer, who broke rhythm, made a thick little blur of sound, and produced a new rhythm. This was more exciting, the inner images it evoked more definite, and the singers' expressions became fatuous and languid. They loved all men, the whole universe, and scraps of their past, tiny splinters of detail, emerged for a moment to melt into the universal warmth. Thus Godbole, though she was not important to him, remembered an old woman he had met in Chandrapore days. Chance brought her into his mind while it was in this heated state, he did not select her, she happened to occur among the throng of soliciting images, a tiny splinter, and he impelled her by his spiritual force to that place where completeness can be found. Completeness, not reconstruction. His senses grew thinner, he remembered a wasp seen he forgot where, perhaps on a stone. He loved the wasp equally, he impelled it likewise, he was imitating God. And the stone where the wasp clung—could he . . . no, he could not, he had been wrong to attempt the stone, logic and conscious effort had seduced, he came back to the strip of red carpet and discovered that he was dancing upon it. Up and down, a third of the way to the altar and back again, clashing his cymbals, his little legs twinkling, his companions dancing with him and each other. Noise, noise, the Europeanized band louder, incense on the altar, sweat, the blaze of lights, wind in the bananas, noise, thunder, eleven-fifty by his wrist-watch, seen as he threw up his hands and detached the tiny reverberation that was his soul. Louder shouts in the crowd. He danced on. The boys and men who were squatting in the aisles were lifted forcibly and dropped without changing their shapes into the laps of their neighbours. Down the path thus cleared advanced a litter.

It was the aged ruler of the state, brought against the advice of his physicians to witness the Birth ceremony.

No one greeted the Rajah, nor did he wish it; this was no moment for human glory. Nor could the litter be set down, lest it defiled the temple by becoming a throne. He was lifted out of it while its feet remained in air, and deposited on the carpet close to the altar, his immense beard was straightened, his legs tucked under him, a paper containing red powder was placed in his hand. There he sat, leaning against a pillar, exhausted with illness, his eyes magnified by many unshed tears.

He had not to wait long. In a land where all else was unpunctual, the hour of the Birth was chronometrically observed. Three minutes before it was due, a Brahman brought forth a model of the village of Gokul (the Bethlehem in that nebulous story) and placed it in front of the altar. The model was on a wooden tray about a yard square; it was of clay, and was gaily blue and white with streamers and paint. Here, upon a chair too small for him and with a head too large, sat King Kansa, who is Herod, directing the murder of some Innocents, and in a corner, similarly proportioned, stood the father and mother of the Lord, warned to depart in a dream. The model was not holy, but more than a decoration, for it diverted men from the actual image of the God, and increased their sacred bewilderment. Some of the villagers thought the Birth had occurred, saying with truth that the Lord must have been born, or they could not see Him. But the clock struck midnight, and simultaneously the rending note of the conch broke forth, followed by the trumpeting of elephants; all who had packets of powder threw them at the altar, and in the rosy dust and incense, and clanging and shouts, Infinite Love took upon itself the form of SHRI KRISHNA, and saved the world. All sorrow was annihilated, not only for Indians, but for foreigners, birds, caves, railways, and the stars; all became joy, all laughter; there had never been disease nor doubt, misunderstanding, cruelty, fear. Some jumped in the air, others flung themselves prone and embraced the bare feet of the universal lover; the women behind the purdah slapped and shrieked; the little girl slipped out and danced by herself, her black pigtails flying. Not an orgy of the body; the tradition of that shrine forbade it. But the human spirit had tried by a desperate contortion to ravish the unknown, flinging down science and history in the struggle, yes, beauty herself. Did it succeed? Books written afterwards say "Yes." But how, if there is such an event, can it be remembered afterwards? How can it be expressed in anything but itself? Not only from the unbeliever are mysteries hid, but the adept himself cannot retain them. He may think, if he chooses, that he has been with God, but as soon as he thinks it, it becomes history, and falls under the rules of time.

A cobra of papier-mâché now appeared on the carpet, also a wooden cradle swinging from a frame. Professor Godbole approached the latter with a red silk napkin in his arms. The napkin was God, not that it was, and the image remained in the blur of the altar. It was just a napkin, folded into a shape which indicated a baby's. The Professor dandled it and gave it to the Rajah, who, making a great effort, said, "I name this child Shri Krishna," and tumbled it into the cradle. Tears poured from his eyes, because he had seen the Lord's salvation. He was too weak to exhibit the silk baby to his people, his privilege in former years. His attendants lifted him up, a new path was cleared through the crowd, and he was carried away to a less sacred part of the palace. There, in a room accessible to Western science by an outer staircase, his physician, Dr. Aziz, awaited him. His Hindu physician, who had accompanied him to the shrine, briefly reported his symptoms. As the ecstasy receded, the invalid grew fretful. The bumping of the steam engine that worked the dynamo disturbed him, and he asked for what reason it had been introduced into his home. They replied that they would enquire, and administered a sedative.

Down in the sacred corridors, joy had seethed to jollity. It was their duty to play various games to amuse the newly born God, and to simulate his sports with the wanton dairymaids of Brindaban.[2] Butter played a prominent part in these. When the cradle had been removed, the principal nobles of the state gathered together for an innocent frolic. They removed their turbans, and one put a lump of butter on his forehead, and waited for it to slide down his nose into his mouth. Before it could arrive, another stole up behind him, snatched the melting morsel, and swallowed it himself. All laughed exultantly at discovering that the divine sense of humour coincided with their own. "God si love!" There is fun in heaven. God can play practical jokes upon Himself, draw chairs away from beneath His own posteriors, set His own turbans on fire, and steal His own petticoats when He bathes. By sacrificing good taste, this worship achieved what Christianity has shirked: the inclusion of merriment. All spirit as well as all matter must participate in salvation, and if practical jokes are banned, the circle is incomplete. Having swallowed the butter, they played another game which chanced to be graceful: the fondling of Shri Krishna under the similitude of a child. A pretty red and gold ball is thrown, and he who catches it chooses a child from the crowd, raises it in his arms, and carries it round to be caressed. All stroke the darling creature for the Creator's sake, and murmur happy words. The child is restored to his parents, the ball thrown on, and another child becomes for a moment the World's desire. And the Lord bounds hither and thither through the aisles, chance, and the sport of chance, irradiating little mortals with His immortality. . . . When they had played this long enough—and being exempt from boredom, they played it again and again, they played it again and again—they took many sticks and hit them together, whack smack, as though they fought the Pandava[3] wars, and threshed and churned with them, and later on they hung from the roof of the temple, in a net, a great black earthenware jar, which was painted here and there with red, and wreathed with dried figs. Now came a rousing sport. Springing up, they struck at the jar with their sticks. It cracked, broke, and a mass of greasy rice and milk poured on to their faces. They ate and smeared one

2. **Brindaban:** a popular center of pilgrimage in north central India.
3. The Pandavas were five brothers who were great heroes of Hindu legend.

another's mouths and dived between each other's legs for what had been pashed upon the carpet. This way and that spread the divine mess, until the line of schoolboys, who had somewhat fended off the crowd, broke for their share. The corridors, the courtyard, were filled with benign confusion. Also the flies awoke and claimed their share of God's bounty. There was no quarrelling, owing to the nature of the gift, for blessed is the man who confers it on another, he imitates God. And those "imitations," those "substitutions," continued to flicker through the assembly for many hours, awaking in each man, according to his capacity, an emotion that he would not have had otherwise. No definite image survived; at the Birth it was questionable whether a silver doll or a mud village, or a silk napkin, or an intangible spirit, or a pious resolution, had been born. Perhaps all these things! Perhaps none! Perhaps all birth is an allegory! Still, it was the main event of the religious year. It caused strange thoughts. Covered with grease and dust, Professor Godbole had once more developed the life of his spirit. He had, with increasing vividness, again seen Mrs. Moore, and round her faintly clinging forms of trouble. He was a Brahman, she Christian, but it made no difference, it made no difference whether she was a trick of his memory or a telepathic appeal. It was his duty, as it was his desire, to place himself in the position of the God and to love her and to place himself in her position and to say to the God, "Come, come, come, come." This was all he could do. How inadequate! But each according to his own capacities, and he knew that his own were small. "One old Englishwoman and one little, little wasp," he thought, as he stepped out of the temple into the grey of a pouring wet morning. "It does not seem much, still it is more than I am myself."

CHAPTER 34

Dr. Aziz left the palace at the same time. As he returned to his house—which stood in a pleasant garden further up the main street of the town—he could see his old patron paddling and capering in the slush ahead. "Hullo!" he called, and it was the wrong remark, for the devotee indicated by circular gestures of his arms that he did not desire to be disturbed. He added, "Sorry," which was right, for Godbole twisted his head till it didn't belong to his body, and said in a strained voice that had no connection with his mind: "He arrived at the European Guest House—at least possibly."

"Did he? Since when?"

But time was too definite. He waved his arm more dimly and disappeared. Aziz knew who "he" was—Fielding—but he refused to think about him, because it disturbed his life, and he still trusted the floods to prevent

him from arriving. A fine little river issued from his garden gate and gave
him much hope. It was impossible that anyone could get across from
Deora in such weather as this. Fielding's visit was official. He had been
transferred from Chandrapore, and sent on a tour through Central India
to see what the remoter states were doing with regard to English education. He had married, he had done the expected with Miss Quested, and
Aziz had no wish to see him again.

"Dear old Godbole," he thought, and smiled. He had no religious curiosity, and had never discovered the meaning of this annual antic, but he
was well assured that Godbole was a dear old man. He had come to Mau
through him and remained on his account. Without him he could never
have grasped problems so totally different from those of Chandrapore.
For here the cleavage was between Brahman and non-Brahman; Moslems
and English were quite out of the running, and sometimes not mentioned
for days. Since Godbole was a Brahman, Aziz was one also for purposes
of intrigue: they would often joke about it together. The fissures in the
Indian soil are infinite: Hinduism, so solid from a distance, is riven into
sects and clans, which radiate and join, and change their names according
to the aspect from which they are approached. Study it for years with
the best teachers, and when you raise your head, nothing they have told
you quite fits. Aziz, the day of his inauguration, had remarked: "I study
nothing, I respect"—making an excellent impression. There was now a
minimum of prejudice against him. Nominally under a Hindu doctor, he
was really chief medicine man to the court. He had to drop inoculation
and such Western whims, but even at Chandrapore his profession had
been a game, centering round the operating table, and here in the back-
woods he let his instruments rust, ran his little hospital at half steam, and
caused no undue alarm.

His impulse to escape from the English was sound. They had frightened him permanently, and there are only two reactions against fright: to
kick and scream on committees, or to retreat to a remote jungle, where
the sahib seldom comes. His old lawyer friends wanted him to stop in
British India and help agitate, and might have prevailed, but for the
treachery of Fielding. The news had not surprised him in the least. A rift
had opened between them after the trial when Cyril had not joined in his
procession; those advocacies of the girl had increased it; then came the
post-cards from Venice, so cold, so unfriendly that all agreed that something was wrong; and finally, after a silence, the expected letter from
Hampstead. Mahmoud Ali was with him at the time. "Some news that
will surprise you. I am to marry someone whom you know. . . ." He did
not read further. "Here it comes, answer for me——" and he threw it to
Mahmoud Ali. Subsequent letters he destroyed unopened. It was the end

of a foolish experiment. And though sometimes at the back of his mind he felt that Fielding had made sacrifices for him, it was now all confused with his genuine hatred of the English. "I am an Indian at last," he thought, standing motionless in the rain.

Life passed pleasantly, the climate was healthy so that the children could be with him all the year round, and he had married again—not exactly a marriage, but he liked to regard it as one—and he read his Persian, wrote his poetry, had his horse, and sometimes got some shikar while the good Hindus looked the other way. His poems were all on one topic —Oriental womanhood. "The purdah must go," was their burden, "otherwise we shall never be free." And he declared (fantastically) that India would not have been conquered if women as well as men had fought at Plassy. "But we do not show our women to the foreigner"—not explaining how this was to be managed, for he was writing a poem. Bulbuls and roses would still persist, the pathos of defeated Islam remained in his blood and could not be expelled by modernities. Illogical poems—like their writer. Yet they struck a true note: there cannot be a mother-land without new homes. In one poem- the only one funny old Godbole liked—he had skipped over the mother-land (whom he did not truly love) and gone straight to internationality. "Ah, that is bhakti [1]; ah, my young friend, that is different and very good. Ah, India, who seems not to move, will go straight there while the other nations waste their time. May I translate this particular one into Hindi? In fact, it might be rendered into Sanskrit almost, it is so enlightened. Yes, of course, all your other poems are very good too. His Highness was saying to Colonel Maggs last time he came that we are proud of you"—simpering slightly.

Colonel Maggs was the Political Agent for the neighbourhood and Aziz' dejected opponent. The Criminal Investigation Department kept an eye on Aziz ever since the trial—they had nothing actionable against him, but Indians who have been unfortunate must be watched, and to the end of his life he remained under observation, thanks to Miss Quested's mistake. Colonel Maggs learnt with concern that a suspect was coming to Mau, and, adopting a playful manner, rallied the old Rajah for permitting a Moslem doctor to approach his sacred person. A few years ago, the Rajah would have taken the hint, for the Political Agent then had been a formidable figure, descending with all the thunders of Empire when it was most inconvenient, turning the polity inside out, requiring motor-cars and tiger-hunts, trees cut down that impeded the view from the Guest House, cows milked in his presence, and generally arrogating the control of internal affairs. But there had been a change of policy in high quarters. Local thunders were no longer endorsed, and the group of little states that

1. **bhakti**: religious devotion.

composed the agency discovered this and began comparing notes with fruitful result. To see how much, or how little, Colonel Maggs would stand, became an agreeable game at Mau, which was played by all the departments of State. He had to stand the appointment of Dr. Aziz. The Rajah did not take the hint, but replied that Hindus were less exclusive than formerly, thanks to the enlightened commands of the Viceroy, and he felt it his duty to move with the times.

Yes, all had gone well hitherto, but now, when the rest of the state was plunged in its festival, he had a crisis of a very different sort. A note awaited him at his house. There was no doubt that Fielding had arrived overnight, nor much doubt that Godbole knew of his arrival, for the note was addressed to him, and he had read it before sending it on to Aziz, and had written in the margin, "Is not this delightful news, but unfortunately my religious duties prevent me from taking any action." Fielding announced that he had inspected Mudkul (Miss Derek's former preserve), that he had nearly been drowned at Deora, that he had reached Mau according to time-table, and hoped to remain there two days, studying the various educational innovations of his old friend. Nor had he come alone. His wife and her brother accompanied him. And then the note turned into the sort of note that always did arrive from the State Guest House. Wanting something. No eggs. Mosquito nets torn. When would they pay their respects to His Highness? Was it correct that a torchlight procession would take place? If so, might they view it? They didn't want to give trouble, but if they might stand in a balcony, or if they might go out in a boat. . . . Aziz tore the note up. He had had enough of showing Miss Quested native life. Treacherous hideous harridan! Bad people altogether. He hoped to avoid them, though this might be difficult, for they would certainly be held up for several days at Mau. Down country, the floods were even worse, and the pale grey faces of lakes had appeared in the direction of the Asirgarh railway station.

CHAPTER 35

Long before he discovered Mau, another young Mohammedan had retired there—a saint. His mother said to him, "Free prisoners." So he took a sword and went up to the fort. He unlocked a door, and the prisoners streamed out and resumed their previous occupations, but the police were too much annoyed and cut off the young man's head. Ignoring its absence, he made his way over the rocks that separate the fort and the town, killing policemen as he went, and he fell outside his mother's house, having accomplished her orders. Consequently there are two shrines to him today—that of the Head above, and that of the Body below—and they are worshipped by the few Mohammedans who live near, and by Hindus also. "There is no God but God"; that symmetrical injunction melts in the mild airs of Mau; it belongs to pilgrimages and universities, not to feudalism and agriculture. When Aziz arrived, and found that even Islam was idolatrous, he grew scornful, and longed to purify the place, like Alamgir. But soon he didn't mind, like Akbar. After all, this saint had freed prisoners, and he himself had lain in prison. The Shrine of the Body lay in his own garden and produced a weekly crop of lamps and flowers, and when he saw them he recalled his sufferings. The Shrine of the Head made a nice short walk for the children. He was off duty the morning after the great pujah,[1] and he told them to come. Jemila held his hand. Ahmed and Karim ran in front, arguing what the body looked like as it came staggering down, and whether they would have been frightened if they met it. He didn't want them to grow up superstitious, so he rebuked them, and they answered yes, father, for they were well brought up, but, like himself, they were impervious to argument, and after a polite pause they continued saying what their natures compelled them to say.

A slim, tall eight-sided building stood at the top of the slope, among some bushes. This was the Shrine of the Head. It had not been roofed, and was indeed merely a screen. Inside it crouched a humble dome, and inside that, visible through a grille, was a truncated gravestone, swathed in calico. The inner angles of the screen were cumbered with bees' nests, and a gentle shower of broken wings and other aerial oddments kept falling, and had strewn the damp pavement with their flue. Ahmed, apprized by Mohammed Latif of the character of the bee, said, "They will not hurt us, whose lives are chaste," and pushed boldly in; his sister was more cautious. From the shrine they went to a mosque, which, in size and design, resembled a fire-screen; the arcades of Chandrapore had shrunk to a flat piece of ornamental stucco, with protuberances at either end to suggest minarets. The funny little thing didn't even stand straight, for the rock on which it had been put was slipping down the hill. It, and the shrine, were a strange outcome of the protests of Arabia.

They wandered over the old fort, now deserted, and admired the various views. The scenery, according to their standards, was delightful—the sky grey and black, bellyfuls of rain all over it, the earth pocked with pools of water and slimy with mud. A magnificent monsoon—the best for three years, the tanks already full, bumper crops possible. Out towards the river (the route by which the Fieldings had escaped from Deora) the downpour had been enormous, the mails had to be pulled across by ropes. They could just see the break in the forest trees where the gorge came through, and the rocks above that marked the site of the diamond mine,

1. **pujah:** religious festival.

glistening with wet. Close beneath was the suburban residence of the Junior Rani, isolated by floods, and Her Highness, lax about purdah, to be seen paddling with her handmaidens in the garden and waving her sari at the monkeys on the roof. But better not look close beneath, perhaps—nor towards the European Guest House either. Beyond the Guest House rose another grey-green gloom of hills, covered with temples like little white flames. There were over two hundred gods in that direction alone, who visited each other constantly, and owned numerous cows, and all the betel-leaf industry, besides having shares in the Asirgarh motor omnibus. Many of them were in the palace at this moment, having the time of their lives; others, too large or proud to travel, had sent symbols to represent them. The air was thick with religion and rain.

Their white shirts fluttering, Ahmed and Karim ran about over the fort, shrieking with joy. Presently they intersected a line of prisoners, who were looking aimlessly at an old bronze gun. "Which of you is to be pardoned?" they asked. For to-night was the procession of the Chief God, when He would leave the palace, escorted by the whole power of the State, and pass by the Jail, which stood down in the town now. As He did so, troubling the waters of our civilization, one prisoner would be released, and then He would proceed to the great Mau tank that stretched as far as the Guest House garden, where something else would happen, some final or subsidiary apotheosis, after which He would submit to the experience of sleep. The Aziz family did not grasp as much as this, being Moslem, but the visit to the Jail was common knowledge. Smiling, with downcast eyes, the prisoners discussed with the gentry their chances of salvation. Except for the irons on their legs, they resembled other men, nor did they feel different. Five of them, who had not yet been brought to trial, could expect no pardon, but all who had been convicted were full of hope. They did not distinguish between the God and the Rajah in their minds, both were too far above them; but the guard was better educated, and ventured to enquire after His Highness's health.

"It always improves," replied the medicine man. As a matter of fact, the Rajah was dead, the ceremony overnight had overtaxed his strength. His death was being concealed lest the glory of the festival were dimmed. The Hindu physician, the Private Secretary, and a confidential servant remained with the corpse, while Aziz had assumed the duty of being seen in public, and misleading people. He had liked the ruler very much, and might not prosper under his successor, yet he could not worry over such problems yet, for he was involved in the illusion he helped to create. The children continued to run about, hunting for a frog to put in Mohammed Latif's bed, the little fools. Hundreds of frogs lived in their own garden, but they must needs catch one up on the fort. They reported two topis

below. Fielding and his brother-in-law, instead of resting after their journey, were climbing the slope to the saint's tomb!

"Throw stones?" asked Karim.

"Put powdered glass in their pan?"

"Ahmed, come here for such wickedness." He raised his hand to smite
his firstborn, but allowed it to be kissed instead. It was sweet to have his
sons with him at this moment, and to know they were affectionate and
brave. He pointed out that the Englishmen were State guests, so must not
be poisoned, and received, as always, gentle yet enthusiastic assent to
words.

The two visitors entered the octagon, but rushed out at once pursued
by some bees. Hither and thither they ran, beating their heads; the children shrieked with derision, and out of heaven, as if a plug had been
pulled, fell a jolly dollop of rain. Aziz had not meant to greet his former
friend, but the incident put him into an excellent temper. He felt compact
and strong. He shouted out, "Hullo, gentlemen, are you in trouble?"

The brother-in-law exclaimed; a bee had got him.

"Lie down in a pool of water, my dear sir—here are plenty. Don't come
near me. . . . I cannot control them, they are State bees; complain to
His Highness of their behaviour." There was no real danger, for the rain
was increasing. The swarm retired to the shrine. He went up to the stranger and pulled a couple of stings out of his wrist, remarking, "Come, pull
yourself together and be a man."

"How do you do, Aziz, after all this time? I heard you were settled in
here," Fielding called to him, but not in friendly tones. "I suppose a couple of stings don't signify."

"Not the least. I'll send an embrocation over to the Guest House. I
heard you were settled in there."

"Why have you not answered my letters?" he asked, going straight for
the point, but not reaching it, owing to buckets of rain. His companion,
new to the country, cried, as the drops drummed on his topi, that the bees
were renewing their attack. Fielding checked his antics rather sharply,
then said: "Is there a short cut down to our carriage? We must give up
our walk. The weather's pestilential."

"Yes. That way."

"Are you not coming down yourself?"

Aziz sketched a comic salaam; like all Indians, he was skilful in the
slighter impertinences. "I tremble, I obey," the gesture said, and it was
not lost upon Fielding. They walked down a rough path to the road—the
two men first; the brother-in-law (boy rather than man) next, in a state
over his arm, which hurt; the three Indian children last, noisy and impudent—all six wet through.

"How goes it, Aziz?"

"In my usual health."

"Are you making anything out of your life here?"

"How much do you make out of yours?"

"Who is in charge of the Guest House?" he asked, giving up his slight effort to recapture their intimacy, and growing more official; he was older and sterner.

"His Highness's Private Secretary, probably."

"Where is he, then?"

"I don't know."

"Because not a soul's been near us since we arrived."

"Really."

"I wrote beforehand to the Durbar, and asked if a visit was convenient. I was told it was, and arranged my tour accordingly; but the Guest House servants appear to have no definite instructions, we can't get any eggs, also my wife wants to go out in the boat."

"There are two boats."

"Exactly, and no oars."

"Colonel Maggs broke the oars when here last."

"All four?"

"He is a most powerful man."

"If the weather lifts, we want to see your torchlight procession from the water this evening," he pursued. "I wrote to Godbole about it, but he has taken no notice; it's a place of the dead."

"Perhaps your letter never reached the Minister in question."

"Will there be any objection to English people watching the procession?"

"I know nothing at all about the religion here. I should never think of watching it myself."

"We had a very different reception both at Mudkul and Deora, they were kindness itself at Deora, the Maharajah and Maharani wanted us to see everything."

"You should never have left them."

"Jump in, Ralph"—they had reached the carriage.

"Jump in, Mr. Quested, and Mr. Fielding."

"Who on earth is Mr. Quested?"

"Do I mispronounce that well-known name? Is he not your wife's brother?"

"Who on earth do you suppose I've married?"

"I'm only Ralph Moore," said the boy, blushing, and at that moment there fell another pailful of the rain, and made a mist round their feet. Aziz tried to withdraw, but it was too late.

"Quested? Quested? Don't you know that my wife was Mrs. Moore's daughter?"

He trembled, and went purplish grey; he hated the news, hated hearing the name Moore.

"Perhaps this explains your odd attitude?"

"And pray what is wrong with my attitude?"

"The preposterous letter you allowed Mahmoud Ali to write for you."

"This is a very useless conversation, I consider."

"However did you make such a mistake?" said Fielding, more friendly than before, but scathing and scornful. "It's almost unbelievable. I should think I wrote you half a dozen times, mentioning my wife by name. Miss Quested! What an extraordinary notion!" From his smile, Aziz guessed that Stella was beautiful. "Miss Quested is our best friend, she introduced us, but . . . what an amazing notion. Aziz, we must thrash this misunderstanding out later on. It is clearly some deviltry of Mahmoud Ali's. He knows perfectly well I married Miss Moore. He called her 'Heaslop's sister' in his insolent letter to me."

The name woke furies in him. "So she is, and here is Heaslop's brother, and you his brother-in-law, and good-bye." Shame turned into a rage that brought back his self-respect. "What does it matter to me who you marry? Don't trouble me here at Mau is all I ask. I do not want you, I do not want one of you in my private life, with my dying breath I say it. Yes, yes, I made a foolish blunder; despise me and feel cold. I thought you married my enemy. I never read your letter. Mahmoud Ali deceived me. I thought you'd stolen my money, but"—he clapped his hands together, and his children gathered round him—"it's as if you stole it. I forgive Mahmoud Ali all things, because he loved me." Then pausing, while the rain exploded like pistols, he said, "My heart is for my own people henceforward," and turned away. Cyril followed him through the mud, apologizing, laughing a little, wanting to argue and reconstruct, pointing out with irrefragable logic that he had married, not Heaslop's betrothed, but Heaslop's sister. What difference did it make at this hour of the day? He had built his life on a mistake, but he had built it. Speaking in Urdu, that the children might understand, he said: "Please do not follow us, whomever you marry. I wish no Englishman or Englishwoman to be my friend."

He returned to the house excited and happy. It had been an uneasy, uncanny moment when Mrs. Moore's name was mentioned, stirring memories. "Esmiss Esmoor . . ."—as though she was coming to help him. She had always been so good, and that youth whom he had scarcely looked at was her son, Ralph Moore, Stella and Ralph, whom he had promised to be kind to, and Stella had married Cyril.

CHAPTER 36

All the time the palace ceased not to thrum and tum-tum. The revelation was over, but its effect lasted, and its effect was to make men feel that the revelation had not yet come. Hope existed despite fulfilment, as it will be in heaven. Although the God had been born, His procession—loosely supposed by many to be the birth—had not taken place. In normal years, the middle hours of this day were signalized by performances of great beauty in the private apartments of the Rajah. He owned a consecrated troupe of men and boys, whose duty it was to dance various actions and meditations of his faith before him. Seated at his ease, he could witness the Three Steps by which the Saviour ascended the universe to the discomfiture of Indra, also the death of the dragon, the mountain that turned into an umbrella, and the saddhu who (with comic results) invoked the God before dining. All culminated in the dance of the milkmaidens before Krishna, and in the still greater dance of Krishna before the milkmaidens, when the music and the musicians swirled through the dark blue robes of the actors into their tinsel crowns, and all became one. The Rajah and his guests would then forget that this was a dramatic performance, and would worship the actors. Nothing of the sort could occur to-day, because death interrupts. It interrupted less here than in Europe, its pathos was less poignant, its irony less cruel. There were two claimants to the throne, unfortunately, who were in the palace now and suspected what had happened, yet they made no trouble, because religion is a living force to the Hindus, and can at certain moments fling down everything that is petty and temporary in their natures. The festival flowed on, wild and sincere, and all men loved each other, and avoided by instinct whatever could cause inconvenience or pain.

Aziz could not understand this, any more than an average Christian could. He was puzzled that Mau should suddenly be purged from suspicion and self-seeking. Although he was an outsider, and excluded from their rites, they were always particularly charming to him at this time; he and his household received small courtesies and presents, just because he was outside. He had nothing to do all day, except to send the embrocation over to the Guest House, and towards sunset he remembered it, and looked round his house for a local palliative, for the dispensary was shut. He found a tin of ointment belonging to Mohammed Latif, who was unwilling it should be removed, for magic words had been spoken over it while it was being boiled down, but Aziz promised that he would bring it back after application to the stings: he wanted an excuse for a ride.

The procession was beginning to form as he passed the palace. A large crowd watched the loading of the State palanquin, the prow of which protruded in the form of a silver dragon's head through the lofty half-opened door. Gods, big and little, were getting aboard. He averted his eyes, for he never knew how much he was supposed to see, and nearly collided with the Minister of Education. "Ah, you might make me late"—meaning that the touch of a non-Hindu would necessitate another bath; the words were spoken without moral heat. "Sorry," said Aziz. The other smiled, and again mentioned the Guest House party, and when he heard that Fielding's wife was not Miss Quested after all, remarked "Ah, no, he married the sister of Mr. Heaslop. Ah, exactly, I have known that for over a year"—also without heat. "Why did you not tell me? Your silence plunged me into a pretty pickle." Godbole, who had never been known to tell anyone anything, smiled again, and said in deprecating tones: "Never be angry with me. I am, as far as my limitations permit, your true friend; besides, it is my holy festival." Aziz always felt like a baby in that strange presence, a baby who unexpectedly receives a toy. He smiled also, and turned his horse into a lane, for the crush increased. The Sweepers' Band was arriving. Playing on sieves and other emblems of their profession, they marched straight at the gate of the palace with the air of a victorious army. All other music was silent, for this was ritually the moment of the Despised and Rejected; the God could not issue from his temple until the unclean Sweepers played their tune, they were the spot of filth without which the spirit cannot cohere. For an instant the scene was magnificent. The doors were thrown open, and the whole court was seen inside, barefoot and dressed in white robes; in the fairway stood the Ark of the Lord, covered with cloth of gold and flanked by peacock fans and by stiff circular banners of crimson. It was full to the brim with statuettes and flowers. As it rose from the earth on the shoulders of its bearers, the friendly sun of the monsoons shone forth and flooded the world with colour, so that the yellow tigers painted on the palace walls seemed to spring, and pink and green skeins of cloud to link up the upper sky. The palanquin moved. . . . The lane was full of State elephants, who would follow it, their howdahs empty out of humility. Aziz did not pay attention to these sanctities, for they had no connection with his own; he felt bored, slightly cynical, like his own dear Emperor Babur, who came down from the north and found in Hindustan no good fruit, no fresh water or witty conversation, not even a friend.

The lane led quickly out of the town on to high rocks and jungle. Here he drew rein and examined the great Mau tank, which lay exposed beneath him to its remotest curve. Reflecting the evening clouds, it filled the nether-world with an equal splendour, so that earth and sky leant toward one another, about to clash in ecstasy. He spat, cynical again, more cynical than before. For in the centre of the burnished circle a small black blot

was advancing—the Guest House boat. Those English had improvised
something to take the place of oars, and were proceeding in their work of
patrolling India. The sight endeared the Hindus by comparison, and looking back at the milk-white hump of the palace, he hoped that they would
enjoy carrying their idol about, for at all events it did not pry into other
people's lives. This pose of "seeing India" which had seduced him to Miss
Quested at Chandrapore was only a form of ruling India; no sympathy lay
behind it; he knew exactly what was going on in the boat as the party
gazed at the steps down which the image would presently descend, and
debated how near they might row without getting into trouble officially.

He did not give up his ride, for there would be servants at the Guest
House whom he could question; a little information never comes amiss.
He took the path by the sombre promontory that contained the royal
tombs. Like the palace, they were of snowy stucco, and gleamed by their
internal light, but their radiance grew ghostly under approaching night.
The promontory was covered with lofty trees, and the fruit-bats were
unhooking from the boughs and making kissing sounds as they grazed the
surface of the tank; hanging upside down all the day, they had grown
thirsty. The signs of the contented Indian evening multiplied; frogs on all
sides, cow-dung burning eternally; a flock of belated hornbills overhead,
looking like winged skeletons as they flapped across the gloaming. There
was death in the air, but not sadness; a compromise had been made between destiny and desire, and even the heart of man acquiesced.

The European Guest House stood two hundred feet above the water, on
the crest of a rocky and wooded spur that jutted from the jungle. By the
time Aziz arrived, the water had paled to a film of mauve-grey, and the
boat vanished entirely. A sentry slept in the Guest House porch, lamps
burned in the cruciform of the deserted rooms. He went from one room
to another, inquisitive, and malicious. Two letters lying on the piano rewarded him, and he pounced and read them promptly. He was not
ashamed to do this. The sanctity of private correspondence has never been
ratified by the East. Moreover, Mr. McBryde had read all his letters in the
past, and spread their contents. One letter—the more interesting of the two
—was from Heaslop to Fielding. It threw light on the mentality of his former friend, and it hardened him further against him. Much of it was about
Ralph Moore, who appeared to be almost an imbecile. "Hand on my
brother whenever suits you. I write to you because he is sure to make a
bad bunderbust." [1] Then: "I quite agree—life is too short to cherish grievances, also I'm relieved you feel able to come into line with the Oppres-
sors of India to some extent. We need all the support we can get. I hope

1. **bunderbust:** elaborate arrangements.

that next time Stella comes my way she will bring you with her, when I will make you as comfortable as a bachelor can—it's certainly time we met. My sister's marriage to you coming after my mother's death and my own difficulties did upset me, and I was unreasonable. It is about time we made it up properly, as you say—let us leave it at faults on both sides. Glad about your son and heir. When next any of you write to Adela, do give her some sort of message from me, for I should like to make my peace with her too. You are lucky to be out of British India at the present moment. Incident after incident, all due to propaganda, but we can't lay our hands on the connecting thread. The longer one lives here, the more certain one gets that everything hangs together. My personal opinion is, it's the Jews."

Thus far the red-nosed boy. Aziz was distracted for a moment by blurred sounds coming from over the water; the procession was under way. The second letter was from Miss Quested to Mrs. Fielding. It contained one or two interesting touches. The writer hoped that "Ralph will enjoy his India more than I did mine," and appeared to have given him money for this purpose—"my debt which I shall never repay in person." What debt did Miss Quested imagine she owed the country? He did not relish the phrase. Talk of Ralph's health. It was all "Stella and Ralph," even "Cyril" and "Ronny"—all so friendly and sensible, and written in a spirit he could not command. He envied the easy intercourse that is only possible in a nation whose women are free. These five people were making up their little difficulties, and closing their broken ranks against the alien. Even Heaslop was coming in. Hence the strength of England, and in a spurt of temper he hit the piano, and since the notes had swollen and stuck together in groups of three, he produced a remarkable noise.

"Oh, oh, who is that?" said a nervous and respectful voice; he could not remember where he had heard its tones before. Something moved in the twilight of an adjoining room. He replied, "State doctor, ridden over to enquire, very little English," slipped the letters into his pocket, and to show that he had free entry to the Guest House, struck the piano again.

Ralph Moore came into the light.

What a strange-looking youth, tall, prematurely aged, the big blue eyes faded with anxiety, the hair impoverished and tousled! Not a type that is often exported imperially. The doctor in Aziz thought, "Born of too old a mother," the poet found him rather beautiful.

"I was unable to call earlier owing to pressure of work. How are the celebrated bee-stings?" he asked patronizingly.

"I—I was resting, they thought I had better; they throb rather."

His timidity and evident "newness" had complicated effects on the malcontent. Speaking threateningly, he said, "Come here, please, allow me to look." They were practically alone, and he could treat the patient as Callendar had treated Nureddin.

"You said this morning——"

"The best of doctors make mistakes. Come here, please, for the diagnosis under the lamp. I am pressed for time."

"Aough——"

"What is the matter, pray?"

"Your hands are unkind."

He started and glanced down at them. The extraordinary youth was right, and he put them behind his back before replying with outward anger: "What the devil have my hands to do with you? This is a most strange remark. I am a qualified doctor, who will not hurt you."

"I don't mind pain, there is no pain."

"No pain?"

"Not really."

"Excellent news," sneered Aziz.

"But there is cruelty."

"I have brought you some salve, but how to put it on in your present nervous state becomes a problem," he continued, after a pause.

"Please leave it with me."

"Certainly not. It returns to my dispensary at once." He stretched forward, and the other retreated to the farther side of a table. "Now, do you want me to treat your stings, or do you prefer an English doctor? There is one at Asirgarh. Asirgarh is forty miles away, and the Ringnod dam broken. Now you see how you are placed. I think I had better see Mr. Fielding about you; this is really great nonsense, your present behaviour."

"They are out in a boat," he replied, glancing about him for support.

Aziz feigned intense surprise. "They have not gone in the direction of Mau, I hope. On a night like this the people become most fanatical." And, as if to confirm him, there was a sob, as though the lips of a giant had parted; the procession was approaching the Jail.

"You should not treat us like this," he challenged, and this time Aziz was checked, for the voice, though frightened, was not weak.

"Like what?"

"Dr. Aziz, we have done you no harm."

"Aha, you know my name, I see. Yes, I am Aziz. No, of course your great friend Miss Quested did me no harm at the Marabar."

Drowning his last words, all the guns of the State went off. A rocket from the Jail garden gave the signal. The prisoner had been released, and was kissing the feet of the singers. Rose-leaves fall from the houses, sacred spices and coco-nut are brought forth. . . . It was the half-way moment;

the God had extended His temple, and paused exultantly. Mixed and confused in their passage, the rumours of salvation entered the Guest House. They were startled and moved on to the porch, drawn by the sudden illumination. The bronze gun up on the fort kept flashing, the town was a blur of light, in which the houses seemed dancing, and the palace waving little wings. The water below, the hills and sky above, were not involved as yet; there was still only a little light and song struggling among the shapeless lumps of the universe. The song became audible through much repetition; the choir was repeating and inverting the names of deities.

> "Radhakrishna Radhakrishna,
> Radhakrishna Radhakrishna,
> Krishnaradha Radhakrishna,
> Radhakrishna Radhakrishna,"

they sang, and woke the sleeping sentry in the Guest House; he leant upon his iron-tipped spear.

"I must go back now, good night," said Aziz, and held out his hand, completely forgetting that they were not friends, and focusing his heart on something more distant than the caves, something beautiful. His hand was taken, and then he remembered how detestable he had been, and said gently, "Don't you think me unkind any more?"

"No."

"How can you tell, you strange fellow?"

"Not difficult, the one thing I always know."

"Can you always tell whether a stranger is your friend?"

"Yes."

"Then you are an Oriental." He unclasped as he spoke, with a little shudder. Those words—he had said them to Mrs. Moore in the mosque in the beginning of the cycle, from which, after so much suffering, he had got free. Never be friends with the English! Mosque, caves, mosque, caves. And here he was starting again. He handed the magic ointment to him. "Take this, think of me when you use it. I shall never want it back. I must give you one little present, and it is all I have got; you are Mrs. Moore's son."

"I am that," he murmured to himself; and a part of Aziz' mind that had been hidden seemed to move and force its way to the top.

"But you are Heaslop's brother also, and alas, the two nations cannot be friends."

"I know. Not yet."

"Did your mother speak to you about me?"

"Yes." And with a swerve of voice and body that Aziz did not follow he added, "In her letters, in her letters. She loved you."

"Yes, your mother was my best friend in all the world." He was silent, puzzled by his own great gratitude. What did this eternal goodness of Mrs. Moore amount to? To nothing, if brought to the test of thought. She had not borne witness in his favour, nor visited him in the prison, yet she had stolen to the depths of his heart, and he always adored her. "This is our monsoon, the best weather," he said, while the lights of the procession waved as though embroidered on an agitated curtain. "How I wish she could have seen them, our rains. Now is the time when all things are happy, young and old. They are happy out there with their savage noise, though we cannot follow them; the tanks are all full so they dance, and this is India. I wish you were not with officials, then I would show you my country, but I cannot. Perhaps I will just take you out on the water now, for one short half-hour."

Was the cycle beginning again? His heart was too full to draw back. He must slip out in the darkness, and do this one act of homage to Mrs. Moore's son. He knew where the oars were—hidden to deter the visitors from going out—and he brought the second pair, in case they met the other boat; the Fieldings had pushed themselves out with long poles, and might get into difficulties, for the wind was rising.

Once on the water, he became easy. One kind action was with him always a channel for another, and soon the torrent of his hospitality gushed forth and he began doing the honours of Mau and persuading himself that he understood the wild procession, which increased in lights and sounds as the complications of its ritual developed. There was little need to row, for the freshening gale blew them in the direction they desired. Thorns scratched the keel, they ran into an islet and startled some cranes. The strange temporary life of the August flood-water bore them up and seemed as though it would last for ever. The boat was a rudderless dinghy. Huddled in the stern, with the spare pair of oars in his arms, the guest asked no questions about details. There was presently a flash of lightning, followed by a second flash—little red scratches on the ponderous sky. "Was that the Rajah?" he asked.

"What—what do you mean?"

"Row back."

"But there's no Rajah—nothing——"

"Row back, you will see what I mean."

Aziz found it hard work against the advancing wind. But he fixed his eyes on the pin of light that marked the Guest House and backed a few strokes.

"There . . ."

Floating in the darkness was a king, who sat under a canopy, in shining royal robes. . . .

"I can't tell you what that is, I'm sure," he whispered. "His Highness is dead. I think we should go back at once."

They were close to the promontory of the tombs, and had looked straight into the chhatri ² of the Rajah's father through an opening in the trees. That was the explanation. He had heard of the image—made to imitate life at enormous expense—but he had never chanced to see it before, though he frequently rowed on the lake. There was only one spot from which it could be seen, and Ralph had directed him to it. Hastily he pulled away, feeling that his companion was not so much a visitor as a guide. He remarked, "Shall we go back now?"

"There is still the procession."

"I'd rather not go nearer—they have such strange customs, and might hurt you."

"A little nearer."

Aziz obeyed. He knew with his heart that this was Mrs. Moore's son, and indeed until his heart was involved he knew nothing. "Radhakrishna Radhakrishna Radhakrishna Radhakrishna Krishnaradha," went the chant, then suddenly changed, and in the interstice he heard, almost certainly, the syllables of salvation that had sounded during his trial at Chandrapore.

"Mr. Moore, don't tell anyone that the Rajah is dead. It is a secret still, I am supposed not to say. We pretend he is alive until after the festival, to prevent unhappiness. Do you want to go still nearer?"

"Yes."

He tried to keep the boat out of the glare of the torches that began to star the other shore. Rockets kept going off, also the guns. Suddenly, closer than he had calculated, the palanquin of Krishna appeared from behind a ruined wall, and descended the carven glistening water-steps. On either side of it the singers tumbled, a woman prominent, a wild and beautiful young saint with flowers in her hair. She was praising God without attributes—thus did she apprehend Him. Others praised Him without attributes, seeing Him in this or that organ of the body or manifestation of the sky. Down they rushed to the foreshore and stood in the small waves, and a sacred meal was prepared, of which those who felt worthy partook. Old Godbole detected the boat, which was drifting in on the gale, and he waved his arms—whether in wrath or joy Aziz never discovered. Above stood the secular power of Mau—elephants, artillery, crowds—and high above them a wild tempest started, confined at first to the upper regions of the air. Gusts of wind mixed darkness and light, sheets of rain cut from the north, stopped, cut from the south, began rising from below, and across them struggled the singers, sounding every note but terror, and preparing to throw God away, God Himself, (not that God can be thrown)

2. **chhatri:** a chapel built over a tomb.

into the storm. Thus was He thrown year after year, and were others thrown—little images of Ganpati,[3] baskets of ten-day corn, tiny tazias after Mohurram—scapegoats, husks, emblems of passage; a passage not easy, not now, not here, not to be apprehended except when it is unattainable: the God to be thrown was an emblem of that.

The village of Gokul reappeared upon its tray. It was the substitute for the silver image, which never left its haze of flowers; on behalf of another symbol, it was to perish. A servitor took it in his hands, and tore off the blue and white streamers. He was naked, broad-shouldered, thin-waisted—the Indian body again triumphant—and it was his hereditary office to close the gates of salvation. He entered the dark waters, pushing the village before him, until the clay dolls slipped off their chairs and began to gutter in the rain, and King Kansa was confounded with the father and mother of the Lord. Dark and solid, the little waves sipped, then a great wave washed and then English voices cried "Take care!"

The boats had collided with each other.

The four outsiders flung out their arms and grappled, and, with oars and poles sticking out, revolved like a mythical monster in the whirlwind. The worshippers howled with wrath or joy, as they drifted forward helplessly against the servitor. Who awaited them, his beautiful dark face expressionless, and as the last morsels melted on his tray, it struck them.

The shock was minute, but Stella, nearest to it, shrank into her husband's arms, then reached forward, then flung herself against Aziz, and her motions capsized them. They plunged into the warm, shallow water, and rose struggling into a tornado of noise. The oars, the sacred tray, the letters of Ronny and Adela, broke loose and floated confusedly. Artillery was fired, drums beaten, the elephants trumpeted, and drowning all an immense peal of thunder, unaccompanied by lightning, cracked like a mallet on the dome.

That was the climax, as far as India admits of one. The rain settled in steadily to its job of wetting everybody and everything through, and soon spoiled the cloth of gold on the palanquin and the costly disc-shaped banners. Some of the torches went out, fireworks didn't catch, there began to be less singing, and the tray returned to Professor Godbole, who picked up a fragment of the mud adhering and smeared it on his forehead without much ceremony. Whatever had happened had happened, and while the intruders picked themselves up, the crowds of Hindus began a desultory move back into the town. The image went back too, and on the following day underwent a private death of its own, when some curtains of magenta and green were lowered in front of the dynastic shrine. The

---

3. **Ganpati:** a fat and cheerful god, with an elephant's head on a human body; a symbol of prosperity and a remover of obstacles in any project.

singing went on even longer . . . ragged edges of religion . . . unsatisfactory and undramatic tangles. . . . "God si love." Looking back at the
great blur of the last twenty-four hours, no man could say where was the
emotional centre of it, any more than he could locate the heart of a cloud.

CHAPTER 37

Friends again, yet aware that they could meet no more, Aziz and Fielding went for their last ride in the Mau jungles. The floods had abated and
the Rajah was officially dead, so the Guest House party were departing
next morning, as decorum required. What with the mourning and the festival, the visit was a failure. Fielding had scarcely seen Godbole, who
promised every day to show him over the King-Emperor George Fifth
High School, his main objective, but always made some excuse. This afternoon Aziz let out what had happened: the King-Emperor had been converted into a granary, and the Minister of Education did not like to admit
this to his former Principal. The school had been opened only last year by
the Agent to the Governor-General, and it still flourished on paper; he
hoped to start it again before its absence was remarked and to collect its
scholars before they produced children of their own. Fielding laughed at
the tangle and waste of energy, but he did not travel as lightly as in the
past; education was a continuous concern to him, because his income and
the comfort of his family depended on it. He knew that few Indians think
education good in itself, and he deplored this now on the widest grounds.
He began to say something heavy on the subject of Native States, but the
friendliness of Aziz distracted him. This reconciliation was a success, anyhow. After the funny shipwreck there had been no more nonsense or bitterness, and they went back laughingly to their old relationship as if nothing had happened. Now they rode between jolly bushes and rocks. Presently the ground opened into full sunlight and they saw a grassy slope
bright with butterflies, also a cobra, which crawled across doing nothing in
particular, and disappeared among some custard apple trees. There were
round white clouds in the sky, and white pools on the earth; the hills in
the distance were purple. The scene was as park-like as England, but did
not cease being queer. They drew rein, to give the cobra elbow-room, and
Aziz produced a letter that he wanted to send to Miss Quested. A charming letter. He wanted to thank his old enemy for her fine behaviour
two years back: perfectly plain was it now that she had behaved well.
"As I fell into our largest Mau tank under circumstances our other
friends will relate, I thought how brave Miss Quested was and decided
to tell her so, despite my imperfect English. Through you I am happy
here with my children, instead of in a prison, of that I make no doubt.

My children shall be taught to speak of you with the greatest affection and respect."

"Miss Quested will be greatly pleased. I am glad you have seen her courage at last."

"I want to do kind actions all round and wipe out the wretched business of the Marabar for ever. I have been so disgracefully hasty, thinking you meant to get hold of my money: as bad a mistake as the cave itself."

"Aziz, I wish you would talk to my wife. She too believes that the Marabar is wiped out."

"How so?"

"I don't know, perhaps she might tell you, she won't tell me. She has ideas I don't share—indeed, when I'm away from her I think them ridiculous. When I'm with her, I suppose because I'm fond of her, I feel different, I feel half dead and half blind. My wife's after something. You and I and Miss Quested are, roughly speaking, not after anything. We jog on as decently as we can, you a little in front—a laudable little party. But my wife is not with us."

"What are you meaning? Is Stella not faithful to you, Cyril? This fills me with great concern."

Fielding hesitated. He was not quite happy about his marriage. He was passionate physically again—the final flare-up before the clinkers of middle age—and he knew that his wife did not love him as much as he loved her, and he was ashamed of pestering her. But during the visit to Mau the situation had improved. There seemed a link between them at last—that link outside either participant that is necessary to every relationship. In the language of theology, their union had been blessed. He could assure Aziz that Stella was not only faithful to him, but likely to become more so; and trying to express what was not clear to himself, he added dully that different people had different points of view. "If you won't talk about the Marabar to Stella, why won't you talk to Ralph? He is a wise boy really. And (same metaphor) he rides a little behind her, though with her."

"Tell him also, I have nothing to say to him, but he is indeed a wise boy and has always one Indian friend. I partly love him because he brought me back to you to say good-bye. For this is good-bye, Cyril, though to think about it will spoil our ride and make us sad."

"No, we won't think about it." He too felt that this was their last free intercourse. All the stupid misunderstandings had been cleared up, but socially they had no meeting-place. He had thrown in his lot with Anglo-India by marrying a countrywoman, and he was acquiring some of its limitations, and already felt surprise at his own past heroism. Would he to-day defy all his own people for the sake of a stray Indian? Aziz was a memento, a trophy, they were proud of each other, yet they must inevitably part. And, anxious to make what he could of this last afternoon, he forced himself to speak intimately about his wife, the person most dear to him. He said: "From her point of view, Mau has been a success. It calmed her—both of them suffer from restlessness. She found something soothing, some solution of her queer troubles here." After a silence—myriads of kisses around them as the earth drew the water in—he continued: "Do you know anything about this Krishna business?"

"My dear chap, officially they call it Gokul Ashtami. All the States offices are closed, but how else should it concern you and me?"

"Gokul is the village where Krishna was born—well, more or less born, for there's the same hovering between it and another village as between Bethlehem and Nazareth. What I want to discover is its spiritual side, if it has one."

"It is useless discussing Hindus with me. Living with them teaches me no more. When I think I annoy them, I do not. When I think I don't annoy them, I do. Perhaps they will sack me for tumbling on to their dolls'-house; on the other hand, perhaps they will double my salary. Time will prove. Why so curious about them?"

"It's difficult to explain. I never really understood or liked them, except an occasional scrap of Godbole. Does the old fellow still say 'Come, come?'"

"Oh, presumably."

Fielding sighed, opened his lips, shut them, then said with a little laugh, "I can't explain, because it isn't in words at all, but why do my wife and her brother like Hinduism, though they take no interest in its forms? They won't talk to me about this. They know I think a certain side of their lives is a mistake, and are shy. That's why I wish you would talk to them, for at all events you're Oriental."

Aziz refused to reply. He didn't want to meet Stella and Ralph again, knew they didn't want to meet him, was incurious about their secrets, and felt good old Cyril to be a bit clumsy. Something—not a sight, but a sound—flitted past him, and caused him to re-read his letter to Miss Quested. Hadn't he wanted to say something else to her? Taking out his pen, he added: "For my own part, I shall henceforth connect you with the name that is very sacred in my mind, namely, Mrs. Moore." When he had finished, the mirror of the scenery was shattered, the meadow disintegrated into butterflies. A poem about Mecca—the Caaba of Union—the thornbushes where pilgrims die before they have seen the Friend—they flitted next; he thought of his wife; and then the whole semi-mystic, semi-sensuous overturn, so characteristic of his spiritual life, came to end like a landslip and rested in its due place, and he found himself riding in the jungle with his dear Cyril.

"Oh, shut up," he said. "Don't spoil our last hour with foolish questions. Leave Krishna alone, and talk about something sensible."

They did. All the way back to Mau they wrangled about politics. Each had hardened since Chandrapore, and a good knock about proved enjoyable. They trusted each other, although they were going to part, perhaps because they were going to part. Fielding had "no further use for politeness," he said, meaning that the British Empire really can't be abolished because it's rude. Aziz retorted, "Very well, and we have no use for you," and glared at him with abstract hate. Fielding said: "Away from us, Indians go to seed at once. Look at the King-Emperor High School! Look at you, forgetting your medicine and going back to charms. Look at your poems."—"Jolly good poems, I'm getting published Bombay side."—"Yes, and what do they say? Free our women and India will be free. Try it, my lad. Free your own lady in the first place, and see who'll wash Ahmed, Karim and Jemila's faces. A nice situation!"

Aziz grew more excited. He rose in his stirrups and pulled at his horse's head in the hope it would rear. Then he should feel in a battle. He cried: "Clear out, all you Turtons and Burtons. We wanted to know you ten years back—now it's too late. If we see you and sit on your committees, it's for political reasons, don't you make any mistake." His horse did rear. "Clear out, clear out, I say. Why are we put to so much suffering? We used to blame you, now we blame ourselves, we grow wiser. Until England is in difficulties we keep silent, but in the next European war—aha, aha! Then is our time." He paused, and the scenery, though it smiled, fell like a gravestone on any human hope. They cantered past a temple to Hanuman—God so loved the world that he took monkey's flesh upon him— and past a Saivite[1] temple, which invited to lust, but under the semblance of eternity, its obscenities bearing no relation to those of our flesh and blood. They splashed through butterflies and frogs; great trees with leaves like plates rose among the brushwood. The divisions of daily life were returning, the shrine had almost shut.

"Who do you want instead of the English? The Japanese?" jeered Fielding, drawing rein.

"No, the Afghans. My own ancestors."

"Oh, your Hindu friends will like that, won't they?"

"It will be arranged—a conference of Oriental statesmen."

"It will indeed be arranged."

"Old story of 'We will rob every man and rape every woman from Peshawar to Calcutta,' I suppose, which you get some nobody to repeat and then quote every week in the *Pioneer* in order to frighten us into retaining you! We know!" Still he couldn't quite fit in Afghans at Mau,

1. **Saivite:** i.e., of Siva, the Hindu god of destruction, procreation, and the arts.

and, finding he was in a corner, made his horse rear again until he re-membered that he had, or ought to have, a mother-land. Then he shouted: "India shall be a nation! No foreigners of any sort! Hindu and Moslem and Sikh and all shall be one! Hurrah! Hurrah for India! Hurrah! Hurrah!"

India a nation! What an apotheosis! Last comer to the drab nineteenth-century sisterhood! Waddling in at this hour of the world to take her seat! She, whose only peer was the Holy Roman Empire, she shall rank with Guatemala and Belgium perhaps! Fielding mocked again. And Aziz in an awful rage danced this way and that, not knowing what to do, and cried: "Down with the English anyhow. That's certain. Clear out, you fellows, double quick, I say. We may hate one another, but we hate you most. If I don't make you go, Ahmed will, Karim will, if it's fifty-five hundred years we shall get rid of you, yes, we shall drive every blasted Englishman into the sea, and then"—he rode against him furiously—"and then," he con-cluded, half kissing him, "you and I shall be friends."

"Why can't we be friends now?" said the other, holding him affection-ately. "It's what I want. It's what you want."

But the horses didn't want it—they swerved apart; the earth didn't want it, sending up rocks through which riders must pass single file; the temples, the tank, the jail, the palace, the birds, the carrion, the Guest House, that came into view as they issued from the gap and saw Mau beneath: they didn't want it, they said in their hundred voices, "No, not yet," and the sky said, "No, not there."

Nonfiction

Oliver Wendell Holmes, Jr.

CIVIL WAR LETTERS

[20th Regiment Hospital, Camp Benton]

Wed: Oct. 23 1861 [1]

My Dear Mother

Here I am flat on my back after our first engagement—wounded but pretty comfortable [2]—I can't write an account now but I felt and acted

From *Touched with Fire: Civil War Letters and Diary of Oliver Wendell Holmes, Jr., 1861–1864*, edited by Mark DeWolfe Howe, copyright 1946 by the President and Fellows of Harvard College. Reprinted by permission of the Harvard University Press.

1. On July 10, 1861, immediately following his graduation from Harvard College, Holmes was commissioned First Lieutenant in Company A of the 20th Regiment Massachusetts Volunteers.

   For this selection certain useful and interesting background information is supplied, in the form of footnotes, from the biography of Oliver Wendell Holmes, *Yankee from Olympus*, by Catherine Drinker Bowen. Other footnotes are taken from the edition of the Holmes letters prepared by Mark DeWolfe Howe. In each instance the source of the footnote is indicated. [The material from *Yankee from Olympus* by Catherine Drinker Bowen, copyright 1943, 1944 by Catherine Drinker Bowen. Reprinted by permission of Little, Brown and Company.]

2. In a field above a cliff on the Virginia side of the river, the Twentieth lay in the high grass and waited for the rest of the Brigade to arrive. Ball's Bluff, the place was called. Across the field the enemy waited too, hidden by thick trees. It had taken men half the night to cross the river in four leaky old scows they had picked up. The current ran very deep and swift. In the middle of the river

413

very cool and did my duty I am sure—I was out in front of our men encouraging 'em on when a spent shot knocked the wind out of me & I
fell—then I crawled to the rear a few paces & rose by help of the 1st
Sergt; & the Colonel who was passing said "That's right Mr Holmes—Go
to the Rear" but I felt that I couldn't without more excuse so up I got
and rushed to the front where hearing the Col. cheering the men on I
waved my sword and asked if none would follow me when down I went
again by the Colonel's side—The first shot (the spent ball) struck me on
the belly below where the ribs separate & bruised & knocked the wind out
of me—The second time I hope only one ball struck me entering the left
& coming out behind the right breast in wh. case I shall probably recover
and this view is seconded by finding a ball in my clothes by the right hand
wound—I may be hit twice in which case the chance is not so good—
But I am now so well that I have good hopes—The first night I made up
my mind to die & was going to take that little bottle of laudanum as soon
as I was sure of dying with any pain—but the doctors told me not to take
it. And now seem to think I have a fair chance and all my friends whatever happens I am very happy in the conviction I did my duty handsomely—Lt Putnam is dead Capt. Putnam lost his right arm. Hallowell
fought like a brick but wasn't hurt—Schmidt badly wounded—Lowell
wounded—Colonel Major & Adjutant probably prisoners Babo & Wes-
selhoeft probably dead—Dreher shot through the head—Sergt Merchant
shot dead (in the head) From a third to a half of our company killed
wounded & prisoners

I have written a few details if you can read 'em—Men are concentrating
in all directions and fighting still going on—They begun by cutting up the

there was an island, a thin strip of land about two miles long. If we have to retreat, Colonel Lee had said, make for that island.

Retreat? Nobody in the Twentieth was thinking of retreat. They were thinking of glory. Holmes heard Colonel Baker congratulate Colonel Lee on the prospect of a battle . . . The lines were formed. At command, Holmes's company
cocked their rifles, fired straight into the wood.

After that things happened too fast for Holmes to ask himself if he were
scared. Charging out of the woods the Rebels yelled, high and savage, like Indians. Up from the river came the Tammany Regiment, and the California, single file in the smoke, scattering like Indians. Holmes had not fired twice when a
spent ball hit him in the stomach. When he got his wind he struggled up . . .
Over by the grove they were fighting hand-to-hand now. Going down on one
knee, Holmes aimed . . . The blow came again, in the chest this time. Wendell
fell, vomited, lay with his eyes shut. The pain in his chest was terrible. In his
tunic pocket was a bottle of laudanum. Cautiously he lifted a hand to see if he
could reach it . . . Why, he had no shirt on! His breast was wet and slippery.

Wendell fainted. Around him the battle went on and on . . . —CATHERINE
DRINKER BOWEN, pp. 154-55.

20th only 8 officers out of 22 in our Regt got home unhurt I hope we'll lick 'em yet though—I was hit in the beginning of the fight,

Yours Always

O W Holmes Jr

God bless you

I can't send a good looking note lying on my back—But I believe Whit. has written you [3]

Tuesday April 7. [1862] [4]

or Wednesday 1 A.M. rather—

((unless I am a day behind time—))

My Dear Parents—

I am on guard tonight and seize the chance to write—John Put. goes to the fort tomorrow and will take my letter—We are on the advance with about 130 000 men & George B.[5] in person—Our division is the center & at present I believe he remains with us—I have seen him twice—It's a campaign now & no mistake—No tents, no trunks—no nothing—it has rained like the devil last night all day and tonight and you may guess what the mud is in a clayey soil where it was a real annoyance before—Marching will have to be slow for the roads have constantly to be made or mended for artillery (of wh. there is a great deal) The men and officers are wet enough you may believe but there is real pluck shown now as these are real hardships to contend with. But yesterday (i.e. Monday unless all my days are one behindhand) it was cold comfort to come back to a camping ground with which the Boston Common parade ground at its worst offers a favorable contrast after a march up to knees in mud all day on a reconnoissance on wh. our Brigade was sent. We are in camp within 4 miles of the enemie's fortifications & approached to within ½ a mile— There was firing (with one piece of artillery with shell from the rebs none on our side—) all day—volleys & scattering shots from the enemy returned by the 19th & Jack Saunder's Sharp Shooters—We knew biz.

---

3. A long letter, dated October 22, from Lieutenant Whittier to Dr. Holmes [Oliver Wendell's father] describing the battle of Ball's Bluff has been preserved—MARK DE WOLFE HOWE.

4. By New Year's Day 1862, Holmes's wound was healed. He then went on recruiting duty, and rejoined his regiment on March 23.

5. On March 11 General [George B.] McClellen, having been removed as General-in-Chief, had assumed command of the Army of the Potomac—MARK DE WOLFE HOWE.

wasn't intended as we went out for Lt? Comstock of the engineers to make drawings—But late in the afternoon after several changes of position on our part we drew into a field on the other side of wh. was an earthwork & aforesaid gun—our posit. was concealed by rising ground or a shell w'ld have blown some of us to pieces—They kept firing into the edge of the woods where the 19th were deployed as skirmishers & succeeded in killing one & wounding 1 or 2. as we were in line of battle had they known our whereabouts it w'ld have been bad.

When we saw Co I (Lt. Abbot—) go forward up the hill I fairly trembled for though they marched with splendid coolness I expected to see some bowled over every minute—but just as they were in sight of the works Comstock & Bartlett (who is much better than Palf. who isn't worth a ——) ran forward and ordered Abbot (who had misunderstood the order) under cover as skirmishers—then Cabots Co. K—(Ned Hallowell, 2nd Lt.) went forward & then the battalion marched by the left flank to posit. no. 2. by the edge of the woods Then the skirmishers fired a little or were fired at rather—and then having found out all we wanted to know we turned round & marched home—well tired out—I am in good spirits though of course I despise the life [6] in itself outside of special circumstances & principles—If I can stand this very rough beginning it will be good for my health I am in Pen's Co. and it makes all the difference in the world—that is an unmixed pleasure—I caught a heavy cold on board the boat—& I have still something of a cough a *fact* wh. annoys me though the thing itself doesn't—I think I shall stand the work—You must write *all the time* though I can but rarely with great uncertainty whether my letter goes—acknowledge the receipt of mine and be constant in writing even if you don't hear for a long time as they have a way of stopping the mails here & at any rate I rarely can—Anything you want to show any of my friends (wh. isn't private that is) you may for I can't write although I long to hear—

God bless you all
O. W. Holmes, Jr.

My hand is cold so that I sling a nasty quill—

6. When he wrote this letter, Holmes was 21 years old; fifty-eight years later, in 1920, when he was 79 years old, Holmes wrote the following in a letter to a close friend: "I loathe war—which I described when at home with a wound in our Civil War as an organized bore—to the scandal of the young women of the day who thought that Captain Holmes was wanting in patriotism."

Written on field of battle—

June 2nd '62

Dear Parents

I am nearly tired out with the constant labors of the last two days but I write a word to say I with all our officers am safe so far and I am in perfect health & spirits [7] [. . .]

May 31st We heard heavy firing from Casey's Div[n] and soon our Div was under arms & marched 4 miles I sh'ld think—the last part through a stream above our knees and then double quick through mud a foot deep on to the field of battle. [. . .] At this time Rickets Battery was firing hard and sheets of flame came fr. the line of Inft[y] as a couple of Co[s], only, (they say) of the Reb[s] tried to charge the guns. They were mowed down and broke—The shingles of the house rattled with the hail of Reb. bullets and many whistled by—mostly over us wounding one or two—Here I saw an officer just in front of our line lying snug behind a stump apparently, too, unhurt—Soon we filed round and *formed under* fire in 2nd posit. left of a N. Y. Regt. and opened fire on the Reb. Line wh. was visible—Our fire was soon stopped (by order) and we could see in the field, (where our 3[d] posit. was later,) Reb[s] moving by twos & threes—apparently broken up—Then the order was given Forward in line—Double quick—At this point thinking there must be a battery nearer than I thought to be charged —I threw away my haversack wh. impeded my motions containing all my food my dressing case my only change of stockings my pipe & tobacco— wh. I have vainly lamented since—(The land was soft fr. ploughing wh. made it hard to get on) When we got to the road the R. wing entered the woods firing hard and the left wing (I am next the colors on the left of the color Co.—Hallowells place, as 9th Capt., but wh. I keep as the previous posit. of Co G. on acc't of the smallness of Co D.) the left wing advancing more slowly to avoid getting fired into by our own men—A Co. of Reb[s] trying to pass out of the woods was knocked to pieces—and thus we soon took the final posit. of the 1st day marked—((Here I was interrupted by firing near at hand—It turns out to be Reb[s] firing at a party

7. On May 4 the 20th Regiment had entered Yorktown after its evacuation by the Confederates. The Regiment did not participate in the Williamsburg campaign but on May 6 was moved by water from Yorktown to a point on the Pamunkey River above West Point. From that time until May 31 it moved up and across the Peninsula, passing through or near Eltham Landing, Cumberland Landing, New Kent Court House, Baltimore Crossroads, and Bottom's Bridge. On May 28 the Regiment, still part of Dana's Brigade, encamped on the north bank of the Chicka-hominy near the Tyler House. It was from this position that the 20th moved forward on the 31st into the Battle of Fair Oaks. It crossed the Chickahominy by the Grapevine Bridge—MARK DE WOLFE HOWE.

of our men who are burying *their dead!*))—marked May 31—Here we
blazed away left oblique into the woods till we were ordered to cease
firing & remained masters of the field (we were the only Reg^t there)
where the enemy had just been—Then the bringing in of the wounded
begun—Among them were the Brig. Genl Pettigrew I think of the Hamp-
ton Legion S. C. (wh. is among their best troops—as indeed were all the
Rebs—engaged—) a Lt. Col. &c. We sat under arms waiting sleepless cold
wet and hungry till morng for the renewal of the fight—June 1st there was
heavy firing from 7 am. till noon in the woods along the R.R. and we
were formed at the place marked June 1st about wh. we have since continued—We are now shoved forward a hundred or two feet to the woods
—June 1st nothing particular occurred—We stayed in line all day—formed
sq. to resist an expected attack of cavalry in the afternoon—OWH in the
front rank of 1st front handling a sword & pistol—and were fired at several times during the day by sharp shooters—A bullet has a most villain-
ous greasy slide through the air—In the night Co^s D, C, & G on picket in
woods in front of Regt. up again nearly all night. Thunder wind & rain
—Our men fired at once by Reb^s & a shell dropped among us from our
own side—We heard the Reb^s working talking & knocking round all night
and this morn'g it seems they have fallen back a little—

Today is pleasant and hot—It is singular with what indifference one gets
to look on the dead bodies in gray clothes wh. lie all around—(or rather
did—We are burying them today as fast as we can—) As you go through
the woods you stumble constantly, and, if after dark, as last night on
picket, perhaps tread on the swollen bodies already fly blown and decaying, of men shot in the head back or bowels—Many of the wounds are
terrible to look at—especially those fr. fragments of shell, Co G although
roughs & poor material fought splendidly especially after the first flurry
when they had settled down to the work—Once when *entre nous* the
right of Lowell's Co begun to waver a little and fall back our left stood
and didn't give an inch—But really as much or rather more is due to the
file closers than anything else I told 'em to shoot any man who ran and
they lustily buffeted every hesitating brother—I gave one (who was cowering) a smart rap over the backsides with the edge of my sword—and
stood with my revolver & swore I'd shoot the first who ran or fired against
orders—Well we licked 'em and this time there was the maneuvering of a
battle to be seen—splendid and awful to behold; especially as the dusk
allowd us to see clearly the lines of flames from the different Regt^s as
they fired—

We have had so far I fancy about fr. 20 to 25 killed & wounded in our
Regt *—No officers though Pen had a bullet cut the rubber blanket he had

* 400 fighting men strong perhaps

round him sack fashion across the breast. Among our prisoners were men fr. V^a N.C.; S.C.; G^a/ Al^a/ Miss./ L^a/ Texas/ Tennessee I doubt if we fight more at present but we are in spirits though worn by fatigue and privation as well as mental anxiety—

If I am killed you will find a Mem. on the back of a picture I carry wh. please attend to. I must sleep a few minutes I can hardly keep my eyelids raised—God bless you both

My love to all
Your aff. son
O W H, Jr.

June 13, 1862 [8]

My dear Father

Today's mail has made up for past injustice and neglect by bringing me five envelopes—4 enclosing letters and one, even better, a toothbrush—3 were from blushing maidens—I am glad you have rec'd mine if it were only to do our Reg^t the justice of saying we were in some of the prettiest fighting—The 19th & Tammany of our brigade weren't there but we were —And I wish that while *local* Regts like the 10th & 15th get cracked up like thunder that the 20th got its due credit. At Ball's Bluff I think we fought better than the 15th Certainly our proportionate loss was greater *than any Regts in this whole army during the whole war*—at least I understand so—Our loss was more than one in 4 killed & wounded. And this time while we hear about the 10th &c&c& how the Tammany stood like veterans (two miles out of the fight) our work is hardly mentioned. After all it makes very little difference except for the sake of justice and one's friends. I wish you wouldn't all be so anxious—Our loss in this last fight of 25 K^d & W^d out of 400 (our whole fighting force) is about the usual proportion for the Regts actively engaged—

We are now for two days a little in the rear (about ¾ mile from the advanced pickets) our brigade having been relieved from the very hard work it or at least *we* have been doing.

For a week and a half mostly rainy—We had hardly any sleep hardly any blankets or anything—Shall I confess a frightful fact? Many of the officers including your beloved son have discovered themselves to have been attacked by body lice in consequence—(Caught perhaps from the

8. After the Battle of Fair Oaks, from June 1 to June 11, the Regiment remained in its advance position south of the Chickahominy. On the 11th it was relieved from the front line and moved a mile or so to high ground along the York River Railroad line, and established a camp there (Camp Lincoln)—MARK DE WOLFE HOWE.

men, perhaps from the dirty places we have been forced to live in or enter.) I shall fix their flints though now.

The men behaved like bricks through it all—I think my men like me—I have heard so—and I find the duties please me better than those of a Lt.[9] My men cheered me after the fight. I have a 2nd Lt. with me by name Murphy who was a 1st Sergt—He was also 1st Sergt. of the small band who held Pickens under Slemmer until Lincoln came into power & relieved them. He's a good soldier and a good fellow.

Well it's too hot to write more—

I have sent one or two notes since the one you rec'd to make sure you heard—& one for the Miff. to Mother with permission to read—on the sly —It's queer that I stand this exposure and hard work better than many a stout fellow who looks more enduring than I.

I am always well and—as things are—contented—

Your loving son
O. W. Holmes, Jr. Capt. Co. G. XX Reg. Mass Hs.

I wrote you a letter in my pocket book while Sunday's fight was going on but didn't send it—as I wrote another more at length wh. you rec'd.

My love to all—

Tell Amelia & my friends to write—There is no other pleasure except receiving letters.
Don't want anything else
Send me some stamps also—& a paper of quinine.

Sept. 18—[1862]

My Dear Parents

Once more I back it as per hint of yesterday's letter—Usual luck—ball entered at the rear passing straight through the central seam of coat & waistcoat collar coming out toward the front on the left hand side [10]—

9. Holmes was commissioned Captain by Governor Andrew [of Massachusetts] by order dated March 23, 1862. In the Peninsula Campaign he commanded Company G—MARK DE WOLFE HOWE.

10. Captain Holmes did not retire. He lay on the ground where he had fallen, shot through the neck. A voice spoke above him. "You're a Christian aren't you?" Holmes tried to open his eyes; the blackness closed on him again. "Well then, *that's* all right!" the voice said, and passed on. It was the regimental chaplain; no man with a bloody hole in his neck could live; better that he should die a Christian. Another voice spoke; this time Holmes did not hear it. "I've no time to waste on dead men." It was an army surgeon; with him was a captain from Ohio named Leduc. Stooping over Wendell, Leduc spoke sharply to the surgeon. "I know this man. He's a valuable officer. I command you to do what you can for him."

yet it don't seem to have smashed my spine or I suppose I should be dead or paralysed or something—It's more than 24 h'rs & I have remained pretty cocky, only of course feverish at times—& some sharp burning pain in left shoulder Pen & I singular to say are the hardest hit officers he I think will lose his left arm—bone smashed above elbow—We lay together for a while in a little house on the field and were one time within the enemies lines, heard their orders &c (they were all round us) but they fell back & we escaped.

Only one doctor Haven the Surgeon of 15. Mass has yet looked—he glanced hastily yesterday & said it wasn't fatal—I shall try to get home as soon as poss. but have no plans yet—

I shall write again soon—

Col. Revere is waiting for this

Your loving

O W H, Jr.

May 3. [1863] [11]

Dear Mother

Ned Paine arrived here last night & is at present occupied in his maiden battle—if not killed Pour moi I'm already hit in the heel—bullet fr. spherical case—[12]

> Whatever the surgeon did, Holmes was unconscious of it; it was Leduc himself who told the story. The next thing Holmes knew, he was on his feet. There was someone on each side of him, holding him up. It was Leduc and a farmer's boy in a ragged straw hat. "We'll have to get off the field," Leduc said. "There's a farmhouse if we can reach it." Holmes took a step, stumbled, found he could walk. As a matter of fact, he was not nearly so badly wounded as at Ball's Bluff. The bullet had gone sidewise through his neck, missing windpipe and jugular vein, and had come out at the back, cutting the seam of his coat collar—CATHERINE DRINKER BOWEN, pp. 168–69.

11. After the events recounted in the last letter, Holmes went on six weeks' convalescence; he was orderd up again on November 15, 1862.

12. The river road to Chancellorsville was the route the Twentieth must follow. Up this road in the early mist Captain Holmes's company advanced. It was still quiet, firing had not begun. At the canal, knowing he was in full view of the enemy's guns from the hills beyond, Holmes ordered his men sharply to lie down. He had not finished speaking when the first shell came over—and tore the cape from his overcoat. He threw himself down full length, grabbed a rifle from one of his men, and sighted it at the enemy.

When the next volley came Holmes's head went down, he buried his face in the grass. His long legs were crossed, one ankle over the other. There was a lull while the enemy took range. The next shells will be lower, Wendell thought. They were. Shrapnel that missed his head caught the heel of the foot that was uppermost. A terrific blow, tearing ligament and tendons.

It was Holmes's third and last wound. It would keep him out of the war for nine months, it would trouble him for years to come.

Pleasant to see a d'd gun brought up to an earthwork deliberately brought to bear on you—to notice that your Co. is exactly in range—1st discharge puff—second puff (as the shell burst) and my knapsack supporter is knocked to pieces (Mem. We are lying down)˙ 2nd discharge man in front of me hit—3d whang the iron enters through garter & shoe into my heel—

They have been firing hard ever since & as the stretcher is waiting for me I stop—

Your loving

O W Holmes, Jr.

later I've been chloroformed & had bone extracted—probably shant lose foot

H.Q. 1st Div. 6th Corps

10 P.M. May 3, 1864 [13]

Dear Parents

In six hours we start—at 4 A.M. tomorrow—You won't get this I suppose for some time—I sent my diary a week or more ago & judge by Amelia's letter (Rec'd today—telling of serenade &c) it hasn't been rec'd—*Be sure to get that when* the mails arc forwarded—This is only a parting word of love to all at home—

I suppose we fight in a day or two—Till then good-bye—I have no new words of affection now—I am well and in excellent spirits—

Your loving

O. W. Holmes, Jr.

I shall see the fight on the Staff in every probability—My love to Amelia, Ned, and doubly to each of you—

1st Div. 6th Corps

May 6th 1864   5.15 o'clock, PM.

Dear Parents

Second day of battle Not done yet—I am all right & Whit & Dalton— I hear Macy wounded in shoulder Abbott wounded *severely* don't know

---

But Holmes, lying face down in the grass below the Virginia hills, knew nothof this. *My leg is gone*, he thought, and fainted—CATHERINE DRINKER BOWEN, p. 184.

13. As a result of the wounds mentioned in his letter of May 3, 1863, Holmes again went on sick leave; he was not called up until January 1864.

where—Col. Frank Bartlett wounded in head—20th said to be comm'ded by 1st L^t—

> Your loving
> O W H, Jr.

It is doubtful if you get this A Tribune Corr^t. will try to get it through—Considerable firing & yells now—

> Hq. 6 Corps
>
> 10.23 A.M. May 11. 64

Dear Mother

I have written every chance I had—so far all right—fighting every day —shan't try to tell particulars till I can write at leisure—Just think of it— Today is the 7th day we have fought, not pitched battles all the time of course, but averaging a loss I guess of 3000 (three thousand) a day at least—

> My love to all
> Goodbye
> O W H, Jr

T. Lyman ⎫
Dalton ⎬ O. K.
Whit. away with body of Gen. S.

> May 16th 1864
>
> H. Q. 6th Corps—

Dear Parents

Rec'd last night enclosed letters—Yesterday & today tolerably quiet, a quiet that you will easily believe was needed after the long series of collisions beginning on the 5th—Before you get this you will know how immense the butchers bill has been—And the labor has been incessant—I have not been & am not likely to be in the mood for writing details. I have kept brief notes in my diary wh. I hope you may see some day—Enough that these nearly two weeks have contained all of fatigue & horror that war can furnish—The advantage has been on our side but nothing decisive has occurred & the enemy is in front of us strongly intrenched—I doubt if the decisive battle is to be fought between here & Richmond—nearly every Regimental off—I knew or cared for is dead or wounded—

I have made up my mind to stay on the staff if possible till the end of the campaign & then if I am alive, I shall resign—I have felt for sometime that I didn't any longer believe in this being a duty & so I mean to leave at the end of the campaign as I said if I'm not killed before. Remember I am now at H.Q. 6th C. & it is *Major* Gen W. Comdg—

The duties & thoughts of the field are of such a nature that one cannot at the same time keep home, parents and such thoughts as they suggest in his mind at the same time as a reality—Can hardly indeed remember their existence—and this too just after the intense yearning which immediately precedes a campaign. Still your letters are the one pleasure & you know my love

Your Aff. Son
O W H Jr

May 30th 64
4.12 P.M.

Dear Parents

Wrote to Anna this morn'g—who may send to you—imprimis rec^d y'r letters of 21st 22^d the latter fr. dad, stupid—I wish you'd take the trouble to read my letters before answering—I am sure I cannot have conveyed the idea, rightfully, that I intended resigning before the campaign was over (i.e. next winter just near the end of my term of service)—then I probably shall for reasons satisfactory to myself—I must say I dislike such a misunderstanding, so discreditable to my feeling of soldierly honor, when I don't believe there was a necessity for it—I shall stay on the staff and wish you'd notify the Governor to commission new field officers to the 20th I waive promotion—I am convinced from my late experience that if I can stand the wear & tear (body & mind) of regimental duty that it is a greater strain on both than I am called on to endure—If I am satisfied I don't really see that anyone else has a call to be otherwise—I talked with Hayward the mentor of the Regt & told him my views on the matter—I am not the same man (may not have quite the same ideas) & certainly am not so elastic as I was and I *will not acknowledge the same claims upon me under those circumstances* that existed formerly—a day & a half have passed since I wrote last word—it is quarter to 12 between May 31. & June 1 I have just been riding through black woods after some H^dQrs—and we are going to have another of those killing night marches as soon as we can start out of a country worse than the wilderness if possible—I have hardly known what a good night's sleep was since the campaign opened—constantly having, as tonight, to be up all night—

The afternoon of the 29th I had my narrowest escape—Dispatch to carry—important—don't spare y'r horse—gallop—1 mile—small boy (one well known as Col. Upton's scout) retreating at a run—reports fired at 2 reb. cav^y—looked round for forces—one straggler (infty) one (unarmed) man on mule, one sick officer—& boy—I spy 4 of our cav^y foraging dismiss former forces & order them with me—trot—when boy was shot at gallop—bend in road—woods cease—bang—bang—whiz—whiz—about 20 reb^8 in line—"Halt. Surrender" I pulled up & sung out "friends" deceived by number & darkness of their clothes—They keep on shooting then I saw & put in licks for straight ahead—Anon a fellow comes riding down the road—I think I'll gobble him—he to me "Halt Surrender" I see others on R. of road—he is unslinging his carbine as I get to him, I put my pistol to his breast & pull—enclosed cap snaps—then I run the gauntlet—bang—whiz– Halt—Surrender lying along the neck of my horse—Got my dispatch through & return in triumph to find myself given over for lost—

Love to all
Afftly
O W H, Jr.

H.Q. 6th Corps

June 7/64

Dear Mother

Here goes for the luxury of writing a decent looking letter, using the cigar box which father sent me as a desk—that is I will write if the enemy will give me time and not go pitching shell & roundshot round our H.Q. as they have been doing earlier this morn'g, and if they will keep decently quiet on the front line of works. A cheerful place the latter, by the way, to be sent to after breakfast to inspect & report on progress—You show your nose anywhere and sizzle come the bullets at it in less than the twinkling of a bedpost—and they shoot pretty well on both sides now. However I am so much safer than any inft^y officer that I don't grumble but also feel that I am earning less honor though learning much more—

But fortunately I have a jewel in the head of this campaign in the shape of my adventure of Sunday week ago—For let me tell you what I wouldn't before as I was a little irritated, that, although I am not aware of the General's knowing the particulars, the staff to whom I spun my yarn intimated that they thought it rather a gallant thing, & it was I think myself to get the order through & not knock under or turn back—

These days of comparative rest though constant loss allow my thoughts to turn longingly & lovingly homeward again—which they couldn't—as I told you—in the wear and tear of alternative march and fight.

The campaign has been most terrible yet believe me I was not demoralized when I announced my intention to leave the service next winter if I lived so long—I started in this thing a boy I am now a man and I have been coming to the conclusion for the last six months that my duty has changed—

I can do a disagreeable thing or face a great danger coolly enough when I *know* it is a duty—but a doubt demoralizes me as it does any nervous man—and now I honestly think the duty of fighting has ceased for me—ceased because I have laboriously and with much suffering of mind and body *earned* the right which I denied Willy Everett [14] to decide for myself how I can best do my duty to myself to the country and, if you choose, to God—

I believe that Governor Andrew understands my determination to waive promotion—please be sure he does so—The ostensible and sufficient reason is my honest belief that I cannot now endure the labors & hardships of the line—Nothing further need be told abroad—

I hope that this will meet your approbation—you are so sure to be right—at all events I have tried to decide conscientiously & I have decided—

If you know Carrie Dehons direction please let Amelia write a note & thank her for a very kind note wh. I rec^d long after it was written & explain the difficulty of answering it in person—

Love, Love, Love to all of you—Why don't F. McG write? I long for a letter from her

Rec^d Amelia's letter last night—I wish she'd write often—and that Ned would also sling ink—

> Your loving
> O W Holmes, Jr.

                                                              June 23^d 7.10 am

Dear Mother

Another infernal nasty time—night before last the Corps moved from right to left of Army—that night no sleep—All day troops changing position—advancing retreating advancing again usual accompaniment of shooting—A brigade of the 2d Div 2d Corps behaved badly yesterday & lost 4 guns the first guns ever taken from the Corps—last up very late—a brief sleep on the floor of a house with all my harness on rose at 3 this a.m. for

14. Presumably William Everett, of the Harvard Class of 1859, who spent the Civil War studying in England—MARK DE WOLFE HOWE.

an attack wh. was ordered—So far there has been nothing but a little picket shooting

The Genl's going out Goodbye

Yr loving Son
W.

Recd father's letter of 19th

June 24th 64/

Dear Parents

Just the time I stopped my last letter to pres^t moment a constant go—fighting—forward & back nothing of any account however except losing several hundred prisoners yesterday & 2^d Corps losing the same & 4 guns day before—20th I hear ran like thunder—

[. . .]

These last few days have been very bad—This morn'g I spent on the picket line it was being pushed forward—hot & nasty as Orcus—I think there is a kind of heroism in the endurance (Interrupted here to carry order to Gen Ricketts Comdg 3d Div 6th C to cut road in rear of line &c— R. of famous battery at 1st Bull Run wounded & prisoner Mrs. R— heroic—goes to see & comfort R. in jug & he is made Brig. Gen.) in the endurance I was going to say of the men—I tell you many a man has gone crazy since this campaign begun from the terrible pressure on mind & body—

I think the Army feels better than it might but theres no use in disguising that the feeling for McClellan has grown this campaign—I hope for success strongly before the end of the summer—but at what a cost & by & by the sickness will begin—I hope to pull through but don't know yet—

Afftly

Goodbye

O W H, Jr.

H.Q. 6th C.

July 8th 1864

Dear Mammy

Prepare for a startler—Unless something unexpected happens I shall probably leave this army for home about the 17th! The Regt. ceases to exist as a Regt and the few old men not reenlisted leave for home to be mustered out—

The rest of the Reg^t continues as a battalion of 6 or 7 Co^s and I of course shall not go in for 3 yrs more as Capt. of Inft^y having given up promotion for the sake of leaving the line—I might, to be sure, stay longer if I were one of the 3 aides allowed the Gen^{ls} by law but as I'm not and am liable to go back to the Regt if any change sh^d take place, I leave—If it should be necessary to go into the service again I should try for a commission from the Presd^t but I shan't bother myself ab^t that for the pres^t

Do you think I could get a place for my Negro boy if I brought him with me? Answer this last by the next mail after getting this—

Yr loving O W H, Jr [15]

15. [Holmes's last battle, on July 12, 1864, took place near Washington, D. C., and was observed by President Lincoln.] The President climbed a parapet. He had never seen a battle. What he had seen, year after year, week after week, was the young recruits, marching by the White House, singing. He had seen them return in ambulances over the long bridge to the crowded hospitals where he had gone to visit them, standing hat in hand by their beds. Now he was to see them in action.

The firing began. "You had better get out of the fire," General Wright said. The President did not move. Even without his tall hat he stood six feet four, a splendid target. Below him on the dusty ground, men ran forward and fell sprawling on their faces. This was the thing for which Lincoln felt responsible. This was the thing he had dreaded, this was the picture he had seen so often at dead of night and that had caused him to leave his bed and pace the floor until morning. [. . .] On the parapet five feet from him a man fell. Three feet away, so close Lincoln could have touched him, an officer fell dead.

"Get down, you fool!" a young voice shouted. Automatically the President stepped back. It was Wendell Holmes, angry and terrified. From the protection of the bulwark, Lincoln looked down at the white face, streaked with dirt, the brown hair wild [. . .] "Captain," he said, "I am glad you know how to talk to a civilian"—CATHERINE DRINKER BOWEN, p. 194.

Ralph Waldo Emerson

JOURNAL

Boston, May 13, 1823

In twelve days I shall be nineteen years old; which I count a miserable thing. Has any other educated person lived so many years and lost so many days? I do not say acquired so little, for by an ease of thought and certain looseness of mind I have perhaps been the subject of as many ideas as many of mine age. But mine approaching maturity is attended with a goading sense of emptiness and wasted capacity. . . .

Look next from the history of my intellect to the history of my heart. A blank, my lord. I have not the kind affections of a pigeon. Ungenerous and selfish, cautious and cold, I yet wish to be romantic; have not sufficient feeling to speak a natural, hearty welcome to a friend or stranger, and yet send abroad wishes and fancies of a friendship with a man I never knew. There is not in the whole wide Universe of God (my relations to Himself I do not understand) one being to whom I am attached with warm and entire devotion,—not a being to whom I have joined fate for weal or wo, not one whose interests I have nearly and dearly at heart;—and this I say at the most susceptible age of man. Perhaps at the distance of a score of years, if I then inhabit this world, or still more, if I do not, these will appear frightful confessions; they may or may not,—it is a true picture of a barren and desolate soul.

Cambridge, undated, 1826

All things are double one against another, said Solomon. The whole of what we know is a system of compensations. Every defect in one manner is made up in another. Every suffering is rewarded; every sacrifice is made up; every debt is paid.

Alexandria, May 19, 1828

Mr. Adams [1] went out a swimming the other day into the Potomac, and went near to a boat which was coming down the river. Some rude black-

From *Journals* by Ralph Waldo Emerson. Reprinted by permission of Houghton Mifflin Company. From *The Heart of Emerson's Journals* by Bliss Perry. Reprinted by permission of Houghton Mifflin Company.

1. **Mr. Adams:** John Quincy Adams, sixth president of the United States, from 1825 to 1829. Alexandria, where Emerson wrote this Journal entry, is in Virginia, near Washington, D. C.

guards were in it, who, not knowing the character of the swimmer, amused themselves with laughing at his bald head as it poppled up and down in the water, and, as they drew nearer, threatened to crack open his round pate if he came nigh them. The President of the United States was, I believe, compelled to waive the point of honour and seek a more retired bathing-place.

Cambridge, Divinity Hall, July 10, 1828

I am always made uneasy when the conversation turns in my presence upon popular ignorance and the duty of adapting our public harangues and writings to the mind of the people. 'Tis all pedantry and ignorance. The people know as much and reason as well as we do. None so quick as they to discern brilliant genius or solid parts. And I observe that all those who use this cant most, are such as do not rise above mediocrity of understanding.

Boston, January 20, 1832

Don't trust children with edge tools. Don't trust man, great God, with more power than he has, until he has learned to use that little better. What a hell should we make of the world if we could do what we would! Put a button on the foil till the young fencers have learned not to put each other's eyes out.

April 11, 1834

Went yesterday to Cambridge and spent most of the day at Mount Auburn; got my luncheon at Fresh Pond, and went back again to the woods. After much wandering and seeing many things, four snakes gliding up and down a hollow for no purpose that I could see—not to eat, not for love, but only gliding; then a whole bed of *Hepatica triloba*, cousins of the Anemone, all blue and beautiful, but constrained by niggard nature to wear their last year's faded jacket of leaves; then a black-capped titmouse, who came upon a tree, and when I would know his name, sang *chick-a-dee-dee;* then a far-off tree full of clamorous birds, I know not what, but you might hear them half a mile; I forsook the tombs,[2] and found a sunny hollow where the east wind would not blow, and lay down against the side of a tree to most happy beholdings. At least I opened my eyes and let what would pass through them into the soul. I saw no more my relation, how near and petty, to Cambridge or Boston; I heeded no more what minute or hour our Massachusetts clocks might indicate—I saw only the noble earth on which I was born, with the great Star which warms and enlightens it. I saw the clouds that hang their significant drapery over us.

2. Mount Auburn was—and is—a cemetery in Cambridge, Massachusetts.

It was Day—that was all Heaven said. The pines glittered with their in-numerable green needles in the light, and seemed to challenge me to read their riddle. The drab oak-leaves of the last year turned their little somer-sets and lay still again. And the wind bustled high overhead in the forest top. This gay and grand architecture, from the vault to the moss and lichen on which I lay,—who shall explain to me the laws of its proportions and adornments?

Newton, April 13, 1834

We are always getting ready to live, but never living. We have many years of technical education; then many years of earning a livelihood, and we get sick, and take journeys for our health, and compass land and sea for improvement by travelling, but the work of self-improvement,—al-ways under our nose,—nearer than the nearest, is seldom seldom engaged in. A few, few hours in the longest life.

October 14, 1834

Every involuntary repulsion that arises in your mind, give heed unto. It is the surface of a central truth.

December 19, 1834

He who makes a good sentence or a good verse exercises a power very strictly analogous to his who makes a fine statue, a beautiful cornice, a staircase like that in Oxford, or a noble head in painting. One writes on air, if he speaks; but no, he writes on mind more durable than marble, and is like him who begets a son, that is, originates a begetter of nations.

The maker of a sentence, like the other artist, launches out into the in-finite and builds a road into Chaos and old Night, and is followed by those who hear him with something of wild, creative delight.

February 17, 1838

My good Henry Thoreau made this else solitary afternoon sunny with his simplicity and clear perception. How comic is simplicity in this double-dealing, quacking world. Everything that boy says makes merry with society, though nothing can be graver than his meaning. I told him he should write out the history of his college life, as Carlyle has his tutor-ing. We agreed that the seeing the stars through a telescope would be worth all the astronomical lectures.

November 10, 1838

My brave Henry Thoreau walked with me to Walden this afternoon and complained of the proprietors who compelled him, to whom, as much as to any, the whole world belonged, to walk in a strip of road and crowded him out of all the rest of God's earth. I begged him, having this maggot of Freedom and Humanity in his brain, to write it out into good poetry and so clear himself of it.

September 14, 1839

We are shut up in schools and college recitation rooms for ten or fifteen years, and come out at last with a bellyful of words and do not know a thing. We cannot use our hands, or our legs, or our eyes, or our arms. We do not know an edible root in the woods. We cannot tell our course by the stars, nor the hour of the day by the sun. It is well if we can swim and skate. We are afraid of a horse, of a cow, of a dog, of a cat, of a spider. Far better was the Roman rule to teach a boy nothing that he could not learn standing.

Now here are my wise young neighbors [3] who, instead of getting, like the woodmen, into a railroad-car, where they have not even the activity of holding the reins, have got into a boat which they have built with their own hands, with sails which they have contrived to serve as a tent, and gone up the Merrimack to live by their wits on the fish of the stream and the berries of the woods. My worthy neighbor Dr. Bartlett expressed a true parental instinct when he desired to send his boy with them to learn something. The farm, the farm, is the right school. The reason of my deep respect for the farmer is that he is a realist, and not a dictionary. The farm is a piece of the world, the school-house is not.

June 24, 1840

Montaigne. The language of the street is always strong. What can describe the folly and emptiness of scolding like the word *jawing?* I feel too the force of the double negative, though clean contrary to our grammar rules. And I confess to some pleasure from the stinging rhetoric of a rattling oath in the mouth of truckmen and teamsters. How laconic and brisk it is by the side of a page of the *North American Review.*[4] Cut these words and they would bleed; they are vascular and alive; they walk and run. Moreover they who speak them have this elegancy, that they do not trip in their speech. It is a shower of bullets, whilst Cambridge men and Yale men correct themselves and begin again at every half sentence.

I know nobody among my contemporaries except Carlyle who writes with any sinew and vivacity comparable to Plutarch and Montaigne. Yet always this profane swearing and bar-room wit has salt and fire in it. I cannot now read Webster's speeches. Fuller and Browne [5] and Milton are

3. John and Henry Thoreau.
4. *North American Review:* a scholarly journal, published in Boston.
5. **Fuller:** Thomas Fuller (1608–1661), an English divine and historian; **Browne:** Sir Thomas Browne (1605–1682), an English physician and writer.

quick, but the list is soon ended. Goethe seems to be well alive, no pedant. Luther too.

September, undated, 1841

I told Henry Thoreau that his freedom is in the form, but he does not disclose new matter. I am very familiar with all his thoughts,—they are my own quite originally drest. But if the question be, what new ideas has he thrown into circulation, he has not yet told what that is which he was created to say.

October, undated, 1842

You shall have joy, or you shall have power, said God; you shall not have both.

October, undated, 1842

Henry Thoreau made, last night, the fine remark that, as long as a man stands in his own way, everything seems to be in his way, governments, society, and even the sun and moon and stars, as astrology may testify.

November 11, 1842

Do not be too timid and squeamish about your actions. All life is an experiment. The more experiments you make the better. What if they are a little coarse, and you may get your coat soiled or torn? What if you do fail, and get fairly rolled in the dirt once or twice? Up again you shall never be so afraid of a tumble.

October, undated, 1848

The salvation of America and of the human race depends on the next election, if we believe the newspapers. But so it was last year, and so it was the year before, and our fathers believed the same thing forty years ago.

December 14, 1849

Natural Aristocracy. It is a vulgar error to suppose that a gentleman must be ready to fight. The utmost that can be demanded of the gentleman is that he be incapable of a lie. There is a man who has good sense, is well informed, well read, obliging, cultivated, capable, and has an absolute devotion to truth. He always means what he says, and says what he means, however courteously. You may spit upon him;—nothing could induce him to spit upon you,—no praises, and no possessions, no compulsion of public opinion. You may kick him;—he will think it the kick of a brute: but he is not a brute, and will not kick you in return. But neither your knife and pistol, nor your gifts and courting will ever make the smallest impression

on his vote or word; for he is the truth's man, and will speak and act the
truth until he dies.

May, undated, 1852

To what base uses we put this ineffable intellect! To reading all day
murders and railroad accidents, to choosing patterns for waistcoats and
scarfs.

October, undated, 1852

The shoemakers and fishermen say in their shops, "Damn learning! it
spoils the boy; as soon as he gets a little, he won't work." "Yes," answers
Lemuel, "but there is learning somewhere, and somebody will have it, and
who has it will have the power, and will rule you: knowledge is power.
Why not, then, let your son get it, as well as another?"

If I have a message to send, I prefer the telegraph to the wheelbarrow.

Cape Cod, September 5, 1853

Went to Yarmouth Sunday, 5th; to Orleans Monday, 6th; to Nauset
Light on the back side of Cape Cod. Collins, the keeper, told us he found
obstinate resistance on Cape Cod to the project of building a lighthouse
on this coast, as it would injure the wrecking business. He had to go to
Boston, and obtain the strong recommendation of the Port Society. From
the high hill in the rear of Higgins's, in Orleans, I had a good view of the
whole Cape and the sea on both sides. The Cape looks like one of the New-
foundland Banks just emerged, a huge tract of sand half-covered with
poverty grass and beach grass, and for trees, abele and locust and planta-
tions of pitch pine. Some good oak, and in Dennis and Brewster were
lately good trees for whip lumber, and they still are well wooded on the
east side. But the view I speak of looked like emaciated Orkneys,—Mull,
Islay, and so forth,—made of salt dust, gravel, and fish bones. They say
the wind makes the roads, and, as at Nantucket, a large part of the real
estate was freely moving back and forth in the air. I heard much of the
coming railroad which is about to reach Yarmouth and Hyannis, and they
hope will come to Provincetown. I fancied the people were only waiting
for the railroad to reach them in order to evacuate the country. For the
stark nakedness of the country could not be exaggerated. But no; nothing
was less true. They are all attached to what they call *the soil.* Mr. Collins
had been as far as Indiana; but, he said, hill on hill,—he felt stifled, and
"longed for the Cape, where he could see out." And whilst I was fancying
that they would gladly give away land to anybody that would come and
live there, and be a neighbor: no, they said, all real estate had risen, all over
the Cape, and you could not buy land at less than fifty dollars per acre.

And, in Provincetown, a lot on the Front Street of forty feet square would cost five or six hundred dollars.

Still, I saw at the Cape, as at Nantucket, they are a little tender about your good opinion: for if a gentleman at breakfast says he don't like Yarmouth, all real estate seems to them at once depreciated two or three per cent.

They are very careful to give you directions what road you shall take from town to town; but, as the country has the shape of a piece of tape, it is not easy to lose your way. For the same reason it behooves everybody who goes to the Cape to behave well, as he must stop on his return at all the same houses, unless he takes the packet at Provincetown for Boston, six hours in good weather, and a week in bad.

The sand grinds the glass at Nauset Light, and soon makes it unfit for use. The sand grinds the tires of the wheels of the stage-coach.

September 8, 1853

Henry Thoreau says he values only the man who goes directly to his needs; who, wanting wood, goes to the woods and brings it home; or to the river, and collects the drift, and brings it in his boat to his door, and burns it: not him who keeps shop, that he may buy wood. One is pleasing to reason and imagination; the other not.

May (?) undated, 1856

Education. Don't let them eat their seed-corn; don't let them anticipate, ante-date, and be young men, before they have finished their boyhood. Let them have the fields and woods, and learn their secret and the base- and foot-ball, and wrestling, and brickbats, and suck all the strength and courage that lies for them in these games; let them ride bare-back, and catch their horse in his pasture, let them hook and spear their fish, and shin a post and a tall tree, and shoot their partridge and trap the wood-chucks, before they begin to dress like collegians and sing in serenades, and make polite calls.

April (?) undated, 1858

Because our education is defective, because we are superficial and ill-read, we are forced to make the most of that position, of ignorance. Hence America is a vast know-nothing party, and we disparage books, and cry up intuition. With a few clever men we have made a reputable thing of that, and denouncing libraries and severe culture, and magnifying the mother-wit swagger of bright boys from the country colleges, we have even come so far as to deceive everybody, except ourselves, into an ad-miration of un-learning and inspiration, forsooth.

October 23, 1863

Lincoln. We must accept the results of universal suffrage, and not try to make it appear that we can elect fine gentlemen. We shall have coarse men, with a fair chance of worth and manly ability, but not polite men, not men to please the English or French.

You cannot refine Mr. Lincoln's taste, extend his horizon, or clear his judgment; he will not walk dignifiedly through the traditional part of the President of America, but will pop out his head at each railroad station and make a little speech, and get into an argument with Squire A. and Judge B. He will write letters to Horace Greeley,[6] and any editor or reporter or saucy party committee that writes to him, and cheapen himself.

But this we must be ready for, and let the clown appear, and hug ourselves that we are well off, if we have got good nature, honest meaning, and fidelity to public interest, with bad manners,—instead of an elegant *roué* and malignant self-seeker.

June, 1871

In my lifetime have been wrought five miracles,—namely, 1, the Steamboat; 2. the Railroad; 3, the Electric Telegraph; 4, the application of the Spectroscope to astronomy; 5, the Photograph;—five miracles which have altered the relations of nations to each other. Add cheap postage; and the mowing-machine and the horse-rake. A corresponding power has been given to maufactures by the machine for pegging shoes, and the power-loom, and the power-press of the printers. And in dentistry and in surgery, Dr. Jackson's discovery of Anæsthesia. It only needs to add the power which, up to this hour, eludes all human ingenuity, namely, a rudder to the balloon, to give us the dominion of the air, as well as of the sea and the land. But the account is not complete until we add the discovery of Oersted,[7] of the identity of Electricity and Magnetism, and the generalization of that conversion by its application to light, heat, and gravitation. The geologist has found the correspondence of the age of stratified remains to the ascending scale of structure in animal life. Add now, the daily predictions of the weather for the next twenty-four hours for North America, by the Observatory at Washington.

6. **Horace Greeley:** (1811–1872), the famous contemporary editor of the New York *Tribune.*
7. **Oersted:** Hans Christian Oersted (1777–1851), a Danish physicist, especially celebrated for his discovery of electromagnetism in 1819.

Frank O'Connor

GO WHERE GLORY
WAITS THEE

BY THE time I was fourteen it was clear that education was something I would never be able to afford. Not that I had any intention of giving it up even then. I was just looking for a job that would enable me to buy the books from which I could pick up the education myself. So, with the rest of the unemployed, I went to the newsroom of the Carnegie Library where on wet days the steam heating warmed the perished bodies in the broken boots and made the dirty rags steam and smell. I read carefully through the advertisements and applied for every job that demanded "a smart boy," but what I really hoped for was to find a new issue of the *Times Literary Supplement, The Spectator, The New Statesman*, or *The Studio* free, so that I could read articles about books and pictures I would never see, but as often as not some hungry old man would have toppled asleep over it, and I was cheated. The real out-of-works always favoured the high-class magazines at which they were unlikely to be disturbed, though occasionally some cranky ratepayer would rouse the Lancashire librarian in his rubber-soled shoes, and the out-of-work would be shaken awake and sent to take his rest elsewhere. Then, divided between the claims of pity and justice, I went out myself and wandered aimlessly round town till hunger or darkness or rain sent me home.

"A smart boy's" was the job I needed, because, when it became clear that I would never be a priest, Mother's only ambition was for me to become a clerk—someone who would wear a white collar and be called "Mister." Knowing no better myself, but always willing—up to a point—always visiting the Carnegie Library or the advertisement board in front of the Cork *Examiner* office, and answering advertisements for a smart boy, I went to the Technical School and the School of Commerce at night to learn whatever I could learn there in the way of arithmetic, book-keeping and short-hand typewriting. Of book-keeping, all I ever could remember was a saying quoted approvingly on the first page of our textbook—written, of course, by the headmaster himself—which ran: "In business, there is no such thing as an out-and-out free gift"; and of typewriting, a fascinating example of punctuation that began: "The splendour falls on

437

castle walls," which I promptly got by heart. Perhaps they stuck so firmly
in my mind because they represented the two irreconcilables that I was
being asked to reconcile in myself.

In the pursuit of what I regarded as serious education, I also worked
hard at a Self-Educator I had picked up, God knows where. From Canon
Sheehan's [1] novels I had deduced that German was the real language of
culture and that the greatest of cultured persons was Goethe, so I read
right through Goethe in English and studied German out of the Self-Educator so as to be able to read him in the original. I was impressed by the
fact that one of the pretty songs Mother had taught me as a child—"Three
Students Went Merrily over the Rhine"— turned up in a German anthology as a real poem by a real German poet, so I learned the German
words and sang them instead. I also made a valiant attempt to learn Greek,
which struck me as a very important cultural medium indeed, being much
more difficult than Latin, but as I had never learned the rudiments of
grammar in any language I never got far with Greek.

I got my first job through my confessor, a gentle old priest who regarded me as a very saintly boy, and regularly asked me to pray for his
intention. If innocence and sanctity are related, he was probably not so
far wrong about me because once I confessed to "bad thoughts," meaning,
I suppose, murdering my grandmother, but Father O'Regan interpreted it
differently, and there ensued an agonizing few minutes in which he asked
me questions I didn't understand, and I gave him answers that he didn't
understand, and I suspect that when I left the confession box, the poor man
was as shaken as I was.

The job was in a pious wholesale drapery business where every member
of the staff had apparently been recommended by his confessor, and
I hated my immediate boss, a small, smug, greasy little shopman with a
waxed black moustache who tried hard to teach me that whenever he
called "O'Donovan!" [2] I was instantly to drop whatever I was doing and
rush to him, crying smartly "Yessir!" I never minded dropping what I
was doing, which was usually folding shirts as if I were laying out a
corpse—the two arms neatly across the breast—and I had no objection to
calling anybody "Sir," but it was several seconds before my armour of
day-dreaming was penetrated by a voice from outside and "The splendour
falls on castle walls" gave place to the stern beauty of "In business, there

1. Earlier in his autobiography Frank O'Connor says: "Sometimes I took out in
   Mother's name an art book or a novel by Canon Sheehan, who was parish priest
   of a County Cork town, and had a most unclerical passion for novel writing.
   [. . .] He [had . . .] a weakness for foreign languages, and printed lengthy
   extracts from Goethe in the original."
2. **O'Donovan:** Michael O'Donovan is the true name of the author; Frank O'Connor is a pen name.

is no such thing as an out-and-out free gift," and it was several seconds more before I realized that it was the voice to which I must reply "Yessir!" so at the end of a fortnight I stopped folding shirts and saying "Yessir!" and went home to put in some more work at Greek. Then I tried a spell in a chemist's shop that was looking for a smart boy, but I soon discovered that I was only needed to deliver messages and that no amount of smartness would ever make a chemist of me. I still have a vivid recollection of the end of this job. I was still a small boy, and I was looking up at a tall counter, and leaning on the counter and looking down at me through his glasses was a tall, thin Dublinman, just back from a visit to the pub next door. He was telling me in a thick Dublin accent that I had no notion of the sort of people I was working for, and begging me earnestly, for Christ's sweet sake and my own good, to get to hell out of it, quick. I got to hell out of it quick all right.

There was an even briefer spell at a job printer's, because while he was showing me the ropes, the printer asked was I any good at spelling, and I replied airily: "Oh, that's my forte!" Now, that was exactly the sort of language we used on the heights, and I wasn't conscious of doing anything wrong in using it, but that evening the man who had recommended me to the printer met me and repeated the story of my reply with a great deal of laughter, and I realized that, as usual, I had made a fool of myself. It was part of the abnormal sensitiveness induced by day-dreaming, and I was so mortified that I never went back. I was sorry for that, because I really was quite good at spelling, and I still feel I should have made an excellent compositor.

Instead, this only became an additional weight in the load of guilt I always carried. It seemed that I could never persevere with anything, school or work, and just as I had always been impressed by the view of other small boys that I was mad, I was beginning to be impressed by their parents' view that I was a good-for-nothing who would never be anything but a burden on his father and mother. God knows, Father had impressed it on me often enough.

I went to the railway as a messenger boy because I despaired of ever becoming anything better, and besides, though the hours—eight to seven— were hard, the pay—a pound a week—was excellent, and with money like that coming in I could buy a lot of books and get a lot of education. It was with real confidence that at last the future had something in store for me that I left the house one morning at half-past seven and went down Summerhill and the tunnel steps to go to the Goods Office on the quay. Upstairs in the long office where the invoice clerks worked under the eye of the Chief Clerk, I met the other junior tracers, Sheehy, Cremin, and Clery, and the two senior tracers. Our job was to assist the invoice and claims clerks, bringing in dockets from the storage shed and enquiring in the storage shed for missing goods—hence our title.

All transport companies have colossal claims for missing goods, many of which are not really missing at all but lying about forgotten. Whisky and tobacco were easy to trace because they had to be loaded into sealed wagons before some old railway policeman who recorded them and the number of the wagon in his little red book. But no one took much responsibility for other articles, and it depended on the memory of the checkers whether or not you could discover what had happened to them. An efficient, friendly checker like Bob St. Leger of the Dublin Bay or Leahy of the Fermoy Bay could often remember a particular consignment, and, if he were in good humour, could fish it out from the corner where it had lain for weeks, covered by a heap of fresh merchandise. This was a triumph, and you marked your memorandum or wire with some code word like "Stag," meaning that the thing was at last on its way. But, more often, nobody remembered anything at all, and then you wrote something else, like "Bison," which meant "Certainly forwarded please say if since received," to which Goold's Cross or Farranfore retorted "Moose," meaning that it wasn't, and then you had to go to the storage shed and search through scores of tall dusty wire files to discover the original docket and the name of the checker or porter who had signed the receipt for it.

It didn't take me long to realize that this was only going to be another version of school, a place where I would be always useless, frightened, or hurt. The other messengers were railwaymen's sons and understood the work as though they had been born to it. Sheehy was thin, with high cheekbones and an impudent smile; Cremin was round-faced, cherry-cheeked, and complacent, and shot about the office and the store almost without raising his feet. Young Sheehy sneered at me all the time, but young Cremin only sneered at me part of the time because he was usually so busy with his own jobs that he hadn't time for anyone else's, but a couple of times when I found myself with some job I could not do, he looked at me for a while with pity and contempt and then took it from me and did it himself. "See?" he would crow. "Dead easy!" Cremin was really what the advertisements meant when they asked for a smart boy. Years later I found myself in the same hut in an internment camp with him, and though our positions had changed somewhat by that time, and I was a teacher, he was still the same smart boy, mixing with nobody in particular though amiable with everybody, briskly hammering rings out of shilling pieces or weaving macramé handbags—a cheerful, noisy, little universe of self-satisfaction. Yet the moment I fell ill, he nursed me with the same amused exasperation with which he had found dockets for me on the railway, cluck-clucking with an amused smile at my inability to do anything for myself.

My boss was obviously a man who had also at one time been a smart boy and owed his promotion to it. He had a neat, swift hand, and I imitated his elegant signature as I imitated Corkery's articulation, in a hopeless attempt at becoming a smart boy myself. He had a fat, pale face, a button of a nose with a pince-nez attached that was for ever dropping off and being retrieved just in time; he dressed excellently and swept through the office and the storage shed with an air of efficiency that must long since have secured his promotion to the job of stationmaster in Borrisokane or Goold's Cross.[3] I fancy he was really clever and not unkind, but as the days went by he became more and more infuriated by my slowness and stupidity; and, having readjusted his pince-nez sternly, he would shout abuse at me till the whole office was listening and the other messengers sniggering, and I slunk away, stupider than ever, muttering aspirations to the Sacred Heart and the Blessed Virgin to assist me in whatever impossible task I was being asked to perform. It was one of the senior tracers who, in mockery of my love of Irish and the gilt ring I wore in my coat, nicknamed me "The Native," but it was the boss who perpetuated it. It was characteristic of Ireland at the time that the mere fact that you spoke Irish could make you be regarded as a freak.

The other clerk for whom I had to do odd jobs was a very different type. He was small, fair-haired, red-cheeked, and untidy, and drifted about the office with his hands in his trousers pockets, wearing an incredible expression of sweetness and wonder as though he were imitating some saint and martyr he had heard of in church. Either he would put his arm about my waist and draw me close to him, calling me "Child," and beg me in a low, quavering voice to assist him—that is if I could spare him a couple of minutes—or else he would call "Boy!" in a faraway tone, and look at me as though wondering who I was, and rush after me, tearing papers from my hand and scolding and nagging till my nerves were on edge. Then he would sit on his high stool, his fat hands clasped between his thighs, staring incredulously after me.

Not that I didn't do my best. God knows I did. One of my jobs was to answer the telephone, and I did it with such intensity that I could never hear a word the other person said, and so developed a hatred of telephones that has lasted to this day. If there is anything unnaturally stupid or compromising a man can say, I am always guaranteed to say it on the telephone. Sometimes, when I was alone in the Goods Office I listened miserably to some message, too ashamed to admit that I hadn't understood it. Sometimes I summoned up courage and said that I couldn't hear, and then

3. **Borrisokane or Goold's Cross:** small towns in Ireland.

the person at the other end always got furious—a fatal thing to do with me as it drives me completely distracted—and asked if there was no one on the Great Southern and Western Railway who was not stone deaf. Having it put to me like that, I could only reply that there was but he was out at lunch. And whatever stupid thing I said always got back to the boss.

The trouble was that I could not believe in the telephone or the messages that came by it. I could not believe that the missing goods I was supposed to trace had ever existed, or if they had, that their loss meant anything to anybody. Being a naturally kind-hearted boy, if I had believed it I would have found them whatever it cost me. All I could believe in was words, and I clung to them frantically. I would read some word like "unsophisticated" and at once I would want to know what the Irish equivalent was. In those days I didn't even ask to be a writer; a much simpler form of transmutation would have satisfied me. All I wanted was to translate, to feel the unfamiliar become familiar, the familiar take on all the mystery of some dark foreign face I had just glimpsed on the quays.

I hated the storeroom where the dockets were kept, and when I worked there with Sheehy, Cremin, or Clery, I realized that they found six dockets in the time it took me to find one. I had poor sight, and often failed to see a docket properly, particularly as it was usually written in the semi-literate scrawl of carters or porters; and even when I should have seen it, my mind was on something else, and when it was not, it was harassed by panic, shyness, and ignorance. Bad as the storage shed was, noisy, evil-smelling, and dark except where it was pitted with pale electric lights, I preferred it to the office because a couple of the men were kind and did not lose their tempers with me. But even here I was at a disadvantage. Sheehy and Cremin, being railwaymen's sons, were protected by their fathers' presence from anything worse than good-natured ragging, but I was anybody's butt, [. . . It was] all just a vast phantasmagoria which I had to pretend to believe in to draw my weekly pay, but I never did believe in it, and when I left the building at seven o'clock it faded like clouds in the sky. At the same time I envied people who did believe in it, like young Cremin, and I pitied myself when I saw him, storming through the shed, from one lamp-lit bay to the next, his bundle of documents in his hand, exchanging noisy greetings with the porters, dodging checkers who tried to grab him, and yelling back laughing insults at them—at home with everybody but most of all with himself. In that whole huge organization there wasn't a soul with whom I felt at home, and so I had no self to be at home with; the only self I knew being then in wait for me until seven o'clock in the passenger station at the other side of the tracks, rather as I waited for Father outside a public house.

There was one checker I liked, and though he always nodded gravely to me and was helpful on the very few occasions when I needed his help, he never became involved with me. I think he realized with the force of revelation that I didn't believe in dockets, and was doomed to trouble and that this trouble would fall on anyone who had anything to do with me. He shuffled through the storage shed with his head buried in his shoulders and a little to one side as though he hoped no one would notice him, his short-sighted blue eyes narrowed into slits. His secret was that he didn't believe in these things either. At the same time the feeling of his own peril gave him a certain guilty feeling of responsibility to me because I was clearly so much more imperilled than he was, and occasionally he stopped to talk to me and shuffled inch by inch out of the way into some corner where we could not be observed. Then, looking furtively over a bale of goods to make sure that no one was listening, he would tell me in a whisper that the country was priest-ridden. I didn't know what he meant by that, but I knew he meant that I had his sympathy. I was for the lions, and family conditions compelled him to burn a pinch of incense now and again, but he and I both knew there was no such God as Jupiter. One day, with a display of caution that would have done credit to an international conspirator, he pulled me aside, opened his blue jacket with the silver buttons, and took out a book which he thrust on me.

"Read that, boy," he whispered. "That'll show you what the country is really like."

The book was *Waiting* by Gerald O'Donovan, an interesting novelist now almost forgotten. He was a priest in Loughrea who had been carried away by the Catholic liberal movement and the Irish national movement. Later, in disgust with his bishop, he became an army chaplain, married, and wrote a number of novels that have authenticity without charm. I read the book with great care, though [I . . .] had little chance of understanding what the country was like. Yet I remember that particular checker for the breath of fresh air he brought for a moment into my life, with its guarantee that the reality of dockets and invoices, smart boys and foul-mouthed workers, was not quite as real as it seemed.

There was one further small reference to the world I really believed in in a kilted man who appeared one day at the office counter, apparently about some missing goods but who refused to speak English. Cremin came back from the counter, looking red, and reported to my boss. Obviously, this was a very tasteless joke, and the boss shot out, adjusting his pince-nez with the air of a man who never stood any nonsense. But it was no joke. French the visitor would speak if he was compelled, but Irish was the language of his choice, and nobody in the office except myself spoke a word of French or Irish. Nobody outside my boss and the other tracers even bothered to jeer me about my weakness for Irish, though one clerk, a small prissy man with pince-nez, did once sniff at me and ask me what literature we had in Irish to compare with Shakespeare. For a few minutes there was consternation as the clerks discussed the irruption. "All right, Native," the boss said at last with the air of a man setting a thief to catch a thief. "You'd better see what he wants."

Of course, the stranger turned out to be an Englishman, the son of an Anglican bishop, who was enjoying the embarrassment he was causing in an Irish railway station by speaking Irish when the only person who could answer him was a messenger boy. And, indeed, the matter didn't end there, because the Englishman had to put in his claim, and put it in in Irish, which I had to translate into English, and the clerks decided to get even with him by making me also translate the official reply into Irish. Of course, he was a sport and I was a fool, but the little incident was a slight indication of a revolution that was already taking place without the smart boys even being aware of it.

It was also an indication of the extraordinary double life I was leading, a life so divided against itself that it comes back to me now as a hallucination rather than as a memory. Usually, there is some connection between the real and imaginary worlds, some acquaintance in whom the two temporarily merge, but when I left the railway I did not leave a friend behind me and never so much as enquired what had happened to any of the decent people I knew there. One life I led in English—a life of drudgery and humiliation; the other in Irish or whatever scraps of foreign languages I had managed to pick up without benefit of grammar, and which any sensible man would describe as day-dreaming, though day-dreaming is a coarse and unrealistic word that might be applied by sensible men to the beliefs of the early Christians. That was the real significance of my passion for languages: they belonged entirely to the world of my imagination, and even today, when some figure of fantasy enters my dreams, he or she is always liable to break into copious and inaccurate French—the imagination seems to have no particular use for grammar. Irish was merely the most convenient of these escape routes into dreams, and that was why, on Saturday nights, with a German book from the Carnegie Library under my arm, I attended lectures in the Gaelic League hall in Queen Street, or stood admiringly in a corner listening to my seniors discussing in Irish profound questions such as "Is Shakespeare national?" and "Is dancing immoral?" or perhaps "Is dancing national?" and "Is Shakespeare immoral?" I still had no education, except such as fitted me for the by-ways of literature like Shakespeare, or the company of the ordinary girls I met, but these I was too shy or too ignorant to compound for, so I read Goethe a few lines at a time with the aid of a translation, or a page from some obscure novel in Spanish, and adored from afar beautiful university girls I should never get to know. Even Turgenev, who became my hero among writers, I read first only because of some novel of his in which there is a description of the Rhineland and German girls passing by in the twilight, murmuring *"Guten Abend."* [4]

This of course, confined my education mainly to poetry, which has a simpler working vocabulary, based on words like *Herz* and *Schmerz*,[5] *amour* and *toujours*, *ardor* and *rumor*, of which I could guess the meaning even when I hadn't a translation. I had taken a checker's discarded notebook from the storage shed, and, having patiently rubbed out all the pencil notes, made a poem book of my own in all the languages I believed I knew. Though my love of poetry sprang from my mother, my taste, I fear, was entirely O'Donovan. Nature would seem to have intended me for an undertaker's assistant, because in any book of verse I read I invariably discovered elegies on dead parents, dead wives, and dead children, and, though my knowledge of poetry expanded, that weakness has persisted, and my favourite poems would be bound to include Bridges' "Perfect Little Body," Landor's "Artemidora, Gods Invisible," De La Mare's mighty poem on the suicide that begins "Steep hung the drowsy street," Hardy's great series on his dead wife, and a mass of Emily Dickinson. And though I was stupid, and went about everything as Father went about putting up a shelf, I did care madly for poetry, good and bad, without understanding why I cared, and coming home at night, still corpse and brass band, I spoke it aloud till people who overheard looked after me in surprise. And this was as it should have been. On the night before his execution at Tyburn Chidiock Tichbourne [6] wrote: "My prime of life is but a frost of cares," and on the night before his in Kilmainham Patrick Pearse [7] wrote: "The beauty of this world hath made me sad." When life is at its harshest, "when so sad thou can'st not sadder be," poetry comes into its own. Even more than music it is the universal speech, but it is spoken fluently only by those whose existence is already aflame with emotion, for then the beauty and order of language are the only beauty and order possible. Above all, it is the art of the boy and girl overburdened by the troubles of their sex and station, for as Jane Austen so wistfully noted, the difficulty with it is that it can best be appreciated by those who should enjoy it the most sparingly.

4. **Guten Abend:** good evening.
5. **Herz** and **Schmerz:** heart (i.e., feeling) and pain, grief.
6. **Chidiock Tichbourne:** (1558?–1586), executed for his part in an unsuccessful attempt to rescue Mary Queen of Scots from imprisonment.
7. **Patrick Pearse:** Irish educator, writer, and patriot, who was a leader in the Easter Rebellion of 1916. He was executed by a British firing squad. Kilmainham, a suburb of Dublin, was the British headquarters in Ireland.

It was a strange double life, and small wonder if it comes back to me only as a hallucination. Each morning, as I made my way across the tracks from the passenger station in the early light, I said good-bye to my real self, and at seven that evening when I returned across the dark railway yard and paused in the well-lit passenger station to see the new books and papers in the railway bookstall, he rejoined me, a boy exactly like myself except that no experience had dinged or dented him, and as we went up Mahoney's Avenue in the darkness, we chattered in Irish diversified by quotations in German, French, or Spanish, and talked knowledgeably of Italy and the Rhineland and the beautiful girls one could meet there, and I recited Goethe's poem that in those days was always in my mind—the perfection of the poet's dream of escape:

> *Kennst du das Land wo die Zitronen blueh'n,*
> *Im dunklem Laub die Goldorangen glueh'n.*[8]

I know I often hurt Mother by my moroseness and churlishness when some innocent question of hers brought me tumbling from the heights of language to the English that belonged to the office and the store. And between Father and myself there was constant friction. Father was a conservative, and he knew the world was full of thieves and murderers. He wouldn't go to bed like a sensible man and let me lock and bolt the doors and quench the lamp. He and Mother might both be burned alive in their beds. But when I went out for an evening walk I hoped frantically to rescue some American heiress whose father would realize the talent that was lost in me, or, failing that, to tag along behind some of the senior members of the Gaelic League and try to talk as grown-up as they seemed, and often and often I wasted my precious couple of hours, walking up and down the Western Road and meeting nobody who would even speak to me. As I came up Summerhill the pleasure of being all of a piece again was overshadowed by the prospect of the morning when once more I should have to part from the half of me that was real, and it was like a blow in the face when I found the door locked, and Mother came scurrying out to open it for me.

"Don't say a word, child!" she would whisper.

"Why?" I would ask defiantly, loud enough to be heard upstairs. "Is he on the war-path again?"

"Ten o'clock that door is locked!" Father would intone from the bedroom.

"Ah, don't answer him! Would you like a cup of tea?"

8. *Kennst . . . glueh'n:* Knowest thou the land where the lemon trees bloom, where the golden oranges gleam through the dark foliage—from Goethe's *Wilhelm Meister*.

"Better fed than taught!" Father would add, as he had added any time in the previous ten years.

When my first wretched effort at composition appeared in a children's paper and word of it got round the office, everyone was astonished, but most of all my boss. He was a decent man, and a clever one, and he knew better than anyone that I was definitely not a smart boy. I remember him sitting at his high desk with the paper open before him and a frown on his bulgy forehead as he nervously readjusted his pince-nez.

"Did you write this, Native?"

"Yessir," I said, feeling I had probably done it again. Everything I did only seemed to get me into fresh trouble.

"Nobody help you?"

"No, sir," I replied warily, because it looked as though someone else might get the blame, and I still clung to the code of the boys' weeklies and was always prepared to own up. The frown deepened on his fat face.

"Then for God's sake, stick to writing!" he snapped. "You'll never be any good on the Great Southern and Western Railway."

And that, as we used to say, was one sure five. As usual, looking for models of fine conduct, I had hit on a left-wing time-keeper who knew all the Italian operas by heart and made it a point of honour not to take off his cap before the bosses. Seeing that anyone who knew so much about opera must know the correct thing for other situations, I decided to do the same, with results that may be imagined. Even then, I should probably have been let off with a reprimand, because I had no self-confidence and merely went about blindly imitating anyone and anything, in the hope of blending somehow into the phantasmagoria, but, with my bad sight, I had also fallen over a hand-truck and injured my shin so badly that I couldn't walk for weeks. But on the railway bad sight was more serious than bad manners, because it might result in a claim.

On the Saturday night I was sacked I read my first paper. It was in Irish, and the subject was Goethe. For me, my whole adolescence is summed up in that extraordinary evening—so much that even yet I cannot laugh at it in comfort. I didn't know much about Irish, and I knew practically nothing about Goethe, and that little was wrong. In a truly anthropomorphic spirit I re-created Goethe in my own image and likeness, as a patriotic young man who wished to revive the German language, which I considered to have been gravely threatened by the use of French. I drew an analogy between the French culture that dominated eighteenth-century Germany and the English culture by which we in Ireland were dominated.

While I was speaking, it was suddenly borne in on me that I no longer had a job or a penny in the world, or even a home I could go back to without humiliation, and that the neighbours would say, as they had so often said before, that I was mad and a good-for-nothing. And I knew that they would be right, for here I was committing myself in public to all the vague words and vaguer impressions that with me passed for thought. I could barely control my voice, because the words and impressions no longer meant anything to me. They seemed to come back to me from the rows of polite blank faces as though from the wall of my prison. All that did matter was the act of faith, the hope that somehow, somewhere I would be able to prove that I was neither mad nor a good-for-nothing; because now I realized that whatever it might cost me, there was no turning back. When as kids we came to an orchard wall that seemed too high to climb, we took off our caps and tossed them over the wall, and then we had no choice but to follow them.

I had tossed my cap over the wall of life, and I knew I must follow it, wherever it had fallen.

Henry David Thoreau

WHERE I LIVED, AND WHAT I LIVED FOR

A T A CERTAIN SEASON of our life we are accustomed to consider every spot as the possible site of a house. I have thus surveyed the country on every side within a dozen miles of where I live. In imagination I have bought all the farms in succession, for all were to be bought, and I knew their price. I walked over each farmer's premises, tasted his wild apples, discoursed on husbandry with him, took his farm at his price, at any price, mortgaging it to him in my mind—even put a higher price on it; took everything but a deed of it; took his word for his deed, for I dearly love to talk; cultivated it, and him to some extent, I trust, and withdrew when I had enjoyed it long enough, leaving him to carry it on. This experience entitled me to be regarded as a sort of real estate broker by my friends. Wherever I sat, there I might live, and the landscape radiated from me accordingly. What is a house but a *sedes*, a seat?—better if a country seat. I discovered many a site for a house not likely to be soon improved, which some might have thought too far from the village, but to my eyes the village was too far from it. Well, there I might live, I said; and there I did live, for an hour, a summer and a winter life; saw how I could let the years run off, buffet the winter through, and see the spring come in. The future inhabitants of this region, wherever they may place their houses, may be sure that they have been anticipated. An afternoon sufficed to lay out the land into orchard, woodlot, and pasture, and to decide what fine oaks or pines should be left to stand before the door, and whence each blasted tree could be seen to the best advantage; and then I let it lie, fallow perchance, for a man is rich in proportion to the number of things which he can afford to let alone.

My imagination carried me so far that I even had the refusal of several farms—the refusal was all I wanted—but I never got my fingers burned by actual possession. The nearest that I came to actual possession was when I bought the Hollowell place, and had begun to sort my seeds, and collected materials with which to make a wheelbarrow to carry it on or off with; but before the owner gave me a deed of it, his wife—every man has such a wife—changed her mind and wished to keep it, and he offered me ten dollars to release him. Now, to speak the truth, I had but ten cents in the world, and it surpassed my arithmetic to tell, if I was that man who had ten cents, or who had a farm, or ten dollars, or all together. However, I let him keep the ten dollars and the farm too, for I had carried it far enough; or rather, to be generous, I sold him the farm for just what I gave for it, and, as he was not a rich man, made him a present of ten dollars, and still had my ten cents, and seeds, and materials for a wheelbarrow left. I found thus that I had been a rich man without any damage to my poverty. But I retained the landscape, and I have since annually carried off what it yielded without a wheelbarrow. With respect to landscapes,

> I am monarch of all I *survey*,
> My right there is none to dispute.

I have frequently seen a poet withdraw, having enjoyed the most valuable part of a farm, while the crusty farmer supposed that he had got a few wild apples only. Why, the owner does not know it for many years when a poet has put his farm in rhyme, the most admirable kind of invisible fence, has fairly impounded it, milked it, skimmed it, and got all the cream, and left the farmer only the skimmed milk.

The real attractions of the Hollowell farm, to me, were: its complete retirement, being about two miles from the village, half a mile from the nearest neighbor, and separated from the highway by a broad field; its bounding on the river, which the owner said protected it by its fogs and frosts in the spring, though that was nothing to me; the gray color and ruinous state of the house and barn, and the dilapidated fences, which put such an interval between me and the last occupant; the hollow and lichen-covered apple trees, gnawed by rabbits, showing what kind of neighbors I should have; but above all, the recollection I had of it from my earliest voyages up the river, when the house was concealed behind a dense grove of red maples, through which I heard the house dog bark. I was in haste to buy it, before the proprietor finished getting out some rocks, cutting down the hollow apple trees, and grubbing up some young birches which had sprung up in the pasture, or, in short, had made any more of his improvements. To enjoy these advantages I was ready to carry it on, like Atlas, to take the world on my shoulders—I never heard what compensation he received for that—and do all those things which had no other motive or excuse but that I might pay for it and be unmolested in my possession of it; for I knew all the while that it would yield the most abundant crop of the kind I wanted if I could only afford to let it alone. But it turned out as I have said.

All that I could say, then, with respect to farming on a large scale (I have always cultivated a garden) was that I had had my seeds ready. Many think that seeds improve with age. I have no doubt that time discriminates between the good and the bad; and when at last I shall plant, I shall be less likely to be disappointed. But I would say to my fellows, once for all: as long as possible live free and uncommitted. It makes but little difference whether you are committed to a farm or the county jail.

Old Cato, whose "De Re Rustica"[1] is my "Cultivator," says, and the only translation I have seen makes sheer nonsense of the passage, "When you think of getting a farm, turn it thus in your mind, not to buy greedily; nor spare your pains to look at it, and do not think it enough to go around it once. The oftener you go there the more it will please you, if it is good." I think I shall not buy greedily, but go round and round it as long as I live, and be buried in it first, that it may please me the more at last.

The present was my next experiment of this kind, which I purpose to describe more at length, for convenience putting the experience of two years into one. As I have said, I do not propose to write an ode to dejection, but to brag as lustily as chanticleer in the morning standing on his roost, if only to wake my neighbors up.

When first I took up my abode in the woods, that is, began to spend my nights as well as days there, which, by accident, was on Independence

---

1. "De Re Rustica," or "On Country Matters," by Marcus Porcius Cato (234–149 B.C.), a Roman statesman, general, and writer, is a work on the subject of farm management.

Day, or the Fourth of July, 1845, my house was not finished for winter, but was merely a defense against the rain, without plastering or chimney, the walls being of rough weather-stained boards, with wide chinks, which made it cool at night. The upright white hewn studs and freshly planed door and window casings gave it a clean and airy look, especially in the morning, when its timbers were saturated with dew, so that I fancied that by noon some sweet gum would exude from them. To my imagination it retained throughout the day more or less of this auroral character, reminding me of a certain house on a mountain which I had visited the year before. This was an airy and unplastered cabin, fit to entertain a traveling god, and where a goddess might trail her garments. The winds which passed over my dwelling were such as sweep over the ridges of mountains, bearing the broken strains, or celestial parts only, of terrestrial music. The morning wind forever blows, the poem of creation is uninterrupted; but few are the ears that hear it. Olympus is but the outside of the earth everywhere.

The only house I had been the owner of before, if I except a boat, was a tent, which I used occasionally when making excursions in the summer, and this is still rolled up in my garret; but the boat, after passing from hand to hand, has gone down the stream of time. With this more substantial shelter about me, I had made some progress toward settling in the world. This frame, so slightly clad, was a sort of crystallization around me, and reacted on the builder. It was suggested somewhat as a picture in outlines. I did not need to go outdoors to take the air, for the atmosphere within had lost none of its freshness. It was not so much within doors as behind a door where I sat, even in the rainiest weather. The Harivansha [2] says, "An abode without birds is like a meat without seasoning." Such was not my abode, for I found myself suddenly neighbor to the birds, not by having imprisoned one, but having caged myself near them. I was not only nearer to some of those which commonly frequent the garden and the orchard, but to those wilder and more thrilling songsters of the forest which never, or rarely, serenade a villager: the woodthrush, the veery, the scarlet tanager, the field-sparrow, the whippoorwill, and many others.

I was seated by the shore of a small pond, about a mile and a half south of the village of Concord and somewhat higher than it, in the midst of an extensive wood between that town and Lincoln, and about two miles south of that our only field known to fame, Concord Battle Ground; but I was so low in the woods that the opposite shore, half a mile off, like the rest, covered with wood, was my most distant horizon. For the first week, whenever I looked out on the pond, it impressed me like a tarn high up on

2. **The Harivansha:** a Sanskrit (i.e., Indian) poem on the subject of the creation of the world.

the side of a mountain, its bottom far above the surface of other lakes, and as the sun arose, I saw it throwing off its nightly clothing of mist, and here and there, by degrees, its soft ripples or its smooth reflecting surface was revealed, while the mists, like ghosts, were stealthily withdrawing in every direction into the woods, as at the breaking up of some nocturnal conventicle. The very dew seemed to hang upon the trees later into the day than usual, as on the sides of mountains.

This small lake was of most value as a neighbor in the intervals of a gentle rain storm in August, when, both air and water being perfectly still, but the sky overcast, mid-afternoon had all the serenity of evening, and the woodthrush sang around, and was heard from shore to shore. A lake like this is never smoother than at such a time; and, the clear portion of the air above it being shallow and darkened by clouds, the water, full of light and reflections, becomes a lower heaven itself so much the more important. From a hilltop near by, where the wood had been recently cut off, there was a pleasing vista southward across the pond, through a wide indentation in the hills which form the shore there, where their opposite sides sloping toward each other suggested a stream flowing out in that direction through a wooded valley, but stream there was none. That way I looked between and over the near green hills to some distant and higher ones in the horizon, tinged with blue. Indeed, by standing on tiptoe I could catch a glimpse of some of the peaks of the still bluer and more distant mountain ranges in the northwest, those true-blue coins from heaven's own mint, and also of some portion of the village. But in other directions, even from this point, I could not see over or beyond the woods which surrounded me. It is well to have some water in your neighborhood to give buoyancy to and float the earth. One value even of the smallest well is that when you look into it you see that earth is not continent but insular. This is as important as that it keeps butter cool. When I looked across the pond from this peak toward the Sudbury meadows, which in time of flood I distinguished elevated perhaps by a mirage in their seething valley, like a coin in a basin, all the earth beyond the pond appeared like a thin crust insulated and floated even by this small sheet of intervening water, and I was reminded that this on which I dwelt was but dry land.

Though the view from my door was still more contracted, I did not feel crowded or confined in the least. There was pasture enough for my imagination. The low shrub-oak plateau to which the opposite shore arose stretched away toward the prairies of the West and the steppes of Tartary, affording ample room for all the roving families of men. "There are none happy in the world but beings who enjoy freely a vast horizon," said Damodara,[3] when his herds required new and larger pastures.

3. **Damodara:** Damodara Misra, an eleventh-century Sanskrit poet.

Both place and time were changed, and I dwelt nearer to those parts of the universe and to those eras in history which had most attracted me. Where I lived was as far off as many a region viewed nightly by astronomers. We are wont to imagine rare and delectable places in some remote and more celestial corner of the system, behind the constellation of Cassiopeia's Chair, far from noise and disturbance. I discovered that my house actually had its site in such a withdrawn, but forever new and unprofaned, part of the universe. If it were worth the while to settle in those parts near to the Pleiades or the Hyades, to Aldebaran or Altair, then I was really there, or at an equal remoteness from the life which I had left behind, dwindled and twinkling with as fine a ray to my nearest neighbor, and to be seen only in moonless nights by him. Such was that part of creation where I had squatted:

> There was a shepherd that did live,
> And held his thoughts as high
> As were the mounts whereon his flocks
> Did hourly feed him by.

What should we think of the shepherd's life if his flocks always wandered to higher pastures than his thoughts?

Every morning was a cheerful invitation to make my life of equal simplicity, and I may say innocence, with Nature herself. I have been as sincere a worshiper of Aurora as the Greeks. I got up early and bathed in the pond; that was a religious exercise, and one of the best things which I did. They say that characters were engraven on the bathing tub of King Tching-thang [4] to this effect: "Renew thyself completely each day; do it again and again, and forever again." I can understand that. Morning brings back the heroic ages. I was as much affected by the faint hum of a mosquito making its invisible and unimaginable tour through my apartments at earliest dawn, when I was sitting with door and windows open, as I could be by any trumpet that ever sang of fame. It was Homer's requiem; itself an Iliad and Odyssey in the air, singing its own wrath and wanderings. There was something cosmical about it, a standing advertisement, till forbidden, of the everlasting vigor and fertility of the world. The morning, which is the most memorable season of the day, is the awakening hour. Then there is least somnolence in us; and for an hour, at least, some part of us awakes which slumbers all the rest of the day and night. Little is to be expected of that day, if it can be called a day, to which we are not awakened by our Genius, but by the mechanical nudgings of some servitor, are not awakened by our own newly acquired force and aspirations from

---

4. **King Tching-thang:** probably Ch'en T'ang, the founder of the Shang dynasty in China, 1766–1122 B.C. Confucius refers to him as "the philosophical Tsang."

within, accompanied by the undulations of celestial music, instead of factory bells, and a fragrance filling the air—to a higher life than we fell asleep from; and thus the darkness bears its fruit, and proves itself to be good, no less than the light. That man who does not believe that each day contains an earlier, more sacred, and auroral hour than he has yet profaned has despaired of life, and is pursuing a descending and darkening way. After a partial cessation of his sensuous life, the soul of man, or its organs rather, are reinvigorated each day, and his Genius tries again what noble life it can make. All memorable events, I should say, transpire in morning time and in a morning atmosphere. The Vedas say, "All intelligences awake with the morning." Poetry and art and the fairest and most memorable of the actions of men date from such an hour. All poets and heroes, like Memnon, are the children of Aurora and emit their music at sunrise. To him whose elastic and vigorous thought keeps pace with the sun the day is a perpetual morning. It matters not what the clocks say or the attitudes and labors of men. Morning is when I am awake and there is a dawn in me. Moral reform is the effort to throw off sleep. Why is it that men give so poor an account of their day if they have not been slumbering? They are not such poor calculators. If they had not been overcome with drowsiness, they would have performed something. The millions are awake enough for physical labor; but only one in a million is awake enough for effective intellectual exertion, only one in a hundred millions to a poetic or divine life. To be awake is to be alive. I have never yet met a man who was quite awake. How could I have looked him in the face?

We must learn to reawaken and keep ourselves awake, not by mechanical aids, but by an infinite expectation of the dawn, which does not forsake us in our soundest sleep. I know of no more encouraging fact than the unquestionable ability of man to elevate his life by a conscious endeavor. It is something to be able to paint a particular picture, or to carve a statue, and so to make a few objects beautiful; but it is far more glorious to carve and paint the very atmosphere and medium through which we look, which morally we can do. To affect the quality of the day, that is the highest of arts. Every man is tasked to make his life, even in its details, worthy of the contemplation of his most elevated and critical hour. If we refused, or rather used up, such paltry information as we get, the oracles would distinctly inform us how this might be done.

I went to the woods because I wished to live deliberately, to front only the essential facts of life, and see if I could not learn what it had to teach, and not, when I came to die, discover that I had not lived. I did not wish to live what was not life, living is so dear; nor did I wish to practice resignation, unless it was quite necessary. I wanted to live deep and suck out all the marrow of life, to live so sturdily and Spartan-like as to put to rout all that was not life, to cut a broad swath and shave close, to drive life into a corner, and reduce it to its lowest terms, and, if it proved to be mean, why then to get the whole and genuine meanness of it, and publish its meanness to the world; or if it were sublime, to know it by experience, and be able to give a true account of it in my next excursion. For most men, it appears to me, are in a strange uncertainty about it, whether it is of the devil or of God, and have somewhat hastily concluded that it is the chief end of man here to "glorify God and enjoy him forever."

Still we live meanly, like ants, though the fable tells us that we were long ago changed into men; like pygmies we fight with cranes; [5] it is error upon error, and clout upon clout, and our best virtue has for its occasion a superfluous and evitable wretchedness. Our life is frittered away by detail. An honest man has hardly need to count more than his ten fingers, or in extreme cases he may add his ten toes, and lump the rest. Simplicity, simplicity, simplicity! I say, let your affairs be as two or three, and not a hundred or a thousand; instead of a million count half a dozen, and keep your accounts on your thumb nail. In the midst of this chopping sea of civilized life, such are the clouds and storms and quicksands and thousand-and-one items to be allowed for, that a man has to live, if he would not founder and go to the bottom and not make his port at all, by dead reckoning, and he must be a great calculator indeed who succeeds. Simplify, simplify. Instead of three meals a day, if it be necessary eat but one; instead of a hundred dishes, five; and reduce other things in proportion. Our life is like a German Confederacy,[6] made up of petty states, with its boundary forever fluctuating so that even a German cannot tell you how it is bounded at any moment. The nation itself, with all its so-called internal improvements, which, by the way, are all external and superficial, is just such an unwieldy and overgrown establishment, cluttered with furniture and tripped up by its own traps, ruined by luxury and heedless expense, by want of calculation and a worthy aim, as the million households in the land; and the only cure for it, as for them, is in a rigid economy, a stern and more than Spartan simplicity of life and elevation of purpose. It lives too fast. Men think that it is essential that the nation have commerce, and export ice, and talk through a telegraph, and ride thirty miles an hour, without a doubt, whether they do or not; but whether we should live like baboons or like men is a little uncertain. If we do not get out sleepers,[7] and forge rails, and devote days and nights to the work, but go to tinkering upon our lives to improve them, who will build railroads? And if rail-

---

5. According to ancient fable, the cranes came annually from Scythia and made war on the pygmies.
6. A loose and ineffective union of German states was established after 1815.
7. **sleepers**: railroad ties.

roads are not built, how shall we get to heaven in season? But if we stay at home and mind our business, who will want railroads? We do not ride on the railroad; it rides upon us. Did you ever think what those sleepers are that underlie the railroad? Each one is a man, an Irishman, or a Yankee man. The rails are laid on them, and they are covered with sand, and the cars run smoothly over them. They are sound sleepers, I assure you. And every few years a new lot is laid down and run over; so that, if some have the pleasure of riding on a rail, others have the misfortune to be ridden upon. And when they run over a man that is walking in his sleep, a supernumerary sleeper in the wrong position, and wake him up, they suddenly stop the cars and make a hue and cry about it, as if this were an exception. I am glad to know that it takes a gang of men for every five miles to keep the sleepers down and level in their beds as it is, for this is a sign that they may sometime get up again.

Why should we live with such hurry and waste of life? We are determined to be starved before we are hungry. Men say that a stitch in time saves nine, and so they take a thousand stitches today to save nine tomorrow. As for work, we haven't any of any consequence. We have the Saint Vitus's dance, and cannot possibly keep our heads still. If I should only give a few pulls at the parish bell-rope, as for a fire, that is, without setting the bell, there is hardly a man on his farm in the outskirts of Concord, notwithstanding that press of engagements which was his excuse so many times this morning, nor a boy, nor a woman, I might almost say, but would forsake all and follow that sound, not mainly to save property from the flames, but, if we will confess the truth, much more to see it burn, since burn it must, and we, be it known, did not set it on fire—or to see it put out, and have a hand in it, if that is done as handsomely; yes, even if it were the parish church itself. Hardly a man takes a half hour's nap after dinner but when he wakes he holds up his head and asks, "What's the news?" as if the rest of mankind had stood his sentinels. Some give directions to be waked every half hour, doubtless for no other purpose; and then, to pay for it, they tell what they have dreamed. After a night's sleep the news is as indispensable as the breakfast. "Pray tell me anything new that has happened to a man anywhere on this globe," and he reads it over his coffee and rolls that a man has had his eyes gouged out this morning on the Wachito River,[8] never dreaming the while that he lives in the dark unfathomed mammoth cave of this world and has but the rudiment of an eye himself.

For my part, I could easily do without the post office. I think that there are very few important communications made through it. To speak criti-

---

8. **Wachito River:** the Ouachita River in Arkansas, at the time still a frontier area, where gouging was a common technique in man-to-man encounters.

cally, I never received more than one or two letters in my life—I wrote this some years ago—that were worth the postage. The pennypost is, commonly, an institution through which you seriously offer a man that penny for his thoughts which is too often safely offered in jest. And I am sure that I never read any memorable news in a newspaper. If we read of one man robbed, or murdered, or killed by accident, or one house burned, or one vessel wrecked, or one steamboat blown up, or one cow run over on the Western Railroad, or one mad dog killed, or one lot of grasshoppers in the winter, we never need read of another. One is enough. If you are acquainted with the principle, what do you care for a myriad instances and applications? To a philosopher all *news*, as it is called, is gossip, and they who edit and read it are old women over their tea. Yet not a few, are greedy after this gossip. There was such a rush, as I hear, the other day at one of the offices to learn the foreign news by the last arrival that several large squares of plate glass belonging to the establishment were broken by the pressure, news which I seriously think a ready wit might write a twelvemonth, or twelve years, beforehand with sufficient accuracy. As for Spain, for instance, if you know how to throw in Don Carlos and the Infanta, and Don Pedro [9] and Seville and Granada, from time to time in the right proportions—they may have changed the names a little since I saw the papers—and serve up a bull-fight when other entertainments fail, it will be true to the letter, and give us as good an idea of the exact state or ruin of things in Spain as the most succinct and lucid reports under this head in the newspapers; and as for England, almost the last significant scraps of news from that quarter was the revolution of 1649; and if you have learned the history of her crops for an average year, you never need attend to that thing again, unless your speculations are of a merely pecuniary character. If one may judge who rarely looks into the newspapers, nothing new does ever happen in foreign parts, a French revolution not excepted.

What news! how much more important to know what that is which was never old! Kieou-he-yu (great dignitary of the state of Wei) sent a man to Khoung-tseu to know his news.[10] Khoung-tseu caused the messenger to be seated near him, and questioned him in these terms: "What is your master doing?" The messenger answered with respect: "My master desires to diminish the number of his faults, but he cannot come to the end of them." The messenger being gone, the philosopher remarked: "What a worthy messenger! What a worthy messenger!" The preacher, instead of vexing the ears of drowsy farmers on their day of rest at the end of the week—for Sunday is the fit conclusion of an ill-spent week, and not the fresh and

---

9. There was a civil war in Spain at the time, and these were the principal participants.
10. Thoreau refers to a tale told by Confucius.

brave beginning of a new one—with this one other draggletail of a sermon, should shout with thundering voice, "Pause! Avast! Why so seeming
fast, but deadly slow?"

Shams and delusions are esteemed for soundest truths, while reality is
fabulous. If men would steadily observe realities only and not allow themselves to be deluded, life, to compare it with such things as we know,
would be like a fairy tale and the Arabian Nights' Entertainments. If we
respected only what is inevitable and has a right to be, music and poetry
would resound along the streets. When we are unhurried and wise, we
perceive that only great and worthy things have any permanent and absolute existence, that petty fears and petty pleasures are but the shadow of
the reality. This is always exhilarating and sublime. By closing the eyes
and slumbering, and consenting to be deceived by shows, men establish
and confirm their daily life of routine and habit everywhere, which still
is built on purely illusory foundations. Children, who play life, discern its
true law and relations more clearly than men, who fail to live it worthily,
but who think that they are wiser by experience, that is, by failure. I have
read in a Hindoo book, that "there was a king's son, who, being expelled in
infancy from his native city, was brought up by a forester, and, growing
up to maturity in that state, imagined himself to belong to the barbarous
race with which he lived. One of his father's ministers, having discovered
him, revealed to him what he was, and the misconception of his character
was removed, and he knew himself to be a prince." "So the soul," continues the Hindoo philosopher, "from the circumstances in which it is
placed, mistakes its own character, until the truth is revealed to it by some
holy teacher, and then it knows itself to be *Brahme*." [11] I perceive that we
inhabitants of New England live this mean life that we do because our
vision does not penetrate the surface of things. (We think that that *is*
which *appears* to be.) If a man should walk through this town and see
only the reality, where, think you, would the "Mill-dam" go to? If he
should give us an account of the realities he beheld there, we should not
recognize the place in his description. Look at a meeting-house, or a
court-house, or a jail, or a shop, or a dwelling-house, and say what that
thing really is before a true gaze, and they would all go to pieces in your
account of them. Men esteem truth remote, in the outskirts of the system,
behind the farthest star, before Adam and after the last man. In eternity
there is indeed something true and sublime. But all these times and places
and occasions are now and here. God himself culminates in the present
moment, and will never be more divine in the lapse of all the ages. And we
are enabled to apprehend at all what is sublime and noble only by the perpetual instilling and drenching of the reality that surrounds us. The uni-

11. **Brahme:** the designation for God in the Hindu trinity. Also Brahma.

verse constantly and obediently answers to our conceptions; whether we travel fast or slow, the track is laid for us. Let us spend our lives in conceiving them. The poet or the artist never yet had so fair and noble a design but some of his posterity at least could accomplish it.

Let us spend one day as deliberately as Nature, and not be thrown off the track by every nutshell and mosquito's wing that falls on the rails. Let us rise early and fast, or breakfast gently and without perturbation; let company come and let company go, let the bells ring and the children cry —determined to make a day of it. Why should we knock under and go with the stream? Let us not be upset and overwhelmed in that terrible rapid and whirlpool called a dinner, situated in the meridian shallows. Weather this danger and you are safe, for the rest of the way is down hill. With unrelaxed nerves, with morning vigor, sail by it, looking another way, tied to the mast like Ulysses. If the engine whistles, let it whistle till it is hoarse for its pains. If the bell rings, why should we run? We will consider what kind of music they are like. Let us settle ourselves and work and wedge our feet downward through the mud and slush of opinion and prejudice, and tradition, and delusion and appearance, that allusion which covers the globe, through Paris and London, through New York and Boston and Concord, through church and state, through poetry and philosophy and religion, till we come to a hard bottom and rocks in place, which we can call reality, and say, This is, and no mistake; and then begin, having a *point d'appui*, below freshet and frost and fire, a place where they might found a wall or a state, or set a lamp-post safely, or perhaps a gauge, not a Nilometer, but a Realometer, that future ages might know how deep a freshet of shams and appearances had gathered from time to time. If you stand right fronting and face to face to a fact, you will see the sun glimmer on both its surfaces, as if it were a cimeter,[12] and feel its sweet edge dividing you through the heart and marrow, and so you will happily conclude your mortal career. Be it life or death, we crave only reality. If we are really dying, let us hear the rattle in our throats and feel cold in the extremities; if we are alive, let us go about our business.

Time is but the stream I go a-fishing in. I drink at it; but while I drink I see the sandy bottom and detect how shallow it is. Its thin current slides away, but eternity remains. I would drink deeper; fish in the sky, whose bottom is pebbly with stars. I cannot count one. I know not the first letter of the alphabet. I have always been regretting that I was not as wise as the day I was born. The intellect is a cleaver; it discerns and rifts its way into the secret of things. I do not wish to be any more busy with my hands than is necessary. My head is hands and feet. I feel all my best faculties concentrated in it. My instinct tells me that my head is an organ for bur-

12. **cimeter**: scimitar, a curved Oriental sword.

rowing, as some creatures use their snout and fore-paws, and with it I would mine and burrow my way through these hills. I think that the richest vein is somewhere hereabouts; so by the divining rod and thin rising vapors I judge; and here I will begin to mine.

G. K. Chesterton

ON MR. THOMAS GRAY

A NEWSPAPER appeared with the news, which it seemed to regard as exciting and even alarming news, that Gray did not write the 'Elegy in a Country Churchyard' in the churchyard of Stoke Poges,[1] but in some other country churchyard of the same sort in the same country. What effect the news will have on the particular type of American tourist who has chipped pieces off trees and tombstones, when he finds that the chips come from the wrong trees, or the wrong tombstones, I do not feel impelled to inquire. Nor, indeed, do I know whether the new theory is proved or not. Nor do I care whether the new theory is proved or not. What is most certainly proved, if it needed any proving, is the complete lack of imagination, in many journalists and archaeologists, about how any poet writes any poem.

In such a controversy it is implied, generally on both sides, that what happens is something like this. The poet comes and sits on a tombstone, or wherever he was supposed to sit, in the one and only churchyard of Stoke Poges, or whatever place be the rival of Stoke Poges. He hears the Curfew; and there is a dreadful doubt and dispute about whether anybody sitting among the tombs of Stoke Poges can hear the Curfew, which does really ring from Windsor, though I imagine it sounds pretty much like any other bell at evening. Then the poet produces a portable pen and ink, preferably a large quill and a scroll (the poet in question lived before the time of

---

"On Mr. Thomas Gray" from *All I Survey* by G. K. Chesterton. Reprinted by permission of D. E. Collins.

1. **Stoke Poges:** a village in Buckinghamshire, England, about 23 miles west of London.

fountain-pens), and writes down the first line: 'The curfew tolls the knell of parting day.' Then he looks round to make quite sure that there are some lowing herds winding over that particular lea, that the plough-man is present and doing his duty in plodding homeward his weary way, and that all the other fittings are in the offing. Later, he will have to in-sist peremptorily on an ivy-mantled tower being in the immediate neigh-bourhood, inhabited by an (if possible) moping owl. It will not be the only owl involved in the business. If there are not all these correct condi-tions provided on the spot, he will not be able to write the Elegy. If, on the other hand, they are all there and everything has been properly pro-vided, he will then write the whole of the Elegy, steadily, right through, and not roll up his scroll or rise from his tombstone until he has left the unfortunate young man in the poem finally safe in the bosom of his Father and his God. Then he will go home to tea; and I should imagine he would need it, after so prolonged and sustained a literary effort achieved in such damp and clammy conditions. That, with very little exaggeration, is what is really suggested by those who talk about Gray writing the poem in this place or that place, and under this or that condition of local colour.

Now, I should have thought that anybody would know that poetry is not written like that. But perhaps, in this case, even a bad poet is better than a good critic. Anybody who has ever written any verse, good, bad, or indifferent, will know that calculations of this sort are calculations about the incalculable. Gray might have written the poem, or any part of the poem, in any place on the map; he might have visited the New Stoke Poges or the Old Stoke Poges, or quite probably both, or possibly neither. But, if I may be allowed to pick out one thread of speculation from a thousand threads of possibility, I would suggest that the 'Elegy in a Country Churchyard,' even if it did refer to one particular churchyard, is very likely to have been begun, continued, and ended rather like this:

Mr. Thomas Gray was sitting one evening in a coffee-house; let us hope a coffee-house that did not confine itself to coffee. Something or other, a fiddle or a few glasses of wine, or a good dinner, had thrown him into a mood of musing, of pleasant musing, though touched with a manly and generous melancholy. His thoughts turned round and round, as they do at such times, the tantalizing old riddle of what we really feel about life and death; about the toy God gave us which is beautiful and brittle, yet certainly not trivial. He said to himself: 'After all, who doesn't really feel that it really matters, with all its botherations? . . . A queer business . . . pleasing . . . anxious. . . .' Then something stirred quicker within him, and he said to himself, in warm poetic emotion——

> For who tytumpty tumpty tumpty tum,
> This pleasing anxious being e'er resign'd.

Then his impulse gathered speed and power; and he struck the table and said the next line straight off——

> Left the warm precincts of the cheerful day.

He said that line several times. He liked it very much. Then it was almost a matter of form, certainly a matter of facility, to put the tail on the verse——

> Nor cast one longing, ling'ring look behind.

Then he got up and put on his hat. He left the warm precincts of the cheerful coffee-house, and went home and forgot all about it.

Some time afterwards, perhaps quite a long time afterwards, he was walking in the countryside at dusk. It is quite possible that he was walking in Stoke Poges, or through Stoke Poges, or through any number of other places in the neighbourhood. Perhaps he did hear the Curfew, or what he thought was the Curfew, or what he pretended was the Curfew. He made up another verse or two about the twilight landscape, full of the same spirit of stoical thankfulness and genial resignation. Then he noticed, with great joy, that they would work into the same metre as the lines he had made up in the coffee-house. They were very much in the same mood. But he did not write many of the verses in the churchyard. Possibly he did not write any of the verses in the churchyard. It is more likely that the third act has for its scene Mr. Gray's private study, lined with classics in old leather bindings, and adorned with the celebrated cat and the bowl of goldfish. There he jotted down disjointed verses, and began to put them together; until it looked as if they might some day make a poem. But, subject to any information that may exist on the subject, it would not in the ordinary way surprise me to learn that it was a devil of a long time before they did make a poem. It is most likely, in the abstract, that he got sick of it halfway through, and chucked it away, and found it again years afterwards. It is extremely likely that there was another very long interval, when he was just finishing it, but could not finish finishing it. Many a man writing such a poem has held it up for a year for want of one verse. Nor would the newspaper assist him, in such a difficulty, by pointing out that there was another churchyard much more suitable than that of Stoke Poges.

Now, it is possible—nay, it is probable—that there is not one word of truth in this particular description of the proceedings of Mr. Gray. I have not read any of the literary and biographical records of Mr. Gray, at least for a long time; and there are plenty of records to read. It is quite likely that there are details of his daily life that destroy altogether the details I have here suggested. It is even possible that, by some amazing eccentricity, he did write the whole thing in a churchyard; or, by some unscrupulous exaggeration, pretended that he had done so. But my story is a great deal nearer to the normal story of the production of a poem than any story that supposes particular places and conditions to be *necessary* to the poem. Even if Gray did write with all the stage properties stuck up around him, the lowing cow, the plodding ploughman, the moping owl, they were not the materials of the poem; and he would probably have written pretty much the same sort of poem without them. All this business of clues and tests is not criticism. It is a very good thing that people are applying literature to detective stories and detectives. But it is not a good thing to apply detectives to literature. Gray's unmistakable footmark or favourite tobacco-ash may be found in Stoke Poges or anything else. But it is not in those ashes that there lived his wonted fires.

The real relation of Gray's great poem to the present stage of our history will probably not be understood until a later stage. Yet the poem is a monument, a trophy, and, at the same time, a beacon or signal, standing up as solid and significant as the monument stands up in the Stoke Poges fields. Many poems have been written since, and grown more fashionable, if not more famous, which have not the particular meaning for the modern world stored up in this very storied urn. For Gray wrote at the very beginning of a certain literary epoch of which we, perhaps, stand at the very end. He represented that softening of the Classic which slowly turned it into the Romantic. We represent that ultimate hardening of the Romantic which has turned it into the Realistic. Both changes have, of course, been criticized in their time by the more conservative critics. Dr. Johnson said, probably with a partly humorous impatience, that Gray had only proved that he 'could be dull in a new way.' And most of us will agree that the modern realistic writers, who have in their turn replaced the romantic writers, have indubitably discovered a marvellous and amazing number of new ways of being dull.

But the change, as it hung uncompleted in Gray, strangely resembled the twilight changes of that landscape which the poem describes. Indeed, the whole episode has a curious, almost uncanny, harmony that even includes coincidence. Concerned as he was with a fine shade of twilight, it is even odd that his name was Gray. The whole legend is like that of something colourless and classical fading into mere shadow. For something was, indeed, fading before the eyes of Thomas Gray, the poet, and it was something that he did not wish to see fade. It may be noted that the first impression, especially in the first verses, is one of things moving away from the poet and leaving him alone. We see only the back of the ploughman, so to speak, as he plods away into the darkness; the herds of cattle have the perspective of vanishing things; for a whole world was indeed passing out of the sight and reach of that learned and sensitive and secluded gentleman, who represented the culture of eighteenth-century England, and could only watch a twilight transformation which he could not understand. For when the ploughman comes back out of that twilight, he will come back different. He will be either a scientific works-manager [2] or an entirely new kind of agrarian citizen, great as in the first days of Rome; a free peasant or a servant of alien machinery; but never the same again.

I am not very fond of committees and societies of specialists or amateurs who sit upon this or that sort of problem; but in the particular problem of the preservation of the rural and cultural traditions of our own countryside, I cannot see at the moment that any other machinery is possible. And it seems to me that the Penn-Gray Society is a good example of a machine suited to its work and doing work that is wanted. The trouble is that the typical cultured Englishman, like Gray or the traditional admirer of Gray, was generally a certain kind of gentleman, of the sort that had some kind of country seat. Since then, to continue the figure, the gentleman with the country seat has rather fallen between two stools. He is no longer so rich and powerful as a landlord. He generally has not become so rich and powerful as a local politician. There were any number of men, of course, who appreciated the country without owning a country seat. But if they were not the sort of men to own a country seat, still less were they the sort of men to stand for a county council. And, as the old organization of England went, the organization that has been gradually dying since the days of Gray, men of this artistic sort were mostly attached in some more or less indirect way to the gentry. That is the point; that, for good or ill, it was the system peculiar to a gentry. It was never, for instance, the system peculiar to a peasantry. When there is anything like a peasantry, even as there is in Scotland, it was possible to produce a peasant poet like Burns. And the memory of a peasant like Burns would be preserved by other peasants, even if there were nobody else to preserve it. But nobody could expect the agricultural labourers to preserve the memory of a scholar like Gray. It is amusing to remember that Burns put a verse from the Elegy as a motto to his own homely and pungent picture of peasant life; as some thought, consciously stressing the contrast between his own realism and the scholar's classicism:

> Let not Ambition mock their useful toil,
>   Their homely joys, and destiny obscure;
> Nor Grandeur hear, with a disdainful smile,
>   The short and simple annals of the poor.

Indeed, I rather fancy that, in citing those rather patronizing lines, it was the poor poet who had the disdainful smile.

2. **works-manager:** factory manager.

But we must take the rough with the smooth in that noble aristocratic story that made South England like a garden among the nations. And with it weakened the only organization for protecting the art and antiquities of rural life. Gray could not be a popular poet like Burns; at least, not in that sort of rural life. Perhaps there is a hint of it in his own phrase; that the Village Milton would have remained mute and inglorious. Perhaps he deliberately did not finish the tale of the Village Hampden,[3] who was possibly a poacher but could not possibly be a peasant. Anyhow, the old organization of culture has weakened; and the new organization of local politics is not an organization of culture. There can be a culture of peasants, but not a culture of petty politicians. In this dilemma there is nothing to be done except to work through groups of sympathetic individuals, students or artists or lovers of landscape, who take the trouble to support each other in defending the tradition of the national history and poetry. Otherwise the whole country will be swept bare for the sort of motorist to whom every object is an obstacle to rushing from nowhere to nowhere. Roads will not be roads, for there will be no places for them to go to; there will be only those ominously called arterial, and resembling, indeed, those open and spouting arteries that are an inevitable sign of death. I should say the ultimate moral is that we ought to have made up our minds between real aristocracy and real democracy, and should have either preserved a gentry or created a peasantry. But the immediate moral is that we must preserve what we can of all that reminds us that rural life was a civilization and not a savagery, and especially support such groups as the society here in question, which is defending the great tradition of Gray.

3. In the poem (lines 57–58) Gray writes: "Some village-Hampden, that with dauntless breast/The little tyrant of his fields withstood." He was referring to John Hampden (1594–1643), famous as a leader of the resistance to royal tyranny in the time of Cromwell in England.

Robert Louis Stevenson

WALKING TOURS

IT MUST not be imagined that a walking tour, as some would have us fancy, is merely a better or worse way of seeing the country. There are many ways of seeing landscape quite as good; and none more vivid, in spite of canting dilettantes, than from a railway train. But landscape on a walking tour is quite accessory. He who is indeed of the brotherhood does not voyage in quest of the picturesque, but of certain jolly humours —of the hope and spirit with which the march begins at morning, and the peace and spiritual repletion of the evening's rest. He cannot tell whether he puts his knapsack on, or takes it off, with more delight. The excitement of the departure puts him in key for that of the arrival. Whatever he does is not only a reward in itself, but will be further rewarded in the sequel; and so pleasure leads on to pleasure in an endless chain. It is this that so few can understand; they will either be always lounging or always at five miles an hour; they do not play off the one against the other, prepare all day for the evening, and all evening for the next day. And, above all, it is here that your overwalker fails of comprehension. His heart rises against those who drink their curaçoa in liqueur glasses, when he himself can swill it in a brown john. He will not believe that the flavour is more delicate in the smaller dose. He will not believe that to walk this unconscionable distance is merely to stupefy and brutalise himself, and come to his inn, at night, with a sort of frost on his five wits, and a starless night of darkness in his spirit. Not for him the mild luminous evening of the temperate walker! He has nothing left of man but a physical need for bedtime and a double nightcap; and even his pipe, if he be a smoker, will be savourless and disenchanted. It is the fate of such an one to take twice as much trouble as is needed to obtain happiness, and miss the happiness in the end; he is the man of the proverb, in short, who goes further and fares worse.

Now to be properly enjoyed, a walking tour should be gone upon alone. If you go in a company, or even in pairs, it is no longer a walking tour in anything but name; it is something else, and more in the nature of a picnic. A walking tour should be gone upon alone, because freedom is of the essence; because you should be able to stop and go on, and follow this way or that, as the freak takes you; and because you must have your own pace, and neither trot alongside a champion walker, nor mince in time with a girl. And then you must be open to all impressions and let your thoughts take colour from what you see. You should be as a pipe for any wind to play upon. "I cannot see the wit," says Hazlitt, "of walking and talking at the same time. When I am in the country, I wish to vegetate like the country," which is the gist of all that can be said upon the matter. There should be no cackle of voices at your elbow, to jar on the meditative silence of the morning. And so long as a man is reasoning he cannot surrender himself to that fine intoxication that comes of much motion in the open air, that begins in a sort of dazzle and sluggishness of the brain, and ends in a peace that passes comprehension.

During the first day or so of any tour there are moments of bitterness, when the traveller feels more than coldly towards his knapsack, when he is half in a mind to throw it bodily over the hedge and, like Christian [1] on a similar occasion, "give three leaps and go on singing." And yet it soon acquires a property of easiness. It becomes magnetic; the spirit of the journey enters into it. And no sooner have you passed the straps over your shoulder than the lees of sleep are cleared from you, you pull yourself together with a shake, and fall at once into your stride. And surely, of all possible moods, this, in which a man takes the road, is the best. Of course, if he *will* keep thinking of his anxieties, if he *will* open the merchant Abudah's chest [2] and walk arm in arm with the hag—why, wherever he is, and whether he walk fast or slow, the chances are that he will not be happy. And so much the more shame to himself! There are perhaps thirty men setting forth at the same hour, and I would lay a large wager there is not another dull face among the thirty. It would be a fine thing to follow, in a coat of darkness, one after another of these wayfarers, some summer morning, for the first few miles upon the road. This one, who walks fast, with a keen look in his eyes, is all concentrated in his own mind; he is up at his loom, weaving and weaving, to set the landscape to words. This one peers about, as he goes, among the grasses; he waits by the canal to watch the dragon-flies; he leans on the gate of the pasture, and cannot look enough upon the complacent kine. And here comes another talking, laughing, and gesticulating to himself. His face changes from time to time, as indignation flashes from his eyes or anger clouds his forehead. He is composing articles, delivering orations, and conducting the most impassioned interviews, by the way. A litle farther on, and it is as like as not he will begin to sing. And well for him, supposing him to be no great master in that art, if he stumble across no stolid peasant at a corner; for on such an occasion, I scarcely know which is the more troubled, or whether it is worse to suffer the confusion of your troubadour or the unfeigned alarm

1. **Christian:** the hero of *Pilgrim's Progress*, by John Bunyan (1628–1688).
2. Abudah is a character in *Tales of the Genii*, a series of tales published in 1764, supposedly translated from the Persian by Sir Charles Morell, but actually the original compositions of James Ridley. Abudah is a wealthy merchant of Bagdad who is hag-ridden (i.e., conscience-ridden) until he finds a talisman that frees him.

of your clown. A sedentary population, accustomed, besides, to the strange mechanical bearing of the common tramp, can in no wise explain to itself the gaiety of these passers-by. I knew one man who was arrested as a runaway lunatic because, although a full-grown person with a red beard, he skipped as he went like a child. And you would be astonished if I were to tell you all the grave and learned heads who have confessed to me that, when on walking tours, they sang—and sang very ill—and had a pair of red ears when, as described above, the inauspicious peasant plumped into their arms from round a corner. And here, lest you should think I am exaggerating, is Hazlitt's own confession, from his essay *On Going a Journey*, which is so good that there should be a tax levied on all who have not read it:—

"Give me the clear blue sky over my head," says he, "and the green turf beneath my feet, a winding road before me, and a three hours' march to dinner—and then to thinking! It is hard if I cannot start some game on these lone heaths. I laugh, I run, I leap, I sing for joy."

Bravo! After that adventure of my friend with the policeman, you would not have cared, would you, to publish that in the first person? But we have no bravery nowadays, and, even in books, must all pretend to be as dull and foolish as our neighbours. It was not so with Hazlitt. And notice how learned he is (as, indeed, throughout the essay) in the theory of walking tours. He is none of your athletic men in purple stockings, who walk their fifty miles a day: three hours' march is his ideal. And then he must have a winding road, the epicure!

Yet there is one thing I object to in these words of his, one thing in the great master's practice that seems to me not wholly wise. I do not approve of that leaping and running. Both of these hurry the respiration; they both shake up the brain out of its glorious open-air confusion; and they both break the pace. Uneven walking is not so agreeable to the body, and it distracts and irritates the mind. Whereas, when once you have fallen into an equable stride, it requires no conscious thought from you to keep it up, and yet it prevents you from thinking earnestly of anything else. Like knitting, like the work of a copying clerk, it gradually neutralises and sets to sleep the serious activity of the mind. We can think of this or that, lightly and laughingly, as a child thinks, or as we think in a morning doze; we can make puns or puzzle out acrostics, and trifle in a thousand ways with words and rhymes; but when it comes to honest work, when we come to gather ourselves together for an effort, we may sound the trumpet as loud and long as we please; the great barons of the mind will not rally to the standard, but sit, each one, at home, warming his hands over his own fire and brooding on his own private thought!

In the course of a day's walk, you see, there is much variance in the mood. From the exhilaration of the start, to the happy phlegm of the arrival, the change is certainly great. As the day goes on, the traveller moves from the one extreme towards the other. He becomes more and more incorporated with the material landscape, and the open-air drunkenness grows upon him with great strides, until he posts along the road, and sees everything about him, as in a cheerful dream. The first is certainly brighter, but the second stage is the more peaceful. A man does not make so many articles towards the end, nor does he laugh aloud; but the purely animal pleasures, the sense of physical wellbeing, the delight of every inhalation, of every time the muscles tighten down the thigh, console him for the absence of the others, and bring him to his destination still content.

Nor must I forget to say a word on bivouacs. You come to a milestone on a hill, or some place where deep ways meet under trees; and off goes the knapsack, and down you sit to smoke a pipe in the shade. You sink into yourself, and the birds come round and look at you, and your smoke dissipates upon the afternoon under the blue dome of heaven; and the sun lies warm upon your feet, and the cool air visits your neck and turns aside your open shirt. If you are not happy, you must have an evil conscience. You may dally as long as you like by the roadside. It is almost as if the millennium were arrived, when we shall throw our clocks and watches over the house-top, and remember time and seasons no more. Not to keep hours for a lifetime is, I was going to say, to live for ever. You have no idea, unless you have tried it, how endlessly long is a summer's day, that you measure out only by hunger, and bring to an end only when you are drowsy. I know a village where there are hardly any clocks, where no one knows more of the days of the week than by a sort of instinct for the *fête* on Sundays, and where only one person can tell you the day of the month, and she is generally wrong; and if people were aware how slow Time journeyed in that village, and what armfuls of spare hours he gives, over and above the bargain, to its wise inhabitants, I believe there would be a stampede out of London, Liverpool, Paris, and a variety of large towns, where the clocks lose their heads, and shake the hours out each one faster than the other, as though they were all in a wager. And all these foolish pilgrims would each bring his own misery along with him, in a watch-pocket! It is to be noticed, there were no clocks and watches in the much-vaunted days before the flood. It follows, of course, there were no appointments, and punctuality was not yet thought upon. "Though ye take from a covetous man all his treasure," says Milton, "he has yet one jewel left; ye cannot deprive him of his covetousness." And so I would say of a modern man of business, you may do what you will for him, put him in Eden, give him the elixir of life—he has still a flaw at heart, he still has his business habits. Now, there is no time when business habits are more mitigated than a walking tour. And so during these halts, as I say, you will feel almost free.

But it is at night, and after dinner, that the best hour comes. There are no such pipes to be smoked as those that follow a good day's march; the flavour of the tobacco is a thing to be remembered, it is so dry and aromatic, so full and so fine. If you wind up the evening with grog, you will own there was never such grog; at every sip a jocund tranquility spreads about your limbs, and sits easily in your heart. If you read a book—and you will never do so save by fits and starts—you find the language strangely racy and harmonious; words take a new meaning; single sentences possess the ear for half an hour together; and the writer endears himself to you, at every page, by the nicest coincidence of sentiment. It seems as if it were a book you had written yourself in a dream. To all we have read on such occasions we look back with special favour. "It was on the 10th of April 1798," says Hazlitt, with amorous precision, "that I sat down to a volume of the new *Héloïse*,[3] at the Inn of Llangollen, over a bottle of sherry and a cold chicken." I should wish to quote more, for though we are mighty fine fellows nowadays, we cannot write like Hazlitt. And talking of that, a volume of Hazlitt's essays would be a capital pocket-book on such a journey; so would a volume of Heine's songs; and for *Tristram Shandy* [4] I can pledge a fair experience.

If the evening be fine and warm, there is nothing better in life than to lounge before the inn door in the sunset, or lean over the parapet of the bridge, to watch the weeds and the quick fishes. It is then, if ever, that you taste joviality to the full significance of that audacious word. Your muscles are so agreeably slack, you feel so clean and so strong and so idle that whether you move or sit still, whatever you do is done with pride and a kingly sort of pleasure. You fall in talk with anyone, wise or foolish, drunk or sober. And it seems as if a hot walk purged you, more than of anything else, of all narrowness and pride, and left curiosity to play its part freely, as in a child or a man of science. You lay aside all your own hobbies, to watch provincial humours develop themselves before you, now as a laughable farce, and now grave and beautiful like an old tale.

Or perhaps you are left to your own company for the night, and surly weather imprisons you by the fire. You may remember how Burns, numbering past pleasures, dwells upon the hours when he has been "happy thinking." It is a phrase that may well perplex a poor modern girt about on every side by clocks and chimes, and haunted, even at night, by flaming

---

3. **the new Héloïse:** Hazlitt was referring to one of the most famous and popular books of the period, Rousseau's *Julie ou la Nouvelle Héloïse*, published in 1761.
4. *Tristram Shandy: Life and Opinions of Tristram Shandy*, a novel written by Laurence Sterne (1713–1768).

dial-plates. For we are all so busy, and have so many far-off projects to realise, and castles in the fire to turn into solid, habitable mansions on a gravel soil, that we can find no time for pleasure trips into the Land of Thought and among the Hills of Vanity. Changed times, indeed, when we must sit all night, beside the fire, with folded hands; and a changed world for most of us, when we find we can pass the hours without discontent, and be happy thinking. We are in such haste to be doing, to be writing, to be gathering gear, to make our voice audible a moment in the derisive silence of eternity, that we forget that one thing, of which these are but the parts—namely to live. We fall in love, we drink hard, we run to and fro upon the earth like frightened sheep. And now you are to ask yourself if, when all is done, you would not have been better to sit by the fire at home, and be happy thinking. To sit still and contemplate,—to remember the faces of women without desire, to be pleased by the great deeds of men without envy, to be everything and everywhere in sympathy, and yet content to remain where and what you are—is not this to know both wisdom and virtue, and to dwell with happiness? After all, it is not they who carry flags, but they who look upon it from a private chamber who have the fun of the procession. And once you are at that, you are in the very humour of all social heresy. It is no time for shuffling, or for big empty words. If you ask yourself what you mean by fame, riches, or learning, the answer is far to seek; and you go back into that kingdom of light imaginations, which seem so vain in the eyes of Philistines perspiring after wealth, and so momentous to those who are stricken with the disproportions of the world, and in the face of the gigantic stars, cannot stop to split differences between two degrees of the infinitesimally small, such as a tobacco pipe or the Roman Empire, a million of money or a fiddlestick's end.

You lean from the window, your last pipe reeking whitely into the darkness, your body full of delicious pains, your mind enthroned in the seventh circle [5] of content; when suddenly the mood changes, the weather-cock goes about, and you ask yourself one question more: whether, for the interval, you have been the wisest philosopher or the most egregious of donkeys? Human experience is not yet able to reply; but at least you have had a fine moment, and looked down upon all the kingdoms of the earth. And whether it was wise or foolish, tomorrow's travel will carry you, body and mind, into some different parish of the infinite.

5. **seventh circle:** the last and highest of the abodes of bliss according to the Mohammedan religion.

William Hazlitt

ON THE FEELING OF
IMMORTALITY IN YOUTH

N O YOUNG MAN believes he shall ever die. It was a saying of my brother's, and a fine one. There is a feeling of Eternity in youth, which makes us amends for everything. To be young is to be as one of the Immortal Gods. One half of time indeed is flown—the other half remains in store for us with all its countless treasures; for there is no line drawn, and we see no limit to our hopes and wishes. We make the coming age our own.—

> The vast, the unbounded prospect lies before us.

Death, old age, are words without a meaning, that pass by us like the idle air which we regard not. Others may have undergone, or may still be liable to them—we "bear a charmed life," which laughs to scorn all such sickly fancies. As in setting out on a delightful journey, we strain our eager gaze forward—

> Bidding the lovely scenes at distance hail,—

and see no end to the landscape, new objects presenting themselves as we advance; so, in the commencement of life, we set no bounds to our inclinations, nor to the unrestricted opportunities of gratifying them. We have as yet found no obstacle, no disposition to flag; and it seems that we can go on so forever. We look round in a new world, full of life, and motion, and ceaseless progress; and feel in ourselves all the vigour and spirit to keep pace with it, and do not foresee from any present symptoms how we shall be left behind in the natural course of things, decline into old age, and drop into the grave. It is the simplicity, and as it were *abstractedness* of our feelings in youth, that (so to speak) identifies us with nature, and (our experience being slight and our passions strong) deludes us into a belief of being immortal like it. Our short-lived connection with existence, we fondly flatter ourselves, is an indissoluble and lasting union—a honeymoon that knows neither coldness, jar, nor separation. As infants smile and sleep, we are rocked in the cradle of our wayward fancies, and lulled into security by the roar of the universe around us—we quaff the cup of life with eager haste without draining it, instead of which it only overflows the more—objects press around us, filling the mind with their magnitude and with the throng of desires that wait upon them, so that we have no room for the thoughts of death. From that plenitude of our being, we cannot change all at once to dust and ashes, we cannot imagine "this sensible, warm motion, to become a kneaded clod"—we are too much dazzled by the brightness of the waking dream around us to look into the darkness of the tomb. We no more see our end than our beginning: the one is lost in oblivion and vacancy, as the other is hid from us by the crowd and hurry of approaching events. Or the grim shadow is seen lingering in the horizon, which we are doomed never to overtake, or whose last, faint, glimmering outline touches upon Heaven and translates us to the skies! Nor would the hold that life has taken of us permit us to detach our thoughts from present objects and pursuits, even if we would. What is there more opposed to health, than sickness; to strength and beauty, than decay and dissolution; to the active search of knowledge than mere oblivion? Or is there none of the usual advantage to bar the approach of Death, and mock his idle threats; Hope supplies their place, and draws a veil over the abrupt termination of all our cherished schemes. While the spirit of youth remains unimpaired, ere the "wine of life is drank up," we are like people intoxicated or in a fever, who are hurried away by the violence of their own sensations: it is only as present objects begin to pall upon the sense, as we have been disappointed in our favourite pursuits, cut off from our closest ties, that passion loosens its hold upon the breast, that we by degrees become weaned from the world, and allow ourselves to contemplate, "as in a glass, darkly," the possibility of parting with it for good. The example of others, the voice of experience, has no effect upon us whatever. Casualties we must avoid: the slow and deliberate advances of age we can play at *hide-and-seek* with. We think ourselves too lusty and too nimble for that blear-eyed decrepid old gentleman to catch us. Like the foolish fat scullion, in Sterne, when she hears that Master Bobby is dead, our only reflection is—"So am not I!" The idea of death, instead of staggering our confidence, rather seems to strengthen and enhance our possession and our enjoyment of life. Others may fall around us like leaves, or be mowed down like flowers by the scythe of Time: these are but tropes and figures to the unreflecting ears and overweening presumption of youth. It is not till we see flowers of Love, Hope, and Joy, withering around us, and our own pleasures cut up by the roots, that we bring the moral home to ourselves, that we abate something of the wanton extravagance of our pretensions, or that the emptiness and dreariness of the prospect before us reconciles us to the stillness of the grave!

> Life! thou strange thing, that hast a power to feel
> Thou art, and to perceive that others are.

Well might the poet begin his indignant invective against an art, whose professed object is its destruction, with this animated apostrophe to life.

Life is indeed a strange gift, and its privileges are most miraculous. Nor is it singular that when the splendid boon is first granted us, our gratitude, our admiration, and our delight should prevent us from reflecting on our own nothingness, or from thinking it will ever be recalled. Our first and strongest impressions are taken from the mighty scene that is opened to us, and we very innocently transfer its durability as well as magnificence to ourselves. So newly found, we cannot make up our minds to parting with it yet and at least put off that consideration to an indefinite term. Like a clown at a fair, we are full of amazement and rapture, and have no thoughts of going home, or that it will soon be night. We know our existence only from external objects, and we measure it by them. We can never be satisfied with gazing; and nature will still want us to look on and applaud. Otherwise, the sumptuous entertainment, "the feast of reason and the flow of soul," to which they were invited, seems little better than a mockery and a cruel insult. We do not go from a play till the scene is ended, and the lights are ready to be extinguished. But the fair face of things still shines on; shall we be called away, before the curtain falls, or ere we have scarce had a glimpse of what is going on? Like children, our step-mother Nature holds us up to see the raree-show of the universe; and then, as if life were a burthen to support, lets us instantly down again. Yet in that short interval, what "brave sublunary things" does not the spectacle unfold; like a bubble, at one minute reflecting the universe, and the next, shook to air!—To see the golden sun and the azure sky, the outstretched ocean, to walk upon the green earth, and to be lord of a thousand creatures, to look down giddy precipices or over the distant flowery vales, to see the world spread out under one's finger in a map, to bring the stars near, to view the smallest insects in a microscope, to read history, and witness the revolutions of empires and the succession of generations, to hear of the glory of Sidon and Tyre, of Babylon and Susa, as of a faded pageant, and to say all these were, and are now nothing, to think that we exist in such a point of time, and in such a corner of space, to be at once spectators and a part of the moving scene, to watch the return of the seasons, of spring and autumn, to hear—

> The stockdove plain amid the forest deep,
> That drowsy rustles to the sighing gale—

to traverse desert wildernesses, to listen to the midnight choir, to visit lighted halls, or plunge into the dungeon's gloom, or sit in crowded theatres and see life itself mocked, to feel heat and cold, pleasure and pain, right and wrong, truth and falsehood, to study the works of art and refine the sense of beauty to agony, to worship fame and to dream of immortality, to have read Shakespeare and belong to the same species as Sir

Isaac Newton; to be and to do all this, and then in a moment to be nothing, to have it all snatched from one like a juggler's ball or a phantasmagoria; there is something revolting and incredible to sense in the transition, and no wonder that, aided by youth and warm blood, and the flush of enthusiasm, the mind contrives for a long time to reject it with disdain and loathing as a monstrous and improbable fiction, like a monkey on a housetop, that is loath, amidst its fine discoveries and specious antics, to be tumbled headlong into the street, and crushed to atoms, the sport and laughter of the multitude!

The change, from the commencement to the close of life, appears like a fable, after it has taken place; how should we treat it otherwise than as a chimera before it has come to pass? There are some things that happened so long ago, places or persons we have formerly seen, of which such dim traces remain, we hardly know whether it was sleeping or waking they occurred; they are like dreams within the dream of life, a mist, a film before the eye of memory, which, as we try to recall them more distinctly, elude our notice altogether. It is but natural that the lone interval that we thus look back upon, should have appeared long and endless in prospect. There are others so distinct and fresh, they seem but of yesterday—their very vividness might be deemed a pledge of their permanence. Then, however, far back our impressions may go, we find others still older (for our years are multiplied in youth); descriptions of scenes that we had read, and people before our time, Priam and the Trojan war; and even then, Nestor was old and dwelt delighted on his youth, and spoke of the race, of heroes that were no more;—what wonder that, seeing this long line of being pictured in our minds, and reviving as it were in us, we should give ourselves involuntary credit for an indeterminate period of existence? In the Cathedral at Peterborough there is a monument to Mary, Queen of Scots, at which I used to gaze when a boy, while the events of the period, all that had happened since, passed in review before me. If all this mass of feeling and imagination could be crowded into a moment's compass, what might not the whole of life be supposed to contain? We are heirs of the past; we count on the future as our natural reversion. Besides, there are some of our early impressions so exquisitely tempered, it appears that they must always last—nothing can add to or take away from their sweetness and purity—the first breath of spring, the hyacinth dipped in the dew, the mild lustre of the evening-star, the rainbow after a storm—while we have the full enjoyment of these, we must be young; and what can ever alter us in this respect? Truth, friendship, love, books, are also proof against the canker of time; and while we live, but for them, we can never grow old. We take out a new lease of existence from the objects on which we set our affections, and become abstracted, impassive, immortal in them. We

cannot conceive how certain sentiments should ever decay or grow cold in
our breasts; and, consequently, to maintain them in their first youthful
glow and vigour, the flame of life must continue to burn as bright as ever,
or rather, they are the fuel that feed the sacred lamp, that kindle "the
purple light of love," and spread a golden cloud around our heads! Again,
we not only flourish and survive in our affections (in which we will not
listen to the possibility of a change, any more than we foresee the wrinkles
on the brow of a mistress), but we have a farther guarantee against the
thoughts of death in our favourite studies and pursuits, and in their con-
tinual advance. Art we know is long; life, we feel, should be so too. We
see no end of the difficulties we have to encounter: perfection is slow of
attainment, and we must have time to accomplish it in. Rubens complained
that when he had just learnt his art, he was snatched away from it: we
trust we shall be more fortunate! A wrinkle in an old head takes whole
days to finish it properly: but to catch "the Raphael grace, the Guido air,"
no limit should be put to our endeavours. What a prospect for the future!
What a task we have entered upon! and shall we be arrested in the middle
of it? We do not reckon our time thus employed lost, or our pains thrown
away, or our progress slow—we do not droop or grow tired, but "gain new
vigour at our endless task;"—and shall Time grudge us the opportunity to
finish what we have auspiciously begun, and have formed a sort of compact with nature to achieve? The fame of the great names we look up to
is also imperishable; and shall not we, who contemplate it with such intense yearnings, imbibe a portion of ethereal fire, the *divinæ particula
auræ*,[1] which nothing can extinguish? I remember to have looked at a
print of Rembrandt for hours together, without being conscious of the
flight of time, trying to resolve it into its component parts, to connect its
strong and sharp gradations, to learn the secret of its reflected lights, and
found neither satiety nor pause in the prosecution of my studies. The
print over which I was poring would last long enough; why should the
idea of my mind, which was finer, more impalpable, perish before it? At
this, I redoubled the ardour of my pursuit, and by the very subtlety and
refinement of my inquiries, seemed to bespeak for them an exemption from
corruption and the rude grasp of Death.

Objects, on our first acquaintance with them, have that singleness and
integrity of impression that it seems as if nothing could destroy or obliterate them, so firmly are they stamped and riveted on the brain. We repose
on them with a sort of voluptuous indolence, in full faith and boundless
confidence. We are absorbed in the present moment, or return to the
same point—idling away a great deal of time in youth, thinking we have
enough and to spare. There is often a local feeling in the air, which is as

1. *divinæ particula auræ:* divine spirit (in man) (Latin).

fixed as if it were of marble; we loiter in dim cloisters, losing ourselves in thought and in their glimmering arches; a winding road before us seems as long as the journey of life, and as full of events. Time and experience dissipate this illusion; and by reducing them to detail, circumscribe the limits of our expectations. It is only as the pageant of life passes by and the masques turn their backs upon us, that we see through the deception, or believe that the train will have an end. In many cases, the slow progress and monotonous texture of our lives, before we mingle with the world and are embroiled in its affairs, has a tendency to aid the same feeling. We have a difficulty, when left to ourselves, and without the resource of books or some more lively pursuit, to "beguile the slow and creeping hours of time," and argue that if it moves on always at this tedious snail's-pace, it can never come to an end. We are willing to skip over certain portions of it that separate us from favourite objects, that irritate ourselves at the unnecessary delay. The young are prodigal of life from a superabundance of it; the old are tenacious on the same score, because they have little left, and cannot enjoy even what remains of it.

For my part, I set out in life with the French Revolution, and that event had considerable influence on my early feelings, as on those of others. Youth was then doubly such. It was the dawn of a new era, a new impulse had been given to men's minds, and the sun of Liberty rose upon the sun of Life in the same day, and both were proud to run their race together. Little did I dream, while my first hopes and wishes went hand in hand with those of the human race, that long before my eyes should close, that dawn would be overcast, and set once more in the night of despotism—"total eclipse!" Happy that I did not. I felt for years, and during the best part of my existence, *heart-whole* in that cause, and triumphed in the triumphs over the enemies of man! At that time, while the fairest aspirations of the human mind seemed about to be realized, ere the image of man was defaced and his breast mangled in scorn, philosophy took a higher, poetry could afford a deeper range. At that time, to read *The Robbers*,[2] was indeed delicious, and to hear

> From the dungeon of the tower time-rent,
> That fearful voice, a famish'd father's cry,

could be borne only amidst the fulness of hope, the crash of the fall of the strongholds of power, and the exulting sounds of the march of human freedom. What feelings the death-scene in *Don Carlos* sent into the soul! In that headlong career of lofty enthusiasm, and the joyous opening of the prospects of the world and our own, the thought of death crossing it,

2. *The Robbers:* a play by the German poet and dramatist, Johann Schiller (1759–1805), who also wrote *Don Carlos*.

smote doubly cold upon the mind; there was a stifling sense of oppression and confinement, an impatience of our present knowledge, a desire to grasp the whole of our existence in one strong embrace, to sound the mystery of life and death, and in order to put an end to the agony of doubt and dread, to burst through our prison-house, and confront the King of Terrors in his grisly palace!—As I was writing out this passage, my miniature picture when a child lay on the mantle-piece, and I took it out of the case to look at it. I could perceive few traces of myself in it; but there was the same placid brow, the dimpled mouth, the same timid, inquisitive glance as ever. But its careless smile did not seem to reproach me with having become a recreant to the sentiments that were then sown in my mind, or with having written a sentence that could call up a blush in this image of ingenuous youth!

"That time is past with all its giddy raptures." Since the future was barred to my progress, I have turned for consolation to the past, gathering up the fragments of my early recollections, and putting them into a form that might live. It is thus, that when we find our personal and substantial identity vanishing from us, we strive to gain a reflected and substituted one in our thoughts: we do not like to perish wholly, and wish to bequeath our names at least to posterity. As long as we can keep alive our cherished thoughts and nearest interests in the minds of others, we do not appear to have retired altogether from the stage, we still occupy a place in the estimation of mankind, exercise a powerful influence over them, and it is only our bodies that are trampled into dust or dispersed to air. Our darling speculations still find favour and encouragement, and we make as good a figure in the eyes of our descendants, nay, perhaps, a better than we did in our lifetime. This is one point gained; the demands of our self-love are so far satisfied. Besides, if by the proofs of intellectual superiority we survive ourselves in this world, by exemplary virtue or unblemished faith, we are taught to ensure an interest in another and a higher state of being, and to anticipate at the same time the applauses of men and angels.

> Even from the tomb the voice of nature cries;
> Even in our ashes live their wonted fires.

As we advance in life, we acquire a keener sense of the value of time. Nothing else, indeed, seems of any consequence; and we become misers in this respect. We try to arrest its few last tottering steps, and to make it linger on the brink of the grave. We can never leave off wondering how that which has ever been should cease to be, and would still live on, that we may wonder at our own shadow, and when "all the life of life is flown," dwell on the retrospect of the past. This is accompanied by a mechanical tenaciousness of whatever we possess, by a distrust and a sense of fallacious hollowness in all we see. Instead of the full, pulpy feeling of youth, everything is flat and insipid. The world is a painted witch, that puts us off with false shews and tempting appearances. The ease, the jocund gaiety, the unsuspecting security of youth are fled: nor can we, without flying in the face of common sense,

> From the last dregs of life, hope to receive
> What its first sprightly runnings could not give.

If we can slip out of the world without notice or mischance, can tamper with bodily infirmity, and frame our minds to the becoming composure of *still-life*, before we sink into total insensibility, it is as much as we ought to expect. We do not in the regular course of nature die all at once: we have mouldered away gradually long before; faculty after faculty, attachment after attachment, we are torn from ourselves piece-meal while living; year after year takes something from us; and death only consigns the last remnant of what we were to the grave. The revulsion is not so great, and a quiet *euthanasia* is a winding-up of the plot, that is not out of reason or nature.

That we should thus in a manner outlive ourselves, and dwindle imperceptibly into nothing, is not surprising, when even in our prime the strongest impressions leave so little traces of themselves behind, and the last object is driven out by the succeeding one. How little effect is produced on us at any time by the books we have read, the scenes we have witnessed, the sufferings we have gone through! Think only of the variety of feelings we experience in reading an interesting romance, or being present at a fine play—what beauty, what sublimity, what soothing, what heart-rending emotions! You would suppose these would last forever, or at least subdue the mind to a correspondent tone and harmony—while we turn over the page, while the scene is passing before us, it seems as if nothing could ever after shake our resolution, that "treason domestic, foreign levy, nothing could touch us farther!" The first splash of mud we get, on entering the street, the first pettifogging shop-keeper that cheats us out of two-pence, and the whole vanishes clean out of our remembrance, and we become the idle prey of the most petty and annoying circumstances. The mind soars by an effort to the grand and lofty: it is at home, in the grovelling, the disagreeable, and the little. This happens in the height and hey-day of our existence, when novelty gives a stronger impulse to the blood and takes a faster hold of the brain, (I have known the impression on coming out of a gallery of pictures then last half a day)—as we grow old, we become more feeble and querulous, every object "reverbs its own hollowness," and both worlds are not enough to satisfy the peevish importunity and extravagant presumption of our desires! There are a few superior, happy beings, who are born with a temper exempt from every trifling annoyance. This spirit sits serene and smiling as in its native skies, and a divine harmony (whether heard or not) plays around them. This is to be at peace. Without this, it is in vain to fly into deserts, or to build a hermitage on the top of rocks, if regret and ill-humour follow us there: and with this, it is needless to make the experiment. The only true retirement is that of the heart; the only true leisure is the repose of the passions. To such persons it makes little difference whether they are young or old; and they die as they have lived, with graceful resignation.

William James

ON A CERTAIN BLINDNESS IN HUMAN BEINGS

OUR JUDGMENTS concerning the worth of things, big or little, depend on the *feelings* the things arouse in us. Where we judge a thing to be precious in consequence of the *idea* we frame of it, this is only because the idea is itself associated already with a feeling. If we were radically feelingless, and if ideas were the only things our mind could entertain, we should lose all our likes and dislikes at a stroke, and be unable to point to any one situation or experience in life more valuable or significant than any other.

Now the blindness in human beings, of which this discourse will treat, is the blindness with which we all are afflicted in regard to the feelings of creatures and people different from ourselves.

We are practical beings, each of us with limited functions and duties to perform. Each is bound to feel intensely the importance of his own duties and the significance of the situation that call these forth. But this feeling is in each of us a vital secret, for sympathy with which we vainly look to others. The others are too much absorbed in their own vital secrets to take an interest in ours. Hence the stupidity and injustice of our opinions, so far as they deal with the significance of alien lives. Hence the falsity of our judgments, so far as they presume to decide in an absolute way on the value of other persons' conditions or ideals.

Take our dogs and ourselves, connected as we are by a tie more intimate than most ties in this world; and yet, outside of that tie of friendly fondness, how insensible, each of us, to all that makes life significant for the other!—we to the rapture of bones under hedges, or smells of trees and lamp-posts, they to the delights of literature and art. As you sit reading the most moving romance you ever fell upon, what sort of a judge is your fox-terrier of your behavior? With all his good will toward you, the nature of your conduct is absolutely excluded from his comprehension. To sit there like a senseless statue, when you might be taking him to walk and throwing sticks for him to catch! What queer disease is this that comes over you every day, of holding things and staring at them like that for hours together, paralyzed of motion and vacant of all conscious life? The African savages came nearer the truth; but they, too, missed it, when they gathered wonderingly round one of our American travellers who, in the interior, had just come into possession of a stray copy of the New York *Commercial Advertiser*, and was devouring it column by column. When he got through, they offered him a high price for the mysterious object; and, being asked for what they wanted it, they said: 'For an eye medicine,' —that being the only reason they could conceive of for the protected bath which he had given his eyes upon its surface.

The spectator's judgment is sure to miss the root of the matter, and to possess no truth. The subject judged knows a part of the world of reality which the judging spectator fails to see, knows more while the spectator knows less; and, wherever there is conflict of opinion and difference of vision, we are bound to believe that the truer side is the side that feels the more, and not the side that feels the less.

Let me take a personal example of the kind that befalls each one of us daily:—

Some years ago, while journeying in the mountains of North Carolina, I passed by a large number of 'coves,' as they call them there, or heads of small valleys between the hills, which had been newly cleared and planted. The impression on my mind was one of unmitigated squalor. The settler had in every case cut down the more manageable trees, and left their charred stumps standing. The larger trees he had girdled and killed, in order that their foliage should not cast a shade. He had then built a log cabin, plastering its chinks with clay, and had set up a tall zigzag rail fence around the scene of his havoc, to keep the pigs and cattle out. Finally, he had irregularly planted the intervals between the stumps and trees with

Indian corn, which grew among the chips; and there he dwelt with his wife and babes—an axe, a gun, a few utensils, and some pigs and chickens feeding in the woods, being the sum total of his possessions.

The forest had been destroyed; and what had 'improved' it out of existence was hideous, a sort of ulcer, without a single element of artificial grace to make up for the loss of Nature's beauty. Ugly, indeed, seemed the life of the squatter, scudding, as the sailors say, under bare poles, beginning again away back where our first ancestors started, and by hardly a single item the better off for all the achievements of the intervening generations.

Talk about going back to nature! I said to myself, oppressed by the dreariness, as I drove by. Talk of a country life for one's old age and for one's children! Never thus, with nothing but the bare ground and one's bare hands to fight the battle! Never, without the best spoils of culture woven in! The beauties and commodities gained by the centuries are sacred. They are our heritage and birthright. No modern person ought to be willing to live a day in such a state of rudimentariness and denudation.

Then I said to the mountaineer who was driving me, 'What sort of people are they who have to make these new clearings?' 'All of us,' he replied. 'Why, we ain't happy here, unless we are getting one of these coves under cultivation.' I instantly felt that I had been losing the whole inward significance of the situation. Because to me the clearings spoke of naught but denudation, I though that to those whose sturdy arms and obedient axes had made them they could tell no other story. But, when *they* looked on the hideous stumps, what they thought of was personal victory. The chips, the girdled trees, and the vile split rails spoke of honest sweat, persistent toil, and final reward. The cabin was a warrant of safety for self and wife and babes. In short, the clearing, which to me was a mere ugly picture on the retina, was to them a symbol redolent with moral memories and sang a very paean of duty, struggle, and success.

I had been as blind to the peculiar ideality of their conditions as they certainly would also have been to the ideality of mine, had they had a peep at my strange indoor academic ways of life at Cambridge.

Wherever a process of life communicates an eagerness to him who lives it, there the life becomes genuinely significant. Sometimes the eagerness is more knit up with the motor activities, sometimes with the perceptions, sometimes with the imagination, sometimes with reflective thought. But, wherever it is found, there is the zest, the tingle, the excitement of reality; and there *is* 'importance' in the only real and positive sense in which importance ever anywhere can be.

Robert Louis Stevenson has illustrated this by a case, drawn from the sphere of the imagination, in an essay which I really think deserves to become immortal, both for the truth of its matter and the excellence of its form.

'Toward the end of September,' Stevenson writes, 'when school-time was drawing near, and the nights were already black, we would begin to sally from our respective villas, each equipped with a tin bull's-eye lantern. The thing was so well known that it had worn a rut in the commerce of Great Britain; and the grocers, about the due time, began to garnish their windows with our particular brand of luminary. We wore them buckled to the waist upon a cricket belt, and over them, such was the rigor of the game, a buttoned top-coat. They smelled noisomely of blistered tin. They never burned aright, though they would always burn our fingers. Their use was naught, the pleasure of them merely fanciful, and yet a boy with a bull's-eye under his top-coat asked for nothing more. The fishermen used lanterns about their boats, and it was from them, I suppose, that we had got the hint; but theirs were not bull's-eyes, nor did we ever play at being fishermen. The police carried them at their belts, and we had plainly copied them in that; yet we did not pretend to be policemen. Burglars, indeed, we may have had some haunting thought of; and we had certainly an eye to past ages when lanterns were more common, and to certain story-books in which we had found them to figure very largely. But take it for all in all, the pleasure of the thing was substantive; and to be a boy with a bull's-eye under his top-coat was good enough for us.

'When two of these asses met, there would be an anxious "Have you got your lantern?" and a gratified "Yes!" That was the shibboleth, and very needful, too; for, as it was the rule to keep our glory contained, none could recognize a lantern-bearer unless (like the polecat) by the smell. Four or five would sometimes climb into the belly of a ten-man lugger, with nothing but the thwarts above them,—for the cabin was usually locked,—or choose out some hollow of the links where the wind might whistle overhead. Then the coats would be unbuttoned, and the bull's-eyes discovered; and in the chequering glimmer, under the huge, windy hall of the night, and cheered by a rich steam of toasting tinware, these fortunate young gentlemen would crouch together in the cold sand of the links, or on the scaly bilges of the fishing-boat, and delight them with inappropriate talk. Woe is me that I cannot give some specimens! . . . But the talk was but a condiment, and these gatherings themselves only accidents in the career of the lantern-bearer. The essence of this bliss was to walk by yourself in the black night, the slide shut, the top-coat buttoned, not a ray escaping, whether to conduct your footsteps or to make your glory public,—a mere pillar of darkness in the dark; and all the while, deep down in the privacy of your fool's heart, to know you had a bull's-eye at your belt, and to exult and sing over the knowledge.

'It is said that a poet has died young in the breast of the most stolid. It may be contended rather that a (somewhat minor) bard in almost every case survives, and is the spice of life to his possessor. Justice is not done to the versatility and the unplumbed childishness of men's imagination. His life from without may seem but a rude mound of mud: there will be some golden chamber at the heart of it, in which he dwells delighted; and for as dark as his pathway seems to the observer, he will have some kind of bull's-eye at his belt.

. . . 'There is one fable that touches very near the quick of life,—the fable of the monk who passed into the woods, heard a bird break into song, hearkened for a trill or two, and found himself at his return a stranger at his convent gate; for he had been absent fifty years, and of all his comrades there survived but one to recognize him. It is not only in the woods that this enchanter carols, though perhaps he is native there. He sings in the most doleful places. The miser hears him and chuckles, and his days are moments. With no more apparatus than an evil-smelling lantern, I have evoked him on the naked links. All life that is not merely mechanical is spun out of two strands,—seeking for that bird and hearing him. And it is just this that makes life so hard to value, and the delight of each so incommunicable. And it is just a knowledge of this, and a remembrance of those fortunate hours in which the bird *has* sung to *us*, that fills us with such wonder when we turn to the pages of the realist. There, to be sure, we find a picture of life in so far as it consists of mud and of old iron, cheap desires and cheap fears, that which we are ashamed to remember and that which we are careless whether we forget; but of the note of that time-devouring nightingale we hear no news.

. . . 'Say that we came [in such a realistic romance] on some such business as that of my lantern-bearers on the links, and described the boys as very cold, spat upon by flurries of rain, and drearily surrounded, all of which they were; and their talk as silly and indecent, which it certainly was. To the eye of the observer they *are* wet and cold and drearily surrounded; but ask themselves, and they are in the heaven of a recondite pleasure, the ground of which is an ill-smelling lantern.

'For, to repeat, the ground of a man's joy is often hard to hit. It may hinge at times upon a mere accessory, like the lantern; it may reside in the mysterious inwards of psychology . . . It has so little bond with externals . . . that it may even touch them not, and the man's true life, for which he consents to live, lie altogether in the field of fancy . . . In such a case the poetry runs underground. The observer (poor soul, with his

documents!) is all abroad. For to look at the man is but to court deception. We shall see the trunk from which he draws his nourishment; but
he himself is above and abroad in the green dome of foliage, hummed
through by winds and nested in by nightingales. And the true realism
were that of the poets, to climb up after him like a squirrel, and catch
some glimpse of the heaven for which he lives. And the true realism, always and everywhere, is that of the poets: to find out where joy resides,
and give it a voice far beyond singing.

'For to miss the joy is to miss all. In the joy of the actors lies the sense of
any action. That is the explanation, that the excuse. To one who has not
the secret of the lanterns the scene upon the links is meaningless. And
hence the haunting and truly spectral unreality of realistic books . . . In
each we miss the personal poetry, the enchanted atmosphere, that rainbow
work of fancy that clothes what is naked and seems to ennoble what is
base; in each, life falls dead like dough, instead of soaring away like a balloon into the colors of the sunset; each is true, each inconceivable; for no
man lives in the external truth, among salts and acids, but in the warm,
phantasmagoric chamber of his brain, with the painted windows and the
storied walls.'

These paragraphs are the best thing I know in all Stevenson. 'To miss
the joy is to miss all.' Indeed, it is. Yet we are but finite, and each one of
us has some single specialized vocation of his own. And it seems as if energy in the services of its particular duties might be got only by hardening
the heart toward everything unlike them. Our deadness toward all but
one particular kind of joy would thus be the price we inevitably have to
pay for being practical creatures. Only in some pitiful dreamer, some
philosopher, poet, or romancer, or when the common practical man becomes a lover, does the hard externality give way, and a gleam of insight
into the ejective world, as Clifford [1] called it, the vast world of inner life
beyond us, so different from that of outer seeming, illuminate our mind.
Then the whole scheme of our customary values gets confounded, then
our self is riven and its narrow interests fly to pieces, then a new center
and a new perspective must be found.

The change is well described by my colleague, Josiah Royce:—

'What, then, is our neighbor? Thou hast regarded his thought, his feeling, as somehow different from thine. Thou hast said, "A pain in him is
not like a pain in me, but something far easier to bear." He seems to thee
a little less living than thou; his life is dim, it is cold, it is a pale fire beside
thy own burning desires . . . So, dimly and by instinct hast thou lived
with thy neighbor, and hast known him not, being blind. Thou hast made

---

1. **Clifford:** William Clifford (1845–1879), an English mathematician and philosopher.

[of him] a thing, no Self at all. Have done with this illusion, and simply try to learn the truth. Pain is pain, joy is joy, everywhere, even as in thee. In all the songs of the forest birds; in all the cries of the wounded and dying, struggling in the captor's power; in the boundless sea where the myriads of water-creatures strive and die; amid all the countless hordes of savage men; in all sickness and sorrow; in all exultation and hope, everywhere, from the lowest to the noblest, the same conscious, burning, wilful life is found, endlessly manifold as the forms of the living creature, unquenchable as the fires of the sun, real as these impulses that even now throb in thine own little selfish heart. Lift up thy eyes, behold that life, and then turn away, and forget it as thou canst; but, if thou hast *known* that, thou hast begun to know thy duty.'

This higher vision of an inner significance in what, until then, we had realized only in the dead external way, often comes over a person suddenly; and, when it does so, it makes an epoch in his history. As Emerson says, there is a depth in those moments that constrains us to ascribe more reality to them than to all other experiences. The passion of love will shake one like an explosion, or some act will awaken a remorseful compunction that hangs like a cloud over all one's later day.

This mystic sense of hidden meaning starts upon us often from non-human natural things. I take this passage from 'Obermann,' a French novel that had some vogue in its day: 'Paris, March 7.—It was dark and rather cold. I was gloomy, and walked because I had nothing to do. I passed by some flowers placed breast-high upon a wall. A jonquil in bloom was there. It is the strongest expression of desire: it was the first perfume of the year. I felt all the happiness destined for man. This unutterable harmony of souls, the phantom of the ideal world, arose in me complete. I never felt anything so great or so instantaneous. I know not what shape, what analogy, what secret of relation it was that made me see in this flower a limitless beauty . . . I shall never enclose in a conception this power, this immensity that nothing will express; this form that nothing will contain; this ideal of a better world which one feels, but which it would seem that nature has not made.'

Wordsworth and Shelley are similarly full of this sense of a limitless significance in natural things. In Wordsworth it was a somewhat austere and moral significance,—a 'lonely cheer.'

> To every natural form, rock, fruit, or flower,
> Even the loose stones that cover the highway,
> I gave a moral life: I saw them feel
> Or linked them to some feeling: the great mass
> Lay bedded in some quickening soul, and all
> That I beheld respired with inward meaning.

'Authentic tidings of invisible things!' Just what this hidden presence in nature was, which Wordsworth so rapturously felt, and in the light of which he lived, tramping the hills for days together, the poet never could explain logically or in articulate conceptions. Yet to the reader who may himself have had gleaming moments of a similar sort the verses in which Wordsworth simply proclaims the fact of them come with a heart-satisfying authority:—

> Magnificent
> The morning rose, in memorable pomp,
> Glorious as ere I had beheld. In front
> The sea lay laughing at a distance; near
> The solid mountains shone, bright as the clouds,
> Grain-tinctured, drenched in empyrean light;
> And in the meadows and the lower grounds
> Was all the sweetness of a common dawn,—
> Dews, vapors, and the melody of birds,
> And laborers going forth to till the fields.
>
> Ah! need I say, dear Friend, that to the brim
> My heart was full; I made no vows, but vows
> Were then made for me; bond unknown to me
> Was given, that I should be, else sinning greatly,
> A dedicated Spirit. On I walked,
> In thankful blessedness, which yet survives.

As Wordsworth walked, filled with this strange inner joy, responsive thus to the secret life of nature round about him, his rural neighbors, tightly and narrowly intent upon their own affairs, their crops and lambs and fences, must have thought him a very insignificant and foolish personage. It surely never occurred to any one of them to wonder what was going on inside of *him* or what it might be worth. And yet that inner life of his carried the burden of a significance that has fed the souls of others, and fills them to this day with inner joy.

Richard Jefferies[2] has written a remarkable autobiographic document entitled, 'The Story of My Heart.' It tells, in many pages, of the rapture with which in youth the sense of the life of nature filled him. On a certain hill-top he says:—

'I was utterly alone with the sun and the earth. Lying down on the grass, I spoke in my soul to the earth, the sun, the air, and the distant sea, far beyond sight . . . With all the intensity of feeling which exalted me, all the intense communion I held with the earth, the sun and sky, the stars hidden by the light, with the ocean,—in no manner can the thrilling depth of these feelings be written,—with these I prayed as if they were the keys of an instrument . . . The great sun, burning with light, the strong earth,

---

2. **Richard Jefferies:** (1848–1887), an English writer who had a remarkable power of observing and representing nature.

—dear earth,—the warm sky, the pure air, the thought of ocean, the inex-
pressible beauty of all filled me with a rapture, an ectasy, an inflatus.[3] With
this inflatus, too, I prayed . . . The prayer, this soul-emotion, was in
itself, not for an object: it was a passion. I hid my face in the grass. I was
wholly prostrated, I lost myself in the wrestle, I was rapt and carried
away . . . Had any shepherd accidentally seen me lying on the turf, he
would only have thought I was resting a few minutes. I made no outward
show. Who could have imagined the whirlwind of passion that was going
on in me as I reclined there!'

Surely, a worthless hour of life, when measured by the usual standards
of commercial value. Yet in what other *kind* of value can the precious-
ness of any hour, made precious by any standard, consist, if it consist not
in feelings of excited significance like these, engendered in some one, by
what the hour contains?

Yet so blind and dead does the clamor of our own practical interests
make us to all other things, that it seems almost as if it were necessary to
become worthless as a practical being, if one is to hope to attain to any
breadth of insight into the impersonal world of worths as such, to have
any perception of life's meaning on a large objective scale. Only your
mystic, your dreamer, or your insolvent tramp or loafer, can afford so
sympathetic an occupation, an occupation which will change the usual
standards of human value in the twinkling of an eye, giving to foolish-
ness a place ahead of power, and laying low in a minute the distinctions
which it takes a hard-working conventional man a lifetime to build up.
You may be a prophet, at this rate; but you cannot be a worldly success.

Walt Whitman, for instance, is accounted by many of us a contemporary prophet. He abolishes the usual human distinctions, brings all conven-
tionalisms into solution, and loves and celebrates hardly any human attributes save those elementary ones common to all members of the race. For
this he becomes a sort of ideal tramp, a rider on omnibus-tops and ferry-
boats, and, considered either practically or academically, a worthless, un-
productive being. His verses are but ejaculations—things mostly without
subject or verb, a succession of interjections on an immense scale. He felt
the human crowd as rapturously as Wordsworth felt the mountains, felt
it as an overpowering significant presence, simply to absorb one's mind in
which should be business sufficient and worthy to fill the days of a serious
man. As he crosses Brooklyn ferry, this is what he feels:—

Flood-tide below me! I watch you, face to face;
Clouds of the west! sun there half an hour high! I see you also face to face.
Crowds of men and women attired in the usual costumes! how curious you are
    to me!

3. **inflatus:** inspiration.

On the ferry-boats, the hundreds and hundreds that cross, returning home, are
more curious to me than you suppose;
And you that shall cross from shore to shore hence, are more to me and more
in my meditations, than you might suppose.
Others will enter the gates of the ferry, and cross from shore to shore;
Others will watch the run of the flood-tide;
Others will see the shipping of Manhattan north and west, and the heights of
Brooklyn to the south and east;
Others will see the islands large and small;
Fifty years hence, others will see them as they cross, the sun half an hour high.
A hundred years hence, or ever so many hundred years hence, others will see
them,
Will enjoy the sunset, the pouring in of the flood-tide, the falling back to the
sea of the ebb-tide.
It avails not, neither time or place—distance avails not.
Just as you feel when you look on the river and sky, so I felt;
Just as any of you is one of a living crowd, I was one of a crowd;
Just as you are refresh'd by the gladness of the river and the bright flow, I was
refresh'd;
Just as you stand and lean on the rail, yet hurry with the swift current, I stood,
yet was hurried;
Just as you look on the numberless masts of ships, and the thick-stemmed pipes
of steamboats, I looked.
I too many and many a time cross'd the river, the sun half an hour high;
I watched the Twelfth-month [4] sea-gulls—I saw them high in the air, with
motionless wings, oscillating their bodies,
I saw how the glistening yellow lit up parts of their bodies, and left the rest in
strong shadow,
I saw the slow-wheeling circles, and the gradual edging toward the south.
Saw the white sails of schooners and sloops, saw the ships at anchor,
The sailors at work in the rigging, or out astride the spars;
The scallop-edged waves in the twilight, the ladled cups, the frolicsome crests
and glistening;
The stretch afar growing dimmer and dimmer, the gray walls of the granite
store-houses by the docks;
On the neighboring shores, the fires from the foundry chimneys burning
high . . . into the night,
Casting their flicker of black . . . into the clefts of streets.
These, and all else, were to me the same as they are to you.

And so on, through the rest of a divinely beautiful poem. And, if you
wish to see what this hoary loafer considered the most worthy way of
profiting by life's heaven-sent opportunities, read the delicious volume of
his letters to a young car-conductor who had become his friend:—

'New York, Oct. 9, 1868.
'Dear Pete,—It is splendid here this forenoon—bright and cool. I was out
early taking a short walk by the river only two squares from where I

4. **Twelfth-month**: December.

live . . . Shall I tell you about [my life] just to fill up? I generally spend
the forenoon in my room writing, etc., then take a bath, fix up and go out
about twelve and loafe somewhere or call on someone down town or on
business, or perhaps if it is very pleasant and I feel like it ride a trip with
some driver friend on Broadway from 23rd Street to Bowling Green,
three miles each way. (Every day I find I have plenty to do, every hour is
occupied with something.) You know it is a never ending amusement and
study and recreation for me to ride a couple of hours on a pleasant afternoon on a Broadway stage in this way. You see everything as you pass, a
sort of living, endless panorama—shops and splendid buildings and great
windows: on the broad sidewalks crowds of women richly dressed continually passing, altogether different, superior in style and looks from any
to be seen anywhere else—in fact a perfect stream of people—men too
dressed in high style, and plenty of foreigners—and then in the streets the
thick crowd of carriages, stages, carts, hotel and private coaches, and in
fact all sorts of vehicles and many first class teams, mile after mile, and the
splendor of such a great street and so many tall, ornamental, noble buildings many of them of white marble, and the gayety and motion on every
side; you will not wonder how much attraction all this is on a fine day, to
a great loafer like me, who enjoys so much seeing the busy world move by
him, and exhibiting itself for his amusement, while he takes it easy and
just looks on and observes.'

Truly a futile way of passing the time, some of you may say, and not altogether creditable to a grown-up man. And yet, from the deepest point
of view, who knows the more of truth, and who knows the less,—Whitman
on his omnibus-top full of the inner joy with which the spectacle inspires
him, or you, full of the disdain which the futility of his occupation excites?

When your ordinary Brooklynite or New Yorker, leading a life replete
with too much luxury, or tired and careworn about his personal affairs,
crosses the ferry or goes up Broadway, *his* fancy does not thus 'soar away
into the colors of the sunset' as did Whitman's, nor does he inwardly realize at all the indisputable fact that this world never did anywhere or at any
time contain more of essential divinity, or of eternal meaning, than is embodied in the fields of vision over which his eyes so carelessly pass. There
is life; and there, a step away, is death. There is the only kind of beauty
there ever was. There is the old human struggle and its fruits together.
There is the text and the sermon, the real and the ideal in one. But to the
jaded and unquickened eye it is all dead and common, pure vulgarism,
flatness, and disgust. 'Hech! it is a sad sight!' says Carlyle, walking at night
with some one who appears to him to note the splendor of the stars. And
that very repetition of the scene to new generations of men *in secula*

seculorum, [5] that eternal recurrence of the common order, which so fills a Whitman with mystic satisfaction, is to a Schopenhauer, with the emotional anæsthesia, the feeling of 'awful inner emptiness' from out of which he views it all, the chief ingredient of the tedium it instils. What is life on the largest scale, he asks, but the same recurrent inanities, the same dog barking, the same fly buzzing, forevermore? Yet of the kind of fiber of which such inanities consist is the material woven of all the excitements, joys, and meanings that ever were, or ever shall be, in this world.

To be rapt with satisfied attention, like Whitman, to the mere spectacle of the world's presence, is one way, and the most fundamental way, of confessing one's sense of its unfathomable significance and importance. But how can one attain to the feeling of the vital significance of an experience, if one have it not to begin with? There is no receipt which one can follow. Being a secret and a mystery, it often comes in mysteriously unexpected ways. It blossoms sometimes from out of the very grave wherein we imagined that our happiness was buried. Benvenuto Cellini, after a life all in the outer sunshine, made of adventures and artistic excitements, suddenly finds himself cast into a dungeon in the Castle of San Angelo. The place is horrible. Rats and wet and mould possess it. His leg is broken and his teeth fall out, apparently with scurvy. But his thoughts turn to God as they have never turned before. He gets a Bible, which he reads during the one hour in the twenty-four in which a wandering ray of daylight penetrates his cavern. He has religious visions. He sings psalms to himself, and composes hymns. And thinking, on the last day of July, of the festivities customary on the morrow in Rome, he says to himself: 'All these past years I celebrated this holiday with the vanities of the world: from this year henceforth I will do it with the divinity of God. And then I said to myself, "Oh, how much more happy I am for this present life of mine than for all those things remembered!"'

But the great understander of these mysterious ebbs and flows is Tolstoi. They throb all through his novels. In his 'War and Peace,' the hero, Peter, is supposed to be the richest man in the Russian empire. During the French invasion he is taken prisoner, and dragged through much of the retreat. Cold, vermin, hunger, and every form of misery assail him, the result being a revelation to him of the real scale of life's values. 'Here only, and for the first time, he appreciated, because he was deprived of it, the happiness of eating when he was hungry, of drinking when he was thirsty, of sleeping when he was sleepy, and of talking when he felt the desire to exchange some words . . . Later in life he always recurred with joy to this month of captivity, and never failed to speak with enthusiasm of the

5. *in secula seculorum:* unto eternity.

powerful and ineffaceable sensations, and especially of the moral calm
which he had experienced at this epoch. When at daybreak, on the morrow of his imprisonment, he saw [I abridge here Tolstoi's description] the
mountains with their wooded slopes disappearing in the grayish mist;
when he felt the cool breeze caress him; when he saw the light drive away
the vapors, and the sun rise majestically behind the clouds and cupolas,
and the crosses, the dew, the distance, the river, sparkle in the splendid,
cheerful rays,—his heart overflowed with emotion. This emotion kept
continually with him, and increased a hundred-fold as the difficulties of his
situation grew grave . . . He learnt that man is meant for happiness, and
that this happiness is in him, in the satisfaction of the daily needs of existence, and that unhappiness is the fatal result, not of our need, but of our
abundance . . . When calm reigned in the camp, and the embers paled,
and little by little went out, the full moon had reached the zenith. The
woods and the fields roundabout lay clearly visible; and, beyond the in-
undation of light which filled them, the view plunged into the limitless
horizon. Then Peter cast his eyes upon the firmament, filled at that hour
with myriads of stars. "All that is mine," he thought. "All that is in me,
is me! And that is what they have taken prisoner! That is what they have
shut up in a cabin." So he smiled, and turned in to sleep among his comrades.'

The occasion and the experience, then, are nothing. It all depends on the
capacity of the soul to be grasped, to have its life-currents absorbed by
what is given. 'Crossing a bare common,' says Emerson, 'in snow puddles,
at twilight, under a clouded sky, without having in my thoughts any occurrence of special good fortune, I have enjoyed a perfect exhilaration. I
am glad to the brink of fear.'

Life is always worth living, if one have such responsive sensibilities. But
we of the highly educated classes (so called) have most of us got far, far
away from Nature. We are trained to seek the choice, the rare, the exquisite exclusively, and to overlook the common. We are stuffed with abstract conceptions, and glib with verbalities and verbosities; and in the
culture of these higher functions the peculiar sources of joy connected
with our simpler functions often dry up, and we grow stoneblind and insensible to life's more elementary and general goods and joys.

The remedy under such conditions is to descend to a more profound
and primitive level. To be imprisoned or shipwrecked or forced into the
army would permanently show the good of life to many an overeducated
pessimist. Living in the open air and on the ground, the lopsided beam of
the balance slowly rises to the level line; and the over-sensibilities and in-
sensibilities even themselves out. The good of all the artificial schemes and
fevers fades and pales; and that of seeing, smelling, tasting, sleeping, and

daring and doing with one's body, grows and grows. The savages and children of nature, to whom we deem ourselves so much superior, certainly
are alive where we are often dead, along these lines; and could they write
as glibly as we do, they would read us impressive lectures on our impatience for improvement and on our blindness to the fundamental static
goods of life. 'Ah! my brother,' said a chieftain to his white guest, 'thou
wilt never know the happiness of both thinking of nothing and doing
nothing. This, next to sleep, is the most enchanting of all things. Thus we
were before our birth, and thus we shall be after death. Thy people . . .
when they have finished reaping one field, they begin to plough another;
and, if the day were not enough, I have seen them plough by moonlight.
What is their life to ours,—the life that is as naught to them? Blind that
they are, they lose it all! But we live in the present.'

The intense interest that life can assume when brought down to the
non-thinking level, the level of pure sensorial perception, has been beautifully described by a man who *can* write,—Mr. W. H. Hudson, in his
volume, 'Idle Days in Patagonia.'

'I spent the greater part of one winter,' says this admirable author, 'at
a point on the Rio Negro, seventy or eighty miles from the sea.

. . . 'It was my custom to go out every morning on horseback with my
gun, and, followed by one dog, to ride away from the valley; and no
sooner would I climb the terrace, and plunge into the gray, universal
thicket, than I would find myself as completely alone as if five hundred instead of only five miles separated me from the valley and river. So wild
and solitary and remote seemed that gray waste, stretching away into in-
finitude, a waste untrodden by man, and where the wild animals are so
few that they have made no discoverable path in the wilderness of
thorns . . . Not once nor twice nor thrice, but day after day I returned to
this solitude, going to it in the morning as if to attend a festival, and
leaving it only when hunger and thirst and the westering sun compelled
me. And yet I had no object in going,—no motive which could be put into
words; for, although I carried a gun, there was nothing to shoot,—the
shooting was all left behind in the valley . . . Sometimes I would pass a
whole day without seeing one mammal, and perhaps not more than a
dozen birds of any size. The weather at that time was cheerless, generally
with a gray film of cloud spread over the sky, and a bleak wind, often cold
enough to make my bridle-hand quite numb . . . At a slow pace, which
would have seemed intolerable under other circumstances, I would ride
about for hours together at a stretch. On arriving at a hill, I would slowly
ride to its summit, and stand there to survey the prospect. On every side
it stretched away in great undulations, wild and irregular. How gray it
all was! Hardly less so near at hand than on the haze-wrapped horizon

where the hills were dim and the outline obscured by distance. Descending from my outlook, I would take up my aimless wanderings again, and visit other elevations to gaze on the same landscape from another point; and so on for hours. And at noon I would dismount, and sit or lie on my folded poncho for an hour or longer. One day in these rambles I discovered a small grove composed of twenty or thirty trees, growing at a convenient distance apart, that had evidently been resorted to by a herd of deer or other wild animals. This grove was on a hill differing in shape from other hills in its neighborhood; and, after a time, I made a point of finding and using it as a resting-place every day at noon. I did not ask myself why I made choice of that one spot, sometimes going out of my way to sit there, instead of sitting down under any one of the millions of trees and bushes on any other hillside. I thought nothing about it, but acted unconsciously. Only afterward it seemed to me that, after having rested there once, each time I wished to rest again, the wish came associated with the image of that particular clump of trees, with polished stems and clean bed of sand beneath; and in a short time I formed a habit of returning, animal like, to repose at that same spot.

'It was, perhaps, a mistake to say that I would sit down and rest, since I was never tired; and yet, without being tired, that noon-day pause, during which I sat for an hour without moving, was strangely grateful. All day there would be no sound, not even the rustling of a leaf. One day, while *listening* to the silence, it occurred to my mind to wonder what the effect would be if I were to shout aloud. This seemed at the time a horrible suggestion, which almost made me shudder. But during those solitary days it was a rare thing for any thought to cross my mind. In the state of mind I was in, thought had become impossible. My state was one of *suspense* and *watchfulness;* yet I had no expectation of meeting an adventure, and felt as free from apprehension as I feel now while sitting in a room in London. The state seemed familiar rather than strange, and accompanied by a strong feeling of elation; and I did not know that something had come between me and my intellect until I returned to my former self,—to thinking, and the old insipid existence [again].

'I had undoubtedly *gone back;* and that state of intense watchfulness or alertness, rather, with suspension of the higher intellectual faculties, represented, the mental state of the pure savage. He thinks little, reasons little, having a surer guide in his [mere sensory perceptions]. He is in perfect harmony with nature, and is nearly on a level, mentally, with the wild animals he preys on, and which in their turn sometimes prey on him.'

For the spectator, such hours as Mr. Hudson writes of form a mere tale of emptiness, in which nothing happens, nothing is gained, and there is nothing to describe. They are meaningless and vacant tracts of time. To him who feels their inner secret, they tingle with an importance that unutterably vouches for itself. I am sorry for the boy or girl, or man or woman, who has never been touched by the spell of this mysterious sensorial life, with its irrationality, if so you like to call it, but its vigilance and its supreme felicity. The holidays of life are its most vitally significant portions, because they are, or at least should be, covered with just this kind of magically irresponsible spell.

And now what is the result of all these considerations and quotations? It is negative in one sense, but positive in another. It absolutely forbids us to be forward in pronouncing on the meaninglessness of forms of existence other than our own; and it commands us to tolerate, respect, and indulge those whom we see harmlessly interested and happy in their own ways, however unintelligible these may be to us. Hands off: neither the whole of truth nor the whole of good is revealed to any single observer, although each observer gains a partial superiority of insight from the peculiar position in which he stands. Even prisons and sick-rooms have their special revelations. It is enough to ask of each of us that he should be faithful to his own opportunities and make the most of his own blessings, without presuming to regulate the rest of the vast field.

E. B. White

A SLIGHT SOUND AT EVENING

I N HIS JOURNAL for July 10–12, 1841, Thoreau wrote: "A slight sound at evening lifts me up by the ears, and makes life seem inexpressibly serene and grand. It may be in Uranus, or it may be in the shutter." The book into which he later managed to pack both Uranus and the shutter was published in 1854, and now, a hundred years having gone by, *Walden*, its serenity and grandeur unimpaired, still lifts us up by the ears, still trans-

"A Slight Sound at Evening" (Allen Cove, Summer, 1954) from *The Points of My Compass* by E. B. White, copyright 1954 by E. B. White. Reprinted with the permission of Harper & Row, Publishers, Incorporated. Originally appeared in *The Yale Review* under the title of "Walden—1954."

lates for us that language we are in danger of forgetting, "which all things and events speak without metaphor, which alone is copious and standard."

Walden is an oddity in American letters. It may very well be the oddest of our distinguished oddities. For many it is a great deal too odd, and for many it is a particular bore. I have not found it to be a well-liked book among my acquaintances, although usually spoken of with respect, and one literary critic for whom I have the highest regard can find no reason why anyone gives *Walden* a second thought. To admire the book is, in fact, something of an embarrassment, for the mass of men have an indistinct notion that its author was a sort of Nature Boy.

I think it is of some advantage to encounter the book at a period in one's life when the normal anxieties and enthusiasms and rebellions of youth closely resemble those of Thoreau in that spring of 1845 when he borrowed an axe, went out to the woods, and began to whack down some trees for timber. Received at such a juncture, the book is like an invitation to life's dance, assuring the troubled recipient that no matter what befalls him in the way of success or failure he will always be welcome at the party—that the music is played for him, too, if he will but listen and move his feet. In effect, that is what the book is—an invitation, unengraved; and it stirs one as a young girl is stirred by her first big party bid. Many think it a sermon; many set it down as an attempt to rearrange society; some think it an exercise in nature-loving; some find it a rather irritating collection of inspirational puffballs by an eccentric show-off. I think it none of these. It still seems to me the best youth's companion yet written by an American, for it carries a solemn warning against the loss of one's valuables, it advances a good argument for traveling light and trying new adventures, it rings with the power of positive adoration, it contains religious feeling without religious images, and it steadfastly refuses to record bad news. Even its pantheistic note is so pure as to be noncorrupting—pure as the flute-note blown across the pond on those faraway summer nights. If our colleges and universities were alert, they would present a cheap pocket edition of the book to every senior upon graduating, along with his sheepskin, or instead of it. Even if some senior were to take it literally and start felling trees, there could be worse mishaps: the axe is older than the Dictaphone and it is just as well for a young man to see what kind of chips he leaves before listening to the sound of his own voice. And even if some were to get no farther than the table of contents, they would learn how to name eighteen chapters by the use of only thirty-nine words and would see how sweet are the uses of brevity.

If Thoreau had merely left us an account of a man's life in the woods, or if he had simply retreated to the woods and there recorded his complaints about society, or even if he had contrived to include both records in one essay, *Walden* would probably not have lived a hundred years. As things turned out, Thoreau, very likely without knowing quite what he was up to, took man's relation to nature and man's dilemma in society and man's capacity for elevating his spirit and he beat all these matters together, in a wild free interval of self-justification and delight, and produced an original omelette from which people can draw nourishment in a hungry day. *Walden* is one of the first of the vitamin-enriched American dishes. If it were a little less good than it is, or even a little less queer, it would be an abominable book. Even as it is, it will continue to baffle and annoy the literal mind and all those who are unable to stomach its caprices and imbibe its theme. Certainly the plodding economist will continue to have rough going if he hopes to emerge from the book with a clear system of economic thought. Thoreau's assault on the Concord society of the mid-nineteenth century has the quality of a modern Western: he rides into the subject at top speed, shooting in all directions. Many of his shots ricochet and nick him on the rebound, and throughout the melee there is a horrendous cloud of inconsistencies and contradictions, and when the shooting dies down and the air clears, one is impressed chiefly by the courage of the rider and by how splendid it was that somebody should have ridden in there and raised all that ruckus.

When he went to the pond, Thoreau struck an attitude and did so deliberately, but his posturing was not to draw the attention of others to him but rather to draw his own attention more closely to himself. "I learned this at least by my experiment: that if one advances confidently in the direction of his dreams, and endeavors to live the life which he has imagined, he will meet with a success unexpected in common hours." The sentence has the power to resuscitate the youth drowning in his sea of doubt. I recall my exhilaration upon reading it, many years ago, in a time of hesitation and despair. It restored me to health. And now in 1954 when I salute Henry Thoreau on the hundredth birthday of his book, I am merely paying off an old score—or an installment on it.

In his journal for May 3–4, 1838—Boston to Portland—he wrote: "Midnight—head over the boat's side—between sleeping and waking—with glimpses of one or more lights in the vicinity of Cape Ann. Bright moonlight—the effect heightened by seasickness." The entry illuminates the man, as the moon the sea on that night in May. In Thoreau the natural scene was heightened, not depressed, by a disturbance of the stomach, and nausea met its match at last. There was a steadiness in at least one passenger if there was none in the boat. Such steadiness (which in some would be called intoxication) is at the heart of *Walden*—confidence, faith, the discipline of looking always at what is to be seen, undeviating gratitude for the life-everlasting that he found growing in his front yard. "There is nowhere recorded a simple and irrepressible satisfaction with the gift of life, any memorable praise of God." He worked to correct that deficiency. *Walden* is his acknowledgment of the gift of life. It is the testament of a man in a high state of indignation because (it seemed to him) so few ears heard the uninterrupted poem of creation, the morning wind that forever blows. If the man sometimes wrote as though all his readers were male, unmarried, and well-connected, it is because he gave his testimony during the callow years, and, for that matter, never really grew up. To reject the book because of the immaturity of the author and the bugs in the logic is to throw away a bottle of good wine because it contains bits of the cork.

Thoreau said he required of every writer, first and last, a simple and sincere account of his own life. Having delivered himself of this chesty dictum, he proceeded to ignore it. In his books and even in his enormous journal, he withheld or disguised most of the facts from which an understanding of his life could be drawn. *Walden,* subtitled *Life in the Woods,* is not a simple and sincere account of a man's life, either in or out of the woods; it is an account of a man's journey into the mind, a toot on the trumpet to alert the neighbors. Thoreau was well aware that no one can alert his neighbors who is not wide awake himself, and he went to the woods (among other reasons) to make sure that he would stay awake during his broadcast. What actually took place during the years 1845–47 is largely unrecorded, and the reader is excluded from the private life of the author, who supplies almost no gossip about himself, a great deal about his neighbors and about the universe.

As for me, I cannot in this short ramble give a simple and sincere account of my own life, but I think Thoreau might find it instructive to know that this memorial essay is being written in a house that, through no intent on my part, is the same size and shape as his own domicile on the pond—about ten by fifteen, tight, plainly finished, and at a little distance from my Concord. The house in which I sit this morning was built to accommodate a boat, not a man, but by long experience I have learned that in most respects it shelters me better than the larger dwelling where my bed is, and which, by design, is a manhouse not a boathouse. Here in the boathouse I am a wilder and, it would appear, a healthier man, by a safe margin. I have a chair, a bench, a table, and I can walk into the water if I tire of the land. My house fronts a cove. Two fishermen have just arrived to spot fish from the air—an osprey and a man in a small yellow plane who works for the fish company. The man, I have noticed, is less well equipped than the hawk, who can dive directly on his fish and carry it away, without telephoning. A mouse and a squirrel share the house with me. The building is, in fact, a multiple dwelling, a semidetached affair. It is because I am semidetached while here that I find it possible to transact this private business with the fewest obstacles.

There is also a woodchuck here, living forty feet away under the wharf. When the wind is right, he can smell my house; and when the wind is contrary, I can smell his. We both use the wharf for sunning, taking turns, each adjusting his schedule to the other's convenience. Thoreau once ate a woodchuck. I think he felt he owed it to his readers, and that it was little enough, considering the indignities they were suffering at his hands and the dressing-down they were taking. (Parts of *Walden* are pure scold.) Or perhaps he ate the woodchuck because he believed every man should acquire strict business habits, and the woodchuck was destroying his market beans. I do not know. Thoreau had a strong experimental streak in him. It is probably no harder to eat a woodchuck than to construct a sentence that lasts a hundred years. At any rate, Thoreau is the only writer I know who prepared himself for his great ordeal by eating a woodchuck; also the only one who got a hangover from drinking too much water. (He was drunk the whole time, though he seldom touched wine or coffee or tea.)

Here in this compact house where I would spend one day as deliberately as Nature if I were not being pressed by *The Yale Review*,[1] and with a woodchuck (as yet uneaten) for neighbor, I can feel the companionship of the occupant of the pondside cabin in Walden woods, a mile from the village, near the Fitchburg right of way. Even my immediate business is no barrier between us: Thoreau occasionally batted out a magazine piece, but was always suspicious of any sort of purposeful work that cut into his time. A man, he said, should take care not to be thrown off the track by every nutshell and mosquito's wing that falls on the rails.

There has been much guessing as to why he went to the pond. To set it down to escapism is, of course, to misconstrue what happened. Henry went forth to battle when he took to the woods, and *Walden* is the report of a man torn by two powerful and opposing drives—the desire to enjoy the world (and not be derailed by a mosquito wing) and the urge to set the world straight. One cannot join these two successfully, but sometimes, in rare cases, something good or even great results from the attempt of the tormented spirit to reconcile them. Henry went forth to battle, and if he set the stage himself, if he fought on his own terms and with his own weapons, it was because it was his nature to do things differently from most men, and to act in a cocky fashion. If the pond and the woods seemed a more plausible site for a house than an in-town location, it was because a cowbell made for him a sweeter sound than a churchbell. *Walden*, the book, makes the sound of a cowbell, more than a churchbell, and proves

1. Mr. White's essay first appeared in *The Yale Review*, Autumn, 1954.

the point, although both sounds are in it, and both remarkably clear and sweet. He simply preferred his churchbell at a little distance.

I think one reason he went to the woods was a perfectly simple and commonplace one—and apparently he thought so, too. "At a certain season of our life," he wrote, "we are accustomed to consider every spot as the possible site of a house." There spoke the young man, a few years out of college, who had not yet broken away from home. He hadn't married, and he had found no job that measured up to his rigid standards of employment, and like any young man, or young animal, he felt uneasy and on the defensive until he had fixed himself a den. Most young men, of course, casting about for a site, are content merely to draw apart from their kinfolks. Thoreau, convinced that the greater part of what his neighbors called good was bad, withdrew from a great deal more than family: he pulled out of everything for a while, to serve everybody right for being so stuffy, and to try his own prejudices on the dog.

The house-hunting sentence above, which starts the Chapter called "Where I Lived, and What I Lived For," is followed by another passage that is worth quoting here because it so beautifully illustrates the offbeat prose that Thoreau was master of, a prose at once strictly disciplined and wildly abandoned. "I have surveyed the country on every side within a dozen miles of where I live," continued this delirious young man. "In imagination I have bought all the farms in succession, for all were to be bought, and I knew their price. I walked over each farmer's premises, tasted his wild apples, discoursed on husbandry with him, took his farm at his price, at any price, mortgaging it to him in my mind; even put a higher price on it—took everything but a deed of it—took his word for his deed, for I dearly love to talk—cultivated it, and him too to some extent, I trust, and withdrew when I had enjoyed it long enough, leaving him to carry it on." A copydesk man would get a double hernia trying to clean up that sentence for the management, but the sentence needs no fixing, for it perfectly captures the meaning of the writer and the quality of the ramble.

"Wherever I sat, there I might live, and the landscape radiated from me accordingly." Thoreau, the home-seeker, sitting on his hummock with the entire State of Massachusetts radiating from him, is to me the most humorous of the New England figures, and *Walden* the most humorous of the books, though its humor is almost continuously subsurface and there is nothing funny anywhere, except a few weak jokes and bad puns that rise to the surface like the perch in the pond that rose to the sound of the maestro's flute. Thoreau tended to write in sentences, a feat not every writer is capable of, and *Walden* is, rhetorically speaking, a collection of certified sentences, some of them, it would now appear, as indestructible as they are errant. The book is distilled from the vast journals, and this accounts for its intensity: he picked out bright particles that pleased his eye, whirled them in the kaleidoscope of his content, and produced the pattern that has endured—the color, the form, the light.

On this its hundredth birthday, Thoreau's *Walden* is pertinent and timely. In our uneasy season, when all men unconsciously seek a retreat from a world that has got almost completely out of hand, his house in the Concord woods is a haven. In our culture of gadgetry and the multiplicity of convenience, his cry "Simplicity, simplicity, simplicity!" has the insistence of a fire alarm. In the brooding atmosphere of war and the gathering radioactive storm, the innocence and serenity of his summer afternoons are enough to burst the remembering heart, and one gazes back upon that pleasing interlude—its confidence, its purity, its deliberateness—with awe and wonder, as one would look upon the face of a child asleep.

"This small lake was of most value as a neighbor in the intervals of a gentle rain-storm in August, when, both air and water being perfectly still, but the sky overcast, midafternoon had all the serenity of evening, and the wood-thrush sang around, and was heard from shore to shore." Now, in the perpetual overcast in which our days are spent, we hear with extra perception and deep gratitude that song, tying century to century.

I sometimes amuse myself by bringing Henry Thoreau back to life and showing him the sights. I escort him into a phone booth and let him dial Weather. "This is a delicious evening," the girl's voice says, "when the whole body is one sense, and imbibes delight through every pore." I show him the spot in the Pacific where an island used to be, before some magician made it vanish. "We know not where we are," I murmur. "The light which puts out our eyes is darkness to us. Only that day dawns to which we are awake." I thumb through the latest copy of *Vogue* with him. "Of two patterns which differ only by a few threads more or less of a particular color," I read, "the one will be sold readily, the other lie on the shelf, though it frequently happens that, after the lapse of a season, the latter becomes the most fashionable." Together we go outboarding on the Assabet,[2] looking for what we've lost—a hound, a bay horse, a turtledove. I show him a distracted farmer who is trying to repair a hay baler before the thunder shower breaks. "This farmer," I remark, "is endeavoring to solve the problem of a livelihood by a formula more complicated than the problem itself. To get his shoe strings he speculates in herds of cattle."

I take the celebrated author to Twenty-One[3] for lunch, so the waiters may study his shoes. The proprietor welcomes us. "The gross feeder," remarks the proprietor, sweeping the room with his arm, "is a man in the

2. the Assabet: a river near Concord.
3. Twenty-One: a well-known restaurant in New York City.

larva stage." After lunch we visit a classroom in one of those schools conducted by big corporations to teach their superannuated executives how to retire from business without serious injury to their health. (The shock to men's systems these days when relieved of the exacting routine of amassing wealth is very great and must be cushioned.) "It is not necessary," says the teacher to his pupils, "that a man should earn his living by the sweat of his brow, unless he sweats easier than I do. We are determined to be starved before we are hungry."

I turn on the radio and let Thoreau hear Winchell beat the red hand around the clock. "Time is but the stream I go a-fishing in," shouts Mr. Winchell, rattling his telegraph key. "Hardly a man takes a half hour's nap after dinner, but when he wakes he holds up his head and asks, 'What's the news?' If we read of one man robbed, or murdered, or killed by accident, or one house burned, or one vessel wrecked, or one steamboat blown up, or one cow run over on the Western Railroad, or one mad dog killed, or one lot of grasshoppers in the winter—we need never read of another. One is enough."

I doubt that Thoreau would be thrown off balance by the fantastic sights and sounds of the twentieth century. "The Concord nights," he once wrote, "are stranger than the Arabian nights." A four-engined air liner would merely serve to confirm his early views on travel. Everywhere he would observe, in new shapes and sizes, the old predicaments and follies of men—the desperation, the impedimenta, the meanness—along with the visible capacity for elevation of the mind and soul. "This curious world which we inhabit is more wonderful than it is convenient; more beautiful than it is useful; it is more to be admired and enjoyed than used." He would see that today ten thousand engineers are busy making sure that the world shall be convenient if they bust doing it, and others are determined to increase its usefulness even though its beauty is lost somewhere along the way.

At any rate, I'd like to stroll about the countryside in Thoreau's company for a day, observing the modern scene, inspecting today's snowstorm, pointing out the sights, and offering belated apologies for my sins. Thoreau is unique among writers in that those who admire him find him uncomfortable to live with—a regular hairshirt of a man. A little band of dedicated Thoreauvians would be a sorry sight indeed: fellows who hate compromise and have compromised, fellows who love wildness and have lived tamely, and at their side, censuring them and childing them, the ghostly figure of this upright man, who long ago gave corroboration to impulses they perceived were right and issued warnings against the things they instinctively knew to be their enemies. I should hate to be called a Thoreauvian, yet I wince every time I walk into the barn I'm pushing before me, seventy-five feet by forty, and the author of *Walden* has served as my conscience through the long stretches of my trivial days.

Hairshirt or no, he is a better companion than most, and I would not swap him for a soberer or more reasonable friend even if I could. I can reread his famous invitation with undiminished excitement. The sad thing is that not more acceptances have been received, that so many decline for one reason or another, pleading some previous engagement or ill health. But the invitation stands. It will beckon as long as this remarkable book stays in print—which will be as long as there are August afternoons in the intervals of a gentle rainstorm, as long as there are ears to catch the faint sounds of the orchestra. I find it agreeable to sit here this morning, in a house of correct proportions, and hear across a century of time his flute, his frogs, and his seductive summons to the wildest revels of them all.

H. W. Fowler

THE SPLIT INFINITIVE

THE English-speaking world may be divided into (1) those who neither know nor care what a split infinitive is; (2) those who do not know, but care very much; (3) those who know and condemn; (4) those who know and approve; and (5) those who know and distinguish.

Those who neither know nor care are the vast majority, and are a happy folk, to be envied by most of the minority classes; 'to really understand' comes readier to their lips and pens than 'really to understand', they see no reason why they should not say it (small blame to them, seeing that reasons are not their critics' strong point), and they do say it, to the discomfort of some among us, but not to their own.

To the second class, those who do not know but do care, who would as soon be caught putting their knives in their mouths as splitting an infinitive but have hazy notions of what constitutes that deplorable breach of etiquette, this article is chiefly addressed. These people betray by their practice that their aversion to the split infinitive springs not from instinctive

From *A Dictionary of Modern English Usage* by H. W. Fowler, copyright 1926 by Oxford University Press. Reprinted by permission of the publishers.

good taste, but from tame acceptance of the misinterpreted opinion of others; for they will subject their sentences to the queerest distortions, all to escape imaginary split infinitives, 'To really understand' is a split infinitive; 'to really be understood' is a split infinitive; 'to be really understood' is not one; the havoc that is played with much well-intentioned writing by failure to grasp that distinction is incredible. Those upon whom the fear of infinitive-splitting sits heavy should remember that to give conclusive evidence, by distortions, of misconceiving the nature of the split infinitive is far more damaging to their literary pretensions than an actual lapse could be; for it exhibits them as deaf to the normal rhythm of English sentences. No sensitive ear can fail to be shocked, if the following examples are read aloud, by the strangeness of the indicated adverbs. Why on earth, the reader wonders, is that word out of its place? He will find, on looking through again, that each has been turned out of a similar position, viz between the word *be* and a passive participle. Reflection will assure him that the cause of dislocation is always the same—all these writers have sacrificed the run of their sentences to the delusion that 'to be really understood' is a split infinitive. It is not; and the straitest non-splitter of us all can with a clear conscience restore each of the adverbs to its rightful place:

He was proposed at the last moment as a candidate likely *generally* to be accepted.

When the record of this campaign comes *dispassionately* to be written, and in just perspective, it will be found that . . .

The leaders have given instructions that the lives and property of foreigners shall *scrupulously* be respected.

New principles will have *boldly* to be adopted if the Scottish case is to be met.

This is a very serious matter, which clearly ought *further* to be inquired into.

There are many points raised in the report which need *carefully* to be explored.

Only two ways of escaping from the conflict without loss, by this time become too serious *squarely* to be faced, have ever offered themselves.

The Headmaster of a public school possesses very great powers, which ought *most carefully* and *considerately* to be exercised.

The time to get this revaluation put through is when the amount paid by the State to the localities is *very largely* to be increased.

But the party whose Leader in the House of Commons acts in this way cannot fail *deeply* to be discredited by the way in which he flings out and about these false charges.

The above writers are bogy-haunted creatures who for fear of splitting an infinitive abstain from doing something quite different, i.e. dividing *be* from its complement by an adverb. Those who presumably do know what split infinitives are, and condemn them, are not so easily identified, since they include all who neither commit the sin nor flounder about in saving themselves from it, all who combine with acceptance of conventional rules a reasonable dexterity. But when the dexterity is lacking, disaster follows. It does not add to a writer's readableness if readers are pulled up now and again to wonder—Why this distortion? Ah, to be sure, a non-split die-hard! That is the mental dialogue occasioned by each of the adverbs in the examples below. It is of no avail merely to fling oneself desperately out of temptation; one must so do it that no traces of the struggle remain; that is, sentences must be thoroughly remodelled instead of having a word lifted from its original place and dumped elsewhere:

What alternative can be found which the Pope has not condemned, and which will make it possible *to organize legally* public worship?

If it is to do justice between the various parties and not *unduly to burden* the State, it will . . .

It will, when better understood, tend *firmly to establish* relations between Capital and Labour.

Both Germany and England have done ill in not combining *to forbid flatly* hostilities.

Nobody expects that the executive of the Amalgamated Society is going *to assume publicly* sackcloth and ashes.

Every effort must be made *to increase adequately* professional knowledge and attainments.

We have had *to shorten somewhat* Lord Denbigh's letter.

The kind of sincerity which enables an author *to move powerfully* the heart would . . .

Safeguards should be provided *to prevent effectually* cosmopolitan financiers from manipulating these reserves.

Just as those who know and condemn the split infinitive include many who are not recognizable, only the clumsier performers giving positive proof of resistance to temptation, so too those who know and approve are not distinguishable with certainty; when a man splits an infinitive, he may be doing it unconsciously as a member of our class 1, or he may be deliberately rejecting the trammels of convention and announcing that he means to do as he will with his own infinitives. But, as the following examples are from newspapers of high repute, and high newspaper tradition is strong against splitting, it is perhaps fair to assume that each specimen is a manifesto of independence:

It will be found possible *to considerably improve* the present wages of the miners without jeopardizing the interests of capital.

Always providing that the Imperialists do not feel strong enough *to decisively assert* their power in the revolted provinces.

But even so, he seems *to still be allowed* to speak at Unionist demonstrations.

It is the intention of the Minister of Transport *to substantially increase* all present rates by means of a general percentage.

The men in many of the largest districts are declared *to strongly favour* a strike if the minimum wage is not conceded.

It should be noticed that in these the separating adverb could have been placed outside the infinitive with little or in most cases no damage to the sentence-rhythm (*considerably* after *miners, decisively* after *power, still* with clear gain after *be, substantially* after *rates,* and *strongly* at some loss after *strike*), so that protest seems a safe diagnosis.

The attitude of those who know and distinguish is something like this: We admit that separation of *to* from its infinitive (viz *be, do, have, sit, doubt, kill,* or other verb inflexionally similar) is not in itself desirable, and we shall not gratuitously say either 'to mortally wound' or 'to mortally be wounded'; but we are not foolish enough to confuse the latter with 'to be mortally wounded', which is blameless English, nor 'to just have heard' with 'to have just heard', which is also blameless. We maintain, however, that a real split infinitive, though not desirable in itself, is preferable to either of two things, to real ambiguity, and to patent artificiality. For the first, we will rather write 'Our object is to further cement trade relations' than, by correcting into 'Our object is further to cement . . .', leave it doubtful whether an additional object or additional cementing is the point. And for the second, we take it that such reminders of a tyrannous convention as 'in not combining to forbid flatly hostilities' are far more abnormal than the abnormality they evade. We will split infinitives sooner than be ambiguous or artificial; more than that, we will freely admit that sufficient recasting will get rid of any split infinitive without involving either of those faults, and yet reserve to ourselves the right of deciding in each case whether recasting is worth while. Let us take an example: 'In these circumstances, the Commission, judging from the evidence taken in London, has been feeling its way to modifications intended to better equip successful candidates for careers in India and at the same time to meet reasonable Indian demands'. To better equip? We refuse 'better to equip' as a shouted reminder of the tyranny; we refuse 'to equip better' as ambiguous (*better* an adjective?); we regard 'to equip successful candidates better' as lacking compactness, as possibly tolerable from an anti-splitter, but not good enough for us. What then of recasting? 'intended to make successful candidates fitter for' is the best we can do if the exact sense is to be kept; it takes some thought to arrive at the correction; was the game worth the candle?

After this inconclusive discussion, in which, however, the author's opinion has perhaps been allowed to appear with indecent plainness, readers may like to settle for themselves whether, in the following sentence, 'either to secure' followed by 'to resign', or 'to either secure' followed by 'resign', should have been preferred—an issue in which the meaning and the convention are pitted against each other:—The speech has drawn an interesting letter from Sir Antony MacDonnell, who states that his agreement with Mr Wyndham was never cancelled, and that Mr Long was too weak *either to secure* the dismissal of Sir Antony or himself to resign office.

It is perhaps hardly fair that this article should have quoted no split infinitives except such as, being reasonably supposed to be deliberate, are likely to be favourable specimens. Let it therefore conclude with one borrowed from a reviewer, to whose description of it no exception need be taken: 'A book . . . of which the purpose is thus—with a deafening split infinitive—stated by its author:—"Its main idea is *to* historically, even while events are maturing, and divinely—from the Divine point of view—*impeach* the European system of Church & States".'.

George Orwell

POLITICS AND THE ENGLISH LANGUAGE

Most people who bother with the matter at all would admit that the English language is in a bad way, but it is generally assumed that we cannot by conscious action do anything about it. Our civilization is decadent and our language—so the argument runs—must inevitably share in the general collapse. It follows that any struggle against the abuse of language is a sentimental archaism, like preferring candles to electric light or hansom cabs to aeroplanes. Underneath this lies the half-conscious belief that language is a natural growth and not an instrument which we shape for our own purposes.

Now, it is clear that the decline of a language must ultimately have political and economic causes: it is not due simply to the bad influence of this or that individual writer. But an effect can become a cause, reinforcing the original cause and producing the same effect in an intensified form, and so on indefinitely. A man may take to drink because he feels himself to be a failure, and then fail all the more completely because he drinks. It is rather the same thing that is happening to the English language. It becomes ugly and inaccurate because our thoughts are foolish, but the slovenliness of our language makes it easier for us to have foolish thoughts. The point is that the process is reversible. Modern English, especially written English, is full of bad habits which spread by imitation and which can be avoided if one is willing to take the necessary trouble. If one gets rid of these habits one can think more clearly, and to think clearly is a necessary first step toward political regeneration: so that the fight against bad English is not frivolous and is not the exclusive concern of professional writers. I will come back to this presently, and I hope that by that time the meaning of what I have said here will have become clearer. Meanwhile, here are five specimens of the English language as it is now habitually written.

These five passages have not been picked out because they are especially bad—I could have quoted far worse if I had chosen—but because they illustrate various of the mental vices from which we now suffer. They are a little below the average, but are fairly representative samples. I number them so that I can refer back to them when necessary:

(1) I am not, indeed, sure whether it is not true to say that the Milton who once seemed not unlike a seventeenth-century Shelley had not become, out of an experience ever more bitter in each year, more alien [*sic*] to the founder of that Jesuit sect which nothing could induce him to tolerate.
Professor Harold Laski (Essay in *Freedom of Expression*)

(2) Above all, we cannot play ducks and drakes with a native battery of idioms which prescribes such egregious collocations of vocables as the Basic [1] *put up with* for *tolerate* or *put at a loss* for *bewilder*.
Professor Lancelot Hogben (*Interglossa*)

1. Professor Hogben is referring to Basic English, a highly simplified form of English, containing only 850 words in its general vocabulary.

(3) On the one side we have the free personality: by definition it is not neurotic, for it has neither conflict nor dream. Its desires, such as they are, are transparent, for they are just what institutional approval keeps in the forefront of consciousness; another institutional pattern would alter their number and intensity; there is little in them that is natural, irreducible, or culturally dangerous. But *on the other side*, the social bond itself is nothing but the mutual reflection of these self-secure integrities. Recall the definition of love. Is not this the very picture of a small academic? Where is there a place in this hall of mirrors for either personality or fraternity?

Essay on psychology in Politics (New York)

(4) All the "best people" from the gentlemen's clubs, and all the frantic fascist captains, united in common hatred of Socialism and bestial horror of the rising tide of the mass revolutionary movement, have turned to acts of provocation, to foul incendiarism, to medieval legends of poisoned wells, to legalize their own destruction of proletarian organizations, and rouse the agitated petty-bourgeoisie to chauvinistic fervor on behalf of the fight against the revolutionary way out of the crisis.

Communist pamphlet

(5) If a new spirit *is* to be infused into this old country, there is one thorny and contentious reform which must be tackled, and that is the humanization and galvanization of the B.B.C. Timidity here will bespeak canker and atrophy of the soul. The heart of Britain may be sound and of strong beat, for instance, but the British lion's roar at present is like that of Bottom in Shakespeare's *Midsummer Night's Dream*—as gentle as any sucking dove. A virile new Britain cannot continue indefinitely to be traduced in the eyes or rather ears, of the world by the effete languors of Langham Place,[2] brazenly masquerading as "standard English." When the Voice of Britain is heard at nine o'clock, better far and infinitely less ludicrous to hear aitches honestly dropped than the present priggish, inflated, inhibited, school-ma'amish arch braying of blameless bashful mewing maidens!

Letter in Tribune

Each of these passages has faults of its own, but, quite apart from avoidable ugliness, two qualities are common to all of them. The first is staleness of imagery; the other is lack of precision. The writer either has a meaning and cannot express it, or he inadvertently says something else, or he is al-

---

2. **Langham Place:** the London address of the B.B.C., the British Broadcasting Corporation.

most indifferent as to whether his words mean anything or not. This mixture of vagueness and sheer incompetence is the most marked characteristic of modern English prose, and especially of any kind of political writing. As soon as certain topics are raised, the concrete melts into the abstract and no one seems able to think of turns of speech that are not hackneyed: prose consists less and less of *words* chosen for the sake of their meaning, and more and more of *phrases* tacked together like the sections of a prefabricated henhouse. I list below, with notes and examples, various of the tricks by means of which the work of prose-construction is habitually dodged:

Dying metaphors. A newly invented metaphor assists thought by evoking a visual image, while on the other hand a metaphor which is technically "dead" (e.g. *iron resolution*) has in effect reverted to being an ordinary word and can generally be used without loss of vividness. But in between these two classes there is a huge dump of worn-out metaphors which have lost all evocative power and are merely used because they save people the trouble of inventing phrases for themselves. Examples are: *Ring the changes on, take up the cudgels for, toe the line, ride roughshod over, stand shoulder to shoulder with, play into the hands of, no axe to grind, grist to the mill, fishing in troubled waters, on the order of the day, Achilles' heel, swan song, hotbed.* Many of these are used without knowledge of their meaning (what is a "rift," for instance?), and incompatible metaphors are frequently mixed, a sure sign that the writer is not interested in what he is saying. Some metaphors now current have been twisted out of their original meaning without those who use them even being aware of the fact. For example, *toe the line* is sometimes written *tow the line.* Another example is *the hammer and the anvil,* now always used with the implication that the anvil gets the worst of it. In real life it is always the anvil that breaks the hammer, never the other way about: a writer who stopped to think what he was saying would be aware of this, and would avoid perverting the original phrase.

Operators or *verbal false limbs.* These save the trouble of picking out appropriate verbs and nouns, and at the same time pad each sentence with extra syllables which give it an appearance of symmetry. Characteristic phrases are *render inoperative, militate against, make contact with, be subjected to, give rise to, give grounds for, have the effect of, play a leading part (role) in, make itself felt, take effect, exhibit a tendency to, serve the purpose of, etc., etc.* The keynote is the elimination of simple verbs. Instead of being a single word, such as *break, stop, spoil, mend, kill,* a verb becomes a *phrase,* made up of a noun or adjective tacked on to some general-purpose verb such as *prove, serve, form, play, render.* In addition, the passive voice is wherever possible used in preference to the active, and noun constructions are used instead of gerunds (*by examination of* instead of *by examining*). The range of verbs is further cut down by means of the -*ize* and *de-* formations, and the banal statements are given an appearance of profundity by means of the *not un-* formation. Simple conjunctions and prepositions are replaced by such phrases as *with respect to, having regard to, the fact that, by dint of, in view of, in the interests of, on the hypothesis of, on the hypothesis that;* and the ends of sentences are saved by anticlimax by such resounding commonplaces as *greatly to be desired, cannot be left out of account, a development to be expected in the near future, deserving of serious consideration, brought to a satisfactory conclusion,* and so on and so forth.

Pretentious diction. Words like *phenomenon, element, individual* (as noun), *objective, categorical, effective, virtual, basic, primary, promote, constitute, exhibit, exploit, utilize, eliminate, liquidate,* are used to dress up simple statements and give an air of scientific impartiality to based judgments. Adjectives like *epoch-making, epic, historic, unforgettable, triumphant, age-old, inevitable, inexorable, veritable,* are used to dignify the sordid processes of international politics, while writing that aims at glorifying war usually takes on an archaic color, its characteristic words being: *realm, throne, chariot, mailed fist, trident, sword, shield, buckler, banner, jackboot, clarion.* Foreign words and expressions such as *cul de sac, ancien régime, deus ex machina, mutatis mutandis, status quo, gleichschaltung, weltanschauung,*[3] are used to give an air of culture and elegance. Except for the useful abbreviations *i.e., e.g.,* and *etc.,* there is no real need for any of the hundreds of foreign phrases now current in English. Bad writers, and especially scientific, political, and sociological writers, are nearly always haunted by the notion that Latin or Greek words are grander than Saxon ones, and unnecessary words like *expedite, ameliorate, predict, extraneous, deracinated, clandestine, subaqueous,* and hundreds of others constantly gain ground from their Anglo-Saxon opposite numbers.* The jargon peculiar to Marxist writing (*hyena, hangman, cannibal, petty bourgeois, these gentry, lackey, flunkey, mad dog, White Guard,* etc.) consists largely of words and phrases translated from Russian, German, or French; but the normal way of coining a new word is to use a Latin or Greek root with the appropriate affix and, where necessary, the size formation. It is

---

3. *gleichschaltung:* political coordination (the bringing into line or elimination of opponents) (German); *weltanschauung:* a comprehensive philosophy of life, nature, and history (German).

* An interesting illustration of this is the way in which the English flower names which were in use till very recently are being ousted by Greek ones, *snapdragon* becoming *antirrhinum, forget-me-not* becoming *myosotis,* etc. It is hard to see any practical reason for this change of fashion: it is probably due to an instinctive turning away from the more homely word and a vague feeling that the Greek word is scientific.

often easier to make up words of this kind (*deregionalize, impermissible, extramarital, nonfragmentary* and so forth) than to think up the English words that will cover one's meaning. The result, in general, is an increase in slovenliness and vagueness.

Meaningless words. In certain kinds of writing, particularly in art criticism and literary criticism, it is normal to come across long passages which are almost completely lacking in meaning.* Words like *romantic, plastic, values, human, dead, sentimental, natural, vitality*, as used in art criticism, are strictly meaningless, in the sense that they not only do not point to any discoverable object, but are hardly ever expected to do so by the reader. When one critic writes, "The outstanding feature of Mr. X's work is its living quality," while another writes, "The immediately striking thing about Mr. X's work is its peculiar deadness," the reader accepts this as a simple difference of opinion. If words like *black* and *white* were involved, instead of the jargon words *dead* and *living*, he would see at once that language was being used in an improper way. Many political words are similarly abused. The word *Fascism* has now no meaning except in so far as it signifies "something not desirable." The words *democracy, socialism, freedom, patriotic, realistic, justice*, have each of them several different meanings which cannot be reconciled with one another. In the case of a word like *democracy*, not only is there no agreed definition, but the attempt to make one is resisted from all sides. It is almost universally felt that when we call a country democratic we are praising it: consequently the defenders of every kind of régime claim that it is a democracy, and fear that they might have to stop using the word if it were tied down to any one meaning. Words of this kind are often used in a consciously dishonest way. That is, the person who uses them has his own private definition, but allows his hearer to think he means something quite different. Statements like *Marshal Pétain was a true patriot, The Soviet press is the freest in the world*, [. . .] are almost always made with intent to deceive. Other words used in variable meanings, in most cases more or less dishonestly, are: *class, totalitarian, science, progressive, reactionary, bourgeois, equality*.

Now that I have made this catalogue of swindles and perversions, let me give another example of the kind of writing that they lead to. This time it must of its nature be an imaginary one. I am going to translate a passage of good English into modern English of the worst sort. Here is a well-known verse from *Ecclesiastes*:

---

* Example: "Comfort's catholicity of perception and image, strangely Whitmanesque in range, almost the exact opposite in aesthetic compulsion, continues to evoke that trembling atmospheric accumulative hinting at a cruel, an inexorably serene timelessness. . . . Wrey Gardiner scores by aiming at simple bull's-eyes with precision. Only they are not so simple, and through this contented sadness runs more than the surface bittersweet of resignation" (*Poetry Quarterly*).

I returned and saw under the sun, that the race is not to the swift, nor the battle to the strong, neither yet bread to the wise, nor yet riches to men of understanding, or yet favour to men of skill; but time and chance happeneth to them all.

Here it is in modern English:

Objective considerations of contemporary phenomena compels the conclusion that success or failure in competitive activities exhibits no tendency to be commensurate with innate capacity, but that a considerable element of the unpredictable must invariably be taken into account.

This is a parody, but not a very gross one. Exhibit (3), above, for instance, contains several patches of the same kind of English. It will be seen that I have not made a full translation. The beginning and ending of the sentence follow the original meaning fairly closely, but in the middle the concrete illustrations—race, battle, bread—dissolve into the vague phrase "success or failure in competitive activities." This had to be so, because no modern writer of the kind I am discussing—no one capable of using phrases like "objective consideration of contemporary phenomena"—would ever tabulate his thoughts in that precise and detailed way. The whole tendency of modern prose is away from concreteness. Now analyze these two sentences a little more closely. The first contains forty-nine words but only sixty syllables, and all its words are those of everyday life. The second contains thirty-eight words of ninety syllables: eighteen of its words are from Latin roots, and one from Greek. The first sentence contains six vivid images, and only one phrase ("time and chance") that could be called vague. The second contains not a single fresh, arresting phrase, and in spite of its ninety syllables it gives only a shortened version of the meaning contained in the first. Yet without a doubt it is the second kind of sentence that is gaining ground in modern English. I do not want to exaggerate. This kind of writing is not yet universal, and outcrops of simplicity will occur here and there in the worst-written page. Still, if you or I were told to write a few lines on the uncertainty of human fortunes, we should probably come much nearer to my imaginary sentence than to the one from *Ecclesiastes*.

As I have tried to show, modern writing at its worst does not consist in picking out words for the sake of their meaning and inventing images in order to make the meaning clearer. It consists in gumming together long strips of words which have already been set in order by someone else, and making the results presentable by sheer humbug. The attraction of this way of writing is that it is easy. It is easier—even quicker, once you have the habit—to say *In my opinion it is not an unjustifiable assumption that*

than to say *I think*. If you use ready-made phrases, you not only don't
have to hunt about for words; you also don't have to bother with the
rhythms of your sentences, since these phrases are generally so arranged as
to be more or less euphonious. When you are composing in a hurry—when
you are dictating to a stenographer, for instance, or making a public
speech—it is natural to fall into a pretentious, Latinized style. Tags like *a
consideration which we should do well to bear in mind* or *a conclusion to
which all of us would readily assent* will save many a sentence from coming down with a bump. By using stale metaphors, similes, and idioms, you
save much mental effort, at the cost of leaving your meaning vague, not
only for your reader but for yourself. This is the significance of mixed
metaphors. The sole aim of a metaphor is to call up a visual image. When
these images clash—as in *The Fascist octopus has sung its swan song, the
jackboot is thrown into the melting pot*—it can be taken as certain that the
writer is not seeing a mental image of the objects he is naming; in other
words he is not really thinking. Look again at the examples I gave at the
beginning of this essay. Professor Laski (1) uses five negatives in fifty-
three words. One of these is superfluous, making nonsense of the whole
passage, and in addition there is the slip—*alien* for akin—making further
nonsense, and several avoidable pieces of clumsiness which increase the
general vagueness. Professor Hogben (2) plays ducks and drakes with a
battery which is able to write prescriptions, and, while disapproving of the
everyday phrase *put up with*, is unwilling to look *egregious* up in the dictionary and see what it means; (3), if one takes an uncharitable attitude towards it, is simply meaningless: probably one could work out its intended
meaning by reading the whole of the article in which it occurs. In (4), the
writer knows more or less what he wants to say, but an accumulation of
stale phrases chokes him like tea leaves blocking a sink. In (5), words and
meaning have almost parted company. People who write in this manner
usually have a general emotional meaning—they dislike one thing and want
to express solidarity with another—but they are not interested in the detail
of what they are saying. A scrupulous writer, in every sentence that he
writes, will ask himself at least four questions, thus: What am I trying to
say? What words will express it? What image or idiom will make it
clearer? Is this image fresh enough to have an effect? And he will probably ask himself two more: Could I put it more shortly? Have I said anything that is avoidably ugly? But you are not obliged to go to all this trouble. You can shirk it by simply throwing your mind open and letting the
ready-made phrases come crowding in. They will construct your sentences for you—even think your thoughts for you, to a certain extent—and
at need they will perform the important service of partially concealing

your meaning even from yourself. It is at this point that the special connection between politics and the debasement of language becomes clear.

In our time it is broadly true that political writing is bad writing. Where it is not true, it will generally be found that the writer is some kind of rebel, expressing his private opinions and not a "party line." Orthodoxy, of whatever color, seems to demand a lifeless, imitative style. The political dialects to be found in pamphlets, leading articles, manifestoes, White Papers and the speeches of undersecretaries do, of course, vary from party to party, but they are all alike in that one almost never finds in them a fresh, vivid, homemade turn of speech. When one watches some tired hack on the platform mechanically repeating the familiar phrases—*bestial atrocities, iron heel, bloodstained tyranny, free peoples of the world, stand shoulder to shoulder*—one often has a curious feeling that one is not watching a live human being but some kind of dummy: a feeling which suddenly becomes stronger at moments when the light catches the speaker's spectacles and turns them into blank discs which seem to have no eyes behind them. And this is not altogether fanciful. A speaker who uses that kind of phraseology has gone some distance toward turning himself into a machine. The appropriate noises are coming out of his larynx, but his brain is not involved as it would be if he were choosing his words for himself. If the speech he is making is one that he is accustomed to make over and over again, he may be almost unconscious of what he is saying, as one is when one utters the responses in church. And this reduced state of consciousness, if not indispensable, is at any rate favorable to political conformity.

In our time, political speech and writing are largely the defense of the indefensible. Things like the continuance of British rule in India, the Russian purges and deportations, the dropping of the atom bombs on Japan, can indeed be defended, but only by arguments which are too brutal for most people to face, and which do not square with the professed aims of political parties. Thus political language has to consist largely of euphemism, question-begging and sheer cloudy vagueness. Defenseless villages are bombarded from the air, the inhabitants driven out into the countryside, the cattle machine-gunned, the huts set on fire with incendiary bullets: this is called *pacification*. Millions of peasants are robbed of their farms and sent trudging along the roads with no more than they can carry: this is called *transfer of population* or *rectification of frontiers*. People are imprisoned for years without trial, or shot in the back of the neck or sent to die of scurvy in Arctic lumber camps: this is called *elimination of unreliable elements*. Such phraseology is needed if one wants to name things without calling up mental pictures of them. Consider for instance some

comfortable English professor defending Russian totalitarianism. He cannot say outright, "I believe in killing off your opponents when you can
get good results by doing so." Probably, therefore, he will say something
like this:

"While freely conceding that the Soviet régime exhibits certain features which the humanitarian may be inclined to deplore, we must, I think,
agree that a certain curtailment of the right to political opposition is an
unavoidable concomitant of transitional periods, and that the rigors which
the Russian people have been called upon to undergo have been amply justified in the sphere of concrete achievement."

The inflated style is itself a kind of euphemism. A mass of Latin words
falls upon the facts like soft snow, blurring the outlines and covering up
all the details. The great enemy of clear language is insincerity. When
there is a gap between one's real and one's declared aims, one turns as it
were instinctively to long words and exhausted idioms, like a cuttlefish
squirting out ink. In our age there is no such thing as "keeping out of politics." All issues are political issues, and politics itself is a mass of lies, eva-
sions, folly, hatred, and schizophrenia. When the general atmosphere is
bad, language must suffer. I should expect to find—this is a guess which I
have not sufficient knowledge to verify—that the German, Russian and
Italian languages have all deteriorated in the last ten or fifteen years, as a
result of dictatorship.

But if thought corrupts language, language can also corrupt thought. A
bad usage can spread by tradition and imitation, even among people who
should and do know better. The debased language that I have been discussing is in some ways very convenient. Phrases like *a not unjustifiable
assumption, leaves much to be desired, would serve no good purpose, a
consideration which we should do well to bear in mind*, are a continuous
temptation, a packet of aspirins always at one's elbow. Look back through
this essay, and for certain you will find that I have again and again committed the very faults I am protesting against. By this morning's post I
have received a pamphlet dealing with conditions in Germany. The author
tells me that he "felt impelled" to write it. I open it at random, and here is
almost the first sentence that I see: "[The Allies] have an opportunity not
only of achieving a radical transformation of Germany's social and political structure in such a way as to avoid a nationalistic reaction in Germany
itself, but at the same time of laying the foundations of a co-operative and
unified Europe." You see, he "feels impelled" to write—feels, presumably,
that he has something new to say—and yet his words, like cavalry horses
answering the bugle, group themselves automatically into the familiar
dreary pattern. This invasion of one's mind by ready-made phrases (*lay
the foundations, achieve a radical transformation*) can only be prevented

if one is constantly on guard against them, and every such phrase anaesthetizes a portion of one's brain.

I said earlier that the decadence of our language is probably curable. Those who deny this would argue, if they produced an argument at all, that language merely reflects existing social conditions, and that we cannot influence its development by any direct tinkering with words and constructions. So far as the general tone or spirit of a language goes, this may be true, but it is not true in detail. Silly words and expressions have often disappeared, not through any evolutionary process but owing to the conscious action of a minority. Two recent examples were *explore every avenue* and *leave no stone unturned*, which were killed by the jeers of a few journalists. There is a long list of flyblown metaphors which could similarly be got rid of if enough people would interest themselves in the job; and it should also be possible to laugh the *not un-* formation out of existence,* to reduce the amount of Latin and Greek in the average sentence, to drive out foreign phrases and strayed scientific words, and, in general, to make pretentiousness unfashionable. But all these are minor points. The defense of the English language implies more than this, and perhaps it is best to start by saying what it does *not* imply.

To begin with it has nothing to do with archaism, with the salvaging of obsolete words and turns of speech, or with the setting up of a "standard English" which must never be departed from. On the contrary, it is especially concerned with the scrapping of every word or idiom which has outworn its usefulness. It has nothing to do with correct grammar and syntax, which are of no importance so long as one makes one's meaning clear, or with the avoidance of Americanisms, or with having what is called a "good prose style." On the other hand it is not concerned with fake simplicity and the attempt to make written English colloquial. Nor does it even imply in every case preferring the Saxon word to the Latin one, though it does imply using the fewest and shortest words that will cover one's meaning. What is above all needed is to let the meaning choose the word, and not the other way about. In prose, the worst thing one can do with words is to surrender to them. When you think of a concrete object, you think wordlessly, and then, if you want to describe the thing you have been visualizing you probably hunt about till you find the exact words that seem to fit it. When you think of something abstract you are more inclined to used words from the start, and unless you make a conscious effort to prevent it, the existing dialect will come rushing in and do the job for you, at the expense of blurring or even changing your meaning. Probably it is better to put off using words as long as possible

---

* One can cure oneself of the *not un-* formation by memorizing this sentence: *A not unblack dog was chasing a not unsmall rabbit across a not ungreen field.*

and get one's meaning as clear as one can through pictures or sensations. Afterward one can choose—not simply *accept*—the phrases that will best cover the meaning, and then switch round and decide what impression one's words are likely to make on another person. This last effort of the mind cuts out all stale or mixed images, all prefabricated phrases, needless repetitions, and humbug and vagueness generally. But one can often be in doubt about the effect of a word or a phrase, and one needs rules that one can rely on when instinct fails. I think the following rules will cover most cases:

(i) Never use a metaphor, simile, or other figure of speech which you are used to seeing in print.

(ii) Never use a long word where a short one will do.

(iii) If it is possible to cut a word out, always cut it out.

(iv) Never use the passive where you can use the active.

(v) Never use a foreign phrase, a scientific word, or a jargon word if you can think of an everyday English equivalent.

(vi) Break any of these rules sooner than say anything outright barbarous.

These rules sound elementary, and so they are, but they demand a deep change of attitude in anyone who has grown used to writing in the style now fashionable. One could keep all of them and still write bad English, but one could not write the kind of stuff that I quoted in those five specimens at the beginning of this article.

I have not here been considering the literary use of language, but merely language as an instrument for expressing and not for concealing or preventing thought. Stuart Chase [4] and others have come near to claiming that all abstract words are meaningless, and have used this as a pretext for advocating a kind of political quietism. Since you don't know what Fascism is, how can you struggle against Fascism? One need not swallow such absurdities as this, but one ought to recognize that the present political chaos is connected with the decay of language, and that one can probably bring about some improvement by starting at the verbal end. If you simplify your English, you are freed from the worst follies of orthodoxy. You cannot speak any of the necessary dialects, and when you make a stupid remark its stupidity will be obvious, even to yourself. Political language—and with variations this is true of all political parties, from Conservatives to Anarchists—is designed to make lies sound truthful and murder respectable, and to give an appearance of solidity to pure wind. One cannot change this all in a moment, but one can at least change one's own

4. **Stuart Chase:** an American writer. One of his best-known books is *The Tyranny of Words,* published in 1938.

habits, and from time to time one can even, if one jeers loudly enough, send some worn-out and useless phrase—some *jackboot, Achilles' heel, hotbed, melting pot, acid test, veritable inferno,* or other lump of verbal refuse—into the dustbin where it belongs.

James Thurber

SUCH A PHRASE AS DRIFTS THROUGH DREAMS

SOMETHING central and essential in the mechanism of meaning began losing its symmetry last summer. It was as if the maiden spring of sense had suddenly become matron-sprung. At first I thought the fault must be in myself, some flaw of comprehension or concentration, aggravated by the march of time. Then I realized one June afternoon at a cocktail party in Bermuda that the trouble was largely female, or at least seemed to originate in that sex, like so many other alarming things.

At this party, a woman from the Middle West began telling me about some legal involvement her daughter and son-in-law had got into. I didn't have the vaguest idea what it was all about, and was merely feigning attention, when she ended her cloudy recital on a note of triumph. "So finally they decided to leave it where sleeping dogs lie," she said. I was upon it in a moment, hastily assuming my best Henry James garden-party manner. "How perfectly charming of them both, dear lady," I wonderfully cried. "One can only hope the barristers for the other side will tumble for it, hook, line, and barrel. To be sure, they may overtake it in their stride, in which case may the devil pay the hindmost." Upon this my companion cautiously withdrew to the safer company of younger minds.

The charmingly tainted idiom of the lady of the sleeping dogs must have infected other members of her circle in Somerset,[1] among them a beautiful young woman from Geneva, New York, who told me, in another Bermuda landscape with figures, "We are not going to hide our heads in the sand like kangaroos." This was just what my harassed understanding and tortured spirits needed. I was, it is not too much to say, saved by the twisted and inspired simile, and whenever I think I hear the men coming with the stretcher or the subpoena, I remember those kangaroos with their heads in the sand, and I am ready to face anything again.

The kangaroo, it has always seemed to me, is Exhibit A among the evidence supporting the contention of some of us that Nature has a grotesque and lovely sense of humor. I think the Geneva lady's kangaroos would be far more effective head-hiders than ostriches. Any creature coming upon a kangaroo upright would not be frightened by its comic head and little forelegs, but a sudden view of its strange and enormous rear quarters, protruding from the earth, would surely be enough to give pause to a prowling tiger or a charging rhino. (Quibblers who have pounced upon the fact that there are no tigers or rhinos in Australia should remember that these kangaroos are Bermuda kangaroos.) I was not the first to think of the head-hiding kangaroos of Bermuda, alas, but I shall be the last to forget them.

It was only a fortnight later that a counterpart of the Bermuda ladies, this one the proud mother of a young man who had just completed his first year as a history teacher, sat down beside me at an indoor cocktail party in New York and leaped into a discussion of history professors in general. "It is not easy to make them colleagues," she said. "They are always looking down each other's noses."

I let my awareness deal with this troubled idiom for a long Jamesian moment before replying. "At least," I said, with an old-world smile, "when there is so much smoke one knows one is in Denmark. But be of good cheer. I can fairly see the butter melting in their mouths now." My companion was delightfully equal to it. "Oh, but I am sure that he will," she said.

The summer malady of incoherence soon spread, as I was afraid it would, to printers and proofreaders, or, at any rate, to one or two saddled with the admittedly onerous task of helping to get some stories of mine into book form. Ours is a precarious language, as every writer knows, in which the merest shadow line often separates affirmation from negation, sense from nonsense, and one sex from the other. Forty years ago, *The Candle*, a literary monthly published at Ohio State University, ruined the point of a mild little essay of mine by garbling a salient quotation so that it came out "The gates of hell shall now prevail."

1. **Somerset:** one of the Bermuda islands.

One linotyper I have never met became co-author of a piece of mine last year by introducing a bear into the story. He simply made one out of a bead that was lying around in the middle of the narrative. This set me to brooding, and for weeks I lay awake at night, in my fashion, playing unhappily with imaginary havoc wrought by single letter changes in the printed word. I still remember a few of them: "A stitch in time saves none . . . There's no business like shoe business . . . Lafayette, we ate here . . . Don, give up the ship."

[. . .]

In Martha's Vineyard last August—is there something about islands that fogs the clarity of speech?—I fell into conversation with an actress I had known in my Greenwich Village, or devil-may-care days, and we began counting our Village friends of thirty years ago, separating the dead from the crazy, and both from those who had moved to Hollywood, or at least uptown. It turned out that Gloria Mundy, as I shall call her, was still living in the same old place on Christopher Street, or Commerce or Wherever. "Her apartment was broken into so often this year, she finally had to have it burglarized," my old friend told me.

My aging mind had to turn that over several times before I could find anything to say. "You mean there's a *company* that burglarizes apartments now?" I finally demanded. "What do you do—call them up and tell them when you won't be home?"

My companion eyed me warily. "You don't have to not be home," she said.

"Most people are not home when their apartments are burglarized," I told her. "It's like foolproofing a part in a play. The author would rather not have anybody around. Are you sure Gloria didn't have the place just alarmed?"

"I don't know what you're talking about," said my old friend quietly, moving a foot or so farther away.

"It's much simpler and a lot cheaper to install a burglar alarm than to have your apartment completely burglarized," I told her.

"I hate writers," she said, after a long pause. "They're such Puritans about everything. You can't even use a figure of speech the wrong way."

"We are a brave lot, though," I insisted. "We stand at Armageddon and we battle for the word while the very Oedipus of reason crumbles beneath us."

"Let's go to the Harborside [2] and have a drink," she said, and we went there and had a long, cold drink, in silence. That is the best way to commune with an actress.

I am back at my home in Connecticut, now resting up after a bad year

2. the **Harborside:** a hotel in Edgartown, Martha's Vineyard.

among the meaning-manglers, the lunatype machines, and the typo-writers. The worst that has happened in the realm of the anti-perspicuous was a letter I got whose third sentence began like this: "Even whether you haven't been there or not yet . . ." I just threw it away. To be sure, radio and television go on speaking their special kind of broken English, but it is rather comforting after a long day of trying to write simple declarative English sentences. "It is possible that the killer is probably in the house now," said a man on one of TV's half-hour mysteries. It gave me a moral for a future fable, which I jotted down and filed: "A pinch of probably is worth a pound of perhaps." Then there was the moment in a Sherlock Holmes television program when Doctor Watson stoutly defended (or tried to, anyway) the innocence of a guilty woman. "Mrs. *Burchard?* She couldn't be less harmless!"

Our community in the lovely foothills of the Berkshires wears a special radiance the year round in the person of a French lady whom I shall call Renée. The accuracy of her English and the quality of her clarity depend on the weather in her heart, which changes with the caprice of island winds. In an hour of impatience she once said to the local telephone operator, "What is the name of the Macleans?" The operator, who loves and understands Renée, like everybody else, did not say, "The Macleans," but simply, "Orchard 2–6338."

Renée is mistress of what I call not the dangling participle, but the dazzling participle, often, when excited, using it in place of the past tense. "How did you like the concert at Tanglewood [3] last night?" I asked her one day.

"I was fascinating," she said.

Renée is always fascinating, but never more so than on two unforgettable occasions. One of these was the evening she told a little circle of her admirers about a visit she had made years ago to Andalusia. "I am with this airedale in Spain," was the way she began her recital, and I shall never forget it. [. . .]

Some fifteen years ago, our usually tranquil community was violently upset by the attempted murder of a woman. The State Police questioned us all, and did not come off very well with either Renée or me. "What kind of an artist are you?" a detective asked me, and I must have looked guilty as hell. I finally said, "I refuse to answer that question on the ground that it might incriminate me."

The detective had even tougher sledding with Renée. "One thing I am certain of," he said to her. "Somebody in this town is guilty."

"So am I," said the innocent and wonderful Renée.

3. **Tanglewood:** a town in western Massachusetts noted for its summer music festivals.

The cop stared at her for a long time without a word and then asked, "Where do you live?"

Renée, who was standing on her front porch at the time, waved a hand at her house and said, "I am leeving here." The harassed police officer gave her another long and rueful look, sighed, and said, "So am I," and he went away.

I must go now and feed those Bermuda kangaroos, if I can get their heads out of the sand.

Bertrand Russell

CHARACTERISTICS OF SCIENTIFIC METHOD

SCIENTIFIC method has been often described, and it is not possible, at this date, to say anything very new about it. Nevertheless, it is necessary to describe it if we are to be in a position later to consider whether any other method of acquiring general knowledge exists.

In arriving at a scientific law there are three main stages: the first consists in observing the significant facts; the second in arriving at a hypothesis, which, if it is true, would account for these facts; the third in deducing from this hypothesis consequences which can be tested by observation. If the consequences are verified, the hypothesis is provisionally accepted as true, although it will usually require modification later on as the result of the discovery of further facts.

In the existing state of science, no facts and no hypotheses are isolated; they exist within the general body of scientific knowledge. The significance of a fact is relative to such knowledge. To say that a fact is significant in science, is to say that it helps to establish or refute some general law; for science, though it starts from observation of the particular, is not concerned essentially with the particular, but with the general. A fact, in science, is not a mere fact, but an instance. In this the scientist differs from the artist, who, if he deigns to notice facts at all, is likely to notice them in all their particularity. Science, in its ultimate ideal, consists of a set of propositions arranged in a hierarchy, the lowest level of the hierarchy being concerned with particular facts, and the highest with some general law, governing everything in the universe. The various levels in the hierarchy have a twofold logical connexion, travelling one up, one down; the upward connexion proceeds by induction, the downward by deduction. That is to say, in a perfected science, we should proceed as follows: the particular facts, A, B, C, D, etc., suggest as probable a certain general law, of which, if it is true, they are all instances. Another set of facts suggests another general law, and so on. All these general laws suggest, by induction, a law of a higher order of generality of which, if it is true, they are instances. There will be many such stages in passing from the particular facts observed to the most general law as yet ascertained. From this general law we proceed in turn deductively, until we arrive at the particular facts from which our previous induction had started. In textbooks the deductive order will be adopted, but in the laboratory the inductive order.

The only science which has, as yet, come anywhere near this perfection is physics. The consideration of physics may help us to give concreteness to the above abstract account of scientific method. Galileo discovered the law of falling bodies in the neighbourhood of the earth's surface. He discovered that, apart from the resistance of the air, they fall with a constant acceleration, which is the same for all. This was a generalization from a comparatively small number of facts, namely, the cases of actual falling bodies which Galileo had timed; but his generalization was confirmed by all subsequent experiments of a like nature. Galileo's result was a law of the lowest order of generality, as little removed from the crude facts as a general law could be. Meanwhile, Kepler had observed the motions of the planets, and formulated his three laws as to their orbits. These, again, were laws of the lowest order of generality. Newton collected together Kepler's laws and Galileo's law of falling bodies, and the laws of the tides, and what was known as to the motions of comets, in one law, namely, the law of gravitation, which embraced them all. This law, moreover, as usually happens with a successful generalization, showed not merely why the previous laws were right, but also why they were not quite right. Bodies near the earth's surface do not fall with an acceleration which is quite constant: as they approach the earth, the acceleration is slightly increased. Planets do not move exactly in ellipses: when they approach near to other planets, they are pulled a little out of their orbits. Thus Newton's law of gravitation superseded the older generalizations, but could scarcely have been arrived at except from them. For over two hundred years no new generalization was found to swallow up Newton's law of gravitation, as it had swallowed up Kepler's laws. When, at last, Einstein arrived at such a generalization it placed the law of gravitation in the most unexpected company. To everybody's surprise, it was found to be a law of geometry rather than of physics in the old sense. The proposition with which it has most affinity is the theorem of Pythagoras, to the effect that the squares on the two shorter sides of a right-angled triangle are together equal to the square on the longest side. Every schoolboy learns the proof of this proposition, but only those who read Einstein learn the disproof. To the Greeks—and to the moderns until a hundred years ago—geometry was an *a priori* study like formal logic, not an empirical science based upon observation. Lobachevsky, in the year 1829, demonstrated the falsehood of this opinion, and showed that the truth of Euclidean geometry could only be established by observation, not by reasoning. Although this view gave rise to important new branches of pure mathematics, it did not bear fruit in physics until the year 1915, when Einstein embodied it in his general theory of relativity. It now appears that the theorem of Pythagoras is not quite true, and that the exact truth which it adumbrates contains within itself the law of gravitation as an ingredient or consequence. Again, it is not quite Newton's law of gravitation, but a law whose observable consequences are slightly different. Where Einstein differs from Newton in an observable manner it is found that Einstein is right as against Newton. Einstein's law of gravitation is more general than Newton's, since it applies not only to matter, but also to light and to every form of energy. Einstein's general theory of gravitation demanded as a preliminary not only Newton's theory, but also the theory of electro-magnetism, the science of spectroscopy, observation of light pressure, and the power of minute astronomical observation, which we owe to large telescopes and the perfecting of the technique of photography. Without all these preliminaries, Einstein's theory could not have been both discovered and demonstrated. But when the theory is set forth in mathematical form we start with the generalized law of gravitation, and arrive at the end of our argument at those verifiable consequences upon which, in the inductive order, the law was based. In the deductive order, the difficulties of discovery are obscured, and it becomes hard to be aware of the immense extent of preliminary knowledge required for the induction which led to our major premise. The same sort of development has happened with a rapidity which is truly astonishing in regard to quantum theory. The first discovery that there were facts necessitating such a theory was made in 1900, yet already the subject can be treated in an utterly abstract way which scarcely reminds the reader that a universe exists.

Throughout the history of physics, from the time of Galileo onward, the importance of the *significant* fact has been very evident. The facts that are significant at any one stage in the development of a theory are quite different from those that are significant at another stage. When Galileo was establishing the law of falling bodies, the fact that in a vacuum a feather and a lump of lead fall equally fast, was more important than the fact that, in air, a feather falls more slowly, since the first step in understanding falling bodies consisted in realizing that, so far as the earth's attraction alone is concerned, all falling bodies have the same acceleration. The effect of the resistance of the air must be treated as something superadded to the earth's attraction. The essential thing is always to look for such facts as illustrate one law in isolation, or at any rate, only in combination with laws whose effects are well known. This is why experiment plays such an important part in scientific discovery. In an experiment the circumstances are artificially simplified, so that some one law in isolation may become observable. In most concrete situations, what actually happens requires for its explanation a number of laws of nature, but in order to discover these one by one it is usually necessary to invent circumstances such that only one of them is relevant. Moreover, the most instructive phenomena may be very difficult to observe. Consider, for example, how much our knowledge of matter has been enhanced by the discovery of X-rays and of radio-activity; yet both of these would have remained unknown but for the most elaborate experimental technique. The discovery of radio-activity was an accident due to the perfecting of photography. Becquerel had some very sensitive photographic plates, which he was meaning to employ; but as the weather was bad, he put them away in a dark cupboard in which there happened to be some uranium. When they were taken out again they were found to have photographed the uranium, in spite of the complete darkness. It was this accident which led to the discovery that uranium is radio-active. This accidental photograph affords another illustration of the significant fact.

Outside physics, the part played by deduction is much less, while the part played by observation, and by laws immediately based upon observation, is much greater. Physics, owing to the simplicity of its subject matter, has reached a higher stage of development than any other science. I do not think it can be doubted that the ideal is the same for all sciences; but it can be doubted whether human capacity will ever be able to make physiology, for example, as perfect a deductive edifice as theoretical physics is now. Even in pure physics the difficulties of calculation swiftly become insuperable. In the Newtonian gravitation theory it was impossible to calculate how three bodies would move under their mutual attractions, except approximately when one of them was much larger than the other two. In the theory of Einstein, which is much more complicated than Newton's, it is impossible to work out with theoretical exactness even how two bodies will move under their mutual attraction, though it is possible to obtain a sufficiently good approximation for all practical purposes. Fortunately for physics there are methods of averaging, by which the behaviour of large bodies can be calculated with a quite sufficient approximation to the truth, although a wholly exact theory is utterly beyond human powers.

Although this may seem a paradox, all exact science is dominated by the idea of approximation. When a man tells you that he knows the exact truth about anything, you are safe in inferring that he is an inexact man. Every careful measurement in science is always given with the probable error, which is a technical term, conveying a precise meaning. It means: that amount of error which is just as likely to be greater than the actual error as to be less. It is characteristic of those matters in which something is known with exceptional accuracy that, in them, every observer admits that he is likely to be wrong, and knows about how much wrong he is likely to be. In matters where the truth is not ascertainable, no one admits that there is the slightest possibility of even the minutest error in his opinions. Who ever heard of a theologian prefacing his creed, or a politician concluding his speeches, with a statement as to the probable error in his opinions? It is an odd fact that subjective certainty is inversely proportional to objective certainty. The less reason a man has to suppose himself in the right, the more vehemently he asserts that there is no doubt whatever that he is exactly right. It is a practice of theologians to laugh at science because it changes. "Look at us," they say. "What we asserted at the Council of Nicea we still assert; whereas what the scientists asserted only two or three years ago is already forgotten and antiquated." Men who speak in this way have not grasped the great idea of successive approximations. No man who has the scientific temper asserts that what is now believed in science is *exactly* right; he asserts that it is a stage on the road towards the exact truth. When a change occurs in science, as, for example, from Newton's law of gravitation to Einstein's, what had been done is not overthrown, but is replaced by something slightly more accurate. Suppose you measured yourself with a rough apparatus, and came to the conclusion that you were 6 ft. tall: you would not suppose, if you were wise, that your height was exactly 6 ft., but rather that your height was (say) between 5 ft. 11 in. and 6 ft. 1 in.; and if a very careful measurement showed that your height was (within a tenth of an inch) 5 ft. 11 9/10 in. you would not consider that that had overthrown the previous result. The previous result was that your height was *about* 6 ft., and this remains true. The case with the changes in science is precisely analogous.

The part played by measurement and quantity in science is very great, but is, I think, sometimes overestimated. Mathematical technique is powerful, and men of science are naturally anxious to be able to apply it whenever possible; but a law may be quite scientific without being quantitative. Pavlov's laws concerning conditioned reflexes may serve as an illustration. It would probably be impossible to give quantitative precision to these laws; the number of repetitions required to establish conditioned reflexes depends upon many conditions, and varies not only with different animals, but with the same animal at different times. In the pursuit of quantitative precision we should be driven first to the physiology of the cortex and the physical nature of nerve-currents, and we should find ourselves unable to stop short of the physics of electrons and protons. There, it is true, quantitative precision may be possible, but to pass back by calculation from pure physics to the phenomena of animal behaviour is beyond human power, at any rate at present, and probably for many ages to come. We must, therefore, in dealing with such a matter as animal behaviour, be content in the meantime with qualitative laws which are none the less scientific for not being quantitative.

One advantage of quantitative precision, where it is possible, is that it gives much greater strength to inductive arguments. Suppose, for example, that you invent a hypothesis, according to which a certain observable quantity should have a magnitude which you work out to five significant figures; and suppose you then find by observation that the quantity in question has this magnitude. You will feel that such a coincidence between theory and observation can hardly be an accident, and that your theory and observation must contain at least some important element of truth. Experience shows, however, that it is easy to attach too much importance to such coincidences. Bohr's theory of the atom was originally commended by a remarkable power of calculating theoretically certain quantities which had until then been known only by observation. Nevertheless, Bohr's theory, though a necessary stage in progress, has already been virtually abandoned. The truth is, that men cannot frame sufficiently abstract hypotheses; imagination is always intruding upon logic, and causing men to make pictures of occurrences which are essentially incapable of being visualized. In Bohr's theory of the atom, for example, there was a highly abstract constituent, which was in all likelihood true, but this abstract element was embedded in imaginative details which had no inductive justification. The world that we can picture is the world that we see; but the world of physics is an abstract world that cannot be seen. For this reason, even a hypothesis which accounts with a minute exactitude for all known relevant facts must not be regarded as certainly true, since it is probably only some highly abstract aspect of the hypothesis that is logically necessary in the deductions which we make from it to observable phenomena.

All scientific laws rest upon induction, which, considered as a logical process, is open to doubt, and not capable of giving certainty. Speaking crudely, an inductive argument is of the following kind. If a certain hypothesis is true, the such and such facts will be observable; now these facts are observable; therefore the hypothesis is probably true. An argument of this sort will have varying degrees of validity according to circumstances. If we could prove that no other hypothesis was compatible with the observed facts we could arrive at certainty, but this is hardly ever possible. In general, there will be no method of thinking of all the possible hypotheses, or, if there is, it will be found that more than one of them is compatible with the facts. When this is the case, the scientist adopts the simplest as a working hypothesis, and only reverts to more complicated hypotheses if new facts show that the simplest hypothesis is inadequate. If you had never seen a cat without a tail, the simplest hypothesis to account for this fact would be: "all cats have tails"; but the first time that you saw a Manx cat, you would be compelled to adopt a more complicated hypothesis. The man who argues that because all cats he has seen have tails, therefore all cats have tails, is employing what is called "induction by simple enumeration." This is a very dangerous form of argument. In its better forms, induction is based upon the fact that our hypothesis leads to consequences which are found to be true, but which, if they had not been observed, would seem extremely improbable. If you meet a man who has a pair of dice that always throw double sixes, it is possible that he is lucky; but there is another hypothesis which would make the observed facts less astonishing. You will therefore be well advised to adopt this other hypothesis. In all good inductions, the facts accounted for by the hypothesis are such as would be antecedently improbable, and the more improbable they would be, the greater becomes the probability of the hypothesis which accounts for them. This, as we remarked a moment ago, is one of the advantages of measurement. If something which might have any size, is found to have just the size that your hypothesis had led you to expect, you feel that your hypothesis must at least have something in it. As common sense this seems evident, but as logic it has certain difficulties.

There is one remaining characteristic of scientific method about which something must be said, namely, analysis. It is generally assumed by men of science, at any rate as a working hypothesis, that any concrete occurrence is the resultant of a number of causes, each of which, acting separately, might produce some different result from that which actually occurs; and that the resultant can be calculated when the effects of the separate causes are known. The simplest examples of this occur in mechanics. The moon is attracted both by the earth and by the sun. If the earth acted alone, the moon would describe one orbit; if the sun acted alone, it would describe another; but its actual orbit is calculable when we know the effects which the earth and the sun separately would produce. When we know how bodies fall in a vacuum, and also the law of resistance of the air, we can calculate how bodies will fall in air. The principle that causal laws can, in this way, be separated, and then recombined, is in some degree essential to the procedure of science, for it is impossible to take account of everything at once, or to arrive at causal laws unless we can isolate them one at a time. It must be said, however, that there is no reason *a priori* to suppose that the effect of two causes, acting simultaneously, will be calculable from the effects which they have severally; and in the most modern physics, this principle is found to have less truth than was formerly supposed. It remains a practical and approximate principle in suitable circumstances, but it cannot be laid down as a general property of the universe. Undoubtedly, where it fails, science becomes very difficult; but, so far as can be seen at present, it retains sufficient truth to be employed as a hypothesis, except in the most advanced and delicate calculations.

Loren Eiseley

THE SNOUT

I HAVE long been an admirer of the octopus. The cephalopods are very old, and they have slipped, protean, through many shapes. They are the wisest of the mollusks, and I have always felt it to be just as well for us that they never came ashore, but—there are other things that have.

There is no need to be frightened. It is true some of the creatures are odd, but I find the situation rather heartening than otherwise. It gives one a feeling of confidence to see nature still busy with experiments, still dynamic, and not through nor satisfied because a Devonian fish managed to end as a two-legged character with a straw hat. There are other things brewing and growing in the oceanic vat. It pays to know this. It pays to know there is just as much future as there is past. The only thing that doesn't pay is to be sure of man's own part in it.

There are things down there still coming ashore. Never make the mistake of thinking life is now adjusted for eternity. It gets into your head—the certainty, I mean—the human certainty, and then you miss it all: the things on the tide flats and what they mean, and why, as my wife says, "they ought to be watched."

The trouble is we don't know what to watch for. I have a friend, one of these Explorers Club people, who drops in now and then between trips to tell me about the size of crocodile jaws in Uganda, or what happened on some back beach in Arnhem Land.

"They fell out of the trees," he said. "Like rain. And into the boat."

"Uh?" I said, noncommittally.

"They did *so*," he protested, "and they were hard to catch."

"Really—" I said.

"We were pushing a dugout up one of the tidal creeks in northern Australia and going fast when *smacko* we jam this mangrove bush and the things come tumbling down.

"What were they doing sitting up there in bunches? I ask you. It's no place for a fish. Besides that they had a way of sidling off with those popeyes trained on you. I never liked it. Somebody ought to keep an eye on them."

"Why?" I asked.

"I don't know why," he said impatiently, running a rough, square hand through his hair and wrinkling his forehead. "I just mean they make you feel that way, is all. A fish belongs in the water. It ought to stay there—just as we live on land in houses. Things ought to know their place and stay in it, but those fish have got a way of sidling off. As though they had mental reservations and weren't keeping any contracts. See what I mean?"

"I see what you mean," I said gravely. "They ought to be watched. My wife thinks so too. About a lot of things."

"She does?" He brightened. "Then that's two of us. I don't know why, but they give you that feeling."

He didn't know why, but I thought that he did.

It began as such things always begin—in the ooze of unnoticed swamps, in the darkness of eclipsed moons. It began with a strangled gasping for air.

The pond was a place of reek and corruption, of fetid smells and of oxygen-starved fish breathing through laboring gills. At times the slowly contracting circle of the water left little windrows of minnows who skittered desperately to escape the sun, but who died, nevertheless, in the fat, warm mud. It was a place of low life. In it the human brain began.

There were strange snouts in those waters, strange barbels nuzzling the bottom ooze, and there was time—three hundred million years of it—but mostly, I think, it was the ooze. By day the temperature in the world outside the pond rose to a frightful intensity; at night the sun went down in smoking red. Dust storms marched in incessant progression across a wilderness whose plants were the plants of long ago. Leafless and weird and stiff they lingered by the water, while over vast areas of grassless uplands the winds blew until red stones took on the polish of reflecting mirrors. There was nothing to hold the land in place. Winds howled, dust clouds rolled, and brief erratic torrents choked with silt ran down to the sea. It was a time of dizzying contrasts, a time of change.

On the oily surface of the pond, from time to time a snout thrust upward, took in air with a queer grunting inspiration, and swirled back to the bottom. The pond was doomed, the water was foul, and the oxygen almost gone, but the creature would not die. It could breathe air direct through a little accessory lung, and it could walk. In all that weird and lifeless landscape, it was the only thing that could. It walked rarely and under protest, but that was not surprising. The creature was a fish.

In the passage of days the pond became a puddle, but the Snout survived. There was dew one dark night and a coolness in the empty stream bed. When the sun rose next morning the pond was an empty place of cracked mud, but the Snout did not lie there. He had gone. Down stream there were other ponds. He breathed air for a few hours and hobbled slowly along on the stumps of heavy fins.

It was an uncanny business if there had been anyone there to see. It was a journey best not observed in daylight, it was something that needed swamps and shadows and the touch of the night dew. It was a monstrous penetration of a forbidden element, and the Snout kept his face from the light. It was just as well, though the face should not be mocked. In three hundred million years it would be our own.

There was something fermenting in the brain of the Snout. He was no longer entirely a fish. The ooze had marked him. It takes a swamp-and-tide-flat zoologist to tell you about life; it is in this domain that the living suffer great extremes, it is here that the water-failures, driven to desperation, make starts in a new element. It is here that strange compromises are made and new senses are born. The Snout was no exception. Though he breathed and walked primarily in order to stay in the water, he was coming ashore.

He was not really a successful fish except that he was managing to stay alive in a noisome, uncomfortable, oxygen-starved environment. In fact the time was coming when the last of his kind, harried by more ferocious and speedier fishes, would slip off the edge of the continental shelf, to seek safety in the sunless abysses of the deep sea. But the Snout was a fresh-water Crossopterygian, to give him his true name, and cumbersome and plodding though he was, something had happened back of his eyes. The ooze had gotten in its work.

It is interesting to consider what sort of creatures we, the remote descendants of the Snout, might be, except for that green quagmire out of which he came. Mammalian insects perhaps we should have been—solid-brained, our neurones wired for mechanical responses, our lives running out with the perfection of beautiful, intricate, and mindless clocks. More likely we should never have existed at all. It was the Snout and the ooze that did it. Perhaps there also, among rotting fish heads and blue, night-burning bog lights, moved the eternal mystery, the careful finger of God. The increase was not much. It was two bubbles, two thin-walled little balloons at the end of the Snout's small brain. The cerebral hemispheres had appeared.

Among all the experiments in that dripping, ooze-filled world, one was vital: the brain had to be fed. The nerve tissues are insatiable devourers of oxygen. If they do not get it, life is gone. In stagnant swamp waters, only the development of a highly efficient blood supply to the brain can prevent disaster. And among those gasping, dying creatures, whose small brains winked out forever in the long Silurian drought, the Snout and his brethren survived.

Over the exterior surface of the Snout's tiny brain ran the myriad blood vessels that served it; through the greatly enlarged choroid plexuses, other vessels pumped oxygen into the spinal fluid. The brain was a thin-walled tube fed from both surfaces. It could only exist as a thing of thin walls permeated with oxygen. To thicken, to lay down solid masses of nervous tissue such as exist among the fishes in oxygenated waters was to invite disaster. The Snout lived on a bubble, two bubbles in his brain.

It was not that his thinking was deep; it was only that it had to be thin. The little bubbles of the hemispheres helped to spread the area upon which higher correlation centers could be built, and yet preserve those areas from the disastrous thickenings which meant oxygen death to the swamp dweller. There is a mystery about those thickenings which culminate in the so-called solid brain. It is the brain of insects, of the modern fishes, of some reptiles and all birds. Always it marks the appearance of elaborate patterns of instinct and the end of thought. A road has been taken which, anatomically, is well-nigh irretraceable; it does not lead in the direction of a high order of consciousness.

Wherever, instead, the thin sheets of gray matter expand upward into the enormous hemispheres of the human brain, laughter, or it may be sorrow, enters in. Out of the choked Devonian waters emerged sight and sound and the music that rolls invisible through the composer's brain. They are there still in the ooze along the tideline, though no one notices. The world is fixed, we say: fish in the sea, birds in the air. But in the mangrove swamps by the Niger, fish climb trees and ogle uneasy naturalists who try unsuccessfully to chase them back to the water. There are things still coming ashore.

The door to the past is a strange door. It swings open and things pass through it, but they pass in one direction only. No man can return across that threshold, though he can look down still and see the green light waver in the water weeds.

There are two ways to seek the doorway: in the swamps of the inland waterways and along the tide flats of the estuaries where rivers come to the sea. By those two pathways life came ashore. It was not the magnificent march through the breakers and up the cliffs that we fondly imagine. It was a stealthy advance made in suffocation and terror, amidst the leaching bite of chemical discomfort. It was made by the failures of the sea.

Some creatures have slipped through the invisible chemical barrier between salt and fresh water into the tidal rivers, and later come ashore, some have crept upward from the salt. In all cases, however, the first adventure into the dreaded atmosphere seems to have been largely determined by the inexorable crowding of enemies and by the retreat further and further into marginal situations where the oxygen supply was depleted. Finally, in the ruthless selection of the swamp margins, or in the scramble for food on the tide flats, the land becomes home.

Not the least interesting feature of some of the tide-flat emergents is their definite antipathy for the full tide. It obstructs their food-collecting on the mud banks and brings their enemies. Only extremes of fright will drive them into the water for any period.

I think it was the great nineteenth-century paleontologist Cope who first clearly enunciated what he called the "law of the unspecialized," the contention that it was not from the most highly organized and dominant forms of a given geological era that the master type of a succeeding period evolved, but that instead the dominant forms tended to arise from more lowly and generalized animals which were capable of making new adaptations, and which were not narrowly restricted to a given environment.

There is considerable truth to this observation, but, for all that, the idea is not simple. Who is to say without foreknowledge of the future which animal is specialized and which is not? We have only to consider our remote ancestor, the Snout, to see the intricacies into which the law of the unspecialized may lead us.

If we had been making zoological observations in the Paleozoic Age, with no knowledge of the strange realms life was to penetrate in the future, we would probably have regarded the Snout as specialized. We would have seen his air-bladder lung, his stubby, sluggish fins, and his odd ability to wriggle overland as specialized adaptations to a peculiarly restricted environmental niche in stagnant continental waters. We would have thought in water terms and we would have dismissed the Snout as an interesting failure off the main line of progressive evolution, escaping from his enemies and surviving successfully only in the dreary and marginal surroundings scorned by the swift-finned teleost fishes who were destined to dominate the seas and all quick waters.

Yet it was this poor specialization—this bog-trapped failure—whose descendants, in three great movements, were to dominate the earth. It is only now, looking backward, that we dare to regard him as "generalized." The Snout was the first vertebrate to pop completely through the water membrane into a new dimension. His very specializations and failures, in a water sense, had preadapted him for a world he scarcely knew existed.

The day of the Snout was over three hundred million years ago. Not long since I read a book in which a prominent scientist spoke cheerfully of some ten billion years of future time remaining to us. He pointed out happily the things that man might do throughout that period. Fish in the sea, I thought again, birds in the air. The climb all far behind us, the species fixed and sure. No wonder my explorer friend had had a momentary qualm when he met the mudskippers with their mental reservations and lack of promises. There is something wrong with our world view. It is still Ptolemaic, though the sun is no longer believed to revolve around the earth.

We teach the past, we see farther backward into time than any race before us, but we stop at the present, or, at best, we project far into the future idealized versions of ourselves. All that long way behind us we see, perhaps inevitably, through human eyes alone. We see ourselves as the culmination and the end, and if we do indeed consider our passing, we think that sunlight will go with us and the earth be dark. We are the end. For us continents rose and fell, for us the waters and the air were mastered, for us the great living web has pulsated and grown more intricate.

To deny this, a man once told me, is to deny God. This puzzled me. I went back along the pathway to the marsh. I went, not in the past, not by the bones of dead things, not down the lost roadway of the Snout. I went instead in daylight, in the Now, to see if the door was still there, and to see what things passed through.

I found that the same experiments were brewing, that up out of that ancient well, fins were still scrambling toward the sunlight. They were small things, and which of them presaged the future I could not say. I saw only that they were many and that they had solved the oxygen death in many marvelous ways, not always ours.

I found that there were modern fishes who breathed air, not through a lung but through their stomachs or through strange chambers where their gills should be, or breathing as the Snout once breathed. I found that some crawled in the fields at nightfall pursuing insects, or slept on the grass by pond sides and who drowned, if kept under water, as men themselves might drown.

Of all these fishes the mudskipper *Periophythalmus* is perhaps the strangest. He climbs trees with his fins and pursues insects; he snaps worms like a robin on the tide flats; he sees as land things see, and above all he dodges and evades with a curious popeyed insolence more suggestive of the land than of the sea. Of a different tribe and a different time he is, nevertheless, oddly reminiscent of the Snout.

But not the same. There lies the hope of life. The old ways are exploited and remain, but new things come, new senses try the unfamiliar air. There are small scuttlings and splashings in the dark, and out of it come the first croaking, illiterate voices of the things to be, just as man once croaked and dreamed darkly in that tiny vesicular forebrain.

Perpetually, now, we search and bicker and disagree. The eternal form eludes us—the shape we conceive as ours. Perhaps the old road through the marsh should tell us. We are one of many appearances of the thing called Life; we are not its perfect image, for it has no image except Life, and life is multitudinous and emergent in the stream of time.

John Hay

AN UNIMAGINED FRONTIER

O NE afternoon in the middle of June I set off from Race Point at Provincetown, carrying a pack and sleeping bag, with Nauset Light Beach in Eastham, twenty-five miles away, as my destination, and my purpose simply to be on the beach, to see it and feel it for whatever it turned out to be, since most of my previous visits had been of the sporadic hop, skip, and jump kind to which our automotivated lives seem to lead us.

The summer turmoil was not yet in full voice but the barkers were there on behalf of beach-buggy tours over the dunes, and a sight-seeing plane flew by; cars drew up and droned away, and families staggered up from the beach with their load of towels, shoes, bags, or portable radios. The beach did not contain quite the great wealth of paper, cans, bottles, and general garbage that it would later on, in July and August, but one of the first things to catch my eye as I lunged down on to the sands was an electric-light bulb floating in the water, a can of shaving soap, the remains of a rubber doll, and a great scattering of sliced onions—probably thrown off a fishing boat.

The air was dancing with heat. The sun seemed to have the power to glare through all things. With the exception of a camper's tent on the upper part of the beach, and a few isolated gray shacks perched on dune tops behind it, there was nothing ahead but the wide belt of sand curving around one unseen corner after another with the flat easing and stretching sea beside me. Two boys waved to me from where they were perched high up on a dune, and I waved back.

Then I heard an insistent, protesting bird note behind me, and a piping plover flew past. It was very pale, and sand colored, being a wild personification of the place it lived in. It suddenly volplaned down the slope of the beach ahead of me, fluttering, half disappearing in holes made by human feet, side-winged, edged away, still fluttering, in the direction of the shore line, and when it reached the water, satisfied, evidently, that it had led me far enough, it flew back. These birds nest on the beach above the high-tide line, and like a number of other species, try to lead intruders away when they come too close to their eggs and young.

With high, grating cries, terns flew over the beach and low over the water, occasionally plummeting in after fish. Among the larger species, principally common terns, there were some least terns—a tiny, dainty version of the "sea swallow," chasing each other back and forth. They have the graceful, sharply defined bodies and deep wingbeat of the other terns, but in their littleness and excitability they seem to show a kind of baby anger.

Also there were tree swallows gathering and perching on the hot, glittering sand, and on smooth gray driftwood just below the dunes. It was a band of them, adults, and young hatched during the early spring, chittering and shining with their brilliant blue-green backs and white bellies.

It seemed to me that out of these birds—my unwilling or indifferent companions—came a protest, the protest of a desert in its beauty, an ancient sea land claiming its rarity, with these rare inhabitants, each with its definition and assertion, each having the color and precision of life and place, out of an unknown depth of devising.

Behind the beach at Provincetown and Truro are eight square miles of dunes, making a great series of dips and pockets, innumerable smooth scourings, hollows within wide hollows. Standing below their rims are hills, mounds, and cones, chiseled by the wind, sometimes flattened on the top like mesas. These dunes give an effect of motion, rolling, dipping, roving, dropping down and curving up like sea surfaces offshore. When I climbed the bank to see them I heard the clear, accomplished notes of a song sparrow. There were banks of rugosa roses in bloom, with white or pink flowers sending off a lovely scent, and the dunes were patched with the new green of beach grass, bayberry, and beach plum, many of the shrubs looking clipped and rounded, held down by wind and salt spray. The purple and pink flowers of the beach pea, with purselike petals, were in bloom too, contrasting with dusty miller with leaf surfaces like felt, a soft, clear grayish-green. Down at the bottom of the hollows the light and wind catching heads of bunch grass, pinkish and brown, waved continually; and the open sandy slopes were swept as by a free hand with curving lines and striations.

A mile or so at sea, over the serene flatness of the waters, a fishing boat moved very slowly by. I started down the beach again, following another swallow that was twisting and dipping in leafy flight along the upper edge of the beach. On the tide line slippery green sea lettuce began to glimmer as if it had an inner fire, reflecting the evening sun. I stopped somewhere a mile or two north of Highland Light in Truro, built a small fire of driftwood to heat up a can of food, and watched a bar appearing above the water as the tide ebbed. Low white waves conflicted and ran across a dome of sand, occasionally bursting up like hidden geysers.

The terns were still crying and diving as the sun's metal light, slanting along the shore, began to turn a soft yellow, to spread and bloom. They hurried back and forth, as if to make use of the time left them, and fell sharply like stones into the shimmering road of light that led across the water.

Where I live on the upper Cape, that part of it which lies between the Cape Cod canal and Orleans, the land heads out directly to the sea, toward the east from the continental west. Cape Cod Bay lies to the north and Nantucket Sound to the south. The arm of the lower Cape turns in the Orleans area and heads up on a north-south axis, the head of it, or hand if you like, curving around so that the sandy barrens in the Provincetown area are oriented in an east to west direction again. I am used to looking toward Kansas to see the setting sun, and from the curving shore line of Truro I had the illusion that it was setting in the north and that when it rose the next morning it appeared to be located not very far from where it set, a matter of ninety or a hundred degrees. In fact it does set closer to the north at this time of year, and along the flat ocean horizon this becomes more clear to the eye, as well as its relative position at dawn and its arc during the day. On the open beach in spring and summer you are not only at the sun's mercy in a real sense, but you are also under wider skies. In the comparative isolation of the beach, which is convex, slanting steeply toward the water, and therefore hides its distances, I felt reoriented, turned out and around through no effort of my own, and faced in many possible directions.

Shortly before sundown a beach buggy, curtains at its windows and a dory attached, lumbered slowly down some preordained ruts in the sand, and then a smaller one passed by at the top of the low dunes behind me. Fishing poles were slung along the outside of both machines. It was getting to be a good time to cast for striped bass.

I sat on the sands and listened to the sonorous heave and splash of low waves. The sun, like a colossal red balloon filled with water, was sinking in to the horizon. It swelled, flattened, and disappeared with a final rapidity, leaving a foaming, fiery band behind it. I suddenly heard the wild, trembling cry of a loon behind me, and then saw it fly over, heading north. The wind grew cool, after a hot day when the light shone on metallic, glittering slow waters, and sharp, pointed beach grasses clicked together, while I watched the darkness falling around me.

A small seaplane flew by at low altitude, parallel to the shore. A sliver of a moon appeared and then a star; and then single lights began to shine on the horizon, while from the direction of Highland Light an arm of light shot up and swung around. A fishing boat passed slowly by with a light at its masthead and two—port and starboard—at its stern. A few night-flying moths fluttered near me. The sky began to be massive with its stars. I thought of night's legitimacies now appearing, the natural claim of all these single lights on darkness, and then, making my bed in a hollow just above the beach, I lowered down into infinity, waking up at about one o'clock in the morning to the sound of shouting, a strange direct interruption to the night. It was the loud implacable voice of the human animal, something very wild in itself, filling the emptiness.

"For Chrisake bring her higher up! I can't have her dig in that way." The tide had come in and someone was having trouble maneuvering his beach buggy along the thin strip of sand now available.

The light of dawn opened my eyes again before the sun showed red on the horizon, and I first saw the tiny drops of dew on tips and stems of beach grass that surrounded me. A sparrow sang, and then, somewhere behind the dunes, a prairie warbler with sweet notes on an ascending scale.

When I started walking again I caught sight of a young fox. Its fur was still soft and woolly and its gait had a cub's limpness where it moved along the upper edge of the beach. I wished the young one well, though I suspected it might have an uncomfortable life. In spite of an excessive population of rabbits, and their role in keeping it down, foxes have not been too highly regarded on the Cape. In recent years they seem to have been a skinny and somewhat dilapidated bunch for the most part, suffering from parasitic skin diseases, and ticks in season. I once saw a fox out on an asphalt road sliding along on his chin and side, shoving and dragging himself in such a frantic way that I began to feel very itchy myself. I have heard them referred to in scornful way as "spoilers," fond of scavenging and rolling in dead meat. In other words, they are smelly, diseased and, to add another epithet, "tricky," not to be trusted.

Yet this cub exploring an early morning on the sands had a future, however limited, and I remembered the lively trot of foxes when they are in good health, and their intelligence and curiosity, and simply their right to whatever special joys they might inherit.

I carried a pair of field glasses with me, along with the somewhat thoughtlessly assembled equipment I wore on my back and which seemed increasingly heavy as time went on. When not too conscious of my burden I would use the glasses to bring an inland or offshore bird closer to me. I noticed five eider ducks across the troughs of the waves, a remnant of the thousands that winter off the Cape along with such other sea birds as brant, Canada geese, scoters, mergansers, old squaws, and various members of the auk family. I passed a dead gannet lying on the sand. It had been badly oiled, reminding me of the hazards of jettisoned tanker or freighter oil to all those water birds which land on the sea to rest or feed.

There were a number of kingbirds on the dune rims, and they kept dropping down over the beach in their special way, to hover with fast wingbeat and flutter after flying insects. I heard the grating call of redwings, indicating marshy areas inland of the beach, but the cliffs above began to increase until they were 100 to 150 feet high or more, and the sun was so fierce that I had little interest in trying to scale them to see what was on the other side.

I plodded on, noticing very little after a while, my attention blunted, reduced to seeing that one foot got in front of the other. The more level upper parts of the beach provided fairly good walking, but the sand was soft, and to relieve my aching muscles I would then angle down to the water's edge where it was firmer, and there I was obliged to walk with one leg below the other because of the inclination of the beach. So I would return to the upper beach again and push ahead. I walked on, very hot and slow, seeing no one for miles until I came up to a group of bathers below a road and parking lot giving access to the beach, of the kind that are scattered along its reaches; and there I refilled my canteen at a cottage and went on.

I found that if I rested too long during this hike I had little desire to go on again, so I confined myself to an army "break" of ten minutes every hour. Renewed walking unlimbered me a little and the wind off the water cooled my sweating skin. I listened to the sound of the waves. In addition to their rhythmic plunge and splash, their breathing, they clashed occasionally with a sound like the breaking of heavy glass, the falling of timber, or a load of bricks.

I passed what was left of two shipwrecks during the day, a reminder of the dangers that still face ships along this coast with its fogs, its shifting winds, its storms, the hidden, treacherous offshore bars. The sands often reveal the timbers of old ships. One day their ribs, sodden and dark, barnacle encrusted, may reach up out of oblivion, and not long after that the water buries them under tons of sand. From them a local history calls out for recognition. Thousands of ships over three centuries wrecked on shoals, engulfed by violent seas, men with the dark of doom in them, to drown or to survive, and only a few timbers left to declare the ultimate dangers and their terror.

I was not in Death Valley, or on a raft at sea. My walk was not unusually long, and I could leave the beach if I had to, but the enormity of the area filled me more and more. It had so much in it that was without recourse. Its emptiness, the great tidal range beyond it and through it, the raw heartbeat of the waves, the implacable sun, established the kind of isolation and helplessness in me which the commerce and community of our lives tries so hard to disguise. Even the birds, I began to think, were more secure than I. They had their strong bright threads of cognizance to the areas they came to, the water, the sands, the marsh. They were fixed in entity and grace, eating what was theirs by evolution to be eaten, using land and air in the ways that had come to them, knowing this place and all places like it in terms of its bounds and boundlessness, meeting its naked eye in the ways they had been sent to do.

I started off in the morning admiring the brilliance of the sun, the small shadows from the dunes and across the beach, through driftwood, isolated beach plants and tidal wrack, with the wide flooding of light ahead and the variation in reflected light across the sea. I felt the sea moving quietly beside me. The waves heaved and sighed and spray was tossed lightly above the sand. Everything was continuous, untroubled, and deliberate; but as the day wore on the sun became my enemy, and I had very little rage or resource in me to fight it with. I was not fitted to environmental stability, like a bird, or fox or fish. I found myself in an area of whose reaches I had never been wholly aware, and in me there was no mastery. The sun was not only hostile. It was an ultimate, an impossibility; and the waters beside me began to deepen from their pleasant daytime sparkle and freshness into an incalculable realm which I had hardly entered. I was touching on an unimagined frontier.

I spent my second night on the beach a few miles from Nauset Light where I left it the following morning. It was in the South Wellfleet area, and as I started to sleep on the sand a little above the high-tide line, I remembered that this was about the same place where a fishing boat had been wrecked two years before and two men drowned. I had seen the boat, with its cargo of fish, and some of the men's clothing strewn along the shore, and I had heard a little about the depths of their ordeal. Their story haunted me; and then I began to feel that I might be caught by the tide while I was asleep. There were only about twelve feet between the bottom of a steep cliff and the high-tide line. I would soon be lying on a narrow shelf at the sea's edge. So as the vague thought of being engulfed began to invade me, I took up my pack and sleeping bag again, retraced my steps down the beach, and found a way to the top of the cliff, where I spent the night in another hollow.

The light of dawn, lifting quickly out of the sea, flooding into the range of low-lying land, woke me up again, and it signaled to the birds, who started singing in all the thickets and heath around me with a sweet, high, shrill intensity, a kind of automatic worship; and after a while they quieted down again.

Little dirt roads dropped back from headlands through green slopes covered with bearberry and patches of yellow-flowered Hudsonia, or "poverty grass," and there were hollows dipping back inland, and woods of stunted pitch pine. From the top of the cliff I watched the sun starting to send light running across the blue table of the sea, making it glitter and move. The intensity of light and heat began to grow steadily as I walked down the beach again for the last stretch toward Nauset.

The beach is not so very far from where I live, or for that matter where anyone lives on the Cape. It is a few miles down the road, beyond the trees; and yet when I came back from my walk I felt as if I had been at enormous remove from my surroundings, caught out where I might have feared to be. The long line of sand and surf, the intensity of the sun, the cover of stars had come close enough to put me in council with that which had no answers. I was in awe of nature; and I understood that the sun and sea could be our implacable enemies. It was in this context that I saw our human world as subject to a stature that it never made.

Samuel Eliot Morison

FIRST CROSSING OF THE ATLANTIC

B Y THE second day of August, 1492, everything at last was ready. That night every man and boy of the fleet confessed his sins, received absolution and made his communion at the church of Palos,[1] which by happy coincidence was dedicated to Saint George, patron saint of Genoa. Columbus went on board his flagship in the small hours of Friday the third and gave the signal to get under way. Before the sun rose, all three vessels had anchors aweigh, and with sails hanging limp from their yards were floating down the Rio Tinto on the morning ebb, using their long sweeps

1. Palos is a town situated on the Rio (River) Tinto in southwestern Spain; La Rábida, a monastery, is also on the river, just below Palos, where the Tinto meets the Rio Odiel to form the Rio Saltés, only a short distance before the open sea.

to maintain steerageway. As they swung into the Saltés and passed La Rábida close aboard, they could hear the friars chanting the ancient hymn *Iam lucis orto sidere* [2] with its haunting refrain *Et nunc et in perpetuum,* which we render "Evermore and evermore."

This fleet of good hope, whose achievements would radically alter world history, sailed parallel to another fleet of misery and woe. On the very same tide there dropped down the Saltés the last vessel carrying the Jews whom Ferdinand and Isabella had expelled from Spain. August 2 was their deadline; any who remained thereafter were to be executed unless they embraced Christianity. Thousands of pitiful refugees, carrying what few household goods they could stow in the crowded ships, were bound for the more tolerant lands of Islam, or for the only Christian country, the Netherlands, which would receive them. Columbus in all his writings dropped no word of pity for the fate of this persecuted race, and even expressed the wish to exclude them from the lands he discovered. But if there had been a new prophet among the Spanish Jews, he might have pointed out the Columbian fleet to his wretched compatriots on that August morning and said, "Behold the ships that in due time will carry the children of Israel to the ends of the earth."

Columbus's plan for the voyage was simple, and its simplicity insured his success. Not for him the boisterous head winds, the monstrous seas and the dark, unbridled waters of the North Atlantic, which had already baffled so many Portuguese. He would run south before the prevailing northerlies to the Canary Islands, and there make, as it were, a right-angle turn; for he had observed on his African voyages that the winter winds in the latitude of the Canaries blew from the east, and that the ocean around them, more often than not, was calm as a millpond. An even better reason to take his departure from the Canaries was their position astride latitude 28 degrees North, which, he believed, cut Japan, passing en route the mythical Isle of Antilia, which would make a good break in the westward passage. Until about a hundred years ago when chronometers became generally available to find longitude, sailors always tried to find the latitude of their destination and then would "run their westing" (or easting) down until they hit it.* That is what Columbus proposed to do with respect to Japan, which he had figured out to be only 2400 nautical miles due west of the Canaries.

The first leg of the voyage was made in less than a week. Then, within sight of the Grand Canary, the fleet ran into a calm that lasted two or

2. *Iam lucis orto sidere:* the daystar having already risen, i.e., now that day begins (Latin).
* A New England shipmaster of whom someone inquired the route from Cape Cod to Barbados said, "Run South until your butter melts, then West!"

three days. Columbus decided to send *Pinta* into Las Palmas for some needed repairs while *Santa María* and *Niña* went to Gomera, westernmost of the Canaries that the Spaniards had wrested from their native inhabitants. At Gomera the Captain General (as we should call Columbus on this voyage before he made Admiral) sent men ashore to fill extra water casks, buy breadstuffs and cheese, and put a supply of native beef in pickle. He then sailed to Las Palmas to superintend *Pinta's* repairs and returned with her to Gomera.

On September 2 all three ships were anchored off San Sebastián, the port of that island. Columbus then met for the first time Doña Beatriz de Bobadilla, widow of the former captain of the island. Beatriz was a beautiful lady still under thirty, and Columbus is said to have fallen in love with her; but if that is true, he did not love her warmly enough to tarry to the next full moon. Additional ship's stores were quickly hoisted on board and struck below, and on September 6, 1492, the fleet weighed anchor for the last time in the Old World. They had still another island to pass, the lofty Ferro or Hierro. Owing to calms and variables Ferro and the 12,000-foot peak of Tenerife were in sight until the ninth, but by nightfall that day, every trace of land had sunk below the eastern horizon, and the three vessels were alone on an uncharted ocean. Columbus himself gave out the course: "West; nothing to the north, nothing to the south."

Before going into the details of the voyage, let us see how those vessels were navigated, and how a day was passed at sea. Celestial navigation was then in its infancy, but rough estimates of latitude could be made from the height of the North Star above the horizon and its relation to the two outer stars (the "Guards") of the Little Dipper. A meridian altitude of the sun, applied to available tables of the sun's declination, also gave latitude, by a simple formula. But the instruments of observation—a solid wood or brass quadrant and the seaman's astrolabe—were so crude, and the movement of a ship threw them off to such an extent, that most navigators took their latitude sights ashore. Columbus relied almost completely on "dead reckoning," which means plotting your course and position on a chart from the three elements of direction, time and distance.

The direction he had from one or more compasses which were similar to those used in small craft until recently—a circular card graduated to the 32 points (N, N by E, NNE, NE by N, NE, and so on), with a lodestone under the north point, mounted on a pin and enclosed in a binnacle with gimbals so it could swing freely with the motion of the ship. Columbus's standard compass was mounted on the poop deck where the officer of the watch could see it. The helmsman, who steered with a heavy tiller attached directly to the rudder head, was below decks and could see very little. He may have had another compass to steer by, but in the smaller vessels, at least, he was conned by the officer of the deck and kept a steady course by the feel of the helm. On a sailing vessel you can do that; it would be impossible in any power craft.

Time on the vessels of that day was measured by a half-hour glass which hung from a beam so the sand could flow freely from the upper to the lower half. As soon as the sand was all down, a ship's boy turned the glass and the officer of the deck recorded it by making a stroke on a slate. Eight glasses made a watch; the modern ship's bells were originally a means of marking the glasses. This half-hour-glass time could be corrected daily in fair weather by noting the moment when the sun lay due south, which was local noon.

Distance was the most variable of these three elements. Columbus had no chip log [3] or other method of measuring the speed of his vessels. He and the watch officers merely estimated it and noted it down. By carefully checking Columbus's Journal of his First Voyage, Captain J. W. McElroy [4] ascertained that he made an average 9 per cent overestimate of his distance. This did not prevent his finding the way home, because the mistake was constant, and time and course were correct. It only resulted in Columbus placing the islands of his discovery farther west than they really were.

Even after making the proper reduction for this overestimate, the speed of his vessels is surprising. Ships of that day were expected to make 3 to 5 knots in a light breeze, up to $9\frac{1}{2}$ in a strong, fair gale, and at times to be capable of 12 knots. In October 1492, on the outward passage, the Columbus fleet made an average of 142 miles per day for five consecutive days, and the best day's run, 182 miles, averaged 8 knots. On the homeward passage, in February 1493, *Niña* and *Pinta* covered 198 miles one day, and at times hit it up to 11 knots. Any yachtsman today would be proud to make records that the great Admiral did on some of his transatlantic crossings in the fifteenth century. Improvements in sailing vessels since 1492 have been more in seaworthiness and comfort than in speed.

One reason Columbus always wanted two or more vessels was to have someone to rescue survivors in case of sinking. But he made an unusual record for that era by never losing a ship at sea, unless we count the *Santa María*, grounded without loss of life. Comforts and conveniences were almost totally lacking. Cooking was done on deck over a bed of sand in a wooden firebox protected from the wind by a hood. The diet was a mo-

3. **chip log**: a chip or log of wood trailed aft on the end of a line and used to measure the motion of a ship through the water.

4. **Captain J. W. McElroy**: chief navigating officer of the Harvard Columbus Expedition, which, under Admiral Morison's command, traced the courses of Columbus's various voyages.

notonous one of salt meat, hardtack and dried peas. For drink they had wine, while it lasted, and water in casks, which often went bad. Only the Captain General and the ships' captains had cabins with bunks; the others slept where they could, in their clothes.

In those days, sailors were the most religious of laymen. On each vessel a boy was charged with singing a ditty at daybreak, which began:

> Blessed be the light of day
> And the Holy Cross, we say;

after which he recited the Lord's Prayer and the Ave Maria, and invoked a blessing on the ship's company. Every half hour a boy sang out when turning the glass. For instance, at what we would call five bells, he sang:

> Five is past and six floweth,
> More shall flow if God willeth,
> Count and pass make voyage fast.

After sunset, and before the first night watch was set, all hands were called to evening prayers. The services began with the boy whose duty it was to light the binnacle lamp singing:

> God give us a good night and good sailing;
> May our ship make a good passage,
> Sir Captain and Master and good company.

All hands then said the Lord's Prayer, the Creed and the Ave Maria, and concluded by singing the *Salve Regina*. [. . .] Columbus himself said, "Seamen sing or say it after their own fashion," bawling it out in several keys at once and murdering the stately Latin words. But was it the less acceptable to the Virgin, under whose protection all sailors felt secure?

Now the boy who turns up the glass for the eighth time sings:

> The watch is called,
> The glass floweth.
> We shall make a good voyage
> If God willeth.

And as the vessels sail westward through the soft tropic night, rolling and pitching, sails bellying and slatting, cordage straining, bows throwing foam, every half hour is marked by this chantey:

> To our God let's pray
> To give us a good voyage,
> And through the Blessed Mother,
> Our advocate on high,
> Protect us from the waterspout
> And send no tempest nigh.

So much for the sea ritual that went on every day, whatever the weather. Now for the events of the voyage.

On September 9, the day he dropped the last land below the horizon, Columbus decided to keep a true reckoning of his course for his own use and a false one to give out to the people, so that they would not be frightened at sailing so far from land. But, owing to his overestimate of speed, the "false" reckoning was more nearly correct than the "true"!

During the first ten days (September 9 to 18), the easterly trade wind blew steadily, and the fleet made 1163 nautical miles' westing. This was the honeymoon of the voyage. *Que era plazer grande el gusto de las mañanas*—"What a delight was the savor of the mornings!" wrote Columbus in his Journal. That entry speaks to the heart of anyone who has sailed in the trades; it recalls the beauty of the dawn, kindling clouds and sails rose color, the smell of dew drying on a wooden deck, and, something Columbus didn't have, the first cup of coffee. Since his ships were at the northern edge of the northeast trades, where the wind first strikes the water, the sea was smooth, and the air, remarked the Captain General in his Journal, was "like April in Andalusia; the only thing wanting was to hear the song of the nightingale." But there were plenty of other birds following the ships: the little Mother Carey's chickens, dabbling for plankton in the bow waves and wakes; the boatswain bird, so called (as old seamen used to say) because it carries a marlinspike in its tail; the man-of-war or frigate bird, "thou ship of the air that never furl'st thy sails," as Walt Whitman wrote; and when the fleet passed beyond the range of these birds, the big Jaeger gulls gave it a call. During this period the fleet encountered its first field of sargassum or gulfweed and found that it was no hindrance to navigation. "Saw plenty weed" was an almost daily notation in the Captain General's log. The gulfweed bothered him much less than observing a westerly variation of the compass, for in European waters the variation is always easterly.

On September 19, only ten days out from Ferro, the fleet temporarily ran into an area of variable winds and rain. It was near the point on Columbus's chart where the fabled island of Antilia should have been, and all hands expected to sight land. The Captain General even had the deep-sea lead hove, and found no bottom at 200 fathoms; no wonder, since the ocean is about 2300 fathoms deep at the point he had reached. But the seamen who, on the tenth day of the northeast trades, were beginning to wonder whether they could ever beat back home were cheered by the change of wind.

During the next five days only 234 miles were made good. During this spell of moderate weather it was easy to converse from ship to ship and to talk about this or that island, St. Brendan's or Antilia, which they might pick up. In the middle of one of these colloquies, a seaman of *Pinta* gave the "Land Ho!" and everyone thought he saw an island against the setting sun. Columbus fell on his knees to thank God, ordered *Gloria in excelsis Deo* [5] to be sung by all hands, and set a course for the island. But at dawn no island was visible; there was none. It was simply a cloud bank above the western horizon resembling land, a common phenomenon at sea. Martín Alonso Pinzón [6] apparently wished to beat about and search for this island, but Columbus refused, because, he said, "his object was to reach the Indies, and if he delayed, it would not have made sense."

The trade wind now returned, but moderately, and during the six days September 26 to October 1, the fleet made only 382 miles. Under these circumstances the people began to mutter and grumble. Three weeks was probably more than they had ever been outside sight of land before. They were all getting on each other's nerves, as happens even nowadays on a long voyage to a known destination. There was nothing for the men to do in the light wind except to follow the ship's routine, and troll for fish. Grievances, real or imaginary, were blown up; cliques were formed; Spain was farther away every minute, and what lay ahead? Probably nothing, except in the eye of that cursed Genoese. Let's make him turn back, or throw him overboard!

On the first day of October the wind increased, and in five days (October 2 to 6) the fleet made 710 miles. On the sixth, when they had passed longitude 65 degrees West and actually lay directly north of Puerto Rico, Martín Alonso Pinzón shot his agile *Pinta* under the flagship's stern and shouted, "Alter course, sir, to southwest by west . . . Japan!" Columbus did not understand whether Martín Alonso meant that he thought they had missed Japan and should steer southwest by west for China, or that Japan lay in that direction; but he knew and Pinzón knew that the fleet had sailed more than the 2400 miles which, according to their calculations, lay between the Canaries and Japan. Naturally Columbus was uneasy, but he held to the west course magnetic, which, owing to the variation for which he did not allow, was about west by south, true.

On October 7, when there was another false landfall, great flocks of birds passed over the ships, flying westsouthwest; this was the autumn migration from eastern North America to the West Indies. Columbus decided that he had better follow the birds rather than his chart, and changed course accordingly that evening. That was "good joss" [7]; it was his shortest course to the nearest land. Now, every night, the men were heartened by seeing against the moon (full on October 5) flocks of birds flying their way. But by the tenth, mutiny flared up again. No land for thirty-

5. *Gloria in excelsis Deo:* Glory to God in the highest.
6. **Martín Alonso Pinzón:** commanded the *Pinta;* his younger brother, Vicente Yáñez, commanded the *Niña.*
7. **good joss:** good luck ("joss" is pidgin English for "God"; the word was used for "luck" among sailors in the eighteenth and nineteenth centuries).

one days. Even by the phony reckoning which Columbus gave out they had sailed much farther west than anyone had expected. Enough of this nonsense, sailing west to nowhere; let the Captain General turn back or else—! Columbus, says the record, "cheered them as best he could, holding out good hope of the advantages they might gain; and, he added, it was useless to complain, *since he had come to go to the Indies, and so had to continue until he found them, with Our Lord's help.*"

That was typical of Columbus's determination. Yet even he, conscious of divine guidance, could not have kept on indefinitely without the support of his captains and officers. According to one account, it was Martín Alonzo Pinzón who cheered him by shouting, *Adelante! Adelante!* which an American poet has translated, "Sail on! Sail on!" But, according to Oviedo, one of the earliest historians who talked with the participants, it was Columbus alone who persuaded the Pinzóns and La Cosa [8] to sail on, with the promise that if land were not found within three days, he would turn back. If this version is correct, as I believe it is, the Captain General's promise to his captains was made on October 9. Next day the trade wind blew fresher, sending the fleet along at 7 knots; it so continued on the eleventh, with a heavy following sea. But signs of land, such as branches of trees with green leaves and flowers, became so frequent that the people were content with their Captain General's decision, and the mutinous mutterings died out in the keen anticipation of making a landfall in the Indies.

As the sun set under a clear horizon October 11, the northeast trade breezed up to gale force, and the three ships tore along at 9 knots. But Columbus refused to shorten sail, since his promised time was running out. He signaled everyone to keep a particularly sharp watch, and offered extra rewards for first landfall in addition to the year's pay promised by the Sovereigns. That night of destiny was clear and beautiful with a late rising moon, but the sea was the roughest of the entire passage. The men were tense and expectant, the officers testy and anxious, the Captain General serene in the confidence that presently God would reveal to him the promised Indies.

At 10 P.M., an hour before moonrise, Columbus and a seaman, almost simultaneously, thought they saw a light "like a little wax candle rising and falling." Others said they saw it too, but most did not; and after a few minutes it disappeared. Volumes have been written to explain what this light was or might have been. To a seaman it requires no explanation. It was an illusion, created by overtense watchfulness. When uncertain of your exact position, and straining to make a night landfall, you are apt to see imaginary lights and flashes and to hear nonexistent bells and breakers.

8. **La Cosa:** Juan de la Cosa, commander of the *Santa María.*

On rush the ships, pitching, rolling, throwing spray—white waves at their bows and white wakes reflecting the moon. *Pinta* is perhaps half a mile in the lead, *Santa María* on her port quarter, *Niña* on the other side. Now one, now another forges ahead, but they are all making the greatest speed of which they are capable. With the sixth glass of the night watch, the last sands are running out of an era that began with the dawn of history. A few minutes now and destiny will turn up a glass the flow of whose sands we are still watching. Not since the birth of Christ has there been a night so full of meaning for the human race.

At 2 A.M., October 12, Rodrigo de Triana, lookout on *Pinta*, sees something like a white cliff shining in the moonlight, and sings out, *Tierra! tierra!* "Land! land!" Captain Pinzón verifies the landfall, fires a gun as agreed, and shortens sail to allow the flagship to catch up. As *Santa María* approaches, the Captain General shouts across the rushing water, "Señor Martín Alonso, you *did* find land! Five thousand maravedis [9] for you as a bonus!"

Yes, land it was this time, a little island of the Bahamas group. The fleet was headed for the sand cliffs on its windward side and would have been wrecked had it held course. But these seamen were too expert to allow that to happen. The Captain General ordered sail to be shortened and the fleet to jog off and on until daylight, which was equivalent to a southwesterly drift clear of the island. At dawn they made full sail, passed the southern point of the island and sought an opening on the west coast, through the barrier reef. Before noon they found it, sailed into the shallow bay now called Long or Fernandez, and anchored in the lee of the land, in five fathoms.

Here on a gleaming beach of white coral occurred the famous first landing of Columbus. The Captain General (now by general consent called Admiral) went ashore in the flagship's boat with the royal standard of Castile displayed, the two Captains Pinzón in their boats, flying the banner of the Expedition—the green crowned cross on a white field. "And, all having rendered thanks to Our Lord, kneeling on the ground, embracing it with tears of joy for the immeasurable mercy of having reached it, the Admiral rose and gave this island the name *San Salvador*"—Holy Saviour.*

9. **maravedis:** the maravedi, a Spanish copper coin unit, was introduced by Ferdinand and Isabella.

* Although there is still some difference of opinion, the generally accepted identification of Columbus's island is the one formerly called Watlings. It has been officially renamed San Salvador.

Carl Sandburg

GETTYSBURG

WHEN Lee's army had vanished into the Shenandoah Valley to reappear in Pennsylvania, Lincoln's instructions to Meade ran that not Richmond but Lee's army must be the objective. Meade followed Lee with orders from Lincoln "to find and fight" the enemy. From day to day neither Meade nor Lee had been certain where the other was. Lee would rather have taken Harrisburg, its stores and supplies, and then battled Meade on the way to Philadelphia. In that case Lee would have had ammunition enough to keep his artillery firing with no letup, no orders during an infantry charge that ammunition was running low and must be saved.

Lee rode his horse along roads winding through bright summer landscapes to find himself suddenly looking at the smoke of a battle he had not ordered nor planned. Some of his own marching divisions had become entangled with enemy columns, traded shots, and a battle had begun that Lee could draw away from or carry on. He decided to carry on. He said Yes. His troops in their last two battles and on general form looked unbeatable. Against him was an untried commander with a jealous staff that had never worked as smoothly as his own. If he could repeat his performances with his men at Fredericksburg and Chancellorsville, he could then march to Harrisburg, use the State capitol for barracks, replenish his needs, march on to Philadelphia, Baltimore, and Washington, lay hold of money, supplies, munitions, win European recognition and end the war.

The stakes were immense, the chances fair. The new enemy commander had never planned a battle nor handled a big army in the wild upsets of frontal combat on a wide line. Also fifty-eight regiments of Northern veterans who had fought at Antietam, Fredericksburg, Chancellorsville, had gone home, their time up, their places filled by militia and raw recruits.

One factor was against Lee: he would have to tell his cannoneers to go slow and count their shells, while Meade's artillery could fire on and on from an endless supply. Another factor too was against Lee: he was away from his Virginia, where he knew the ground and the people, while Meade's men were fighting for their homes, women, barns, cattle, and fields against invaders and strangers, as Meade saw and felt it.

To Lee's words, "If the enemy is there, we must attack him," Longstreet, who now replaced Stonewall Jackson, spoke sharply, "If he is there, it will be because he is anxious that we should attack him—a good reason, in my judgment, for not doing so." This vague and involved feeling Longstreet nursed in his breast; attack was unwise, and his advice rejected. It resulted in hours of delay and wasted time that might have counted.

Lee hammered at the Union left wing the first day, the right wing the second day, Meade on that day sending word to Lincoln that the enemy was "repulsed at all points." On the third day, July 3, of '63, Lee smashed at Meade's center. Under Longstreet's command, General George Edward Pickett, a tall arrow of a man, with mustache and goatee, with long ringlets of auburn hair flying as he galloped his horse, headed 15,000 men who had nearly a mile to go up a slow slope of land to reach the Union center. Pickett might have had thoughts in his blanket under the stars some night that week of how long ago it was, twenty-one years, since he, a Virginia boy schooled in Richmond, had been studying law in his uncle's office in Quincy, Illinois, seeing men daily who tried cases with the young attorney Abraham Lincoln. And the Pickett boy had gone on to West Point, graduated at the bottom of his class, the last of all, though later he had been first to go over the parapets at Chapultepec in 1847, and still later, in 1859, had taken possession of San Juan Island at Puget Sound on the delicate mission of accommodating officials of the Buchanan Administration in bringing on a war with Great Britain, with the hope of saving his country from a threatened civil war by welding its divided sections. British diplomacy achieved joint occupation of the island by troops of two nations and thus averted war. On the Peninsula, Pickett's men had earned the nickname of "The Game Cock Brigade," and he considered love of woman second only to the passion of war.

Before starting his men on their charge to the Union center, Pickett handed Longstreet a letter to a girl in Richmond he was to marry if he lived. Longstreet had ordered Pickett to go forward and Pickett had penciled on the back of the envelope, "If Old Peter's [Longstreet's] nod means death, good-bye, and God bless you, little one!" An officer held out a flask of whisky to Pickett: "Take a drink with me; in an hour you'll be in hell or glory." And Pickett said No; he had promised "the little girl" he wouldn't.

Across the long rise of open ground, with the blue flag of Virginia floating ahead, over field and meadow Pickett's 15,000 marched steadily and smoothly, almost as if on a drill ground. Solid shot, grape and canister, from the Union artillery plowed through them, and later a wild rain of rifle bullets. Seven-eighths of a mile they marched in the open sunlight, every man a target for the Union marksmen behind stone fences and breastworks. They obeyed orders; Uncle Robert had said they would go anywhere and do anything.

As men fell their places were filled, the ranks closed up. As officers tumbled off horses it was taken as expected in battle.

Perhaps half who started reached the Union lines surmounting Cemetery Ridge.

Then came cold steel, the bayonet, the clubbed musket. The strongest and last line of the enemy was reached. "The Confederate battle flag waved over his defences," said a Confederate major, "and the fighting over the wall became hand to hand, but more than half having already fallen, our line was too weak to rout the enemy."

Meade rode up white-faced to hear it was a repulse and cried, "Thank God!" Lee commented: "They deserved success as far as it can be deserved by human valor and fortitude. More may have been required of them than they were able to perform." To one of his colonels Lee said, "This has been a sad day for us, a sad day, but we cannot expect always to gain victories."

As a heavy rainfall came on the night of July 4 Lee ordered a retreat toward the Potomac.

Meade was seen that day sitting in the open on a stone, his head held in his hand, willing it should rain, thankful that his army had, as he phrased it, driven "the invaders from our soil." For three days and nights Meade wasn't out of his clothes, took only snatches of sleep, while he had spoken the controlling decisions to his corps commanders in the bloodiest battle of modern warfare up till that time. Tabulations ran that the Union Army lost 23,000 killed, wounded and missing, the Confederate Army 28,000. Pickett came out of it alive to write his Virginia girl, "Your soldier lives and mourns and but for you, he would rather, a million times rather, be back there with his dead to sleep for all time in an unknown grave."

One tree in line of fire had 250 bullets in it, another tree 110 lead messengers that missed human targets. Farmer Rummel's cow lane was piled with thirty dead horses. Farmer Rummel found two cavalrymen who had fought afoot, killed each other and fallen with their feet touching, each with a bloody saber in his hand. A Virginian and a 3d Pennsylvania man had fought on horseback, hacking each other head and shoulders with sabers; they clinched and their horses ran out from under them; they were found with stiff and bloody fingers fastened in each other. The pegleg Confederate General Ewell, struck by a bullet, had chirped merrily to General John B. Gordon, "It don't hurt a bit to be shot in a wooden leg."

Military experts studied 27,000 muzzle-loading muskets picked up on the battlefield; 24,000 were loaded, one half had two loads, many had ten loads; and the experts deduced that in the bloody work and the crying out loud that day many soldiers lost their heads, loaded, forgot to fire, and then forgot their muskets were loaded. Also they figured it out that each soldier in battle fired away about his own weight in lead before he killed one of the opposition.

Where cannon and muskets had roared with sheets of flame on Cemetery Ridge was a tall graveyard gate with a sign forbidding the use of firearms out of respect to the dead and decently buried on the premises. The dead on the battlefield lay where they had fallen during three days' fighting, and on July 3 Fremantle noticed an "offensive" odor of decomposing bodies. "Through the branches of the trees and among the gravestones in the cemetery a shower of destruction crashed ceaselessly," wrote the *New York World* correspondent. He noted with one storm of shell from the Confederate guns that soldiers and officers leaping from rest on the grass died "some with cigars in their teeth, some with pieces of food in their fingers, and one, a pale young German, with a miniature of his sister in his hands."

The brave and able General John F. Reynolds, who had once peremptorily refused Lincoln's offer of command of the Army of the Potomac, felt a bullet sink into his neck, called to his men, "Forward! For God's sake, forward!" and fell into the arms of a captain with the words, "Good God, Wilcox, I am killed."

Companies of students from the Lutheran Theological Seminary and from the Pennsylvania College of Gettysburg took a hand in the action. A seventy-year-old farmer, John L. Burns, in a swallowtail coat with brass buttons, joined up with the Iron Brigade, went under fire, amazed the youngsters with his coolness, took three wounds and was carried to the rear. When a Wisconsin sergeant asked Burns whatever made him step out into the war without being enlisted, the old man said "the rebels had either driven away or milked his cows and he was going to be even with them." A son of Harriet Beecher Stowe was sent to the rear with bad wounds. Joseph Revere, a grandson of the famous Paul Revere of Boston, was killed.

Confederate bayonets had taken Union cannon and Union bayonets had retaken the cannon. Round Top, Little Round Top, Culp's Hill, rang with the yells of men shooting and men shot. Meadows of white daisies were pockmarked with horse hoofs. Dead and wounded lay scattered in rows, in little sudden piles, in singles and doubles, the spindrift of a storm wave.

The names of Plum Run, Peach Orchard, Devil's Den, Ziegler's Grove, Trostle's Barnyard, became sacred and terrible to those who had touched a mystery of human struggle and suffering in those ordinarily peaceful landscape corners where spiders could ordinarily weave their webs and linger in the sunshine without interruption. The *Richmond Enquirer* man wrote when the firing ceased: "One by one the stars came out in the quiet sky, and over that field of carnage hung the sweet influences of the Pleiades."

Bernard De Voto

MARK TWAIN

THE first truly American literature grew out of the tidewater culture of the early republic. It was the culture of a people who, whatever their diversity, were more homogeneous in feeling and belief than Americans as a people have ever been since them. We have come to think of the literature whose greatest names are Emerson and Poe, Thoreau and Melville, Hawthorne and Whitman, as our classic period, and in a very real sense the republic that shaped their mind was classical. It felt a strong affinity for the Roman Republic, it believed that Roman virtues and ideas had been expressed in the Constitution, it gave us a great architectural style because it identified its own emotions in the classic style. When Horatio Greenough [1] let a toga fall from Washington's naked shoulders he was not out of tune with contemporary taste: Washington seemed a kind of consul, so did Jefferson, and in the portraits of them which our stamps and coins preserve they have a Roman look. This classical republican culture was at its most vigorous when our classic writers were growing up. But there is an element of anachronism in all literature, and while these men were themselves in full vigor American culture entered a new phase.

The culture of the early republic crossed the Alleghenies in two streams, one Southern, the other mainly New England; but they were more like each other than either was like the one which their mingling presently helped to produce. For beyond the mountains people found different landscapes, different river courses, different relationships of sky and wind

From *The Portable Mark Twain*, copyright 1946. Reprinted by permission of The Viking Press, Inc.

1. **Horatio Greenough:** (1805–1852), an American sculptor. His enormous statue of George Washington is now in the Smithsonian Institution.

and water, different conceptions of space and distance, different soils and climates—different conditions of life. Beyond still farther mountains lay Oregon and California—and they were implicit in the expanding nation as soon as the treaty that gave us Louisiana was signed—but first the United States had to incorporate the vast expanse between the eastern and the western heights of land. That area is the American heartland. Its greatest son was to call it the Egypt of the West because nature had organized it round a central river and it touched no ocean, but it came into the American consciousness as the Great Valley. When the tidewater culture came to the Great Valley it necessarily broke down: new conditions demanded adaptations, innovations, new combinations and amplifications. The new way of life that began to develop there had a different organization of feeling, a different metabolism of thought. It was no more native, no more "American," than that of the first republic, but it was different and it began to react on it.

The heartland was midcontinental and its energies were oriented toward the river at its center—and were therefore turned away from Europe, which had been a frontier of the early republic. And life in the heartland, with its mingling of stocks, its constant shifting of population, and its tremendous distances, led people in always increasing numbers to think continentally. Both facts were fundamental in the thought and feeling of the new culture.

The American littoral came only slowly, with greater slowness than the fact demanded, to realize that the nation's center of gravity was shifting westward. It tragically failed to understand one consequence of that shift, thirty years of contention between the Northeast and the South to dominate the Great Valley or at least achieve a preferential linkage with it. The failure to understand was in great part a failure to think continentally —as was made clear at last when the Civil War demonstrated that no peaceful way of resolving the contention had been found. Even now too many Americans fail to understand that the war, the resolution by force, only made explicit the organization of our national life that is implicit in the geography which the Great Valley binds together. Abraham Lincoln understood our continental unity; he argued it persistently down to the outbreak of the war and from then on. And Lincoln was a distillation of the heartland culture.

Lincoln's feeling for the continentalism of the American nation was so intense that it almost transcended the transcendent facts. It was a deposit in the very cells of his bones from the soil of the Great Valley. He was, Herndon [2] rightly says, one of the limestone men, the tall, gaunt, power-

2. **Herndon:** William Henry Herndon (1818–1891), a law partner of Lincoln and author of *Herndon's Lincoln: the True Story of a Great Life* (1889).

ful, sallow, saturnine men who appear in quantity enough to constitute a
type when the wilderness on both sides of the Ohio comes under the
plow. His radical democracy was wrought from the experience of the
Great Valley. In his ideas and beliefs as in the shadowed depths of his personality there is apparent a new articulation of American life. His very
lineaments show it. When you turn from the Jefferson nickel to the Lincoln penny as when you turn from Jefferson's first inaugural address to
any of Lincoln's state papers, in the flash of a total and immediate response you understand that you have turned from one era to a later one.
You have turned from the tidewater republic to the continental empire.

Lincoln expressed a culture and brought a type to climax. Similarly,
when that culture found major literary expression it did so from a rich
and various, if humble, literary tradition. As always, the literary expression was the later one; the economic, social, and political impact was felt
much earlier. The lag, however, was not so great as Walt Whitman
thought. Whitman was sixty when in 1879 he traveled across the Great
Valley to its western limit, where the Front Range walls it off. He tra-
versed it with a steadily growing conviction that here in the flesh were the
people whose society he had envisioned in so many rhapsodies, Americans
who had been fused, annealed, compacted (those are his words) into a new
identity. He felt that literature had not yet spoken to these prairie people,
"this continental inland West," that it had not yet spoken for them, that
it had not made images for their spirit.

The poet supposed that he was speaking of things still to come but he
was already wrong by a full ten years. The thing had happened. And the
first notification that it had happened can be dated with an exactness not
often possible in the history of literature. That notification came in 1869
with the appearance of a book of humorous travel sketches by Samuel
Langhorne Clemens, who, faithful to the established tradition, signed it
with a pen name, Mark Twain.

Innocents Abroad was greeted with an enthusiasm that made Mark
Twain a celebrity overnight, and with too much misunderstanding of a
kind that was to persist throughout his career. It was a funny book and a
cardinal part of its fun was its disdain of European culture. This disdain,
the mere fact of making humor of such disdain, and its frequent exaggeration into burlesque all produced an effect of shock—in most ways a delightful shock but in some ways an uneasy one. Yet the point was not the pro-
vinciality of such humor, though it was frequently provincial, and not its
uncouthness, though it was sometimes uncouth, but the kind of consciousness it implied. Again it is absurd to speak of this as the first American
literature that was independent of European influence, for our literature
had obediently divorced itself, from Europe as soon as Emerson ordered

it to. The humorous core of *Innocents Abroad* was not independence of Europe, but indifference to it. Thoreau and Emerson and Poe were detached from Europe but completely aware of being heirs to it, but here was a literature which had grown up in disregard of Europe—which had looked inward toward the Mississippi and not outward beyond the Atlantic. Failure to appreciate the implications of this difference was one reason, no doubt the weightiest one, why for two full generations literary critics thought of Mark Twain as no more than a clown. But the same identity, the same organization of personality, that made Lincoln the artificer of our continental unity was what made Mark Twain a great writer.

There are striking affinities between Lincoln and Mark Twain. Both spent their boyhoods in a society that was still essentially frontier; both were rivermen. Both absorbed the midcontinental heritage: fiercely equalitarian democracy, hatred of injustice and oppression, the man-to-man individualism of an expanding society. Both were deeply acquainted with melancholy and despair; both were fatalists. On the other hand, both were instinct with the humor of the common life and from their earliest years made fables of it. As humorists, both felt the basic gravity of humor; with both it was an adaptation of the mind, a reflex of the struggle to be sane; both knew, and Mark Twain said, that there is no humor in heaven. It was of such resemblances that William Dean Howells was thinking when he called Mark Twain "the Lincoln of our literature."

2

Samuel Clemens was born at Florida, Monroe County, Missouri, on November 30, 1835, a few months after his parents reached the village from Tennessee. His father was a Virginian, his mother a Kentuckian, and as a family they had made three moves before this one. Florida was a handful of log cabins only two hundred miles east of the Indian Country and in the earliest stage of frontier economy. Though he could have only a generalized memory of it, Sam's earliest years were thus spent in the "Sweet Betsy from Pike" [3] society which has contributed a color and a flavor of its own to American legendry. More: the town was located at the forks of that Salt Creek which figures in the folk proverbs. He could retain little conscious memory of the chinked-log, open-fireplace hamlet with its woods-runners and movers; mostly it would mean the immediacy of nature, the infinity of the forest, the ease of escape into solitude and an all-encompassing freedom. He was still short of four when the Clemenses made their last move, this time eastward. They seem to have been movers

3. **"Sweet Betsy from Pike"**: a popular American folk song of the period.

by force of circumstance, not instinct; it was always the pressure of poverty and the hope of betterment that impelled them on. But they bequeathed restlessness to their son.

The final move brought them to Hannibal, an older settlement than Florida and perhaps four times as large but still short of five hundred inhabitants. Hannibal is the most important single fact in the life of Samuel Clemens the person and Mark Twain the writer. It too was lapped round by forest; it maintained the romantic mystery, the subliminal dread, and the intimacy with nature that he had been born to; but it had passed the pioneering stage. It must be seen as a later stage that characterized all our frontiers east of the great plains, after the actual frontier of settlement had pushed westward, after the farms had been brought in and functional communities had been established, but while the frontier crafts and values and ways of thinking lingered on, a little mannered perhaps, a little nostalgic, but still vital. The frontier thugs had passed to other fields or degenerated to village loafers and bullies. There were a few Indians near by and sizable numbers not too far away but they were a spectacle, not a threat. A few hunters and trappers ranged the woods but they were relics, brush folk, not of the great race. There were as many frame houses as log cabins; if the schoolhouse had a puncheon floor, the squire's wife had a silk dress from St. Louis. Caste lines were almost nonexistent. Hannibal was a farmers' market village. More than half of its inhabitants were Southerners, but Southerners modified by the Great Valley. Its slaves were servants, not gang laborers.

But also Hannibal was on the Mississippi. Here enters the thread of cosmopolitanism that is so paradoxically interwoven with the extreme provincialism of this society. Steamboats bore the travelers and commerce of half a continent past the town wharf. Great rafts of logs and lumber—it was the latter kind that Huck and Jim traveled on—came down from Wisconsin. A population of freighters, movers, and mere drifters in shanty boats, keelboats, broadhorns, mackinaws, and scows added pageantry. Other types and other costumery came down from the lakes and northern rivers: voyageurs, trappers, winterers, Indians of the wilderness tribes always seen in ceremonial garments on their way to make treaties or collect annuities. All these belonged to the rapidly widening movement of the expanding nation. Moreover, Hannibal was within the aura of St. Louis, eighty miles away, and St. Louis was the port through which the energies of a truly imperial expansion were moving toward Santa Fe, Oregon, and California. Perhaps dimly but quite permanently any river town so near St. Louis would give even the most local mind an awareness of the continental divide, the Columbia, the Pacific, the Southwest. A town that may have never heard of Zebulon Pike or John Ledyard or Jonathan Carver [4] nevertheless felt the national will that had turned them westward. The year of Mark's birth, 1835, may properly be taken as the year when the final phase of our continental expansion began. And the fruitfulness of Hannibal for Mark's imagination may reasonably be said to have stopped with this tenth year, just before that final phrase raised up the irrepressible conflict.

For two things remain to be said of the society that shaped Sam Clemens's mind and feelings: that its postpioneer, frontier stage stops short of the industrial revolution, and that the sectional conflict which produced the Civil War has not yet shown itself. The life which is always most desirable in Mark's thinking is the preindustrial society of a little river town; it is a specific identification of Hannibal. Whereas the evils of life are the eternal cruelties, hypocrisies, and stupidities of mankind which have nothing to do with time or place but result from Our Heavenly Father's haste in experimenting when He grew dissatisfied with the monkey.

As the St. Petersburg of *Tom Sawyer*, Hannibal is one of the superb idyls of American literature, perhaps the supreme one. A town of sun, forest shade, drowsy peace, limpid emotions, simple humanity—and eternity going by on the majestic river. Even here, however, a mood of melancholy is seldom far away: a melancholy of the river itself, of our westering people who had always known solitude, and of a child's feeling, which was to grow through the years, that he was a stranger and a mysterious one under the stars. And below the melancholy there is a deeper stratum, a terror or disgust that may break through in a graveyard at midnight or at the sound of unidentified voices whispering above the water. This is in part fantasy, but in part also it is the weary knowledge of evil that paints Hannibal in far different colors in *Pudd'nhead Wilson* or *Huckleberry Finn*.

Almost as soon as he begins to write, Mark Twain is a citizen of the world, but he is always a citizen of Hannibal too. He frequently misunderstood himself, but he knew that quite clearly. In a postscript to the fragment of a letter "to an unidentified person," he says:

And yet I can't go away from the boyhood period & write novels because *capital* [that is, personal experience] is not sufficient by itself & I lack the other essential: interest in handling the men & experiences of later times.

4. Pike (1779–1813), Ledyard (1751–1789), and Carver (1710–1780) were American explorers and adventurers.

While still a boy, he was apprenticed to a printer and so got the education that served more nineteenth-century American writers than any other. (It was a surprisingly extensive education. By twenty he knew the English classics thoroughly, was an inveterate reader of history, and had begun to cultivate his linguistic bent.) The trade eventually led him to newspaper reporting but first it took him on a series of *Wanderjahre* [5] toward which heredity may have impelled him. At eighteen he went to St. Louis and on to New York. Philadelphia followed, Muscatine, St. Louis again, Keokuk (where he began to write humorous newspaper sketches), and Cincinnati, always setting type on a newspaper or in a job shop. He was twenty-two years old (and, if his memory can be trusted, ripe with a characteristic fantasy of South American adventure) when the American spectacle caught him up. In 1857 he began his apprenticeship to a Mississippi pilot.

"Old Times on the Mississippi," a study in pure ecstasy, is of course stamped from his memory, which was always nostalgic, and from the romancing half of his twinned talent. It records a supreme experience about whose delight there can be no doubt whatever, and it testifies to Mark's admiration of all skills and his mastery of one of the most difficult. But piloting gave him more than ever got into "Old Times" or its enlargement, *Life on the Mississippi*. "Flush Times" would have done as well as "Old Times" to describe the climactic years of the prewar Mississippi Valley, with the rush and fever of the expanding nation. Those years vastly widened Mark's knowledge of America and fed his insatiable enjoyment of men, his absorbed observation of man's depravity, and his delight in spectacle.

The Civil War put an end to piloting. Mark has described his experience and that of many others in that war, in all wars, in a sketch which is one of the best things he ever wrote. "The Private History of a Campaign That Failed" could not be spared from the mosaic of our national catastrophe; it is one of the contexts in which Mark Twain has perfectly refracted a national experience through a personal one. When his military career petered out in absurdity, he joined the great national movement which even civil war could not halt. His older brother, the gentle zany Orion, was made Secretary of the Territory of Nevada and, paying the Secretary's passage west, Mark went along. In Nevada he found another national retort, another mixed and violent society, another speculative flush times. He became a drunkard of speculation, a prospector, a hunter of phantasmal mines, a silver miner, a laborer in a stamp mill, and at last a newspaperman. He went to work for that fabulous paper *The Territorial*

5. *Wanderjahre:* wanderyears, i.e., years of wandering or traveling before settling down to one's profession (German).

Enterprise of Virginia City as an "editor," that is to say a reporter. And it was here that he took his immortal *nom de plume*, a phrase from the pilot's mystery. "Mark Twain" was signed to a species of humor in which Sam Clemens had been immersed ever since his apprenticeship, the newspaper humor of the Great Valley, which was in turn a development of the pungent oral humor he had heard from childhood on. Far from establishing a literary tradition, Mark Twain brought one to culmination.

After less than two years on the *Enterprise* he went to California, in 1864. He had met Artemus Ward in Nevada; now he joined the transient, bright Bohemia of the Golden Gate: Bret Harte, Prentice Mulford, Charles Warren Stoddard, Charles H. Webb, Ada Clare, Ina Coolbrith,[6] still slighter and more forgotten names. He got a new kind of companionship and his first experience of literary sophistication. After a short time as a reporter he began to write humor for the Coast's literary papers, the *Californian* and the *Golden Era*. Promptly his work developed a strain of political and ethical satire which it never lost: the humorist was seldom separable from the satirist from this year on. That is to say, the individual humor of Mark Twain with its overtones of extravaganza and its undercurrent of misanthropy was, however crude and elliptical, fully formed by the end of 1864. He had not yet revealed the novelist's power to endow character with life, but it—together with a memorable talent for the vernacular—was made clear to anyone with eyes on December 16, 1865, when the New York *Saturday Press* published "Jim Smiley and His Jumping Frog."

The immortal story derived from still another Western experience, one which had made Mark, however lackadaisically, a pocket miner. He had sent it east at Artemus Ward's suggestion, but only an accident got it into type. It was a momentary smash hit, and so Mark was not altogether an unknown when he went to New York in 1867. Before he went there, however, he had reached the farthest limit of the expansionist dream, having gone to the Sandwich Islands as a newspaper correspondent. That voyage in turn had initiated his career as a lecturer. He had a marked histrionic talent; for years he barnstormed or made occasional appearances as a public "reader" and story-teller; all his life he was making the after-dinner appearance of that vanished age, which pleased his vanity and gratified the longings of an actor *manqué*. But he went to New York as a correspondent: he had arranged to travel to Europe and the Holy Land with a conducted tour. In 1867 he published his first book, a collection of sketches called *The Celebrated Jumping Frog of Calaveras County* after the best of them, but the year is more notable for the travel letters he

6. Short story writers, poets, and journalists who lived in the San Francisco area.

wrote for the *Alta California* [7] and the New York *Tribune*. He made a
book of them after his return, meanwhile writing free-lance humor and
Washington correspondence. The book, *Innocents Abroad*, was published
in 1869.

All this has been detailed to show how deep and various an experience
of American life Mark Twain had had when he began to write. The rest
of his biography is also strikingly typical of nineteenth-century America,
but the seed-time has now been accounted for. It is not too much to say
that he had seen more of the United States, met more kinds and castes and
conditions of Americans, observed the American in more occupations and
moods and tempers—in a word had intimately shared a greater variety of
the characteristic experiences of his countrymen—than any other major
American writer. [. . .]

3

Mark Twain was a man of moods, of the extreme of moods. He had a
buoyancy which, twinned as it was with gentleness and intuition and wit,
gave him a personal magnetism which his friends did not hesitate to call
enchantment. Yet it alternated with an anger that readily became fury and
was rooted in a revulsion between disgust and despair. The alternation suggests a basic split; it is clearly marked in his personality and equally evident in his books. The splendor his friends felt, his kindness to the unfortunate and the lowly and the oppressed, his generosity, his sensitiveness
unite in a singular luminosity of spirit. Yet he was capable of savage vin-
dictiveness, he exaggerated small or imaginary grievances out of all reason,
and on little or no provocation he repeatedly believed himself misrepre-
sented or betrayed. One doubts if any other American writer was ever
so publicly beloved or privately adored; one is certain that no other was
involved in so many lawsuits. "I am full of malice, saturated with malignity," he wrote eight months before his death. His malice and malignity
of that moment were for the damned human race, but he could feel them
in his private life whenever he thought he had been wronged. When *A
Connecticut Yankee* was finished he wrote Howells that if he could write
it over again "there wouldn't be so many things left out. They burn in me
and they keep multiplying and multiplying, but now they can't even be
said. And besides they would require a library—and a pen warmed up in
hell." With a pen warmed up in hell he did fill a library and an extraordinary bulk of letters too. If it was sometimes avenging personal, usually
imaginary wrongs, that private activity was only a reflex of the public
function. For what burned in him was hatred of cruelty and injustice, a

7. *Alta California:* a San Francisco newspaper (*Alta* is Spanish for "Upper").

deep sense of human evil, and a recurrent accusation of himself. Like Swift he found himself despising man while loving Tom, Dick, and Harry so warmly that he had no proper defense against the anguish of human relationships. The trouble was that in terms of either earth or heaven he was never sure what to make of Samuel L. Clemens and so is recorded on both sides.

He is usually to be found on both sides of any question he argues. His intelligence was intuitive, not analytical. He reasoned fluently, with an avidity that touched most of the surface flow of his time, but superficially and with habitual contradictions. He had little capacity for sustained thought and to get to the heart of a question had to abandon analysis and rely on feeling. The philosophy which he spent years refining and supposed he had perfected is a sophomoric determinism. Even so, it is less a philosophy than a symbol or a rationalization; the perceptions it stood for are expressed at the level of genius in his fiction—not as idea but in terms of human life. Most of the nineteenth century's optimisms were his also. He fiercely championed the democratic axioms; they are the ether of his fiction and the fulcrum of his satire. He thought too that the nineteenth century, especially as Progress, and more especially as Progress in the United States, was the happiest estate of man; he believed that it was bringing on a future of greater freedom and greater happiness. This was basic and spontaneous in his mind, but at the same time he felt something profoundly wrong. There seemed to be some limitation to freedom, some frustration of happiness. He never really came to grips with the conflict. Only in the last fifteen years of his life did he ascribe any part of what might be wrong to any but superficial injustices in American life or any but slight dislocations in our system. By the time he became aware of serious threats to freedom they did not seem to matter much: he was so absorbed in the natural depravity of man that the collapse or frustration of democracy, which he was by then taking for granted, seemed only an unimportant detail. Ideally, his last years would have been spent in more rigorous analysis—if not of the objective data, then of his intuitive awareness of them. They were not and so his judgments remained confused—and his principal importance in our literature belongs to his middle years, the period when his mind and feelings are in healthy equilibrium. It is an importance of his perceptions, not his thinking, and it exists primarily in his fiction, most purely in *Huckleberry Finn*. The best of Mark Twain's fiction is, historically, the first mature realization in our literature of a conflict between the assumptions of democracy and the limitations on democracy. Between the ideal of freedom and the nature of man.

Not less important is the fact that there is a reconciliation, even an affirmation. Detachment could be no greater but it is still somehow compas-

sionate; condemnation could be no more complete, but it is somehow mag-
nanimous. The damned human race is displayed with derision and
abhorrence, yet this is on the ground that it has fallen short of its own decencies. Moreover at least *Huckleberry Finn* has a hero, the only heroic
character (apart from Joan of Arc, a debauch of gyneolatry [8]) he ever
drew, and it is the essence of what Mark Twain had to say that the hero
is a Negro slave. It has also a vindication not only of freedom, but of loyalty and decency, kindness and courage; and it is the essence of Mark
Twain that this vindication is made by means of a boy who is a spokesman
of the folk mind and whom experience has taught wariness and skepticism.
Like all great novels *Huckleberry Finn* moves on many levels of significance, but it describes a flight and a struggle for freedom, and the question
it turns on is a moral question.

Mark found zest and gusto—nouns that do not describe very much
American literature of the first rank—in whatsoever was alive. He liked
few novels except those of his intimate friends. What he praised in the
ones he did like was reality of behavior, speech, or motive; his notebooks
are sulphurous with comments on merely literary, that is false, characters.
His taste was for biography, autobiography, history—life direct, men revealing themselves. No doubt the race was damned but it was fascinating.
And that was proper, for if his fiction is the best of his work, his most
salient talent as a novelist is the life-giving power. It is a careless and
prodigal fecundity, but nevertheless remarkably concentrated. Old Man
Finn, for instance, is greatly imagined and he seems to fill the first half of
the book, yet he appears in only a few pages. Mrs. Judith Loftus lives
completely in a single chapter. A mere passer-by, a casual of the river or a
thug heard talking in a frowzy town, may reveal a whole personality in a
few paragraphs. Nor is this fecundity confined to Mark's fiction, for the
framework of all his books is anecdotal and all the people in them are
dramatized. The whole population of his principal books, nine-tenths of
the population of all his books, has the same vividness. Boys, villagers, the
rivermen, the Negroes, Colonel Sellers, the two great vagabonds—there is
nothing quite like the Mark Twain gallery elsewhere in American literature.

But there is a striking limitation: nowhere in that gallery are there
women of marriageable age. No white women, that is, for the slave Rox-
ana in *Pudd'nhead Wilson* lives as vividly as Old Man Finn himself. It must
be significant that the only credible woman of an age that might sanction
desire is withdrawn from desire behind the barrier of race. None of Mark
Twain's nubile girls, young women, or young matrons are believable; they
are all bisque, saccharine, or tears. He will do girl children in the romantic

8. **gyneolatry:** worship of women.

convention of boys' books and he is magnificent with the sisterhood of worn frontier wives whom Aunt Polly climaxes, but something like a taboo drains reality from any woman who might trouble the heart or the flesh. There is no love story in Mark Twain, there is no love at all beyond an occasional admission, for purposes of plot only, that someone is married or is going to be. Women seldom have husbands and men seldom have wives unless they are beyond middle age. Mark's endless absorption in human motives did not, for literary purposes at least, extend to sexual motives. Sex seems to be forbidden unless it can be treated mawkishly, and this writer of great prose who habitually flouted the genteel proprieties of language was more prudish than the most tremulous of his friends in regard to language that might suggest either desire or its gratification. So there is a sizable gap in the world he created. That gap has never been accounted for. Certainly there was nothing bloodless about Mark Twain; and his marriage, one of the happiest of literary marriages, was clearly passionate. Yet he did not marry till he was thirty-five (1870), and there may have been something permissive—to a man whose characters have usually lost a father if not both parents—in the fact that he married an invalid.

Few Americans have written as much as Mark Twain. His published works are not much greater in bulk than his unpublished manuscripts, the books he finished fewer than the ones he broke off and abandoned. He wrote on impulse and enthusiasm and while they lasted he wrote easily, but he wrote as needs must, for he had little faculty of self-criticism and but small ability to sustain or elaborate an idea. He was best at the short haul. Not only his fiction but the personalized narrative that is the vehicle of *Innocents Abroad, A Tramp Abroad, Life on the Mississippi*, and much else is episodic. When what he was writing was in circuit with his deepest perceptions he was superb. The breaking of the circuit always threw him into extemporization, which meant that fiction fell away into extravaganza and satire into burlesque. At such times he did not know that he was flatting; the serious artist could become a vaudeville monologuist in a single page without being aware that the tone had changed. That such a well-imagined novel as *Pudd'nhead Wilson* was written round the grotesque joke called "Those Extraordinary Twins" [9] would be incredible if the same tone-deafness were not plentifully evident elsewhere. He thought the mawkish *Joan of Arc* and the second-rate *The Prince and the Pauper* his best work. He interrupted his masterpiece before it was half-finished, liking it so little that he threatened to burn it, and ignored it for six years during which, though he wrote constantly, he wrote nothing of impor-

9. "Those Extraordinary Twins": a grotesque tale of a circus freak by Mark Twain, published in 1892.

tance. Then he finished it almost as casually as he had begun it. There is no greater book in American literature, but critics agree that the last quarter of it is impaired by the extravaganza that begins when Huck gets to Uncle Silas's farm. It is typical of Mark Twain that he felt no difference in kind or key between this admittedly superb extravaganza and the searching of American society and human experience that precedes it. In fact, the delivery of Jim from the dungeon was one of Mark's favorite platform readings.

Furthermore, he lacked the attribute of the artist—whatever it may be—that enables him to think a novel through till its content has found its own inherent form. Of his novels only *Joan of Arc, The Prince and the Pauper*, and *Tom Sawyer* have structures that have developed from within; significantly, all are simple and only one is first-rate. Mark lived with his material for a long time, sometimes for many years, but not consciously, not with critical or searching dissatisfaction. A book must come of its own momentum from the unconscious impulse, be it as a whole, as a fragment, or as something that hardly got started before it broke off. This is to say that he had no conscious esthetic. He stood at the opposite pole from Henry James, with the other great contemporary of both, Howells, in between but nearer to James. Yet he had as large a share as either of them in creating the modern American novel.

The explanation for his lack of self-criticism and for his innocence of esthetics is not to be found in the supposed naïveté of the society that bore him. In the first place, that society was far from naïve; in the second place, not only did the fine artist Howells come from it, but Mark himself raised its native tale-telling to a fine art, which surely establishes a discipline. He had, besides, two other disciplines: that of the daily job, which he observed as faithfully as any writer who ever lived, and the taskmastership of a great style. Nor can Mark's own explanation, which he pleads so earnestly in the letter to Andrew Lang, be supported: that he wrote for the belly and members [10] only. *Huckleberry Finn* is no more written for the belly and members only than *War and Peace* is or *Recherche du Temps Perdu*.[11] But it is written at the behest of an instinctive drive, and explanation need go no farther if it could, for this time at least Mark's whole personality was behind it. In short, he wrote trivially or splendidly or magnificently as what appears to have been little more than chance might determine: he was not a fully self-conscious artist. But when he wrote greatly he was writing from an inner harmony of desire and will.

10. **members:** limbs.
11. *War and Peace* (1865–1868) and *Recherche du Temps Perdu* (Remembrance of Things Past) (1913–1927) by the Russian Count Leo Tolstoy (1828–1910) and the Frenchman Marcel Proust (1871–1922), respectively, are generally considered to be among the greatest novels of the past century.

Or call it a harmony of his deepest self and his inheritance from the Great Valley.

Only that harmony, seen in relation to time and history, can explain him. For no man ever became a great writer more inadvertently than Mark Twain. He first became famous as a superior Artemus Ward, and that corresponded to his idea of himself. A long time passed before he had any desire to be more. He exploited a joke-maker's talent as systematically as a production manager could have done it for him, delighted by the discovery that he could raise his status, prestige, and income beyond Tom Sawyer's dreams. Nevertheless there is the paradox that almost from the beginning the attack of the funny man had been supported by that of a serious artist. Already in "The Jumping Frog" mastery of fictional character is clearly presaged, and the prophecy is fulfilled as early as *The Gilded Age* (1874). By *The Gilded Age* also a satirist is dealing maturely with a wide expanse of American life. From this composite the funny man cannot be separated out for a long time, and during that time there are only sporadic indications that Mark saw either the novelist or the satirist as more than instrumentalities of the humorist. The paradox resists criticism. One can only repeat that Mark Twain's greatness developed because the time and the continent had shaped him at their core.

This representative centrality goes on undiminished after the establishment of his fame. Following his marriage he was briefly a newspaper owner in Buffalo but abandoned that career to move to a provincial New England city, Hartford, and set up as a professional writer. His periodic restlessness continued; he never spent the full year in Hartford, he made at least twelve trips abroad, and he once expatriated himself for nine years. The Hartford period, 1874–1891, covered his greatest happiness and the beginning of his catastrophe. His was an unusually happy family life, and he was the center of an always widening circle. Howells and the Rev. Joseph Twichell [12] were his closest friends; Cable, Aldrich, most of the leading writers of his generation were of the circle, and it widened to include the rich, the famous, the powerful, and the great. Mark ruled it by divine right: there have always been conflicting opinions about his books, but only one has ever been possible about his dominion over men's affections. He seemed alien to mortality. A fantasy of his childhood is frequently set down in notes and fragments of manuscript: the child had identified himself with a romantic stranger in Hannibal, a mysterious, perhaps supernatural visitor from Elsewhere. As the one-gallus village boy

12. **the Rev. Joseph Twichell:** (1838–1918), a Congregational clergyman of Hartford. It was he who suggested to Mark Twain that he write *Life on the Mississippi*, and he accompanied the author on the European tour that is described in *A Tramp Abroad*, in which he is "Harris."

came to be a world figure, that fantasy seemed on the way to being confirmed. There was further confirmation as the author of *The Gilded Age* entered with a blithe and innocent heart on another career as a spectator, and the stamp-mill operator and tramp printer, who sincerely believed all his life that he was a member of the laboring class, undertook with the same innocence to be an industrial promoter.

Always convinced that his publishers were defrauding him, Mark had established his own firm to publish his books. The expansion it underwent in order to handle the bestseller of the generation, *Personal Memoirs of U. S. Grant*, could not be sustained. The firm sank into insolvency and finally went bankrupt. It could probably have been saved except that the most fantastic of Mark's promotions failed at the same time and left him bankrupt. For years he had been pouring his earnings and his wife's fortune into a mechanical typesetter which would indeed have made him a multimillionaire if it had succeeded. Its failure and that of the publishing firm were only the beginning of a series of disasters on the same scale as his fantastic rise. He paid off his indebtedness by a heroic lecture tour that took him round the world but his health broke. The oldest of his three daughters, the one who seemed most like him in temperament and talent, died during his absence. An agonizing personality change in his youngest daughter was finally diagnosed as epilepsy. Mrs. Clemens declined into permanent invalidism and in 1904 died.

This prolonged catastrophe brought Mark's misanthropy out of equilibrium; it dominated the rest of his life. The disasters were, of course, personal and yet it is hardly straining the facts to find him here also representative of the nineteenth-century America that had already found so much expression in him. As the century neared its end there was a good deal of pessimism and disenchantment in the United States. A wave of doubt and questioning swept many minds. The people who began an imperialistic adventure in the Pacific with the same naïve enthusiasm that had taken Mark Twain into the industrial life were widely, at the very time they stepped out on the world stage, beginning to be troubled about themselves. The nineteenth century, looking back on its course, found cause to be dismayed. Was the democratic dream being served as well as the nation had assumed? Had the United States gone wrong somewhere during the avalanche of expansion? Were there, then, limits to what democracy could do, or flaws or contradictions in its theses, or impassable barriers in its path? Was the good time ending, were the vigorous years running out under a gathering shadow?

However deep or shallow this *fin de siècle* weariness may have been in the United States at large, Mark Twain's last fifteen years must be seen as related to it, if only distantly. During this period he wrote as much as in any similar length of time in his life, perhaps more, but most of it is fragmentary, unfinished. Almost all of it deals with the nature of man, man's fate, and man's conceptions of honor and morality. There are fables, dialogues, diatribes—sometimes cold, sometimes passionate, derisive, withering, savage. Mark sees the American republic perishing, like republics before it, through the ineradicable cowardice, corruption, and mere baseness of mankind. He elaborates theories, which he embodies in imaginary histories of the world (and sometimes of extra-mundane societies) to support his prophecy, and yet he cannot be much troubled by the going-down of this western land, for year by year he is writing a general apocalypse. The Old Testament fables had always served him for humorous derision of man's gullibility, but now he uses them as missiles in a ferocious attack on human stupidity and cruelty. Man is compact of malignity, cowardice, weakness, and absurdity, a diseased organism, a parasite on nature, a foolish but murderous animal much lower than the swine.

Yet *What Is Man?* (published anonymously in 1906 but written before the turn of the century), the fullest of many developments of these themes, cannot be seen solely as a document in anthropophobia.[13] It is also in complex ways a justification, even a self-justification. Its fixed universe, with an endless chain of cause and effect from the beginning of time, permits Mark to compose many variations on the theme of human pettiness, but also it serves to free man of blame—and thus satisfies a need deeply buried in Mark's personal remorse. To this period also belongs *Mark Twain's Autobiography*, which serves him as an escape into the security of the boyhood idyl he had made immortal in *Tom Sawyer*. The need to escape is significant, but the release is even more so, for it breaks the obsession signified by *What Is Man?* But a much truer release and a fulfillment as well came, as always, when Mark turned from reasoning to the instinctual portions of his mind. The highest reach of his last period is *The Mysterious Stranger*. It is an almost perfect book—perfect in expression of his final drive, in imaginative projection of himself, in tone and tune, in final judgment on the nature of man and the experience of Mark Twain. It is on a humbler level than his great books. More than any of them it is Mark Twain somewhat in disregard of America. It is not, finally, a major work; but in its small way it is a masterpiece. Those who know and love Mark Twain will always find it as revealing as *Huckleberry Finn*.

4

Mark Twain died in 1910 with, as he had foretold, the return of the mysterious visitor from beyond the solar system under whose sign he had

13. **anthropophobia:** hatred of mankind.

been born, Halley's comet. His last years had been as full of honors as his middle years had been of fame. Even so, in 1910 it was hardly possible to define his importance in American literature as clearly as we can after another generation.

No doubt his first importance in that literature is the democratizing effect of his work. It is a concretely liberating effect, and therefore different in kind from Whitman's vision of democracy, which can hardly be said to have been understood by or to have found a response among any considerable number of Americans. Mark Twain was the first great American writer who was also a popular writer, and that in itself is important. Much more important is the implicit and explicit democracy of his books. They are the first American literature of the highest rank which portrays the ordinary bulk of Americans, expresses them, accepts their values, and delineates their hopes, fears, decencies, and indecencies as from within. The area proper to serious literature in the United States was enormously widened by them, in fact widened to the boundaries it still observes today. There have been no acknowledged priorities of caste in American writing since Mark Twain. Moreover, in his native equalitarian point of view, in his assertion of the basic democratic axioms, in his onslaught on privilege, injustice, vested power, political pretense, and economic exploitation (much of it admittedly superficial or confused, though much else is the most vigorous satire we have), in his transmutation of the town-meeting or country-store sharpness of judgment into a fine art—he is midnineteenth-century American democracy finding its first major voice in literature, ultimately its strongest voice. In him the literature of democracy becomes more robust than it had been before, such part of that literature, at least, as may be said to contain multitudes and speak to them. And this, to return to our starting point, embodies the transforming experience of the American people as they occupied the Great Valley and pushed beyond it, on the way forging the continental mind.

The nature of his writing is hardly less important. Mark Twain wrote one of the great styles of American literature, he helped develop the modern American style, he was the first writer who ever used the American vernacular at the level of art. [. . .] Mark Twain wrote English of a remarkable simplicity and clarity, and of singular sensitiveness, flexibility, and beauty as well. Its simplicity might deceive a patronizing reader, for the sentence structure is not involved, usually consisting of short elements in natural sequence, and in order to understand without analysis how much art has gone into it one must have an ear for the tones and accents of speech as well as some feeling for the vigor of words. It is so lucid that it seems effortless—but just what is style?

Now, it is important that Mark made the American vernacular the medium of a great novel. Even before that he had used local, class, and racial dialects with immeasurably greater skill than anyone before him in our literature. "The Jumping Frog" raised such dialects above the merely humorous use which was the only one they had previously had and gave them a function in the writing of fiction. And the first two chapters of *The Gilded Age* bring to American literature genuine Negro speech and a rural dialect that are both genuine and an instrument of art—literally for the first time. In the rendition of Negro speech he may have had one equal, though there are those who will not grant that Harris [14] is an equal; but it is doubtful if anyone has used the dialects of the middle South, or for that matter any other American dialect, as well as he. This on the basis of *The Gilded Age* and its immediate successors: the achievement of *Huckleberry Finn* is greater still. Huck's style, which is the spoken language of the untutored American of his place and time, differentiates the most subtle meanings and emphases and proves capable of the most difficult psychological effects. In a single step it made a literary medium of the American language; the liberating effect on American writing could hardly be overstated. Since *Huckleberry Finn* the well of American undefiled has flowed confidently.

Nevertheless, Mark's principal service to the American language was not Huck's vernacular: it lay within the recognized limits of literary prose. Within those limits he was a radical innovator, a prime mover who changed the medium by incorporating in it the syntax, the idioms, and especially the vocabulary of the common life. The vigor of his prose comes directly from the speech of the Great Valley and the Far West. A superlative may be ventured: that Mark Twain had a greater effect than any other writer on the evolution of American prose.

His place in that evolution cannot be analyzed or even illustrated here. He is in the direct succession and he powerfully accelerates the movement. The evolution is of course older than our independence, even older than our nationality—which it helped to produce. Only an American could have said, "We must all hang together, or assuredly we shall all hang separately" in the traditional context. Only an American could have written, "It is not necessary that a man should earn his living by the sweat of his brow unless he sweats easier than I do." Only an American could have written, "the calm confidence of a Christian with four aces." The sequence is Franklin, Thoreau, Mark Twain; and the point here made lightly can be made with as profound a search into the fusion of thought, expression, and nationality as anyone may care to undertake. But before Mark Twain no American, no one writing in English, could have launched a novel into the movement of fiction with such a passage as:

14. **Harris:** Joel Chandler Harris (1848–1908), author of *Uncle Remus*.

At the end of an hour we saw a far-away town sleeping in a valley
by a winding river, and beyond it on a hill, a vast gray fortress with
towers and turrets, the first I had ever seen out of a picture.

"Bridgeport?" said I, pointing.

"Camelot," said he.

Such questions as these, however, interest the historian of literature
more than the general reader. The general reader who, it may be worth
reminding you, continues to read Mark Twain, here and in Europe, more
often by far than any other of our great dead. It is not difficult to say
why.

The Americanism just mentioned is part of it. Any unidentified quotation from Mark Twain will be recognized at sight as American. It is,
furthermore, a national Americanism; his great books are set along the
Mississippi, but no one can think of them as local or regional. But there
is also a kind of centripetal Americanism, so that he seems frequently to
speak for the nation. The character of national spokesman is in his work
as early as *Innocents Abroad;* by *Huckleberry Finn* it is self-evident. Fifteen years before he died it was generally acknowledged—so that if the
nation's mood changed or its honor came in peril, the newspapers could
hardly be put to bed till Mark Twain had spoken.

But there is something more basic. What the millions who have gone
on reading Mark Twain since 1869 have chiefly wanted and received from
him is precisely those images which, three years after *Tom Sawyer* and
four years after "Old Times on the Mississippi" had been published, Walt
Whitman was still hoping someone would forge from the new national life.

[. . .]

The Adventures of Tom Sawyer and *Adventures of Huckleberry Finn:*
Here the images Walt Whitman desired of and for the new society are
actually forged. They are the America of their time speaking with many
voices—and the sharp difference between them corresponds not only to
the dichotomy in Mark's mind but to one that is basic in our thinking
about ourselves. Between them the idyllic *Tom* and the corrosive *Huck*
express most of the American consciousness. Forgetting that he himself
had made several plays of it, Mark once refused to let an applicant dramatize *Tom Sawyer* because you cannot make a hymn into a play. It is a
hymn: to boyhood, to the fantasies of boyhood, to the richness and security of the child's world, to a phase of American society now vanished
altogether, to the loveliness of woods and prairies that were the Great
Valley, to the river, to many other things in which millions of readers
have recognized themselves and their inheritance. It is wrought out of
beauty and nostalgia. Yet Mark is nowhere truer to us, to himself, or to

childhood than in the dread which holds this idyl inclosed. The book so superbly brings the reader within its enchantment that some reflection is required before he can realize of what ghastly stuff it is made—murder and starvation, grave-robbery and revenge, terror and panic, some of the darkest emotions of men, some of the most terrible fears of children, and the ghosts and demons and death portents of the slaves. The book could have been written nowhere but in America and by no American but Mark Twain, but it has passed out of our keeping. It is the fantasy of boyhood in world literature.

Huckleberry Finn also has become a universal possession. It is a much deeper book than *Tom Sawyer*—deeper as of Mark Twain, of America, and of humanity. When after some stumbling it finds its purpose, it becomes an exploration of an entire society, the middle South along the river. In accomplishing this purpose it maintains at the level of genius Mark's judgment in full on the human race. It is well to remember that no one had spoken so witheringly to Americans about themselves before Huck raised his voice. But the book is not only the judgment on the damned human race which the much later *What Is Man?* only tried to be, it is also incomparably rich with the swarming life that so absorbed Mark Twain—and contains a forthright assertion of the inalienable dignity of man. It is the most complete expression of Mark Twain.

Like *Tom* and in much greater measure it has a mythic quality. This is in part the river itself, the Mississippi which had dominion over Mark's imagination and here becomes a truly great symbol. It is in part the symbol of the downriver journey—made the more momentous by a boy's bewilderment and a slave's flight for freedom. But in greater part it is the developing pageantry which becomes ecstatic when two vagabonds join Jim and Huck, and the Duke of Bilgewater and the "pore disappeared Dauphin, Looy the Seventeen," take their place in a small company of literature's immortals.

Thus realism, fantasy, satire, mythology, and the tragic knowledge of man, all of them a good many layers deep, united in Mark Twain's masterpiece. It is the book he was meant to write. A book of itself alone, unlike any other, unique, essentially Mark Twain, essentially America, it also has transcended our national literature. Every new generation of readers discovers that it belongs to mankind.

Walter Lippmann

THE PASSAGE INTO MATURITY

THE critical phase of human experience is the passage from childhood to maturity; the critical question is whether childish habits and expectations are to persist or to be transformed. We grow older. But it is by no means certain that we shall grow up. The human character is a complicated thing, and its elements do not necessarily march in step. It is possible to be a sage in some things and a child in others, to be at once precocious and retarded, to be shrewd and foolish, serene and irritable. For some parts of our personalities may well be more mature than others; not infrequently we participate in the enterprises of an adult with the mood and manners of a child.

The successful passage into maturity depends, therefore, on a breaking up and reconstruction of those habits which were appropriate only to our earliest experience.

In a certain large sense this is the essence of education. For unless a man has acquired the character of an adult, he is a lost soul no matter how good his technical equipment. The world unhappily contains many such lost souls. They are often in high places, men trained to manipulate the machinery of civilization, but utterly incapable of handling their own purposes in any civilized fashion. For their purposes are merely the relics of an infancy when their wishes were law, and they knew neither necessity nor change.

When a childish disposition is carried over into an adult environment the result is a radically false valuation of that environment. The symptoms are fairly evident. They may appear as a disposition to feel that everything which happens to a man has an intentional relation to himself; life becomes a kind of conspiracy to make him happy or to make him miserable. In either case it is thought to be deeply concerned with his destiny. The childish pattern appears also as a deep sense that life owes him something, that somehow it is the duty of the universe to look after him, and to listen sharply when he speaks to it. The notion that the universe is full of purposes utterly unknown to him, utterly indifferent to him, is as outrageous to one who is imperfectly matured as would be the conduct of a mother who forgot to give a hungry child its lunch. The childish pattern appears also as a disposition to believe that he may reach out for anything in sight and take it, and that having gotten it nobody must ever under any circumstances take it away. Death and decay are, therefore, almost an insult, a kind of mischief in the nature of things, which ought not to be there, and would not be there, if everything only behaved as good little boys believe it should. There is indeed authority for the belief that we are all being punished for the naughtiness of our first grandmother; that work and trouble and death would not really be there to plague us but for her unhappy transgression; that by rights we ought to live in paradise and have everything we want for ever and ever.

Here, too, is the source of that common complaint of the world-weary that they are tired of their pleasures. They have what they yearned for; yet having it they are depressed at finding that they do not care. Their inability to enjoy what they can have is the obverse of the desire to possess the unattainable: both are due to carrying over the expectations of youth into adult life. They find themselves in a world unlike the world of their youth; they themselves are no longer youths. But they retain the criteria of youth, and with them measure the world and their own deserts.

Here, too, is the origin of the apparent paradox that as men grow older they grow wiser but sadder. It is not a paradox at all if we remember that this wisdom which makes them sadder is, after all, an incompleted wisdom. They have grown wiser as to the character of the world, wiser too about their own powers, but they remain naive as to what they may expect of the world and themselves. The expectations which they formed in their youth persist as deeply ingrained habits to worry them in their maturity. They are only partially matured; they have become only partially wise. They have acquired skill and information, but the parts of them which are adult are embedded in other parts of their natures which are childish. For men do not necessarily mature altogether and in unison; they learn to do this and that more easily than they learn what to like and what to reject. Intelligence is often more completely educated than desire; our outward behavior has an appearance of being grown up which our inner vanities and hopes, our dim but powerful cravings, often belie. In a word, we learn the arts and the sciences long before we learn philosophy.

If we ask ourselves what is this wisdom which experience forces upon us, the answer must be that we discover the world is differently constituted than we had supposed it to be. It is not that we learn more about its physical elements, or its geography, or the variety of its inhabitants, or the ways in which human society is governed. Knowledge of this sort can be taught to a child without in any fundamental way disturbing his childishness. In fact, all of us are aware that we once knew a great many things which we have since forgotten. The essential discovery of maturity has little if anything to do with information about the names, the locations, and the sequences of facts; it is the acquiring of a different sense of life, a different kind of intuition about the nature of things.

A boy can take you into the open at night and show you the stars; he might tell you no end of things about them, conceivably all that an astronomer could teach. But until and unless he feels the vast indifference of the universe to his own fate, and has placed himself in the perspective of cold and illimitable space, he has not looked maturely at the heavens. Until he has felt this, and unless he can endure this, he remains a child, and in his childishness he will resent the heavens when they are not accommodating. He will demand sunshine when he wishes to play, and rain when the ground is dry, and he will look upon storms as anger directed at him, and the thunder as a personal threat.

The discovery that our wishes have little or no authority in the world brings with it experience of the necessity that is in the nature of things. The lesson of this experience is one from which we shrink and to which few ever wholly accommodate themselves. The world of the child is a kind of enchanted island. The labor that went into procuring his food, his clothes, his toys, is wholly invisible at first. His earliest expectations are, therefore, that somehow the Lord will provide. Only gradually does the truth come home to him how much effort it costs to satisfy his wants. It takes even longer for him to understand that not only does he not get what he wants by asking for it but he cannot be sure to get what he wants by working for it. It is not easy to accept the knowledge that desire, that prayer, that effort can be and often are frustrated, that in the nature of things there is much fumbling, trial and error, deadlock and defeat.

The sense of evil is acquired late; by many persons it is never acquired at all. Children suffer, and childhood is by no means so unreservedly happy as some make it out to be. But childish suffering is not inherently tragic. It is not stamped with the irrevocability which the adult feels to be part of the essence of evil. Evil for the child is something which can be explained away, made up for, done away with. Pretentious philosophies have been built on this fancy purporting somehow to absorb the evil of the world in an all-embracing goodness, as a child's tears are dried by its mother's kisses. The discovery that there is evil which is as genuine as goodness, that there is ugliness and violence which are no less real than joy and love, is one of those discoveries that the adult is forced somehow to accept in his valuation of experience.

And then there is the knowledge, which only experience can give, that everything changes and that everything comes to an end. It is possible to tell a child about mortality, but to realize it he must live long enough to experience it. This knowledge does not come from words; it comes in feeling, in the feeling that he himself is older, in the death of kin and friends, in seeing well-known objects wear out, in discarding old things, in awakening to the sense that there is a whole new generation in the world which looks upon him as old. There is an intimation of immortality in our youth because we have not yet had experience of mortality. The persons and the things which surround us seem eternal because we have known them too briefly to realize that they change. We have seen neither their beginning nor their end.

In the last analysis we have no right to say that the world of youth is an illusion. For the child it is a true picture of the world in that it corresponds to, and is justified in, his experience. If he did not have to grow older, it would be quite sufficient because nothing in his experience would contradict it. Our sense of life as we mature is quite different, but there is no reason to think that it has any absolute finality. Perhaps if we lived several hundred years we should acquire a wholly different sense of life, compared with which all our adult philosophy would seem quite callow.

The child's sense of life can be called an illusion only if it is carried over into manhood, for then it ceases to fit his experience and to be justified by events. The habits formed in a childish environment become progressively unworkable and contradictory as the youth is thrust out from the protection of his family into an adult environment. Then the infantile conviction that his wants will somehow be met collides with the fact that he must provide for himself. The world begins to seem out of joint. The child's notion that things are to be had for the asking becomes a vast confusion in which words are treated as laws, and rhetoric as action. The childish belief that each of us is the center of an adoring and solicitous universe becomes the source of endless disappointments because we cannot reconcile what we feel is due us with what we must resign ourselves to. The sense of the unreality of evil, which our earliest experience seemed to justify, becomes a deep preference for not knowing the truth, an habitual desire to think of the world as we should prefer it to be; out of this rebellion against truth, out of this determination that the facts shall conform to our wishes, are born all manner of bigotry and uncharitableness. The child's sense that things do not end, that they are there forever, becomes, once it is carried over into maturity, a vain and anxious effort to possess things forever. The incapacity to realize that the objects of desire will last only a little while makes us put an extravagant value upon them, and to care for them, not as they are and for what they can actually give us, but for what we foolishly insist they ought to be and ought always to give us.

The child's philosophy rests upon the assumption that the world outside is in gear with his own appetites. For this reason an adult with a childish character will ascribe an authority to his appetites which may easily land

him in fanaticism or frustration, in a crazy indulgence or a miserable starvation. And to the environment he will ascribe a willingness to conform
to him, a capacity to be owned by him, which land him in all sorts of delusions of grandeur. Only the extreme cases are in the asylums. The world
is full of semi-adult persons who secretly nurse the notion that they are,
or that by rights they ought to be, Don Juan, Crœsus, Napoleon, or the
Messiah.

They have brought with them the notion that they are still as intimately attached to nature and to society as the child is to its household.
The adult has to break this attachment to persons and things. His world
does not permit him to remain fused with it, but compels him to stand
away from things. For things no longer obey his wishes. And therefore
he cannot let his wishes become too deeply involved in things. He can no
longer count on possessing whatever he may happen to want. And therefore he must learn to want what he can possess. He can no longer hold
forever the things at which he grasps; for they change, and slip away.
And therefore he must learn to hold on to things which do not slip away
and change, to hold on to things not by grasping them, but by understanding them and by remembering them. Then he is wholly an adult.
Then he has conquered mortality in the only way mortal men can con-
quer it. For he has ceased to expect anything of the world which it cannot give, and he has learned to love it under the only aspect in which it is
eternal.

Arnold Toynbee

RACE AND CIVILIZATION

I T IS an established fact of Physiology that, in all human beings, the pigment secreted in the skin is qualitatively the same; and that the different shades of colour which strike the eye and affect the feelings and give

rise to theories and classifications correspond to mere differences in the quantity in which this qualitatively uniform human pigment happens to be present beneath the skin of any given specimen of the Human Race. We can verify this on the body of an African Negro; for the palms of his hands and the soles of his feet are of a different shade from the rest of his skin and of practically the same shade as the whole skin of a White man —the explanation being that, on his palms and soles, a Negro has about the same quantity of pigment that a White man has all over, while on the rest of his body the Negro has rather more. This fact indicates that our colour-prejudice has not a shadow of physiological justification and shows it up for what it is: a particular instance of the irrational but universal aversion from whatever is abnormal. 'Nordic Man,' who rejoices in the rather low quantity of pigment in his skin, eyes, and hair which happens to be normal in human beings of his kind, is repelled by the abnormal case in which this quantity is reduced to zero and 'the Blond Beast' transformed into an albino, though logically, if colourlessness is the pink of perfection, the rare albino ought to be hailed by his commonplace Nordic relatives as a king of men. Again, even the relative lack of colour which is normal and therefore comely in the sight of a White man is abnormal and therefore unbecoming in the sight of a Red Indian, who expresses his aversion by calling the White man a 'pale-face.' It even happens that a human being comes to regard his own colour with aversion if he lives for some time in a minority of one among people of a different colour—the colour of the majority setting the norm. For example, it is said that David Livingstone, on one of his expeditions, after passing many months in Central Africa with no White companions and none but Negroes round him, began to find that the sight of his own naked skin turned him sick, as though he were looking at some deformity of nature.

This craving for the normal in physical appearance (whatever the normal may be in the particular circumstances) is not of course confined to the single feature of colour. For example, in the United States, where the physical appearance of the White people is the norm for the Coloured people, the Coloured women try to lessen their unlikeness from the White women by straightening their hair. On the other hand, the White women, who have no fear of looking like Negroes, take pleasure, as White women do in other countries, in having their hair waved or curled. Thus, in the same American town at the same moment, some barbers may be busy straightening women's hair in the Negro quarter while others are busy curling women's hair in the White quarter—in both cases alike, for the satisfaction of the universal human craving to be 'in the fashion.'

Hair, indeed, is just as good—or just as bad—a criterion of Race as pigment. The North American Whites and Negroes are sensitive to the straightness or curliness of the hair on the head. The Japanese are sensitive to the general hairiness of the human body, because, in Japan, this happens to be a more significant feature than the colour of the skin. The Japanese people (like almost every other people that has ever distinguishd itself) is of mixed race; and its original racial components must have differed widely in colour; for there is a considerable diversity of colour among the Japanese people to this day. In the same district and in the same social class and in the same family you may find skins varying from copper-colour to what White people call white. Hence, the differences of colour within this range do not excite race-feeling among the Japanese any more than this is excited among Europeans by differences in the quantity of hair on their bodies. On the other hand, Japanese of all shades of skin are alike in being more or less hairless except on their heads, in contrast to the aboriginal inhabitants of the Japanese Islands who, like Nordic Man in the unshaven state of nature, have bushy beards and hairy chests. For this reason, the Japanese call these aborigines (the remnant of whom are now philanthropically preserved, on the northern island of Hokkaido, in 'reservations') 'the Hairy Ainu.' In the local circumstances of Japan, it is just as natural to emphasize the hairiness of the inferior race as it is in the United States or in the Union of South Africa to emphasize their colour; and as the people of European origin apply the colour-classification, which suggests itself in their own local circumstances, to the whole of Mankind, so we might expect the Japanese to divide the human family, not into a 'White Race' and a 'Coloured Race' but into a 'Hairless Race' and a 'Hairy.'

Logically there is nothing to choose between one classification and the other; but it may be edifying for us to glance at the classification with which we are less familiar. It yields what, to our minds, are disconcerting results. It brackets 'Nordic Man' with the Hairy Ainu of Hokkaido and the Blackfellows of Australia and the Veddahs of Ceylon and the Todas of the Nilgiri Hills in Southern India, as one of the representatives of a race whose abnormal hairiness makes them not as other men are.

'What nonsense,' the indignant Nordic ethnologist exclaims. 'Is it likely that there is any racial relation between these tribes, considering that their homes are separated by the whole breadth of Europe and Asia?' But the Japanese ethnologist has his answer up his sleeve. Courteously he points out to his Nordic colleague that 'the Hairy Race' is the nearest of all living races to the Apes in that feature which is fundamental for Japanese purposes of racial classification. It follows that 'the Hairy Race' is the nearest of all living breeds of Man to the common ancestor of Apes and Men. In other words, 'the Hairy Race' is the most primitive, rudimentary experiment in *Homo Sapiens* [1] that survives; and it is natural enough that it should only survive in holes and corners. If we assume that the original breeding-ground of Mankind lay somewhere in the heart of the Old World, and that 'the Hairy Race' was one of the earliest human swarms to hive off, then we should expect to find *Homo Hirsutus* pushed outwards in all directions, to the ends of the Earth, to Australia and to Hokkaido and to Ultima Thule, by younger and superior races—*Homo Mediterraneus* and *Homo Dravidicus*, *Homo Alpinus* and *Homo Mongolicus*—which have issued from the common breeding-ground at later dates to multiply and replenish the Earth in their turns. Thus the vast distances which separate the several surviving tribes of *Homo Hirsutus* to-day are presumptive evidence for and not against the racial kinship of these tribes which their common shagginess betrays. Their present homes are not their respective cradles but their respective retreats from a common birthplace. They are fragments of the circumference of the circle in which *Homo Hirsutus* has spread—or has been chevied—over the face of the Earth from his original centre of dispersion. We may compare his now widely dispersed representatives with the disturbances which remain here and there on the surface of a pond when the last of the ripples produced by the fall of a stone into the water is dying away. If the Japanese ethnologist presents his case on these lines, it will be difficult for the Nordic ethnologist to rebut it.

Another racial feature which acts as a stimulus of race-feeling, no less powerfully than hairiness or colour, is smell.

'I hope you have been enjoying yourself,' said an English dramatic critic to a celebrated Japanese actress who had been having a season in the West End of London. 'Yes, on the whole,' the lady replied, 'but of course there have been hardships to put up with.' 'Hardships? I am sorry to hear that,' the Englishman exclaimed (rather taken aback, for the Japanese artist had been received enthusiastically by the English public). 'Oh yes,' she burst out. 'And the worst of all was the smell. The people in this country smell like lions and tigers. . . . But not you, of course,' she added hastily, solicitous for her own manners and for her interlocutor's feelings, 'you only smell of mutton-fat and scented soap.' The truth is that the Japanese, whose national odour is kept sweet and wholesome by a mainly vegetarian

---

1. The Latin word *homo* means "man." The meanings of the other Latin words in the paragraph are as follows: *Sapiens:* to have sense, to know (thus *homo sapiens* has come to mean "man," regarded as an organic species); *Hirsutus:* rough, i.e., hairy; *Mediterraneus:* Mediterranean, i.e., the Mediterranean race, a subdivision of the Caucasoid stock inhabiting the shores of the Mediterranean Sea; *Dravidicus:* Dravidian, an ancient people inhabiting southern India; *Alpinus:* Alps, i.e., a European stock found in the Alps and adjacent districts; *Mongolicus:* Mongolian, i.e., an ancient stock that inhabited most of Asia and was found in many other parts of the world.

diet, are considerably distressed by the rank and foetid odour of the
carnivorous peoples of the West—an odour of which we are hardly conscious ourselves because we are living in the reek of it all the time.

It is not only the Japanese who are upset by the White Race's smell.
A highly cultivated and fastidious English lady of my acquaintance once
went to stay for several months in South Africa and engaged a staff of
native servants—among them, a little Kaffir maid. It happened several times
that the maid, on being summoned into her employer's presence, fell into
a sudden faint; and the lady, who was kind-hearted, felt some concern.
What could be the matter with the girl? Was it heart-disease? Or was it
just acute nervousness at finding herself *tête-à-tête* with a member of the
superior race? The lady questioned the other servants, only to have her
questions parried and eluded in the usual provoking fashion; but at last
an older servant, who saw that her mistress was becoming really upset and
alarmed, succeeded in conquering her own reserve and embarrassment.
'You needn't worry, Madam,' she assured my friend, 'there is nothing serious the matter with the girl. The fact is, she has come straight from her
village to you; this is her first place in White people's service, and she isn't
yet quite used to the White people's smell. But don't you worry. She will
get used to it soon enough. Why, look at us! We all used to faint at first,
but now we have quite got over it. It will be the same with her, you'll see!'

Here, then, are three different physical features—colour, hairiness, and
smell—which all excite race-feeling and are all equally suitable, or unsuitable, for being taken as bases for racial classifications. For our purpose it
has merely to be pointed out that these alternative classifications, between
which there is nothing to choose from a logical standpoint, yield results
which are quite incompatible with one another.

[. . .]

Plato, in a famous passage of *The Republic*, has propounded 'a noble lie'
which is to reconcile the citizens of his utopia to the different stations in
life to which it may please the Government to call them after having
tested and brought out their innate abilities by a strenuously competitive
course of education.

'What we now need,' I said, 'is some dodge in the nature of an oppor-
tune lie: a single noble lie which will do the trick of convincing—if possible the Government themselves and in any case the rest of the community.'

'What do you mean?' he said.

'Nothing out of the way,' I said; 'just a *welsh* which has been worked
on ever so many occasions before now, as the poets credibly inform us,
though it has not been worked in our time and now could only be

worked, if at all (of which I am not sure), at the cost of a great deal of tact and patience.'

'How shy you seem to be of your idea,' he said.

'You will feel,' I said, 'that I have every reason to be shy when I tell you what it is.'

'Speak out,' he said, 'and don't be afraid.'

'Here goes, then—though I don't know how I shall have the face to say it or whether I shall find words to say it in. Well, I shall try to convince first the Government and the Army and then the rest of the community that the upbringing and education which we gave them was all a dream and that all the time they were really being moulded and brought up underground in the bosom of the Earth, they and their arms and the rest of their equipment, which was likewise being manufactured there. Then, I shall tell them, when they had been completely finished off, their mother the Earth produced them—thus placing them under an obligation to defend their country, if she is attacked, with all their mind and all their strength, as their mothers and their nurse, and also to look after their fellow-citizens as their brothers born of the same Mother Earth.'

'Really,' he said, 'how can you have the effrontery to go on and on with a lie like that?'

'You have every reason to be shocked,' I said, 'but, all the same, do hear my fairy-story out. It goes on like this: "All of you members of the community are brothers; but when God moulded you, he put a streak of metal into each at the moment of birth—gold into those of you who were fit to govern, because they were the most precious; silver into the soldiers; and iron and bronze into the peasants and the workmen. As you are all akin, you will generally breed true to type; but it will occasionally happen that the golden stock will have silver offspring and the silver stock golden offspring and so on, *mutatis mutandis*. Now the first and chiefest commandment that God lays upon members of the Government is this: the paramount call upon their honour and efficiency as guardians of Society is to be on the watch for any of these flaws in the psychic composition of the members of the rising generation and to take the proper action in each case. If it is a case of their own children showing traces of bronze or iron, they must have no mercy on them but must degrade them to the ranks of the workmen or the peasants to which they intrinsically belong. Conversely, if the children of peasants or workmen show traces of gold or silver, they must rate them at their intrinsic value and must promote them to be members of the Government or of the Army, as the case may be." We must find scriptural authority for the prophecy that the community will come to

grief on the day when a member of the iron race or the bronze race enters the Government. Well, can you think of any dodge for getting this
fairy-story believed?'

'Certainly not for getting it believed by grown-up people now alive;
but we might manage it with their children and their descendants and
the whole of posterity.'

In this passage, Plato drives home the truth that the racial explanation
of differences in human ability and achievement cannot be put forward by
any rational mind except as a deliberate and cold-blooded piece of deception, in which the differentiating effects of 'upbringing and education' are
mendaciously ascribed to pre-existing differences of a racial order—and
this with the calculated object of producing certain effects in the practical
field of social and political action.

In Plato's 'noble lie,' the fallacy of Race thus receives its final exposure.

George Santayana

THE SENTIMENTAL BANDIT

IN WALKING through a Zoological Garden we may admire the dignity of
the animals—except the monkeys and the peering spectators. True,
those animals are caged; if they were free they might make more manifest
the normal condition of living beings where each is radically the enemy of
all the rest. Here they are artificially prevented from attacking one another; yet the intense way they have of burrowing or prowling or peck-
ing expresses clearly enough the absoluteness of their will. Their noble
indifference lasts only as long as their digestion: if all is well within, all is
well or non-existent without. But at the call of hunger or lust or fear, the
brave war of each atom begins against the universe; and the universe itself
is so tolerant and so indifferent that it suffers the brave atom, sometimes,
to win.

A curious complication arises in the absolute will when it becomes senti-mental. Are the lower animals, the vultures or the bisons, ever senti-mental? They seem so at times: as if the infinite vacuity of a world that doesn't concern them made them aware of their own pathetic predicament in having to act as if they were important. They *must* act so, on occasion, with an absolute conviction and ferocity; but in the long intervals of sleepy leisure, as they blink at the world, they may dimly feel that the world is as helpless and as innocent as themselves, and they may grow sentimental. For they can't change that state of things; they can only be sorry for their victims, and sorry for themselves at having to victimize them.

Such at least, among men, is the sentiment of the romantic criminal. He has reverted to animal war against society; but he was a social being in childhood; he remains a social being in respect to his comrades, and to his wife and children; it is easy for him therefore to extend an impotent benevolence to the people he robs and murders. Poor things, especially if they are young women, and good-looking. He would much prefer to be nice to them; but his professional duty obliges him to waylay or to gag or perhaps to kill them. It is too bad. His professional duty is far more merciless to him than his heart is to his fellow-creatures.

The sentimental bandit is not always a highwayman or a burglar: some-times he is a monarch or a general or the founder of a colony, or of a great business enterprise. Sometimes too he is a revolutionary leader, an enthusi-astic humanitarian. He is not robbing and murdering for his own benefit; he is doing it for the greatness of his country or for the emancipation of the poor. He is cruel only in order to dry the people's tears, or those of a part of the people, or those which he himself has been shedding all his life long at the sight of human misery. Nothing could be nobler than the language and sentiments of such a romantic bandit. His every word is a eulogy of himself. He talks of his honor: tells you how unjustly fortune has treated him, and how wickedly his enemies have maligned him; how he has been driven unwillingly to defend himself; how he detests and de-spises the decrepit society of which he was a victim; although he may ad-mit that his own victims personally were sometimes innocent. But invec-tive and apology are not his only themes; he is even more eloquent in prophecy and self-glorification. The pure will of man, he says, is above all: if you have the gift of commanding you have the right, even the duty, to command; for the only duty of a free man is that which he imposes upon himself. But ah, what noble storms often agitate his free bosom! He will confess that in the midst of his hard cruel actions a strange wave of sensibility sometimes overwhelms him; suddenly he will cross himself or say the Lord's prayer or found a hospital or endow a college.

All this, however, will be a passing weakness, unless, like the improbable Don Juan of history, he is sincerely converted and reformed. Absolute will rejects religion as it rejects chivalry; it is on the make. The bandit, however sentimental, is not a gentleman crossing swords in a specific quarrel with a particular person, whom he recognizes as an equal, with rights and liberties of his own to defend. The bandit's greed is indefinite, his enemies are simply obstacles to be kicked out of the way. His avowed art is to take them at a disadvantage. You should never, he says, attack the strong; that would be foolish and dangerous; you would be likely to come off crippled even if victorious. And when you think what great losses and sufferings such an equal war might impose, the mere idea of it will become repulsive, and you will make any sacrifice for the sake of peace. The wise, the efficient, the ultimately kind policy is to attack the weak. Then the struggle will be brief, the victims few, and the settlement decisive.

The sentimental bandit, or the bandit pure and simple, can seem a hero to children or to awestruck peasants; they admire his courage, and sympathize with the absolute will let loose in a play world. Yet this benevolence is itself fanciful; at close quarters and in the long run the sentimental bandit will impose his own absoluteness and lack of chivalry upon his enemies. The lack of chivalry is even more catching than the example of it; it appeals to a deeper and more universal impulse of animal life. Any absolute asserters of themselves, any other sentimental bandits will be suppressed by him without mercy, hunted down by police-dogs, and thoroughly extirpated like so many rats.

Of late we have seen, in art, in war, and in social theory, a rehabilitation of savagery. It is not for me to deny that a great deal of affectation, mere restlessness, and ignorant folly is mixed up in these revivals. They are archaistic and the work of people not savages except by choice. Yet these modish or doctrinaire poses have an instructive side. They remind us that savagery, like every form of animal life, may suddenly be recovered and loved by those in whom it lay latent; and then free impulse may be defended more hotly than life itself; because it is less dreadful to die than to live contrary to one's deepest inclinations.

C. S. Lewis

SCREWTAPE PROPOSES A TOAST

(The scene is in Hell at the annual dinner of the Tempters' Training College for young Devils. The Principal, Dr. Slubgob, has just proposed the health of the guests. Screwtape, a very experienced Devil, who is the guest of honour, rises to reply:)

MR. PRINCIPAL, your Imminence, your Disgraces, my Thorns, Shadies, and Gentledevils:

It is customary on these occasions for the speaker to address himself chiefly to those among you who have just graduated and who will very soon be posted to official Tempterships on Earth. It is a custom I willingly obey. I well remember with what trepidation I awaited my own first appointment. I hope, and believe, that each one of you has the same uneasiness tonight. Your career is before you. Hell expects and demands that it should be—as Mine was—one of unbroken success. If it is not, you know what awaits you.

I have no wish to reduce the wholesome and realistic element of terror, the unremitting anxiety, which must act as the lash and spur to your endeavours. How often you will envy the humans their faculty of sleep! Yet at the same time I would wish to put before you a moderately encouraging view of the strategical situation as a whole.

Your dreaded Principal has included in a speech full of points something like an apology for the banquet which he has set before us. Well, gentledevils, no one blames *him*. But it would be vain to deny that the human souls on whose anguish we have been feasting tonight were of pretty poor quality. Not all the most skilful cookery of our tormentors could make them better than insipid.

Oh to get one's teeth again into a Farinata,[1] a Henry VIII, or even a Hitler! There was real crackling there; something to crunch; a rage, an egotism, a cruelty only just less robust than our own. It put up a delicious resistance to being devoured. It warmed your inwards when you'd got it down.

"Screwtape Proposes a Toast" from *The World's Last Night and Other Essays* by C. S. Lewis, © 1959 by Helen Joy Lewis. Reprinted by permission of Harcourt, Brace & World, Inc.

1. **Farinata:** a political leader in Florence (Italy) in the thirteenth century.

Instead of this, what have we had tonight? There was a municipal authority with Graft sauce. But personally I could not detect in him the flavour of a really passionate and brutal avarice such as delighted one in the great tycoons of the last century. Was he not unmistakably a Little Man—a creature of the petty rake-off pocketed with a petty joke in private and denied with the stalest platitudes in his public utterances—a grubby little nonentity who had drifted into corruption, only just realizing that he was corrupt, and chiefly because everyone else did it? [. . .] The Trade Unionist stuffed with sedition was perhaps a shade better. He had, not quite unknowingly, worked for bloodshed, famine, and the extinction of liberty. Yes, in a way. But what a way! He thought of those ultimate objectives so little. Toeing the party line, self-importance, and above all mere routine, were what really dominated his life.

But now comes the point. Gastronomically, all this is deplorable. But I hope none of us puts gastronomy first. Is it not, in another and far more serious way, full of hope and promise?

Consider, first, the mere quantity. The quality may be wretched; but we never had souls (of a sort) in more abundance.

And then the triumph. We are tempted to say that such souls—or such residual puddles of what once was soul—are hardly worth damning. Yes, but the Enemy (for whatever inscrutable and perverse reason) thought them worth trying to save. Believe me, He did. You youngsters who have not yet been on active service have no idea with what labour, with what delicate skill, each of these miserable creatures was finally captured.

The difficulty lay in their very smallness and flabbiness. Here were vermin so muddled in mind, so passively responsive to environment, that it was very hard to raise them to that level of clarity and deliberateness at which mortal sin becomes possible. To raise them just enough; but not that fatal millimetre of "too much." For then of course all would possibly have been lost. They might have seen; they might have repented. On the other hand, if they had been raised too little, they would very possibly have qualified for Limbo, as creatures suitable neither for Heaven nor for Hell; things that, having failed to make the grade, are allowed to sink into a more or less contented sub-humanity forever.

In each individual choice of what the Enemy would call the "wrong" turning such creatures are at first hardly, if at all, in a state of full spiritual responsibility. They do not understand either the source or the real character of the prohibitions they are breaking. Their consciousness hardly exists apart from the social atmosphere that surrounds them. And of course we have contrived that their very language should be all smudge and blur; what would be a *bribe* in someone else's profession is a *tip* or a *present* in theirs. The job of their Tempters was first, of course, to harden these choices of the Hell-ward roads into a habit by steady repetition. But then (and this was all-important) to turn the habit into a principle—a principle the creature is prepared to defend. After that, all will go well. Conformity to the social environment, at first merely instinctive or even mechanical —how should a *jelly* not conform?—now becomes an unacknowledged creed or ideal of Togetherness or Being Like Folks. Mere ignorance of the law they break now turns into a vague theory about it—remember they know no history—a theory expressed by calling it *conventional* or *puritan* or *bourgeois* "morality." Thus gradually there comes to exist at the centre of the creature a hard, tight, settled core of resolution to go on being what it is, and even to resist moods that might tend to alter it. It is a very small core; not at all reflective (they are too ignorant) nor defiant (their emotional and imaginative poverty excludes that); almost, in its own way, prim and demure; like a pebble, or a very young cancer. But it will serve our turn. Here at last is a real and deliberate, though not fully articulate, rejection of what the Enemy calls Grace.

These, then, are two welcome phenomena. First, the abundance of our captures; however tasteless our fare, we are in no danger of famine. And secondly, the triumph; the kill of our Tempters has never stood higher. But the third moral, which I have not yet drawn, is the most important of all.

The sort of souls on whose despair and ruin we have—well, I won't say feasted, but at any rate subsisted—tonight are increasing in numbers and will continue to increase. Our advices from Lower Command assure us that this is so; our directives warn us to orient all our tactics in view of this situation. The "great" sinners, those in whom vivid and genial passions have been pushed beyond the bounds and in whom an immense concentration of will has been devoted to objects which the Enemy abhors, will not disappear. But they will grow rarer. Our catches will be ever more numerous; but they will consist increasingly of trash—trash which we should only have thrown to Cerberus and the hellhounds as unfit for diabolical consumption. And there are two things I want you to understand about this. First, that however depressing it may seem, it is really a change for the better. And secondly, I would draw your attention to the means by which it has been brought about.

It is a change for the better. The great (and toothsome) sinners are made out of the very same material as those horrible phenomena, the great Saints. The virtual disappearance of such material may mean insipid meals for us. But is it not utter frustration and famine for the Enemy? He did not create the humans—He did not become one of them and die among them by torture—in order to produce candidates for Limbo; "failed" humans. He wanted to make Saints; gods; things like Himself. Is the dullness of your present fare not a very small price to pay for the delicious knowledge that His whole great experiment is petering out? But not only that. As the great sinners grow fewer, and the majority lose all individuality, the great sinners become far more effective agents for us. Every dictator or even demagogue—almost every film-star or crooner—can now draw tens of thousands of the human sheep with him. They give themselves (what there is of them) to him; in him, to us. There may come a time when we shall have no need to bother about *individual* temptation at all, except for the few. Catch the bell-wether and his whole flock comes after him.

But do you realize how we have succeeded in reducing so many of the human race to the level of ciphers? This has not come about by accident. It has been our answer—and a magnificent answer it is—to one of the most serious challenges we ever had to face.

Let me recall to your minds what the human situation was in the latter half of the nineteenth century—the period at which I ceased to be a practising Tempter and was rewarded with an administrative post. The great movement towards liberty and equality among men had by then borne solid fruits and grown mature. Slavery had been abolished. The American War of Independence had been won. The French Revolution had succeeded. Religious toleration was almost everywhere on the increase. In that movement there had originally been many elements which were in our favour. Much Atheism, much Anti-Clericalism, much envy and thirst for revenge, even some (rather absurd) attempts to revive Paganism, were mixed in it. It was not easy to determine what our own attitude should be. On the one hand it was a bitter blow to us—it still is—that any sort of men who had been hungry should be fed or any who had long worn chains should have them struck off. But on the other hand, there was in the movement so much rejection of faith, so much materialism, secularism, and hatred, that we felt we were bound to encourage it.

But by the latter part of the century the situation was much simpler, and also much more ominous. In the English sector (where I saw most of my front-line service) a horrible thing had happened. The Enemy, with His usual sleight of hand, had largely appropriated this progressive or liberalizing movement and perverted it to His own ends. Very little of its old anti-Christianity remained. The dangerous phenomenon called Christian Socialism was rampant. Factory owners of the good old type who grew rich on sweated labour, instead of being assassinated by their workpeople—we could have used that—were being frowned upon by their own class. The rich were increasingly giving up their powers not in the face of revolution and compulsion, but in obedience to their own consciences. As for the poor who benefited by this, they were behaving in a most dis-

appointing fashion. Instead of using their new liberties—as we reasonably
hoped and expected—for massacre, rape, and looting, or even for perpetual
intoxication, they were perversely engaged in becoming cleaner, more
orderly, more thrifty, better educated, and even more virtuous. Believe
me, gentledevils, the threat of something like a really healthy state of society seemed then perfectly serious.

Thanks to our Father Below the threat was averted. Our counter-attack
was on two levels. On the deepest level our leaders contrived to call into
full life an element which had been implicit in the movement from its
earliest days. Hidden in the heart of this striving for Liberty there was
also a deep hatred of personal freedom. That invaluable man Rousseau
first revealed it. In his perfect democracy, you remember, only the state
religion is permitted, slavery is restored, and the individual is told that he
has really willed (though he didn't know it) whatever the Government
tells him to do. From that starting point, *via* Hegel (another indispensable
propagandist on our side) we easily contrived both the Nazi and the
Communist state. Even in England we were pretty successful. I heard the
other day that in that country a man could not, without a permit, cut
down his own tree with his own axe, make it into planks with his own
saw, and use the planks to build a tool-shed in his own garden.

Such was our counter-attack on one level. You, who are mere begin-
ners, will not be entrusted with work of that kind. You will be attached
as Tempters to private persons. Against them, or through them, our
counter-attack takes a different form.

Democracy is the word with which you must lead them by the nose.
The good work which our philological experts have already done in the
corruption of human language makes it unnecessary to warn you that they
should never be allowed to give this word a clear and definable meaning.
They won't. It will never occur to them that *Democracy* is properly the
name of a political system, even a system of voting, and that this has only
the most remote and tenuous connection with what you are trying to sell
them. Nor of course must they ever be allowed to raise Aristotle's question: whether "democratic behaviour" means the behaviour that democracies like or the behaviour that will preserve a democracy. For if they
did, it could hardly fail to occur to them that these need not be the same.

You are to use the word purely as an incantation; if you like, purely
for its selling power. It is a name they venerate. And of course it is connected with the political ideal that men should be equally treated. You
then make a stealthy transition in their minds from this political ideal to
a factual belief that all men *are* equal. Especially the man you are working
on. As a result you can use the word *Democracy* to sanction in his
thought the most degrading (and also the least enjoyable) of all human

feelings. You can get him to practise, not only without shame but with a positive glow of self-approval, conduct which, if undefended by the magic word, would be universally derided.

The feeling I mean is of course that which prompts a man to say *I'm as good as you.*

The first and most obvious advantage is that you thus induce him to enthrone at the centre of his life a good, solid resounding lie. I don't mean merely that his statement is false in fact, that he is no more equal to everyone he meets in kindness, honesty, and good sense than in height or waist-measurement. I mean that he does not believe it himself. No man who says *I'm as good as you* believes it. He would not say it if he did. The St. Bernard never says it to the toy dog, nor the scholar to the dunce, nor the employable to the bum, nor the pretty woman to the plain. The claim to equality, outside the strictly political field, is made only by those who feel themselves to be in some way inferior. What it expresses is precisely the itching, smarting, writhing awareness of an inferiority which the patient refuses to accept.

And therefore resents. Yes, and therefore resents every kind of superiority in others; denigrates it; wishes its annihilation. Presently he suspects every mere difference of being a claim to superiority. No one must be different from himself in voice, clothes, manners, recreations, choice of food. "Here is someone who speaks English rather more clearly and euphoniously than I—it must be a vile, upstage, lah-di-dah affectation. Here's a fellow who says he doesn't like hot dogs—thinks himself too good for them no doubt. Here's a man who hasn't turned on the jukebox —he's one of those goddam highbrows and is doing it to show off. If they were honest-to-God all right Joes they'd be like me. They've no business to be different. It's undemocratic."

Now this useful phenomenon is in itself by no means new. Under the name of Envy it has been known to the humans for thousands of years. But hitherto they always regarded it as the most odious, and also the most comical, of vices. Those who were aware of feeling it felt it with shame; those who were not gave it no quarter in others. The delightful novelty of the present situation is that you can sanction it—make it respectable and even laudable—by the incantatory use of the word *democratic*.

Under the influence of this incantation those who are in any or every way inferior can labour more wholeheartedly and successfully than ever before to pull down everyone else to their own level. But that is not all. Under the same influence, those who come, or could come, nearer to a full humanity, actually draw back from it for fear of being *undemocratic*. I am credibly informed that young humans now sometimes suppress an incipient taste for classical music or good literature because it might prevent their Being Like Folks; that people who would really wish to be—and are offered the Grace which would enable them to be—honest, chaste, or temperate, refuse it. To accept might make them Different, might offend against the Way of Life, take them out of Togetherness, impair their Integration with the Group. They might (horror of horrors!) become individuals.

All is summed up in the prayer which a young female human is said to have uttered recently: "Oh God, make me a normal twentieth-century girl!" Thanks to our labours, this will mean increasingly, "Make me a minx, a moron, and a parasite."

Meanwhile, as a delightful by-product, the few (fewer every day) who will not be made Normal and Regular and Like Folks and Integrated, increasingly tend to become in reality the prigs and cranks which the rabble would in any case have believed them to be. For suspicion often creates what it suspects. ("Since whatever I do, the neighbours are going to think me a witch, or a Communist agent, I might as well be hanged for a sheep as a lamb and become one in reality.") As a result we now have an intelligentsia which, though very small, is very useful to the cause of Hell.

But there is a mere by-product. What I want to fix your attention on is the vast, over-all movement towards the discrediting, and finally the elimination, of every kind of human excellence—moral, cultural, social, or intellectual. And is it not pretty to notice how *Democracy* (in the incantatory sense) is now doing for us the work that was once done by the most ancient Dictatorships, and by the same methods? You remember how one of the Greek Dictators (they called them "tyrants" then) sent an envoy to another Dictator to ask his advice about the principles of government. The second Dictator led the envoy into a field of grain, and there he snicked off with his cane the top of every stalk that rose an inch or so above the general level. The moral was plain. Allow no pre-eminence among your subjects. Let no man live who is wiser, or better, or more famous, or even handsomer than the mass. Cut them all down to a level; all slaves, all ciphers, all nobodies. All equals. Thus Tyrants could practise, in a sense, "democracy." But now "democracy" can do the same work without any other tyranny than her own. No one need now go through the field with a cane. The little stalks will now of themselves bite the tops off the big ones. The big ones are beginning to bite off their own in their desire to Be Like Stalks.

I have said that to secure the damnation of these little souls, these creatures that have almost ceased to be individual, is a laborious and tricky work. But if proper pains and skill are expended, you can be fairly confident of the result. The great sinners *seem* easier to catch. But then they are incalculable. After you have played them for seventy years, the Enemy may snatch them from your claws in the seventy-first. They are capable, you see, of real repentance. They are conscious of real guilt. They are, if things take the wrong turn, as ready to defy the social pressures around them for the Enemy's sake as they were to defy them for ours. It is in some ways more troublesome to track and swat an evasive wasp than to shoot, at close range, a wild elephant. But the elephant is more troublesome if you miss.

My own experience, as I have said, was mainly on the English sector, and I still get more news from it than from any other. It may be that what I am now going to say will not apply so fully to the sectors in which some of you may be operating. But you can make the necessary adjustments when you get there. Some application it will almost certainly have. If it has too little, you must labour to make the country you are dealing with more like what England already is.

In that promising land the spirit of *I'm as good as you* has already become something more than a generally social influence. It begins to work itself into their educational system. How far its operations there have gone at the present moment, I would not like to say with certainty. Nor does it matter. Once you have grasped the tendency, you can easily predict its future developments; especially as we ourselves will play our part in the developing. The basic principle of the new education is to be that dunces and idlers must not be made to feel inferior to intelligent and industrious pupils. That would be "undemocratic." These differences between the pupils—for they are obviously and nakedly *individual* differences—must be disguised. This can be done on various levels. At universities, examinations must be framed so that nearly all the students get good marks. Entrance examinations must be framed so that all, or nearly all, citizens can go to universities, whether they have any power (or wish) to profit by higher education or not. At schools, the children who are too stupid or lazy to learn languages and mathematics and elementary science can be set to doing the things that children used to do in their spare time. Let them, for example, make mud-pies and call it modelling. But all the time there must be no faintest hint that they are inferior to the children who are at work. Whatever nonsense they are engaged in must have—I believe the English already use the phrase—"parity of esteem." An even more drastic scheme is not impossible. Children who are fit to proceed to a higher class may be artificially kept back, because the others would get a *trauma*—Beelzebub, what a useful word—by being left behind. The bright pupil thus remains democratically fettered to his own age-group throughout his school career, and a boy who would be capable of tackling Aeschylus or Dante sits listening to his coaeval's attempts to spell out A CAT SAT ON A MAT.

In a word, we may reasonably hope for the virtual abolition of education when *I'm as good as you* has fully had its way. All incentives to learn and all penalties for not learning will vanish. The few who might want to learn will be prevented; who are they to overtop their fellows? And anyway the teachers—or should I say, nurses?—will be far too busy reassuring the dunces and patting them on the back to waste any time on real teaching. We shall no longer have to plan and toil to spread imperturbable conceit and incurable ignorance among men. The little vermin themselves will do it for us.

Of course this would not follow unless all education became state education. But it will. That is part of the same movement. Penal taxes, designed for that purpose, are liquidating the Middle Class, the class who were prepared to save and spend and make sacrifices in order to have their children privately educated. The removal of this class, besides linking up with the abolition of education, is, fortunately, an inevitable effect of the spirit that says *I'm as good as you*. This was, after all, the social group which gave to the humans the overwhelming majority of their scientists, physicians, philosophers, theologians, poets, artists, composers, architects, jurists, and administrators. If ever there was a bunch of tall stalks that needed their tops knocked off, it was surely they. As an English politician remarked not long ago, "A democracy does not want great men."

It would be idle to ask of such a creature whether by *want* it meant "need" or "like." But you had better be clear. For here Aristotle's question comes up again.

We, in Hell, would welcome the disappearance of Democracy in the strict sense of that word; the political arrangement so called. Like all forms of government it often works to our advantage; but on the whole less often than other forms. And what we must realize is that "democracy" in the diabolical sense (*I'm as good as you*, Being Like Folks, Togetherness) is the finest instrument we could possibly have for extirpating political Democracies from the face of the earth.

For "democracy" or the "democratic spirit" (diabolical sense) leads to a nation without great men, a nation mainly of subliterates, full of the cocksureness which flattery breeds on ignorance, and quick to snarl or whimper at the first hint of criticism. And that is what Hell wishes every democratic people to be. For when such a nation meets in conflict a nation where children have been made to work at school, where talent is placed in high posts, and where the ignorant mass are allowed no say at all in public affairs, only one result is possible.

The Democracies were surprised lately when they found that Russia had got ahead of them in science. What a delicious specimen of human blindness! If the whole tendency of their society is opposed to every sort of excellence, why did they expect their scientists to excel?

It is our function to encourage the behaviour, the manners, the whole attitude of mind, which democracies naturally like and enjoy, because these are the very things which, if unchecked, will destroy democracy. You would almost wonder that even humans don't see it themselves. Even if they don't read Aristotle (that would be undemocratic) you would have thought the French Revolution would have taught them that the behaviour aristocrats naturally like is not the behaviour that preserves aristocracy. They might then have applied the same principle to all forms of government.

But I would not end on that note. I would not—Hell forbid!—encourage in your own minds that delusion which you must carefully foster in the minds of your human victims. I mean the delusion that the fate of nations is *in itself* more important than that of individual souls. The overthrow of free peoples and the multiplication of slave-states are for us a means (besides, of course, being fun); but the real end is the destruction of individuals. For only individuals can be saved or damned, can become sons of the Enemy or food for us. The ultimate value, for us, of any revolution, war, or famine lies in the individual anguish, treachery, hatred, rage, and despair which it may produce. *I'm as good as you* is a useful means for the destruction of democratic societies. But it has a far deeper value as an end in itself, as a state of mind which, necessarily excluding humility, charity, contentment, and all the pleasures of gratitude or admiration, turns a human being away from almost every road which might finally lead him to Heaven.

But now for the pleasantest part of my duty. It falls to my lot to propose on behalf of the guests the health of Principal Slubgob and the Tempters' Training College. Fill your glasses. What is this I see? What is this delicious bouquet I inhale? Can it be? Mr. Principal, I unsay all my hard words about the dinner. I see, and smell, that even under wartime conditions the College cellar still has a few dozen of sound old vintage *Pharisee*. Well, well, well. This is like old times. Hold it beneath your nostrils for a moment, gentledevils. Hold it up to the light. Look at those fiery streaks that writhe and tangle in its dark heart, as if they were contending. And so they are. You know how this wine is blended? Different types of Pharisee have been harvested, trodden, and fermented together to produce its subtle flavour. Types that were most antagonistic to one another on Earth. Some were all rules and relics and rosaries; others were all drab clothes, long faces, and petty traditional abstinences from wine or cards or the theatre. Both had in common their self-righteousness and the almost infinite distance between their actual outlook and anything the Enemy really is or commands. The wickedness of other religions was the really live doctrine in the religion of each; slander was its gospel and denigration its litany. How they hated each other up there where the sun shone! How much more they hate each other now that they are forever conjoined but not reconciled. Their astonishment, their resentment, at the combination, the festering of their eternally impenitent spite, passing into our spiritual digestion, will work like fire. Dark fire. All said and done, my friends, it will be an ill day for us if what most humans mean by "religion" ever vanishes from the Earth. It can still send us the truly delicious sins. The fine flower of unholiness can grow only in the close neighbourhood of the Holy. Nowhere do we tempt so successfully as on the very steps of the altar.

Your Imminence, your Disgraces, my Thorns, Shadies, and Gentledevils: I give you the toast of—Principal Slubgob and the College!

Part
TWO

CRITICAL COMMENT

THE NATURE OF CRITICISM

BEFORE WE EXAMINE the critical comments in Part Two, we should try to gain some familiarity with the broad principles of literary criticism.

Criticism has been called "the science of art," which, when we apply a dictionary definition of the word *science*, means simply "an orderly presentation of facts, reasonings, doctrines, and beliefs concerning" art. The critic may blame or praise, but he does so secondarily: his primary task is to understand and interpret. Ralph Waldo Emerson, in his Journal, wrote: "Criticism should not be querulous and wasting, all knife and root-puller, but guiding, instructive, inspiring, a south wind, not an east wind." Only after—or, perhaps more correctly, *by*—understanding and interpreting does the critic judge.

The fact that the critic himself has not written—most probably could not write—a work of literature comparable to the one on which he is commenting does not mean he cannot fairly and intelligently appraise that work. We can recognize greatness in a painting without ourselves being able to produce a great painting. "This notion," said H. L. Mencken (himself a notable American critic of the 1920's), "is always absurd—that the critic, to be competent, must be a practitioner of the specific art he ventures to deal with; i.e., that a doctor, to cure a belly-ache, must have a belly-ache." At the same time, it is true that many creative artists, and especially writers, are also able critics: notably, among the writers in this book, William Hazlitt, George Orwell, George Santayana, C. S. Lewis, Henry James, D. H. Lawrence, and E. M. Forster.

But why do we need criticism and critics at all? Isn't intuitive appreciation enough, or, indeed, even better—because it is more personal and free and spontaneous—than analysis? Can we not simply enjoy the beauty of the flower—without pulling it apart to try to discover where its scent comes from? David Daiches, a contemporary critic, writes: "Literature has been produced since long before people began to worry about its nature and value, and there is something to be said for the naiveté which enjoys art without asking questions about it. But civilized man cannot afford innocence: there comes a stage at which he must be prepared to justify all the activities which he considers significant. [. . .]" [1]

When first confronted with a work of art, our reaction is likely to be purely intuitive, chiefly emotional. We may or may not like the work, but our response to it is based on what we have known in the past, the associations the work has for us—not on our knowledge of how it was put together or our recognition of its good or bad qualities. When we learn how to analyze a book or a picture—how to separate and examine the elements of a work—we go back to it with a fresh eye. Analysis has added to our original appreciation. We see the work more deeply—more completely.

Another critic, Percy Lubbock, writes:

Nobody can work in material of which the properties are unfamiliar, and a reader who tries to get possession of a book with nothing but his apprecia-

1. *A Study of Literature*, Ithaca: Cornell University Press, 1948, p. 1.

603

tion of the life and the ideas and the story in it is like a man who builds a wall without knowing the capacities of wood and clay and stone. Many different substances, as distinct to the practised eye as stone and wood, go to the making of a novel, and it is necessary to see them for what they are. So only is it possible to use them aright, and to find, when the volume is closed, that a complete, coherent, appraisable book remains in the mind.[2]

What, then, is criticism? One critic, Francis Connolly, defines it as follows:

Criticism, as the word implies, is a judgment on the merit or value of a literary work. A critic says, in effect, that a work is good or bad, successful or unsuccessful, for reasons that may be found in the work itself. To a certain degree, every careful reader is a critic. A reader of a book forms an opinion about individual stories, poems, or essays by asking and answering questions like these: What was the author of the selection trying to say? Did he achieve his purpose? If he did, how did he do it? Was his purpose worth achieving in the first place? If so, is his achievement comparable to that of other writers who wrote in the same genre? Why? The reader's answers to such questions provide grounds for his judgment whether the selection is ineffective, merely competent, or highly successful.

If the reader arrives at his judgment by fair, unbiased study, and if he expresses his judgment clearly and reasonably, he is entitled to be called, if not a critic, then at least a critical reader.[3]

In short, criticism, "the science of art," by orderly analysis and evaluation makes a work of literature more meaningful, and therefore more effective and rewarding.

Let us turn now to various comments that may help us evaluate criticism itself as a creative art. The parallels among these comments will suggest to you some of the aspects of literature that attract the interest of readers and critics, and their differences will help illumine the difficulties of the critic in trying to be balanced in his judgments. We begin, then, not with criticism of creative writing, but with critics writing about their own function and problems.

2. *The Craft of Fiction,* New York: Viking Press, 1957, p. 20.
3. *The Types of Literature,* New York: Harcourt, Brace & World, 1955, pp. 787–88.

Edmund Gosse

CRITICISM

CRITICISM is the art of judging the qualities and values of an aesthetic object, whether in literature or the fine arts. It involves, in the first instance, the formation and expression of a judgment on the qualities of anything, and Matthew Arnold defined it in this general sense as "a disinterested endeavour to learn and propagate the best that is known and thought in the world." It has come, however, to possess a secondary and specialized meaning as a published analysis of the qualities and characteristics of a work in literature or fine art, itself taking the form of independent literature. The sense in which criticism is taken as implying censure, the "picking holes" in any statement or production, is frequent, but it is entirely unjustifiable. There is nothing in the proper scope of criticism which presupposes blame. On the contrary, a work of perfect beauty and fitness, in which no fault could possibly be found with justice, is as proper a subject for criticism to deal with as a work of the greatest imperfection. It may be perfectly just to state that a book or a picture is "beneath criticism," *i.e.* is so wanting in all qualities of originality and technical excellence that time would merely be wasted in analysing it. But it can never be properly said that a work is "above criticism," although it may be "above censure," for the very complexity of its merits and the fulness of its beauties tempt the skill of the analyser and reward it.

It is necessary [. . .] to expose this laxity of speech, since nothing is more confusing to a clear conception of this art than to suppose that it consists in an effort to detect what is blameworthy. Candid criticism should be neither benevolent nor adverse; its function is to give a just judgment, without partiality or bias. A critic is one who exercises the art of criticism, who sets himself up, or is set up, as a judge of literary and artistic merit. The irritability of mankind, which easily forgets and neglects praise, but cannot forgive the rankling poison of blame, has set upon the word *critic* a seal which is even more unamiable than that of *criticism*. It takes its most savage form in Benjamin Disraeli's celebrated and deplorable *dictum*, "the critics are the men who have failed in literature and art." It is plain that such names as those of Aristotle, Dante, Dryden, Joshua Reynolds, Sainte-Beuve and Matthew Arnold are not to be thus swept by a reckless fulmination. There have been many critics who brought from failure in imaginative composition a cavilling, jealous and ignoble temper, who have mainly exercised their function in indulging the evil passion of envy. But, so far as they have done this, they have proved themselves bad critics, and neither minute care, nor a basis of learning, nor wide experience of literature, salutary as all these must be, can avail to make that criticism valuable which is founded on the desire to exaggerate faultfinding and to emphasize censure unfairly. The examination of what has been produced by other ages of human thought is much less liable to this dangerous error than the attempt to estimate contemporary works of art and literature. There are few indeed whom personal passion can blind to

From "Criticism" from *Encyclopaedia Britannica*, Eleventh Edition. Reprinted by permission of Encyclopaedia Britannica.

the merits of a picture of the fifteenth or a poem of the seventeenth century. In the higher branches of historical criticism, prejudice of this ignoble sort is hardly possible, and therefore, in considering criticism in its ideal forms, it is best to leave out of consideration that invidious and fugitive species which bears the general name of "reviewing." This pedestrian criticism, indeed, is useful and even indispensable, but it is, by its very nature, ephemeral, and it is liable to a multitude of drawbacks. Even when the reviewer is, or desires to be, strictly just, it is almost impossible for him to stand far enough back from the object under review to see it in its proper perspective. He is dazzled, or scandalized, by its novelty; he has formed a preconceived notion of the degree to which its author should be encouraged or depressed; he is himself, in all cases, an element in the mental condition which he attempts to judge, and if not positively a defendant is at least a juryman in the court over which he ought to preside with remote impartiality.

It may be laid down as the definition of criticism in its pure sense, that it should consist in the application, in the most competent form, of the principles of literary composition. Those principles are the general aesthetics upon which taste is founded; they take the character of rules of writing. From the days of Aristotle the existence of such rules has not been doubted, but different orders of mind in various ages have given them diverse application, and upon this diversity the fluctuations of taste are founded. It is now generally admitted that in past ages critics have too often succumbed to the temptation to regulate taste rigidly, and to lay down rules that shall match every case with a formula. Over-legislation has been the bane of official criticism, and orig-

inality, especially in works of creative imagination, has been condemned because it did not conform to existing rules. Such instances of want of contemporary appreciation as the reception given to William Blake or Keats, or even Milton, are quoted to prove the futility of criticism. As a matter of fact they do nothing of the kind. They merely prove the immutable principles which underlie all judgment of artistic products to have been misunderstood or imperfectly obeyed during the life-times of those illustrious men. False critics have built domes of glass, as Voltaire put it, between the heavens and themselves, domes which genius has to shatter in pieces before it can make itself comprehended. In critical application formulas are often useful, but they should be held lightly; when the formula becomes the tyrant where it should be the servant of thought, fatal error is imminent. What is required above all else by a critic is knowledge, tempered with good sense, and combined with an exquisite delicacy of taste. He who possesses these qualities may go wrong in certain instances, but his error cannot become radical, and he is always open to correction. It is not his business crudely to pronounce a composition "good" or "bad"; he must be able to show why it is "good" and wherein it is "bad"; he must admire with independence and blame with careful candour. He must above all be assiduous to escape from pompous generalizations, which conceal lack of thought under a flow of words. The finest criticism should take every circumstance of the case into consideration, and hold it necessary, if possible, to know the author as well as the book. A large part of the reason why the criticism of productions of the past is so much more fruitful than mere contemporary reviewing, is that by remoteness from the scene of action the critic is able to make himself familiar with all the elements of age, place and medium which affected the writer at the moment of his composi-tion. In short, knowledge and even taste are not sufficient for perfect crit-icism without the infusion of a still rarer quality, breadth of sympathy.

Theodore Meyer Greene

THE THREE ASPECTS OF CRITICISM

A WORK of art is a unique, individ-ual whole—a self-contained ar-tistic "organism" with a "life" and reality of its own. But it is also an his-torical phenomenon—the product of a specific artist in a specific school, pe-riod, and culture, and an exemplifica-tion of stylistic characteristics which it shares with other works by the same artist and of the same school, period, and culture. Finally, works of art vary in artistic excellence, truth, and sig-nificance: every work of art possesses its own degree of perfection and its own measure of truth or falsity, trivi-ality or greatness.

The competent critic takes all three aspects of the work of art into ac-count, and so, though with less sys-tematic and historical rigor, does the artistically sensitive layman. He ap-prehends the individual work of art in all its self-contained uniqueness through sensitive artistic re-creation. But to re-create it adequately he must understand the artist's "language," and this implies familiarity with the ge-neric style of the composition and its cultural setting. Historically oriented re-creation, in turn, does not exhaust critical response, for such response also implies appraisal of the work of art with respect both to its artistic quality and to its truth and spiritual significance. Criticism has therefore three aspects, the historical, the re-creative, and the judicial. Each aspect relates itself to a corresponding aspect of the work of art itself—historical criticism, to the work's historical char-acter and orientation; re-creative crit-icism, to its unique artistic individual-ity; and judicial criticism, to its artistic value. These aspects of criticism are mutually conditioning factors of a single organic process: their relation to one another is strictly analogous to the interrelation of style, individual-ity, and value in the work of art itself.

The special task of historical criti-cism is that of determining the nature and expressive intent of works of art in their historical context. It involves, on the one hand, the authentication of texts and monuments, and, on the other, their interpretation in the light of available biographical, social, cul-tural, and other types of evidence. It is only thus that we can hope to un-derstand what it was that the authors or makers of works of art intended to express, and to interpret this intention in the light of *their* interests and cul-tural background.

The special task of re-creative criticism is that of apprehending imaginatively, through sensitive artistic response, what the artist has actually succeeded in expressing in a specific work of art. The re-creative critic will inevitably, and quite properly, *also* relate what he thus apprehends to his own interests and needs. But this act is not in itself integral to re-creative criticism, save in so far as it contributes positively to the critic's understanding of the work of art itself and *its* expressed content. The prefix "re," in the term "re-creation," is of crucial importance.

The special task of judicial criticism is that of estimating the value of a work of art in relation to other works of art and to other human values. [. . .]

It must be emphasized that these three aspects of criticism are in reality three complementary approaches to the work of art, and that each approach can be explored effectively only in conjunction with the other two. Historical inquiry divorced from sensitive re-creation and judicial appraisal can merely produce an uninspired chronicle of "objective" historical "facts" which, by themselves, must fail to determine the artistic nature and value of the works of art under consideration. The effort to re-create a work of art without any understanding of its historical context must fail to be truly *re*-creative and must remain a purely subjective reaction. And man's aesthetic response to art must lack all artistic significance if it is not accompanied by an appraisal of it in terms of appropriate artistic standards. But this evaluation of a work of art must remain purely academic, scientific, or moralistic, if it is undertaken without historical perspective and without artistic sensitivity.

Elizabeth Drew

THE CRITIC AND THE WORLD TODAY

THERE are all kinds of creative artists in the field of literature, but there is only one kind of critic of books who is of the least value, and that is the critic who makes us want to go and read the books he criticizes. The function of criticism is to send people to literature. [. . .]

Every piece of literature is the communication of the experience of one individual man or woman, living in a particular age of the world's history, and in particular circumstances and environment. It will inevitably reflect a personality, but there is the further question of how much that personality is influenced by the society in which he lives. What is the relation of literature to what we call the spirit of the age, of the artist to his contemporary world? [. . .]

The very fact that the artist possesses a sensibility beyond the ordinary makes him acutely impressionable to his environment and the temper of his times. These impose on him certain predispositions which are inescapable. Unconsciously they color the texture of his thought, and open certain channels of intellectual and emotional development to him, while they block others. He can achieve fullness of life only if his individuality can consort in some kind of vital sympathy with the culture of his own day. [. . .]

And the limitations of the individual in criticism can be paralleled in the limitations of the spirit of the age. For the critic, like the artist, lives in a particular age of the world's history and in particular circumstances and environment. Each age in turn revalues works of art according to its own needs and the quality of its own outlook, and there is always that element in the appreciation of literature which is summed up by Charles II's comment on the popularity of a certain preacher among the Londoners of that day: 'Well, I suppose his nonsense suits their nonsense.'

But no age is the law and the prophets. The men and women of today, whatever their peculiarities of outlook, are the descendants of many centuries of men and women very much like themselves, and the literature of today is a living part of the literary traditions of many centuries. As individuals each of us passes, and as an age, our age will pass just as other ages have passed. Future epochs will see us in perspective in the vision of time, as we cannot see ourselves. They will be able to sift what is ephemeral from what is lasting in our personalities and our achievements and our writings; they will sort and catalogue our catchwords and our affectations, our habits of mind, our beliefs and disillusionments, our sincerities and our shams; and label us 'twentieth century.'

But that is not all. Behind the grouping of ideas and fashions which create the particular pattern of our own epoch, there are the eternal

rhythms of life itself: behind our particular disillusionments, there are the faiths and the disillusionments of all time: behind our psychoanalysis, there are the passions and frustrations of the centuries, and behind our exploration of the unconscious there is the age-old knowledge of the human heart.

Where then shall the critic stand? 'I care not much for new books,' wrote Montaigne in the sixteenth century, 'because the old seem fuller and of stronger reason.' It is the eternal plea of the middle-aged lover of reading in all ages. Beside it we can put D. H. Lawrence, 'damn their discipline. If you've got to make mistakes— and who hasn't—make your own, not theirs': which is the eternal taunt of the rebel. What position shall the critic choose? What shall be his advice to those who want to know what books they shall read and how they shall read them?

There are many answers. [. . .]

To Hazlitt, the aim of criticism is to receive and to define the characteristic quality of works of art. That is, criticism is interpretation of literature. Taste cannot be taught by criticism: it is familiarity with books which alone can bring the real enjoyment of literature, but the companionship of sympathetic interpreters can itself be one of the great delights of reading.

There are no laws of criticism which are immutable, and no opinions in powerful rhyme or prose which can be cast into the monument of absolute values. Criticism, like art itself, must always remain personal. But behind all personal views there *is* a standard, which if it is not absolute, is at least rooted and durable, just as behind the vagaries of any one age there is the stability of the reiterated values of all the ages. Dr. Johnson said of *The Pilgrim's Progress* that it had the best of all recommendations, 'the general and continued approbation of mankind':

and that is a standard which nothing can shake. 'He was on the side of sense and taste and civilization'; is that not the summing up of his standpoint which any reader of literature would choose? Problems of pure aesthetics will always fascinate the lover of abstract speculation. As Bradley said: 'Metaphysics is the finding of bad reasons for what we believe upon instinct; but to find these reasons is no less an instinct.' But the enjoyment of literature is a more general and humane occupation. It is bound to be influenced in some degree by the rigidities and prejudices which are inseparable from individual human nature, but the art of criticism (for it is an art, although a small one) has much in common with the art of living. In both, the positive is of more value than the negative: it is of more importance to be cultivated than to be censorious; to have intellectual and emotional good breeding than mere brains; to enjoy than to dislike; to love than to hate. Knowledge must be there, to be sure, but to it the man of taste brings a kind of intellectual wisdom, a general spirit of discrimination and good judgment, a power to recognize and to value the width and variety of life's scope, and to relate the experiences of the mind with those of the emotions and the senses. To him life and literature challenge each other at every turn: memory and revelation go hand in hand. As knowledge of men and experience of living come to him, he responds more fully and sensitively to literature: as his knowledge of literature increases, he responds more fully and sensitively to life. 'One cannot be seriously interested in literature and remain purely literary in interests.'

E. M. Forster

PSEUDO-SCHOLARSHIP

Genuine scholarship is one of the highest successes which our race can achieve. No one is more triumphant than the man who chooses a worthy subject and masters all its facts and the leading facts of the subjects neighbouring. He can then do what he likes. He can, if his subject is the novel, lecture on it chronologically if he wishes because he has read all the important novels of the past four centuries, many of the unimportant ones, and has adequate knowledge of any collateral facts that bear upon English fiction. [. . .] The scholar, like the philosopher, can contemplate the river of time. He contemplates it not as a whole, but he can see the facts, the personalities, floating past him, and estimate the relations between them, and if his conclusions could be as valuable to us as they are to himself he would long ago have civilized the human race. As you know, he has failed. True scholarship is incommunicable, true scholars rare. [. . .] Most of us are pseudo-scholars, and I want to consider our characteristics with sympathy and respect, for we are a very large and quite a powerful class, eminent in Church and State, we control the education of the Empire, we lend to the Press such distinction as it consents to receive, and we are a welcome asset at dinner-parties.

Pseudo-scholarship is, on its good side, the homage paid by ignorance to learning. [. . .]

It is when he comes to criticism—to a job like the present—that [the pseudo-scholar] can be so pernicious, because he follows the method of a true scholar without having his equipment. He classes books before he has understood or read them; that is his first crime. Classification by chronology. Books written before 1847, books written after it, books written after or before 1848. The novel in the reign of Queen Anne, the pre-novel, the ur-novel, the novel of the future. Classification by subject matter—sillier still. The literature of Inns, beginning with *Tom Jones;* the literature of the Women's Movement, beginning with *Shirley;* the literature of Desert Islands, from *Robinson Crusoe* to *The Blue Lagoon;* the literature of Rogues —dreariest of all, though the Open Road runs it pretty close; the literature of Sussex (perhaps the most devoted of the Home Counties); improper books—a serious thought dreadful branch of inquiry, only to be pursued by pseudo-scholars of riper years; novels relating to industrialism, aviation, chiropody, the weather. I include the weather on the authority of the most amazing work on the novel that I have met for many years. It came over the Atlantic to me, nor shall I ever forget it. It was a literary manual entitled *Materials and Methods of Fiction.* The writer's name shall be concealed. He was a pseudo-schol-ar and a good one. He classified novels by their dates, their length, their locality, their sex, their point of view, till no more seemed possible. But he still had the weather up his sleeve, and when he brought it out, it had nine heads. He gave an example under each head, for he was anything but slovenly, and we will run through his list. In the first place the weather can be "decorative," as in Pierre Loti; then "utilitarian," as in *The Mill on the Floss* (no Floss, no Mill; no Mill, no Tullivers); "illustrative," as in *The Egoist;* "planned in pre-established harmony," as by Fiona MacLeod; "in emotional contrast," as in *The Master of Ballantrae;* "determinative of action," as in a certain Kipling story, where a man proposes to the wrong girl on account of a mud storm; "a controlling influence," *Richard Feverel;* "itself a hero," like Vesuvius in *The Last Days of Pompeii;* and ninthly, it can be "nonexistent," as in a nursery tale. I liked him flinging in nonexistence. It made everything so scientific and trim. But he himself remained a little dissatisfied, and having finished his classification he said yes, of course there was one more thing, and that was genius; it was useless for a novelist to know that there are nine sorts of weather, unless he has genius also. Cheered by this reflection, he classified novels by their tones. There are only two tones, personal and impersonal, and having given examples of each he grew pensive again and said, "Yes, but you must have genius too, or neither tone will profit."

This constant reference to genius is another characteristic of the pseudo-scholar. He loves mentioning genius, because the sound of the word exempts him from trying to discover its meaning. Literature is written by geniuses. Novelists are geniuses. There we are; now let us classify them. Which he does. Everything he says may be accurate but all is useless because he is moving round books instead of through them, he either has not read them or cannot read them properly. Books have to be read (worse luck, for it takes a long time); it is the only way of discovering what they contain. A few savage tribes eat them, but reading is the only method of assimilation revealed to the West. The reader must sit down alone and struggle with the writer, and this the pseudo-scholar will not do. He would rather relate a book to the history of its time, to events in the life of its author, to the events it describes, above all to some tendency. As soon as he can use the word "tendency" his spirits rise, and though those of his audience may sink, they often pull out their pencils at this point and make a note, under the belief that a tendency is portable.

The critical statements that follow will show that there are many kinds of criticism or, more properly, many kinds of critical approach. As Theodore Greene noted above, the critic may discuss the work's relation to the period in which it was written; the work's intrinsic quality—its style and language; or the work's truth or significance—its meaning. Thus criticism may be chiefly historical or biographical, aesthetic, or philosophical or interpretative.

This has been called an age of criticism. Whether it is, in fact, any more so than other ages is debatable; but that there exists today, especially in America, a great body of excellent criticism is not debatable, and we shall find many examples of it in the pages that follow.

THE NATURE OF LITERATURE

IN *Hamlet* Polonius characterizes the various kinds of drama as

[. . .] tragedy, comedy, history, pastoral, pastoral-comical, historical-pastoral, tragical-historical, tragical-comical-historical-pastoral, scene individable or poem unlimited.

Fortunately, we need not chop our categories quite so fine. In this text we are concerned with the short story, the novel, and the essay (including history and biography)—but not with poetry and drama—and we will limit our investigation into the nature and function of literature to these forms.

"Literature," a contemporary poet, Ezra Pound, has said, "is language charged with meaning. Great literature is simply language charged with meaning to the utmost degree." "The function of literature," George Santayana stated, is "to turn events into ideas." Literature, then, gives meaning; it also incites participation: "[. . .] the man who succeeds in finishing the reading of *War and*

Peace—not everybody does—may not feel himself the same man afterward, and this change of heart may reflect itself so clearly in his daily conduct that other people will recognize the change." [1]

Meaning, participation—and life: "Literature is [. . .] a revelation of life. It is the communication, in words, of every imaginable kind of human experience, from the most profound to the most trivial, from the pinnacle to the pinpoint, from a nutshell to infinite space." [2]

The three selections that follow will fortify your understanding of the term *literature*.

David Daiches

THE LITERARY USE OF LANGUAGE

Let us take a very simple example. Consider that a journalist has been asked to stand for a while in a city street and then write up an account of the street and what took place there. As soon as he begins to write he will have to make his own definition of his subject. What in fact is meant by "the street and what took place there"? To define even the street requires a choice: is it simply the thoroughfare leading from one place to another, or are we to include the buildings which flank it, and if we include the buildings what aspects of them are we to include? A street, in fact, can be considered in an indefinite number of ways. As for defining "what took place there," we strike here immediately the problem of selection. Clearly, it would be physically impossible as well as wholly pointless for the writer to give an account of every single event which in fact occurred while he was there, or even of every single event which he observed. Our journalist would have to select from among the plethora of events—the actions and gestures of people, the movement of traffic, all the innumerable activities of city life—what he considered of importance or of interest on some standard or other. He would have to define "street" and "what took place there" before writing or in the process of writing. And he would have to make up his mind about his perspective. Should he try to get closer to some things than to others; should he vary the distance at which he stood from people and things, or maintain a simple gradation from foreground to background? These and other questions he will have to answer, consciously or unconsciously, in presenting us with a verbal picture of that street at that time. Having done so, he will have presented to us aspects of a situation which we can recognize as one which we either have known or might have known. If he can use the language

From *A Study of Literature* by David Daiches, copyright 1948 by Cornell University. Reprinted by permission of Cornell University Press.

1. Caroline Gordon in *How to Read a Novel*.
2. Elizabeth Drew in *The Modern Novel*.

with any ability at all, even if he can put together a number of sentences which say, however badly or crudely, what he saw (or, rather, what he thought he saw) that he considered worth mentioning, we shall be able to recognize his account as corresponding to something of which we have had experience—assuming, of course, that we are products of the same civilization and are familiar with that kind of city street. That is to say, we should *recognize* the description as, in a general sort of way at least, true. The writer, without using any other skill than is required of a reasonably competent journalist, would have defined his subject intelligibly and recognizably. Out of the moving chaos of reality he will have isolated a static picture, which a certain class of readers would consent to, as reflecting in some sense an actual state of affairs.

Our journalist might do more than that. He might manage to convey to readers who have not had experience of that kind of city street at all a sense of the authenticity of his picture. He can do this by "style," by the selection and organization of his imagery, by using words in such a way that the reader is persuaded into recognizing not what he has seen but what he might have seen. The first stage is where we recognize what we know, the second is where we recognize what we might have known, and there is a third—where, while we recognize what we have known or might have known, we at the same time see, and know to be authentic, what we should never have seen for ourselves. The interesting fact is that where a writer succeeds in making authentic a picture of a kind that his readers might not have seen, he will very probably be doing more—he will be giving them at the same time a new insight which coexists with the feel-

ing of recognition. This is because "style," that way of writing which makes convincing in its own right what would otherwise be merely recognizable, can rarely do this without going further. For such a style is the result of the ability to choose and order words in such a way that what is described becomes not merely something existing, something which happens to be in a particular place at a particular time, but something that is linked with man's wider fate, that suggests, and keeps on suggesting the more we read, ever wider categories of experience until there is included something with which we can make contact, which touches what we, too, find recognizable. And then it becomes irrelevant whether what is described exists in fact in the real world or not. The mere journalist drops his words one by one, and there they lie, in the order in which he dropped them, specific but still, corresponding accurately enough to what the author intends to say, but having no further life of their own. But the true creative writer drops his words into our mind like stones in a pool, and the ever-widening circles of meaning eventually ring round and encompass the store of our own experience. And —to continue the metaphor—in doing so they provide a new context for familiar things, and what has been lying half dead in our mind and imagination takes on new life in virtue of its new context, so that we not only recognize what we feel we knew but see the familiar take on rich and exciting new meanings.

If, therefore, the journalist who described what went on in a particular city street during a given period of time had the literary skill (and the initial combination of feeling for life and feeling for language which alone can make such a skill *realizable*) to present his observations in such a way that when he wrote of businessmen entering and leaving the bank, children coming home from school, housewives out shopping, loiterers, barking dogs, lumbering buses, or whatever else he cared to note, he was able to convey to the reader something of the tragedy or the comedy of human affairs, wringing some human insight out of these multifarious incidents so that the reader not only sees what he already knew or even admits as authentic what he did not know, but sees simultaneously what he knew and what he never saw before, recognizes the picture in the light of his deepest, half-intuitive knowledge of what man's experience is and can be and at the same time sees it as a new illumination—if he can do this, then he has moved from journalism into art. He has shown that he can make the means of expression comment on what is expressed so as simultaneously to define and expand

his subject matter: define it by using words that block off the wrong meanings, which show with complete compulsion that what is meant is *this* rather than *that*, and expand it by choosing and arranging words and larger units of expression so that they set going the appropriate overtones and suggestions which help to elevate a description of people's behavior to an account of man's fate.

"Style" then—to employ this term for that use of language which distinguishes art from mere communication—is a handling of words in such a way as to produce both recognition *and* insight. [. . .]

Language can thus be regarded as either a medium of communication or as a medium which can, while communicating, simultaneously expand the significance of the communication. The latter is the literary use of language.

Henry A. Myers

LITERATURE

At CORNELL UNIVERSITY, where the College of Agriculture maintains an Extension Bulletin Service which furnishes New Yorkers with pamphlets on a great variety of practical subjects, a professor of literature is often reminded that many people call *any* valuable piece of writing literature. One letter which we received recently will serve as a fair example of many. It was addressed to the Department of Literature, Cornell University, but it was clear from the contents that it was intended for the Extension Bulletin Service, which the writer obviously regarded as the center of literary activity at Cornell. "Dear Sirs," he wrote. "Will you please send me as soon as possible your latest literature on how to make sauerkraut?"

What is the essential difference between literature and other kinds of

Part I from "Literature, Science, and Democracy" by Henry Alonzo Myers, first published in the *Pacific Spectator*, Volume VIII, Number 4, Autumn 1954. Reprinted by permission of Mrs. Henry Myers.

writing? Dictionaries still label as a colloquialism the use of the word literature to describe such current printed matter as advertising circulars, income tax directions, and college announcements, but the dictionary definition of literature as "the total of the preserved writings belonging to a given language or people" would certainly include a time-tested treatise on how to make sauerkraut, and would seem also to include old handbills or any kind of printed matter venerable enough to be called "preserved." In recent years the editors who compile anthologies for the use of students of Ameircan literature have confirmed popular usage by leaning more and more toward the broadest possible definition. A recent anthology, for example, subtitled "Selections from the Literature of the United States," includes in its offerings passages from John Smith's *Description of New England*, Noah Webster's *Grammatical Institute of the English Language*, Alexander Hamilton's *Report on Manufactures*, Andrew Carnegie's *Empire of Business*, and Mr. Justice Field's concurring opinion in the Slaughterhouse cases of 1884.

In textbooks designed to show the growth of the American mind, or of American civilization, the selection of a wide variety of writings is defensible, and even desirable, but the literary critics and historians who confirm loose popular usage by including purely impersonal, factual, informative, and descriptive writings under the heading of literature make doubly necessary a reconsideration of what we mean when we speak of literature in its narrower sense as one of the humanities, in the narrower sense which includes only such writings as *Oedipus the King*, or *Hamlet*, or *Moby Dick*.

The traditional distinction between the supposedly purely aesthetic values of belles-lettres and the informational and utilitarian values of other kinds of writing is vague and misleading. Everyone understands what is meant by informational and utilitarian values, but what is meant by purely aesthetic values? If the traditional definition of belles-lettres is understood to mean that the reading of poems, plays, novels, and essays is, generally speaking, a pleasurable experience, it affirms an undeniable fact, but it seems also to imply that literature in the narrow sense is valuable only because it offers recreation, diversion, and even escape from the actualities of a practical and troubled world. In the United States amusements have always been considered a matter more of private than of public concern, and the traditional identification of belles-lettres with purely aesthetic values may explain why the federal and state governments have done so little to encourage creative artists and why, for example, Cornell's Extension Bulletin Service is cheerfully supported by the taxpayers of New York State while its program in literature is dependent upon tuition payments and income from endowments.

Inherited from aristocratic theorists, the distinction between writings that afford aesthetic pleasure and writings that serve useful purposes is misleading on both sides, and is particularly unlikely to attract the citizens of a democratic society to the serious study of literature. On one side, this traditional distinction, contrary to the evidence, implies that writings intended primarily to be informative and useful are necessarily lacking in aesthetic qualities. On the other side, and worse, the distinction implies that great literature is neither informative nor useful. Nothing could be farther from the truth.

A cookbook or a textbook may have aesthetic qualities; a mathematical or scientific demonstration may be a thing of beauty; and *King Lear*, properly read, may be as informative and as useful as a treatise on sauerkraut.

The true difference between literature and other kinds of writing is indicated by the simple, but often forgotten, fact that there are two fundamentally different views of life, two ways of looking at man and the universe, one from within, the other from the outside. These views are equally valuable and indispensable: a culture or a civilization which glorifies one view and belittles the other is out of balance and in danger.

The first view is personal and insighted. This view is more than anthropocentric; it places each individual at the center of the universe and makes it possible for him to say, as Schopenhauer said: "The world is my idea."

From the individual's own point of view, the world begins and ends with his awareness of it. As long as he clings to this point of view, and believes in its validity, man is at home in the universe. As he sees the world from his personal, insighted point of view, it is a world of values: of pleasure and pain, of joy and sorrow, of beauty and ugliness, of victory and defeat, of success and failure, of good deeds and bad deeds, of rewards and punishments, of satisfaction and remorse.

In its beginnings this personal, insighted view is the simple awareness of the individual human consciousness, but in its highest reaches it is the vision, the poetic insight of the artist who sees other people as he sees himself, from within, and who strengthens the bonds of society by demonstrating that the inner world of one individual is in its basic conditions the same as the inner world of another.

The second view is impersonal and external: it had its beginnings in the invention of the weights, measures, scales, clocks, thermometers, and calendars which make impersonal and external description possible. In turn external, impersonal description makes possible a variety of writings, ranging from almanacs and encyclopedias through scholarly monographs on literary history and on to the chemist's periodic table and Newton's *Principia*.

When man sees himself from within and the world as his world, he is the measure of all things; when he insists upon viewing himself from the outside only, he discovers that he is no longer the measure of anything.

What, then, is the indispensable quality, the distinguishing trait, of literature? What essential characteristic distinguishes the *Orestcia* from Aristotle's *Poetics*, *King Lear* from the footnotes in a scholarly edition, Whitman's *Leaves of Grass* from a treatise on the care of lawns?

My genial and talented colleague at Cornell, Professor Morris Bishop, once wrote a book of light verse which carried on its cover the title, *Paramount Poems*, followed by the assertion: "If it isn't a Paramount, it isn't a Poem."

Although negative in form, this is the shortest and clearest definition of poetry that I have ever seen. In the interest of clarity I propose now to offer first a definition of literature in similar negative form. My sentence is much longer than Morris Bishop's because it is much less exclusive.

If it doesn't open up for you the inner life of at least one other human being, who may be either the author or one of his fictional creations; if it doesn't release you for a moment from your lonely island in the sea of the individual's isolation; if it doesn't inform you of some of the resources of the human spirit, of its triumphs and frustrations, or of its complexities, perversities, and incongruities; if it doesn't convince you that the inner world of the human spirit is as boundless and wonderful as the outer world of the seven seas and the starry heavens; if it doesn't indicate that the moral law is as important as the laws of thermodynamics; if it doesn't lead you toward an insighted understanding that, in spite of all outward and measurable differences, inwardly all human beings are akin—if it affects you in none of these ways, then no matter how great its other merits of diction and form and style may be, what you have been reading is not literature.

And now to turn this into positive form:

Other qualities of poetry and literary prose are important, but insight— the writer's personal view and his ability to see others as he sees himself, from within, his ability to estimate those inner values which cannot be checked by measuring rods, weights, clocks, and thermometers—is the indispensable quality, the distinguishing trait, of literature. Literature may offer more than insight, but it cannot offer less, it cannot lack insight without becoming another kind of writing. Literature without insight is a contradiction in terms.

Thomas De Quincey

THE LITERATURE OF KNOWLEDGE
AND THE LITERATURE OF POWER

IN THAT great social organ, which, collectively, we call literature, there may be distinguished two separate offices that may blend and often *do* so, but capable, severally, of a severe insulation, and naturally fitted for reciprocal repulsion. There is, first, the literature of *knowledge;* and, secondly, the literature of *power*. The function of the first is—to *teach;* the function of the second is—to *move:* the first is a rudder; the second, an oar or a sail. The first speaks to the *mere* discursive understanding; the second speaks ultimately, it may happen, to the higher understanding or reason, but always *through* affections of pleasure and sympathy. [. . .]

[. . .] What do you learn from *Paradise Lost?* Nothing at all. What do you learn from a cookery-book? Something new—something that you did not know before, in every paragraph. But would you therefore put the wretched cookery-book on a higher level of estimation than the divine poem? What you owe to Milton is not any knowledge, of which a million separate items are still but a million of advancing steps on the same earthly level; what you owe, is *power,* that is, exercise and expansion to your own latent capacity of sympathy with the infinite, where every pulse and each separate influx is a step upwards—a step ascending as upon a

Jacob's ladder from earth to mysterious altitudes above the earth. *All* the steps of knowledge, from first to last, carry you further on the same plane, but could never raise you one foot above your ancient level of earth: whereas, the very *first* step in power is a flight—is an ascending movement into another element where earth is forgotten. [. . .]

All the literature of knowledge builds only ground-nests, that are swept away by floods, or confounded by the plough; but the literature of power builds nests in aërial altitudes of temples sacred from violation, or of forests inaccessible to fraud. *This* is a great prerogative of the *power* literature; and it is a greater which lies in the mode of its influence. The *knowledge* literature, like the fashion of this world, passeth away. An Encyclopædia is its abstract; and, in this respect, it may be taken for its speaking symbol—that, before one generation has passed, an Encylopædia is superannuated; for it speaks through the dead memory and unimpassioned understanding, which have not the repose of higher faculties, but are continually enlarging and varying their phylacteries. But all literature, properly so called—literature κατ' ἐξοχήν,[1] for the very reason that it is so much more durable than the literature of knowledge, is (and by the very same proportion it is) more intense and electrically searching in its impressions. The directions in which the tragedy of this planet has trained our human feelings to play, and the combinations into which the poetry of this planet has thrown our human passions of love and hatred, of admiration and contempt, exercise a power bad or good over human life, that cannot be contemplated, when stretching through many generations, without a sentiment allied to awe. And of this let every one be assured—that he owes to the impassioned books which he has read, many a thousand more of emotions than he can consciously trace back to them. Dim by their origination, these emotions yet arise in him, and mould him through life like forgotten incidents of his childhood.

Our main concern in this section has been to work out an understanding of the meaning of literature. But our concern should be with the writer too, with how a work is created. Art, after all, is produced by artists; it takes a writer to make literature. "Artists," Ezra Pound has said, "are the antennae of the race"; and one artist, Ernest Hemingway, suggested once in an interview why—and how—the writing artist writes:

> From things that have happened and from things as they exist and from all things that you know and all those you cannot know, you make something through your invention that is not a representation but a whole new thing truer than anything true and alive, and you make it alive, and if you make it well enough, you give it immortality. That is why you write and for no other reason that you know of.[2]

It is the *writer's* sense of meaning and purpose, *his* understanding of life and truth; and through the conscious use of language he strives to make all vivid and to tempt the reader to participate. Thus he creates literature.

1. of highest excellence.
2. From *Writers at Work*, Second Series, New York: Viking Press, 1963, p. 239.

FICTION

Fiction, to use Joseph Conrad's phrase, is "the creation of a world," whereas nonfiction is fundamentally the *reporting* of a world. One is the literature of power, the other the literature of knowledge; one deals with the fiction writer's *re-creation* of a segment of life, the other with the essayist's or historian's or biographer's *recording* of a segment of life. Both fiction and nonfiction, however, are equally concerned with life. Let us examine what three of the fiction writers represented in this anthology have to say on this point. First, Ernest Hemingway, emphasizing the writer's "creation of a world":

> All good books are alike in that they are truer than if they had really happened and after you are finished reading one you will feel that all that happened to you and afterwards it all belongs to you: the good and the bad, the ecstasy, the remorse and sorrow, the people and the places and how the weather was.

Second, Henry James—a writer-critic seriously concerned with fiction as "truth" and with the problem of verisimilitude:

> [T]he novel is history. That is the only general description (which does it justice) that we may give of the novel. [. . .] The subject-matter of fiction is stored up likewise in documents and records, and if it will not give itself away, as they say in California, it must speak with assurance, with the tone of the historian. Certain accomplished novelists have a habit of giving themselves away which must often bring tears to the eyes of people who take their fiction seriously. I was lately struck, in reading over many pages of Anthony Trollope, with his want of discretion in this particular. In a digression, a parenthesis or an aside, he concedes to the reader that he and this trusting friend are only "making believe." He admits that the events he narrates have not really happened, and that he can give his narrative any turn the reader may like best. Such a betrayal of a sacred office seems to me, I confess, a terrible crime; it is what I mean by the attitude of apology, and it shocks me every whit as much in Trollope as it would have shocked me in Gibbon or Macaulay. It implies that the novelist is less occupied in looking for the truth (the truth, of course I mean, that he assumes, the premises that we must grant him, whatever they may be) than the historian, and in doing so it deprives him at a stroke of all his standing-room. To represent and illustrate the past, the actions of men, is the task of either writer, and the only difference that I can see is, in proportion as he succeeds, to the honor of the novelist, consisting as it does in his having more difficulty in collecting his evidence, which is so far from being purely literary.[1]

Third, Joseph Conrad, who notes that this concern with fiction as "truth" is not unique with James, and tries to clarify and expand the idea:

> In one of his critical studies, published some fifteen years ago, Mr. Henry James claims for the novelist the standing of the historian as the only ade-

1. "The Art of Fiction."

quate one, as for himself and before his audience. I think that the claim cannot be contested, and that the position is unassailable. Fiction is history, human history, or it is nothing. But it is also more than that; it stands on firmer ground, being based on the reality of forms and the observation of social phenomena, whereas history is based on documents and the reading of print and handwriting—on second-hand impression. Thus fiction is nearer truth. But let that pass. A historian may be an artist too, and a novelist is a historian, the preserver, the keeper, the expounder, of human experience.[2]

On this same point, consider the statements of two present-day critics: "The novel," says Mark Schorer, "is not journalism, philosophy, poetry; not politics, theology, sociology; not even morality. But if it finds its proper structure [. . .] it can include, in some sense, the interests of all of these. It stands halfway between poetry and history." And in the following passage David Daiches suggests just how the "truth" of fiction differs from the "truth" of a report:

If one summarizes the plot of Stevenson's *Treasure Island,* one will not convey the slightest impression of the meaning of the book as it actually emerges to the reader. From a summary, for example, one would gather that the important thing in the novel was to obtain the treasure. As we read the book, however, we realize that the nearer we get to the treasure the less important it becomes—in fact, when it is finally obtained it is dismissed in a sentence: "All of us had an ample share of the treasure, and used it wisely or foolishly, according to our natures." The search for the treasure—an example of the age-old device of the quest—is but a part of a pattern of incident and characterization which, expressed as Stevenson expressed it, builds up in the reader as he reads that whole sense of picturesque danger, of colorful evil and purposeful virtue, of mystery as an essential flavor of life, of contrast between the familiar and the remote, the routine and the unexpected, the known and the unknown, which combine to symbolize persuasively and irresistibly that whole tract of human experience which can be labeled "love of adventure." The book is not about a hunt for treasure: it is about Treasure Island, and Treasure Island is itself a potent symbol, standing for the quest, and for a special kind of quest, the boy's quest, with all the implied further symbols of pirates, hidden maps, and southern seas. [. . .] Fiction [. . .] is the narration of real [3] or imaginary events in which the incidents and characters are arranged in such a pattern, both in relation to each other and to the work as a whole, and in which the method of expression at any given point is such, that the resultant work is at the same time recognizable and convincing as a report on aspects of the human situation and illuminating as a series of original insights into human experience.[4]

2. *Notes on Life and Letters,* London: Dent, 1905.
3. Mr. Daiches refers to narratives based on actual events, such as one would find in a historical novel.
4. *A Study of Literature,* Ithaca: Cornell University Press, 1948, pp. 52–53, 59–60.

Each of the five critics has made the same fundamental point: *both* fiction and nonfiction are concerned with a truthful account of life, though the account of one is a re-creation and the account of the other a report. Now let us see why we should be concerned with a fictional approach to life.

Robert Gorham Davis

FICTION

JAMES says that "the air of reality" is the supreme virtue in fiction, the merit on which all other merits depend. The purpose of the writer is "to represent life," to give "a personal, a direct impression of life." The greater the intensity of the impression, the greater the value of his fiction.

[. . .] Nearly every writer defines his purpose in almost precisely these terms. Chekhov put it most directly and flatly when he wrote, "The aim of fiction is absolute and honest truth."

At first this insistence on truth by fiction writers seems a little puzzling. If they are interested primarily in truth, why do they write fiction? Fiction and fact, imagination and reality are often presented as opposites. Fiction is something "made up," imagined, invented. The short story in the past has been, above all, the form used for the unreal and untrue, for accounts of magic, witches and fairies, strange quests, impossible tasks, miraculous transformations. Now it claims to be equal to science and philosophy in conveying truth.

Or even superior to them. How can this be?

Much depends, of course, on our definition of truth or reality. Maupassant had his own, which most people would not be willing to accept. "How childish," he wrote, "to believe in reality, since we each carry our own in our thought and in our organs. Our eyes, our ears, our sense of smell, of taste, differing from one person to another, create as many truths as there are men upon earth. And our minds, taking instruction from these organs so diversely impressed, understand, analyze, judge, as if each of us belonged to a different race."

Maupassant is obviously exaggerating human separateness. And yet this separateness is something which we all feel acutely at times. The sense of isolation and alienation has been particularly acute in the twentieth century. Scientists and philosophers, to be sure, offer general ideas which they hold to be true for all men. But these are ideas which they have abstracted from experience, and which take on life for most people only

From the Introduction to *Ten Modern Masters*, edited by Robert Gorham Davis, copyright 1953 by Harcourt, Brace & World, Inc. Reprinted by permission of the publishers.

when they are put back into experience. General ideas are based on experience and tested by experience. Experience itself, however, is always individual, occurring here and now to a particular body and mind, different from all the other bodies and minds in the world.

Everyone has to view the world—or reality—from his own limited perspective, with such faculties as his birth and upbringing have given him. He can never view life from inside anyone else, except in imagination. He can never be angry with other people's anger. He can never remember with their memories, feel their toothaches or their thrills of ecstasy. He can never know whether the color red looks to them as it looks to him. And yet in the totality of our life experience, our sensations, feelings, observations, emotions and memories play a much larger part than do our ideas.

What imaginative literature does is to break through the barriers of personal identity, of personal separateness. It lets us know what goes on inside other persons, what it is like to be another person. It literally "communicates"; that is, makes common, or available to others, what otherwise would have been shut up within a single self. It extends immeasurably our sense of direct experience of life. [. . .]

The classic distinction between fiction and history appears in Aristotle's treatise on poetry. It was written in the fourth century B.C., but still holds good. In fact, most modern textbooks can add little to what Aristotle said about plot construction. Aristotle said that poetry—by which he meant imaginative literature generally—"is a more philosophic and higher thing than history: for poetry tends to ex-

press the universal; history, the particular." The business of the poet, he said, is not to state what *did* happen, but to describe what *may* happen; that is, how a person of a certain type will behave and feel in a certain situation "according to the laws of probability."

What Aristotle says is consistent with ordinary experience. History does not repeat itself. The mere fact that a thing has happened once does not mean that it will happen again. No science of history has yet been developed that enables us to predict the future certainly, nor does the science of psychology enable us to predict certainly the behavior of our friends. [. . .]

And yet in living our lives, in planning for the future, we have to try to predict. In making the decisions that constantly face us, we ask what is *likely* to happen, what consequences, moral and otherwise, are *likely* to follow from our decisions, how people are *likely* to feel about it, how the values we cherish or the larger ends we seek are *likely* to be affected. These are the probabilities of which Aristotle spoke [. . .]

Fiction, in its likeness to life, deals with probabilities rather than certainties. Expectation, suspense, surprise and revelation provide the dramatic interest in a plot. What happens must not be fully predictable, at least not in the way it happens. [. . .] Full predictability would not only be boring, but untrue to life. The accidental, the immeasurable, the unaccounted-for play their essential parts in life as in fiction. If they seem more common in fiction, it is because fiction prepares us imaginatively for what we do not expect or are likely to overlook. This is part of its great value.

Robert Penn Warren

WHY DO WE READ FICTION?

WHY do we read fiction? The answer is simple. We read it because we like it. And we like it because fiction, as an image of life, stimulates and gratifies our interest in life. But whatever interests may be appealed to by fiction, the special and immediate interest that takes us to fiction is always our interest in a story.

A story is not merely an image of life, but of life in motion—specifically, the presentation of individual characters moving through their particular experiences to some end that we may accept as meaningful. And the experience that is characteristically presented in a story is that of facing a problem, a conflict. To put it bluntly: No conflict, no story.

OUR AMBIVALENT ATTITUDE

It is no wonder that conflict should be at the center of fiction, for conflict is at the center of life. But why should we, who have the constant and often painful experience of conflict in life and who yearn for inner peace and harmonious relations with the outer world, turn to fiction, which is the image of conflict? The fact is that our attitude toward conflict is ambivalent. If we do find a totally satisfactory adjustment in life, we tend to sink into the drowse of the accustomed. Only when our surroundings—or we ourselves—become problematic again do we wake up and feel that surge of energy which is life. And life more abundantly lived is what we seek.

So we, at the same time that we yearn for peace, yearn for the problematic. The adventurer, the sportsman, the gambler, the child playing hide-and-seek, the teen-age boys choosing up sides for a game of sandlot baseball, the old grad cheering in the stadium—we all, in fact, seek out or create problematic situations of greater or lesser intensity. Such situations give us a sense of heightened energy, of life. And fiction, too, gives us that heightened awareness of life, with all the fresh, uninhibited opportunity to vent the rich emotional charge—tears, laughter, tenderness, sympathy, hate, love, and irony—that is stored up in us and short-circuited in the drowse of the accustomed. Furthermore, this heightened awareness can be more fully relished now, because what in actuality would be the threat of the problematic is here tamed to mere imagination, and because some kind of resolution of the problem is, owing to the very nature of fiction, promised.

The story promises us a resolution, and we wait in suspense to learn how things will come out. We are in suspense, not only about what will happen, but even more about what the event will mean. We are in suspense about the story in fiction because we are in suspense about another story far closer and more important to us—the story of our own life as we live it. We do not know how that story of our own life is going to come out. We do not know what it will mean. So, in that deepest suspense of life, which will be shadowed in the suspense we feel about the story in fiction, we turn to fiction for some slight hint about the story in the life we live. The rela-

"Why Do We Read Fiction?" by Robert Penn Warren from *The Saturday Evening Post* of October 20, 1962, © 1962 by The Curtis Publishing Company. Reprinted by permission of William Morris Agency, Inc.

tion of our life to the fictional life is what, in a fundamental sense, takes us to fiction.

Even when we read, as we say, to "escape," we seek to escape not from life but to life, to a life more satisfying than our own drab version. Fiction gives us an image of life—sometimes of a life we actually have and like to dwell on, but often and poignantly of one we have had but do not have now, or one we have never had and can never have. The ardent fisherman, when his rheumatism keeps him housebound, reads stories from *Field and Stream*. The baseball fan reads *You Know Me, Al*, by Ring Lardner. The little co-ed worrying about her snub nose and her low mark in Sociology 2, dreams of being a debutante out of F. Scott Fitzgerald; and the thin-chested freshman, still troubled by acne, dreams of being a granite-jawed Neanderthal out of Mickey Spillane. When the Parthians in 53 B.C. beat Crassus, they found in the baggage of Roman officers some very juicy items called *Milesian Tales*, by a certain Aristides of Miletus; and I have a friend who, in A.D. 1944, supplemented his income as a GI by reading aloud *Forever Amber*, by a certain Kathleen Winsor, to buddies who found that the struggle over three-syllable words somewhat impaired their dedication to that improbable daydream.

And that is what, for all of us, fiction, in one sense, is—a daydream. It is, in other words, an imaginative enactment. In it we find, in imagination, not only the pleasure of recognizing the world we know and of reliving our past, but also the pleasure of entering worlds we do not know and of experimenting with experiences which we deeply crave but which the limitations of life, the fear of consequences, or the severity of our principles forbid to us. Fiction can give us this pleasure without any painful consequences, for there is no price tag on the magic world of imaginative enactment. But fiction does not give us only what we want; more importantly, it may give us things we hadn't even known we wanted.

COMPENSATING FOR REALITY

In this sense then, fiction painlessly makes up for the defects of reality. Long ago Francis Bacon said that poetry—which, in his meaning, would include our fiction—is "agreeable to the spirit of man" because it affords "a greater grandeur of things, a more perfect order, and a more beautiful variety" than can "anywhere be found in nature. . . ." More recently we find Freud putting it that the "meager satisfactions" that man "can extract from reality leave him starving," and John Dewey saying that art "was born of need, lack, deprivation, incompleteness." But philosophers aside, we all know entirely too well how much we resemble poor Walter Mitty.

If fiction is—as it clearly is for some readers—merely a fantasy to redeem the liabilities of our private fate, it is flight from reality and therefore the enemy of growth, of the life process. But is it necessarily this? Let us look at the matter in another way.

The daydream which is fiction differs from the ordinary daydream in being publicly available. This fact leads to consequences. In the private daydream you remain yourself—though nobler, stronger, more fortunate, more beautiful than in life. But when the little freshman settles cozily with his thriller by Mickey Spillane, he finds that the granite-jawed hero is not named Slim Willett, after all—as poor Slim, with his thin chest, longs for it to be. And Slim's college instructor, settling down to

For Whom the Bell Tolls, finds sadly that this other college instructor who is the hero of the famous tale of sleeping bags, bridge demolition, tragic love and lonely valor, is named Robert Jordan.

HOW READERS "IDENTIFY"

In other words, to enter into that publicly available daydream which fiction is, you have to accept the fact that the name of the hero will never be your own; you will have to surrender something of your own identity to him, have to let it be absorbed in him. But since that kind of daydream is not exquisitely custom-cut to the exact measure of your secret longings, the identification can never be complete. In fact, only a very naive reader tries to make it thrillingly complete. The more sophisticated reader plays a deep double game with himself; one part of him is identified with a character—or with several in turn—while another part holds aloof to respond, interpret and judge. How often have we heard some sentimental old lady say of a book: "I just loved the heroine—I mean I just went through everything with her and I knew exactly how she felt. Then when she died I just cried." The sweet old lady, even if she isn't very sophisticated, is instinctively playing the double game too: She identifies herself with the heroine, but she survives the heroine's death to shed the delicious tears. So even the old lady knows how to make the most of what we shall call her role-taking. She knows that doubleness, in the very act of identification, is of the essence of role-taking: There is the taker of the role and there is the role taken. And fiction is, in imaginative enactment, a role-taking.

For some people—those who fancy themselves hardheaded and realistic—the business of role-taking is as reprehensible as indulgence in a daydream. But in trying to understand our appetite for fiction, we can see that the process of role-taking not only stems from but also affirms the life process. It is an essential part of growth.

Role-taking is, for instance, at the very center of children's play. This is the beginning of the child's long process of adaptation to others, for only by feeling himself into another person's skin can the child predict behavior; and the stakes in the game are high, for only thus does he learn whether to expect the kiss or the cuff. In this process of role-taking we find, too, the roots of many of the massive intellectual structures we later rear—most obviously psychology and ethics, for it is only by role-taking that the child comes to know, to know "inwardly" in the only way that finally counts, that other people really exist and are, in fact, persons with needs, hopes, fears, and even rights. So the role-taking of fiction, at the same time that it gratifies our deep need to extend and enrich our own experience, continues this long discipline in human sympathy. And this discipline in sympathy, through the imaginative enactment of role-taking, gratifies another need deep in us: our yearning to enter and feel at ease in the human community.

Play when we are children, and fiction when we are grown up, lead us, through role-taking, to an awareness of others. But all along the way role-taking leads us, by the same token, to an awareness of ourselves; it leads us, in fact, to the creation of the self. For the individual is not born with a self. He is born as a mysterious bundle of possibilities which, bit by bit, in a long process of trial and error, he sorts out until he gets some sort of unifying self, the ringmaster self, the official self.

The official self emerges, but the

soul, as Plato long ago put it, remains full of "ten thousand opposites occurring at the same time," and modern psychology has said nothing to contradict him. All our submerged selves, the old desires and possibilities, are lurking deep in us, sleepless and eager to have another go. There is knife-fighting in the inner dark. The fact that most of the time we are not aware of trouble does not mean that trouble is any the less present and significant; and fiction, most often in subtly disguised forms, liberatingly reenacts for us such inner conflict. We feel the pleasure of liberation even when we cannot specify the source of the pleasure.

ROUSING SHADOWY SELVES

Fiction brings up from their dark, forgotten dungeons our shadowy, deprived selves and gives them an airing in, as it were, the prison yard. They get a chance to participate, each according to his nature, in the life which fiction presents. When in Thackeray's *Vanity Fair* the girl Becky Sharp, leaving school for good, tosses her copy of Doctor Johnson's *Dictionary* out of the carriage, something in our own heart leaps gaily up, just as something rejoices at her later adventures in Victorian society, and suffers, against all our sense of moral justice, when she comes a cropper. When Holden Caulfield, of Salinger's *Catcher in the Rye*, undertakes his gallant and absurd little crusade against the "phony" in our world, our own nigh-doused idealism flares up again, for the moment without embarrassment. When in Faulkner's *Light in August* Percy Grimm pulls the trigger of the black, blunt-nosed automatic and puts that tight, pretty little pattern of slugs in the top of the overturned table behind which Joe Christmas cowers, our trigger finger tenses, even while, at the same

time, with a strange joy of release and justice satisfied, we feel those same slugs in our heart. When we read Dostoevski's *Crime and Punishment*, something in our nature participates in the bloody deed, and later, something else in us experiences, with the murderer Raskolnikov, the bliss of repentance and reconciliation.

AWESOME CONFRONTATIONS

For among our deprived selves we must confront the redeemed as well as the damned, the saintly as well as the wicked; and strangely enough, either confrontation may be both humbling and strengthening. In having some awareness of the complexity of self we are better prepared to deal with that self. As a matter of fact, our entering into the fictional process helps to redefine this dominant self—even, as it were, to recreate, on a sounder basis—sounder because better understood—that dominant self, the official "I." As Henri Bergson says, fiction "brings us back into our own presence"—the presence in which we must make our final terms with life and death.

The knowledge in such confrontations does not come to us with intellectual labels. We don't say, "Gosh, I've got 15 percent of sadism in me"—or 13 percent of unsuspected human charity. No, the knowledge comes as enactment; and as imaginative enactment, to use our old phrase, it comes as knowledge. It comes, rather, as a heightened sense of being, as the conflict in the story evokes the conflict in ourselves, evokes it with some hopeful sense of meaningful resolution, and with, therefore, an exhilarating sense of freedom.

Part of this sense of freedom derives, to repeat ourselves, from the mere fact that in imagination we are getting off scot-free with something which we, or society, would never permit in real life; from the fact that our paradoxical relation to experience presented in fiction—our involvement and noninvolvement at the same time—gives a glorious feeling of mastery over the game of life. But there is something more important that contributes to this sense of freedom, the expansion and release that knowledge always brings; and in fiction we are permitted to know in the deepest way, by imaginative participation, things we would otherwise never know—including ourselves. We are free from the Garden curse: We may eat of the Tree of Knowledge, and no angel with flaming sword will appear.

But in the process of imaginative enactment we have, in another way, that sense of freedom that comes from knowledge. The image that fiction presents is purged of the distractions, confusions and accidents of ordinary life. We can now gaze at the inner logic of things—of a personality, of the consequences of an act or a thought, of a social or historical situation, of a lived life. One of our deepest cravings is to find logic in experience, but in real life how little of our experience comes to us in such a manageable form!

We have all observed how a person who has had a profound shock needs to tell the story of the event over and over again, every detail. By telling it he objectifies it, disentangling himself, as it were, from the more intolerable effects. This objectifying depends, partly at least, on the fact that the telling is a way of groping for the logic of the event, an attempt to make the experience intellectually manageable. If a child—or a man—who is in a state of blind outrage at his fate can come to understand that the fate which had seemed random and gratuitous is really the result of his own previous behavior or is part of the

general pattern of life, his emotional response is modified by that intellectual comprehension. What is intellectually manageable is, then, more likely to be emotionally manageable.

This fiction is a "telling" in which we as readers participate and is, therefore, an image of the process by which experience is made manageable. In this process experience is foreshortened, is taken out of the ruck of time, is put into an ideal time where we can scrutinize it, is given an interpretation. In other words, fiction shows, as we have said, a logical structure which implies a meaning. By showing a logical structure, it relieves us, for the moment at least, of what we sometimes feel as the greatest and most mysterious threat of life —the threat of the imminent but "unknowable," of the urgent but "unsayable." Insofar as a piece of fiction is original and not merely a conventional repetition of the known and predictable, it is a movement through the "unknowable" toward the "knowable"—the imaginatively knowable. It says the "unsayable."

THE WRITER AS PROPHET

This leads us, as a sort of aside, to the notion that fiction sometimes seems to be, for the individual or for society, prophetic. Now looking back we can clearly see how Melville, Dostoevski, James, Proust, Conrad and Kafka tried to deal with some of the tensions and problems which have become characteristic of our time. In this sense they foretold our world— and even more importantly, forefelt it. They even forefelt us.

Or let us remember that F. Scott Fitzgerald and Hemingway did not merely report a period, they predicted it in that they sensed a new mode of behavior and feeling. Fiction, by seizing on certain elements in its time and imaginatively pursuing them with the unswerving logic of projected enactment, may prophesy the next age. We know this from looking back on fiction of the past. More urgently we turn to fiction of our own time to help us envisage the time to come and our relation to it.

But let us turn to more specific instances of that inner logic which fiction may reveal. In *An American Tragedy* Dreiser shows us in what subtle and pitiful ways the materialism of America and the worship of what William James called the "bitch-goddess Success" can corrupt an ordinary young man and bring him to the death cell. In *Madame Bovary* Flaubert shows us the logic by which Emma's yearning for color and meaning in life leads to the moment when she gulps the poison. In both novels we sense this logic most deeply because we, as we have seen, are involved, are accomplices. We, too, worship the bitch-goddess—as did Dreiser. We, too, have yearnings like Emma's, and we remember that Flaubert said that he himself was Emma Bovary.

We see the logic of the enacted process, and we also see the logic of the end. Not only do we have now, as readers, the freedom that leads to a knowledge of the springs of action; we have also the more difficult freedom that permits us to contemplate the consequences of action and the judgment that may be passed on it. For judgment, even punishment, is the end of the logic we perceive. In our own personal lives, as we well know from our endless secret monologues of extenuation and alibi, we long to escape from judgment; but here, where the price tag is only that of imaginative involvement, we can accept judgment. We are reconciled to the terrible necessity of judgment —upon our surrogate self in the story, our whipping boy and scapegoat. We

find a moral freedom in this fact that we recognize a principle of justice, with also perhaps some gratification of the paradoxical desire to suffer.

It may be objected here that we speak as though all stories were stories of crime and punishment. No, but all stories, from the gayest farce to the grimmest tragedy, are stories of action and consequence—which amounts to the same thing. All stories, as we have said, are based on conflict; and the resolution of the fictional conflict is, in its implications, a judgment too, a judgment of values. In the end some shift of values has taken place. Some new awareness has dawned, some new possibility of attitude has been envisaged.

SENSING RECONCILIATION

Not that the new value is necessarily "new" in a literal sense. The point, to come back to an old point, is that the reader has, by imaginative enactment, lived through the process by which the values become valuable. What might have been merely an abstraction has become vital, has been lived, and is, therefore, "new"—new because newly experienced. We can now rest in the value as experienced; we are reconciled in it, and that is what counts.

It is what counts, for in the successful piece of fiction, a comic novel by Peter de Vries or a gut-tearing work like Tolstoy's *War and Peace*, we feel, in the end, some sense of reconciliation with the world and with ourselves. And this process of moving through conflict to reconciliation is an echo of our own life process. The life process, as we know it from babyhood on, from our early relations with our parents on to our adult relation with the world, is a long process of conflict and reconciliation. This process of enriching and deepening experience is a pattern of oscillation—a pattern resembling that of the lovers' quarrel: When lovers quarrel, each asserts his special ego against that of the beloved and then in the moment of making up finds more keenly than before the joy of losing the self in the love of another. So in fiction we enter imaginatively a situation of difficulty and estrangement—a problematic situation that, as we said earlier, sharpens our awareness of life—and move through it to a reconciliation which seems fresh and sweet.

Reconciliation—that is what we all, in some depth of being, want. All religion, all philosophy, all psychiatry, all ethics involve this human fact. And so does fiction. If fiction begins in daydream, if it springs from the cramp of the world, if it relieves us from the burden of being ourselves, it ends, if it is good fiction and we are good readers, by returning us to the world and to ourselves. It reconciles us with reality.

Let us pause to take stock. Thus far what we have said sounds as though fiction were a combination of opium addiction, religious conversion without tears, a home course in philosophy and the poor man's psychoanalysis. But it is not; it is fiction.

AN IMAGE OF EXPERIENCE

It is only itself, and that *itself* is not, in the end, a mere substitute for anything else. It is an art—an image of experience formed in accordance with its own laws of imaginative enactment, laws which, as we have seen, conform to our deep needs. It is an "illusion of life" projected through language, and the language is that of some individual man projecting his own feeling of life.

The story, in the fictional sense, is not something that exists of and by itself, out in the world like a stone or a tree. The materials of stories—certain events or characters, for example —may exist out in the world, but they are not fictionally meaningful to us until a human mind has shaped them. We are, in other words, like the princess in one of Hans Christian Andersen's tales; she refuses her suitor when she discovers that the bird with a ravishing song which he has offered as a token of love is only a real bird after all. We, like the princess, want an artificial bird—an artificial bird with a real song. So we go to fiction because it is a *created* thing.

Because it is created by a man, it draws us, as human beings, by its human significance. To begin with, it is an utterance, in words. No words, no story. This seems a fact so obvious, and so trivial, as not to be worth the saying, but it is of fundamental importance in the appeal fiction has for us. We are creatures of words, and if we did not have words we would have no inner life. Only because we have words can we envisage and think about experience. We find our human nature through words. So in one sense we may say that insofar as the language of the story enters into the expressive whole of the story we find the deep satisfaction, conscious or unconscious, of a fulfillment of our very nature.

As an example of the relation of words, of style, to the expressive whole which is fiction, let us take Hemingway. We readily see how the stripped, laconic, monosyllabic style relates to the tight-lipped, stoical ethic, the cult of self-discipline, the physicality and the anti-intellectualism and the other such elements that enter into his characteristic view of the world. Imagine Henry James writing Hemingway's story *The Killers*. The complicated sentence structure of James, the deliberate and subtle rhythms, the careful parentheses—

all these things express the delicate intellectual, social and aesthetic discriminations with which James concerned himself. But what in the Lord's name would they have to do with the shocking blankness of the moment when the gangsters enter the lunchroom, in their tight-buttoned identical blue overcoats, with gloves on their hands so as to leave no fingerprints when they kill the Swede?

The style of a writer represents his stance toward experience, toward the subject of his story; and it is also the very flesh of our experience of the story, for it is the flesh of our experience as we read. Only through his use of words does the story come to us. And with language, so with the other aspects of a work of fiction. Everything there—the proportioning of plot, the relations among the characters, the logic of motivation, the speed or retardation of the movement —is formed by a human mind into what it is, into what, if the fiction is successful, is an expressive whole, a speaking pattern, a form. And in recognizing and participating in this form, we find a gratification, though often an unconscious one, as fundamental as any we have mentioned.

We get a hint of the fundamental nature of this gratification in the fact that among primitive peoples decorative patterns are developed long before the first attempts to portray the objects of nature, even those things on which the life of the tribe depended. The pattern images a rhythm of life and intensifies the tribesman's sense of life.

Or we find a similar piece of evidence in psychological studies made of the response of children to comic books. "It is not the details of development," the researchers tell us, "but rather the general aura which the child finds fascinating." What the child wants is the formula of the accelerating buildup of tension followed by the glorious release when the righteous Superman appears just in the nick of time. What the child wants, then, is a certain "shape" of experience. Is his want, at base, different from our own?

ADDING TO LIFE'S RHYTHM

At base, no. But if the child is satisfied by a nearly abstract pattern for the feelings of tension and release, we demand much more. We, too, in the build and shape of experience, catch the echo of the basic rhythm of our life. But we know that the world is infinitely more complicated than the child thinks. We, unlike the child, must scrutinize the details of development, the contents of life and of fiction. So the shaping of experience to satisfy us must add to the simplicity that satisfies the child something of the variety, roughness, difficulty, subtlety and delight which belongs to the actual business of life and our response to it. We want the factual richness of life absorbed into the pattern so that content and form are indistinguishable in one expressive flowering in the process that John Dewey says takes "life and experience in all its uncertainties, mystery, doubt and half-knowledge and turns that experience upon itself to deepen and intensify its own qualities." Only then will it satisfy our deepest need— the need of feeling our life to be, in itself, significant.

The Short Story

As a short story can be as short as 50 words and a novel as long as 1,000,000 words, and, even more significant, as on occasion a short story may be longer than a novel (or novelette), you will understand that definitions based on mere word count are necessarily arbitrary; more pertinent is the writer's purpose or intent. A short story tells a tale in one way, and a novel tells it in another way. One of the earliest analyses of the short story form, Edgar Allan Poe's review of Hawthorne's *Twice-Told Tales*, touches upon this point:

> A skillful literary artist has constructed a tale. If wise, he has not fashioned his thoughts to accommodate his incidents; but having conceived, with deliberate care, a certain unique or single *effect* to be wrought out, he then invents such incidents—he then combines such events as may best aid him in establishing this preconceived effect. If his very initial sentence tends not to the outbringing of this effect, then he has failed in his first step. In the whole composition there should be no word written, of which the tendency, direct or indirect, is not to the one pre-established design. And by such means, with such care and skill, a picture is at length painted which leaves in the mind of him who contemplates it with a kindred art, a sense of the fullest satisfaction.[1]

William Faulkner also suggests that the difference between the short story and the novel is one of kind and not of size: "Maybe every novelist wants to write poetry first, finds he can't, and then tries the short story, which is the most demanding form after poetry. And, failing at that, only then does he take up novel writing."

Professor Robert Adams, in a recent review, had this to say about the term *short story:*

> Of all the ridiculous critical categories—"short story"—as if there were something in a mere word count which entitled one to bundle together parables and sketches, fantasies and fables, romances, burlesques, narrations, satires, character studies, moralities, enigmas (not to mention all the subject categories—mystery stories, love stories, adventure stories, ghost stories, *ad infinitum*) indiscriminately. Yet, if only as a nondescript, catch-all phrase, the term "short story" is probably inevitable[. . .]

Even so, the critical analyses that follow will seek to define the short story and to clarify those distinctions in treatment or development between the short story and the novel. H. E. Bates and Walter Havighurst are primarily addressing readers and students; Eudora Welty is addressing story writers.

1. *The Works of Edgar Allan Poe*, Stedman and Woodbury, eds., Chicago, 1896, Vol. VII.

H. E. Bates

DEFINING THE SHORT STORY

THE history of the novel is short: covering only, if we date its invention from Richardson, a period of two hundred years. The history of the short story, through its phases of myth and legend, fable and parable, anecdote and pictorial essay, sketch, and even down to what the crudest provincial reporter calls "a good story," cannot be measured. The account in Genesis of the conflict between Cain and Abel is a short story; the parable of the Prodigal Son is a short story, and in itself a masterpiece of compression for all time; the stories of Salome, Ruth, Judith, and Susannah are all examples of an art that was already old, civilized, and highly developed some thousands of years before the vogue of *Pamela*. At what date, then, shall we begin an examination of its history? The paradoxical answer is that the history of the short story, as we know it, is not vast but very brief. "The short story proper," says Mr. A. J. J. Ratcliff, "that is, a deliberately fashioned work of art, and not just a straightforward tale of one or more events, belongs to modern times"; "the short story is a young art," says Miss Elizabeth Bowen, "as we know it, it is a child of this century"; to this I shall only add an earlier judgment of my own that "the history of the English short story is very brief, for the simple reason that before the end of the nineteenth century it had no history." [. . .]

The basis of almost every argument or conclusion I can make is the axiom that the short story can be anything the author decides it shall be; it can be anything from the death of a horse to a young girl's first love affair, from the static sketch without plot to the swiftly moving machine of bold action and climax, from the prose poem, painted rather than written, to the piece of straight reportage in which style, colour, and elaboration have no place, from the piece which catches like a cobweb the light subtle iridescence of emotions that can never be really captured or measured to the solid tale in which all emotion, all action, all reaction is measured, fixed, puttied, glazed, and finished, like a well-built house, with three coats of shining and enduring paint. In that infinite flexibility, indeed, lies the reason why the short story has never been adequately defined.

Many definitions have been, and always are being, attempted. Wells defined the short story as any piece of short fiction that could be read in half an hour. Poe, sometimes acclaimed its modern originator, declared that "in the whole composition there should be no word written, of which the tendency, direct or indirect, is not to one pre-established design." Chekhov held that a story should have neither beginning nor end, but reminded authors that if they described a gun hanging on the wall on page one, sooner or later that gun must go off. Mr. John Hadfield describes the short story as "a story that is not long." The late Sir Hugh Walpole, in a moment of truly remarkable perception, asserted that "a story should be a story: a record of things happening, full of incident and

From "The Modern Short Story" by H. E. Bates from *The Writer*. Reprinted by permission of the publishers.

accident, swift movement, unexpected development, leading through suspense to a climax and a satisfying dénouement." Jack London declared that it should be "concrete, to the point, with snap and go and life, crisp and crackling and interesting." Miss Elizabeth Bowen, rightly wary of the concrete definition, says, "the first necessity of the short story, at the set out, is *necessariness*. The story, that is to say, must spring from an impression or perception pressing enough, acute enough, to have made the writer write." The late E. J. O'Brien, to whom the short story in Britain and America owes an unpayable debt, holds that "the first test of a short story, in any qualitative analysis, is the measure of how vitally compelling the writer makes his selected facts or incidents." Mr. Ellery Sedgewick, who pounced on the genius of Hemingway's *Fifty Grand* when that story had been rejected by half the editors of America, holds that "a story is like a horse race. It is the start and finish that count most." Finally, Mr. A. E. Coppard bases the whole theory of his work on the essential difference between a story, as something which is written, and a tale, as something which is told.

All of these definitions have one thing in common. None of them has a satisfactory finality; none defines the short story with an indisputable epigrammatic accuracy which will fit all short stories. For Chekhov, the craftsman, beginning and end do not matter; for Mr. Sedgewick, the editor, beginning and end are everything. Yet both are right. Mr. Hadfield's definition will fit a thousand stories yet fail to account satisfactorily for *Death in Venice*, *Family Happiness*, or *The Gentleman from San Francisco*. Sir Hugh Walpole's definition will do admirably for a work by O. Henry but fails miser-

ably on application to Chekhov's *The Darling*, Mrs. Malachi Whitaker's *Frost in April*, or the unpredictable sketches of Mr. Saroyan. One does not measure the beauty of landscape with a tape measure. Jack London's demand for a concoction with "snap and go and life" is a perfect answer for those who like whisky, but it will be lost on those whose taste has been educated to the bouquet of Turgenev or James Joyce's *The Dead*. It is only when Mr. Ellery Sedgewick asserts, in his extremely perceptive essay written for American schools, "So it is that the short story has become all sorts of things, situation, episode, characterization, or narrative—in effect a vehicle for every man's talent," that we come back again to the sensible conclusion that the short story, whether short or long, poetical or reported, plotted or sketched, concrete or cobweb, has an insistent and eternal fluidity that slips through the hands.

This is, and has always been, my own view. The impression that the short story has something of the indefinite and infinitely variable nature of a cloud is one which sooner or later must be forced on anyone who not only reads, but attempts to break down analytically, the work of writers differing so vastly as Turgenev and Hemingway, Sherwood Anderson and O. Henry, George Moore and Stephen Crane, Kipling and Katherine Mansfield. Is the cumulus or the cirrus more beautiful? The thunder-cloud or the flotilla of feathers? The calm blue and white of noon, or the savagery of sunset? There is no definition, no measure, which will aptly contain the structure, effect, and beauty of them all. As the sky is not made of bricks, so it is worth remembering that stories are not put together with plumb-line and trowel.

There is one other thing which these many and varied definitions all have in common. All omit to point out the advantages of elasticity, in both choice of character and use of time, which the short story holds over the novel. The novel is predominantly an exploration of life: reflecting and describing in some form the impact, entanglement, fruition, destruction or fulfilment of human emotions and desires. "Characters begin young; they grow old; they move from scene to scene, from place to place," said Virginia Woolf. This development of character, this forward movement of time, have always been and perhaps always will be the pulse and nerve of the novel. But in the short story time need not move, except by an infinitesimal fraction; the characters themselves need not move; they need not grow old; indeed there may be no characters at all. A novel without characters would be a tiresome affair; but a novel with characters who never spoke a word would surely be more tiresome still. Yet many a good short story has characters who never open their lips. A novel whose characters were never named, whose location and time were never stated, might well impose on its readers a strain that they would justifiably refuse to bear. Yet many a short story has characters which bear no more marks of identification than the anonymous and universal label of "boy" or "girl," "man" or "woman," "the traveller" or "the commercial traveller," "the barmaid" or "the soldier," and no more topographical exactitude than "the street," "the field," "the room," or any seashore between Brighton and Botany Bay.

"The Novel," said Edward Garnett, "can be anything according to the hands which use it"—a truth far more widely applicable to the short story. For the short story remains plastic, and continues to increase its plasticity, as long as human nature remains the infinitely plastic and variable thing it is. In the 'nineties Kipling was writing of India from a viewpoint that was so popular and so widely endorsed that it might well have seemed, to the Empire-drunken Britisher of the day, to give the only right and proper view; in 1940 young native Indian writers have something to say of their own country from a viewpoint so unsuspected, so unheard of, and so real that Kipling seems guilty of nothing but plain falsification. Again in the 'nineties, when O. Henry was performing elaborate conjuring tricks with an amazing collection of comic human paraphernalia and the result was accepted with the same universal applause as Kipling had enjoyed, who could have guessed that fifty years later a young American-Armenian named Saroyan would demonstrate how a conjuring trick could be performed without any human paraphernalia at all, but with only a pair of eyes, a typewriter, and a handkerchief to dry his tears?

In its various stages of development the short story has frequently been compared with some other literary form, sometimes with some artistic form outside literature. It is thus declared to have affinities with the drama; with the narrative ballad; with the lyric and the sonnet. In the last thirty years it has shown itself, as in fact much other writing has, to be pictorial rather than dramatic, to be more closely allied to painting and the cinema than to the stage. Mr. A. E. Coppard has long cherished the theory that short story and film are expressions of the same art, the art of telling a story by a series of subtly implied gestures, swift shots, moments of suggestion, an art in which elaboration and above all explanation are superfluous and tedious. Miss

Elizabeth Bowen advances the same idea:

> The short story . . . in its use of action is nearer to the drama than to the novel. The cinema, itself busy with a technique, is of the same generation: in the last thirty years the two arts have been accelerating together. They have affinities—neither is sponsored by a tradition; both are, accordingly, free; both, still, are self-conscious, show a self-imposed discipline and regard for form; both have, to work on, immense matter—the disorientated romanticism of the age.

This is strikingly true. Indeed the two arts have not only accelerated together but have, consciously or not, taught each other much. The scrap of dirty paper blown by wind along the empty morning street, a girl sewing, on a railway station, the tear in her lover's jacket and he hiding it by holding up a suitcase, a mother staring dumbly at her returned gangster son—these tiny moments, seen as it were telescopically, brightly focused, unelaborated and unexplained, stamp swiftly on the mind the impressions of desolation, embarrassed love, or maternal despair. Each moment implies something it does not state; each sends out a swift brief signal on a certain emotional wave-length, relying on the attuned mental apparatus of the audience to pick it up.

That audience, it seems to me, becomes of increasingly greater importance; but more important still, I feel, becomes the attitude of writer or director towards that audience. Are its powers of reception and perception to be consistently underestimated? In a process of under-estimation what happens? At the extreme a writer takes a character and describes not only his physique, his weight, his moustache and glasses, but also his clothes, his manner, and his mannerisms, his taste in food and drink, all in minute detail—in order to eliminate any possibility, it seems, of his being confused with the clothes-prop.

This, a century ago, and indeed with some writers for long afterwards, was the accepted convention. Dickens, artist though he was, played throughout novel after novel, with gusto and brilliance, this game of underestimating the reader: so much so that he not only described every character by the system of catalogue but, in many cases, and because he was often writing a serial story that was to be read in parts, reissued that catalogue after an interval in which he judged the reader might have forgotten what goods were for sale.

This was all very well, and in many cases delightful fun, in a novel of 200,000 words; but to apply the same method to the short story was rather like dressing a six-months-old baby in a top-hat and fur coat, with the inevitable result—suffocation. Hence, I think, the languishing of the short story in England throughout the first three-quarters of the nineteenth century, when no single writer applied to it a technique different from that of the novel; and its gradual emergence, accelerated during the last thirty years, as a separate form addressed to a reader who was presumed to be able to take many previously elaborated things such as physical descriptions for granted.

The evolution of the short story may therefore, I think, have something to do with the evolution of the general reader. We must be wary of condemning Dickens, when it would be more just, perhaps, to condemn an age more confined to compartments of class, place, and prejudice than our own. Dickens, often publishing a novel in monthly parts, found it necessary to devote some hundreds of words, and if necessary repeat those words a month later, to a single character. In 1920 Sherwood Anderson remarked simply that "she was a tall silent woman with a long nose and troubled gray eyes"; in 1930 Mr. Ernest Hemingway in a moment, for him, of unusual expansion, said, "He wore a derby hat and a black overcoat buttoned across his chest. His face was small and white and he had tight lips. He wore a silk muffler and gloves." In 1940 Mr. V. S. Pritchett writes, "He had a cape on, soaked with rain, and the rain was in beads in his hair. It was fair hair. It stood up on end."

Anderson took up fourteen words, Mr. Hemingway thirty-one, Mr. Pritchett twenty-six. Between Dickens and Mr. Pritchett, then, something has happened. Is it only the evolution of the short story? May it not also be, perhaps, the parallel evolution of the reader? Education, travel, wider social contact, the increased uniformity of life, dress, and manners have made us all familiar with things that were once remote enough to need to be described. To-day all of us have seen Sherwood Anderson's woman, the tragic, anonymous representative of a whole inarticulate class; we have seen Mr. Hemingway's tough with the black overcoat and bowler hat; we know Mr. Pritchett's type with its fair hair that stands up on end. The widening of social contact, among other things, has relieved these three writers, and their generation, of an oppressive obligation. It is no longer necessary to describe; it is enough to suggest. The full-length portrait, in full dress, with scenic background, has become superfluous; now it is enough that we should know a woman by the shape of her hands.

In this way the short story can be seen not as a product evolved by generations of writers united in a revolutionary intention to get the short story more simply, more economically, and more truthfully written, but as something shaped also by readers, by social expansion, and by what Miss Bowen calls "peaks of common experience." For there has not been, and rarely is, any such united revolution among writers. Writers work, die, and leave legacies. Other writers draw on those inheritances, as Katherine Mansfield did on Chekhov's, and in turn leave others. But in their turn, too, readers live and perhaps succeed in raising, by an infinitely small fraction, the level of common experience and artistic receptivity. To that level the short story must adjust itself.

Walter Havighurst

THE RANGE OF THE SHORT STORY

A SHORT story is an exploration of a point of interest in the course of experience. In the flow of life there are unhurried currents and slowly gathering tides. The short story cannot trace these deliberate movements with the complex play of forces—physical, social, and psychological—that hasten and retard them. But there are points at which experience rises to some crest of interest, like the crest of a sea; here is the moment of the short story. It deals with a point of experience that is crucial and revealing.

Four hundred years ago Sir Philip Sidney spoke of "a tale which holdeth children from play, and old men from the chimney corner." Much has changed in the world since Sidney wrote his *Defence of Poesy*, but stories still have this lifelong spell. Fiction appeals to two ancient and lasting desires: the desire for delight and the desire for meaning. Like all other artists, the short-story writer offers delight; he pictures experience in its endless color and variety. A story has form—beginning, development, outcome—and it has its appropriate mood and atmosphere. These qualities contribute to the pleasure of reading; they give delight. But a story offers something more. It deals with questions of good and evil, of strength and weakness, of success and failure. It contains truth.

The story writer looks at experience with endless curiosity and with constant reflection. He shows where life is well lived and where it is poorly lived, where it contains prob-lems and perplexities, where it finds fulfillment. In the story, meaning is enriched by delight, as delight is increased by the presence of meaning; the two are inseparable. A dull and lifeless story has little chance of making its meaning felt; a skillful and absorbing story needs some significance to make its appeal complete. Conrad once said to Galsworthy: "Whatever you do people look beyond your art to your ideas." The realization of this dual nature of the story, coming to her early in her career, led Katherine Mansfield to say: "They believe I can only write satire, but I'm not a very satiric person really. I believe in something. Let's call it Truth. Truth is a big thing—a very big thing. We have to discover it—that's what the artist is for, to become true by discovering truth. Truth is so important that when you discover it, you forget about everything else—and all about yourself."

The short story, then, is experience portrayed so as to reveal its meaning. Truth is implicit in the story's action, lurking in it, accompanying it like a shadow. The story is a sharply focused glimpse of experience—warm, alive, and urgent. But the picture of life is not complete without its implicit meaning. James Branch Cabell once explained that a writer's task is to take the reader from the blinding confusion of the street into the darkness and quiet of a theater where he tries to explain, concisely and quietly, the meaning of the chaos outside. The story, therefore, is a paradox. It uses clarity to reveal the world's confu-

From the Introduction to *Masters of the Modern Short Story*, Brief Edition, edited by Walter E. Havighurst, copyright 1945, 1955 by Harcourt, Brace & World, Inc. Reprinted by permission of the publishers.

sion; it employs unity to show life's complexity. It selects and simplifies, making its people and their actions suggest something more general than themselves. The story happens once, in one time and place, to one set of persons, but its meaning widens out to many other situations. The story joins incident and reflection. It tells of a limited happening and of an unlimited meaning which that happening embodies.

The world's first stories were fables—arresting, shrewd, meaningful. Their meaning added to their delight, and the fables with most meaning were best remembered. See the difference in the two primitive stories below—two very short, very simple beast fables.

In the woods of Upper Michigan the Chippewa Indians told a legend: "Once there was a young wolf cub that climbed a hill and stared all around at the horizon. After he had looked awhile he began to wonder how big the world was and what lay at the end of it. Soon he set out. He loped over plains and prairies. He crept through thickets and trotted through forests and climbed the steep sides of mountains. He drank out of rivers and went thirsty in arid places. He pressed on, day after day, season after season, and at last he died of old age. He had not found the end."

What does this story say? It says that America is a huge and varied country. Though the wolf is personified, he does not express human motives and emotions beyond a vague curiosity. He is merely a means of measuring the extent of a wilderness country.

From ancient Persia came this fable: "A fox awoke one morning and saw his shadow huge on the desert sand. He was hungry and he said, 'I shall have a camel for breakfast.' So he set out. He loped over the land,

hour after hour, looking for camels. But he never found one. By noon he was tired and he stopped to rest. Looking down, he saw his tiny midday shadow on the sand. He said, 'A mouse will do.' "

What does this story say? It says that youth has bold anticipations which maturity surrenders. It shows intention defeated by effort and hope mocked by reality. It makes an ironical statement about human character and experience. The wolf story is about the huge extent of America: the woods and mountains, the rivers and deserts are literal, and the journey of the wolf is a literal search for the literal limit of the land. In the fox story the details are figurative: morning is youth, noon is maturity, the camel is great expectations, the mouse is reality. It is a wholly symbolic tale.

Every age must write its own books and its own stories, and beast fables are rarely written now. The modern story shows believable people in the midst of recognizable experience, and beyond that verisimilitude the story contains some significant appraisal of the human condition. It is a representation of life accompanied by a reflection about it. Its action casts a shadow of meaning.

A writer makes his story significant by presenting human problems Always people are perplexed, sometimes they are bewildered and hard-beset, and when he touches these problems a writer touches the reader's interest and concern. The world has an abundance of problems, but not all are equally pertinent at all times. Early in this century Jack London wrote a stark story about an Alaskan miner on the frozen trail, whose numb fingers could not strike a match to make a fire. That elemental problem—how to survive in a hostile world of nature —while of lasting human interest is not a pressing concern of most readers today. Our struggle is not with Arctic cold but with the perverse human self and its social involvement. [. . .]

Long after the incidents of a story are forgotten [. . .] we remember the problem around which the story has unfolded. [. . .] Once James Branch Cabell had a feeling that if he should rise from his study chair and look out the window as far as the Mill Road, he might see, passing away from him and traveling in motley companionship through the gray March weather, all the various people whose lives he had fashioned in his books. They were not all admirable, but all had been at some time of intense interest to him. He understood their joys, and, even more, he understood their struggles and failures—it was his characters who had the hardest problems whom he could best remember.

In presenting human problems a writer enlarges the significance of his story by making it representative. Any writer of fiction knows that all persons are distinct, separate, individual. But he also knows that these separate persons have similar joys and sorrows, hopes and fears, struggles and aspirations. This knowledge leads a story writer to present the experience of an imaginary person so that it resembles the lives of many actual people. Though his characters are distinctly individual, they are at the same time representative. [. . .]

In Ernest Hemingway's "The Undefeated" the veteran bullfighter is a definite character; from the first paragraph of the story he is undeniably distinct and individual. But his experience and attitudes are not unique. His past success, his recent injury, his determination to try again are to be found, in various terms, in many people's experience. Manuel Garcia, with the wounds of his pro-

fession and the pigtail that is his proud badge of bullfighting, is any man who chooses to live (and die) on his own terms. A reader cannot fail to see in the life and death of this "undefeated" bullfighter a code of conduct which may belong to persons who have never seen a bull ring. Manuel Garcia's story is dramatic and singular; at the same time it represents the experience of all who face great odds and win an inward victory. [. . .]

Imaginative writing often appeals to a reader on two levels; beneath the literal statement there is a figurative meaning. When a poet says: "We've each a darkening hill to climb," it is clear that he is not talking about topography. Similarly a short-story writer frequently makes use of symbols. It is only a step from the creation of representative character and situation to the creation of symbols. Indeed, a symbol is a specific and pointed representation in which a material object, like a hill, stands for something immaterial, like difficulty; or a specific detail, like morning, conveys an abstract idea, like youth. [. . .] Again and again the story writer persuades a reader to see as he sees, to view as symbol what might be regarded as bare fact. [. . .]

A story's ultimate symbolism is the story itself—the entire story casting an enlarging shadow of meaning. After reading Stephen Crane's "The Open Boat," Conrad said: "The deep and simple humanity of its presentation seems somehow to illustrate the essentials of life itself, like a symbolic tale." He was not referring to the sea, or the wave-tossed dinghy, or the injured captain, or the oiler who died in the furious surf; he was thinking of the entire story as existing on two levels—real and symbolic. The tale of shipwrecked men struggling to reach shore is a symbolic account of humanity's struggle to endure in the vast and indifferent world. Because he meant his own "Youth" to be such a symbolic tale Conrad objected to calling it a sea-story. The sea is its circumstance, but the story is a portrayal of the genius of youth for transmuting hardship and peril into glamour and romance. [. . .] In such ways as these the story writer becomes a maker of metaphor.

One of William Faulkner's most familiar stories, the often-reprinted short version of "The Bear," contains an unusually candid statement of the writer's double interest in explicit event and implicit meaning. After the fierce and chivalrous bear hunt, following his encounter with the enormous bear, the boy comes into his father's study. His father crosses the room in the spring twilight and takes down a book from the shelves. "Listen," he says, and in his quiet, deliberate voice he reads the five stanzas of a poem by John Keats about the figures on an antique Grecian urn. The boy waits, and at the end his father says again, "Listen," and he reads again: "She cannot fade, though thou hast not thy bliss; for ever wilt thou love, and she be fair."

That poem seems far indeed from a bear hunt, or anything else that concerns him, and the boy is puzzled. He says, "He's talking about a girl." His father explains: "He had to talk about something." (Something, he seemed to imply, more specific than the unattainable in human experience which forever mocks the attained.) Then the father says, "He was talking about truth. Truth doesn't change. It covers all things which touch the heart—honor and pride and pity and justice and courage and love. Do you see now?"

The boy does not exactly see. He feels it is simpler than that. He prefers to go back to the hunt itself—and

this is like going from the theme of a story to its living incident.

—There was an old bear, fierce and ruthless, not merely just to stay alive, but with the fierce pride of liberty and freedom, proud enough of the liberty and freedom to see it threatened without fear or even alarm; nay who at times even seemed deliberately to put that freedom and liberty in jeopardy in order to savor them, to remind his old strong bones and flesh to keep supple and quick to defend and preserve them. There was an old man, son of a Negro slave and an Indian king, inheritor on one side of the long chronicle of a people who had learned humility through suffering, and pride through the endurance which survived the suffering and injustice, and on the other side, the chronicle of a people even longer in the land than the first, yet who no longer existed in the land at all save in the solitary brotherhood of an old Negro's alien blood and the wild and invincible spirit of an old bear. There was a boy who wished to learn humility and pride in order to become skillful and worthy in the woods, who suddenly found himself becoming so skillful so rapidly that he feared he would never become worthy because he had not learned humility and pride, although he had tried to, until one day and as suddenly he discovered that an old man who could not have defined either had led him, as though by the hand, to that point where an old bear and a little mongrel of a dog showed him that, by possessing one thing other, he would possess them both. . . .

That was all. It was simple, much simpler than somebody talking in a book about youth and a girl he would never need to grieve over, because he could never approach any nearer her and would never have to get any farther away. He had heard about a bear, and finally got big enough to trail it, and he trailed it four years and at last met it with a gun in his hands and he didn't shoot. Because a little dog— But he could have shot long before the little dog covered the twenty yards to where the bear waited, and Sam Fathers could have shot at any time during that interminable minute while Old Ben stood on his hind feet over them. He stopped. His father was watching him gravely across the spring-rife twilight of the room; when he spoke his words were as quiet as the twilight, too, not loud, because they did not need to be because they would last. "Courage and honor and pride," his father said, "and pity, and love of justice and of liberty. They all touch the heart, and what the heart holds to becomes truth, as far as we know the truth. Do you see now?"

Sam, and Old Ben, and Nip, he thought. And himself too. He had been all right too. His father had said so. "Yes, sir," he said.

So at last the boy does see. The incident has found its meaning, and from this hour the two will be inseparable in his memory.

One reason for the perennial appeal of this story is that here Faulkner has suggested how all literature uses things seen to call up things unseeable. The hunt for the huge, primordial bear is not merely a metaphor in itself; it becomes the occasion for pointing out that all stories "have to talk about something" while they are concerned with something beyond. Truth is not confined to a youth and a girl he could never overtake, or a boy and a bear he could never kill. But it can be glimpsed and grasped only in particular human instances like these.

[. . .] The story writer embodies truth in people (from which all meaning must come), giving it the warmth and vitality of human experience; he uses specific incidents to symbolize universal conditions of life. That method of conveying truth can be considered indirect, or it can be considered the most concrete and direct method possible. At any rate, it is the storyteller's way.

Eudora Welty

ON SHORT STORIES

THE first thing to say is that I owe you one promise: you'll forget anything I as another writer have had to say as soon as you begin your next story, if not sooner. This is exactly as it should be. In fact the whole nature of my remarks will be—Don't worry. There is much advice going around about writing, but when you come to the actual writing yourself—doesn't your experience match mine?—no memory outside your own story's needs will come to you, and if it does, you had better push it away. Your story will have hold of you and everything else will touch you and tag you in vain. When we are in the act of writing we are alone and on our own, in a kind of absolute state of Do Not Disturb.

And our experience tells us further that each story is a specific thing, never a general thing—never. The words in the story we're writing now might as well never have been used before. They all shine. Stories are *new* things, stories make words new; that is one of their illusions and part of their beauty. The rest of the world —talk, criticism, conferences—all that will be old, and our story new. And of course the great stories of the world are the ones that seem new to their readers besides their writers, on and on, always new because they keep their power of revealing something.

But although all stories in the throes of being written seem new and although good stories are new and persist, there'll always be some characteristics and some functions about them as old as time, as human nature itself, to keep them more or less alike, of a family; and there may be other things, undiscovered yet, in the language, in technique, in the world's body of knowledge, to change them out of our present recognition. Critics, historians, and scholars deal with these affairs—and keep good track of them—while for us, the practitioners, the writing of stories seems to simmer down—between stories—into some generalities that are, we all think from time to time, worth talking about.

Between stories—yes, that's when we can talk.

They are entirely different states, composing a story and talking about the composing of stories. Makers of jelly will know what we mean and may feel with us. When the pot is cooking along, simmering, there's the generality, and there's time to gaze in and dip up and match experiences and speculate how this batch is going to turn out and the state of blackberries this year. But when it boils up! Then there's your state of active composing—there's a cauldron of heat and energy on your hands, and there's only one thing to do, attend to that jelly on the fire—do what's needed the best you can, get it tested and poured out in the glasses, and at the right instant, or you'll be sorry. It's changed from a matter of dreaming along and thinking of jelly—just jelly, abstractly—to a matter of now or never. A condition of crisis is at hand; and out of the past—hearsay or experience—a *practical* knowledge is all you can really use. That is, somebody could have told you to use a safer kind of test at one point, somebody else could have warned you how to keep the glasses from breaking, somebody can always come along and say "I'd have added a little lemon juice"—but that's about as far as outside aid can come—little things. Household hints.

High principled persons here will say, But what about Communication? Get back on a higher level. How can you speak of jelly-making in the same breath with writing a story? Communication? Yes, I think we write stories in the ultimate hope of communication, but so do we make jelly in that hope. Communication and hope of it are conditions of life itself. Let's take that for granted, and not get sidetracked by excitement. We hope somebody will taste our jelly and eat it with even more pleasure than it deserves and ask for another helping— no more can we hope for in writing a story. Always in the back of our heads and in our hearts are such hopes, and attendant fears that we may fail—we do everything out of the energy of some form of love or desire to please. The writing of a story uses the *power* of this love or hope, of course, and not its simple, surface form such as comes out—rather nicely—in jelly making.

During the writing of a story, all the energy we have is put to pressure and reaches a changed-over state—so as to act for the sole and concentrated purpose of making our work excellent and to the pattern of some preconceived idea we have of beauty. The escape or diffusion of this energy will, in the long run, prevent our story from communicating, in the degree that it prevents it from being pure, or our own.

But the practical problems of the story at hand are, on the whole, minutiae. We could call them the problem of How the Old Woman Got Home. With much sweat, maybe, and by burning much light, we get her there—only in the next story to have to get her there again. The little things, that plague and absorb us in every story, never let up. There, help is possible. And that they are little things explains, possibly, how it is that we can shed such problems so entirely once a story is done. Who remembers afterwards the nuisance of counting the children, or preparing the reader (if necessary) for the murder, or getting the moon in the right part of the sky? They aren't truly important problems, and patience is the answer—time and patience. (Time, I think, by the way, one of the important components of a story—give it its time and on the greater issues.) The little things get worked out—successfully or unsuccessfully, and possibly with the aid of outside criticism—and then they're done. One story's prob-

lem is no more than a nuisance. To get at general problems we have to go deeper, in fact, the deepest we can go, into the act of writing itself.

On subjects like this, we can all express ourselves as blithely as critics and be as happy as kings—as though we had authority. We have. For the whole thing is subjective. All any of us can *know* about writing is what it seems like to us. It's not an imitative process. And I don't mean it's a holy estate—one perspires too much—but it's private.

Direct connection is all we have with short stories—reading and writing them. It is not ours to note influences, trace histories, and consider trends. We are in the thick of stories by being personally and directly concerned with them. It is from this close, unromantic, perhaps much less sure and much more passionate point of view, that we writers gaze at the art of the short story.

If we learn mostly little things from correction—from critics—do we learn the big things by doing? I think it the only way, but not an infallible way. That is, there is nothing that will guarantee our writing a better story next time than the one we just finished. We will have passed through the experience of writing a story—we will have meditated some, our perceptions will have been put to use somewhat, and our senses will have garnered things in, and we will carry around on our faces the telltale glow that follows all effort and pleasure—so we could "call ourselves" learning, as we say in my part of the country. At any rate, here's a story, the evidence of something we went through, and if our judgment is clear and steady, we can, at last, see our story out in the world—an object apart from ourselves—a good one or a bad one—in new light. This is more accurate than to say we've learned more about writing itself. Some first stories remain a writer's best work. We work by the story—by the piece. The next story will always be a different thing. There are no two days alike—time moves. There are no two stories alike—*our* time moves. We were in one story and now we are in another —two worlds—and there are many more, though the thought neither helps nor hinders us any in the one where we now struggle.

How do we write a story?

Our own way.

Beyond that, I think it's hard to assign a process to it. There is one great fact [. . .] —we all know it, it's this: that the mind in writing a story is in the throes of imagination, and it is not in the calculations of analysis. [. . .] The mind [. . .] creates in imagination, and it tears down in analysis.

The two ways of working have a great way of worrying the life out of each other. But why can't they both go their ways in peace?

Let's not, to begin with, deny the powers and achievements of good criticism. That would be smug, ignorant, and blind. Story criticism can seem blind itself, when it is ingrown and tedious; on the other hand it can see things in large wholes and in subtle relationships we should be only stupid not to investigate. It can illuminate and reveal, even though in the face of all its achievements, its business is not: to tell *how*. [. . .]

I feel like saying as a friend, to beginning writers—don't be unduly worried by the analyses of stories you might see in some textbooks or critical articles. They are brilliant, no doubt useful to their own ends, but should not be alarming, for in a practical sense they just do not bear in a practical way on writing. To use my own case, that being the only one I can rightly speak of, I have been baffled by analysis and criticism of some of my stories. When I see these analyses—most usually, "reduced to elements"—sometimes I think, "This is none of me," like the old woman with her petticoat trimmed off. Not that I am too proud to like being reduced, especially—but that I could not remember *starting* with those elements—with anything that I could so label. The fact that a story will reduce to elements, can be analyzed, does not necessarily mean it started with them, certainly not consciously. A story can start with a bird song.

Criticism, or more strictly, analysis, is an impossible way to learn how the story was written. Analysis is a one-way process, and is only good after the event. In the newsreel pictures when the dive is shown in reverse, a swimmer can come back out of the water, the splash is swallowed up, he rises in the air and is safe and dry back on the diving board. But in truth you can't come by way of analysis back to the starting point of inspiration; that's against some law of the universe, it might almost seem, I myself lack a scientific upbringing; I hear the arrow of time exists, and I feel quite certain, by every instinct, so does the arrow of creation.

[. . .] You can't analyze a story back to its beginning and truly find thereby what the story started out to do, what then modified and determined it, and what eventually made it a superior story for instance and not just a good story? A story is not the same thing when it ends as it was when it began. Something happens—the writing of it. It *becomes*. And as a story becomes, I believe we as readers understand by becoming too—by enjoying.

The Short Story:
Critical Comments on Part One

So much for a critical analysis of the short story in general. There follows now a series of critical commentaries in which we shall observe how the techniques of critical analysis may be put to work to provide a close study of particular stories—and, inevitably, the authors of those stories. Under consideration here are nine of the stories appearing in Part One of this volume.

Newton Arvin

NATHANIEL HAWTHORNE

IT HAPPENS that we can follow part way the process of [Hawthorne's] art; from an early period Hawthorne, like James and Chekhov after him, had had the habit of keeping notebooks, and on these, when he came to write his tales, he constantly drew. We often find in them, therefore, what James would call the "germs" or "seeds" from which the stories, in their own good season, unfolded. We find, too, the seeds from which they did not unfold: the observations of real people, queer or humorsome or even ordinary individuals who, unlike those in Chekhov, rarely reappear in the tales; the overheard or communicated fragments of "true" stories out of real lives which, unlike those in James, almost never made the transition from hearsay to art. The germ of a typical Hawthorne tale is not a "real" individual or an actual and firsthand story—his imagination needed a further withdrawal from things than that—but either some curious passage that had quickened his fancy in his reading or some

abstractly phrased idea, moral or psychological, that he had arrived at in his endless speculative reveries.

He had been struck, to take an example of the first of these, by an anecdote about Gilbert Stuart which William Dunlap tells in his history of the fine arts in America. Stuart, according to Dunlap, had been commissioned by Lord Mulgrave to paint the portrait of his brother, General Phipps, on the eve of the General's sailing for India. When the portrait was finished and Mulgrave, for the first time, examined it, he broke out with an exclamation of horror: "What is this?—this is very strange!" "I have painted your brother as I saw him," said Stuart, and Mulgrave rejoined: "I see insanity in that face." Some time later the news reached England that Phipps, in India, had indeed gone mad and taken his own life by cutting his throat. The great painter, as Dunlap adds, had seen into a deeper reality behind the man's outward semblance, and with the insight of genius had painted that. Upon this hint Hawthorne wrote, and the result was "The Prophetic Pictures."

Consider, however, what he ends by doing with the hint. An anecdote, strange enough in itself and told for the sake of its deeper meaning, but naked and meager in circumstance and shape, has been worked over into an enriched and molded narrative, in which the original suggestion is only barely recognizable. Back into a remoter past goes the time of the action; back into a past which, as James would say, was "far enough away without being too far"; not the too recent past, at any rate, of Stuart himself, who had died less than ten years before and whose memory was much too fresh in men's minds. The tone of time is to count, but it is the tone of a dimmer time; and Hawthorne, with a few touches of his delicate, poetic erudition, evokes for us, only just fully enough, the simpler Boston of the mid-colonial day. The painter himself remains nameless and a little mythical; he has no actual counterpart in history—not in Smibert, certainly, nor Blackburn—and of course he could have none. As for his sitter, that sitter has become, to deepen the interest, two people, a young man and his bride: two lives, not merely one, are to be darkened and destroyed. The premonitions of madness, as in Dunlap, are to be detected in Walter Ludlow's countenance, but so too are the premonitions of passive suffering and all-enduring love in Elinor's. The painter himself, indeed, is to be involved in a way that did not hold for Stuart, but meanwhile the gloomy sequence of incidents moves from its natural prologue (the ordering of the portraits) to its first and second "acts"

(the painting and then the displaying of them) through its long interval of latency (the years of the painter's absence) to its scene of violent culmination (the painter's return and the onset of Walter's madness). Such was the form—carefully pictorial, narratively deliberate, in a derived sense dramatic—that Hawthorne worked out for himself in his most characteristic tales.

Dunlap's anecdote, however, has undergone a still more revealing metamorphosis. The "moral" of Hawthorne's actual story is not, as Dunlap's was, the great painter's power of seeing beyond the physical countenance into the mind and heart of the sitter, though Hawthorne does, with a deliberate turn of the ironic screw, put just that thought into Walter Ludlow's mouth. What interested him was not so much the sitters and their tragedy as the artist and his: for him the artist's power was always a potential and here an actual curse; his art might so easily become "an engrossing purpose" which would "insulate him from the mass of humankind," as this painter's does, and transform him indeed from the mere reader of men's souls into an agent of their destinies. Hawthorne's portraits here—like Hoffmann's in "Doge and Dogaressa," which he might have known, or like Gogol's in "The Portrait," which he certainly did not know—become the symbols not only of the artist's clairvoyance but of a malignant fatality of which he may be the guilty medium. Certainly Hawthorne shared with several of his contemporaries—Poe and Balzac are other examples—their delight in the use of paintings as poetic symbols.

Mary E. Dichmann

HAWTHORNE'S "PROPHETIC PICTURES"

THE theme which I shall first consider, since it first becomes evident to the reader, is Hawthorne's conception of the ideal artist, whom he presents as the painter of the prophetic pictures. Significantly, this character has no name; he is known merely as "the painter"—a title that implies him to be the quintessence of all painters and, by extension, of all artists. Furthermore, we know from the first paragraph of the tale, when Walter Ludlow eulogizes his accomplishments, that he is the epitome of all that is desirable in man:

"But this painter!" cried Walter Ludlow, with animation. "He not only excels in his peculiar art, but possesses vast acquirements in all other learning and science. He talks Hebrew with Dr. Mather, and gives lectures in anatomy to Dr. Boylston. In a word, he will meet the best instructed man among us on his own ground. Moreover, he is a polished gentleman—a citizen of the world—yes, a true cosmopolite; for he will speak like a native of each clime and country of the globe except our own forests, whither he is now going."

Because his "vast acquirements" have equipped the painter with tools for universal communication and understanding, he transcends the individual being and becomes a representation of the universal; he is a microcosm of the macrocosm, or—to use a juster image, and one that is a favorite with Hawthorne himself—a mirror in which all men and all women will find themselves reflected. Like a mirror, the artist "catches the secret sentiments and passions" of those whose portraits he paints; however, because of his power to strip the spirit of its physical mask and his ability to transfer to canvas the spiritual truth which he perceives, he also gives to them a "duration," an "earthly immortality," which a mirrored image does not achieve.* Thus, he so informs his creatures of paint and canvas with spiritual force that it is difficult for the observer "to separate the idea of life and intellect from such striking counterfeits." In the intense moment of creation, he has recreated the souls as well as the bodies of his originals, for, as he himself says of his art, "The artist—the true artist—must look beneath the exterior. It is his gift—his proudest, but often a melancholy one—to see the inmost soul, and, by a power indefinable even to himself, to make it glow or darken upon the canvas. . . ."

Just as the artist whom Hawthorne here presents has superhuman qualities, so is his act of artistic creation a superhuman act. It is, in fact, a godlike act, analogous to—if not a duplicate of—God's divine artistry in

"Hawthorne's 'Prophetic Pictures'" by Mary E. Dichmann from *American Literature*, May 1951. Reprinted by permission of Mary E. Dichmann and Duke University Press.

* It should also be noted that, according to Hawthorne, the painter was a mirror for natural objects as well as for human beings. We are told that "he had . . . lain in a canoe on the bosom of Lake George, making his soul the mirror of its loveliness and grandeur."

His creation of man.* Like Adam, who was first shaped of clay and then animated by the spirit, the painter's portraits assume first their physical and then their spiritual identities. We are told, for example, that, as the artist proceeds with the portraits of Walter and Elinor, their features begin to assume such vividness that they appear to be disengaged from the canvas. However, since the facial expressions of the portraits are as yet unfixed and "more vague than in most of the painter's works," we know that these shapes are only the lovers' "phantom selves," their unmeaningful physical likeness, not the abode of their spirits. Like God in creating Adam, the painter completes the physical details of his portraits before he inspires them with their souls. At the end of the last sitting, the portraits are still mere painted likenesses, but before the next day, when Walter and Elinor call to examine them, they have been given spiritual vitality.

An even more specific identification of the artist with the Divinity appears in the painter's apostrophe to art, in which he claims for the artist a creative power similar to the Creator's own:

"Oh glorious Art . . . thou art the image of the Creator's own. The innumerable forms that wander in nothingness start into being at thy beck. The dead live again. Thou recallest them to their old scenes, and givest their gray shadows the luster of a better life, at once earthly and immortal. Thou snatchest back the fleeting moments of History. With thee there is no Past; for, at thy touch, all that is great becomes forever present; and illustrious men live through long ages, in the visible performance of the very deeds which made them what they are. Oh potent Art! as thou bringest the faintly revealed Past to stand in that narrow strip of sunlight which we call Now, canst thou summon the shrouded Future to meet her there? Have I not achieved it? Am I not thy Prophet?"

Since the power to synthesize past, present, and future gives to the artist's vision an eternal validity and to the artist an omniscience which is normally attributed only to the mind of God, it is logical to assume in the artist the ability to use his knowledge in a Godlike fashion—in other words, to create, and to comprehend the past, the present, and the future in his creation.

Thus far we have considered chiefly the sunlit features of Hawthorne's artist, without pausing to reflect upon certain gloomy characteristics and dark potentialities that shadow his figure in ambiguities. The first of these is the suggestion that the painter's talents may be a sort of witchcraft, deriving from the "Black Man" rather than from God.† This hinted association of the painter with

---

* The completed portraits, the result of the painter's creative act, duplicated God's creations, a circumstance that again suggests the divine nature of art: "In most of the pictures, the whole mind and character were brought out on the countenance, and concentrated into a single look, so that, to speak paradoxically, the originals hardly resembled themselves so strikingly as the portraits did."

† "Some deemed it an offence against the Mosaic law, and even a presumptuous mockery of the Creator, to bring into existence such lively images of his creatures. Others, frightened at the art which could raise phantoms at will, and keep the form of the dead among the living, were inclined to consider the painter as a magician, or perhaps the famous Black Man, of old witch times, plotting mischief in a new guise."

the "Black Man" casts a doubt over the value of his vision for mankind: if it is satanic in its origins, its revelation of the universal truths which lie buried in material substance may lead men to evil rather than to good.

Another indication of the artist's potentialities for evil is his cold and analytic heart.* His art is to the painter a monomania that has stifled all his sympathies, all his warmth of feeling, and all his tenderness towards his fellows. His preoccupation is so great that his art has become more important in his eyes than God's creations, its prototype, and he has lost interest in the destiny of everything except his paintings. When he visits Walter and Elinor after his long absense, his thoughts are for the pictures, not for the human beings whose tragedy they prophesied: " 'The Portraits! Are they within?' inquired he of the domestic; then recollecting himself—'your master and mistress! Are they at home?' "

As Hawthorne has already indicated, this reversal of human values, this self-imposed isolation from actuality, may have resulted in the artist's becoming a madman rather than a prophet:

It is not good for man to cherish a solitary ambition. Unless there be those around him by whose example he may regulate himself, his thoughts, desires, and hopes will become extravagant, and he the semblance, perhaps the reality, of a madman. Reading other bosoms with an acuteness almost preternatural, the painter failed to see the disorder of his own.

To call the painter mad is, of course, to judge him by human values. In actuality, he lives apart from humanity on the plane of his own ideas, where he finds his meaningful existence, becoming there a synthesizing energy, a symbol for all artistic creativeness. This semi-abstract though potent being is to Hawthorne the quintessential artist and, as such, an ambiguous figure. Although his attributes are in themselves praiseworthy—a superhuman creativeness, a clear perception of eternal truth, and a gift of prophecy which derives from this perception—he is touched by a suggestion of diabolic madness, which implies that he may use them evilly. Hawthorne does not by explicit statement resolve the doubt which he raises concerning the relative malevolence or benignity of the artist's power. Instead, he places him in a social situation and then proceeds to study his influence on those whose lives he enters and to examine his responsibility to society.

2

The second problem to be considered in "The Prophetic Pictures," the relationship and responsibility of the

---

* The following description of the painter is frequently quoted to illustrate Hawthorne's fear of the cold isolation which, he felt, might prove to be the lot of every artist: "Like all other men around whom an engrossing purpose wreathes itself, he was insulated from the mass of human kind. He had no aim—no pleasure —no sympathies—but what were ultimately connected with his art. Though gentle in manner and upright in intent and action, he did not posses kindly feelings; his heart was cold; no living creature could be brought near enough to keep him warm. For these two beings [Walter and Elinor], however, he had felt, in its greatest intensity, the sort of interest which always allied him to the subjects of his pencil. He had pried into their souls with his keenest insight, and pictured the result upon their features with his utmost skill, so as barely to fall short of that standard which no genius ever reached, his own severe conception."

artist to society, is implicit in the narrative itself, through which the painter moves as a powerful but almost abstract force. In describing the artist, Hawthorne dwells upon the effect of his personality on the people of Boston and upon his impressive spiritual and mental qualities, ignoring almost entirely his physical appearance.* Furthermore, he tells us that the painter's countenance is "well worthy of his own pencil"—in fact, that it recalls one of his portraits, which are, after all, painted images, not creatures of flesh and blood. This hint of unreality about the painter reinforces our conception of him as a disembodied force, particularly when we remember that he is famous for painting the minds and hearts, rather than the features, of his subjects.

The two more solidly human characters of the tale are Walter Ludlow and Elinor, into whose lives the painter steps with what Hawthorne indicates may be the footfall of destiny. Nothing about them suggests abstraction. At the beginning of the story, Walter is presented as an excitable young man, given to sudden enthusiasms, such as the one which he develops for the painter, and inclined to an unreasoned half-belief in the superstitions of ignorant folk. Elinor, who is quiet in manner and reserved in her emotions, is the more sensitive of the two, her disposition to belief in the occult deriving from an intuitive perceptiveness rather than from a timorous ignorance. It is from Elinor that we learn, even before the artist has entered the lives of the two lovers, that her coming marriage, which appears superficially to be destined for happiness, may be overshadowed by evil. When Walter mentions the artist's ability to paint the souls as well as the bodies of his subjects, he is startled by Elinor's frightened look. She hastily dismisses his perplexed enquiry about what ails her, but she cannot dismiss the emotion that caused it:

> . . . when the young man had departed, it cannot be denied that a remarkable expression was again visible on the fair and youthful face of his mistress. It was a sad and anxious look, little in accordance with what should have been the feelings of a maiden on the eve of wedlock. Yet Walter Ludlow was the chosen of her heart.

Elinor then reflects that she should not be surprised at Walter's being startled by a look, because she remembers from her own experience "how frightful a look may be." Yet, she remarks, it may be that she is fanciful, for she has seen that look but once.

Walter's superstitious awe of the painter's talents and Elinor's fearful reluctance to face him prepare the reader for the portentous interest which their appearance arouses in the painter, who cancels appointments with two influential Bostonians in order to have time for their sittings. He feels, he says, that he "*must not lose this opportunity*, for the sake of painting a few ells of broadcloth and brocade." † What the painter has

---

* The only physical characteristic of the painter which Hawthorne mentions is his "deep eyebrows," beneath which he watches the countenances of his sitters.

† Italics mine. The reader is also prepared to accept the artist's cavalier dismissal of wealth and influence by Hawthorne's previous description of his attitude towards those who applied to him for sittings: "Whenever such proposals were made, he fixed his piercing eyes on the applicant, and seemed to look him through and through. If he beheld only a sleek and comfortable visage, though there were a gold-laced coat to adorn the picture and golden guineas to pay for it, he civilly

seen in their faces, however, is hard to determine: although Elinor's fears have suggested that it must be gloom and grief, the painter himself was struck by the appearance of the lovers at the moment when, standing in a shaft of sunlight, they seemed to be "living pictures of youth and beauty, gladdened by bright fortune." It is possible, of course, that the artist's interest was aroused by the dramatic irony of the situation—by the contrast of the physical brightness which enveloped Walter and Elinor with the aura of spiritual gloom that he perceived emanating from them. The artist's powers have been so described that the reader easily assumes that he has seen through the sunlight and the physical beauty of these two youthful figures into the eternal truth of their souls.

Having carefully plotted the situation in which these three characters are to be involved, Hawthorne then begins to examine the complicated relationship of the artist with his sitters, who are in actuality the raw materials of his new creation. The question of whether or not the painter is able to influence the future lives of those whom art has placed in his power is handled ambiguously. Walter, whom we have seen to be half-disposed to accept the validity of superstitions, does not dismiss the thought. Although he smiles about it, it lingers in his mind, even after he and Elinor have definitely arranged for their sittings:

After they had taken leave [of the artist], Walter Ludlow asked Elinor, with a smile, whether she knew what an influence over their

fates the painter was about to acquire.

"The old women of Boston affirm," continued he, "that after he has once got possession of a person's face and figure, he may paint him in any act or situation whatever—and the picture will be prophetic. Do you believe it?"

When the sittings begin, it is evident that the painter sees in his subjects more than reveals itself to the superficial observer. Having been forced to reject his first plan of introducing the lovers on the same canvas, he nevertheless works on the paintings simultaneously, because, he explains in his "mystical language," the faces throw light upon each other. And extending his study of the influence that each lover has on the other, he executes secretly a crayon sketch, in which, it is to be presumed, he shows the lovers in the "appropriate action" that he wished originally to represent on the large canvas. During this period of studious analysis, the painter has no apparent effect, either deleterious or benevolent, on Walter and Elinor; he himself, however, is ill occupied with violating their hearts by attempting to uncover their hidden characters.

The idea that the futures of Walter and Elinor are within the painter's control is re-emphasized by what occurs after the portraits have been completed and the lovers come to inspect them. Their stepping across the painter's threshold seems at this moment to be symbolic of their entering his sphere of influence: they step from sunshine into shadow, thus leaving the light of nature which has

rejected the task and the reward. But if the face were the index of anything uncommon, in thought, sentiment, or experience; or if he met a beggar in the street, with a white beard and a furrowed brow; or if sometimes a child happened to look up and smile, he would exhaust all the art on them that he denied to wealth."

hitherto illumined them, to stand in the brooding gloom which emanates from the portraits. The portraits, too, are portentous of change: of grief and terror in Elinor and of some temperamental development in Walter, which he interprets as a "livelier" mood, but which frightens the sensitive Elinor. And then the artist, who sees in Elinor a comprehension of the meaning of his portraits, frightens her still more by showing her the sketch that he has made of what he has seen will be the culmination of her relationship with Walter.

The question now arises concerning the responsibility of the artist for the future events in the lives of Elinor and Walter. When he shows Elinor the crayon sketch, which, as we know from the conclusion of the tale, is a drawing of Walter about to plunge a knife into her bosom, he tells her that he has represented only recognizable truth. He says,

> "If I have failed . . . if your heart does not see itself reflected in your own portrait—if you have no secret cause to trust my delineation of the other—it is not yet too late to alter them. I might change the action of these figures too [referring to the crayon sketch]. But would it influence the event?"

Elinor, in whom we have observed sensitive premonitions of the artistic revelation before her, is evidently convinced that changing the portraits and the sketch will not "influence the event." She refuses to have the pictures altered, but she also refuses to acknowledge their fundamental truth, remarking merely that, if her picture is sad, she will look the gayer by contrast.

On the ideal level, then, it appears that the painter has no responsibility for the futures of Walter and Elinor; his painting, which synthesizes past, present, and future, is a facet of eternal and unalterable truth—the truth of the relationship between Walter and Elinor, which must result in the tragedy that he has foreseen, unless the lovers themselves avoid it by separation. In an absolute sense, the painter has fulfilled his responsibility to society by revealing to the world the truth which he has perceived. Further action he cannot take; that lies with those to whom he has revealed his meaning. That they fail to act is due, not to the artist's irresponsibility, but to their own inability fully to grasp the revelation or to their wilful disregard of its import.*

On the psychological level the problem has greater complexity. Hawthorne suggests from this standpoint that the meaning of the paintings may not be absolute, but may conform to the attitude and the character of the beholder. He hints at this possibility when Walter and Elinor, on their first visit to the painter's apartment, study the portraits hang-

---

* Although those friends of Walter and Elinor who were "people of natural sensibility" speculated endlessly on the meaning of the portraits, scrutinizing them "like the pages of a mystic volume," they were unable to agree on their significance. The failure of this group to act upon the artist's revelation was due to their lacking a full comprehension of his meaning. One person among them, however, seems to have understood it: announcing "that both these pictures were parts of one design, and that the melancholy strength of feeling, in Elinor's countenance, bore reference to the more vivid emotion, or, as he termed it, the wild passion, in that of Walter . . . he even began a sketch, in which the action of the two figures was to correspond with their mutual expression." However, like Elinor, he failed to act on this perception, perhaps because of the inherent weakness that causes men to reject the truth of an unpleasant revelation.

ing on the walls and find different meanings in the painted faces:

"The dark old St. Peter has a fierce and ugly scowl, saint though he be," [said Walter] . . . . "He troubles me. But the Virgin looks kindly at us."

"Yes; but very sorrowfully, methinks," said Elinor.

The easel stood beneath these . . . old pictures, sustaining one that had been recently commenced. After a little inspection, they began to recognize the features of their own minister, the Reverend Dr. Colman, growing into shape and life, as it were, out of a cloud.

"Kind old man!" exclaimed Elinor. "He gazes at me as if he were about to utter a word of paternal advice."

"And at me," said Walter, "as if he were about to shake his head and rebuke me for some suspected iniquity. But so does the original. I shall never feel quite comfortable under his eye till we stand before him to be married."

Nothing in Hawthorne's manner of relating this incident justifies our deducing that Elinor's vision is true and Walter's, false. In fact, when we consider Hawthorne's treatment of Elinor's intuitions, we find that he seems to imply that she is sensitive to psychological suggestion. At the opening of the story, we are told that Elinor has only suspected a strangeness in Walter: she was once frightened by a look—a look which does not reappear upon his face until she sees it again in the completed portrait. After her horrified examination of the portrait, her frame of mind is such that, by the time the artist shows

her the crayon sketch, she has been psychologically conditioned to accept the dark prophecy of her future. Her growing melancholy may, therefore, be easily attributed to the suggestion which he planted in her mind.

Elinor, however, is passive; she does nothing to bring about the artist's prophecy, except in so far as her melancholy may have the natural effect of increasing Walter's moroseness. It is Walter, the active member of the pair, whose behavior, it is to be expected, will demonstrate most forcibly the painter's influence, if any influence he have. The lack of sensitive perception in Walter, combined with his susceptibility to superstitious belief, predisposes him to accept the old wives' report that once the painter "has got possession of a person's face and figure, he may paint him in any act or situation whatever—and the picture will be prophetic." Therefore, if Walter saw the crayon sketch, which the artist intended for the eyes of Elinor alone—and here, characteristically, Hawthorne leaves the matter in doubt*—its effect may have been so great that he was unconsciously forced to consummate the action therein depicted.

The progress of the narrative sustains the validity of this psychological interpretation of the tale. Elinor, who understands the spiritual basis of the artist's prophecy, grows daily in resemblance to her portrait; Walter, who cannot comprehend the artistic ideal, accepts the future certainty of the culminating physical act alone and does not grow to resemble his portrait until the moment when he raises his knife to perform that act. At the same moment the painter, who has just appeared in the open door, cries, " 'Hold, madman!' " and Wal-

---

* Hawthorne's account of the situation is this: "Turning from the table, [Elinor] . . . perceived that Walter had advanced near enough to have seen the sketch, though she could not determine whether it had caught his eye."

ter subsides into passivity, muttering, "'Does Fate impede its own decree?'" This half-mad mutter tells us that Walter, at least, regards the artist as the agent of destiny and that he has acted on an impulse to fulfil the fate that was pronounced upon him.

Although Walter's identification of the artist with destiny may be dismissed as the irrational fancy of a disordered mind, the plausibility of the idea is strengthened by its having already suggested itself to the painter. After entering the house, as he approached the room in which he knew the portraits hung, he "seemed to hear the step of Destiny approaching behind him, on its progress towards its victims. A strange thought darted into his mind. Was not his own the form in which that destiny had embodied itself, and he a chief agent of the coming evil which he foreshadowed?"

Then, when he steps between Walter and his victim, he seems to be the embodiment of their fate: "He had advanced from the door, and interposed himself between the wretched beings, with the same sense of power to regulate their destiny as to alter a scene upon the canvas. He stood like a magician, controlling the phantoms which he had evoked."

Despite these strong suggestions of the fatality of artistic powers, a close reading of the text will show that both the painter and Walter are deluded: the artist is not the agent of destiny among mankind. His power to arrest Walter's hand is proof enough that the murder was not preordained. It does, however, indicate that his skill in probing his subjects' hearts, coupled with their own natural dispositions, caused Walter and Elinor to act the parts which he envisioned for them, and that the capacity for patient suffering in Elinor and the capacity for criminal madness in Walter are indeed the essence of their souls.

Morton Dauwen Zabel

HENRY JAMES

HENRY JAMES was born in 1843 in New York City; he died in 1916 in London. His life began in what was still a young nation and a young metropolis of the New World, eighteen years before the outbreak of the American Civil War; it ended in the largest metropolis of the Old and in the middle of the greatest "world war" that history had yet seen. These two cities and two historic crises may be described as the poles and decisive events of the age he witnessed. The first three decades of his life were spent in America but with three periods of travel and schooling in Europe and England that began in the first year of his childhood and continued at intervals through his later boyhood. His last four decades were spent in continuous European and English residence, punctuated by four important return-visits to his native land. His schooling was irregular and in the end inconclusive, but he happened to be born "a native of the James family," and between his membership in that stimulating circle, his youthful explorations of the American and foreign scenes, and his passion for books, he received the education he needed and so discovered his vocation by the time he was twenty.

He published his first story and essay in 1864, his first novel in 1871, his last story in 1910, and he still had in hand two unfinished novels at the time of his death. Altogether he brought out during his career nineteen novels, an equal number of volumes of tales comprising over a hundred shorter narratives, three volumes of plays, eight of critical essays, six of travel reports, a biography and two personal memoirs, as well as a large quantity of uncollected tales, critical papers, and occasional journalism; and since 1916 his editors have published his two uncompleted novels, a third unfinished memoir, his complete plays, and some twenty posthumous volumes of fiction, criticism, writings on art and drama, working notebooks, and letters, all this still leaving a considerable body of prose and correspondence for future collecting. During the forty years following his first book in 1875 there were only four which did not see the appearance of a new book from his hand; there were sometimes as many as three, four, or five volumes within a twelve-month period, and sometimes as many as forty contributions to magazines. The two most comprehensive collected editions of his fiction occupy twenty-six and thirty-five volumes, but his total literary output would perhaps amount to more than sixty such volumes. His private life was devoted to family ties and affections, travel, many friendships in two hemispheres, and the practical affairs of his literary business; but these remained marginal to the vocation to which he dedicated himself without interruption from early manhood to old age and over a span of more than five decades.

Like all the men whose lives covered that momentous period in modern history, he lived through changes, crises, and events in human thought and action that virtually recreated the simpler world of his youth. These became part of his subject matter and consciousness. He lived between two hemispheres, two continents, two countries, and two centuries, and that fact constitutes another essential feature of his creative and critical material. His achievement is today claimed equally by the two nations in which he made his home and to which he gave his allegiance. His work, since its beginnings a hundred years ago, has passed through many phases of recognition, popularity, unpopularity, critical esteem and controversy. Today it stands as one of the largest and most impressive achievements in modern literature. Since his centenary in 1943 James has become, on a scale he never knew in his lifetime, one of the most read, reprinted, edited, collected, argued, debated, and influential writers of the English-speaking world—a subject and model for schools, a major exponent of the practice and theory of his art, a "special type" and cardinal example in his vocation, a recognized master and an established classic. He is one of the five or six finest novelists and men of letters that America has produced, and in the opinion of many the greatest.

Always basic and fundamental to any reading or evaluation of James's work there lie these considerations—his knowledge and citizenship of two worlds, his passionate dedication to his craft, his enormous productivity in it, his alertness to the social and moral crises he witnessed, and a "sense of the past" that competed in his imagination with his equally avid sense of the present. The focus to which he brought these forces was his ambition to create an art commensurate in scope, insight, and craftsmanship with the history he lived through, the discoveries he and his contemporaries made about man and the world he inhabits. He set out at the beginning of his career to compete with the masters of his profession in America and Europe, and even at the age of twenty he deliberately set for himself the most formidable models available to him—Hawthorne, Balzac, Sainte-Beuve, George Eliot, and Turgenev. By the time he was forty he had made himself one of their company; by seventy he had achieved a life-work comparable in size and scope with that of the most productive of them. If the question of his ultimate rank among the masters of fiction is still undecided; if his distrust of some of the greatest creators of his age (Tolstoy and Dostoevsky among them) or of some of the more original tendencies in modern writing leaves his authority in doubt among the skeptical; if his example as a craftsman and moralist is still open to dispute by a good many of the writers and critics who have succeeded him; and if the limitations of his personal life, his long career in exile, and his division between two cultures leave him open to debate, this only testifies to the fact that he remains as vital a force in modern literature today as he was during his lifetime; that if he is a classic he has not become an inert monument; and that his work has not

lost its force as a challenge to his readers and fellow-writers. He still occupies the position he defined for himself during his active career—a focus of debate, an intellectual and artistic stimulus, a test of personal and literary principle, an "aesthetic war-cry." [. . .]

To any such definition of James's character and rank as the above there have always been, and there will doubtless always recur, opposing arguments. By some of the tests of greatness that are applied to the world's great writers, he is an artist of marked limitations. The world of his fiction, in spite of its geographical scope, is a small one: it is confined to very definite and selected segments of society. He made only one really serious full-scale attempt to dramatize the greater social and political conflicts of his time. He is poles apart from the novelists whose comprehensive powers as historians he respected—Balzac, Dickens, Zola. He repudiated the historical novel as an artistic risk and thus produced nothing comparable to *War and Peace*, the *Comédie humaine*, *I Promessi Sposi*, Scott's vast panorama, or in a later time the teeming canvases of Faulkner, Malraux, Romains, Sartre, or Pasternak. He was a novelist of "philosophic" mind and direction, yet he did not make the novel a vehicle of explicit philosophic or metaphysical speculation as Melville, Dostoevsky, Tolstoy, and Proust did. His art was exploratory, but not in the revolutionary sense that we associate with moral or technical innovators like Lawrence and Joyce. It can be argued that either because of privations in his experience or of cautions of taste, he never fully attacked or dramatized the major conflicts and disruptions of his century-modern politics and warfare, political and social revolution, the collision of re-

ligion and science, the revolution in
sexual morals, the discoveries of
physical and psychological theory,
and the crises of democracy, imperialism, and economic progress that led
to the overwhelming shock of 1914.
Except in the few early stories about
the Civil War and in two of his middle and one of his final novels, these
world-shaking events are hardly
touched on in his fiction. (They are
more anxiously present in his letters
and memoirs and in *The American
Scene*, but even in his journalistic reports from Europe he usually shirked
dealing with them.) The direct attack
on contemporary history which engaged even such sensitive contemporaries as Flaubert, Turgenev, and
George Eliot was, except on two occasions, rejected by James; and it can
still be a matter for surprise to his
readers, knowing the sensitiveness of
his nerves to disturbance, that such
large and urgent areas of modern history were left out of account in his
books, or, if noticed, left obliquely or
marginally implied.

His cast of characters also shows
some notable omissions. There are
among the major personages of his
books no public heroes, great popular
idols, leaders of states and government, generals of armies, moral or
philosophic Titans, inspirers of politics and society, discoverers in
thought or science, any more than
there are peasants, labor leaders,
miners, industrial workers, criminals,
or financial speculators—types that
throng the books of Scott, Tolstoy,
Balzac, Trollope, Dickens, Dostoevsky, Zola, and in more recent times
those of Conrad, Dreiser, Dos Passos,
Wells, Orwell, Sartre, and Pasternak.
If he introduces the modern million-
aire he portrays him at a time when
money-making has been achieved and
put aside in favor of personal rewards
that prove elusive or humiliating

(*The American* and *The Golden
Bowl*). If he describes social reform-
ers or revolutionists (in *The Princess
Casamassima* and *The Bostonians*), it
is to leave the center of his stage to a
confused young bookbinder who fails
as a revolutionist, or to a convinced
reactionary. If he touches on the phenomenon of great wealth (in *The
Wings of the Dove* and *The Ivory
Tower*), it is to show not its power
but its pathos and evil. [. . .] Instead,
the foreground of his stage is occupied by a "poor sensitive gentleman,"
a "certain young woman affronting
her destiny," a young man caught in
a dream of the past, an old man who
finds too late that the chief glory of
life is "to have lived," an artist who
either fails in his art or must realize
his success secretly and without the
rewards of public recognition, an innocent youth or a child preyed upon
by a corrupt world. It was out of
such privations, denials, reticences,
renunciations, disappointments, or
failures that James usually shaped the
destinies of his heroes and heroines.
He left the dramas of public triumph,
leadership, heroic inspiration or mar-
tyrdom to others.

Yet his age and a large part of its
conflict, ordeal, and crisis live in his
books and succeed in making them
both essential documents on the life
of James's century and researches of
permanent validity into the truths of
experience. The paradox of their
highly specialized and selective pictures of life combined with their
largeness of vision is a clue to their
power to fascinate and compel. Instead of attempting the large-scale,
highly populated panorama of history or society, James concentrated
his attention on the selected fragment
of destiny, the particular and esoteric
workings of fate, even at times on
the seemingly trivial crises of petty,
selfish, or obscure existences. [. . .]

What he chose was to be the recorder of the moments and temperaments in which acuteness of nerves, emotion, and intelligence is made possible by scrupulosity of manners, by keenly developed strategies of behavior and communication, by a sense of the evil and treachery that constantly prey upon life, and by an awareness that experience is never so vivid as when its security is threatened and its confidence rebuffed. Danger, risk, and evil thus become the instruments whereby intelligence realizes its highest potentialities. Privation and tragedy become modes of awareness and vision. "The figures in any picture, the agents in any drama," said James in one of his prefaces, "are interesting only in proportion as they feel their respective situations. . . . But there are degrees of feeling—the muffled, the faint, the just sufficient, the barely intelligent, as we may say; and the acute, the intense, the complete, in a word—the power to be finely aware and richly responsible. It is those moved in this latter fashion who 'get most' out of all that happens to them and who in doing so enable us, as readers of their record, as participators by a fond attention, also to get most. Their being finely aware—as Hamlet and Lear, say, are finely aware—*makes* absolute the intensity of their adventure, gives a maximum of sense to what befalls them. We care, our curiosity and our sympathy care, comparatively little for what happens to the stupid, the coarse and the blind. . . . Experience, as I see it, is our apprehension and our measure of what happens to us as social creatures . . ."

It was by his exercise of this principle that James was able to make his characters and their situations, often so obscure or marginal to the greater events and forces of their time, registers or reflectors of what those events actually meant and of what was becoming of mankind during one of its great periods of social change and moral crisis. It is the same faculty of "awareness," of intense sensitivity to the world through which he moved and had his being, that makes James himself so compelling a mind —that makes his reactions to people, writers, events, and the human spectacle so fascinating. Anyone who reads his essays and letters becomes aware of this fascination—of an eagerness to hear what he has to say about the men he met (Turgenev, Ruskin, Flaubert, Wilde, Tennyson); about the books he read (*Our Mutual Friend* or Whitman's *Drum-Taps* in 1865, *Middlemarch* in 1873, *Nana* in 1880, *Du Côté de chez Swann* in 1913, the latest books of Conrad or Lawrence in 1914); about the challenges he met in the arts (the Impressionist painters, Zola's realism, the aesthetes of the '90's, Ibsen's plays, Wells's tales); about the events of his time (the end of the Civil War, Lincoln's death, the outbreak of War in 1914). He makes us acquainted with a registering sensibility which can catch, even at a distance or casually, the nuances of personality, art, and history that count for most, and that lodge in the mind as definitions. He brought this faculty of concentrated insight to his study of literature, and he made it the essential fact in the characters he created, thus permitting even the least of them to become in some degree persons in whom the meaning of society, of morals, or of the reality of history becomes focused and defined.

Henry James

FROM THE NOTEBOOKS:
"THE REAL THING"

Paris, Hotel Westminster,
February 22d. 1891.

IN PURSUANCE of my plan of writing some very short tales—things of from 7000 to 10,000 words the easiest length to 'place,' I began yesterday the little story that was suggested to me some time ago by an incident related to me by George du Maurier [1] the lady and gentleman who called upon him with a word from Frith, an oldish, faded, ruined pair—he an officer in the army—who unable to turn a penny in any other way, were trying to find employment as models. I was struck with the pathos, the oddity and typicalness of the situation—the little tragedy of good-looking gentlefolk, who had been all their life stupid and well-dressed, living, on a fixed income, at country-houses, watering places and clubs, like so many others of their class in England, and were now utterly unable to *do* anything, had no cleverness, no art nor craft to make use of as a *gagne-pain* [2] —could only show themselves, clumsily, for the fine, clean, well-groomed animals that they were, only hope to make a little money by—in this manner—just simply *being*. I thought I saw a subject for very brief treatment in this *donnée* [3]—and I think I do still; but to do anything worth while with it I must (as always, great Heavens!)

be very clear as to what is in it and what I wish to get out of it. I tried a beginning yesterday, but I instantly became conscious that I must straighten out the little idea. It must be an idea—it can't be a 'story' in the vulgar sense of the word. It must be a picture; it must illustrate something. God knows that's enough—if the thing *does* illustrate. To make little anecdotes of this kind real *morceaux de vie* [4] is a plan quite inspiring enough. *Voyons un peu*, therefore, what one can put into this one—I mean how much of life. One must put a little action—not a stupid, mechanical, arbitrary action, but something that is of the real essence of the subject. I thought of representing the husband as jealous of the wife—that is, jealous of the artist employing her, from the moment that, in point of fact, she begins to sit. But this is vulgar and obvious—worth nothing. What I wish to represent is the baffled, ineffectual, incompetent character of their attempt, and how it illustrates once again the everlasting English amateurishness—the way superficial, untrained, unprofessional effort goes to the wall when confronted with trained, competitive, intelligent, qualified art—in whatever line it may be a question of. It is out of *that* element that my little action and move-

From *The Notebooks of Henry James*, edited by F. O. Matthiessen and Kenneth B. Murdock, copyright 1947 by Oxford University Press, Inc. Reprinted by permission of the publishers.

1. **George du Maurier:** an English artist and writer of French birth (1834–1896), who illustrated certain of James's works.
2. *gagne-pain:* means of livelihood.
3. By *donnée*, "what is given," James, as he suggests, means the topic rather than the handling of the topic, which is the whole story.
4. *morceaux de vie:* morsels of life.

ment must come; and now I begin to see just how—as one always *does*—Glory be to the Highest—when one begins to look at a thing hard and straight and seriously—to fix it—as I am so sadly lax and desultory about doing. What subjects I should find—for *everything*—if I could only achieve this more as a habit! Let my contrast and complication here come from the opposition—to my melancholy Major and his wife—of a couple of little vulgar professional people *who know*, with the consequent bewilderment, vagueness, depression of the former—their failure to understand how such people can be better than *they*—their failure, disappointment, disappearance—going forth into the vague again. *Il y a bien quelque chose à tirer de ça.*[5] They have no pictorial sense. They are only clean and stiff and stupid. The others are dirty, even—the melancholy Major and his wife remark on it, wondering. The artist is beginning a big illustrated book, a new edition of a famous novel—say *Tom Jones:* and he is willing to try to work them in—for he takes an interest in their predicament, and feels—sceptically, but, with his flexible artistic sympathy—the appeal of their type. He is willing to give them a trial. Make it out that *he* himself is on trial—he is young and 'rising,' but he has still his golden spurs to win. He can't afford, *en somme*, to make many mistakes. He has regular work in drawing every week for a serial novel in an illustrated paper; but the great project—that of a big house—of issuing an illustrated Fielding promises him a big lift. He has been intrusted with (say) *Joseph Andrews*,[6] experimentally; he will have to do this brilliantly in order to have the engagement for the

rest confirmed. He has already 2 models in his service—the 'complication' must come from *them*. One is a common, clever, London girl, of the smallest origin and without conventional beauty, but of aptitude, of perceptions—knowing thoroughly *how*. She says 'lydy' and 'plice,' but she has the pictorial sense; and can look like anything he wants her to look like. She poses, in short, in perfection. So does her colleague, a professional Italian, a little fellow—ill dressed, smelling of garlic, but admirably serviceable, quite universal. They must be contrasted, confronted, *juxtaposed* with the others; whom they take for people who *pay*, themselves, till they learn the truth when they are overwhelmed with derisive amazement. The denouement simply that the melancholy Major and his wife won't do—they're not 'in it.' Their surprise —their helpless, proud assent—without other prospects: yet at the same time *their* degree of more silent amazement at the success of the two inferior people—who are so much less nice-looking than themselves. Frankly, however, is this contrast enough of a *story*, by itself? It seems to me Yes—for it's an IDEA—and how the deuce should I get *more* into 7000 words? It must be simply 50 pp. of my manuscript. The little tale of *The Servant* (*Brooksmith*) which I did the other day for *Black and White* and which I thought of at the same time as this, proved a very tight squeeze into the same tiny number of words, and I probably shall find that there is much more to be done with this than the compass will admit of. Make it tremendously succinct—with a very short pulse or rhythm—and the closest selection of detail—in other words *summarize* intensely and keep down

5. *Il y a . . . ça:* "there's certainly something to be got out of that."
6. *Joseph Andrews:* a novel (1742) by Henry Fielding (1707-1754), who also wrote *Tom Jones* (1749).

the lateral development. It *should* be a little gem of bright, quick, vivid form. I shall get every grain of 'action' that the space admits of if I make something, for the artist, hang in the balance—depend on the way he does this particular work. It's when he finds that he shall lose his great opportunity if he keeps on with them, that he has to tell the gentlemanly couple, that, frankly, they won't serve his turn—and make them wander forth into the cold world again. I must keep them the age I've made them—50 and 40—because it's more touching; but I must bring up the age of the 2 real models to almost the same thing. That increases the incomprehensibility (to the amateurs) of their usefulness. Picture the immanence, in the latter, of the idle, provided-for, country-house habit—the blankness of their *manière d'être*.[7] But in how tremendously few words I must do it. This is a lesson—a *magnificent* lesson—if I'm to do a good many. Something as admirably compact and *selected* as a Maupassant.

Robert F. Haugh

CONRAD'S "YOUTH"

"YOUTH" is a modest gem of a story with rare felicity of style and event. Youth and the ancient East; youth and an old skipper in his first command; youth and an old rotting coaler—when one examines the story he is astonished to find the magic in images of age which permeate it. In a story of darkness, inspired attention to patterns of light; in a story of youth, inspired attention to patterns of age. Here is the key to Conrad's magnificent verve and sparkle in "Youth." The reader finds youth in odd places, myriad images of decay. Yet so deftly does Conrad manage point of view that his ancients are not weary, hopeless relics of lost vitality, but sprightly like a child's vision of Saint Nick. Conrad's squalor here is like Dickens': brightened by a sparkling spirit, forever young. Conrad creates a joyful world of sombre events by two methods: the dichromatic refraction of his style; and the *progression d'effet* which makes the tale vibrate with energy the more it plunges into disaster.

"Youth" is a Marlow story, but barely so. Marlow appears at the opening curtain, reappears at intervals to say, "Pass the bottle," and the rest of the time remains in the anonymity of the "I" telling the story.

The skipper of the "*Judea*: London, 'Do or Die'" is a sixty-year-old neophyte with cottony hair and blue eyes amazingly like a boy's. He is on his first cruise as captain—a boyish circumstance oddly matching Marlow's twenty years. His wife, whom we meet shortly, has "the figure of a young girl, with a face . . . wrinkled and ruddy like a winter apple."

7. *manière d'être*: way of life.

When the collision comes—one of the early disasters—Captain Beard snatches her up like a bride, runs nimbly across deck and down a ladder to a boat. What could be more youthful and surprising—more delightfully like the capering Saint Nick?

The second mate is elderly as well, white-bearded: "—between those two old chaps I felt like a small boy between two grandfathers." Like the skipper, the mate "had something wrong with his luck, and had never got on." But of course Marlow has a wondrous faith in his luck, and is certain with the immortal certitude of youth, that he will get on, never fear.

The ship is old, all rust and grime, but it has "Do or die" under the scrollwork of the stern, and to young Marlow it is the very spirit of adventure.

Another oldster is Jermyn, the North Sea pilot with the perpetual tear on the end of his nose, whose ideas are hostile to hopeful young Marlow's dreams: "We either had been in trouble, or were in trouble, or expected to be in trouble." Scornful as the young seaman is, he recognizes trouble when it comes. First, the October gale that shifts the ballast of sand while underway for Tyne coal. It was the famous gale of that year; it sends men into the cavernous hold to shovel back the shifting sand, "falling down with a great flourish of shovels."

At Tyne, Mrs. Beard comes aboard while the ship is loaded. The grandmotherly old lady with the figure of a young girl mends Marlow's socks and shirts. The ship, tied alongside a dock, is rammed in a drizzle by sheer bad luck. In an astonishing sequence of events, the climax is the hail from the captain, out in a small boat even before the crew had wits enough to miss him.

After repairs they set out, loaded with coal. It is January in "beautiful sunny winter weather that has more charm than in the summertime, because it is unexpected, and crisp, and you know it won't, can't last long." It is weather like youth in the company of wintry old men. In the channel a gale from the southwest punishes the *Judea* "with spite, without interval, without mercy." The ship begins to leak badly. Marlow and the others work at the pumps that wheeze like a bad heart, but work as they will, they barely keep even with the water. Young Marlow thinks, "What an adventure!" in exultation at the test life is offering him.

They put into Falmouth for repairs, take her out once more, and are back in a week with the crew refusing duty. Yet Marlow loves the ship more than ever. A third time they try it and come back. Now this adventurous craft, this white-winged bird of the seas, repository of nomadic youth's dreams—becomes a fixed museum freak, the familiar sight of townspeople, pointed out to tourists. Sailors become like citizens, known to grocers and tobacconists. Still young Marlow's love burgeons; he defends her hotly from disparagement.

Finally the *Judea* has a new copper bottom; the cargo is reshipped—then the rats leave her. But she breaks the spell of England at last and plunges ponderously into southern latitudes. She lumbers through an interminable procession of days, while the gilt flashes her youthful slogan: "Do or die."

She is to die, but her death, climaxing other images of age in the story, illuminates magnificently the spirit of youth. The first signs of her mortality come in the Indian Ocean, when young Marlow notices a "funny smell." Soon the dread explanation is known—the cargo is afire. Spontaneous combustion has occurred in coal made into powder by repeated loading and unloading.

Captain Beard is steadfast for Bangkok; no turning aside to Australia or closer ports. They try to smother the fire by cutting off air; they pump water into the hold.

It was our fate to pump into that ship; to pump out of her; to pump into her; and after keeping water out of her to save ourselves from being drowned, we frantically poured water into her to save ourselves from being burned . . . the bright stream flashed in the sunshine . . . vanished on the black surface of the coal . . . a pestiferous cloud, unclean vapors . . . defiling the splendor of sea and sky.

Yet the splendor and brightness are there, in young Marlow's heart. Trial by water, trial by fire, then trial by concussion—for the ship explodes after apparent and deceptive quiescence. Marlow finds himself sprawled on the black cargo after the blast. He clambers back to the unfamiliar deck to encounter the captain. "Where's the cabin table?" is Captain Beard's first inquiry. He must find the cabin table, center of his rational life, before he can order his senses. Then, "Trim the yards," of that floating disaster, and trim them the crew does, to steer for Bangkok. Young Marlow thinks, 'This is great. Now, this is something like. I wonder what will happen?'

A mail ship takes them in tow for Batavia, but towing fans the fire, which now leaps high above the ship. The *Judea* must be abandoned. Not a one of the crew but decides to stay with her to the last. The last of the *Judea* is a dazzling flame towering into the night sky, a Phoenix flame to feed the spirit of young Marlow, eternal youth.

Oh, the glamour of youth! Oh, the fire of it, more dazzling than the flames of the burning ship, throwing a magic light on the wide earth, leaping audaciously to the sky—

First thought of the exultant Marlow is that he will first see the romantic East as skipper of his own craft—a small boat it is true, but what is that to youth?

Captain Beard wants to save precious mementoes of his first command—a length of old stream cable; a kedge anchor. The crew says, "Aye, aye, sir" respectfully, then lets it slip over the side at first opportunity. Marlow stands off in his small command, but goes aboard one last time to fetch the captain. Where his imagination had created panic, shouting, terror, instead he finds the captain asleep on a settee, the mate and a few of the crew serenely eating cheese and bread and ale amidst the disaster.

The *Judea* burns in glorious triumph, her "magnificent death like a grace." The small boats set out under orders to keep together for safety. Not young Marlow.

Do you know what I thought? I thought I would pull clear—part company as soon as I could. I wanted to have my first command all to myself.

Then come days of scorching sea, the boat seeming to stand still as if bewitched, with the men's mouths dry as tinder. They drag at oars with aching arms. Then one night, after the blistering desolation, comes an aromatic puff, laden with the strange odors of blossoms: "the mysterious East, perfumed like a flower." The youth sits, weary beyond expression at the journey's end, but exulting like a conqueror. Soon the captain follows. "I had a terrible time of it," he murmurs.

Marlow's first encounter with the people of the East finds him cursed for a native merchant as he approaches a ship in the harbor. Even this he thinks fascinating, and even a bit flattering.

"Youth" closes on a brilliant image of the jetty lined with exotic faces, all attentive and silent in a blaze of color. They gaze without a sigh at the weary men, the old skipper who "looked as if he would never wake," old Mahon the mate, white beard upturned as though he had been shot, all sleeping "unconscious of the land and the people and the violence of sunshine." Youth, a blaze of color . . . the ancient East and the ancient men . . . these are the images that key the events in "Youth." They are events of disaster, defeat, frustration, deadly monotony, yet made to shine by the magic of style.

Conrad's design here has none of the menace of universal evil to be found in *Nigger of the Narcissus*. But the split vision of his artistic consciousness permeates scene and event: age and youth; splendor and stifling fumes; frustration and exuberance; disaster and courage—these are the orderings and designs of his art.

Stephen Crane

STEPHEN CRANE'S OWN STORY

He Tells How the *Commodore* Was Wrecked and How He Escaped

Fear-Crazed Negro Nearly Swamps Boat

Young Writer Compelled to Work in Stifling Atmosphere of the Fire Room

Bravery of Captain Murphy and Higgins

Tried to Tow Their Companions Who Were on the Raft—Last Dash for the Shore Through the Surf

JACKSONVILLE, FLA., Jan. 6.— It was the afternoon of New Year's. The *Commodore* lay at her dock in Jacksonville and negro stevedores processioned steadily toward her with box after box of ammunition and bundle after bundle of rifles. Her hatch, like the mouth of a monster, engulfed them. It might have been the feeding time of some legendary creature of the sea. It was in broad daylight and the crowd of gleeful Cubans on the pier did not forbear to sing the strange patriotic ballads of their island.

Everything was perfectly open. The *Commodore* was cleared with a cargo of arms and munition for Cuba. There was none of that extreme modesty about the proceeding which had marked previous departures of the famous tug. She loaded up as placidly as if she were going to carry oranges to New York, instead of Remingtons to Cuba. Down the river, furthermore, the revenue cutter *Boutwell*, the old isosceles triangle that protects United States interests in the St. John's, lay at anchor, with no sign of excitement aboard her.

EXCHANGING FAREWELLS

On the decks of the *Commodore* there were exchanges of farewells in two languages. Many of the men who were to sail upon her had many intimates in the old Southern town, and we who had left our friends in the remote North received our first touch of melancholy on witnessing these strenuous and earnest goodbys.

It seems, however, that there was more difficulty at the custom house. The officers of the ship and the Cuban leaders were detained there until a mournful twilight settled upon the St. John's, and through a heavy fog the lights of Jacksonville blinked dimly. Then at last the *Commodore* swung clear of the dock, amid a tumult of goodbys. As she turned her bow toward the distant sea the Cubans ashore cheered and cheered. In response the *Commodore* gave three long blasts of her whistle, which even to this time impressed me with their sadness. Somehow, they sounded as wails.

Then at last we began to feel like filibusters.[1] I don't suppose that the most stolid brain could contrive to believe that there is not a mere trifle of danger in filibustering, and so as we watched the lights of Jacksonville swing past us and heard the regular thump, thump, thump of the engines we did considerable reflecting.

But I am sure that there were no hifalutin emotions visible upon any of the faces which fronted the speeding shore. In fact, from cook's boy to captain, we were all enveloped in a gentle satisfaction and cheerfulness. But less than two miles from Jacksonville, this atrocious fog caused the pilot to ram the bow of the *Commodore* hard upon the mud and in this ignominious position we were compelled to stay until daybreak.

1. **filibusters**: pirates.

HELP FROM THE *BOUTWELL*

It was to all of us more than a physical calamity. We were now no longer filibusters. We were men on a ship stuck in the mud. A certain mental somersault was made once more necessary.

But word had been sent to Jacksonville to the captain of the revenue cutter *Boutwell*, and Captain Kilgore turned out promptly and generously fired up his old triangle, and came at full speed to our assistance. She dragged us out of the mud, and again we headed for the mouth of the river. The revenue cutter pounded along a half mile astern of us, to make sure that we did not take on board at some place along the river men for the Cuban army.

This was the early morning of New Year's Day, and the fine golden southern sunlight fell full upon the river. It flashed over the ancient *Boutwell*, until her white sides gleamed like pearl, and her rigging was spun into little threads of gold.

Cheers greeted the old *Commodore* from passing ship and from the shore. It was a cheerful, almost merry, beginning to our voyage. At Mayport, however, we changed our river pilot for a man who could take her to open sea, and again the *Commodore* was beached. The *Boutwell* was fussing around us in her venerable way, and, upon seeing our predicament, she came again to assist us, but this time, with engines reversed, the *Commodore* dragged herself away from the grip of the sand and again headed for the open sea.

The captain of the revenue cutter grew curious. He hailed the *Commodore*: "Are you fellows going to sea today?"

Captain Murphy of the *Commo-*

dore called back: "Yes, sir."

And then as the whistle of the *Commodore* saluted him, Captain Kilgore doffed his cap and said: "Well, gentlemen, I hope you have a pleasant cruise," and this was our last word from shore.

When the *Commodore* came to enormous rollers that flee over the bar a certain lightheartedness departed from the ship's company.

SLEEP IMPOSSIBLE

As darkness came upon the waters, the *Commodore* was a broad, flaming path of blue and silver phosphorescence, and as her stout bow lunged at the great black waves she threw flashing, roaring cascades to either side. And all that was to be heard was the rhythmical and mighty pounding of the engines. Being an inexperienced filibuster, the writer had undergone considerable mental excitement since the starting of the ship, and in consequence he had not yet been to sleep and so I went to the first mate's bunk to indulge myself in all the physical delights of holding one's-self in bed. Every time the ship lurched I expected to be fired through a bulkhead, and it was neither amusing nor instructive to see in the dim light a certain accursed valise aiming itself at the top of my stomach with every lurch of the vessel.

THE COOK IS HOPEFUL

The cook was asleep on a bench in the galley. He is of a portly and noble exterior, and by means of a checker board he had himself wedged on this bench in such a manner the motion of the ship would be unable to dislodge him. He woke as I entered the galley and delivered himself of some dolorous sentiments: "God," he said in the course of his observations, "I don't feel right about this ship, some-how. It strikes me that something is going to happen to us. I don't know what it is, but the old ship is going to get it in the neck, I think."

"Well, how about the men on board of her?" said I. "Are any of us going to get out, prophet?"

"Yes," said the cook. "Sometimes I have these damned feelings come over me, and they are always right, and it seems to me, somehow, that you and I will both get and meet again somewhere, down at Coney Island, perhaps, or some place like that."

ONE MAN HAS ENOUGH

Finding it impossible to sleep. I went back to the pilot house. An old seaman, Tom Smith, from Charleston, was then at the wheel. In the darkness I could not see Tom's face, except at those times when he leaned forward to scan the compass and the dim light from the box came upon his weatherbeaten features.

"Well, Tom," said I, "how do you like filibustering?"

He said "I think I am about through with it. I've been in a number of these expeditions and the pay is good, but I think if I ever get back safe this time I will cut it."

I sat down in the corner of the pilot house and almost went to sleep. In the meantime the captain came on duty and he was standing near me when the chief engineer rushed up the stairs and cried hurriedly to the captain that there was something wrong in the engine room. He and the captain departed swiftly.

I was drowsing there in my corner when the captain returned, and, going to the door of the little room directly back of the pilothouse, he cried to the Cuban leader:

"Say, can't you get those fellows to work. I can't talk their language and I can't get them started. Come on and get them going."

HELPS IN THE FIREROOM

The Cuban leader turned to me and said: "Go help in the fireroom. They are going to bail with buckets."

The engine room, by the way, represented a scene at this time taken from the middle kitchen of hades. In the first place, it was insufferably warm, and the lights burned faintly in a way to cause mystic and grewsome shadows. There was a quantity of soapish sea water swirling and sweeping and swishing among machinery that roared and banged and clattered and steamed and, in the second place, it was a devil of a ways down below.

Here I first came to know a certain young oiler named Billy Higgins. He was sloshing around this inferno filling buckets with water and passing them to a chain of men that extended up the ship's side. Afterward we got orders to change our point of attack on water and to operate through a little door on the windward side of the ship that led into the engine room.

NO PANIC ON BOARD

During this time there was much talk of pumps out of order and many other statements of a mechanical kind, which I did not altogether comprehend but understood to mean that there was a general and sudden ruin in the engine room.

There was no particular agitation at this time, and even later there was never a panic on board the *Commodore*. The party of men who worked with Higgins and me at this time were all Cubans, and we were under the direction of the Cuban leaders. Presently we were ordered again to the afterhold, and there was some hesitation about going into the abominable fireroom again, but Higgins dashed down the companionway with a bucket.

LOWERING BOATS

The heat and hard work in the fireroom affected me and I was obliged to come on deck again. Going forward, I heard as I went talk of lowering the boats. Near the corner of the galley the mate was talking with a man.

"Why don't you send up a rocket?" said this unknown man. And the mate replied: "What the hell do we want to send up a rocket for? The ship is all right."

Returning with a little rubber and cloth overcoat, I saw the first boat about to be lowered. A certain man was the first person in this first boat, and they were handing him in a valise about as large as a hotel. I had not entirely recovered from astonishment and pleasure in witnessing this noble deed when I saw another valise go to him.

HUMAN HOG APPEARS

This valise was not perhaps so large as a hotel, but it was a big valise anyhow. Afterward there went to him something which looked to me like an overcoat.

Seeing the chief engineer leaning out of his little window, I remarked to him:

"What do you think of that blank, blank, blank?"

"Oh, he's a bird," said the old chief.

It was now that was heard the order to get away the lifeboat, which was stowed on top of the deckhouse. The deckhouse was a mighty slippery place, and with each roll of the ship, the men there thought themselves likely to take headers into the deadly black sea.

Higgins was on top of the deckhouse, and, with the first mate and two colored stokers, we wrestled with that boat, which, I am willing to swear, weighed as much as a Broadway cable car. She might have been spiked to the deck. We could have pushed a little brick schoolhouse along a corduroy road as easily as we could have moved this boat. But the first mate got a tackle to her from a leeward davit, and on the deck below the captain corralled enough men to make an impression upon the boat.

We were ordered to cease hauling then, and in this lull the cook of the ship came to me and said: "What are you going to do?"

I told him of my plans, and he said: "Well, my God, that's what I am going to do."

A WHISTLE OF DESPAIR

Now the whistle of the *Commodore* had been turned loose, and if there ever was a voice of despair and death, it was in the voice of this whistle. It had gained a new tone. It was as if its throat was already choked by the water, and this cry on the sea at night, with a wind blowing the spray over the ship, and the waves roaring over the bow, and swirling white along the decks, was to each of us probably a song of man's end.

It was now that the first mate showed a sign of losing his grip. To us who were trying in all stages of competence and experience to launch the lifeboat he raged in all terms of fiery satire and hammerlike abuse. But the boat moved at last and swung down toward the water.

Afterward, when I went aft, I saw the captain standing, with his arm in a sling, holding on to a stay with his one good hand and directing the launching of the boat. He gave me a five-gallon jug of water to hold, and asked me what I was going to do. I told him what I thought was about the proper thing, and he told me then that the cook had the same idea, and ordered me to go forward and be ready to launch the ten-foot dingy.

IN THE TEN-FOOT DINGY

I remember well that he turned then to swear at a colored stoker who was prowling around, done up in life preservers until he looked like a feather bed. I went forward with my five-gallon jug of water, and when the captain came we launched the dingy, and they put me over the side to fend her off from the ship with an oar.

They handed me down the water jug, and then the cook came into the boat, and we sat there in the darkness, wondering why, by all our hopes of future happiness, the captain was so long in coming over to the side and ordering us away from the doomed ship.

The captain was waiting for the other boat to go. Finally he hailed in the darkness: "Are you all right, Mr. Graines?"

The first mate answered: "All right, sir."

"Shove off, then," cried the captain.

The captain was just about to swing over the rail when a dark form came forward and a voice said: "Captain, I go with you."

The captain answered: "Yes, Billy; get in."

HIGGINS LAST TO LEAVE SHIP

It was Billy Higgins, the oiler. Billy dropped into the boat and a moment later the captain followed, bringing with him an end of about forty yards of lead line. The other end was attached to the rail of the ship.

As we swung back to leeward the captain said: "Boys, we will stay right near the ship till she goes down."

This cheerful information, of course, filled us all with glee. The line kept us headed properly into the wind, and as we rode over the monstrous waves we saw upon each rise the swaying lights of the dying *Commodore*.

When came the gray shade of dawn, the form of the *Commodore* grew slowly clear to us as our little ten-foot boat rose over each swell. She was floating with such an air of buoyancy that we laughed when we had time, and said "What a gag it would be on those other fellows if she didn't sink at all."

But later we saw men aboard of her, and later still they began to hail us.

HELPING THEIR MATES

I had forgot to mention that previously we had loosened the end of the lead line and dropped much further to leeward. The men on board were a mystery to us, of course, as we had seen all the boats leave the ship. We rowed back to the ship, but did not approach too near, because we were four men in a ten-foot boat, and we knew that the touch of a hand on our gunwale would assuredly swamp us.

The first mate cried out from the ship that the third boat had foundered alongside. He cried that they had made rafts, and wished us to tow them.

The captain said, "All right."

Their rafts were floating astern. "Jump in!" cried the captain, but there was a singular and most harrowing hesitation. There were five white men and two negroes. This scene in the gray light of morning impressed one as would a view into some place where ghosts move slowly. These seven men on the stern of the sinking *Commodore* were silent. Save the words of the mate to the captain there was no talk. Here was death, but here also was a most singular and indefinable kind of fortitude.

Four men, I remember, clambered over the railing and stood there watching the cold, steely sheen of the sweeping waves.

"Jump," cried the captain again.

The old chief engineer first obeyed the order. He landed on the outside raft and the captain told him how to grip the raft and he obeyed as promptly and as docilely as a scholar in riding school.

THE MATE'S MAD PLUNGE

A stoker followed him, and then the first mate threw his hands over his head and plunged into the sea. He had no life belt and for my part, even when he did this horrible thing, I somehow felt that I could see in the expression of his hands, and in the very toss of his head, as he leaped thus to death, that it was rage, rage, rage unspeakable that was in his heart at the time.

And then I saw Tom Smith, the man who was going to quit filibustering after this expedition, jump to a raft and turn his face toward us. On board the *Commodore* three men strode, still in silence and with their faces turned toward us. One man had his arms folded and was leaning against the deckhouse. His feet were crossed, so that the toe of his left foot pointed downward. There they stood gazing at us, and neither from the deck nor from the rafts was a voice raised. Still was there this silence.

TRIED TO TOW THE RAFTS

The colored stoker on the first raft threw us a line and we began to tow. Of course, we perfectly understood the absolute impossibility of any such thing; our dingy was within six inches of the water's edge, there was an enormous sea running, and I knew that under the circumstances a tugboat would have no light task in moving these rafts.

But we tried it, and would have continued to try it indefinitely, but that something critical came to pass. I was at an oar and so faced the rafts. The cook controlled the line. Suddenly the boat began to go backward and then we saw this negro on the first raft pulling on the line hand over hand and drawing us to him.

He had turned into a demon. He was wild—wild as a tiger. He was crouched on this raft and ready to spring. Every muscle of him seemed to be turned into an elastic spring. His eyes were almost white. His face was the face of a lost man reaching upward, and we knew that the weight of his hand on our gunwale doomed us.

THE *COMMODORE* SINKS

The cook let go of the line. We rowed around to see if we could not get a line from the chief engineer, and all this time, mind you, there were no shrieks, no groans, but silence, silence and silence, and then the *Commodore* sank.

She lurched to windward, then swung afar back, righted and dove into the sea, and the rafts were suddenly swallowed by this frightful maw of the ocean. And then by the men on the ten-foot dingy were words said that were still not words—something far beyond words.

The lighthouse of Mosquito Inlet stuck up above the horizon like the point of a pin. We turned our dingy toward the shore.

The history of life in an open boat for thirty hours would no doubt be instructive for the young, but none is to be told here and now. For my part I would prefer to tell the story at once, because from it would shine the splendid manhood of Captain Edward Murphy and of William Higgins, the oiler, but let it suffice at this time to say that when we were swamped in the surf and making the best of our way toward the shore the captain gave orders amid the wildness of the breakers as clearly as if he had been on the quarter deck of a battleship.

John Kitchell of Daytona came running down the beach, and as he ran the air was filled with clothes. If he had pulled a single lever and undressed, even as the fire horses harness, he could not seem to me to have stripped with more speed. He dashed into the water and dragged the cook. Then he went after the captain, but the captain sent him to me, and then it was that he saw Billy Higgins lying with his forehead on sand that was clear of the water, and he was dead.

Robert Wooster Stallman

"THE OPEN BOAT": A SYMBOLIC INTERPRETATION

CRANE did not have to invent any plot for "The Open Boat": he transcribed the whole from his own experience. Yet it is as much an invention as "The Reluctant Voyagers." [1] Crane always was concerned

From *Stephen Crane: An Omnibus*, edited by Robert Wooster Stallman, copyright 1952 by Alfred A. Knopf, Inc. Reprinted by permission of the publishers.

1. Another story by Crane.

to get facts down with scrupulous fidelity to the truth of experience, and he went to extraordinary pains to be certain that the facts in "The Open Boat" squared with what actually happened. To find out whether he had them right, he checked them with the captain of the *Commodore*. Their conversation was overheard by Ralph Paine and recorded in his *Roads of Adventure* (1922):

—Listen, Ed, I want to have this right, from your point of view. How does it sound so far?—
—You've got it, Steve—said the other man.
—That is just how it happened and how we felt. Read me some more of it.—

Accounts of the wreck in dispatches to the *New York Press* and the *Florida Times-Union* . . . together with Crane's own report, furnished a history of the tragedy. Crane did not alter the facts or their sequence, yet the difference between what happened and what Crane reconstructed from his experience is immense. It is the difference that distinguishes life from art. In "The Open Boat" the whole event is charged with significance. Every fact has been charged with meaning and patterned into a scheme of relationships. Realistic details have been converted into symbols, and their sequence forms a designed whole possessing a life of its own.

By what methods has Crane brought about this symbolic conversion? Let us examine some of his symbols and see how symbols are created.

Symbols are created by establishing correlations between the plight of the characters and their environment (for example, battlefield, forest, or sea). The mental state, feeling, or mood is transposed and objectified in things, in natural objects, or in other persons whose plight parallels the central situation or stands in contrast to it. Thus in *The Red Badge* Henry's mental state is objectified in a single recurrent object, the flag, and the meaning of the whole book gradually accretes around this dominant or focal symbol. In "The Open Boat" the confused mental state of the men is identified with the confused and "broken sea," and it is obversely objectified in the contradictory gulls that hover "comfortably" over them, gruesome and ominous birds utterly indifferent to the plight of the men. The bird's "black eyes were *wistfully* fixed upon the captain's head." The unconcern of the universe is symbolized by the wind-tower as it appears to them when they head for the beach:

This tower was a giant, standing with its back to the plight of the ants. It represented in a degree, to the correspondent, the serenity of nature amid the struggles of the individual—nature in the wind, and nature in the vision of the men. She did not seem cruel to him then, nor beneficent, nor treacherous, nor wise. But she was indifferent, flatly indifferent.

Symbols are generated by parallelisms and repetitions. A symbolic detail at the very beginning of "The Open Boat" prepares for the final incident, the death of the oiler. He is represented by the oar he steers: "It was a thin little oar and it seemed often ready to snap." In *The Red Badge* the chattering fear of a frightened squirrel, fleeing when Henry Fleming throws a pine cone at him (Chapter 7), parallels the plight of the hero under shellfire.

Symbols are at their most effective when they radiate multiple correspondences or different contents—at different times or at the same time.

Colors, used *only* as decorative pattern in *Maggie* and "An Experiment in Misery," are symbolically employed in *The Red Badge*. Here the symbolic value of any given color varies according to its location in a specific context. Symbolic patterns of life and death are established, for example, by the *same* color. The one is signified by the *yellow* of the sun and the other by the *yellow* of uniforms on dead soldiers.

"The Open Boat" and *The Red Badge* are indentical in form, in theme, and even in their patterns of leitmotivs and imagery. In "The Open Boat" the despair-hope mood of the men is established (and the point of view prepared for) in the opening sentence: "None of them knew the color of the sky"; and the final scene repeats the same contrast mood. At the end, when the men are tossed upon "the lonely and indifferent shore," the once barbarously abrupt waves now pace "to and fro in the moonlight." As the sea changes, so the men change. They experience a change of heart. Their serenity, we are made to feel, is signified by the seemingly quieted waves. But the serenity of the waves is deceptive, for the violent sea actually remains unabated. Their victory over nature has cost them one of their brotherhood—the oiler lies face-downward in the shallows.

The death of Higgins symbolizes nature's injustice, her treachery and indifference, but it is *through* his death that this truth is revealed to the others. It is his death that changes their vision. (Similarly, in *The Red Badge*, it is the death of Jim Conklin that changes Henry Fleming's vision.) At the end, when the men hear "the great sea's voice," they understand what it says, what life means, because they have suffered the worst that the sea can exact from them—"they felt that they could *then* be *interpreters*." Life—represented by the ritual of comfort bestowed on the saved men by the people on the beach—life now becomes "sacred to their minds."

This theme of insight through suffering is prepared for by the very first image of the story: "None of them knew the color of the sky." It is foreshadowed and epitomized in the song that the correspondent recites to himself: "A soldier of the Legion lay dying in Algiers." The correspondent had known this verse when a child, but *then* he had not regarded the death of that soldier as important or meaningful. He had never felt any sympathy for the soldier's plight because he himself had not yet experienced it. "It was less to him than the breaking of a pencil's point." The soldier's plight parallels and foremirrors the oiler's plight. The image of the delicate pencil point correlates with the image of the thin oar of the oiler that "seemed often ready to snap." The whole meaning of "The Open Boat" is focused in the death of the oiler.

Cleanth Brooks AND
Robert Penn Warren

AN INTERPRETATION OF "ARABY"

ON WHAT may be called the simplest level this is a story of a boy's disappointment. A great part of the story, however, does not directly concern itself with the boy's love affair, but with the world in which he lives—the description of his street, the information about the dead priest and the priest's abandoned belongings, the relations with the aunt and uncle. These matters seem to come very naturally into the story; that is, they may be justified individually in the story on realistic grounds. But if such elements *merely* serve as "setting" or as mere atmosphere, then the story is obviously overloaded with nonfunctional material. Obviously, for any reader except the most casual, these items do have a function. If we find in what way these apparently irrelevant items in "Araby" are related to each other and to the disappointment of the boy, we shall have defined the theme of the story.

What, then, is the relation of the boy's disappointment to such matters as the belongings of the dead priest, the fact that he stands apart talking to the girl while his friends are quarreling over the cap, the gossip over the tea table, the uncle's lateness, and so on? One thing that is immediately suggested by the mention of these things is the boy's growing sense of isolation, the lack of sympathy between him and his friends, teachers, and family. He says, "I imagined that I bore my chalice safely through a throng of foes." For instance, when the uncle is standing in the hall, the boy could not go into the front parlor and lie at the window; or at school his ordinary occupations began to seem "ugly monotonous child's play." But this sense of isolation has, also, moments which are almost triumphant, as for example, is implied when the porters at the station wave the crowds back, "saying that it was a special train for the bazaar" and was not for them. The boy is left alone in the bare carriage, but he is going to "Araby," moving triumphantly toward some romantic and exotic fulfillment. The metaphor of the chalice implies the same kind of precious secret triumph. It is not only the ordinary surrounding world, however, from which he is cruelly or triumphantly isolated. He is also isolated from the girl herself. He talks to her only once, and then is so confused that he does not know how to answer her. But the present which he hopes to bring her from Araby would somehow serve as a means of communicating his feelings to her, a symbol for their relationship in the midst of the inimical world.

In the last scene at the bazaar, there is a systematic, though subtle, preparation for the final realization on the part of the boy. There is the "improvised wooden platform" in contrast with the "magical name" displayed above the building. Inside, most of the stalls are closed. The young lady and young men who talk together are important in the preparation. They pay the boy no mind, except in so far as the young lady is compelled by her position as clerk to ask him what he wants. But her tone is not "encouraging." She, too, belongs to the inimical world. But she, also, belongs to a world into which he is trying to penetrate: she and her admirers are on terms of easy intimacy—an intimacy in contrast to his relation to Mangan's sister. It is an exotic, rich world into which he cannot penetrate: he can only look "humbly at the great jars that stood like eastern guards at either side of the dark entrance to the stall. . . ." But, ironically, the young lady and her admirers, far from realizing that they are on holy, guarded ground, indulge in a trivial, easy banter, which seems to defile and cheapen the secret world from which the boy is barred. How do we know this? It is not stated, but the contrast between the conversation of the young lady and her admirers, and the tone of the sentence quoted just above indicates such an interpretation.

This scene, then, helps to point up and particularize the general sense of isolation suggested by the earlier descriptive materials, and thereby to prepare for the last sentence of the story, in which, under the sudden darkness of the cheap and barnlike bazaar, the boy sees himself as "a creature driven and derided by vanity," while his eyes burn with anguish and anger.

We have seen how the apparently casual incidents and items of description do function in the story to build up the boy's sense of intolerable isolation. But this is only part of the function of this material. The careful reader will have noticed how many references, direct or indirect, there are to religion and the ritual of the church. We have the dead priest, the Christian Brothers' School, the aunt's hope that the bazaar is not "some

Freemason affair," her remark when the uncle has been delayed, to "this night of Our Lord." At one level, these references merely indicate the type of community in which the impressionable boy is growing up. But there are other, less obvious, references, which relate more intimately to the boy's experience. Even the cries of the shop boys for him are "shrill litanies." He imagines that he bears a "chalice safely through a throng of foes." When he is alone the name of Mangan's sister springs to his lips "in strange prayers and praises." For this reason, when he speaks of his "confused adoration," we see that the love of the girl takes on, for him, something of the nature of a mystic, religious experience. The use of the very word *confused* hints of the fact that romantic love and religious love are mixed up in his mind.

It has been said that the boy is isolated from a world which seems ignorant of, and even hostile to, his love. In a sense he knows that his aunt and uncle are good and kind, but they do not understand him. He had once found satisfaction in the society of his companions and in his school work, but he has become impatient with both. But there is also a sense in which he accepts his isolation and is even proud of it. The world not only does not understand his secret but would cheapen and contaminate it. The metaphor of the chalice borne through a throng of foes, supported as it is by the body of the story, suggests a sort of consecration like that of the religious devotee. The implications of the references to religion, then, help define the boy's attitude and indicate why, for him, so much is staked upon the journey to the bazaar. It is interesting to note, therefore, that the first overt indication of his disillusionment and disappointment is expressed in a metaphor involving a church: "Nearly all the stalls were closed and the greater part of the hall was in darkness. I recognized a silence like that which pervades a church after a service. . . . Two men were counting money on a salver. I listened to the fall of the coins." So, it would seem, here we have the idea that the contamination of the world has invaded the very temple of love—there are, as it were, money-changers in the very temple. (The question may arise as to whether this is not reading too much into the passage. Perhaps it is. But whatever interpretation is to be made of the particular incident, it is by just such suggestion and implication that closely wrought stories, such as this one, are controlled by the author and embody their fundamental meaning.)

Is this a sentimental story? It is about an adolescent love affair, about "calf love," a subject which usually is not to be taken seriously and is often an occasion for amusement. The boy of the story is obviously investing casual incidents with a meaning which they do not deserve; and himself admits, in the end, that he has fallen into self-deception. How does the author avoid the charge that he has taken the matter over-seriously?

The answer to this question would involve a consideration of the point of view from which the story is told. It is told by the hero himself, but after a long lapse of time, after he has reached maturity. This fact, it is true, is not stated in the story, but the style itself is not that of an adolescent boy. It is a formal and complicated style, rich, as has already been observed, in subtle implications. In other words, the man is looking back upon the boy, detached and judicial. For instance, the boy, in the throes of the experience, would never have said of himself: "I had never spoken to her, except for a few casual words, and yet her name was like a summons to all my foolish blood." The man knows, as it were, that the behavior of the boy was, in a sense, foolish. The emotions of the boy are confused, but the person telling the story, the boy grown up, is not confused. He has unraveled the confusion long after, knows that it existed and why it existed.

If the man has unraveled the confusions of the boy, why is the event still significant to him? Is he merely dwelling on the pathos of adolescent experience? It seems, rather, that he sees in the event, as he looks back on it, a kind of parable of a problem which has run through later experience. The discrepancy between the real and the ideal scarcely exists for the child, but it is a constant problem, in all sorts of terms, for the adult. This story is about a boy's first confrontation of that problem—that is, about his growing up. The man may have made adjustments to this problem, and may have worked out certain provisional solutions, but, looking back, he still recognizes it as a problem, and an important one. The sense of isolation and disillusion which, in the boy's experience, may seem to spring from a trivial situation, becomes not less, but more aggravated and fundamental in the adult's experience. So, the story is not merely an account of a stage in the process of growing up—it does not merely represent a clinical interest in the psychology of growing up—but is a symbolic rendering of a central conflict in mature experience.

Robert Penn Warren

IRONY WITH A CENTER:
KATHERINE ANNE PORTER

THE FICTION of Katherine Anne Porter, despite widespread critical adulation, has never found the public which its distinction merits. Many of her stories are unsurpassed in modern fiction, and some are not often equaled. She belongs to the relatively small group of writers—extraordinarily small, when one considers the vast number of stories published every year in English and American magazines—who have done serious, consistent, original, and vital work in the form of short fiction—the group which would include James Joyce, Katherine Mansfield, Sherwood Anderson, and Ernest Hemingway. This list does not include a considerable number of other writers who, though often finding other forms more congenial—the novel or poetry—have scored occasional triumphs in the field of short fiction. Then, of course, there is a very large group of writers who have a great facility, a great mechanical competence, and sometimes moments of real perception, but who work from no fundamental and central conviction.

It was once fashionable to argue complacently that the popular magazine had created the short story—had provided the market and had cultivated an appetite for the product. It is true that the magazine did provide the market, but at the same time, and progressively, the magazine has corrupted the short story. What the magazine encourages is not so much the short story as a conscious or unconscious division of the artistic self of the writer. One can still discover (as in an address delivered by Mr. Frederick Lewis Allen to the American Philosophical Society) a genial self-congratulation in the face of "mass appreciation." But, writes Mr. R. P. Blackmur in reply:

> In fact, mass appreciation of the kind which Mr. Allen approves represents the constant danger to the artist of any serious sort: the danger of popularization *before* creation. . . . The difference between great art and popular art is relatively small; but the difference between either and popularized art is radical, and absolute. Popular art is topical and natural, great art is deliberate and thematic. What can be popularized in either is only what can be sold . . . a scheme which requires the constant replacement of the shoddy goods. He (Mr. Allen) does not mean to avow this; he no doubt means the contrary; but there it is. Until American or any other society is educated either up to the level or back to the level of art with standards, whether popular or great, it can be sold nothing but art without standards. . . .

The fact that Miss Porter has not attempted a compromise may account for the relatively small body of her published fiction. There was the collection of stories published in 1931 under the title *Flowering Judas;* an

From "Irony with a Center: Katherine Anne Porter" from *Selected Essays of Robert Penn Warren,* copyright 1941 by Robert Penn Warren. Reprinted by permission of Random House, Inc.

enlarged collection, under the same title in 1935, which includes two novelettes, *The Cracked Looking-Glass* and *Hacienda*, the latter of which had been previously published by Harrison, in Paris; a collection of three novelettes under the title *Pale Horse, Pale Rider*, in 1939; the Modern Library edition of *Flowering Judas;* and a few pieces, not yet in book form, which have appeared in various magazines—for instance, sections of the uncompleted biography of Cotton Mather and the brilliant story "A Day's Work."

Her method of composition does not, in itself, bend readily to the compromise. In many instances, a story or novelette has not been composed straight off. Instead, a section here and a section there have been written —little germinal scenes explored and developed. Or scenes or sketches of character which were never intended to be incorporated in the finished work have been developed in the process of trying to understand the full potentiality of the material. One might guess at an approach something like this: a special, local excitement provoked by the material—character or incident; an attempt to define the nature of that local excitement, as local—to squeeze it and not lose a drop; an attempt to understand the relationships of the local excitements and to define the implications—to arrive at theme; the struggle to reduce theme to pattern. That would seem to be the natural history of the characteristic story. Certainly, it is a method which requires time, scrupulosity, and contemplation.

The method itself is an index to the characteristics of Miss Porter's fiction —the rich surface detail scattered with apparently casual profuseness and the close structure which makes such detail meaningful; the great compression and economy which one discovers upon analysis; the precision of psychology and observation, the texture of the style.

Most reviewers, commenting upon Miss Porter's distinction, refer to her "style"—struck, no doubt, by an exceptional felicity of phrase, a precision in the use of metaphor, and a subtlety of rhythm. It is not only the appreciation of the obviously poetical strain in Miss Porter's work that has tended to give her reputation some flavor of the special and exquisite, but also the appreciation of the exceptional precision of her language. When one eminent critic praises her for an "English of a purity and precision almost unique in contemporary American fiction," he is giving praise richly merited and praise for a most important quality, but this praise, sad to relate as a commentary on our times, is a kind that does encourage the special reputation. This same eminent critic also praises Miss Porter as an artist, which goes to say that he himself knows very well that her language is but one aspect of her creations; but even so, the word *artist* carries its own overtones of exquisiteness.

The heart of the potential reader may have been chilled—and I believe quite rightly—by the praise of "beautiful style." He is put off by a reviewer's easy abstracting of style for comment and praise; his innocence repudiates the fallacy of agreeable style. The famous common reader is not much concerned with English as such, pure or impure, precise or imprecise, and he is no more concerned with the artist as artist. He is concerned with what the English will say to him, and with what the artist will do for him, or to him.

It is, of course, just and proper for us to praise Miss Porter for her English and her artistry, but we should remind ourselves that we prize those things because she uses them to create vivid and significant images of life. All this is not to say that we are taking the easy moralistic, or easy Philistine, view of English or artistry. We know that the vividness and the significance of any literary work exist only in the proper medium, and that only because of a feeling for the medium and an understanding of artistry did the writer succeed, in the first place, in discovering vividness and significance. We hope that we shall never have to remind ourselves of that fact, and now we remind ourselves of the vividness and significance in which Miss Porter's English and artistry eventuate, only because we would balance praise for the special with praise for the general, praise for subtlety with praise for strength, praise for sensibility with praise for intellect.

But let us linger upon the matter of Miss Porter's style in the hope that it can be used as a point of departure. Take, for example, a paragraph from the title story of *Flowering Judas*, the description of Braggioni, the half-Italian, half-Indian revolutionist in Mexico, "a leader of men, skilled revolutionist, and his skin has been punctured in honorable warfare." His followers "warm themselves in his reflected glory and say to each other, 'He has a real nobility, a love of humanity raised above mere personal affections.' The excess of this self-love has flowed out, inconveniently for her, over Laura"—the puzzled American girl who has been lured to Mexico by revolutionary enthusiasm and before whom he sits with his guitar and sings sentimental songs, while his wife weeps at home. But here is the passage.

Braggioni . . . leans forward, balancing his paunch between his spread knees, and sings with tremendous emphasis, weighing his words. He has, the song relates, no father and no mother, nor even a friend to console him; lonely as a wave of the sea he comes and goes, lonely as a wave. His mouth opens round and yearns sideways, his balloon cheeks grow oily with the labor of song. He bulges marvelously in his expensive garments. Over his lavender collar, crushed upon a purple necktie, held by a diamond hoop: over his ammunition belt of tooled leather worked in silver, buckled cruelly around his gasping middle: over the tops of his glossy yellow shoes Braggioni swells with ominous ripeness, his mauve silk hose stretched taut, his ankles bound with the stout leather thongs of his shoes.

When he stretches his eyelids at Laura she notes again that his eyes are the true tawny yellow cat's eyes. He is rich, not in money, he tells her, but in power, and this power brings with it the blameless ownership of things, and the right to indulge his love of small luxuries. "I have a taste for the elegant refinements," he said once, flourishing a yellow silk handkerchief before her nose. "Smell that? It is Jockey Club, imported from New York." Nonetheless he is wounded by life. He will say so presently. "It is true everything turns to dust in the hand, to gall on the tongue." He sighs and his leather belt creaks like a saddle girth.

The passage is sharp and evocative. Its phrasing embodies a mixture, a fusion, of the shock of surprise and the satisfaction of precision—a resolved tension, which may do much to account for the resonance and vibration of the passage. We have in it the statement, "His mouth opens round and yearns sideways"—and we note the two words *yearns* and *side-*

ways; in the phrase, "labor of song"; in, "he bulges marvelously"; in, "Braggioni swells with ominous ripeness." But upon inspection it may be discovered that the effect of these details is not merely a local effect. The subtle local evocations really involve us in the center of the scene; we are taken to the core of the meaning of the scene, and thence to the central impulse of the story; and thence, possibly to the germinal idea of all of this author's fiction. All of these filaments cannot be pursued back through the web—the occasion does not permit; but perhaps a few can be traced to the meaning of the scene itself in the story.

What we have here is the revolutionist who loves luxury, who feels that power gives blameless justification to the love of elegant refinements, but whose skin has been punctured in "honorable warfare"; who is a competent leader of men, but who is vain and indolent; who is sentimental and self-pitying, but, at the same time, ruthless; who betrays his wife and yet, upon his return home, will weep with his wife as she washes his feet and weeps; who labors for the good of man, but is filled with self-love.

We have here a tissue of contradictions and the very phraseology takes us to these contradictions. For instance, the word *yearns* involves the sentimental, blurred emotion, but immediately afterward the words *sideways* and *oily* remind us of the grossness, the brutality, the physical appetite. So with the implied paradox in the "labor of song." The ammunition belt, we recall, is buckled *cruelly* about his "gasping middle." The ammunition belt reminds us that this indolent, fat, apparently soft, vain man is capable of violent action, is a man of violent profession, and sets the stage for the word *cruelly*, which involves the paradox of the man who loves mankind and is capable of individual cruelties, and which, further, reminds us that he punishes himself out of physical vanity and punishes himself by defining himself in his calling—the only thing that belts in his sprawling, meaningless animality. He swells with "ominous ripeness"—and we sense the violent threat in the man as contrasted with his softness, a kind of great overripe plum as dangerous as a grenade, a feeling of corruption mixed with sentimental sweetness; and specifically we are reminded of the threat to Laura in the situation. We come to the phrase "wounded by life," and we pick up again the motif hinted at in the song and in the lingering rhythms: "He has, the song relates, no father and no mother, nor even a friend to console him; lonely as a wave of the sea he comes and goes, lonely as a wave." In nothing is there to be found a balm—not in revolution, in vanity, in love—for the "vast cureless wound of his self-esteem." Then, after the bit about the wound, we find the sentence: "He sighs and his leather belt creaks like a saddle girth." The defeated, sentimental sigh, the cureless wound, and the bestial creaking of the leather.

If this reading of the passage is acceptable, the passage itself is a rendering of the problem which the character of Braggioni poses to Laura. It is stated, in bare, synoptic form, elsewhere:

The gluttonous bulk of Braggioni has become a symbol of her many disillusions, for a revolutionist should be lean, animated by heroic faith, a vessel of abstract virtues. This is nonsense, she knows it now and is ashamed of it. Revolution must have leaders, and leadership is a career for energetic men. She is, her comrades tell her, full of romantic error, for what she defines as a cynicism is to them merely a developed sense of reality.

What is the moral reality here? This question is, I should say, the theme of the story, which exists in an intricate tissue of paradox, and is posed only in the dream Laura has at the end, a dream which embodies but does not resolve the question.

With all the enchanting glitter of style and all the purity of language and all the flow and flicker of feeling, Miss Porter's imagination, as a matter of fact, is best appreciated if we appreciate its essential austerity, its devotion to the fact drenched in God's direct daylight, its concern with the inwardness of character, and its delight in the rigorous and discriminating deployment of a theme. [. . .]

[. . .] The skeptical and ironical bias is, I think, important in Miss Porter's work, and it is true that her work wears an air of detachment and contemplation. But, I should say, her irony is an irony with a center, never an irony for irony's sake. It simply implies, I think, a refusal to accept the formula, the ready-made solution, the hand-me-down morality, the word for the spirit. It affirms, rather, the constant need for exercising discrimination, the arduous obligation of the intellect in the face of conflicting dogmas, the need for a dialectical approach to matters of definition, the need for exercising as much of the human faculty as possible.

This basic attitude finds its correlation in her work, in the delicacy of phrase, the close structure, the counterpoint of incident and implication. That is, a story must test its thematic line at every point against its total circumstantiality; the thematic considerations must, as it were, be validated in terms of circumstance and experience, and never be resolved in the poverty of statement.

In one sense, it is the intellectual rigor and discrimination that gives Miss Porter's work its classic distinction and control—that is, if any one quality can be said to be uniquely responsible. No, no single quality can take that credit, but where many writers have achieved stories of perception, feeling, sensibility, strength, or charm, few have been able to achieve stories of a deep philosophic urgency in the narrow space, and fewer still have been able to achieve the kind of thematic integration of a body of stories, the mark of the masters, the thing that makes us think first of the central significance of a writer rather than of some incidental and individual triumph. For Miss Porter's bright indicative poetry is, at long last, a literally metaphysical poetry, too. The luminosity is from inward.

Mary Burchard Orvis

CONVERSATION IN "ROPE"

An extremely effective use of conversation is to be found in Katherine Anne Porter's story "Rope," where the comedy is that of husband and wife bickering over trivialities, the kind of bickering that reveals underlying tensions, larger issues. It is interesting to study this unusual technique. Paragraph one introduces the scene with the husband returning from the grocery store. Paragraph two asks:

Had he brought the coffee? She had been waiting all day long for coffee. They had forgot it when they ordered at the store the first day.

Paragraph three contains the germ of the conflict:

Gosh, no, he hadn't. Lord, now he'd have to go back. Yes, he would if it killed him. He thought, though, he had everything else. She reminded him it was only because he didn't drink coffee himself. If he did he would remember it quick enough. Suppose they ran out of cigarettes? Then she saw the rope. What was that for? Well, he thought it might do to hang clothes on, or something. Naturally she asked him if he thought they were going to run a laundry? They already had a fifty foot line hanging right before his eyes? Why, hadn't he noticed it, really? It was a blot on the landscape to her.

This paragraph is woven with the intricacy and craftsmanship which one expects from Miss Porter. First it sets a *tone* of mild irony and amusement at the sight of the young couple quarreling about nothing at all. This situation itself is so common that the reader also experiences the feeling of having seen it many times. (Dorothy Parker used it in "Here We Are," with much the same effect, but nowhere near the same degree of artistry.) This sense of truth to life is brought out primarily through the exact reproduction of bickering conversation, tones, rhythms, and oratorical questions in particular. These questions are ironic and sarcastic and they also show that the young couple are "on" to each other's rationalizations and psychological processes. (This fact is conveyed through their pointing out to each other the interest in coffee or cigarettes, which are the special concern of one or the other—very human, indeed is this.)

Most revealing is the way in which the author has shown a mountain growing out of a mole-hill: all this excitement and tension about a rope! The quarrel advances steadily from its trivial inception to its happy ending, which makes one wonder if this isn't a case of quarreling in order to make up. The tension mounts with each question and answer; slowly but consistently the wife's irritation is revealed, largely through her sarcastic questions and her observation of the man's ability to remember his own cigarettes. One can easily supply the implied italics of her emphasized words: "What was *that* for?" "run a *laundry*," "*already*," "right before his *eyes*," "*really*," "*blot*."

682

It would hardly be possible to pack more revelation of scene, conflict, character, more human nature into a few words. The economy is clear and the tonal integration is memorable, however slight the narrative itself. And this brings us to our last point in regard to this story. It is very important.

One can make a big lather out of a little soap—if one is an artist! This is very simple, everyday material available to all of us. But how many of us could do with it what has been done here? The achievement is, as we have noted, similar to the kind of thing accomplished by Dorothy Parker. The effect in this kind of writing arises largely from skillful reporting on human foibles. But to the student of techniques—and every writer had better be a student of techniques—there are the added values of craftsmanship.

The mechanical details to be noticed here, the devices used, are *original*, or at least uncommon. The Porter story in no way depends upon techniques used earlier by Dorothy Parker. It does, indeed, go her one better as a reporter of conversation.

The student will observe that there are neither quotation marks nor "saids." But—and this is not always the case when either is omitted—the action is entirely clear. We always know who says what and we know it at once, without any annoying looking back and checking over. (One of the commonest faults of amateurs in attempting to dispense with quotes and saids is a maddening obscurity. Every teacher of narration will certify to this!) Dispensing with the customary devices and forms, Katherine Anne Porter has accomplished results simply by her knowledge of speech rhythms and accents used by bickering people, and by an exact reproduction of these sound elements. She has attuned her ears to recognize the revelations of everyday talk in moments of emotion. And she knows that emotions out of proportion to the situation are in themselves revealing of underlying frictions. One sees this clearly as one goes along with the story to the end. "It's all," we are prone to say, "in the way a thing is said." By that we mean tone and emphasis as well as phraseology.

Arthur Mizener

F. SCOTT FITZGERALD:
THE POET OF BORROWED TIME

THE commonplace about Scott Fitzgerald is that he was "the laureate of the Jazz Age." If this means anything, it means that he was a kind of eulogistic fictional historian of the half dozen years following the first World War when there was such a marked change in American

"F. Scott Fitzgerald: The Poet of Borrowed Time" by Arthur Mizener from *The Lives of Eighteen from Princeton*, edited by Willard Thorp, copyright 1946 by Princeton University Press. Reprinted by permission of the publishers.

manners. In fact, however, Fitzgerald never simply reported experience; every one of his books is an attempt to recreate experience imaginatively. It is true that the objects, the people, the events, and the convictions in terms of which his imagination functioned were profoundly American and of his time. Even in his worst book, as John O'Hara once remarked, "the people were right, the talk was right, the clothes, the cars were real." The substance out of which Fitzgerald constructed his stories, that is to say, was American, perhaps more completely American than that of any other writer of his time. It is possible, therefore, to read his books simply for their sensitive record of his time; but there is a great deal more to them than this.

Fitzgerald's great accomplishment is to have realized in completely American terms the developed romantic attitude, in the end at least in that most responsible form in which all the romantic's sensuous and emotional responses are disciplined by his awareness of the goodness and evilness of human experience. He had a kind of instinct for the tragic view of life and remarked himself how even at the very beginning of his career, "all the stories that came into my head had a touch of disaster in them—the lovely young creatures in my novels went to ruin, the diamond mountains of my short stories blew up, my millionaires were as beautiful and damned as Thomas Hardy's peasants." He had, moreover, with all its weakness and strength and in a time when the undivided understanding was very rare, an almost exclusively creative kind of intelligence, the kind that understands things, not abstractly, but only concretely, in terms of people and situations and events.

From the very beginning he showed facility and that minute awareness of the qualities of times and places and persons which is sharpened to a fine point in the romantic writer by his acute consciousness of the irrevocable passage of everything into the past. "He was haunted," as Malcolm Cowley has said, "by time, as if he wrote in a room full of clocks and calendars." A romantic writer of this kind is bound to take as his characteristic subject his own past, building out of the people and places of his time fables of his own inner experience, working his way into his material by identifying himself with others as Fitzgerald, in a characteristic case, made the doctor in "Family in the Wind" an image of what he saw in himself, a talented man who had achieved great early success and then gone to pieces. As a young man he identified himself imaginatively with his beautiful but less clever sister and practically lived her early social career; in middle age he entered so completely into his daughter's career that, as one of his friends remarked, "Scott, not Scottie, went through Vassar." Thus, always, Fitzgerald lived imaginatively the lives of those with whom, through family affection or some obscure similarity of attitude or experience, he was able to identify himself. [. . .]

[. . .] "Taking things hard—" he wrote in his notebooks, "from ——— to ———: that's [the] stamp that goes into my books so that people can read it blind like braill[e]." The first of these references is to the first girl Fitzgerald was ever deeply in love with; he used his recollection of her over and over again (out of that recollection, for example, he made Josephine, who dominates a whole series of stories in *Taps at Reveille*). The second reference is to the producer who hacked to pieces his finest script. The remark thus covers the whole of Fitzgerald's career.

What develops slowly in a writer of this kind is maturity of judgment, for it is not easy to control what is so powerfully felt initially and is never, even in recollection, tranquil. Fitzgerald was three-fifths of the way through his career as novelist, though only five years from its start, before he produced a book in which the purpose and the form it imposes are adequate to the evoked life. With *The Great Gatsby* the "smoldering hatred" of the imaginative obtuseness, the moral vulgarity, and the sheer brutality of the rich—with its tangled roots in Fitzgerald's puritanical Catholic background, in his middle-class, middle-western upbringing, and in his early poverty—had emerged enough to serve as a dramatic balance for the wonderful freedom and beauty which the life of the rich had for him. "Let me tell you about the very rich," he began in one of his finest stories; and with the establishment of this dramatically balanced view of the rich in *The Great Gatsby* he had found his theme and its fable, for wealth was Fitzgerald's central symbol; around it he eventually built a mythology which enabled him to take imaginative possession of American life.

With this view of his material he could at last give expression to his essentially tragic sense of human experience without forcing that feeling on the material so that it ceased to be probable, as it does in *The Beautiful and Damned* where the characters drift without understanding into disaster and our conviction of their suffering is undermined by the inadequacy of its causes. Until he wrote *The Great Gatsby* Fitzgerald's ability to evoke the nightmare terror of disaster was greater than his ability to motivate the disaster. It is different at the moment in *The Great Gatsby* when we are confronted with Daisy's completely prepared betrayal, seeing her sitting with Tom at the kitchen table over a late supper with "an unmistakable air of natural intimacy," and then find Gatsby watching the house from the driveway, imagining that he is guarding Daisy from Tom. "I walked away," says Nick, "and left him standing there in the moonlight—watching over nothing." Here Fitzgerald's view of his material is completely adequate to his feeling about human experience in general, the life of the people he knows has become the fully rounded particular case for the expression of his whole understanding.

Both his admiration for the wonderful possibilities of the life of the rich and his distrust of it probably go back to Fitzgerald's childhood. He was born in St. Paul on September 24, 1896. Very early in his life he began to weave fantasies around the Hill Mansion, only a few blocks but a good many million dollars away from his home on Summit Avenue; and it was certainly Fitzgerald at Newman as well as Basil Lee at St. Regis who "writhed with shame . . . that . . . he was one of the poorest boys in a rich boys' school." But he was proud, too, of his family, which was not rich, particularly of the Francis Scott Key connection, and included his family among what he once called "the few remnants of the old American aristocracy that's managed to survive in communicable form." The Basil Lee stories, with their wonderful recreation of the emotional tensions and social conflicts of middle-class American childhood and youth, give a reasonably accurate impression of the life he lived as a boy and for two years at Newman.

In the fall of 1913 he went to Princeton, full of an intensified but otherwise normal American boy's ambition to succeed. There he plunged with characteristic energy and passion into the race for social prominence. But for all that he wore the right clothes, had the right manners, belonged to one of the best clubs, and was an important figure in the politically powerful Triangle Club, he neither was nor appeared to be a typical Princeton man. Of the highly competitive, socially subtle, ingrown life of Princeton he made for himself, with his gift for romance, an enormously significant world. The very imaginative intensity with which he took the normal preoccupations of a Princeton undergraduate distinguished him radically from his fellows. There was something unusual, almost flamboyant, even about his looks, which set him apart. Twenty-five years later that oddness of appearance was still before Edmund Wilson's eyes when he remembered their first meeting:

> I climbed, a quarter-century and
>   more
> Played out, the college steps, un-
>   latched my door,
> And, creature strange to college,
>   found you there!
> The pale skin, hard green eyes,
>   and yellow hair.

You can still see something of "the glitter of the hard and emerald eyes" in his pictures and, perhaps too, feel in Fitzgerald's personal history something of what Wilson meant by this figure.

Fitzgerald quickly discovered that Cottage Club was not quite the brilliant society he had dreamed of and presently turned to literature. "I want," he said to Wilson at this time, "to be one of the greatest writers who have ever lived, don't you?" But all this extracurricular activity—in addition to his social career and his writing there were the Triangle Club and a debutante in Chicago—was too

much for his health and his academic standing. In November of his junior year he was forced to retire to St. Paul. He returned in 1916 to repeat this year, but his senior year lasted only a couple of months, for he left Princeton in November to join the army.

Before he left he completed the first of three versions of *This Side of Paradise*. This version appears to have contained almost nothing of what is in the final version except the early scenes of Amory's arrival at Princeton, and one of the few people who saw it has remarked that "it was actually flat, something Scott's work almost never was." One of the worst disappointments of his life was that he never got overseas but ended his military career as what he once called "the worst aide-de-camp in the army" to General A. J. Ryan at Camp Sheridan, near Montgomery, Alabama. Here he met and fell in love with Zelda Sayre, and here too, in the officers' club in the evenings, he rewrote his novel and submitted it to a publisher under the title *The Romantic Egotist*. This is the subtitle of Book I of *This Side of Paradise*, which presumably covers about the same ground. *The Romantic Egotist* was rejected.

When he was discharged in February 1919, Fitzgerald came to New York to make his fortune so that he could marry Zelda. He sold one story to *The Smart Set* for $30; for the rest he collected rejection slips and began to realize that he was not going to make a fortune as a copy-writer at $90 a month. So did Zelda, and sometime late in the spring she decided that the whole thing had been a mistake. At this Fitzgerald threw up his job, got drunk, and went back to St. Paul to write his book once more. By the end of the summer it had become *This Side of Paradise* and in the fall

Scribner's accepted it. Fitzgerald hurried off to Montgomery and Zelda. The nightmare of unhappiness was over, but he never forgot it: "The man with the jingle of money in his pocket who married the girl a year later would always cherish an abiding distrust, an animosity, toward the leisure class—not the conviction of a revolutionary but the smoldering hatred of a peasant. In the years since then I have never been able to stop wondering where my friends' money came from, nor to stop thinking that at one time a sort of *droit de seigneur* might have been exercised to give one of them my girl."

This Side of Paradise is in many ways a very bad book. Edmund Wilson's judgment of it, made at the height of its fame, is perfectly just: "Amory Blaine is an uncertain quantity in a phantasmagoria of incident which has no dominating intention to endow it with unity and force. . . . For another thing, it is very immaturely imagined: it is always just verging on the ludicrous. And, finally, it is one of the most illiterate books of any merit ever published. . . . It is not only ornamented with bogus ideas and faked references but it is full of English words misused with the most reckless abandon." [. . .]

This Side of Paradise was an enormous success, and Fitzgerald, in a way very characteristic of him, responded to success with a naïve, pompous, and fundamentally good-humored vanity. He gave interviews in which he told what a great writer he was; he condoled with Heywood Broun over the latter's lost youth (Broun was thirty); he condescended to his elders and betters. He and Zelda were married in April and plunged happily into the gay and strenuous life of New York. Fitzgerald rode down Fifth Avenue on top of a taxi, dove into the Plaza fountain, and in general displayed his exuberance in the ways which were fashionable in 1920. He also worked all night again and again to pay for the fun and "riding in a taxi one afternoon between very tall buildings under a mauve and rosy sky . . . I began to bawl because I had everything I wanted and knew I would never be so happy again."

For a brief period of three years following the publication of *This Side of Paradise* the Fitzgeralds were figures around New York and their house parties at Westport and Great Neck were famous. It was all very gay and lighthearted; the house guests at Great Neck were advised in a set of Rules for Guests at the Fitzgerald House that "Visitors are requested not to break down doors in search of liquor, even when authorized to do so by the host and hostess" and that "invitations to stay over Monday, issued by the host and hostess during the small hours of Sunday morning, must not be taken seriously." There was a trip to Europe in the summer of 1921 and that winter they went to St. Paul for the birth of their only child. ("It was typical of our precarious position in New York," Fitzgerald wrote later, "that when our child was to be born we played safe and went home to St. Paul.") In 1922 there was another novel, *The Beautiful and Damned*, and a second volume of stories, and in 1923 a play, *The Vegetable*, written with the rosiest expectations of profits, for they were, as usual, out of money. But the play flopped dismally in Atlantic City, and there was no attempt to bring it to New York. In 1924, in order to live more cheaply, they went abroad.

The Beautiful and Damned is an enormous improvement on *This Side* of *Paradise*, more than anything else because Fitzgerald, though he has not yet found out how to motivate disaster, has a much clearer sense of the precise feel of the disaster he senses in the life he knows. The book is also a great advance on its predecessor technically, much more unified, much less mixed in tone. The tendency to substitute lectures for dialogue is subdued. [. . .]

[. . .] *The Beautiful and Damned* is full of precisely observed life and Fitzgerald is often able to make us feel the poignancy of his characters' suffering, but he is able to provide neither an adequate cause for their suffering nor an adequate reason within their characters for their surrender. In the end you do not believe they ever were people who wanted the opportunities for fineness that the freedom of wealth provides; you believe them only people who wanted luxury. They are pitiful, and their pathos is often brilliantly realized; but they are not tragic.

With occasional interruptions, the Fitzgeralds remained abroad from 1924 until the autumn of 1931, traveling a good deal and living in a great many hotels but usually returning for the summer to the Cap d'Antibes. They came back to America in 1927, went to California for a while, and then rented a big old house on the Delaware "to bring us a judicious tranquility." But they were soon back in Europe where they remained, except for a short trip in 1929, until their final return. Fitzgerald later described the period quite simply as "seven years of waste and tragedy," but at the time their life, particularly the summers on the Riviera, seemed the life of freedom and culture and charm. The little group which made the summer Riviera its private style for a few years before everyone else began to come there was brilliant and varied. There were the rich and cultivated like the Gerald Murphys, the writers like Charles MacArthur and Alexander Woollcott, and the musicians like Grace Moore. They led a busy, unconventional, and, as it seemed to them, somehow significant life; "whatever happened," Fitzgerald wrote later, "seemed to have something to do with art." They made private movies about such characters as "Princess Alluria, the wickedest woman in Europe," writing the unprintable subtitles on the pink walls of Grace Moore's villa and deliberately forgetting to erase them after they had been photographed; they kidnaped orchestras to play for them all night; they gave high-comedy dinners; and they drank a great deal.

But all the time Fitzgerald's almost animal sensitivity to potential disaster was at work: "By 1927, a wide-spread neurosis began to be evident, faintly signalled like a nervous beating of the feet, by the popularity of cross-word puzzles. I remember a fellow expatriate opening a letter from a mutual friend of ours, urging him to come home and be revitalized by the hardy, bracing qualities of the native soil. It was a strong letter and it affected us both deeply, until we noticed that it was headed from a nerve sanitorium in Pennsylvania." Looking back at the period afterwards he could see its weaknesses clearly without forgetting its charm. "It was borrowed time anyhow—the whole upper tenth of a nation living with the insouciance of grand ducs and the casualness of chorus girls. But moralizing is easy now and it was pleasant to be in one's twenties in such a certain and unworried time."

It was a period during which Fitzgerald produced very little serious work. *The Great Gatsby* was written during the fall and winter of 1924 and he published no other novel until

Tender Is the Night, ten years later. This was not, however, wholly the fault of the kind of life he and Zelda were living, even indirectly; it was partly the result of the extremely ambitious plans Fitzgerald laid for himself after *The Great Gatsby's* critical success. [. . .]

After *The Great Gatsby* Fitzgerald set himself a task which, as Edmund Wilson once remarked, would have given Dostoevski pause. It was to be a story of matricide, and though an immense amount of work was done on it, he was never able to complete a novel on this subject. As if to mock his failure, and perhaps too his deep concern for the subject, Fitzgerald wrote a comic ballad about matricide which he used to perform with great effect as a parlor trick.

In 1930 Zelda, who had been working for several years with all her energy to become a ballet dancer, broke down, and late in 1931 the Fitzgeralds returned to America and settled in a rambling old brown house at Rodgers Forge, between Baltimore and Towson. Here they remained until Fitzgerald went to Hollywood in 1937. [. . .]

In 1935 Fitzgerald had a recurrence of the tuberculosis which had first attacked him when he was an undergraduate and he was never entirely free from it again. In August 1937 he signed a contract with Metro-Goldwyn-Mayer and settled down in Hollywood to write for them. He worked on a number of important scripts, including *Three Comrades, Gone with the Wind,* and *Madame Curie;* he produced a large number of short stories, mostly for *Esquire;* and he began to work on a novel, *The Last Tycoon.* He said himself that he had been thinking about the subject almost from the time of his arrival in Hollywood; he certainly had a great deal of work done on it by late 1939

when he apparently began the actual writing. About half the story was written when he died, though none of it in the final form he had visualized for it.

Thanks to Edmund Wilson's brilliant unraveling of Fitzgerald's notes, it is possible to see pretty clearly what his plans for *The Last Tycoon* were, how rich its theme was to be, and how tight its structure. Of what he planned to make of the book he said: "Unlike *Tender Is the Night,* it is not a story of deterioration. . . . If one book could ever be 'like' another, I should say it is more 'like' *The Great Gatsby.* But I hope it will be entirely different—I hope it will be something new, arouse new emotions, perhaps even a new way of looking at certain phenomena."

On the evidence of what he had actually written there is every reason for supposing that, had he lived, he would have fulfilled these hopes. The material and the people he is dealing with are entirely new, yet his command of the tangled social, industrial, and creative life of Hollywood is so complete that there is no moment in what he has written which is not utterly convincing, at the same time that it exists, not for itself alone, but for what Fitzgerald wanted to say, about Hollywood, about American life, about human experience as a whole. The writing, even though none of it is final, is as subtle and flexible as anything he ever did, and so unremittingly disciplined by the book's central intention that it takes on a kind of lyric intensity, glowing with the life of Fitzgerald's feelings for everything he was trying to say. This intensity is a remarkable achievement for a man who thought—and at least on physical grounds had some reason for thinking—a year before he started to write *The Last Tycoon* that he had only enough talent left "to stretch out over two more novels" (and "I may have to stretch it a little thin"). Most remarkable of all, though less final, is the evidence that he was succeeding, as he never had before with so much to say, in holding everything within the focusing form to which he had committed his story in the beginning.

Around December 1, 1940, Fitzgerald had a serious heart attack. He went on working on his novel, however, with such persistence that on December 20 he put off a visit from his doctor in order to finish a draft of the first episode of Chapter VI. The next day he had another, fatal, heart attack. In some sense Fitzgerald's wonderful natural talent was always haunted by the exigencies of his life. This final exigency aborted what promised to be his best novel, so that it is possible to say of it only what can be said of his work as a whole, that it is very fine and that, with a little more—or a little less—help from circumstances, it might, such was his talent, have been far finer. As John Peale Bishop said in his elegy for Fitz-

gerald, when we think of his death we

> think of all you did
> And all you might have done, before undone
> By death, but for the undoing of despair.
>
> [. . .]

It is not easy at this close range to separate our opinion of the man from our opinion of the writer, particularly since circumstances combined to make the man a legendary, eponymous figure. But as the accidents of the man's life—and the lies about it—gradually fade, we may well come to feel about the writer, with his purity of imagination and his imperviousness to the abstract theories and intellectual fads which have hag-ridden our times, as Stephen Vincent Benét did when he remarked after Fitzgerald's death: "You can take off your hats, now, gentlemen, and I think perhaps you had better. This is not a legend, this is a reputation—and, seen in perspective, it may well be one of the most secure reputations of our time."

Kenneth Eble

THE BASIL DUKE LEE STORIES

THE stories which most clearly and connectedly explore Fitzgerald's youth are the nine Basil Duke Lee stories, eight of which appeared in the Saturday Evening Post from April, 1928, to April, 1929. Five were collected in Taps at Reveille, three

others in Arthur Mizener's Afternoon of an Author.

The stories are as excellent in craftsmanship as any stories Fitzgerald ever wrote. [. . .] The stories are evidence of Fitzgerald's meticulous attention to dates and events and

From *F. Scott Fitzgerald* by Kenneth Eble. Reprinted by permission of Twayne Publishers, Inc.

of his ability to evoke the precise
shades of feeling that accompanied
events of the past. The dates during
which the stories take place—the earliest in 1909 while Basil is still attending
Mrs. Cary's Academy, the last in the
fall he enrolls at Yale—tally exactly
with Fitzgerald's life from his last
year in Buffalo to his enrollment at
Princeton. White Bear Lake, where
Fitzgerald spent part of his summers
(he was a member of the White Bear
Lake Yacht Club), becomes Black
Bear Lake; *The Captured Shadow*,
the play Fitzgerald wrote and produced in 1912, is the same play Basil
writes and produces the same year;
the note in Fitzgerald's "Ledger,"
September, 1911, "Attended State
Fair and took children on roller-
coaster," refers to the same fair that
Basil attends the same fall; even the
small size of Newman Academy (actually only sixty pupils) is used in the
Basil story in which St. Regis loses
valiantly to Exeter: "good for a
school of only 158."

But more important than the fact
that the fictional details fit the actuality of Fitzgerald's experience is that
these stories, written as they were at
the peak of Fitzgerald's skill, are able
to capture with precision the emotions and attitudes of Fitzgerald's
youth. Fitzgerald had not, as Basil
vowed he would, become president
at twenty-five; but he had become almost as famous. He had fulfilled his
dreams and had proved the practical-
ity of dreaming large. And yet
through all the stories and all the
dreams of success runs the theme of
desires not quite satisfied, of last-min-
ute rescues from shame and despair,
of the "worst things" as later recorded in his Notebook: "To be in
bed and sleep not, / To want for one
who comes not, / To try to please
and please not." [. . .]
"Basil and Cleopatra" brings the

series to a close. It does so, Arthur
Mizener concludes, because Basil, now
on the verge of manhood, is forced
to recognize with grief and regret
that "you couldn't be with women
incessantly." Since the stories were
written in 1928, there is a more obvious reason for its ending the series:
the stories which followed Basil into
Yale and after had already been written. Basil leaves off where Amory
Blaine of *This Side of Paradise* begins.
The fine passage with which "Basil
and Cleopatra" ends is very close to a
similar passage in *This Side of Paradise:*

> Jubal the impossible came up
> with an air of possession, and Basil's
> heart went bobbing off around the
> ballroom in a pink silk dress. Lost
> again in a fog of indecision, he
> walked out on the veranda. There
> was a flurry of premature snow in
> the air and the stars looked cold.
> Staring up at them he saw that they
> were his stars as always—symbols
> of ambition, struggle and glory.
> The wind blew through them,
> trumpeting that high white note
> for which he always listened, and
> the thin-blown clouds, stripped for
> battle, passed in review. The scene
> was of an unparalleled brightness
> and magnificence, and only the
> practiced eye of the commander
> saw that one star was no longer
> there.

A comparison with the other passage,
written ten years earlier, shows how
Fitzgerald developed as a writer over
these first ten years:

> No more to wait the twilight of
> the moon in this sequestered vale
> of star and spire, for one eternal
> morning of desire passes to time
> and earthy afternoon. Here, Hera-
> clitus, did you find in fire and shift-
> ing things the prophecy you hurled

down the dead years; this midnight my desire will see, shadowed among the embers, furled in flame, the splendor and the sadness of the world.

Romantic longing inspired both passages; only in the first has he developed the style which captures the feelings convincingly.

The story "Basil and Cleopatra" is one in which fulfillment and disappointment, the comic and the serious, the real and the imagined, are neatly and effectively balanced. The irony throughout is deft. Basil finds out that Erminie has not merely passed him over for his football rival, Littleboy Le Moyne, but has already passed Le Moyne over for "a sad bird named Jubal." Le Moyne, less wary than Basil, saves him from making a fool of himself over a lost cause. Basil passes up the invitation to succumb to Cleopatra once more, but not without the regret that goes with leaving the immortal woman "who wore her sins like stars."

Throughout the story, Fitzgerald's preoccupation with the truth (and the falsity) of the romantic vision gives the story a substantiality beyond its rather thin plot. Basil as a man of destiny, an idea playfully treated in all the stories of this series, is here treated with some depth. His destiny, in turn, is involved in that Faustian desire for the moment of satisfaction. It is Fitzgerald's singular ability to dignify the trivial while remaining faintly ironic toward it that gives this story its best effects. Thus, the football game is treated as the counterpart of Antony's conquests of empire, and Fitzgerald's authorial reflections stand out as quite superior to the context: "Like most Americans,

he was seldom able really to grasp the moment, to say: 'This, for me, is the great equation by which everything else will be measured; this is the golden time,' but for once the present was sufficient. He was going to spend two hours in a country where life ran at the pace he demanded of it."

The highly developed technique in all these stories may be suggested by a number of observations about this one. First, the irony in "Basil and Cleopatra" makes the comparison with Antony and Cleopatra more than a mere use of an obvious parallel. The closing paragraph, in its imagery as in its explicit meaning, creates the heightened feelings of the classical story even as it illuminates the untragic romance being described. The foreshadowing in the second paragraph is as effective in this way as it is felicitous in its phrasing: "He was almost unconscious that they stood in a railroad station and entirely unconscious that she had just glanced over his shoulder and fallen in love with another young man." Second, the ordering of events and use of events is precisely right. The movement from the Southern city, to New Haven, to the Yale football field puts the world of dalliance against the world of conquest. And, after the conquest, the temptation that always reaches out to the victor provides the final drama of the story. Finally, the characters: Erminie, Littleboy Le Moyne, Jobena Dorsey, and Basil are used with more fullness than in other stories. Basil still is mortgaged to the past even as he is steadily pulled into the future, but his awareness of what is happening and his judgment of it have increased greatly.

Jean Stein

AN INTERVIEW WITH
WILLIAM FAULKNER

INTERVIEWER. Is there any possible formula to follow in order to be a good novelist?

FAULKNER. Ninety-nine per cent talent . . . 99 per cent discipline . . . 99 per cent work. He must never be satisfied with what he does. It never is as good as it can be done. Always dream and shoot higher than you know you can do. Don't bother just to be better than your contemporaries or predecessors. Try to be better than yourself. An artist is a creature driven by demons. He don't know why they choose him and he's usually too busy to wonder why. He is completely amoral in that he will rob, borrow, beg, or steal from anybody and everybody to get the work done.

INTERVIEWER. Do you mean the writer should be completely ruthless?

FAULKNER. The writer's only responsibility is to his art. He will be completely ruthless if he is a good one. He has a dream. It anguishes him so much he must get rid of it. He has no peace until then. Everything goes by the board: honor, pride, decency, security, happiness, all, to get the book written. If a writer has to rob his mother, he will not hesitate; the "Ode on a Grecian Urn" is worth any number of old ladies.

INTERVIEWER. Then could the *lack* of security, happiness, honor, be an important factor in the artist's creativity?

FAULKNER. No. They are important only to his peace and contentment, and art has no concern with peace and contentment.

INTERVIEWER. Then what would be the best environment for a writer?

FAULKNER. Art is not concerned with environment either; it doesn't care where it is. [. . .]

So the only environment the artist needs is whatever peace, whatever soiltude, and whatever pleasure he can get at not too high a cost. All the wrong environment will do is run his blood pressure up; he will spend more time being frustrated or outraged. My own experience has been that the tools I need for my trade are paper, tobacco, food, and a little whisky.

INTERVIEWER. Bourbon, you mean?

FAULKNER. No, I ain't that particular. Between scotch and nothing, I'll take scotch.

INTERVIEWER. You mentioned economic freedom. Does the writer need it?

FAULKNER. No. The writer doesn't need economic freedom. All he needs is a pencil and some paper. I've never known anything good in writing to come from having accepted any free gift of money. The good writer never applies to a foundation. He's too busy writing something. If he isn't first rate he fools himself by saying he hasn't got time or economic freedom. Good art can come out of thieves, bootleggers, or horse swipes. People really are afraid to find out just how much hardship and poverty they can stand. They are afraid to find out how tough they are. Nothing can destroy the good writer. The only thing that can alter the good writer is death. Good ones don't have time to bother with success or getting rich. Success is feminine and like a woman; if you cringe before her, she will override you. So the way to treat her is to show her the back of your hand. Then maybe she will do the crawling.

INTERVIEWER. Can working for the movies hurt your own writing?

FAULKNER. Nothing can injure a man's writing if he's a first-rate writer. If a man is not a first-rate writer, there's not anything can help it much. The problem does not apply if he is not first rate, because he has already sold his soul for a swimming pool.

INTERVIEWER. Does a writer compromise in writing for the movies?

FAULKNER. Always, because a moving picture is by its nature a collaboration, and any collaboration is compromise because that is what the word means—to give and to take.

[. . .]

INTERVIEWER. You say that the writer must compromise in working for the motion pictures. How about his writing? Is he under any obligation to his reader?

FAULKNER. His obligation is to get the work done the best he can do it; whatever obligation he has left over after that he can spend any way he likes. I myself am too busy to care about the public. I have no time to wonder who is reading me. I don't care about John Doe's opinion on my or anyone else's work. Mine is the standard which has to be met, which is when the work makes me feel the way I do when I read *La Tentation de Saint Antoine*, or the Old Testament. They make me feel good. So does watching a bird make me feel good. You know that if I were reincarnated, I'd want to come back a buzzard. Nothing hates him or envies him or wants him or needs him. He is

never bothered or in danger, and he can eat anything.

INTERVIEWER. What technique do you use to arrive at your standard?

FAULKNER. Let the writer take up surgery or bricklaying if he is interested in technique. There is no mechanical way to get the writing done, no short cut. The young writer would be a fool to follow a theory. Teach yourself by your own mistakes; people learn only by error. The good artist believes that nobody is good enough to give him advice. He has supreme vanity. No matter how much he admires the old writer, he wants to beat him.

INTERVIEWER. Then would you deny the validity of technique?

FAULKNER. By no means. Sometimes technique charges in and takes command of the dream before the writer himself can get his hands on it. That is *tour de force* and the finished work is simply a matter of fitting bricks neatly together, since the writer knows probably every single word right to the end before he puts the first one down. This happened with *As I Lay Dying*. It was not easy. No honest work is. It was simple in that all the material was already at hand. It took me just about six weeks in the spare time from a twelve-hour-a-day job at manual labor. I simply imagined a group of people and subjected them to the simple universal natural catastrophes, which are flood and fire, with a simple natural motive to give direction to their progress. But then, when technique does not intervene, in another sense writing is easier too. Because with me there is always a point in the book where the characters themselves rise up and take charge and finish the job—say somewhere about page 275. Of course I don't know what would happen if I finished the book on page 274. The quality an artist must have is objectivity in judging his work, plus the honesty and courage not to kid himself about it. [. . .]

INTERVIEWER. How much of your writing is based on personal experience?

FAULKNER. I can't say. I never counted up. Because "how much" is not important. A writer needs three things, experience, observation, and imagination, any two of which, at times any one of which, can supply the lack of the others. With me, a story usually begins with a single idea or memory or mental picture. The writing of the story is simply a matter of working up to that moment, to explain why it happened or what it caused to follow. A writer is trying to create believable people in credible moving situations in the most moving way he can. Obviously he must use as one of his tools the environment which he knows. I would say that music is the easiest means in which to express, since it came first in man's experience and history. But since words are my talent, I must try to express clumsily in words what the pure music would have done better. That is, music would express better and simpler, but I prefer to use words, as I prefer to read rather than listen. I prefer silence to sound, and the image produced by words occurs in silence. That is, the thunder and the music of the prose take place in silence.

INTERVIEWER. Some people say they can't understand your writing, even after they read it two or three times. What approach would you suggest for them?

FAULKNER. Read it four times.

INTERVIEWER. You mentioned experience, observation, and imagination as being important for the writer. Would you include inspiration?

FAULKNER. I don't know anything about inspiration, because I don't know what inspiration is—I've heard about it, but I never saw it.

INTERVIEWER. As a writer you are said to be obsessed with violence.

FAULKNER. That's like saying the carpenter is obsessed with his hammer. Violence is simply one of the carpenter's tools. The writer can no more build with one tool than the carpenter can.

[. . .]

INTERVIEWER. Do you read your contemporaries?

FAULKNER. No, the books I read are the ones I knew and loved when I was a young man and to which I return as you do to old friends: the Old Testament, Dickens, Conrad, Cervantes—Don Quixote. I read that every year, as some do the Bible. Flaubert, Balzac—he created an intact world of his own, a bloodstream running through twenty books—Dostoevsky, Tolstoi, Shakespeare. I read Melville occasionally, and of the poets Marlowe, Campion, Jonson, Herrick, Donne, Keats, and Shelley. I still read Housman. I've read these books so often that I don't always begin at page one and read on to the end. I just read one scene, or about one character, just as you'd meet and talk to a friend for a few minutes.

INTERVIEWER. And Freud?

FAULKNER. Everybody talked about Freud when I lived in New Orleans, but I have never read him. Neither did Shakespeare. I doubt if Melville did either, and I'm sure Moby Dick didn't.

INTERVIEWER. Do you ever read mystery stories?

FAULKNER. I read Simenon because he reminds me something of Chekhov.

INTERVIEWER. What about your favorite characters?

FAULKNER. My favorite characters are Sarah Gamp—a cruel, ruthless woman, a drunkard, opportunist, unreliable, most of her character was bad, but at least it was character; Mrs. Harris, Falstaff, Prince Hal, Don Quixote, and Sancho of course. Lady Macbeth I always admire. And Bottom, Ophelia, and Mercutio—both he and Mrs. Gamp coped with life, didn't ask any favors, never whined. Huck Finn, of course, and Jim. Tom Sawyer I never liked much—an awful prig. And then I like Sut Lovingood, from a book written by George Harris about 1840 or '50 in the Tennessee mountains. He had no illusions about himself, did the best he could; at certain times he was a coward and knew it and wasn't ashamed; he never blamed his misfortunes on anyone and never cursed God for them.

INTERVIEWER. Would you comment on the future of the novel?

FAULKNER. I imagine as long as people will continue to read novels, people will continue to write them, or vice versa; unless of course the pictorial magazines and comic strips finally atrophy man's capacity to read, and literature really is on its way back to the picture writing in the Neanderthal cave.

INTERVIEWER. And how about the function of the critics?

FAULKNER. The artist doesn't have time to listen to the critics. The ones who want to be writers read the reviews, the ones who want to write don't have the time to read reviews. The critic too is trying to say "Kilroy was here." His function is not directed toward the artist himself. The artist is a cut above the critic, for the artist is writing something which will move the critic. The critic is writing something which will move everybody but the artist.

INTERVIEWER. So you never feel the need to discuss your work with anyone?

FAULKNER. No, I am too busy writing it. It has got to please me and if it does I don't need to talk about. If it doesn't please me, talking about it won't improve it, since the only thing to improve it is to work on it some more. I am not a literary man but only a writer. I don't get any pleasure from talking shop.

INTERVIEWER. Critics claim that blood relationships are central in your novels.

FAULKNER. That is an opinion and, as I have said, I don't read critics. I doubt that a man trying to write about people is any more interested in blood relationships than in the shape of their noses, unless they are necessary to help the story move. If the writer concentrates on what he does need to be interested in, which is the truth and the human heart, he won't have much time left for anything else, such as ideas and facts like the shape of noses or blood relationships, since in my opinion ideas and facts have very little connection with truth.

INTERVIEWER. Critics also suggest that your characters never consciously choose between good and evil.

FAULKNER. Life is not interested in good and evil. Don Quixote was constantly choosing between good and evil, but then he was choosing in his dream state. He was made. He entered reality only when he was so busy trying to cope with people that he had no time to distinguish between good and evil. Since people exist only in life, they must devote their time simply to being alive. Life is motion, power, pleasure. What time a man can devote to morality, he must take by force from the motion of which he is a part. He is compelled to make choices between good and evil sooner or later, because moral conscience demands that from him in order that he can live with himself tomorrow. His moral conscience is the curse he had to accept from the gods in order to gain from them the right to dream.

INTERVIEWER. Could you explain more what you mean by motion in relation to the artist?

FAULKNER. The aim of every artist is to arrest motion, which is life, by artificial means and hold it fixed so that a hundred years later, when a stranger looks at it, it moves again since it is life. Since man is mortal, the only immortality possible for him is to leave something behind him that is immortal since it will always move. This is the artist's way of scribbling "Kilroy was here" on the wall of the final and irrevocable oblivion through which he must someday pass.

William Faulkner

THE AUTHOR DISCUSSES "THE BEAR"

Q. In "The Bear," Mr. Faulkner, was there a dog, a real Lion?

A. Yes, there was. I can remember that dog—I was about the age of that little boy—and he belonged to our pack of bear and deer dogs, and he was a complete individualist. He didn't love anybody. The other dogs were all afraid of him, he was a savage, but he did love to run the bear. Yes, I remember him quite well. He was mostly airedale, he had some hound and Lord only knows what else might have been in him. He was a tremendous big brute—stood about that high, must have weighed seventy-five or eighty pounds.

Q. In any bear hunt that Lion participated in, did he ever perform a heroic action like the one in the story?

A. No, not really. There's a case of the sorry, shabby world that don't quite please you, so you create one of your own, so you make Lion a little braver than he was, and you make the bear a little more of a bear than he actually was. I am sure that Lion could have done that and would have done it, and it may be at times when I wasn't there to record the action, he did do things like that.

[. . .]

. . . Q. Mr. Faulkner, you seem to put so much meaning in the hunt. Could you tell us just why you hunted when you were a little boy, or what meaning the hunt has to you?

A. The hunt was simply a symbol of pursuit. Most of anyone's life is a pursuit of something. That is, the only alternative to life is immobility, which is death. This was a symbolization of the pursuit which is a normal part of anyone's life, while he stays alive, told in terms which were familiar to me and dramatic to me. The protagonist could have been anything else besides that bear. I simply told a story which was a natural, normal part of anyone's life in familiar and to me interesting terms without any deliberate intent to put symbolism in it. I was simply telling something which was in this case the

From *Faulkner in the University*, edited by Frederick L. Gwynn and Joseph L. Blotner. Reprinted by permission of The University Press of Virginia.

child—the need, the compulsion of the child to adjust to the adult world. It's how he does it, how he survives it, whether he is destroyed by trying to adjust to the adult world or whether despite his small size he does adjust within his capacity. And always to learn something, to learn something of—not only to pursue but to overtake and then to have the compassion not to destroy, to catch, to touch, and then let go because then tomorrow you can pursue again. If you destroy it, what you caught, then it's gone, it's finished. And that to me is sometimes the greater part of valor but always it's the greater part of pleasure, not to destroy what you have pursued. The pursuit is the thing, not the reward, not the gain.

[. . .]

Q. Sir, one of the most interesting aspects of "The Bear" to me is the conflict between man and the wilderness. I would like to ask you if you intend for the reader to sympathize more with Old Ben in his conflict with the hunters or towards the hunters in their conflict with Old Ben.

A. Well, not "sympathize." I doubt if the writer's asking anyone to sympathize, to choose sides. That is the reader's right. What the writer's asking is compassion, understanding, that change must alter, must happen, and change is going to alter what was. That no matter how fine anything seems, it can't endure, be-

cause once it stops, abandons motion, it is dead. It's to have compassion for the anguish that the wilderness itself may have felt by being ruthlessly destroyed by axes, by men who simply wanted to make that earth grow something they could sell for a profit, which brought into it a condition based on an evil like human bondage. It's not to choose sides at all—just to compassionate the good splendid things which change must destroy, the splendid fine things which are a part of man's past too, part of man's heritage too, but they were obsolete and had to go. But that's no need to not feel compassion for them simply because they were obsolete.

[. . .]

. . . *Q.* I'd like to ask you . . . if you saw a symbol in the bear in the short story "The Bear."

A. Since I've been up here and discussed it I've seen lots of symbols that I was too busy at the time—

Q. [I wish you'd please] tell me one so that I could tell my class.

A. Well, one symbol was the bear represented the vanishing wilderness. The little dog that wasn't scared of the bear represented the indomitable spirit of man. I'll have to dig back and get up some more of those symbols, because I have learned around an even dozen that I put into that story without knowing it. But there are two pretty good ones that you can hold to.

Ernest V. Trueblood*

AFTERNOON OF A COW

MR. FAULKNER and I were sitting under the mulberry with the afternoon's first julep while he informed me what to write on the morrow, when Oliver appeared suddenly around the corner of the smokehouse, running and with his eyes looking quite large and white. "Mr. Bill!" he cried. "Day done sot fire to de pasture!"

"——" cried Mr. Faulkner, with that promptitude which quite often marks his actions, "—— those boys to ——!" springing up and referring to his own son, Malcolm, and to his brother's son, James, and to the cook's son, Rover or Grover. Grover his name is, though both Malcolm and James (they and Grover are of an age and have, indeed, grown up not only contemporaneously but almost inextricably) have insisted upon calling him Rover since they could speak, so that now all the household, including the child's own mother and naturally the child itself, call him Rover too, with the exception of myself, whose practice and belief it has never been to call any creature, man, woman, child or beast, out of its rightful name—just as I permit no one to call me out of mine, though I am aware that behind my back both Malcolm and James (and doubtless Rover or Grover) refer to me as Ernest be Toogood—a crass and low form of so-called wit or humor to which children, these two in particular—are only too prone. I have attempted on more than one occasion (this was years ago; I have long since ceased) to explain to them that my position in the household is in no sense menial, since I have been writing Mr. Faulkner's novels and short stories for years. But I long ago became convinced (and even reconciled) that neither of them knew or cared about the meaning of the term.

I do not think that I anticipate myself in saying that we did not know where the three boys would now be. We would not be expected to know, beyond a general feeling or conviction that they would by now be concealed in the loft of the barn or stable —this from previous experience, though experience had never before included or comprised arson. Nor do I feel that I further violate the formal rules or order, unity and emphasis by saying that we would never for one moment have conceived them to be where later evidence indicated that they now were. But more on this subject anon: we were not thinking of the boys now; as Mr. Faulkner himself might have observed someone should have been thinking about them ten or fifteen minutes ago; that now it was too late. No, our concern was to reach the pasture, though not with any hope of saving the hay which had been Mr. Faulkner's pride and even hope—a fine, though small, plantation of this grain or forage fenced lightly away from the pasture proper and the certain inroads of the three stocks whose pleasance the pasture was, which had been intended as an alternative or balancing factor in the winter's victualing of the three

From "The Afternoon of a Cow" by Ernest V. Trueblood (William Faulkner) from *Furioso*, Summer 1947, copyright 1947 by William Faulkner. Reprinted by permission of Harold Ober Associates Incorporated.

* Mr. Faulkner's ghost writer.

beasts. We had no hope of saving this, since the month was September following a dry summer, and we knew that this as well as the remainder of the pasture would burn with almost the instantaneous celerity of gunpowder or celluloid. That is, I had no hope of it and doubtless Oliver had no hope of it. I do not know what Mr. Faulkner's emotion was, since it appears (or so I have read and heard) a fundamental human trait to decline to recognize misfortune with regard to some object which man either desires or already possesses and holds dear, until it has run him down and then over like a Juggernaut itself. I do not know if this emotion would function in the presence of a field of hay, since I have neither owned nor desired to own one. No, it was not the hay which we were concerned about. It was the three animals, the two horses and the cow, in particular the cow, who, less gifted or equipped for speed than the horses, might be overtaken by the flames and perhaps asphyxiated, or at least so badly scorched as to be rendered temporarily unfit for her natural function; and that the two horses might bolt in terror, and to their detriment, into the further fence of barbed wire or might even turn and rush back into the actual flames, as is one of the more intelligent characteristics of this so-called servant and friend of man.

Philip Young

HEMINGWAY: THE ORIGINS AND MEANING OF A STYLE

MANY serious writers have learned from [Hemingway], among other things, the values of objectivity, of honesty (what you really felt, and not what you ought or had been taught to feel) and something of how to write a hard and clean prose style. In such ways his influence has been all to the good. He has helped to purify our writing of sentimentality, literary embellishment, padding and a superficial artfulness. Almost singlehanded he has revitalized the writing of dialogue.

Hemingway's prose is easy to mimic, but hard to reproduce; efforts to write a style like it become tedious. And at best it is not a style suitable for all kinds of writing. However, when Hemingway writes it well, it is full of meaning, is pure and clear and does not spoil. In some ways a leader bears a responsibility for the excesses and defects of his followers, but we seldom weigh it against him. If we did, the greatest man in history, whoever he might be, would find it hard to survive the atrocities committed in his name.

It is of course as a stylist that

From *Ernest Hemingway* by Philip Young, copyright 1952 by Philip Young. Reprinted by permission of Holt, Rinehart and Winston, Inc.

Hemingway commands the most respect, and has had his widest and deepest effect on serious writers. When he is at his best we have no better, as even his detractors will occasionally and reluctantly admit. There is no need to describe the style at any great length, so well is it known. It is for the most part a colloquial and, apparently, a nonliterary prose, characterized by a conscientious simplicity of diction and of sentence structure. The words are chiefly short and common ones, and there is a severe and austere economy in their use. The typical sentence is a simple declarative sentence, or a couple of these joined by a conjunction; there is very little subordination of clauses. The rhythms are simple and direct, and the effect is of crispness, leanness and clarity, and sometimes of a monotony that the author does little to relieve.

It is a style which normally keeps out of sight the intelligence behind it. The sequence in which events are described is strictly the sequence in which they occurred; no mind reorders or analyzes them. Perceptions come direct to the reader, unmixed with editorial comment. Consequently, the impression is of an intense and disciplined objectivity, a matter-of-fact offering of whatever details are chosen to build in the reader the response for which the author has provided only the stimulus. Since the subject matter is, most often, violence and pain, the result of this tensely unemotional, "primitive" and "objective" presentation of experience is frequently a characteristic effect of irony and understatement. The vision which selects the details is narrow and sharply focused. A great deal is not seen at all, but what is looked at is caught brilliantly and the images strike the eye as if it had never caught them before.

Equally remarkable is the dialogue, which at its best shows Hemingway to have an ear for the sound of human speech that is as sensitive as his nose for the smells of animals or as acute as the eyes of his father for birds. His ear picks up and records the accents and mannerisms of the characters that the speech is in the process of swiftly revealing. The conversation is as laconic and carefully controlled as the unspoken prose. The customary substitutes for the past of the verb "say" are scrupulously avoided; Roget's "assert, affirm, state, declare" go out the window in an effort to avoid the artful use of synonyms. Since the speech itself is normally eloquent of the way in which it is spoken, the crutch of verbs which explain the manner of the speaking becomes unnecessary, and is thrown away too. But for all the impression of authenticity Hemingway's dialogue gives, it is no simple reproduction of actual human talking. If it were, no particular credit would go to a writer who could turn the trick, for all he would need would be a portable home-recorder, a little meddlesome impudence and the services of a competent typist; few people would care to read much of the transcription. Instead, Hemingway's dialogue strips speech down to the essentials which are typical of the speaker. He builds a pattern of mannerisms and responses which give an illusion of reality that, in its completeness, reality itself does not give. [. . .]

A style has its own content, the manner of prose its own meanings, and there have been two or three fairly incisive attempts to figure out what Hemingway's prose style adds up to, what it does and says. It has been shown, for instance, that the style itself is very suggestive of the dislocated and disunified world which it reflects. Mark Schorer has argued that the bareness of the prose suggests the bareness of life, which is Hemingway's "subject." He also remarks that the style is itself an expression of the novelist's stiff-lipped morality.

But the things that Hemingway's style most suggests are the very things that he has been trying also to say directly and outright. His style is as eloquent of his content as the content itself; the style is a large part of the content. The strictly disciplined controls which he has exerted over his hero and his "bad nerves" are precise parallels to the strictly disciplined sentences he writes. Understatement, abbreviated statement and lack of statement reflect without the slightest distortion the rigid restraint which the man feels he must practice if he is to survive. The "mindlessness" of the style is the result of a need to "stop thinking," and is the purest reflection of that need. The intense simplicity of the prose is a means by which the man says, Things must be *made* simple, or I am lost, in a way you'll never be. There is no rearrangement and reordering of the material because the mind operates no more than it has to. And all these things are being communicated by the manner of the presentation.

The "impersonal tone" speaks the need to escape personality. The "objectivity" exists because subjectivity could mean that a brain could get to "racing like a flywheel with the weight gone." The "directness" and "immediacy" with which objects are seen convey the necessity for seeing for one's self, straight and anew, when so much of what others have said they saw seems a lie. The "economy" of the prose masters the little it can control cleanly. The style is "unemotional" and "primitive" because it has to be, and it says so. It is "tense" because that is the atmosphere in which the struggle for control takes place, and the tension expresses the fact. The prose gives an impression of "bareness" because, as Schorer said, so much of life is barren for the hero. But that is not really Hemingway's "subject." His subject is violence and pain, and their effects, and the recovery from the effects in the face of and partly through more of the same. The style which expresses this subject matter is itself perfectly expressive of these things, and of the message: life, which is the material, must be constantly forced under the most intense and rigorous control, and held in the tightest of rein, for it is savage and can get out of hand. [. . .]

Hemingway reproduces on paper the life he has seen through the eyes which his experiences have made distinctive. What was muddy and messy becomes ordered and clear. The large part of it that was unpleasant is repeated, mastered, exorcised. The discipline that made the new personality made the new prose style, which developed it, and which bespoke the personality. Hemingway's style is the perfect voice of his content. That style, moreover, is the end, or aim, of the man. It is the means of being the man. An old commonplace takes on new force: the style *is* the man.

Leon Edel

HEMINGWAY: THE ART OF EVASION

I WOULD like to offer a mild dissent amid the current cheering for our poet of big-game hunting and bull-fighting. Doubtless we rejoice, as Americans, that our literature has been honored once again by the Swedish Academy; and it is pleasant to feel that a writer as swashbuckling and myth-making as Ernest Hemingway should have been selected. Nevertheless the Swedish Academy has not been very brilliant, on the whole, in its choice of Nobel prize winners; the list, going back to the beginning of the century, is filled with forgotten names, redolent with omissions. They gave the prize to Kipling, but when the time came they did not give it to James Joyce. As Hemingway himself pointed out, they passed over Mark Twain and Henry James and, we might add, Edwin Arlington Robinson. Of the Americans who have received it, only Faulkner, O'Neill, and T. S. Eliot (an American turned Englishman) have had the world stature envisaged when the prize was created.

Ernest Hemingway, I hold, belongs to the second shelf of American fiction, not the first: he can safely be placed beside Sinclair Lewis rather than beside Hawthorne, Melville, or James. But my dissent at this moment is not in matters of classification. It stems from the Academy's bestowing of the prize on the grounds of Hemingway's Style—his "mastery of the art of modern narration." I am not, of course, sure what the Swedish Academy means by "modern narration"—unless indeed it is thinking of brisk journalism, the most characteristic form of narration of our time. But the award has generally been interpreted as an award for Style.

Now Style, I agree, is virtually everything in literature. The writer who forges a Style places himself; in the very nature of things, in the forefront of his period, and provides himself with a shining passkey to the future. But we must be careful here—both myself and critics who have been embalming Hemingway —to be sure we speak of the same thing. A Style involves substance as well as form. No writer has received his key for swaddling meager thought in elegant flowers. Such flowers fade easily. I would argue that Hemingway has not created a Style: he has rather created the artful illusion of a Style, for he is a clever artist and there is a great deal of cleverness in all that he has done. He has conjured up an *effect* of Style by a process of evasion, very much as he sets up an aura of emotion—by walking directly away from emotion!

What I am trying to suggest is that the famous Hemingway Style is not "organic." And any style worthy of the name must be, as the much-worn, but nevertheless truthful *mot*, that *Style is the man*, testifies. Is Hemingway's Style the man? At the risk of a pun, I would answer no, it is the mannerism! It is an artifice, a series of charming tricks, a group of cleverness. Gertrude Stein taught Hemingway that one can obtain wry effects by assembling incongruities,

"The Art of Evasion" by Leon Edel from *Folio* XX, Spring 1955, pp. 18–20, copyright 1955 by the Department of English, Indiana State University. Reprinted by permission of the author and publishers.

and Hemingway really learned how to juxtapose these with high skill. "There were many more guns in the country around and the spring had come." Now the coming of spring is, strictly speaking a *non sequitur*. It has nothing to do with the guns. Spring occurs in many parts of the world where there are no guns. And yet this juxtaposition underlines the ironic effect that in spring, and in this particular time and place, men could still shed blood, at the very season of the year when everything around us is re-born. This is very good, and there are many such examples in Hemingway. There are others which are mere incongruity, as when he writes "The river ran behind us and the town had been captured very handsomely." This is quite simply hodge-podge. It is easily imitated, as a whole school of junior Hemingways has demonstrated. It's a fine trick. But it is hardly a Style. Neither can certain of his long tagged-together sentences, reminiscent of Molly Bloom's internal monologue, be regarded as "organic" prose.

What of the substance? In Hemingway's novels people order drinks —they are always ordering drinks— then they drink, then they order some more; they make love, and the love-making is "fine" and "nice" and it is "good" and it is sufficiently romantic, as in the pulps, that is, sufficiently adolescent. There is some killing. There is some fine riding and shooting and sailing. It is a world of superficial action and almost wholly without reflection—such reflection as there is tends to be on a rather crude and simplified level. It will be argued that all this is a large part of life and thus has validity in fiction. Of course. It is my contention merely that such surface writing, dressed out in prose mannerisms, does not constitute a Style and that the present emphasis

on this quality in Hemingway tends, in effect, to minimize the hollowness of his total production. Hemingway has created a world of Robinson Crusoes, living on lonely islands, with bottle and gun for companions, and an occasional woman to go with the drinks.

I have said that Hemingway belongs to the second shelf of our literature, or at least that is where I would put him, and it would be precisely on this ground: that he has not written an "adult" novel. He has contrived, with great cleverness, some very good novels. He is at his happiest, in reality, in the short story. The short story by its very nature demands simplification; characters need not be developed, plot and drama need not be created—a mood, a nostalgia, a moment of experience, suffice. Hemingway is an artist of the small space, the limited view. And I am not sure that what I have called "evasion" in his work will not be borne out if we search for its roots in his life, from which, after all, an artist's work always springs. To be able to cope with emotion only by indirection, or to write prose which seeks surface expressly to avoid texture—is this not a little like escaping from life by big-game hunting or watching violence in a bull ring or daydreaming through long hours of fishing? These are all fascinating pursuits for our hours of leisure or when given a proper perspective and taken in proper proportion (unless indeed one earns one's living by fighting bulls or is a career-fisherman). When they become a substitute for other forms of life—and granted that they themselves are part of life and partake of it—they can become an evasion of life.

But Hemingway is not as old as his Old Man. There have been striking examples in the history of literature of artists in whom, only at the end, is there a great fusion of experience and of expression that culminates in a large, mature, and durable work. And a Style. We must not at all ex- clude the possibility that Hemingway may yet write a book for the top shelf of our literature. But let us not put him there until he does.

Katherine Anne Porter

EUDORA WELTY

FRIENDS of us both first brought Eudora Welty to visit me three years ago in Louisiana. It was hot mid- summer, they had driven over from Mississippi, her home state, and we spent a pleasant evening together talking in the cool old house with all the windows open. Miss Welty sat listening, as she must have done a great deal of listening on many such occasions. She was and is a quiet, tranquil-looking, modest girl, and un- like the young Englishman of the story, she has something to be modest about, as this collection of short sto- ries proves.

She considers her personal history as hardly worth mentioning, a fact in itself surprising enough, since a vivid personal career of fabulous ups and downs, hardships and strokes of luck, travels in far countries, spiritual and intellectual exile, defensive flight, homesick return with a determined groping for native roots, and a con- fusion of contradictory jobs have long been the mere conventions of an American author's life. Miss Welty was born and brought up in Jackson, Mississippi, where her father, now dead, was president of a Southern in- surance company. Family life was cheerful and thriving; she seems to have got on excellently with both her parents and her two brothers. Edu- cation, in the Southern manner with daughters, was continuous, indulgent, and precisely as serious as she chose to make it. She went from school in Mississippi to the University of Wis- consin, thence to Columbia, New York, and so home again where she lives with her mother, among her lifelong friends and acquaintances, quite simply and amiably. She tried a job or two because that seemed the next thing, and did some pub- licity and newspaper work; but as she had no real need of a job, she gave up the notion and settled down to writing.

She loves music, listens to a great deal of it, all kinds; grows flowers very successfully, and remarks that she is "underfoot locally," meaning that she has a normal amount of so- cial life. Normal social life in a medium-sized Southern town can be- come a pretty absorbing occupation, and the only comment her friends make when a new story appears is, "Why, Eudora, when did you write that?" Not how, or even why, just when. They see her about so much, what time has she for writing? Yet she spends an immense amount of time at it. "I haven't a literary life at all," she wrote once, "not much of a confession, maybe. But I do feel that the people and things I love are of a true and human world, and there is no clutter about them. . . . I would not understand a literary life."

We can do no less than dismiss that topic as casually as she does. Being the child of her place and time, profiting perhaps without being aware of it by the cluttered experiences, foreign travels, and disorders of the generation immediately preceding her, she will never have to go away and live among the Eskimos, or Mexican Indians; she need not follow a war and smell death to feel herself alive: she knows about death already. She shall not need even to live in New York in order to feel that she is having the kind of experience, the sense of "life" proper to a serious author. She gets her right nourishment from the source natural to her—her experience so far has been quite enough for her and of precisely the right kind. She began writing spontaneously when she was a child, being a born writer; she continued without any plan for a profession, without any particular encouragement, and, as it proved, not needing any. For a good number of years she believed she was going to be a painter, and painted quite earnestly while she wrote without much effort.

Nearly all the Southern writers I know were early, omnivorous, insatiable readers, and Miss Welty runs reassuringly true to this pattern. She had at arm's reach the typical collection of books which existed as a matter of course in a certain kind of Southern family, so that she had read the ancient Greek and Roman poetry, history and fable, Shakespeare, Mil-

ton, Dante, the eighteenth-century English and the nineteenth-century French novelists, with a dash of Tolstoy and Dostoievsky, before she realized what she was reading. When she first discovered contemporary literature, she was just the right age to find first W. B. Yeats and Virginia Woolf in the air around her; but always, from the beginning until now, she loved folk tales, fairy tales, old legends, and she likes to listen to the songs and stories of people who live in old communities whose culture is recollected and bequeathed orally.

She has never studied the writing craft in any college. She has never belonged to a literary group, and until after her first collection was ready to be published she had never discussed with any colleague or older artist any problem of her craft. Nothing else that I know about her could be more satisfactory to me than this; it seems to me immensely right, the very way a young artist should grow, with pride and independence and the courage really to face out the individual struggle; to make and correct mistakes and take the consequences of them, to stand firmly on his own feet in the end. I believe in the rightness of Miss Welty's instinctive knowledge that writing cannot be taught, but only learned, and learned by the individual in his own way, at his own pace and in his own time, for the process of mastering the medium is part of a cellular growth in a most complex organism; it is a way of life and a mode of being which cannot be divided from the kind of human creature you were the day you were born, and only in obeying the law of this singular being can the artist know his true directions and the right ends for him.

Miss Welty escaped, by miracle, the whole corrupting and destructive influence of the contemporary, organized tampering with young and promising talents by professional teachers who are rather monotonously divided into two major sorts: those theorists who are incapable of producing one passable specimen of the art they profess to teach; or good, sometimes first-rate, artists who are humanly unable to resist forming disciples and imitators among their students. It is all well enough to say that, of this second class, the able talent will throw off the master's influence and strike out for himself. Such influence has merely added new obstacles to an already difficult road. Miss Welty escaped also a militant social consciousness, in the current radical-intellectual sense, she never professed Communism, and she has not expressed, except implicitly, any attitude at all on the state of politics or the condition of society. But there is an ancient system of ethics, an unanswerable, indispensable moral law, on which she is grounded firmly, and this, it would seem to me, is ample domain enough; these laws have never been the peculiar property of any party or creed or nation, they relate to that true and human world of which the artist is a living part; and when he dissociates himself from it in favor of a set of political, which is to say, inhuman, rules, he cuts himself away from his proper society-living men.

There exist documents of political and social theory which belong, if not to poetry, certainly to the department of humane letters. They are reassuring statements of the great hopes and dearest faiths of mankind and they are acts of high imagination. But all working practical political systems, even those professing to originate in moral grandeur, are based upon and operate by contempt of human life and the individual fate; in accepting any one of them and shaping his mind

and work to that mold, the artist dehumanizes himself, unfits himself for the practise of any art.

Not being in a hurry, Miss Welty was past twenty-six years when she offered her first story, "The Death of a Traveling Salesman," to the editor of a little magazine unable to pay, for she could not believe that anyone would buy a story from her; the magazine was *Manuscript*, the editor John Rood, and he accepted it gladly. Rather surprised, Miss Welty next tried the *Southern Review*, where she met with a great welcome and the enduring partisanship of Albert Erskine, who regarded her as his personal discovery. The story was "A Piece of News" and it was followed by others published in the *Southern Review*, the *Atlantic Monthly*, and *Harper's Bazaar*.

She has, then, never been neglected, never unappreciated, and she feels simply lucky about it. She wrote to a friend: "When I think of Ford Madox Ford! You remember how you gave him my name and how he tried his best to find a publisher for my book of stories all that last year of his life; and he wrote me so many charming notes, all of his time going to his little brood of promising writers, the kind of thing that could have gone on forever. Once I read in the *Saturday Review* an article of his on the species and the way they were neglected by publishers, and he used me as the example chosen at random. He ended his cry with 'What is to become of both branches of Anglo-Saxondom if this state of things continues?' Wasn't that wonderful, really, and typical? I may have been more impressed by that than would other readers who knew him. I did not know him, but I knew it was typical. And here I myself have turned out to be not at all the martyred promising writer, but have had all the good luck and all the good things Ford chided the world for withholding from me and my kind." [. . .]

[Her] stories offer an extraordinary range of mood, pace, tone, and variety of material. The scene is limited to a town the author knows well; the farthest reaches of that scene never go beyond the boundaries of her own state, and many of the characters are of the sort that caused a Bostonian to remark that he would not care to meet them socially: Lily Daw is a half-witted girl in the grip of social forces represented by a group of earnest ladies bent on doing the best thing for her, no matter what the consequences. Keela, the Outcast Indian Maid, is a crippled little Negro who represents a type of man considered most unfortunate by W. B. Yeats: one whose experience was more important than he, and completely beyond his powers of absorption. But the really unfortunate man in this story is the ignorant young white boy, who had innocently assisted at a wrong done the little Negro, and for a most complex reason, finds that no reparation is possible, or even desirable to the victim. . . . The heroine of "Why I Live at the P.O." is a terrifying case of dementia praecox. In this first group—for the stories may be loosely classified on three separate levels—the spirit is satire and the key grim comedy. Of these, "The Petrified Man" offers a fine clinical study of vulgarity—vulgarity absolute, chemically pure, exposed mercilessly to its final subhuman depths. Dullness, bitterness, rancor, self-pity, baseness of all kinds, can be most interesting material for a story provided these are not also the main elements in the mind of the author. There is nothing in the least vulgar or frustrated in Miss Welty's mind. She has simply an eye and an ear sharp, shrewd, and true as

a tuning fork. She has given to this little story all her wit and observation, her blistering humor and her just cruelty; for she has none of that slack tolerance or sentimental tenderness toward symptomatic evils that amounts to criminal collusion between author and character. Her use of this material raises the quite awfully sordid little tale to a level above its natural habitat, and its realism seems almost to have the quality of caricature, as complete realism so often does. Yet, as painters of the grotesque make only detailed reports of actual living types observed more keenly than the average eye is capable of observing, so Miss Welty's little human monsters are not really caricatures at all, but individuals exactly and clearly presented: which is perhaps a case against realism, if we cared to go into it. She does better on another level—for the important reason that the themes are richer—in such beautiful stories as "Death of a Traveling Salesman," "A Memory," "A Worn Path." Let me admit a deeply personal preference for this particular kind of story, where external act and the internal voiceless life of the human imagination almost meet and mingle on the mysterious threshold between dream and waking, one reality refusing to admit or confirm the existence of the other, yet both conspiring toward the same end. This is not easy to accomplish, but it is always worth trying, and Miss Welty is so successful at it, it would seem her most familiar territory. There is no blurring at the edges, but evidences of an active and disciplined imagination working firmly in a strong line of continuity, the waking faculty of daylight reason recollecting and recording the crazy logic of the dream. There is in none of these stories any trace of autobiography in the prime sense, except as the author is omnipresent, and knows each character she writes about as only the artist knows the thing he has made, by first experiencing it in imagination. But perhaps in "A Memory," one of the best stories, there might be something of early personal history in the story of the child on the beach, alienated from the world of adult knowledge by her state of childhood, who hoped to learn the secrets of life by looking at everything, squaring her hands before her eyes to bring the observed thing into a frame—the gesture of one born to select, to arrange, to bring apparently disparate elements into harmony within deliberately fixed boundaries. But the author is freed already in her youth from self-love, self-pity, self-preoccupation, that triple damnation of too many of the young and gifted, and has reached an admirable objectivity. In such stories as "Old Mr. Marblehall," "Powerhouse," "The Hitch-Hikers," she combines an objective reporting with great perception of mental or emotional states, and in "Clytie" the very shape of madness takes place before your eyes in a straight account of actions and speech, the personal appearance and habits of dress of the main character and her family.

In all of these stories, varying as they do in excellence, I find nothing false or labored, no diffusion of interest, no wavering of mood—the approach is direct and simple in method, though the themes and moods are anything but simple, and there is even in the smallest story a sense of power in reserve which makes me believe firmly that, splendid beginning that this is, it is only the beginning.

William M. Jones

EUDORA WELTY'S "A WORN PATH"

UNLIKE many of Eudora Welty's stories, "A Worn Path" has a deceptively uncomplex organization. The major portion of the story simply recounts the journey of an old Negro woman into Natchez at Christmas time to obtain medicine for her grandson. Underneath this seemingly naive account lies a persistently annoying suggestion that there is more to the story than appears at a casual reading.

The first hint of the deeper meaning is the old woman's name: Phoenix Jackson. The third sentence announces this name to the reader. The end of the first paragraph tells the reader that the stick she carries "made a grave and persistent noise in the still air, that seemed meditative like the chirping of a solitary little bird." The next paragraph describes her: first her great age, then her color. ". . . a golden color ran underneath, and the two knobs of her cheeks were illumined by a yellow burning under the dark." Her hair was black, but "with an odor like copper."

These seemingly coincidental references to birds, great age, and gold might be overlooked, but the reader who knows some of Welty's other work is on the lookout for significant names. Some of the more obvious are Mr. Petrie in "Petrified Man," Mrs. Rainy in "Shower of Gold," and Florabel in the early verison of "The Burning" (Delilah in the later version).

By the end of the second paragraph the reader of "A Worn Path" may well suspect that the name Phoenix, like these others, is not a name chosen at random, nor even because it is a very reasonable name for a Southern Negro woman. The references at the beginning of the story announce rather clearly that a comparison with the legendary bird is intended. The similarity becomes more pronounced as the story progresses. After Phoenix's arduous journey into town, she arrives at the charity ward where she is to obtain the medicine for her grandson, "and there she saw nailed up on the wall the document that had been stamped with the gold seal and framed in the gold frame, which matched the dream that was hung up in her head." In this office Phoenix stands, "a fixed and ceremonial stiffness over her body." Obviously, like the embodiment of the original Egyptian sun-god that flew home every five hundred years, this Mississippi Phoenix has returned by instinct to the source of her strength to renew her own youth.

Having said simply, "Here I be," she refuses to speak until "At last there came a flicker and then a flame of comprehension across her face, and she spoke." She tells of her little grandson who has swallowed lye: "He is going to last. He wear a little patch quilt and peep out holding his mouth open like a little bird." When she receives the medicine, the nurse offers her a nickel. "Phoenix rose carefully and held out her hand." Obviously, in the burning and the rising again, the phoenix legend has been carefully paralleled.

There is little doubt that the phoenix is at the core of the story. The main question is why Miss Welty should make the old Negro so completely analogous to this bird. There are numerous possibilities which might involve an allegorical account of the Southern Negro's plight, but in the light of the story's phoenix symbol any such suggestion seems to lack support.

The main reason that Miss Welty chose a Negro seems to be that only a relatively simple, uncivilized individual is worthy of representing the powerful force which inspires such love as hers for her grandchild. Her long journey shows that all her struggles, all her fears, even her petty theft of a nickel from a hunter, were endured almost gaily because she was filled with a love which would cause rejuvenation at the end of the journey. The hunter whom Phoenix met on the path was in the country for what he could get for himself in the form of game; the woman who laced Phoenix's shoes was encumbered with packages; the nurses dispensed cold charity. But Phoenix has no selfish motives, no hate for anything. She does not condemn thorns for holding her, the hunter for pointing his gun at her, or a dog for knocking her into a ditch. She is the one who will last and return down the well-worn path. She moves instinctively, gaily, toward what love demands. As she herself said, "I bound to go on my way." As she leaves the doctor's office she is "going down," but the title itself suggests that she will, like the Phoenix of antiquity, return to the source of her youth again and again.

The Novel

Among "the various demands one can make of a novelist," says W. H. Auden, a major contemporary poet and critic, are the following:

> . . . that he show us the way in which society works, that he show an understanding of the human heart, that he create characters in whose reality we believe and for whose fate we care, that he describe things and people so that we feel their physical presence, that he illuminate our moral consciousness, that he make us laugh and cry, that he delight us by his craftsmanship . . .[1]

We can see by this list of demands that the range of the novel will be broader than that of the short story, that the novel must capture and hold what we might call the flow of life. There will be more people, more conflict, more change. But because the novel is indeed a *form* of literature it does have limitations, just as the short story has limitations. And the novel has its own techniques—different from those of the short story.

Caroline Gordon, in the critical statement that follows, sets forth a general definition of the novel; she is a contemporary novelist, short story writer, and critic.

Caroline Gordon

THE NOVEL AS AN ART FORM

WHAT is a novel? The question is, indeed, more easily asked than answered. I have been writing fiction for twenty-five years but I would be hard put to it to define the essential nature of the novel as an art form. I can more readily say what it is not than what it is. Certainly the idea entertained by many people that a novel or even a short story is, as they say, a "slice of life" is all wrong. This notion appeals not only to the casual reader; many professional writers who are themselves highly gifted also hold to it. [. . .]

[. . .] Why is there such a diversity of opinion among serious readers, and among authors themselves, as to the [. . .] nature of this art form?

I suspect that it is because the novel is different from any other form of art. If we are to become good readers of fiction, we must learn to recognize and in our own minds define this essential difference. But perhaps we might set about defining it by first asking ourselves what the novel has in common with other art forms.

It has this in common with all art forms: it has a medium, and that me-

1. *The Mid-Century*, February 1961.

dium, like all mediums, has limitations or boundaries. It is one of the primary tasks of the artist not only to recognize those boundaries but, on occasion, when his art demands it of him, to exceed them. A man coming into possession of a tract of land that proves to be larger than he had expected it to be might acknowledge this fact by extending the fence which encloses the field. So, any fiction writer who uses a method that has not been used before, or explores a method already in use more thoroughly than it has been explored hitherto, extends the boundaries of the medium. But we come back to a consideration of the nature of the medium itself. The French philosopher Jacques Maritain has put it better than anybody else, I think, when he says, in *Art and Scholasticism,* that the novel differs from other forms of art in being directly concerned with the conduct of life itself.

This is doubtless one reason why there can be such a divergence of opinion, even among professional writers, as to what is a good novel or a bad novel, or even what is a novel and what isn't. It is the very nature of the medium, as complicated, as intractable, as mysterious as life itself, that makes for this confusion, a kind of confusion which does not reign in the other arts. I, for instance, do not know my notes and I have never, even for an instant, labored under the delusion that I could compose a piece of music. But I rarely meet a person who does not feel at the bottom of his heart that he could write a novel if he (half) tried. There is a good reason for this, of course. Everybody who is alive *knows* that he has in his own life the makings of a magnificent piece of fiction. But these happenings, however moving and dramatic, are not in themselves fiction, but only the material out of which we may fashion fiction—if we have the talent and the time and the patience.

Malcolm Cowley has defined a novel as a "long but unified story, designed to be read at more than one sitting, that deals with the relations among a group of characters and leads to a change in those relations." The distinctions made by the philosopher Maritain and the critic Cowley seem to supplement each other. The novel is, indeed, different from other forms of art in that it concerns itself with the conduct of life, but it also concerns itself primarily with a change in those relations that make up the lives of a number of persons— if we adhere to Mr. Cowley's definition, which seems to me a good one. The primary concern of a novel, then, is life, and life as it manifests itself in change, in action [. . .] that is to say, every piece of fiction that was ever written has the same subject: what happened to certain human beings.

"If art contrives to give the illusion of reality, it is done—as they say—with mirrors, and we are concerned with how it is done." [1] In the pages that follow, E. M. Forster, whose critical study *Aspects of the Novel* is an important modern work of criticism, and Percy Lubbock, whose *Craft of Fiction* has been equally influential, discuss the techniques of the novel. You will find that there is some disagreement between the views of these two critics.

1. Harry Levin.

E. M. Forster

FROM *ASPECTS OF THE NOVEL*

WE SHALL all agree that the fundamental aspect of the novel is its story-telling aspect, but we shall voice our assent in different tones, and it is on the precise tone of voice we employ now that our subsequent conclusions will depend.

Let us listen to three voices. If you ask one type of man, "What does a novel do?" he will reply placidly: "Well—I don't know—it seems a funny sort of question to ask—a novel's a novel—well, I don't know—I suppose it kind of tells a story, so to speak." He is quite good-tempered and vague, and probably driving a motor-bus at the same time and paying no more attention to literature than it merits. Another man, whom I visualize as on a golf-course, will be aggressive and brisk. He will reply: "What does a novel do? Why, tell a story of course, and I've no use for it if it didn't. I like a story. Very bad taste on my part, no doubt, but I like a story. You can take your art, you can take your literature, you can take your music, but give me a good story. And I like a story to be a story, mind, and my wife's the same." And a third man he says in a sort of drooping regretful voice, "Yes—oh, dear, yes—the novel tells a story." I respect and admire the first speaker. I detest and fear the second. And the third is myself. Yes—oh, dear, yes—the novel tells a story. That is the fundamental aspect without which it could not exist. That is the highest factor common to all novels, and I wish that it was not so, that it could be something different—melody, or perception of the truth, not this low atavistic form.

For the more we look at the story (the story that is a story, mind), the more we disentangle it from the finer growths that it supports, the less shall we find to admire. It runs like a backbone—or may I say a tapeworm, for its beginning and end are arbitrary. It is immensely old—goes back to neolithic times, perhaps to paleolithic. Neanderthal man listened to stories, if one may judge by the shape of his skull. The primitive audience was an audience of shock-heads, gaping round the campfire, fatigued with contending against the mammoth or the woolly rhinoceros, and only kept awake by suspense. What would happen next? The novelist droned on, and as soon as the audience guessed what happened next, they either fell asleep or killed him. [. . .]

We [. . .] all [. . .] want to know what happens next. That is universal and that is why the backbone of a novel has to be a story. Some of us want to know nothing else—there is nothing in us but primeval curiosity, and consequently our other literary judgments are ludicrous. And now the story can be defined. It is a narrative of events arranged in their time sequence—dinner coming after breakfast, Tuesday after Monday, decay after death, and so on. *Qua* story, it can only have one merit: that of making the audience want to know what happens next. And conversely it can only have one fault: that of making the audience not want to know what happens next. These are the only two criticisms that can be made on the

story that is a story. It is the lowest
and simplest of literary organisms.
Yet it is the highest factor common
to all the very complicated organisms
known as novels.

When we isolate the story like this
from the nobler aspects through
which it moves, and hold it out on
the forceps—wriggling and interminable, the naked worm of time—it
presents an appearance that is both
unlovely and dull. But we have much
to learn from it. Let us begin by considering it in connection with daily
life.

Daily life is also full of the time-
sense. We think one event occurs after or before another, the thought is
often in our minds, and much of our
talk and action proceeds on the assumption. Much of our talk and action, but not all; there seems something else in life besides time,
something which may conveniently be
called "value," something which is
measured not by minutes or hours,
but by intensity, so that when we look
at our past it does not stretch back
evenly but piles up into a few notable
pinnacles, and when we look at the
future it seems sometimes a wall,
sometimes a cloud, sometimes a sun,
but never a chronological chart. Neither memory nor anticipation is
much interested in Father Time, and
all dreamers, artists and lovers are
partially delivered from his tyranny;
he can kill them, but he cannot secure
their attention, and at the very moment of doom, when the clock collected in the tower its strength and
struck, they may be looking the other
way. So daily life, whatever it may be
really, is practically composed of two
lives—the life in time and the life by
values—and our conduct reveals a
double allegiance. "I only saw her for
five minutes, but it was worth it."
There you have both allegiances in a
single sentence. And what the story

does is to narrate the life in time. And
what the entire novel does—if it is a
good novel—is to include the life by
values as well [. . .] It, also, pays a
double allegiance. But in it, in the
novel, the allegiance to time is imperative: no novel could be written
without it. [. . .] It is always possible for you or me in daily life to deny
that time exists and act accordingly
even if we become unintelligible and
are sent by our fellow citizens to what
they choose to call a lunatic asylum.
But it is never possible for a novelist
to deny time inside the fabric of his
novel: he must cling however lightly
to the thread of his story, he must
touch the interminable tapeworm,
otherwise he becomes unintelligible,
which, in his case, is a blunder. [. . .]

[. . .] What the story does do
[. . .] , all it can do, is to transform
us from readers into listeners, to
whom "a" voice speaks, the voice of
the tribal narrator, squatting in the
middle of the cave, and saying one
thing after another until the audience
falls asleep [. . .] The story is primitive, it reaches back to the origins of
literature, before reading was discovered, and it appeals to what is
primitive in us. That is why we are so
unreasonable over the stories we like,
and so ready to bully those who like
something else. [. . .] Intolerance is
the atmosphere stories generate. The
story is neither moral nor is it favourable to the understanding of the novel
in its other aspects. If we want to do
that we must come out of the cave.

We shall not come out of it yet,
but observe already how that other
life—the life by value—presses against
the novel from all sides, how it is
ready to fill and indeed distort it, offering it people, plots, fantasies, views
of the universe, anything except this
constant "and then . . . and then,"
which is the sole contribution of our
present inquiry. The life in time is so

obviously base and inferior that the question naturally occurs: cannot the novelist abolish it from his work, even as the mystic asserts he has abolished it from his experience, and install its radiant alternative alone?

[. . .] The experiment is doomed to failure. The time-sequence cannot be destroyed without carrying in its ruin all that should have taken its place; the novel that would express values only becomes unintelligible and therefore valueless. [. . .]

Having discussed the story—that simple and fundamental aspect of the novel—we can turn to a more interesting topic: the actors. We need not ask what happened next, but to whom did it happen; the novelist will be appealing to our intelligence and imagination, not merely to our curiosity. A new emphasis enters his voice: emphasis upon value.

Since the actors in a story are usually human, it seemed convenient to entitle this aspect People. [. . .]

Since the novelist is himself a human being, there is an affinity between him and his subject-matter which is absent in many other forms of art. The historian is also linked, though, as we shall see, less intimately. The painter and sculptor need not be linked: that is to say they need not represent human beings unless they wish, no more need the poet, while the musician cannot represent them even if he wishes, without the help of a programme. The novelist, unlike many of his colleagues, makes up a number of word-masses roughly describing himself (roughly: niceties shall come later), gives them names and sex, assigns them plausible gestures, and causes them to speak by the use of inverted commas, and perhaps to behave consistently. These word-masses are his characters. [. . .] What is the difference between people in a novel and people like the novelist or like you, or like me, or Queen Victoria?

There is bound to be a difference. If a character in a novel is exactly like Queen Victoria—not rather like but exactly like—then it actually is Queen Victoria, and the novel, or all of it that the character touches, becomes a memoir. A memoir is history, it is based on evidence. A novel is based on evidence + or − x, the unknown quantity being the temperament of the novelist, and the unknown quantity always modifies the effect of the evidence, and sometimes transforms it entirely.

The historian deals with actions, and with the characters of men only so far as he can deduce them from their actions. He is quite as much concerned with character as the novelist, but he can only know of its existence when it shows on the surface. [. . .]

[. . .] The historian records whereas the novelist must create. [. . .] In daily life we never understand each other, neither complete clairvoyance nor complete confessional exists. We know each other approximately, by external signs, and these serve well enough as a basis for society and even for intimacy. But people in a novel can be understood completely by the reader, if the novelist wishes; their inner as well as their outer life can be exposed. And this is why they often seem more definite than characters in history, or even our own friends; we have been told all about them that can be told; even if they are imperfect or unreal they do not contain any secrets, whereas our friends do and must, mutual secrecy being one of the conditions of life upon this globe.

Now let us restate the problem [. . .] You and I are people. Had not we better glance through the main facts in our own lives—not in our individual careers but in our make-up as human beings? Then we shall have something definite to start from.

The main facts in human life are five: birth, food, sleep, love and death. One could increase the number—add breathing for instance—but these five are the most obvious. Let us briefly ask ourselves what part they play in our lives, and what in novels. Does the novelist tend to reproduce them accurately or does he tend to exaggerate, minimize, ignore, and to exhibit his characters going through processes which are not the same through which you and I go, though they bear the same names?

To consider the two strangest first: birth and death; strange because they are at the same time experiences and not experiences. We only know of them by report. We were all born, but we cannot remember what it was like. And death is coming even as birth has come, but, similarly, we do not know what it is like. Our final experience, like our first, is conjectural. We move between two darknesses. Certain people pretend to tell us what birth and death are like: a mother, for instance, has her point of view about birth; a doctor, a religious, have their points of view about both. But it is all from the outside, and the two entities who might enlighten us, the baby and the corpse, cannot do so, because their apparatus for communicating their experiences is not attuned to our apparatus for reception.

So let us think of people as starting life with an experience they forget and ending it with one which they anticipate but cannot understand. These are the creatures whom the novelist proposes to introduce as characters into books; these, or creatures plausibly like them. The novelist is allowed to remember and understand everything, if it suits him.

He knows all the hidden life. How soon will he pick up his characters after birth, how close to the grave will he follow them? And what will he say, or cause to be felt, about these two queer experiences?

Then food, the stoking-up process, the keeping alive of an individual flame, the process that begins before birth and is continued after it by the mother, and finally taken over by the individual himself, who goes on day after day putting an assortment of objects into a hole in his face without becoming surprised or bored: food is a link between the known and the forgotten; closely connected with birth, which none of us remembers, and coming down to this morning's breakfast. Like sleep—which in many ways it resembles—food does not merely restore our strength, it has also an aesthetic side, it can taste good or bad. What will happen to this double-faced commodity in books?

And fourthly, sleep. On the average, about a third of our time is not spent in society or civilization or even in what is usually called solitude. We enter a world of which little is known and which seems to us after leaving it to have been partly oblivion, partly a caricature of this world and partly a revelation. "I dreamt of nothing" or "I dreamt of a ladder" or "I dreamt of heaven" we say when we wake. I do not want to discuss the nature of sleep and dreams—only to point out that they occupy much time and that what is called "History" only busies itself with about two-thirds of the human cycle, and theorizes accordingly. Does fiction take up a similar attitude?

And lastly, love. [. . .] Besides sex, there are other emotions [. . .]: the various upliftings of the spirit, such as affection, friendship, patriotism, mysticism—and as soon as we try to determine the relation between sex and these other emotions we shall of course begin to quarrel [. . .] Let me only tabulate the various points of view. Some people say that sex is basic and underlies all these other loves—love of friends, of God, of country. Others say that it is connected with them, but laterally; it is not their root. Others say that it is not connected at all. All I suggest is that we call the whole bundle of emotions love, and regard them as the fifth great experience through which human beings have to pass. When human beings love they try to get something. They also try to give something, and this double aim makes love more complicated than food or sleep. It is selfish and altruistic at the same time, and no amount of specialization in one direction quite atrophies the other. How much time does love take? This question sounds gross but it must be asked because it bears on our present inquiry. Sleep takes about eight hours out of the twenty-four, food about two more. Shall we put down love for another two? Surely that is a handsome allowance. Love may weave itself into our other activities—so may drowsiness and hunger. Love may start various secondary activities: for instance, a man's love for his family may cause him to spend a good deal of time on the Stock Exchange, or his love for God a good deal of time in church. But that he has emotional communion with any beloved object for more than two hours a day may be gravely doubted, and it is this emotional communion, this desire to give and to get, this mixture of generosity and expectation, that distinguishes love from the other experiences on our list.

That is the human make-up—or part of it. Made up like this himself, the novelist takes his pen in his hand, gets into the abnormal state which it is convenient to call "inspiration," and

tries to create characters. [. . .]

[. . .] A character in a book is real [. . .] when the novelist knows everything about it. He may not choose to tell us all he knows—many of the facts, even of the kind we call obvious, may be hidden. But he will give us the feeling that though the character has not been explained, it is explicable, and we get from this a reality of a kind we can never get in daily life.

For human intercourse, as soon as we look at it for its own sake and not as a social adjunct, is seen to be haunted by a spectre. We cannot understand each other, except in a rough and ready way; we cannot reveal ourselves, even when we want to; what we call intimacy is only a makeshift; perfect knowledge is an illusion. But in the novel we can know people perfectly, and, apart from the general pleasure of reading, we can find here a compensation for their dimness in life. In this direction fiction is truer than history, because it goes beyond the evidence, and each of us knows from his own experience that there is something beyond the evidence, and even if the novelist has not got it correctly, well—he has tried. He can post his people in as babies, he can cause them to go on without sleep or food, he can make them be in love, love and nothing but love, provided he seems to know everything about them, provided they are his creations. [. . .]

That is why novels, even when they are about wicked people, can solace us; they suggest a more comprehensible and thus a more manageable human race, they give us the illusion of perspicacity and of power. [. . .]

The novelist, we are beginning to see, has a very mixed lot of ingredients to handle. There is the story, with its time-sequence of "and then

. . . and then . . ."; there are nine-pins about whom he might tell the story, and tell a rattling good one, but no, he prefers to tell his story about human beings; he takes over the life by values as well as the life in time. The characters arrive when evoked, but full of the spirit of mutiny. For they have these numerous parallels with people like ourselves, they try to live their own lives and are consequently often engaged in treason against the main scheme of the book. They "run away," they "get out of hand": they are creations inside a creation, and often inharmonious towards it; if they are given complete freedom they kick the book to pieces, and if they are kept too sternly in check, they revenge themselves by dying, and destroy it by intestinal decay. [. . .]

We may divide characters into flat and round. Flat characters were called "humorous" in the seventeenth century, and are sometimes called types, and sometimes caricatures. In their purest form, they are constructed round a single idea or quality: when there is more than one factor in them, we get the beginning of the curve towards the round. The really flat character can be expressed in one sentence such as "I never will desert Mr. Micawber." There is Mrs. Micawber —she says she won't desert Mr. Micawber, she doesn't, and there she is. [. . .]

One great advantage of flat characters is that they are easily recognized whenever they come in—recognized by the reader's emotional eye, not by the visual eye, which merely notes the recurrence of a proper name. [. . .] It is a convenience for an author when he can strike with his full force at once, and flat characters are very useful to him, since they never need reintroducing, never run away, have not to be watched for development, and provide their own atmosphere—little luminous disks of a pre-arranged size, pushed hither and thither like counters across the void or between the stars; most satisfactory.

A second advantage is that they are easily remembered by the reader afterwards. They remain in his mind as unalterable for the reason that they were not changed by circumstances; they moved through circumstances, which gives them in retrospect a comforting quality, and preserves them when the book that produced them may decay. [. . .]

All the same, critics who have their eyes fixed severely upon daily life—as were our eyes last week—have very little patience with such renderings of human nature. Queen Victoria, they argue, cannot be summed up in a single sentence, so what excuse remains for Mrs. Micawber? [. . .]

[. . .] But [. . .] a novel that is at all complex often requires flat people as well as round [. . .] The case of Dickens is significant. Dickens' people are nearly all flat (Pip and David Copperfield attempt roundness, but so diffidently that they seem more like bubbles than solids). Nearly every one can be summed up in a sentence, and yet there is this wonderful feeling of human depth. Probably the immense vitality of Dickens causes his characters to vibrate a little, so that they borrow his life and appear to lead one of their own. It is a conjuring trick; at any moment we may look at Mr. Pickwick edgeways and find him no thicker than a gramophone record. But we never get the sideway view. Mr. Pickwick is far too adroit and well-trained. He always has the air of weighing something [. . .] Part of the genius of Dickens is that he does use types and caricatures, people whom we recognize the instant they re-enter, and yet achieves effects that are not mechanical and a vision of humanity that is not shallow. Those who dislike Dickens have an excellent case. He ought to be bad. He is actually one of our big writers, and his immense success with types suggests that there may be more in flatness than the severer critics admit. [. . .]

[Yet] we must admit that flat people are not in themselves as big achievements as round ones, and also that they are best when they are comic. A serious or tragic flat character is apt to be a bore. Each time he enters crying "Revenge!" or "My heart bleeds for humanity!" or whatever his formula is, our hearts sink. [. . .] It is only round people who are fit to perform tragically for any length of time and can move us to any feelings except humour and appropriateness. [. . .]

[. . .] The test of a round character is whether it is capable of surprising in a convincing way. If it never surprises, it is flat. If it does not convince, it is a flat pretending to be round. It has the incalculability of life about it—life within the pages of a book. And by using it sometimes alone, more often in combination with the other kind, the novelist achieves his task of acclimatization and harmonizes the human race with the other aspects of his work.

Now for [. . .] the point of view from which the story may be told.

To some critics this is the fundamental device of novel-writing. "The whole intricate question of method, in the craft of fiction," says Mr. Percy Lubbock, "I take to be governed by the question of the *point of view*— the question of the relation in which the narrator stands to the story." And his book *The Craft of Fiction* examines various points of view with genius and insight. The novelist, he says, can either describe the characters from outside, as an impartial or partial onlooker; or he can assume omniscience and describe them from within; or he can place himself in the position of one of them and affect to be in the dark as to the motives of the rest; or there are certain intermediate attitudes.

Those who follow him will lay a sure foundation for the aesthetics of fiction—a foundation which I cannot for a moment promise. This is a ramshackly survey and for me the "whole intricate question of method" resolves itself not into formulae but into the power of the writer to bounce the reader into accepting what he says—a power which Mr. Lubbock admits and admires, but locates at the edge of the problem instead of at the centre. I should put it plumb in the centre. Look how Dickens bounces us in *Bleak House*. Chapter I of *Bleak House* is omniscient. Dickens takes us into the Court of Chancery and rapidly explains all the people there. In Chapter II he is partially omniscient. We still use his eyes, but for some unexplained reason they begin to grow weak: he can explain Sir Leicester Dedlock to us, part of Lady Dedlock but not all, and nothing of Mr. Tulkinghorn. In Chapter III he is even more reprehensible: he goes straight across into the dramatic method and inhabits a young lady. Esther Summerson. "I have a great deal of difficulty in beginning to write my portion of these pages, for I know I am not clever," pipes up Esther, and continues in this strain with consistency and competence, so long as she is allowed to hold the pen. At any moment the author of her being may snatch it from her, and run about taking notes himself, leaving her seated goodness knows where, and employed we do not care how. Logically, *Bleak House* is all to pieces, but Dickens bounces us, so that we do not mind the shift-ings of the view-point. [. . .]

[. . .] A novelist can shift his view-point if it comes off, and it came off with Dickens [. . .] Indeed this power to expand and contract per-ception (of which the shifting view-point is a symptom), this right to in-termittent knowledge:—I find it one of the great advantages of the novel-form, and it has a parallel in our per-ception of life. We are stupider at some times than others; we can enter into people's minds occasionally but not always, because our own minds get tired; and this intermittence lends in the long run variety and colour to the experiences we receive. A quan-tity of novelists, English novelists es-pecially, have behaved like this to the people in their books: played fast and loose with them, and I cannot see why they should be censured.

They must be censured if we catch them at it at the time. That is quite true, and out of it arises another ques-tion: may the writer take the reader into his confidence about his charac-ters? Answer has already been indi-cated: better not. It is dangerous, it generally leads to a drop in the tem-perature, to intellectual and emotion-al laxity, and worse still to facetious-ness, and to a friendly invitation to see how the figures hook up behind. "Doesn't A look nice—she always was my favourite." "Let's think of why B does that—perhaps there's more in him than meets the eye—yes, see—he has a heart of gold—having given you this peep at it I'll pop it back—I don't think he's noticed." "And C—he al-ways was the mystery man." Inti-macy is gained but at the expense of illusion and nobility. It is like stand-ing a man a drink so that he may not criticize your opinions. With all re-spect to Fielding and Thackeray it is devastating, it is bar-parlour chatti-ness, and nothing has been more

harmful to the novels of the past. To take your reader into your confi-dence about the universe is a different thing. It is not dangerous for a novel-ist to draw back from his characters, as Hardy and Conrad do, and to gen-eralize about the conditions under which he thinks life is carried on. It is confidences about the individual peo-ple that do harm, and beckon the reader away from the people to an examination of the novelist's mind. Not much is ever found in it at such a moment, for it is never in the crea-tive state: the mere process of saying, "Come along, let's have a chat," has cooled it down. [. . .]

[. . .] In most literary works there are two elements: human individuals, whom we have recently discussed, and the element vaguely called art. Art we have also dallied with, but with a very low form of it: the story: the chopped-off length of the tape-worm of time. Now we arrive at a much higher aspect: the plot, and the plot, instead of finding human beings more or less cut to its requirements, as they are in the drama, finds them enormous, shadowy and intractable, and three-quarters hidden like an iceberg. [. . .]

Let us define a plot. We have de-fined a story as a narrative of events arranged in their time-sequence. A plot is also a narrative of events, the emphasis falling on causality. "The king died and then the queen died" is a story. "The king died, and then the queen died of grief" is a plot. The time-sequence is preserved, but the sense of causality overshadows it. Or again: "The queen died, no one knew why, until it was discovered that it was through grief at the death of the king." This is a plot with a mystery in it, a form capable of high develop-ment. It suspends the time-sequence, it moves as far away from the story as its limitations will allow. Consider the death of the queen. If it is in a story we say "and then?" If it is in a plot we ask "why?" That is the fundamental difference between these two aspects of the novel. A plot cannot be told to a gaping audience of cave-men or to a tyrannical sultan or to their modern descendant the movie-public. They can only be kept awake by "and then—and then——" They can only supply curiosity. But a plot demands intelligence and memory also.

Curiosity is one of the lowest of the human faculties. You will have noticed in daily life that when people are inquisitive they nearly always have bad memories and are usually stupid at bottom. The man who begins by asking you how many brothers and sisters you have is never a sympathetic character, and if you meet him in a year's time he will probably ask you how many brothers and sisters you have, his mouth again sagging open, his eyes still bulging from his head. It is difficult to be friends with such a man, and for two inquisitive people to be friends must be impossible. Curiosity by itself takes us a very little way, nor does it take us far into the novel—only as far as the story. If we would grasp the plot we must add intelligence and memory.

Intelligence first. The intelligent novel-reader, unlike the inquisitive one who just runs his eye over a new fact, mentally picks it up. He sees it from two points of view: isolated, and related to the other facts that he has read on previous pages. Probably he does not understand it, but he does not expect to do so yet awhile. The facts in a highly organized novel |. . .] are often of the nature of cross-correspondences and the ideal spectator cannot expect to view them properly until he is sitting up on a hill at the end. This element of sur-

prise or mystery—the detective element as it is sometimes rather emptily called—is of great importance in a plot. It occurs through a suspension of the time-sequence; a mystery is a pocket in time, and it occurs crudely, as in "Why did the queen die?" and more subtly in half-explained gestures and words, the true meaning of which only dawns pages ahead. Mystery is essential to a plot, and cannot be appreciated without intelligence. To the curious it is just another "and then——" To appreciate a mystery, part of the mind must be left behind, brooding, while the other part goes marching on.

That brings us to our second qualification: memory.

Memory and intelligence are closely connected, for unless we remember we cannot understand. If by the time the queen dies we have forgotten the existence of the king we shall never make out what killed her. The plot-maker expects us to remember, we expect him to leave no loose ends. Every action or word ought to count; it ought to be economical and spare; even when complicated it should be organic and free from deadmatter. It may be difficult or easy, it may and should contain mysteries, but it ought not to mislead. And over it, as it unfolds, will hover the memory of the reader (that dull glow of the mind of which intelligence is the bright advancing edge) and will constantly rearrange and reconsider, seeing new clues, new chains of cause and effect, and the final sense (if the plot has been a fine one) will not be of clues or chains, but of something aesthetically compact, something which might have been shown by the novelist straight away, only if he had shown it straight away it would never have become beautiful. We come up against beauty here—for the first time in our inquiry: beauty at which a novelist should never aim, though he fails if he does not achieve it. [. . .]

[. . .] There are in the novel two forces: human beings and a bundle of various things not human beings, and [. . .] it is the novelist's business to adjust these two forces and conciliate their claims. [. . .]

Sometimes a plot triumphs too completely. The characters have to suspend their natures at every turn, or else are so swept away by the course of Fate that our sense of their reality is weakened. [. . .] In the novel, all human happiness and misery does not take the form of action, it seeks means of expression other than through the plot, it must not be rigidly canalized.

In the losing battle that the plot fights with the characters, it often takes a cowardly revenge. Nearly all novels are feeble at the end. This is because the plot requires to be wound up. Why is this necessary? Why is there not a convention which allows a novelist to stop as soon as he feels muddled or bored? Alas, he has to round things off, and usually the characters go dead while he is at work, and our final impression of them is through deadness. [. . .] If it was not for death and marriage I do not know how the average novelist would conclude. Death and marriage are almost his only connection between his characters and his plot, and the reader is more ready to meet him here, and take a bookish view of them, provided they occur later on in the book: the

writer, poor fellow, must be allowed to finish up somehow, he has his living to get like anyone else, so no wonder that nothing is heard but hammering and screwing.

This—as far as one can generalize—is the inherent defect of novels: they go off at the end: and there are two explanations of it: firstly, failure of pep, which threatens the novelist like all workers: and secondly, the difficulty which we have been discussing. The characters have been getting out of hand, laying foundations and declining to build on them afterwards, and now the novelist has to labour personally, in order that the job may be done to time. He pretends that the characters are acting for him. He keeps mentioning their names and using inverted commas. But the characters are gone or dead.

The plot, then, is the novel in its logical intellectual aspect: it requires mystery, but the mysteries are solved later on: the reader may be moving about in worlds unrealized, but the novelist has no misgivings. He is competent, poised above his work, throwing a beam of light here, popping on a cap of invisibility there, and (qua plot-maker) continually negotiating with himself qua character-monger as to the best effect to be produced. He plans his book beforehand: or anyhow he stands above it, his interest in cause and effect give him an air of predetermination.

Percy Lubbock

FROM *THE CRAFT OF FICTION*

IT SEEMS to be a principle of the story-teller's art that a personal narrator will do very well and may be extremely helpful, so long as the story is only the reflection of life beyond and outside him; but that as soon as the story begins to find its centre of gravity in his own life, as soon as the main weight of attention is claimed for the speaker rather than for the scene, then his report of himself becomes a matter which might be strengthened, and which should accordingly give way to the stronger method. [. . .]

The novelist, therefore, returns to the third person again, but he returns with a marked difference. [. . .] It is still the man in the book who sees and judges and reflects; all the picture of life is still rendered in the hero's terms. But the difference is that instead of receiving his report we now see him in the act of judging and reflecting; his consciousness, no longer a matter of hearsay, a matter for which we must take his word, is now before us in its original agitation. Here is a spectacle for the reader, with no obtrusive interpreter, no transmitter of light, no conductor of meaning. This man's interior life is cast into the world of independent, rounded objects; it is given room to show itself, it appears, it *acts*. A distinction is made between the scene which the man surveys, and the energy within him which converts it all into the stuff of his own being. The scene, as much as ever, is watched through his eyes; but now there is this other fact, in front of the scene, actually under the hand of the reader. To this fact the

value of drama has accrued. [. . .]

Thus it is that the novelist pushes his responsibility further and further away from himself. The fiction that he devises is ultimately his; but it looks poor and thin if he openly claims it as his, or at any rate it becomes much more substantial as soon as he fathers it upon another. This is not *my* story, says the author; you know nothing of me; it is the story of this man or woman in whose words you have it, and he or she is a person whom you *can* know; and you may see for yourselves how the matter arose, the man and woman being such as they are; it all hangs together, and it makes a solid and significant piece of life. And having said this, the author has only moved the question a stage further, and it reappears in exactly the same form. The man or the woman, after all, is only telling and stating, and we are still invited to accept the story upon somebody's authority. The narrator may do his best, and may indeed do so well that to hear his account is as good as having seen what he describes, and nothing could be better than that; the matter might rest there, if this were all. But it must depend considerably on the nature of his story, for it may happen that he tells and describes things that a man is never really in a position to substantiate; his account of himself, for example, cannot be thoroughly valid, not through any want of candour on his part, but simply because no man can completely objectify himself, and a credible account of anything must appear to detach it, to set it altogether free for inspection. And so the novelist passes on towards drama, gets behind the narrator, and represents the mind of the narrator as in itself a kind of action.

By so doing, be it noted, he forfeits none of his special freedom, as I have called it, the picture-making faculty that he enjoys as a story-teller. He is not constrained, like the playwright, to turn his story into dramatic action and nothing else. He has dramatized his novel step by step, until the mind of the picture-maker [. . .] is present upon the page; but [the picture-makers are] just as free to project their view of the world, to picture it for the reader, as they might be if they spoke in person. The difference is in the fact that we now see the very sources of the activity within them; we not only share their vision, we watch them absorbing it. [. . .]

It thus becomes clear why the prudent novelist tends to prefer an indirect to a direct method. The simple story-teller begins by addressing himself openly to the reader, and then exchanges this method for another and another, and with each modification he reaches the reader from a further remove. The more circuitous procedure on the part of the author produces a straighter effect for the reader; that is why, other things being equal, the more dramatic way is better than the less. It is indirect, as a method; but it places the thing itself in view, instead of recalling and reflecting and picturing it. For any story, no doubt, there is an ideal point upon this line of progress towards drama, where the author finds the right method of telling the story. The point is indicated by the subject of the story itself, by the particular matter that is to be brought out and made plain; and the author, while he regards the subject and nothing else, is guided to the best manner of treatment by a twofold consideration. In the first place he wishes the story so far as possible to speak for itself, the people and the action to appear independently rather than to be described and explained. To this end the method is raised to the highest dramatic power that the subject allows, until at last, perhaps, it is found that nothing need be explained at all; there need be no revelation of anybody's thought, no going behind any of the appearances on the surface of the action; even the necessary description [. . .] may be so treated that this too gains the value of drama.

The Novel:
A Passage to India

Having read what Caroline Gordon, E. M. Forster, and Percy Lubbock have to say about the novel in general, we now turn to a close examination of *A Passage to India*. The four statements that follow present varying critical approaches and interpretations or evaluations. They are placed here to help you—

to enlarge and deepen your understanding of *A Passage to India*. But every reader is to at least some extent a critic, consciously or subconsciously, and no one critic's appraisal is likely to be wholly right—or, indeed, wholly wrong. You will have to judge for yourself the validity of these various appraisals. In the final analysis, you must have the courage to be your own critic.

Morton Dauwen Zabel

E. M. FORSTER: THE TROPHIES
OF THE MIND

E. M. FORSTER lends himself no more easily to superficial recognition today than he did half a century ago when his first novel was published. His books came into their first general popularity early in the 1940s, when the war spurred the anxious recovery of so much writing which suddenly appeared to defend a threatened tradition or to embody the civilized values that war endangers. During the past fifteen years they have been read, reprinted, and discussed on a scale which no one, least of all perhaps their author, would have had the daring to prophesy in the days of their first appearance. They have become firmly established as Twentieth Century classics. Yet even now Forster offers few of the appeals that qualify a novelist for urgent "importance" or timely respect: no dogmatic beliefs in politics or religion, no radical stylistic novelty or aesthetic oddity, no yearly appeal to his public with a new book. For an author generally described, with admissible justice, as "the most distinguished living English novelist," he suggests few tags of easy distinction; perhaps only one—that he has

practiced the difficult strategy of writing little but making it count for much; of keeping his readers unsatisfied and asking for more. It is now more than thirty years since he published a novel, yet if he were to publish one tomorrow no book—certainly in the English-speaking world would be more eagerly or expectantly read.

This attraction has been strong in his work from its beginnings. He published his first novel in 1905, his fourth in 1910 when he was just over thirty, his fifth and latest in 1924. To these he has on occasion added two collections of tales, three of essays and criticism, a life of Lowes Dickinson, a guide and book of studies on Alexandria, by-products of service in Egypt during the First World War, a chronicle (*The Hill of Devi*) of his two sojourns in Dewas State Senior in India, and a "domestic biography" of his great-aunt Marianne Thornton and her remarkable English family. He has contributed for almost six decades to the English liberal reviews and he has written a sizeable number of broadcasts for the BBC. None of his fictions came announced by the fan-

From *Craft and Character* by Morton Dauwen Zabel, copyright 1938, 1943, 1951 by Morton Dauwen Zabel. Reprinted by permission of The Viking Press, Inc.

fares of innovation or technical experiment. If popularly read, as two of them were, they could be taken as witty and topical comedies in late-Victorian line of Meredith, brisk in language and insight, agreeably diverting in romantic interest. They showed plots of lithe and shapely movement, as insinuating in their darting charm as Jane Austen's, barbed with wit and comment, populated by characters who had the art of springing into quick and recognizable life with their first speeches. Whatever dissent, perplexity, or irritation they might arouse to tease the mind, they did little to disturb the literary conventions. Yet as time has gone on, these books have persisted and cut deeper into the memory and consciousness of the age. Of the new English novelists who made their mark between Hardy's retirement from fiction in 1895 and the war of 1914, Forster is the only one, except for Conrad and Lawrence, who survives as an intimate force among the younger talents of the present day. His books deal with events and circumstances which have now receded to historic distance, yet in effect, style, and meaning they seem as dateless as any novels of the century. His energy has issued from a firm center of moral and intellectual realism. If one were to define the ancestry of Auden's generation, Forster's name—whatever the claims of James, Conrad, Lawrence, or Eliot—would suggest the most accurate combination of critical and temperamental forces, the one most clearly stamped by the peculiarly English skeptical sensibility and moral passion that has survived two wars with sanity and made possible the reassessment of the tradition and delusion that made those wars and their consequences possible in the Twentieth Century. Today as much as thirty years ago, his special position is contested by no other tal-

ent. It is still useful to go back to his beginnings to see what qualities and temperament he brought into modern English fiction, and by what means he impressed these on the intelligence of his time.

In 1905 there appeared quietly in England a short novel by a new writer. It was called *Where Angels Fear to Tread;* its author was then twenty-six years old and had thus far published only a few stories in magazines of small circulation. It carried none of the marks that indicate a bold or unusual originality. The qualities of the masters then dominating the scene in England—the tragic vision of Hardy, the intellectual comedy of Meredith, the complex moral analysis and stylistic density of Henry James— were none of them obviously present in the deceptively modest tale. Nor was it a piece of solid social documentation in the vein of the younger naturalists and social radicals then rising to prominence—Bennett, Wells, Galsworthy, Beresford. The book was brief, lucid, apparently spontaneous and effortless in manner. It told the story of an international marriage, but it was cut along lines markedly different from the established "international theme" as it had for thirty years operated so intricately in the novels and tales of Henry James. Here the reader met, at the outset, a situation making for charming comedy and an absurd collision between cultures—middle-class English folk among the scenes and shrines of Italy. [. . .]

It was fourteen years before Forster produced *A Passage to India,* but when it came, it carried the problem that had taxed him in Cambridge, in Italy, and in London into a deeper and more complex world than any of these—to India and the East, which had always fascinated him and where, by this time, he had made two long sojourns. Here the scene is Chandrapore, a small city on the upper Ganges, tense with antagonisms of class and race. The life of the town is divided between the swarming native populace and the small circle of English officials who form the local outpost of Empire. This is the India already made familiar to English readers in the tales of Kipling, but it no longer has the attributes of romance and reckless adventure of Kipling's military and war-stirred imperial scene. The age of conquest and bravado is past. So too is Kipling's world of aggressive, vulgar action, though not his suggestion of uneasy conscience and morbid hauntings—even if Forster's treatment of these is miles removed from Kipling's style and drama. We are now in the early Twentieth Century. Imperialism has become a thing of hardened routine and of guilty uneasiness. The townsfolk of Chandrapore, part though they are of the teeming sea of Indian life, are dominated by Oxford- or Cambridge-trained natives whose inherited loyalties are mixed with the enlightened yet defensive sensibility bred by their western contacts.

Into this restless situation come two visitors from England—Adela Quested, who has come out to India to get reacquainted with one of the local officials, Ronny Heaslop, with a view to marrying him; and Mrs. Moore, Ronny's mother, who accompanies Adela as chaperon. The two ladies are products again of well-bred English gentility, but they exasperate the English colony, smugly locked in its code of club life and official superiority, by their earnest desire to see "the real India." Adela is serious, sober, plain-natured, earnestly dull, but Mrs. Moore is something more. Mrs. Moore is a character who appears sooner or later in every Forster novel. She is anticipated by Caroline Abbott

in *Where Angels Fear to Tread;* by Charlotte Bartlett, Lucy Honeychurch's family friend and chaperon in Italy, in *A Room with a View;* by Rickie Elliott's mother in *The Longest Journey;* by the first Mrs. Wilcox in *Howards End.* Mrs. Moore also belongs to the English moral tradition, to middle-class life with its guarded, self-protective mores, to the orbit of discreet and defensive ethic which makes her class and nation strong; but she is also gifted—or perhaps damned —by having a secret and inner life of her own, a spirit that protests the complacent confines of her kind and that rebels against the closed mind of a dominant world, the hardened mentality of privilege, the smugness, cant, and intolerance that are bred by power and authority.

These two ladies make contact with two members of the Chandrapore community who are regarded with distrust by the English officials. One is Mr. Fielding, the principal of the Government College, an Englishman but a disillusioned one: a man of middle age and rough experience whose imagination has penetrated the Indian world and made friends there, and who has become a standing threat to the local English solidarity. The other is the Indian physician, Dr. Aziz, educated in England, a small, wiry, witty, half-absurd man, partly a poet, partly a careerist, a widower with three small children, desperately anxious to ingratiate himself with his English superiors, yet nervously defensive of his own intelligence too, and of his race and his loyalties to it. Adela gropes toward the friendship of Aziz and Fielding with a liberal, well-disposed woman's eager decency. But Mrs. Moore has no need to grope or yearn. Old age has dissolved her ambitions and illusions. Like Mrs. Wilcox in *Howards End,* she knows herself to be approaching the mystery of death.

The vast inchoate mystery of India around her is something both to fear and to love: something that means death's horror but also its rewarding release. She has responded instantly to the charms of Dr. Aziz and has become his friend. So it comes about that Aziz, always eager to make alliance with the English, arranges a picnic excursion to the Marabar caves in the mountains that lie across the hot plain beyond Chandrapore. These caves have dominated the landscape from the first page of the novel. Now they become the scene of crisis. Adela is anxious to see the caves out of her alert tourist's curiosity. Mrs. Moore the caves attract but they also repel. They are entrances to the kingdom of death that makes all things alike—life and death, good and evil—and their famous echo spells for her the dissolution of the life and faith she was bred to back in England:

> . . . the echo began in some indescribable way to undermine her hold on life. . . . it had managed to murmur: "Pathos, piety, courage —they exist, but are identical, and so is filth. Everything exists, nothing has value." If one had spoken vileness in that place, or quoted lofty poetry, the comment would have been the same—"ou-boum." If one had spoken with the tongues of angels and pleaded for all the unhappiness and misunderstanding of the world, past, present, and to come, for all the misery men must undergo whatever their opinion and position, and however much they dodge or bluff—it would amount to the same. . . . Devils are of the North, and poems can be written about them, but no one could romanticize the Marabar because it robbed infinity and eternity of their vastness, the only quality that accommodates them to

mankind. . . . But suddenly at the edge of her mind, Religion reappeared, poor little talkative Christianity, and she knew that all its divine words from "Let there be Light" to "It is finished" only amounted to "boum."

So the fatal picnic party stands at the edge of the Indian mystery. And then at last the long-drawn tension and secret hostilities of Chandrapore snap. Abandoning Mrs. Moore to her fatigue and exhaustion, Adela and Dr. Aziz visit the caves. Something happens there—we never learn exactly what—but Adela, her moral and sexual defenses breached by the strange influences working on her that day, believes she has been assaulted by Dr. Aziz and that he has attempted to rape her. She rushes out; she makes her way back to Chandrapore; the news spreads like wild-fire. Aziz is jailed. Every Englishman believes him guilty except Fielding and Mrs. Moore. His trial is set, and its verdict of guilty is assured. Fielding is ostracized by his compatriots for asserting his belief in Aziz's innocence, and Mrs. Moore, since she cannot be trusted to run with her pack, is shipped by her son to England only to die en route and be buried at sea in the tropic depths of the Indian Ocean. Then, at the trial, with the populace of Chandrapore seething with fury and the English colony desperately beleaguered but triumphant in the justice of their cause, the long arm of uncertainty once more reaches out and flaws the defenses of the West. Adela, at her nerve's edge in the witness-box, is suddenly touched by something akin to Mrs. Moore's lucidity and intuition. Her conviction deserts her. She recants her accusation. With the court and city at their highest pitch of suspense, the whole case collapses. Aziz is exonerated.

The town bursts into frenzy and triumph for the Indians. Adela is spurned and cast out by her tribe.

Some years later, Fielding, who has left India to return to England, comes back, now married to Mrs. Moore's daughter Stella. He finds his old friend Aziz living far up-country with his children, a medical officer in a remote Moslem state. The old scars have healed, but they can still throb with remembered pains and unsettled racial scores. Aziz has reverted to his Moslem kind. England nearly ruined his life. He has never forgiven her. But the friends—Aziz and Fielding—know themselves to be brothers beyond any division of race or breed. Yet can they really live as brothers, forget the worlds that divide them, and unite in brotherhood and love? Never, cries Aziz, until "we shall drive every blasted Englishman into the sea." Then, and only then, shall "you and I be friends." "Why can't we be friends now?" asks Fielding. "It's what I want. It's what you want."

But the horses didn't want it—they swerved apart; the earth didn't want it, sending up rocks through which riders must pass single file; The temples, the tank, the jail, the palace, the birds, the carrion, the Guest House, that came into view as they issued from the gap and saw Mau beneath: they didn't want it, they said in their hundred voices, "No, not yet," and the sky said, "No, not there."

In this book, so masterfully shaped, so keenly written, so symbolically suggestive, so nearly miraculous in condensing the huge dimensions of its theme and drama to concise terms, Forster has carried the riddle of human relations and society to its farthest boundary. Here he has driven the tragic evil of human division, of alienation, of hostilities and barriers —man against man, race against race, sex against sex, culture against culture —to its most complex and baffling condition. (England has now withdrawn and restored self-rule to India, but the problem of human and racial alienation remains as basic as it was before 1947. The political situation is only an external aspect of the deep-seated moral situation which is Forster's real concern. *A Passage to India* remains as much of a classic as ever to its Indian readers, as it does to English readers. Even those who challenge the accuracy of Forster's details or historical acumen—like, for instance, Nirad C. Chaudhuri in his article "Passage to and from India" in the June 1954 issue of the London magazine *Encounter*—miss the point, for Forster was writing about something incidental to India but actually applicable to the larger world of human and moral relations in our time.) Here, going beyond his earlier conflicts of England against Italy, of civilized life against the claims of nature, of North against South, of intelligence against instinct, of the business morality of the Wilcoxes against the spiritual morality of the Schlegels, of Cambridge against Sawston, he has placed his characters in a profounder element than he ever fathomed before. It is the element of India, in which the rationality of western man encounters the spiritual mystery and absolutes of the East; but it is also the essential element or realm of the spirit, the final court of human instinct and aspiration. And the argument he poses is the argument, so riddling and elusive, which he proposed at the beginning of his career. It is an argument for integration: a plea for mankind to save itself from defeat or disaster by surmounting its denials of spirit, its refusals of natural instinct, in order to arrive at the wholeness of life and spirit which must always be the final and hardest goal of all endeavor—a goal tragically obscured by the selfish delusions and treacheries that seem to be inevitable in so much of what is called civilized life.

Lionel Trilling

A PASSAGE TO INDIA

IN 1912, Forster, in company with Dickinson and R. C. Trevelyan, sailed for India. Dickinson, traveling on one of the fellowships established by Albert Kahn in the interests of international understanding, had official visits and tours to make and the friends separated at Bombay. But their itineraries crossed several times and they spent a fortnight as guests of the Maharajah of Chhatarpur, who loved Dickinson and philosophy—" 'Tell me, Mr. Dickinson, where is God?' " the Maharajah said. " 'Can Herbert Spencer lead me to him, or should I prefer George Henry Lewes? Oh when will Krishna come and be my friend? Oh Mr. Dickinson!' "

The two travelers came away from India with widely different feelings. Dickinson, who was to love China, was not comfortable in India. Displeased as he was by her British rulers, he was not pleased with India itself. "There is no solution to the problem of governing India," he wrote. "Our presence is a curse both to them and to us. Our going away will be worse. I believe that to the last word. And *why* can't the races meet? Simply because the Indians *bore* the English. That is the simple adamantine fact." It is not an enlightening or even a serious view of the situation, and Forster, dissenting from it, speaks of the "peace and happiness" which he himself found in India in 1912 and again on his second visit ten years later.

The best fruit of the Indian journey was to be *A Passage to India*, but meanwhile Forster wrote several short pieces on Indian life of which two, "The Suppliant" and "Advance, India!" (both reprinted in *Abinger Harvest*) admirably depict the comic, sad confusion of a nation torn between two cultures.

He began to sketch the Indian novel, but the war postponed its completion for a decade. [. . .]

In 1922 Forster made a second journey to India and took up again the Indian story he had projected. *A Passage to India* appeared with great success in 1924.

A Passage to India is Forster's best known and most widely read novel. Public and political reasons no doubt account for this; in England the book was a matter for controversy and its success in America, as Forster himself explains it, was due to the superiority Americans could feel at the English botch of India. But the public, political nature of the book is not extraneous; it inheres in the novel's very shape and texture.

By many standards of criticism, this public, political quality works for good. *A Passage to India* is the most comfortable and even the most conventional of Forster's novels. It is under the control not only of the authors' insight; a huge, hulking physical fact which he is not alone in seeing, requires that the author submit to its veto-power. Consequently, this is the least surprising of Forster's novels, the least capricious and, indeed, the least personal. It quickly establishes the pattern for our emotions and keeps to it. We are at once taught to withhold our sympathies from the English officials, to give them to Mrs. Moore and to the "renegade" Fielding, to regard Adela Quested with remote interest and Aziz and his Indian friends with affectionate understanding.

Within this pattern we have, to be sure, all the quick, subtle modifications, the sudden strictnesses or relentings of judgment which are the best stuff of Forster's social imagination. But always the pattern remains public, simple and entirely easy to grasp. What distinguishes it from the patterns of similarly public and political novels is the rigor of its objectivity; it deals with unjust, hysterical emotion and it leads us, not to intense emotions about justice, but to cool poise and judgment—if we do not relent in our contempt for Ronny, we are at least forced to be aware that he is capable of noble, if stupid, feelings; the English girl who has the hallucination of an attempted rape by a native has engaged our sympathy by her rather dull decency; we are permitted no easy response to the benign Mrs. Moore, or to Fielding, who stands out against his own people, or to the native physician who is wrongly accused. This restraint of our emotions is an important element in the book's greatness.

With the public nature of the story goes a chastened and somewhat more public style than is usual with Forster, and a less arbitrary manner. Forster does not abandon his right to intrude into the novel, but his manner of intrusion is more circumspect than ever before. Perhaps this is because here, far less than in the English and Italian stories, he is in possession of truth; the Indian gods are not his gods, they are not genial and comprehensible. So far as the old Mediterranean deities of wise impulse and loving intelligence can go in India, Forster is at home; he thinks they can go far but not all the way, and a certain retraction of the intimacy of his style reflects his uncertainty. The acts of imagination by which Forster conveys the sense of the Indian gods are truly wonderful; they are, nevertheless, the acts of imagination not of a master of the truth but of an intelligent neophyte, still baffled.

So the public nature of the novel cannot be said to work wholly for good. For the first time Forster has put himself to the test of verisimilitude. Is this the truth about India? Is this the way the English act?—always? sometimes? never? Are Indians like this?—all of them? some of them? Why so many Moslems and so few Hindus? Why so much Hindu religion and so little Moslem? And then, finally, the disintegrating question, What is to be done?

Forster's gallery of English officials has of course been disputed in England; there have been many to say that the English are not like that. Even without knowledge we must suppose that the Indian Civil Service has its quota of decent, devoted and humble officials. But if Forster's portraits are perhaps angry exaggerations, anger can be illuminating— the English of Forster's Chandrapore are the limits toward which the English in India must approach, for Lord Acton was right, power does corrupt, absolute power does corrupt absolutely.

As for the representation of the Indians, that too can be judged here only on *a priori* grounds. Although the Indians are conceived in sympathy and affection, they are conceived with these emotions alone, and although all of them have charm, none of them has dignity; they touch our hearts but they never impress us. Once, at his vindication feast, Aziz is represented as "full of civilization . . . complete, dignified, rather hard" and for the first time Fielding treats him "with diffidence," but this only serves to remind us how lacking in dignity Aziz usually is. Very possibly this is the effect that Indians make upon even sensitive Westerners; Dickinson, as we have seen, was bored by them, and generations of subjection can diminish the habit of dignity and teach grown men the strategy of the little child.

These are not matters that we can settle; that they should have arisen at all is no doubt a fault of the novel. Quite apart from the fact that questions of verisimilitude diminish illusion, they indicate a certain inadequacy in the conception of the story. To represent the official English as so unremittingly bad and the Indians as so unremittingly feeble is to prevent the story from being sufficiently worked out in terms of the characters; the characters, that is, are *in* the events, the events are not in them: we want a larger Englishman than Fielding, a weightier Indian than Aziz.

These are faults, it is true, and Forster is the one novelist who could commit them and yet transcend and even put them to use. The relation of the characters to the events, for ex-

ample, is the result of a severe imbalance in the relation of plot to story. Plot and story in this novel are not coextensive as they are in all Forster's other novels.* The plot is precise, hard, crystallized and far simpler than any Forster has previously conceived. The story is beneath and above the plot and continues beyond it in time. It is, to be sure, created by the plot, it is the plot's manifold reverberation, but it is greater than the plot and contains it. The plot is as decisive as a judicial opinion, the story is an impulse, a tendency, a perception. The suspension of plot in the large circumambient sphere of story, the expansion of the story from the center of plot. requires some of the subtlest manipulation that any novel has ever had. This relation of plot and story tells us that we are dealing with a political novel of an unusual kind. The characters are of sufficient size for the plot; they are not large enough for the story—and that indeed is the point of the story.

This, in outline, is the plot: Adela Quested arrives in India under the chaperonage of the elderly Mrs. Moore with whose son by a first marriage Adela has an "understanding." Both ladies are humane and Adela is liberal and they have an intense desire to "know India." This is a matter of some annoyance to Ronny, Mrs. Moore's son and Adela's fiancé, and of amused condescension to the dull people at the station who try to satisfy the ladies with elephant rides—only very *new* people try to *know* India. Both Mrs. Moore and Adela are chilled by Ronny; he has entirely adopted the point of view of the ruling race and has become a heavy-minded young judge with his dull dignity as his chief recognized asset. But despite Ronny's fussy certainty

* I am not using plot and story in exactly the same sense that Forster uses them in *Aspects of the Novel*.

about what is and is not proper, Mrs.
Moore steps into a mosque one evening and there makes the acquaintance of Aziz, a young Moslem doctor.
Aziz is hurt and miserable, for he has
just been snubbed; Mrs. Moore's
kindness and simplicity soothe him.
Between the two a friendship develops which politely includes Adela
Quested. At last, by knowing Indians,
the travelers will know India, and
Aziz is even more delighted than they
at the prospect of the relationship. To
express his feelings he organizes a fantastically elaborate jaunt to the Marabar Caves. Fielding, the principal of
the local college, and Professor Godbole, a Hindu teacher, were also to
have been of the party but they miss
the train and Aziz goes ahead with
the ladies and his absurd retinue. In
one of the caves Mrs. Moore has a
disturbing psychic experience and
sends Aziz and Adela to continue the
exploration without her. Adela, not
a very attractive girl, has had her
doubts about her engagement to Ronny, not a very attractive man, and
now she ventures to speak of love to
Aziz, quite abstractly but in a way
both to offend him and disturb herself. In the cave the strap of her field-
glasses is pulled and broken by someone in the darkness and she rushes out
in a frenzy of hallucination that Aziz
has attempted to rape her. The accusation makes the English of the station hysterical with noble rage. In
every English mind there is the certainty that Aziz is guilty and the verdict is foregone. Only Fielding and
Mrs. Moore do not share this certainty. Fielding, because of his liking for
the young doctor, and Mrs. Moore,
because of an intuition, are sure that
the event could not have happened
and that Adela is the victim of illusion. Fielding, who openly declares
his partisanship, is ostracized, and
Mrs. Moore, who only hints her

opinion, is sent out of the country by
her son; the journey in the terrible
heat of the Indian May exhausts her
and she dies on shipboard. At the trial
Adela's illusion, fostered by the mass-
hysteria of the English, becomes suddenly dispelled, she recants, Aziz is
cleared, Fielding is vindicated and
promoted, the Indians are happy, the
English furious.

Thus the plot. And no doubt it is
too much a plot of event, too easily
open and shut. Nevertheless it is an
admirable if obvious device for or-
ganizing an enormous amount of observation of both English and native
society; it brings to spectacular viru-
lence the latent antagonisms between
rulers and ruled.

Of the Anglo-Indian society it is
perhaps enough to say that, "more
than it can hope to do in England,"
it lives by the beliefs of the English
public school. It is arrogant, ignorant,
insensitive—intelligent natives estimate that a year in India makes the
pleasantest Englishman rude. And of
all the English it is the women who
insist most strongly on their superiority, who are the rawest and crudest
in their manner. The men have a certain rough liking for the men of the
subject race; for instance, Turton,
Collector of the district, has "a contemptuous affection for the pawns he
had moved about for so many years;
they must be worth his pains." But
the women, unchecked by any professional necessity or pride, think
wholly in terms of the most elementary social prestige and Turton's wife
lives for nothing else. " 'After all,' "
Turton thinks but never dares say,
" 'it's our women who make everything more difficult out here.' "

This is the result of the undeveloped heart. *A Passage to India* is not
a radical novel; its data were gathered
in 1912 and 1922, before the full spate
of Indian nationalism; it is not con-

cerned to show that the English should not be in India at all. Indeed, not until the end of the book is the question of the expulsion of the English mentioned, and the novel proceeds on an imperialistic premise—ironically, for it is not actually Forster's own—its chief point being that by reason of the undeveloped heart the English have thrown away the possibility of holding India. For want of a smile an Empire is to be lost.* Not even justice is enough. " 'Indians know whether they are liked or not,' " Fielding says, " '—they cannot be fooled here. Justice never satisfies them, and that is why the British Empire rests on sand.' " Mrs. Moore listens to Ronny defending the British attitude; "his words without his voice might have impressed her, but when she heard the self-satisfied lilt of them, when she saw the mouth moving so complacently and competently beneath the little red nose, she felt, quite illogically, that this was not the last word on India. One touch of regret—not the canny substitute but the true regret—would have made him a different man, and the British Empire a different institution."

Justice is not enough then, but in the end neither are liking and goodwill enough. For although Fielding and Aziz reach out to each other in friendship, a thousand little tricks of speech, a thousand different assumptions and different tempi keep them apart. They do not understand each other's *amounts* of emotion, let alone kinds of emotion. " 'Your emotions never seem in proportion to their objects, Aziz,' " Fielding says, and Aziz answers, " 'Is emotion a sack of potatoes, so much the pound, to be measured out?' "

The theme of separateness, of fences and barriers, the old theme of the Pauline epistles, which runs through all Forster's novels, is, in *A Passage to India*, hugely expanded and everywhere dominant. The separation of race from race, sex from sex, culture from culture, even of man from himself, is what underlies every relationship. The separation of the English from the Indians is merely the most dramatic of the chasms in this novel. Hindu and Moslem cannot really approach each other; Aziz, speaking in all friendliness to Professor Godbole, wishes that Hindus did not remind him of cow-dung and Professor Godbole thinks, " 'Some Moslems are very violent' "—"Between people of distant climes there is always the possibility of romance, but the various branches of Indians know too much about each other to surmount the unknowable easily." Adela and Ronny cannot meet in sexuality, and when, after the trial, Adela and Fielding meet in an idea, "a friendliness, as of dwarfs shaking hands, was in the air." Fielding, when he marries Mrs. Moore's daughter Stella, will soon find himself apart from his young wife. And Mrs.

---

* H. N. Brailsford in his *Rebel India* (1931) deals at some length with the brutality with which demonstrations were put down in 1930. "Here and there," he says, "mildness and good-temper disarmed the local agitation. I heard of one magistrate, very popular with the people, who successfully treated the defiance of the Salt Monopoly as a joke. The local Congress leaders made salt openly in front of his bungalow. He came out: bought some of the contraband salt: laughed at its bad quality: chaffed the bystanders, and went quietly back to his house. The crowd melted away, and no second attempt was made to defy this genial bureaucrat. On the other hand, any exceptional severity, especially if physical brutality accompanied it, usually raised the temper of the local movement and roused it to fresh daring and further sacrifices," p. 7, footnote.

Moore is separated from her son, from all people, from God, from the universe.

This sense of separateness broods over the book, pervasive, symbolic—at the end the very earth requires, and the sky approves, the parting of Aziz and Fielding—and perhaps accounts for the remoteness of the characters: they are so far from each other that they cannot reach us. But the isolation is not merely adumbrated; in certain of its aspects it is very precisely analyzed and some of the most brilliant and virtuosi parts of the novel are devoted to the delineation of Aziz and his friends, to the investigation of the cultural differences that keep Indian and Englishman apart.

The mold for Aziz is Gino Carella of the first novel. It is the mold of unEnglishness, that is to say, of volatility, tenderness, sensibility, a hint of cruelty, much warmth, a love of pathos, the desire to please even at the cost of insincerity. Like Gino's, Aziz's nature is in many ways child-like, in many ways mature: it is mature in its acceptance of child-like inconsistency. Although eager to measure up to English standards of puritan rectitude, Aziz lives closer to the literal facts of his emotions; for good or bad, he is more human. He, like his friends, is not prompt, not efficient, not neat, not really convinced of Western ideas even in science—when he retires to a native state he slips back to mix a little magic with his medicine—and he, like them, is aware of his faults. He is hyper-sensitive, imagining slights even when there are none because there have actually been so many; he is full of humility and full of contempt and desperately wants to be liked. He is not heroic but his heroes are the great chivalrous emperors, Babur and Alamgir. In short, Aziz is a member of a subject race. A rising nationalism in India may by now have thrust him aside in favor of a more militant type; but we can be sure that if the new type has repudiated Aziz' emotional contradictions it has not resolved them.

Aziz and his friends are Moslems, and with Moslems of the business and professional class the plot of the novel deals almost entirely. But the story is suffused with Hinduism.* It is Mrs. Moore who carries the Hindu theme; it is Mrs. Moore, indeed, who is the story. The theme is first introduced by Mrs. Moore observing a wasp.

> Going to hang up her cloak she found that the tip of the peg was occupied by a small wasp. . . . There he clung, asleep, while jackals in the plain bayed their desires and mingled with the percussion of drums.
> "Pretty dear," said Mrs. Moore to the wasp. He did not wake, but her voice floated out, to swell the night's uneasiness.

This wasp is to recur in Professor Godbole's consciousness when he has left Chandrapore and taken service as director of education in a Hindu native state. He stands, his school quite forgotten—turned into a granary, indeed—and celebrates the birth of Krishna in the great religious festival that dominates the third part of the novel.† The wasp is mixed up in his

---

* The Indian masses appear only as crowds in the novel; they have no individualized representative except the silent, unthinking figure of the man who pulls the *punkah* in the courtroom scene. He is one of the "untouchables" though he has the figure of a god, and in Adela's mind, just before the crisis of the trial, he raises doubts of the "suburban Jehovah" who sanctifies her opinions, and he makes her think of Mrs. Moore.

† The novel is divided: I. Mosque II. Caves III. Temple. In his notes to the Every-

mind—he does not know how it got there in the first place, nor do we—with a recollection of Mrs. Moore.

He was a Brahman, she a Christian, but it made no difference, it made no difference whether she was a trick of his memory or a telepathic appeal. It was his duty, as it was his desire, to place himself in the position of the God and to love her, and to place himself in her position and say to the God: "Come, come, come, come." This was all he could do. How inadequate! But each according to his own capacities, and he knew that his own were small. "One old Englishwoman and one little, little wasp," he thought, as he stepped out of the temple into the grey of a pouring wet morning. "It does not seem much, still it is more than I am myself."

The presence of the wasp, first in Mrs. Moore's consciousness, then in Godbole's, Mrs. Moore's acceptance of the wasp, Godbole's acceptance of Mrs. Moore—in some symbolic fashion, this is the thread of the story of the novel as distinguished from its plot. For the story is essentially concerned with Mrs. Moore's discovery that Christianity is not adequate. In a quiet way, Mrs. Moore is a religious woman; at any rate, as she has grown older she has found it "increasingly difficult to avoid" mentioning God's name "as the greatest she knew." Yet in India God's name becomes less and less efficacious—"outside the arch there seemed always another arch, beyond the remotest echo a silence."

And so, unwittingly, Mrs. Moore has moved closer and closer to Indian ways of feeling. When Ronny and Adela go for an automobile ride with the Nawab Bahadur and the chauffeur swerves at something in the path and wrecks the car, Mrs. Moore, when she is told of the incident, remarks without thinking, " 'A ghost!' " And a ghost it was, or so the Nawab believed, for he had run over and killed a drunken man at that spot nine years before. "None of the English knew of this, nor did the chauffeur; it was a racial secret communicable more by blood than by speech." This "racial secret" has somehow been acquired by Mrs. Moore. And the movement away from European feeling continues: "She felt increasingly (vision or nightmare?) that, though people are important, the relations between them are not, and that in particular too much fuss has been made over marriage; centuries of carnal embracement, yet man is no nearer to understanding man." The occasion of her visit to the Marabar Caves is merely the climax of change, although a sufficiently terrible one.

What so frightened Mrs. Moore in the cave was an echo. It is but one echo in a book which is contrived of echoes. Not merely does Adela Quested's delusion go in company with a disturbing echo in her head which only ceases when she masters her delusion, but the very texture of the story is a reticulation of echoes. Actions and speeches return, sometimes in a better, sometimes in a worse form, given back by the perplexing "arch" of the Indian universe. The recurrence of the wasp is a prime example, but there are many more. If Aziz plays a scratch game of polo with a subaltern who comes to think well of this particular anonymous native, the same subaltern will be particularly virulent in his denunciation of Aziz the rapist, never

man edition Forster points out that the three parts correspond to the three Indian seasons.

knowing that the liked and the detested native are the same. If the natives talk about their inability to catch trains, an Englishman's missing a train will make all the trouble of the story. Mrs. Moore will act with bad temper to Adela and with surly indifference to Aziz, but her action will somehow have a good echo; and her children will be her further echo. However we may interpret Forster's intention in this web of reverberation, it gives his book a cohesion and intricacy usually only found in music. And of all the many echoes, the dominant one is the echo that booms through the Marabar cave.

A Marabar cave had been horrid as far as Mrs. Moore was concerned, for she had nearly fainted in it, and had some difficulty in preventing herself from saying so as soon as she got into the air again. It was natural enough; she had always suffered from faintness, and the cave had become too full, because all their retinue followed them. Crammed with villagers and servants, the circular chamber began to smell. She lost Aziz and Adela in the dark, didn't know who touched her, couldn't breathe, and some vile naked thing struck her face and settled on her mouth like a pad. She tried to regain the entrance tunnel, but an influx of villagers swept her back. She hit her head. For an instant she went mad, hitting and gasping like a fanatic. For not only did the crush and stench alarm her; there was also a terrifying echo.

Professor Godbole had never mentioned an echo; it never impressed him, perhaps. There are some exquisite echoes in India; . . . The echo in a Marabar cave is not like these, it is entirely devoid of distinction. Whatever is said, the same monotonous noise replies, and quivers up and down the walls until it is absorbed in the room. "Boum" is the sound as far as the human alphabet can express it, or "bououm," or "ou-boum"—utterly dull. Hope, politeness, the blowing of a nose, the squeal of a boot, all produce "boum."

Panic and emptiness—Mrs. Moore's panic had been at the emptiness of the universe. And one goes back beyond Helen Schlegel's experience of the Fifth Symphony in *Howards End*: the negating mess of the cave reminds us of and utterly denies the mess of that room in which Caroline Abbott saw Gino with his child. For then the mess had been the source of life and hope, and in it the little child had blossomed; Caroline had looked into it from the "charnel chamber" of the reception room and the "light in it was soft and large, as from some gracious, noble opening." It is, one might say, a representation of the womb and a promise of life. There is also a child in the mess of the Marabar cave —for the "vile, naked thing" that settles "like a pad" on Mrs. Moore's mouth is "a poor little baby, astride its mother's hip." The cave's opening is behind Mrs. Moore, she is facing into the grave; light from the world does not enter, and the universe of death makes all things alike, even life and death, even good and evil.

. . . The echo began in some indescribable way to undermine her hold on life. . . . It had managed to murmur: "Pathos, piety, courage —they exist, but are identical, and so is filth. Everything exists, nothing has value." If one had spoken vileness in that place or quoted lofty poetry, the comment would have been the same—"ou-boum." If one had spoken with the tongues of angels and pleaded for all the unhappiness and misunderstanding in the world, past, present, and to come; for all the misery men must undergo whatever their opinion and position, and however much they dodge or bluff—it would amount to the same. . . . Devils are of the north, and poems can be written about them, but no one could romanticize the Marabar because it robbed infinity and eternity of their vastness, the only quality that accomodates them to mankind. . . . But suddenly at the edge of her mind, religion reappeared, poor little talkative Christianity, and she knew that all its divine words from "Let there be Light" to "It is finished" only amounted to "boum."

"Something snub-nosed, incapable of generosity" had spoken to her—"the undying worm itself." Converse with God, her children, Aziz, is repugnant to her. She wants attention for her sorrow and rejects it when given. Knowing Aziz to be innocent, she says nothing in his behalf except a few sour words that upset Adela's certainty, and though she knows that her testimony will be useful to Aziz, she allows Ronny to send her away. She has had the beginning of the Hindu vision of things and it has crushed her. What the Hindu vision is, is expressed by Professor Godbole to Fielding:

> Good and evil are different, as their names imply. But, in my own humble opinion, they are both of them aspects of my Lord. He is present in the one, absent in the other, and the difference between presence and absence is great, as great as my feeble mind can grasp. Yet absence implies presence, absence is not non-existence, and we are therefore entitled to repeat: "Come, come, come, come."

Although Mrs. Moore abandons everything, even moral duty, she dominates the subsequent action. As "Esmiss Esmoor" she becomes to the crowd around the courthouse, a Hindu goddess who was to save Aziz. And, we are vaguely given to understand, it is her influence that brings Adela to her senses and the truth. She recurs again, together with the wasp, in the mind of Professor Godbole in that wonderful scene of religious muddlement with which the book draws to its conclusion. She remains everlastingly in the mind of Aziz who hates—or tries to hate—all the other English. She continues into the future in her daughter Stella, who marries Fielding and returns to India, and in her son Ralph. Both Stella and Ralph "like Hinduism, though they take no interest in its forms" and are shy of Fielding because he thinks they are mistaken. Despite the sullen disillusionment in which Mrs. Moore died, she had been right when she had said to Ronny that there are many kinds of failure, some of which succeed. No thought, no deed in this book of echoes, is ever lost.

It is not easy to know what to make of the dominant Hinduism of the third section of the novel. The last part of the story is frankly a coda to the plot, a series of resolutions and separations which comment on what has gone before—in it Fielding and Aziz meet and part, this time forever; Aziz forgives Adela Quested and finds a friend in Ralph Moore; Fielding, we learn, is not really at one with his young wife; Hindu and Moslem, Brahman and non-Brahman are shown to be as far apart as Indian and English, yet English and Moslem meet in the flooded river, in a flow of Hindu religious fervor; and everything is encompassed in the spirit of Mrs. Moore, mixed up with a vision of the ultimate nullity, with the birth of Krishna and with joy in the fertile rains.

Certainly it is not to be supposed that Forster finds in Hinduism an answer to the problem of India; and its dangers have been amply demonstrated in the case of Mrs. Moore herself. But here at least is the vision in which the arbitrary human barriers sink before the extinction of all things. About seventy-five years before *A Passage to India*, Matthew Arnold's brother, William Delafield Arnold, went out to India as Director of Public Education of the Punjab. From his experiences he wrote a novel, *Oakfield: Or, Fellowship in the East;* it was a bitter work which denounced the English for making India a "rupee mine" and it declared that the "grand work" of civilizing India was all humbug. William Arnold thought that perhaps socialism, but more likely the Church of England, could bring about some change. This good and pious man felt it "grievous to live among men"—the Indians—"and feel the idea of fraternity thwarted by facts;" he believed that "we must not resign ourselves, without a struggle, to calling the Indians brutes." To such a pass has Christianity come, we can suppose Forster to be saying. We must suffer a vision even as dreadful as Mrs. Moore's if by it the separations can

be wiped out. But meanwhile the separations exist and Aziz in an hysteria of affirmation declares to Fielding on their last ride that the British must go, even at the cost of internal strife, even if it means a Japanese conquest. Only with the British gone can he and Fielding be friends. Fielding offers friendship now: "It's what I want. It's what you want.' " But the horses, following the path the earth lays for them, swerve apart; earth and sky seem to say that the time for friendship has not come, and leave its possibility to events.

The disintegrating question, What, then, must be done? which many readers have raised is of course never answered—or not answered in the language in which the question has been asked. The book simply involves the question in ultimates. This, obviously, is no answer; still, it defines the scope of a possible answer, and thus restates the question. For the answer can never again temporize, because the question, after it has been involved in the moods and visions of the story, turns out to be the most enormous question that has ever been asked, requiring an answer of enormous magnanimity. Great as the problem of India is, Forster's book is not about India alone; it is about all of human life.

Alan Wilde

A PASSAGE TO INDIA: PART III

PART III of the novel, "Temple," does indeed open in India, not now in Chandrapore, but in Mau, a Hindu native state, and opens in the midst of a festival celebrating the birth of the god Krishna. The chapter that describes this festival serves not only to introduce the themes and symbols that are to be developed, as do the first chapters of the earlier sections, but is itself the most important and colorful scene in Part III. *A Passage to India* may be said to consist of a series of tableaux, held together by the overlapping of the three main symbols of the book—the mosque, the caves, the temple—and by various "rhythms"; of these tableaux the one devoted to the birth of Krishna is, deservedly, among the most famous. In it Forster combines skillfully an appreciation of the Hindu spirit with an ironic, Western detachment, so that the reader is made to move now closer to, now further from, the center of the event, alternately sympathizing with and criticizing, but always understanding, the strange ceremony.

To a large degree the things Forster finds to praise in the Hindu spirit are precisely those he finds absent in the West. "Religion," he comments, "is a living force to the Hindus, and can at certain moments fling down everything that is petty and temporary in their natures" (p. 398). In the Hindu ceremony, religion is a response of the total personality to something larger than itself, to the mystery of the universe [. . .] The Hindus who participate in the ceremony feel no need for gravity: their merriment is opposed to the asceticism and the solemnity of Christianity, and indeed it is the inclusiveness of Hinduism that Forster most admires, its ability to hold together all the seemingly irreconcilable feelings and desires of men. In its spirit men are able, if only for a while, to love each other and the universe they symbolize in their god.

Forster does note, however, that the ceremony is a triumph of intuition, and to that extent there is no room for reason in what is otherwise a unified and complete response. In fact, increasingly, even as he reaches the climax of the ceremony, the moment when all men come together, Forster begins to point to the less admirable or acceptable side of Hinduism: the exaltation that overwhelms the believers is temporary and its effects pass with the ceremony. Even the inclusiveness that is symbolized by the Krishna festival has its troubling side: it is in some ways dangerously near to chaos, to the horror Mrs. Moore saw in the Marabar.* The problem of inclusion and exclusion arises again. Forster's Hindus [. . .] shun asceticism and rigidity, but they do not have the "natural order" of the Mediterranean people. The Hindu order is so large as to be almost shapeless. "They did not one thing which the non-Hindu would feel dramatically correct," Forster observes; "this approaching triumph of India was a muddle (as we call it), a

From *Art and Order: A Study of E. M. Forster* by Alan Wilde, © 1964 by New York University. Reprinted by permission of New York University Press.

* Forster told the present writer that the Hindu festival represents the same thing as the scene in the cave, "turned inside out."

frustration of reason and form" (p. 385). And later, commenting on one of the signs before the altar, written in English to symbolize the universality of the god, and bearing the confused motto, "God si love," Forster asks, "Is this the final message of India?" (p. 385).

And indeed what is the final message for Forster, as he dramatizes it in the final section of his novel? The question is an important one, since it has often been assumed that the final answer to the vision of the caves lies in a total affirmation of Hinduism.* Forster did not, I think, intend such an affirmation, and certainly he has not produced one. To be sure, he admires the inclusiveness, the vitality, and the antiascetic attitude of the Hindus, but he is acutely aware of the muddle, the confusion, and the transitory nature of the ceremony that symbolizes their response to life. To the extent that his attitude can be said to be the Hindu one, it involves the recognition that man must have some relation with the unexplained and unexplainable, albeit a relation never totally satisfactory. Godbole has from the beginning an attitude that comes only gradually to Mrs. Moore: the awareness that inadequacy and incompleteness are indelible features of the universe, but that one must go on nonetheless. In that both Godbole and Forster are, to a large extent, pessimistic about this world but convinced that man must do his best with what he is given, the comparison is legitimate.

Still, Forster is by no stretch of the imagination a Hindu, and if his remarks in *A Passage to India* are not sufficient proof of his disagreement,

one may turn for confirmation to *The Hill of Devi*, a collection of letters that Forster sent home from India in 1912–13 and in 1921. One section of the correspondence of 1921, "Gokul Ashtami," is devoted to a description of the Krishna festival. In basic detail the account is very similar to the one in the novel, but the tone and observation of the former are a good deal more critical. One remark will indicate Forster's general feeling: "*I do like Islam, though I have had to come through Hinduism to discover it. After all the mess and profusion and confusion of Gokul Ashtami, where nothing ever stopped or need ever have begun, it was like standing on a mountain*" (p. 193). The generally sympathetic treatment of the ceremony in the novel points much more to Forster's skill as an artist than to his enthusiasm for what occurs. He is interested in what the religion *represents* to a Western mind, and he is criticizing Christianity at least as much as he is affirming Hinduism. Forster's interest in fact is in correcting the West, not in converting it to the East.

The "Temple," then, through its connection with the Hindu festival, becomes like the other symbols in the book, a dual or, better, an ambivalent symbol. It is in one aspect a reaffirmation of Mrs. Moore's vision while crossing the Indian continent, and in another a grotesque monument of the muddle that is described in the book. It signifies not that all is right in the world—quite the contrary—but that there are possibilities of constructive action. It signifies, too, that these possibilities are always subject to frustration, but, at any rate, the affirmation

---

* For other arguments against the idea that Forster is presenting Hinduism as a complete answer, see Crews [Frederick C. Crews, *E. M. Forster: The Perils of Humanism*, Princeton University Press, 1962], pp. 151–55, and the excellent article by David Shusterman, "The Curious Case of Professor Godbole: *A Passage to India* Re-examined," *PMLA*, LXXVI (September, 1961), 426–35.

implicit in the symbol is stronger than that in the symbol of "Caves," where negation is uppermost. The rest of the section is devoted to a working out of the two meanings of "Temple," a balancing of hope and despair, as in all Forster's novels, an attempt that fails here only in that it is not sufficiently developed. Of the Hindu festival Forster has said: "It was architecturally necessary. I needed a lump, or a Hindu temple if you like— a mountain standing up. It is well placed; and it gathers up some strings. But there ought to be more after it. The lump sticks out a little too much." The self-criticism is just; the festival scene does pick up strings left loose in Part II, but it absorbs too much of the space and interest of the third section. Therein seems to lie the explanation of the fact that critics have at times overemphasized the importance of the Hindu element in the book: the fault is in large part Forster's and it is a structural one. One must look to the other side of the "mountain standing up" to discover where exactly Forster intended to lead his readers.

It is the negative meaning of "Temple" that is first apparent after the festival. Forster makes it clear that discord still exists, not only between Indians and English, not only between Mohammedans and Hindus, but within Hinduism itself: "The fissures in the Indian soil are infinite" (p. 390). On a personal level, there is no real meeting in the confrontation of Aziz, now a doctor in Mau, and Fielding, who is making an educational survey for the government and traveling with his wife and brother-in-law (Mrs. Moore's children Ralph and Stella). Fielding is older, sterner, more official, Aziz hos-

tile and guarded, and their conversation goes badly. The encounter ends with a complete separation between the two men, but Aziz "returned to the house excited and happy" (p. 397). Happy is a word that at this point applies to a state of which Aziz is not yet aware: as far as he is conscious of his attitude, he feels himself still angry and hurt, but within him the almost magic name of Mrs. Moore, which has entered the conversation, is beginning to produce its effect, just at the time when the Hindus prepare for the procession that is the aftermath of the festival celebrating the birth of Krishna.

The conjunction is significant: the spirit of Mrs. Moore and the spirit of Hinduism begin to work together toward the same goal—reconciliation and unity. Once again the weather is propitious; it is the rainy season, the most favorable time of the Indian year. Everywhere the cycle of death and life is about to culminate in rebirth, the rebirth of nature, of the god (for to many of the Hindus the procession, rather than the earlier ceremony, symbolizes the birth of Krishna), and of personal relations. In Mau the atmosphere is charged with anticipation, and the time is ready, not indeed for the eradication of all the evil in the world and all difficulties among men, but for some adjustment between man's recognition of chaos and his ideals.

It is Aziz who proves to be the instrument of reconciliation. Alone, as he thinks, in the guest house where Fielding and his party are staying, he suddenly hears a voice that is familiar to him; * it is Ralph Moore's, and on to him Aziz projects all his anger at the English. But in the midst of their conversation Aziz unwittingly re-

---

* It is, of course, Ralph's voice that Aziz hears, but it reminds him of Mrs. Moore's. [. . .] In his interview with Angus Wilson, Forster made a point of saying that Mrs. Moore's influence does reappear in Part III of this novel.

marks to the boy that he is an Oriental and suddenly realizes that these are the words he had once said to his mother. The cycle has begun again. Ralph, like his sister, is attracted to Hinduism and, like her, he is distinctly his mother's child. Aziz is aware of the resemblance and begins to feel for the boy all he had felt for the old woman. As this instinctive communication is set up, intangible forces begin to operate. He offers to take Ralph out for a while onto the tank where the festivities are taking place. As they row, they hear the chanting of the Hindus and, among the syllables, the words "esmiss esmoor." They approach the celebrants and find themselves in the midst of a divine muddle: a model of the village of Gokul, Krishna's birthplace, is made ready to float upon the waters of the tank. It is set adrift by a naked Indian, the counterpart of the punkah wallah of the trial scene. Like the Indian of Chandrapore, he is an inscrutable fate: as he pushes the village out into the waters, his influence combines with those of Mrs. Moore and of the Hindu ceremony, and Aziz' boat collides with Fielding's, which is also out on the tank. "That was the climax," Forster remarks, "as far as India admits of one" (p. 406). The climax is formless, shapeless, but it has its effect upon the English and upon Aziz. Once again Aziz and Fielding are friends, and for the first time Fielding and his wife are completely compatible. It is significant that ultimately an accident is required to bring about the reconciliations, an accident that is the last link in the chain of forces made up of the mysterious influences of Mrs. Moore, Krishna, and the naked Indian. Strange, inexplicable powers have succeeded where Fielding's reasonable attitudes failed. But the accident is different from the one that brought Ronny and Adela together. Here there is not a spurious unity but, Forster would have us believe, a spirit of genuine love: the forcible meeting of the occupants of the boats engenders a triumph of understanding and affection, and indeed the whole festival builds up to a reassertion of the possibility of personal relations. Aziz, Fielding, Ralph, and Stella themselves undergo a baptism by water. Like the Hindus, they are purged of suspicion, hatred, and pettiness; the reconciliations are genuine. But the question remains: Can they last, or will Aziz and the English, like the Hindus, revert to more normal patterns of behavior? Are the fissures in the Indian soil too deep to be mended by the forces of love and harmony?

The somewhat ambiguous answer to that question is given in the final scene of the book, in which [. . .] there is much giving with one hand and taking back with the other. The festival is over and the focus of the last chapter is on Fielding and Aziz, on personal relations, and on the more limited, but more human, capacities of Islam and the West. To be sure, the re-establishment of good relations between the two men is due, in the first instance, to the influence of Hinduism (and Mrs. Moore), but it is clear that, if these relations are to continue, Aziz and Fielding must rely upon themselves. There is sadness in the last pages of the book, but it is sadness rather than the apathy and despair of "Caves." The two men are friends once more—the lines of communication have been repaired—but they know, too, that they cannot see each other again, that the ride they are taking through the Mau jungles will be their last. So brief a reconciliation is, perhaps, basis for small comfort, but in the light of what has gone before it is a triumph of sorts. It is an affirmation, however weak, of the possibility of personal relations, an answer, however limited, to the echo of the Marabar.

Of course, one must not make too much of this answer; the forces of disunion are still powerful, and they become more prominent as the men continue their ride. Both Fielding and Aziz are, and they realize the fact, different from what they were in Chandrapore. Talking about what means most to them, the two men find the conversation floundering; friendship is there, but communication is still difficult. Aziz tells Fielding to talk about something else, and for the rest of the ride they argue politics. The scene is strange; both become angry and excited. They speak more as an Englishman and an Indian then as Fielding and Aziz, and yet they are never closer. Excitement —in large part artificially generated— brings what sincerity and self-revelation cannot, a vital, if temporary, bond between them. They ride on, and "the divisions of daily life were returning" (p. 410), Forster comments in passing. But the curious conversation is prolonged a while longer by yet more intense insults and exacerbated emotions: Aziz begins to shout, and, when Fielding mocks him, he is beside himself with rage. Now, as both transcend their normal selves, as they pass beyond reason into a realm where, perhaps, communication is possible, the climax of their meeting comes. Aziz cries: " 'If it's fifty-five hundred years we shall get rid of you . . . and then'—he rode against him furiously—'and then,' he concluded, half kissing him, 'you and I shall be friends'" (p. 411). But the moment cannot last; consummated in movement (like Adela's and Ronny's), fanned by the wing of a passing emotion, denying the facts

that make for separation, it is, of its own nature and by necessity, transitory. Why can't they be friends now, Fielding asks;

> But the horses didn't want it—they swerved apart; the earth didn't want it, sending up rocks through which riders must pass single file; the temples, the tank, the jail, the palace, the birds, the carrion, the Guest House, that came into view as they issued from the gap and saw Mau beneath: they didn't want it, they said in their hundred voices. "No, not yet," and the sky said, "No, not there" (p. 411).

Professor Brower has said of these final words that "the implication of a celestial 'Sometime, Somewhere' is inescapable. . . . The vision of the Caves is too compelling to be forgotten or to allow us to find solace in pleasing 'hints of infinity.' " * But though the words do imply the possibility of hope deferred to some distant future—that is the pattern of all Forster's novels—it is not necessary that the possibility be considered "celestial" or unreal, not, at any rate, if the hope is accepted, as I believe it is meant to be, as moderate and limited. The vision of the caves *is* compelling, and Forster does not mean for us to forget it. The abyss remains, no matter what man does, but man can do something nonetheless; he can attempt neither to deny it nor to give in to its horror, as Mrs. Moore did at first. He must, as Mrs. Moore later realized, give what meaning he can to his chaotic, orderless world, through his own, unaided efforts. The last chapter of the novel shows, indeed, that such an effort will never be easy; the forces of disorder are powerful and persistent, but they can be fought against and partially subdued, if not

* Reuben A. Brower, "Beyond E. M. Forster: The Unseen." *The Chicago Review*, II (Fall-Winter, 1948), 109.

conquered. Forster's hope is hard won: it is founded upon despair, and its reliance is, ultimately, upon man himself.

A Passage to India is a novel of many impressive qualities, but probably the most impressive of them all lies in the complexity of the vision that it finally communicates. One can point—perhaps too readily—to the bleak despair of Mrs. Moore's experience in the Marabar Cave and to the wild harmony of the Hindu festival —indeed these are central moments. But the total effect of the novel is probably more dependent upon those scenes, and they constitute the majority, in which it is less easy to find a dominant mood. In them the sounds that anticipate and follow from the "boum" of the cave mingle with those generated by the "secret understanding of the heart," and one is hard put to say upon which note the final chord is constructed.

It follows that the whole question of order, which is the primary theme of the novel, is never resolved in any explicit fashion. Forster is never able —or willing—to draw precisely the line where inclusion must stop and exclusion begin, but he is at any rate sure of certain elements that must make part of his new order. Personal relations, love, form, comprehensiveness, reason, intuitive understanding: all, though perhaps limited or partial, are necessary, but Forster stops short of a final synthesis. Perhaps he himself realized the impossibility of one, for, while in *Howards End* Margaret Schlegel was meant to be the cynosure of all the ideals related to connecting, in *A Passage to India* there is a distribution among several people— Fielding, Mrs. Moore, Godbole, Aziz —of the qualities that are meant to be admired. Forster is indicating the paths that lead away from chaos, but he does not make them join; there is no Howards End to serve as the all-embracing symbol of the good life. *A Passage to India* directs the reader back to life again. It is a vision, not an answer, an echo and a counterecho whose monotonous and hopeful sounds spread back through India the primal to the world that was before man and forward through the present to a future that man must make for himself.

Santha Rama Rau

A PASSAGE TO INDIA AS A PLAY

IN A program note for the dramatization of his novel *A Passage to India*, E. M. Forster said, "I began to write the novel in 1913, but the first world war intervened and it did not get published until 1924. Needless to say, it dates. The India I described has been transformed politically and greatly changed socially. I also tried to describe human beings; these may not have altered so much. Furthermore—taking my title from a poem of

"Recollections" by Santha Rama Rau from *E. M. Forster: A Tribute*, edited by K. Natwar-Singh, © 1964 by Harcourt, Brace & World, Inc. Reprinted by permission of William Morris Agency, Inc.

Walt Whitman's—I tried to indicate the human predicament in a universe which is not, so far, comprehensible to our minds."

On another occasion, Mr. Forster summed up the purpose of literature —and indeed the solution, in a way, of "the human predicament"—in two words: "Only connect." Easier said than done, of course, but the brilliance of Mr. Forster's novels lies to a large extent in the giant step they take towards just such "connecting." They are variously set in England, in Italy, in India (his non-fiction takes in Egypt as well), and in every case and country he concerns himself with the misunderstandings between people and nationalities, between manners and points of view, between established mores and the rebel. In short, he is always building the connecting bridge between human beings.

He has never been so crass as to write a Problem Novel; the genre can be excellently handled by, say, Alan Paton. Neither does he write the Novel of Social Reform, as Dickens did. Knowing that each person is a problem and that the bigger questions that surround us are seldom given a neat answer, he writes about individuals and their position in "the human predicament," gallantly keeping them individuals instead of accepting useful stereotypes to prove a point.

My first experience of this sturdy literary independence came when I went to see Mr. Forster about the rewriting of my dramatization of *A Passage to India*. In the charming, unpretentious rooms in King's College, Cambridge, where he lives as a Fellow of King's, surrounded with lovely pieces of china, with pictures, coin collections, the souvenirs, acquisitions, accumulations of a long and travelled life, he discussed my script. We went over it line by line, includ-

ing stage directions, while the pale English sunlight fitfully illuminated the desk where he worked. I soon overcame my acute attack of nervousness—I was meeting him for the first time—when I realized that he was even more nervous than I was, and that in any case there was no reason to tremble before the careful kindness that he displayed.

By then I had gained courage enough to ask him about the one character in the play that puzzled me, Mrs. Moore, an old, rather vague English woman. She has come out to India partly to visit her son, the District Magistrate of the small provincial town of Chandrapore, partly to chaperone the girl who is half engaged to her son and who, by a hallucinatory experience of attempted rape by an Indian, provides the central action.

I wanted a clarification of Mrs. Moore. In the novel, one can cope with her more easily, listen in on her thoughts—she never *said* very much— observe her intuitive understanding of India, and even share her disturbing mystical experience, which arrives through otherwise mundane activities. But a play is a coarser literary form. Everything has to be *said* out loud, not in the mind. With Mrs. Moore this was extremely difficult, because, although she is a pivotal character and expresses much of what the novel and the play are trying to say, she remained obstinately allusive, illusive, and inarticulate. An inexplicable, but absolutely convincing, symbol in the book, but maddening when one has to transfer her to the stage.

"What shall I do?" I asked Mr. Forster, with what seems to me, in retrospect, the most shaming naïveté. "She's got to speak, but every time I try to give her words for her thoughts, she comes out sounding false."

"These things are going on in her

head," he remarked gently.

"Yes, yes. But how will the audience *know* what goes on in her head?"

He shook his head helplessly. "Mrs. Moore was always a very tiresome woman," he said, as if that ended the matter.

All of a sudden I saw what he meant. These were real people, whether he had imagined them or not. You couldn't change their characters or their way of functioning just to suit yourself, or because you wanted to present them through another medium. They are examples of what Graham Greene, in another connection, describes as characters who, at the end of a book, disappear into life. The novel may be concluded, but its people go on living as though only a part of their experience had been recorded. They try your ingenuity, exasperate you, please you, but you can't shake off their reality.

This incontrovertible vitality of the characters in his novels, with all their quirks, their nobility, their stupidity, perhaps characterizes Mr. Forster's writing more than anything else. Yes, he is interested in philosophy and expressive about the forms it takes. Yes, social contretemps appear on every level. And, as he has regretfully said, "Yes—oh, dear, yes—the novel tells a story . . . and I wish that it was not so, that it could be something different—melody, or perception of the truth, not this low atavistic form." (*Aspects of the Novel*)

Certainly, the "story" of *A Passage to India*, or rather, the material involved, is melodramatic to a degree: attempted rape, race relations, mystery and mysticism, a love story on several different levels and meanings— one could go on forever listing its ingredients. One could even call it a "Who-if-anyone-done-it." Yet, when these elements are combined with Mr. Forster's inescapable engagement with human beings, a novel like *A Passage to India* emerges—the kind of novel that critics like to call "timeless."

When it was first published, it shocked the colonial diehards. *Indian* characters, some of them presented *sympathetically?* It would have been all right to be decent about, for instance, a loyal servant ("You're a better man than I am, Gunga Din"), but the educated Indian was a horse of quite another colour. What's more, they were mixed in with *British* characters, some of them presented as *arrogant fools*. Going a bit far, sir, surely? Is it cricket? But Mr. Forster was one of the first Englishmen to remind his countrymen that there are games more important than cricket. He was to say to them, at a time when his nation was involved in a dangerous war, with his quiet, hesitant, donnish voice, ". . . if I had to choose between betraying my country and betraying my friend, I hope I should have the guts to betray my country." In short, in his speeches as in his writing he expresses the basic conviction that people are more important than ideologies, that individuals can "connect" with other individuals only when the accidents of birth, breeding, patriotism, or nationality can be overcome by the larger cause of humanity. One may lose the small unimportant battle, the political one, but must not lose the big universal war—the human one.

In a literary sense, his book was what Mr. Forster himself, in *A Passage to India*, describes as a "Bridge Party"—a little joke of the time referring to the kind of "mixed" party to which both Indians and British were invited—a party, that is, to "bridge" the gulf between nationalities. The varied attitudes of readers were much the same as the attitudes of those distant English Bridge Party-goers. Some were shocked at the mere idea. Others, who had lived in India, thought that Mr. Forster had made a good try, but "no one but a novice would think of such a thing." Yet others felt that it was a dangerous experiment; still, "we all come out here with the honest wish to do well, not exactly mingle socially, but at least to close the gap a little," and admired his courage. A few perceptive and rebellious souls realized that he was not concerned simply with matters of race relations, politics, or social behaviour, but with human beings, faulty, brave, stupid, intelligent, wise, all contributors to our inescapable and universal "human predicament."

His writing excellence was never in any doubt by any faction of opinion, even though he assured Virginia Woolf when he finished *A Passage to India*, "This is a failure." Possibly this is the only time that Mr. Forster's critical judgment was seriously at fault. Mrs. Woolf herself firmly records in her diary that "I suppose I value Morgan's opinion as much as anybody's," or, about a book she had just finished, "Well, Morgan admires. This is a weight off my mind," and also, when she was in literary difficulties, "We can always ask Morgan."

In fact, it is especially because of this kind of treble vision Mr. Forster has—as the sharp-eyed critic, the creative artist, the subtle social philosopher—that his novels, and *A Passage to India* in particular, carry the remarkable force that was to impress Indians so deeply. To us the novel had dimensions that may not have been so striking to the British audience.

Until it was published—and indeed, for many years afterwards—what had we been offered by way of novels about India by foreigners, foreigners who had, after all, been ruling our country for more than a century? Kipling? Yeats-Brown? All the writers that an Indian friend of mine gathers loosely under the classification of "The Lean Bronzed Horseman School" of literature. No humour, though we don't really think of ourselves as an entirely dour nation. No politics, though the struggle for independence had started in India and the life of few nations has been so influenced by political ideas. No sense of social upheaval, though the social revolutions of the past fifty years coloured the upbringing of all Indians. Worst of all, no psychological exploration of Indian characters, though we do not consider ourselves even more unapproachable and reserved than the British are reputed to be.

It is not surprising, then, that *A Passage to India* came as such a shock, such a delight, such a wonder, to Indians, and caused incredulous comment all across the country. As Mr. Forster has said about his own work, "One grows accustomed to being praised, or being blamed, or being advised, but it is unusual to be understood." Here at last was a novel that was, in passages, wonderfully funny, was also profound, with a grasp of that famous inscrutable Hindu mysticism and philosophy; that was, besides, aware of political and social conditions and changes throughout the country, without being a political novel. But the most astonishing aspect of the book for many Indians was that it had the courage to talk and think from the inside of the Indian mind in all its many divergencies, and still convince *Indians* that it was telling the truth.

There are, in dealing with fictional foreigners, two quick and vulgar ways of establishing for the reader the fact that they belong to a different nationality, that the author is setting his novel "abroad." One is a reckless sprinkling of foreign words in the narrative or conversation. "'Fermez la porte,' she said to the concierge." And at once, we know we are in France. Or, "The coolie salaamed to the sahib, who was drinking a chota peg." Sure enough, we are in India. The other way is to translate dialogue literally from another language, as Ernest Hemingway did in *For Whom the Bell Tolls,* and this method, since it produces speeches in curiously tortured and broken English, always leaves me feeling that the characters can't speak their own language properly.

Mr. Forster does something much less obvious and much more complicated. He persuades you, by characterization and without a word of exposition, that his Indians are speaking to each other in their own language, and yet catches the special lilt and idiom of Indian-English when they are talking to the colonial British. This, like his extraordinary evocation of the Indian countryside, might be considered a matter of technique combined with the discriminating and alert eyes and ears of an artist.

The opening chapter of *A Passage to India* would give splendid evidence for this view. In two pages, with dazzling virtuosity, he describes the setting of Chandrapore, the scene of his story, the river, the town, the houses and bazaars, the feel of the heat, and the pervasive sense of the sky embracing it all:

> The sky settles everything—not only climates and seasons but when the earth shall be beautiful. By herself she can do little—only feeble outbursts of flowers. But when the sky chooses, glory can rain into the Chandrapore bazaars or a benediction pass from horizon to horizon. . . . No mountains infringe on the curve. League after league the earth lies flat, heaves a little, is flat again. Only in the south, where a group of fists and fingers are thrust up through the soil, is the endless expanse interrupted. These fists and fingers are the Marabar Hills, containing the extraordinary caves.

However, this is not a landscape without figures. As Mr. Forster peoples it with Indians, one begins to realize that his penetrating presentation of the Indian characters is a far more formidable feat than his sweeping command of description, but due in essence to the same faculties of observation and selection. In *A Passage to India,* he places the whole problem of the novelist squarely before the reader:

> Most of life is so dull that there is nothing to be said about it, and the books and talk that would describe it as interesting are obliged to exaggerate, in the hope of justifying their own existence . . . a perfectly adjusted organism would be silent.

Luckily for us, Mr. Forster is not, by his own definition, a perfectly adjusted organism, and manages to put before us far more than a series of quaint or eccentric characters in an exotic setting. He creates people in startlingly sharp relief and in situations that are both extreme and ordinary. With them, he illustrates his very deep and complex view of life and living.

Effortlessly, or so it seems, he leads his reader through the rarefied mental atmosphere of a devout Brahmin professor, expresses the nature of an affectionate, volatile, touchy Muslim, whose combination of exuberance and retreat lead him sometimes into poetry, sometimes into absurdity. His range of Indians includes a conniving fool of a junior doctor, a charming but histrionic lawyer, a rich local Nawab, and on and on. Each is unmistakably a person in his own right, and each contributes to the vast canvas—not simply of India, but of thoughts, ideas, and human relations anywhere—that Mr. Forster chooses to use in his fiction.

His British characters are, less surprisingly, quite as compelling as his Indians. The "liberal" college teacher, the thickheaded but fundamentally decent City Magistrate, the strange, honest girl who causes so much trouble, and, of course, that endearing, elusive, "tiresome woman," Mrs. Moore —all are alive. All of them are true to themselves and true to the time and place that Mr. Forster decided to record.

It is because of this that his plot, which could, by a lesser writer, be laced with sensationalism, is in *A Passage to India*, subordinated to the life and development of the people involved. Even without the expert sense of prose and the delight of his dialogue, or his handling of—oh, dear, yes, a *story*, the entirely convincing people you meet would be worth the novel.

There is one other major reason why the novel does not date. Conditions may have changed in India— though, goodness knows, one can find comparable conditions in other parts of the world today—but this is, in a way, an advantage in assessing *A Passage to India*. After all, one doesn't need to have lived through the Napoleonic wars to appreciate Tolstoy. Now one can see it without the colouring of social or political bias. History has taken the heat out of partisan views. Now the book can be considered as the novel of ideas that it is, and, as one of Mr. Forster's characters remarks, "I'd far rather leave a thought behind me than a child." His thoughts, his perception of other peo-

ple's thoughts, and his searching understanding of human relations are the qualities that make *A Passage to India* "timeless." Indubitably it is a grasp of life, left to his readers as an experience with indelible impact.

It was because I felt this way about the novel that my dramatization of *A Passage to India* came about. I was dining with a friend one evening, a friend who is involved in the American theatre, and we talked about the curious fact that there had never been a play about India, by an Indian, on Broadway. I remarked casually, without any idea of what a chance comment might start in my mind, that the obvious "first" should be a dramatization of *A Passage to India*, the best novel that I knew about India.

I still don't know quite how I summoned the nerve to attempt it, particularly since I was well aware that Mr. Forster doesn't readily give permission to anyone to dramatize his novels. He feels, entirely reasonably, that if he had written a book as a *novel*, it was because the material was a *novel* and not a play, a film, a short story, or any other literary form. The scope that a novel gives suited his conception of the matters, events, ideas, that he wanted to write about. The necessary compression of his Anglo-Indian world and all its happenings into two and a half hours of playing time could only seem to him a coarsening and debasing of his original, contemplative plan. Still, I couldn't get the project out of my head.

When I reread the book, a world I had half forgotten was suddenly real to me again. Admittedly, India was now free, but a society familiar to my parents and, in a more fragmentary way, familiar to me, was summoned up. I remembered my great-grandmother, very old, deaf, and almost blind, recalling the upheaval and fright of the Indian "mutiny" (now known as the First Indian War for Independence), and remarking that in those days, to scare a child into obedience, instead of saying, "The bogeyman will get you," one said, "*Gora ayega*"—"The white man will come for you."

I remembered from later times my mother saying, with a kind of despairing impatience, "Social insults will break up the British Empire just as fast as political injustice could." Like any Indian—or, indeed, any subject of colonialism—both my mother and I knew about the English clubs which were forbidden to Indians, the houses and occasions that Indians couldn't enter even as guests. A time and a world that only Mr. Forster could capture with irony, compassion, and a true understanding of every side.

I remembered that, years later, the atmosphere in India had changed enough for a taxi driver to make his own political comment on the times, the height of the independence movement. We didn't need guns and machinery to fight the British, he said. "If every Indian spits once, we can *drown* the British." By then there were a good many Englishmen who sincerely wanted "to be friends," and a good many Indians who tried to respond. But under those conditions a friendship of that sort was, if not impossible, at least difficult, embarrassing, inconvenient, for everyone concerned.

All this was part of the Indian air during the twenties and early thirties, and no Englishman, until Mr. Forster, had had the courage to record it honestly and in depth, or to try seriously to "connect." If, however, Mr. Forster had been interested purely in describing political and social conditions, dramatizing his novel after all these years would scarcely have been worth while, since in a free India, life

and its ambiance have changed so profoundly. But that wasn't, as he himself says, his aim. Although colonial conditions, and the frictions and distresses between ruler and ruled still exist, the vitality and human values of *A Passage to India* are of totally another temper. It was those aspects of the novel that I was trying to capture in my dramatization—values that are eternally valid.

It was a matter of incredulous joy that Mr. Forster accepted my version of his book as a play. A joy slowly dampened by the fact that the manuscript was rejected by countless producers in England and in America for five years. Usually, to my bewilderment, the grounds for the refusal were that the situation was out of date. It was eventually produced by a small English repertory company called the Oxford Playhouse. (Someone remarked to me at the time, "Nothing recedes like success.")

To everyone's astonishment—mine most of all—the English, with their unsentimental sense of realism, liked it. A century and a half had passed since their ancestors had conquered India; nearly forty years had passed since the novel was published; a decade had passed since the parents and friends of Oxford audiences had left India. But there were two facts that even the less academic audiences of London could not ignore: first, Mr. Forster had truthfully explored a moment in history; second, similar moments are being lived by human beings almost anywhere in the world.

We, as Indians, were left with questions rather than statements. With the departure of the convenient villains from our country, were the problems solved? Could we manage, within our society, to deal with the Privileged involved in their own privileges, having to take over the role of rulers—because who else has the edu-

cation, money, time, or experience?—
yet committed to a democratic society based on equal human rights? Can
we, after blaming the British for their
lacks, arrive ourselves at the hope of
both governing and "connecting"
with the mass of underprivileged Indians, the millions who are still in a
position we used to share? The
thoughtful British must have faced
many of the same paradoxes. To get
back to Mr. Forster's basic questions
in *A Passage to India*, are friendship,

cooperation, life, love, the brotherhood of man impossible until the first
steps to political and social freedom
are achieved? Are good intentions
enough? And, most important, can
the subjects who become the rulers
keep from perpetuating both a human
and a political dominance?

I wish I could answer any of those
questions. I can't. But I'm very glad
that Mr. Forster posed them—and
posed them so fairly.

NONFICTION

Though the English language has an extraordinarily rich vocabulary, one at
times draws a blank. "Nonfiction" is one of those blanks—a spongy, almost
meaningless word; yet it is the only general term we have to denote writing
that is not fiction or poetry or drama. It is a term, clearly, that covers an
enormous area: reports, letters, articles, printed directions, every kind of document, essays, historical and biographical writings—just about everything that
appears in newspapers, newsmagazines, and other periodicals, as well as books
and pamphlets, except, as we have noted, fiction, poetry, and drama. Probably,
at a guess, "nonfiction" today accounts for ninety percent of all printed matter
the world over.

The Essay

In this book we are concerned only with the literary branch of nonfiction:
the essay, history, and biography. Actually, as the critics make most clear,
"essay," though not so vague a term as "nonfiction," does itself cover a multitude of writings, and we may therefore classify *all* the nonfiction selections in

Part One as essays—the examples of short history (Morison and Sandburg), biography (De Voto) and autobiography (O'Connor), as well as the letters (Holmes), the journal (Emerson), the personal essay (Thoreau, Stevenson, White), the informal essay (Hazlitt, Chesterton, Thurber), the transcribed lecture (William James), the formal essay (Orwell, Lippmann), and all the rest.

In the comments that follow, all three critics agree on two main points: "essay" covers a great quantity and variety of writings; but all such writings, to be classified as essays, must have the quality of literature. The critics are Carl Van Doren, best known as a biographer and historian, Alexander Smith, a nineteenth-century essayist, and Josephine Miles, a contemporary teacher and poet.

Carl Van Doren

A NOTE ON THE ESSAY

THE sonnet has a standard form very much as a man has. Leave off the sestet of your sonnet and you do about what a god does when he leaves the legs off a man. The drama has a standard form very much as a rendezvous has. Write a drama in which no spark is exchanged between the audience and the action, and you have done what fate does when it keeps lovers from their meeting. The novel has a standard form very much as a road has. You may set out anywhere you like and go wherever you please, at any gait, but you must go somewhere, or you have made what is no more a novel than some engineer's road would be a road if it had neither beginning, end, nor direction. But the essay! It may be of any length, breadth, depth, weight, density, color, savor, odor, appearance, importance, value, or uselessness which you can or will give it. The epigram bounds it on one side and the treatise on the other, but it has in its time encroached upon the territory of both of them, and it doubtless will

do so again. Or, to look at the essay from another angle, it is bounded on one side by the hell-fire sermon and on the other by the geometrical demonstration; and yet it ranges easily between these extremes of heat and cold and occasionally steals from both of them. It differs from a letter by being written to more—happily a great many more—than one person. It differs from talk chiefly by being written at all.

Having to obey no regulations as to form, the essay is very free to choose its matter. The sonnet, by reason of its form, tends to deal with solemn and not with gay themes. The drama, for the same reason, tends to look for intense and not for casual incidents. The novel tends to feel that it must carry a considerable amount of human life on its back. The essay may be as fastidious as a collector of carved emeralds or as open-minded as a garbage-gatherer. Nothing human, as the platitude says, is alien to it. The essay, however, goes beyond the platitude and dares to choose matter from numerous non-human sources. Think of the naturalists and their essays. Think, further, of the range of topics for essayists at large. Theodore Roosevelt in an essay urges the strenuous life; Max Beerbohm in an essay defends cosmetics. De Quincey expounds the fine art of murder, Thoreau the pleasures of economy, William Law the blisses of prayer, Hudson the sense of smell in men and in animals, Schopenhauer the ugliness of women, Bacon the advantages of a garden, Plutarch the traits of curiosity, and A. C. Benson the felicity of having nothing much in the mind. All, in fact, an essayist needs to start with is something, anything, to say. He gets up each morning and finds the world spread out before him, as the world was spread out before Adam and Eve the day they left paradise. With the cosmos, past, present, and future, to pick from, the essayist goes to work. If he finds a topic good enough he may write a good essay, no matter how he writes it.

He may. There is still, however, the question of his manner. Thousands of dull men have written millions of true things which no one but their proofreaders, wives, or pupils ever read. If each essayist could take out a patent on each subject into which he dips his pen, and could prevent any other pen from ever dipping into it after him, he might have better luck. But there are no monopolists in this department. Would research find in all the hoards of books or all the morgues of manuscripts a single observation which has never been made twice? Competition in such affairs is free and endless. The only law which gives an essayist a right to his material is the law which rules that the

best man wins. The law does not say in what fashion he must be best. Any fashion will do. Let him be more sententious, like Bacon; or more harmonious, like Sir Thomas Browne; or more elegant, like Addison; or more direct, like Swift; or more hearty, like Fielding; or more whimsical, like Lamb; or more impassioned, like Hazlitt; or more encouraging, like Emerson; or more Olympian, like Arnold; or more funny, like Mark Twain; or more musical, like Pater; or more impish, like Max Beerbohm; or more devastating, like Mencken. Let the essayist be any of these things and he may have a copyright till someone takes it away from him. What matters is the manner. If he has good matter, he *may* write a good essay; if he has a good manner he probably *will* write a good essay.

An essay is a communication. If the subject of the discourse were the whole affair, it would be enough for the essayist to be an adequate conduit. If the manner were the whole affair, any versatile fellow might try all the manners and have a universal triumph. But back of matter and manner both lies the item which is really significant. The person who communicates anything in any way must be a person. His truth must have a tone, his speech must have a rhythm which are his and solely his. His knowledge or opinions must have lain long enough inside him to have taken root there; and when they come away they must bring some of the soil clinging to them. They must, too, have been shaped by that soil—as plants are which grow in cellars, on housetops, on hillsides, in the wide fields, under shade in forests. Many kinds of men, many kinds of essays! Important essays come from important men.

Alexander Smith

ON THE WRITING OF ESSAYS [1]

THE essay, as a literary form, resembles the lyric, in so far as it is moulded by some central mood—whimsical, serious, or satirical. Give the mood, and the essay, from the first sentence to the last, grows around it as the cocoon grows around the silkworm. The essay-writer is [. . .] a law unto himself. A quick ear and eye, an ability to discern the infinite suggestiveness of common things, a brooding meditative spirit, are all that the essayist requires to start business with. [. . .] It is not the essayist's duty to inform, to build pathways through metaphysical morasses, to cancel abuses, any more than it is the duty of the poet to do these things. Incidentally he may do something in that way, just as the poet may, but it is not his duty, and should not be expected of him. Skylarks are primarily created to sing, although a whole choir of them may be baked in pies and brought to table; they were born to make music, although they may incidentally stay the pangs of vulgar hunger. The essayist is a kind of poet in prose, and if questioned harshly as to his uses, he might be unable to render a better apology for his existence than a flower might. The essay should be pure literature as the poem is pure literature. The essayist wears a lance, but he cares more for the sharpness of its point than for the pennon that flutters on it, than for the banner of the captain whom he serves. He plays with death as Hamlet plays with Yorick's skull, and he reads the morals—strangely stern, often, for such fragrant lodging —which are folded up in the bosoms of roses. He has no pride, and is deficient in a sense of the congruity and fitness of things. He lifts a pebble from the ground, and puts it aside more carefully than any gem; and on a nail in a cottage-door he will hang the mantle of his thought, heavily brocaded with the gold of rhetoric. He finds his way into the Elysian fields through portals the most shabby and commonplace.

The essayist plays with his subject, now in whimsical, now in grave, now in melancholy mood. He lies upon the idle grassy bank [. . .] letting the world flow past him, and from this thing and the other he extracts his mirth and his moralities. His main gift is an eye to discover the suggestiveness of common things; to find a sermon in the most unpromising texts. Beyond the vital hint, the first step, his discourses are not beholden to their titles. Let him take up the most trivial subject, and it will lead him away to the great questions over which the serious imagination loves to brood—fortune, mutability, death— just as inevitably as the runnel, trickling among the summer hills, on which sheep are bleating, leads you to the sea; or as, turning down the first street you come to in a city, you are led finally, albeit by many an intricacy, out into the open country, with its waste places and its woods, where you are lost in a sense of strangeness and solitariness. The world is to the meditative man what the mulberry plant is to the silkworm. The essay-writer has no lack of subject-matter. He has the day that is passing over his head; and, if unsatis-

1. Alexander Smith, the reader will discover, is discussing primarily the personal and the informal essay.

fied with that, he has the world's six thousand years to depasture his gay or serious humour upon. I idle away my time here, and I am finding new subjects every hour. Everything I see or hear is an essay in bud. The world is everywhere whispering essays, and one need only be the world's amanuensis. [. . .] Of the essayist, when his mood is communicative, you obtain a full picture. You are made his contemporary and familiar friend. You enter into his humours and seriousness. You are made heir of his whims, prejudices, and playfulness. You walk through the whole nature of him, as you walk through the streets of Pompeii, looking into the interior of stately mansions, reading the satirical scribblings on the walls. And the essayist's habit not only of giving you his thoughts, but telling you how he came by them, is interesting, because it shows you by what alchemy the ruder world becomes transmuted into the finer. We like to know the lineage of ideas, just as we like to know the lineage of great earls and swift race-horses. We like to know that the discovery of the law of gravitation was born of the fall of an apple in an English garden on a summer afternoon. Essays written after this fashion are racy of the soil in which they grow, as you taste the lava in the vines grown on the slopes of Etna, they say. There is a healthy Gascon flavour in Montaigne's *Essays;* and Charles Lamb's are scented with the primroses of Covent Garden.

The essayist does not usually appear early in the literary history of a country: he comes naturally after the poet and the chronicler. His habit of mind is leisurely; he does not write from any special stress or passionate impulse; he does not create material so much as he comments upon material already existing. It is essential for him that books should have been written, and that they should, at least to some extent, have been read and digested. He is usually full of allusions and references, and these his reader must be able to follow and understand.

Josephine Miles

THE ESSAY AS A FORM

IF YOU have ever tried to work out an idea that seemed to you worthwhile, you realize the pleasure of seeing it take shape. This is the pleasure of the essayist—first the tentative thought, then the steps of development through positive and negative evidence, finally the restatement and clarification of the thought in its developed form.

You may ask, how generally true is your idea? What connections and associations does it have? Who cares about it? How may it grow, take on breadth and depth, lead others to think about ideas like it? What is

From the Introduction to *Classic Essays in English*, edited by Josephine Miles, copyright © 1961 by Little, Brown and Company (Inc.). Reprinted by permission of the publishers.

your feeling toward it, your manner in writing of it?

You may ask also, what are the main concerns of your ideas? Perhaps what you like to do—"Fishing is pleasanter than hunting," or "It's a good plan to read the end of a book first." Or they may be concerns about people, with puzzling complexities of character, with a question such as "Why do I like the people I like?" or "What is the difference between an acquaintance and a friend?" Or they may be about concepts of groups and organizations—"Why do people enjoy excluding others?" "How does a church differ from a religion?" "How important are settings in theatrical productions?" "What are the consequences of one vote in an election?"

If you think as you read these suggestions that none of them are ideas that would ever cross your mind, then ask yourself what you think about instead, when you are philosophizing on matters larger than one person or one event, when you are thinking, that is, about matters that may be at least proposed to be generally true.

Some concerns for such matters keep recurring through the centuries. Others change from era to era, as events and situations change. [. . .]

An essay tries to develop an idea. The concept of trying, of tentative effort, is in the term *essay* itself—*essaier* in French is *to attempt*. So it differs from a formal report or a technical work of any kind which supplies evidence as complete and thorough as possible. The evidence offered by the essay is usually just that available to the author at the moment of writing. He searches his mind, maybe asks his friends what they think, but does not necessarily do further research. Much of the finest prose-writing of our day we would not call essay-

writing because it is too technical, too loaded with materials which are themselves as interesting as the argument. An essayist's main interest is his idea, his argument; he is more interested in developing an attitude, a clarification of a thought, than in adding to knowledge.

Why does he usually write in prose rather than in verse? Because, as the word *pro*-se suggests, it *pro*gresses, it carries his idea straight *for*ward, while *verse*, related to *versus*, turns back upon itself, stops at the end of one line and re*verses* its position to the beginning of the next line, using all sorts of repetitions in sound, such as rhythm and rhyme, to create a stronger sense of pattern than the development of an idea may require. A clear idea, in other words, might find a close repetitive emphasis on sound qualities distracting; it would call for emphasis less on syllables, more on words, phrases, and clauses, and thus establish a larger rhythm of repetition, in the straightforward motion of prose. A closely repetitive sound-pattern in prose may cause it to be called "poetic," while, on the other hand, verse, if it stresses sound as little as possible, especially in places that emphasize the argument, comes close to being justly called verse-essay: some of Pope's writing, for example, or of Wallace Stevens' in our own day. The essay is written by those most interested in the general and thoughtful powers of language.

What form do these powers usually take in prose? What shape does the artist in prose give to language by his selection and arrangement of it? The principles of arrangement are similar from art to art. Repetitions in balance, in contrast, in culmination, in analyzed portions of repeated wholes, serve to give first emphasis and then connection to the selected materials, which in prose are the words, phrases, clauses, sentences, paragraphs.

So as we look for the shaping of an idea in an essay, we may look first for its most basic unit—the sentence that states its idea. Then we may look to see how this sentence is repeated, or analyzed, or varied, in each larger paragraph unit. Then finally we may look for supporting patterns: the main ways in which phrases and clauses are combined into sentences, the main ways in which words are combined into phrases and clauses, and the large patterns of sound, of the contours of intonation from phrase to phrase and sentence to sentence.

In the course of English prose we may distinguish certain main patterns. One is often called the *curt* style: short sentences with few connectives but with a good deal of connection by similarity and cumulative force of structures—"He came. He saw. He conquered."—Such a style uses many verbs in short clauses; relatively few participles and other modifiers. [. . . Roger] Ascham's style is most like this. Another pattern is often called the *periodic;* it is modelled upon the Latin style of Cicero, and, in the Latin and later German fashion, suspends the verb until the end of a long complex sentence full of subordinate clauses and phrases, so that one does not know just what the chief meaning will be until he reaches the end. Such a style is More's or Dry-

den's. A third way may be called the *explanatory* or *substantiating*, in which the chief statement is made at the outset, and then is supported by a number of substantiary clauses or participial phrases, adding either topical or material enrichment. Note Russell's style for the clauses, De Quincey's for the phrases. Such differences in style appear to depend partly on the nature and habit of the author, partly on the custom and practice in his time, and partly on his specific substance and purpose. We may notice that while various styles appear in every era and for every main concern, the nineteenth century seemed most interested in the style of phrasal substantiation, using more adjectives and participles, with fewer verbs, than did the essayists of other centuries.

As part of the shape and structure, the ideas themselves have changed in emphasis. In the Renaissance, primary concerns were religion, education, and human relations. Increasingly in recent centuries, the critical essay on literature has developed, the interpretation of meaning through art, and along with it the essay of social interest—Thoreau's, James', Arnold's, Adams', Shaw's, Orwell's. But as we name these names we are carried back to More and Ascham again, and we see that certain basic ethical concerns persist, for man in his daily life, in his way of thought and belief, in his community.

History

History, according to historian Allan Nevins, "is the record of everything in the past which helps explain how the present came to be." And another historian, E. H. Carr, states: "Scientists, social scientists, and historians are all engaged in different branches of the same study: the study of man and his environment, of the effects of man on his environment and of his environment on man." There seems to be no significant conflict between these two definitions, and yet we shall discover in the critical comments that follow that among historians and students of history many points of disagreement do indeed exist. The reading of the two brief historical statements below may help you to understand why the meaning of "history" does, and should, concern the critics:

> To the frontier the American intellect owes its striking characteristics. That coarseness and strength combined with acuteness and inquisitiveness; that practical, inventive turn of mind, quick to find expedients; that masterful grasp of material things, lacking in the artistic but powerful to effect great ends; that restless, nervous energy; that dominant individualism, working for good and for evil; and withal that buoyancy and exuberance which comes with freedom—these are traits of the frontier, or traits called out elsewhere because of the existence of the frontier. Since the days when the fleet of Columbus sailed into the waters of the New World, America has been another name for opportunity, and the people of the United States have taken their tone from the incessant expansion which has not only been open but has even been forced upon them. He would be a rash prophet who should assert that the expansive character of American life has now entirely ceased. Movement has been its dominant fact, and, unless this training has no effect upon a people, the American energy will continually demand a wider field for its exercise. But never again will such gifts of free land offer themselves.[1]

> To Turner the westerner was a radical in both thought and actions, developing new ideas to meet new conditions. The modern trend of thinking, while far from uniform, tends to move in the opposite direction, with more and more people asserting that the West was essentially conservative. True enough the westerner made some unpleasant innovations such as the sod house, was forced to develop several new techniques as in the arid parts of the West, and supported certain drastic actions for his own advantage—as free land and the elimination of Indian power; and yet the great bulk of his customs, including the building of log cabins, was derivative. More basic, however, he accepted in general the virtues and ideals which he had been taught as a youth and which were common in the United States. He was a God-fearing man along traditional lines. He joined the rest of the United States in judging success as the attainment of wealth. He respected personal property and the sanctity of contracts just as did his eastern contemporary. In fact he had moved to the West not in protest at current ideals but to

1. From Frederick Jackson Turner, "The Significance of the Frontier in American History," 1893.

attain them more quickly. His objective was the same kind of life which he had envied in his eastern neighbors.[2]

Each of these conflicting statements is called "history." But which one of them is true? Which objective and unbiased? What, then, *is* history? Let us see what four historians have to say on the subject.

Barbara Tuchman

WHEN DOES HISTORY HAPPEN?

"WHAT is history?" Professional historians have been exercising themselves vehemently over this query for some time. A distinguished exponent, E. H. Carr of Cambridge University, made it the subject of his Trevelyan Lectures and the title of a book in 1962.

Is history, he asked, the examination of past events or is it the past events themselves? By good luck I did not read the book until after I had finished an effort of my own at historical narrative, otherwise I should never have dared to begin. In my innocence I had not been aware that the question posed by Mr. Carr had ever come up. I had simply assumed that history was past events existing independently, whether we examined them or not.

I had thought that we who comment on the past were extraneous to it; helpful, perhaps, to its understanding but not integral to its existence. I had supposed that the Greeks' defeat of the Persians would have given the same direction to Western history whether Herodotus chronicled it or not. But that is not Mr. Carr's position. "The belief in a hard core of historical facts existing independently of the interpretation of the historian," he says, "is a preposterous fallacy but one that is very hard to eradicate."

On first reading this seemed to me to be preposterous nonsense. Was it some sort of recondite joke? But a thinker of such eminence must be taken seriously, and after prolonged silent arguments with Mr. Carr of which he remained happily unaware, I began to see what he was driving at. What he means, I suppose, is that past events cannot exist independently of the historian because without the historian we would know nothing about them; in short, that the unrecorded past is none other than our old friend, the tree in the primeval forest which fell without being heard. I refuse to be frightened by that hoary apparition. The question should

"When Does History Happen?" by Barbara Tuchman from *The New York Times*, March 8, 1964, © 1964 by The New York Times Company. Reprinted by permission of the publishers and Russell & Volkening, Inc.

2. From Robert E. Riegel, *Current Ideas of the Significance of the United States Frontier*, 1952.

not be, let me say at once, whether the fall of the tree made a noise but whether it left a mark on the forest. If it left a space that let in the sun on a hitherto shade-grown species or if it killed a dominant animal and shifted rule of the pack to one of different characteristics or if it fell across a path of animals and caused some small change in their habitual course from which larger changes followed, then the fall made history whether anyone heard it or not.

I therefore declare myself a firm believer in the "preposterous fallacy" of historical facts existing independently of the historian. [. . .] Mr. Carr might just as well say the Grecian Urn would not exist without Keats.

As I see it, evidence is more important than interpretation, and facts are history whether interpreted or not. [. . .]

[. . .] I am content to define history as the past events of which we have knowledge and refrain from worrying about those of which we have none—until, that is, some archeologist digs them up, a thought that raises a new question. What about those facts of which we have the interpretation (in the form of legend) before we have the evidence, like the Flood or the fall of Troy? Was the Trojan War history when Homer interpreted it or only after Schliemann dug it up?

I will leave history out on that limb and come next to historians. Who are they: contemporaries of the event or those who come after? The answer is obviously both. Among contemporaries, first and indispensable are the more-or-less unconscious sources: letters, diaries, memoirs, autobiographies, newspapers and periodicals, business and government documents. These are historical raw material, not history. Their authors may be writing with one eye or possibly both on pos-

terity, but that does not make them historians. To perform that function requires a view from the outside and a conscious craft.

At a slightly different level are the I-was-there recorders, usually journalists, whose accounts often contain golden nuggets of information buried in a mass of daily travelogue which the passage of time has reduced to trivia. Some of the most vivid details that went into my book, "The Guns of August," came from the working press: the rag doll crushed under the wheel of a German gun carriage from Irvin Cobb, the smell of half a million unwashed bodies that hung over the invaded villages of Belgium from Will Irwin, the incident of Col. Max Hoffmann yelling insults at the Japanese general from Frederick Palmer, who reported the Russo-Japanese War. Daily journalism, however, even when collected in book form, is, like letters and the rest, essentially source material, rather than history. [. . .]

Still contemporary but dispensable are the Compilers who hurriedly assemble a book from clippings and interviews in order to capitalize on public interest when it is high. A favorite form of these hasty puddings is the overnight biography, like "The Lyndon Johnson Story," which was in the bookstores within a few weeks of the incident that gave rise to it. [. . .]

[. . .] The Compilers, in their treatment, supply no extra understanding and as historians are ephemeral.

All these varieties being disposed of, there remains a pure vein of conscious historians of whom, among contemporaries, there are two kinds. First, the Onlookers, who deliberately set out to chronicle an episode of their own age—a war or depression or strike or social revolution or whatever it may be—and shape it into a historical narrative with character and validity of its own. Thucydides's "Peloponnesian War," on a major scale, and Theodore White's "The Making of a President," undertaken in the same spirit though on a tiny scale in comparison, are examples.

Second are the Active Participants or Axe-Grinders, who attempt a genuine history of events they have known, but whose accounts are inevitably weighted, sometimes subtly and imperceptibly, sometimes crudely, by the requirements of the role in which they wish themselves to appear. Josephus's "The Jewish War," the Earl of Clarendon's "History of the Rebellion" and Winston Churchill's "World Crisis" and "Second World War" are classics of this category.

For the latter-day historian, these too become source material. Are we now in possession of history when we have these accounts in hand? Yes, in the sense that we are in possession of wine when the first pressing of the grapes is in hand. But it has not fermented, and it has not aged. The great advantage of the latter-day historian is the distance conferred by the passage of time. At a distance from the events he describes and with a wider area of vision, he can see more of what was going on at the time and distinguish what was significant from what was not.

The contemporary has no perspective; everything is in the foreground and appears the same size. Little matters loom big, and great matters are sometimes missed because their outlines cannot be seen. Vietnam and Panama are given four-column headlines today, but the historian 50 or 100 years hence will put them in a chapter under a general heading we have not yet thought of.

The contemporary, especially if he is a participant, is inside his events, which is not an entirely unmixed advantage. What he gains in intimacy through personal acquaintance—which we can never achieve—he sacrifices in detachment. He cannot see or judge fairly both sides in a quarrel, for example the quarrel as to who deserves chief credit for the French victory at the Battle of the Marne in 1914. All contemporary chroniclers were extreme partisans of either Joffre or Gallieni. So violent was the partisanship that no one (except President Poincaré) noticed what is so clearly visible when viewed from a distance, that both generals had played an essential role. Gallieni saw the opportunity and gave the impetus; Joffre brought the Army and the reinforcements into place to fight; but it took 50 years before this simple and just apportionment could be made.

Distance does not always confer objectivity; one can hardly say Gibbon wrote objectively of the Roman Empire or Carlyle of the French Revolution. Objectivity is a question of degree. It is possible for the latter-day historian to be at least *relatively* objective, which is not the same thing as being neutral or taking no sides. There is no such thing as a neutral or purely objective historian. Without an opinion a historian would be simply a ticking clock, and unreadable besides.

Nevertheless, distance does confer a kind of removal that cools the judgment and permits a juster appraisal than is possible to a contemporary. [. . .]

I am not saying that emotion should have no place in history. On the contrary, I think it is an essential element of history, as it is of poetry, whose origin Wordsworth defined as "emotion recollected in tranquility." History, one might say, is emotion plus action recollected or, in the case of latter-day historians, reflected on in tranquility after a close and honest examination of the records. The primary duty of the historian is to stay within the evidence. Yet it is a curious fact that poets, limited by no such rule, have done very well with history, both of their own times and of times long gone before. [. . .]

We know how the American Revolution began from Longfellow's signal lights in the old North Church:

One, if by land, and two, if by sea,
And I on the opposite shore will be,
Ready to ride and spread the alarm
Through every Middlesex village and farm.

And we know what happened next from Emerson who commemorated Concord Bridge where "once the embattled farmers stood and fired the shot heard round the world."

Sometimes poets are lifted above themselves by a theme from history. The man who was happy with the jingle-bell rhythms of "The Raven" and "Annabel Lee" never equaled, nor have many others, the lines to Helen:

On desperate seas long wont to roam,
Thy hyacinth hair, thy classic face,
Thy Naiad airs have brought me home
To the glory that was Greece
And the grandeur that was Rome.
[. . .]

What the poets did was to distill the essence of an episode of history and by their art endow it with an idea or shape or meaning; [. . .] historians do much the same thing, with one major difference: they do it within the discipline of the facts.

What his imagination is to the poet, facts are to the historian. His exercise of judgment comes in their selection, his art in their arrangement. His method is narrative. Narrative is the life-blood of history; it is the vehicle that carries it, the medium through which the historian communicates what he has to tell. Macaulay said history should ideally be a compound of poetry and philosophy. Today they argue whether it is art or science. For myself I incline toward the first of both these choices, but primarily I think of the historian as a story-teller. His subject is the story of man's past. His function is to make it known.

E. H. Carr

WHAT IS HISTORY?

THE empirical theory of knowledge presupposes a complete separation between subject and object.

Facts, like sense-impressions, impinge on the observer from outside, and are independent of his consciousness. The process of reception is passive: having received the data, he then acts on them. This is what may be called the common-sense view of history. History consists of a corpus of ascertained facts. The facts are available to the historian in documents, inscriptions, and so on, like fish on the fishmonger's slab. The historian collects them, takes them home, and cooks and serves them in whatever style appeals to him. [. . .] First get your facts straight, then plunge at your peril into the shifting sands of interpretation—that is the ultimate wisdom of the empirical, common-sense school of history. It recalls the favourite dictum of the great liberal journalist C. P. Scott: "Facts are sacred, opinion is free."

Now this clearly will not do. I shall not embark on a philosophical discussion of the nature of our knowledge of the past. Let us assume for present purposes that the fact that Caesar crossed the Rubicon and the fact that there is a table in the middle of the room are facts of the same or of a comparable order, that both these facts enter our consciousness in the same or in a comparable manner, and that both have the same objective character in relation to the person who knows them. But, even on this bold and not very plausible assumption, our argument at once runs into the difficulty that not all facts about the past are historical facts, or are treated as such by the historian. What is the criterion which distinguishes the facts of history from other facts about the past?

What is a historical fact? This is a crucial question into which we must look a little more closely. According to the common-sense view, there are certain basic facts which are the same for all historians and which form, so to speak, the backbone of history— the fact, for example, that the Battle

of Hastings was fought in 1066. But this view calls for two observations. In the first place, it is not with facts like these that the historian is primarily concerned. It is no doubt important to know that the great battle was fought in 1066 and not in 1065 or 1067, and that it was fought at Hastings and not at Eastbourne or Brighton. The historian must not get these things wrong. But when points of this kind are raised, I am reminded of Housman's remark that "accuracy is a duty, not a virtue." To praise a historian for his accuracy is like praising an architect for using well-seasoned timber or properly mixed concrete in his building. It is a necessary condition of his work, but not his essential function. It is precisely for matters of this kind that the historian is entitled to rely on what have been called the "auxiliary sciences" of history—archaeology, epigraphy, numismatics, chronology, and so forth. The historian is not required to have the special skills which enable the expert to determine the origin and period of a fragment of pottery or marble, to decipher an obscure inscription, or to make the elaborate astronomical calculations necessary to establish a precise date. These so-called basic facts which are the same for all historians commonly belong to the category of the raw materials of the historian rather than of history itself. The second observation is that the necessity to establish these basic facts rests not on any quality in the facts themselves, but on an *a priori* decision of the historian. In spite of C. P. Scott's motto, every journalist knows today that the most effective way to influence opinion is by the selection and arrangement of the appropriate facts. It used to be said that facts speak for themselves. This is, of course, untrue. The facts speak only when the historian calls on them: it is he who decides to which facts to give the floor, and in what order or context. It was, I think, one of Pirandello's characters who said that a fact is like a sack—it won't stand up till you've put something in it. The only reason why we are interested to know that the battle was fought at Hastings in 1066 is that historians regard it as a major historical event. It is the historian who has decided for his own reasons that Caesar's crossing of that petty stream, the Rubicon, is a fact of history, whereas the crossing of the Rubicon by millions of other people before or since interests nobody at all. The fact that you arrived in this building half an hour ago on foot, or on a bicycle, or in a car, is just as much a fact about the past as the fact that Caesar crossed the Rubicon. But it will probably be ignored by historians. [. . .] The historian is necessarily selective. The belief in a hard core of historical facts existing objectively and independently of the interpretation of the historian is a preposterous fallacy, but one which it is very hard to eradicate.

The nineteenth-century fetishism of facts was completed and justified by a fetishism of documents. The documents were the Ark of the Covenant in the temple of facts. The reverent historian approached them with bowed head and spoke of them in awed tones. If you find it in the documents, it is so. But what, when we get down to it, do these documents— the decrees, the treaties, the rent-rolls, the blue books, the official correspondence, the private letters and diaries—tell us? No document can tell us more than what the author of the document thought—what he thought had happened, what he thought ought to happen or would happen, or perhaps only what he wanted others to think he thought, or even only what he himself thought he thought. None of this means anything until the his-

torian has got to work on it and deciphered it. The facts, whether found in documents or not, have still to be processed by the historian before he can make any use of them: the use he makes of them is, if I may put it that way, the processing process. [. . .]

In the first place, the facts of history never come to us "pure," since they do not and cannot exist in a pure form: they are always refracted through the mind of the recorder. It follows that when we take up a work of history, our first concern should not be with the facts which it contains but with the historian who wrote it. [. . .]

[. . .] Study the historian before you begin to study the facts. This is, after all, not very abstruse. It is what is already done by the intelligent undergraduate who, when recommended to read a work by that great scholar Jones of St. Jude's, goes round to a friend at St. Jude's to ask what sort of chap Jones is, and what bees he has in his bonnet. When you read a work of history, always listen out for the buzzing. If you can detect none, either you are tone deaf or your historian is a dull dog. The facts are really not at all like fish on the fishmonger's slab. They are like fish swimming about in a vast and sometimes inaccessible ocean; and what the historian catches will depend partly on chance, but mainly on what part of the ocean he chooses to fish in and what tackle he chooses to use—these two factors being, of course, determined by the kind of fish he wants to catch. By and large, the historian will get the kind of facts he wants. History means interpretation. [. . .]

The second point is the more familiar one of the historian's need of imaginative understanding for the minds of the people with whom he is dealing, for the thought behind their acts: I say "imaginative understanding," not "sympathy," lest sympathy should be supposed to imply agreement. [. . .] Much of what has been written in English-speaking countries in the last ten years about the Soviet Union, and in the Soviet Union about the English-speaking countries, has been vitiated by this inability to achieve even the most elementary measure of imaginative understanding of what goes on in the mind of the other party, so that the words and actions of the other are always made to appear malign, senseless, or hypocritical. History cannot be written unless the historian can achieve some kind of contact with the mind of those about whom he is writing.

The third point is that we can view the past, and achieve our understanding of the past, only through the eyes of the present. The historian is of his own age, and is bound to it by the conditions of human existence. The very words which he uses—words like democracy, empire, war, revolution—have current connotations from which he cannot divorce them. [. . .] Yet the historian is obliged to choose: the use of language forbids him to be neutral. Nor is it a matter of words alone. Over the past hundred years the changed balance of power in Europe has reversed the attitude of British historians to Frederick the Great. The changed balance of power within the Christian churches between Catholicism and Protestantism has profoundly altered their attitude to such figures as Loyola, Luther, and Cromwell. It requires only a superficial knowledge of the work of French historians of the last forty years on the French revolution to recognize how deeply it has been affected by the Russian revolution of 1917. The historian belongs not to the past but to the present. [. . .] The function of the historian is neither to love the past nor to emancipate himself from the past, but to master and understand it as the key to the understanding of the present. [. . .]

The historian starts with a provisional selection of facts and a provisional interpretation in the light of which that selection has been made—by others as well as by himself. As he works, both the interpretation and the selection and ordering of facts undergo subtle and perhaps partly unconscious changes through the reciprocal action of one or the other. And this reciprocal action also involves reciprocity between present and past, since the historian is part of the present and the facts belong to the past. The historian and the facts of history are necessary to one another. The historian without his facts is rootless and futile; the facts without their historian are dead and meaningless. My first answer therefore to the question, What is history?, is that it is a continuous process of interaction between the historian and his facts, an unending dialogue between the present and the past.

Allan Nevins

THE ART OF HISTORY

THE STRUGGLE TO MAKE THE PAST ALIVE

CLIO, the Muse of History, does not dwell (as most people think) in cozy libraries and shaded archives. She presides over a dangerous battlefield, where angry groups charge and grapple, and one cohort no sooner gains a height than an enfilading fire is opened from both flanks. Among skirmishers and guerrillas two great central combats never cease. One is fought between these, who believe that the facts of the past should be pushed and locked into a philosophic system, and those who believe in an open-minded and relativist approach to the data of history. The other unceasing, clangorous battle rages between those who hold that the best approach to historical truth is that of the artist with his power of divination and those who fight for the scientific approach, with its calipers and micrometer.

These two main battles about the writing of history will never end; for history has to be interpretive, and ideas upon the proper method of interpretation must always differ. Nor will minor skirmishes and engagements ever end, for history constantly has to be lifted out of conventional ruts. This is what lends history its deepest interest. To the true student it is never dead; it is always aggressively, challengingly alive. It is never written once and for all, but has incessantly to be rewritten.

The history texts state that Sherman's March to the Sea was one of the great pivotal events of the Civil War. But a writer arises who points out that Lieut. Gen. John M. Schofield believed that the war would have ended just as quickly had Sherman never made that march; that other notable military authorities believed that Thomas' destruction of Hood's army was the really crucial event in the West; and that Sherman himself wrote that his march northward from Savannah was ten times more important than the swath to the sea. Where then stands the old view? [. . .]

The true historical attitude, argues one side, is a search for all the facts about a given situation, force, or event —the Puritan regime, the Abolitionist Movement, Pearl Harbor—which slowly, painfully, accurately dredges up an interpretation *not* mapped out in advance. That is, history should operate by the inductive, not the deductive, use of evidence. An Olympian historian like Gibbon says in effect: "Let us collect and collate all the relevant facts, and find what conclusions emerge from their impartial analysis." Not so, says the other side; the true way to the truth about the past is to use a theory which will grope deep into the confusing array of facts and occurrences. Such a deductive historian as Charles A. Beard remarks, in effect: "Let us take this provocative theory of what happened at a given time, say in making the Constitution, and see if we can collect an array of evidence which offers overwhelming proof." Enemies of this school cry, "Tendentious history!"

And in rebuttal, enemies of the open-minded school shout: "Plodding history! History without ideas!"

But, by contrast, the battle between the literary and the scientific schools of historical interpretation, so stubborn and protracted, does show a definite contemporaneous tendency toward the victory of the artist over the micrometrist. For evidence we need only point to the publishing lists of the last quarter-century, and particularly of the last decade. A century ago, when Prescott and Motley were at the height of their powers, when Irving was still alive and Parkman just well launched in his race, the literary historian was dominant in this country, as he was in the England of Macaulay, Carlyle, and Froude. Francis Parkman, by common consent the greatest of our historians, enunciated in two sentences the creed of his illustrious group: "Faithfulness to history involves far more than a research, however patient and scrupulous, into special facts. Such facts may be detailed with the most scrupulous minuteness, and yet the narrative, taken as a whole, may be unmeaning or untrue."

This was a great truth. The Dryasdusts whom Carlyle so often denounced, with all their dedication to precise fact, often did more to falsify the picture of the past than the most careless artist. Unhappily, for a long generation after Parkman's climactic *Montcalm and Wolfe* (1884) this truth was obscured. A school of Teutonic tradition and training, which exalted monographic throughness, declared that nothing mattered but endless research, laborious sifting of facts, and rigorous analysis of evidence. The scientific element was all-important; the literary element was subsidiary and unessential if not positively harmful. [. . .]

Yet Theodore Roosevelt was entirely correct when, revolting against the arid precisians, he wrote that history is not good unless it is "a vivid and powerful presentation of scientific matter *in literary form.*" For, as Roosevelt himself helped prove in *The Winning of the West*, form and substance are not separable entities; and certain virtues of literary form are as vital to a complete presentation of historical truth as are certain virtues of scientific method. The historian can no more ascertain the truth about the past and convey it to his reader without literary power than without scientific discipline. The over-dull writer falsifies the past. [. . .]

Imagination is an artistic quality. Now imagination does not disable a conscientious writer from presenting facts in accurate form; it enormously assists him in doing so. Any researcher can collect overwhelming masses of facts and yet leave them utterly lifeless, drab and unmeaning. [. . .]

Without life, there is no truth to history, and without imagination there is no life. Imagination joined with research in the wonderful narratives which both Motley and Froude wrote of the destruction of the Great Armada. It was because he possessed the kind of imagination which could convert a handful of prosaic facts into an arresting picture that Macaulay penned so vivid an account of the starvation of Londonderry ("There was scarcely a cellar in which some corpse was not decaying") and the entry of the rescuing army. It was by use of the imagination that Parkman made so real Wolfe's battle-array on the Plains of Abraham; and that capitulation of Vaudreuil at Montreal which he summed up in one unforgettable sentence—"Half the continent had changed hands at the scratch of a pen."

Human warmth and sympathy are

allied qualities which, belonging to the artist and not the scientific researcher, are indispensable to a faithful reconstruction of the past. The power of understanding character is primarily a literary gift; it has little to do with erudite grubbing (though that is not to be despised, but honored) in tons of manuscripts. Human sympathy is a gift which brings novelist, poet and historian near together. We need not wonder that Walter Scott and Victor Hugo wrote history, or that Parkman, Prescott, and Froude all wrote novels. Sympathy extends to places, to things and to atmosphere, but it is most valuable to the historian when used to penetrate human nature. Without a profound sympathy with the people of the North, Carl Sandburg could never have written his chapter on the Deep Shadows of early 1863 in the third volume of his *Abraham Lincoln: The War Years;* without sympathy, Douglas Freeman could never have written his chapter on The Sword of Lee.

For literary and artistic virtues have flowed back, full tide, into the best historical writing of this present gen-eration. Narrative history—a good story, racily told—has regained its old and proper ascendency over analytical discussion. The panoramic theme, as distinguished from the monograph, is no longer neglected. For a time a chasm seemed opening in America between the academic and non-academic writers of history; but now the best academic historians write with as much dash as their outside brethren, and the best non-academic historians with a scholarship unexcelled in ivied walls.

With imagination, with sympathy, and with stylistic eloquence, there has come into historical writing a deepened moral sense much needed in this troubled age. The greatest of all living historians has set on the title page of his greatest series of works, the motto: "In War, Resolution. In Defeat, Defiance. In Victory, Magnanimity. In Peace, Good Will." That furnishes readers of Mr. Churchill's noble chronicle something of what Thomas Carlyle called "the divine idea"; and not a little historical writing of the time is prevaded with the sense that human life has to be given moral dignity, or it is worth nothing.

C. V. Wedgwood

ART, TRUTH AND HISTORY

THE connexion between art and truth, that is, the apprehension of truth and its communication by means of art, is the central problem of every writer and of every creative artist. All writers are confronted with it, and take their own ways to solve it with greater or lesser success. [. . .]

While it is true that the greatest art is to conceal art, and few admire writers who allow the mechanism behind their achievement to become visible,

From *Truth and Opinion* by C. V. Wedgwood. Reprinted by permission of C. V. Wedgwood and Joyce Weiner Associates.

it is equally true that some appreciation of the technical skill of the artist deepens and enriches our pleasure. At the first impact of a beautiful poem or a great work of art we do not want to divert our minds by considering the ingenuity of vocabulary, the sensibility of hearing, the subtlety in the association of ideas which have brought together certain effects of sound, and stimulated certain trains of thought to create in us a spontaneous reaction of delight; so with a great picture we do not want consciously to notice at the first instant the deliberate touches by which the balance and harmony of line and colour have been produced; but—there is no doubt —that at a second and third examination these things enhance our pleasure, because by recognizing the details of craftsmanship we make ourselves at secondhand partners in the act of creation whose results we admire. Moreover, apart from this subtle self-flattery in which all critical readers secretly indulge, the education of the ear, the mind, the eye to detect and value the finer points does actually enhance the initial impact that a work of art has on us, because we are enabled to react more quickly and more fully to the writer's or the painter's intention.

[. . .] For the historian, the relationship of art to truth is a particularly exacting one; it may even seem rather a narrow one. What more is there to be said but that the historian has to tell the truth? At least that is ideally what he is supposed to do, and some would say that art does not come into it at all. But art *does* come into it, for within the limitations of our human condition, truth is not apprehensible without the help of art, since it cannot be communicated to another person without the help of art. To pass on any piece of information intelligibly requires a feat in the arrangement of words and ideas. Some have argued that art comes in at an earlier stage, before that of communication. Simply to apprehend a fact intelligently and intelligibly requires a degree of art. [. . .]

[. . .] The creative writer, the novelist who aims at giving us life as it is, faces the same problem as the historian—the problem of reading the meaning of an incident and conveying it to the reader. [. . .]

The historian has to do very much the same thing, with this difference: that the novelist is free to adapt and invent provided that the material is that of authentic and living experience. The historian, on the other hand, is dealing with events which once occurred independently of him and which he seeks to describe, or, if he is a pioneer, to re-establish accurately. But although everything about which the historian writes had at one time a separate existence in itself, it exists for him in the present only as he is able to re-think it. Thus the quality of our understanding of the past depends on the quality of understanding its interpreters have brought to it. [. . .]

The good historian whatever his theme must be an artist. Without art there may be accumulations of statements, there may be calendars or chronicles, but there is no history.

This then is what I want to emphasize about art and history: that any way of thinking about, or looking at, historical facts, which has any value at all must be an exercise of the imaginative and discriminating faculties; History in any intelligible form *is art*.

But if history is *art* in what way does the historian's attitude to art and truth differ from that of the essentially imaginative writers? The answer is, of course: very profoundly. It is the privilege and indeed the function of the creative artist to use—that is, to manipulate and to intensify the truth about life as he sees it. The bare truth is not enough in itself. [. . .]

The work of creative imagination is *controlled* by experience; it has to spring from knowledge and understanding of life, but the writer is free to use and reject what he wants, to present a heightened or simplified picture; he is not subservient to the facts he has accumulated or the observations he has made. They are his material to be freely used as his art directs, and he can invent or discard as it suits him.

The historian cannot do so. He can only use what he has before him. He cannot invent and—this may be even more difficult—he cannot reject except within very cautious limits. The novelist—and this goes for the historical novelist too—can reject those parts of the material which for one reason or another seem to add nothing to what he wishes to project. Indeed selection of essentials is an important part of his art. The historian can only select in a much more limited manner; naturally he *does* select and reject because everything cannot be included in an intelligible book. There must be some theme or theory, and there must be some parts of the historical material which are adjudged not relevant. But over-selection, over-simplification are major causes of misrepresentation in history, and the historian cannot ask with the novelist: does this fact add anything to the pattern of my novel as I see it? to the projection of this character or this situation as I intend it? He has to ask: does this fact add anything to my knowledge and understanding of this incident, of this situation, of this epoch? And he must be very sure indeed that it adds nothing before he decides to pass it over.

The historian has to decide whether an apparently irrelevant fact is truly irrelevant. He also has to find a place for the awkward fact which does not fit with the pattern of development or the scheme of events as he had at first seen it. This is often a strain on his patience and his conscience. He has to find a place for new evidence which will make sense with the existing evidence whether or not it fits in with his own theories. If his theory is destroyed by new evidence, he must abandon it and start again. It is never safe and it is usually impossible to insert new material into the texture of an older theory. The attempt to do so produces a result like that picture of the Gerbier family which was begun by Rubens during his visit to England in 1630. Gerbier was an engraver, a go-between in the traffic in works of art, who was under the patronage of Charles I. He had a handsome wife and family of pretty, plump children whom Rubens painted when he was staying in their house. But the lady was very fruitful, and had many more children later; so pieces were attached to the canvas at one side and additional little Gerbiers, not by Rubens, were introduced. The effect is very strange, not only because the picture has an extra foot or two that do not fit, but because the original fluid and beautifully placed composition by Rubens has been thrown out of balance.

New material, new evidence, additional historical facts are very like the little Gerbiers. They cannot just be added on. A new picture has to be painted, a new composition thought out, which will include all the children, or all the facts, in a newly thought-out relationship to each other. That is one reason why history is constantly being rewritten.

Biography

Biography is the history of an individual man or woman. Indeed, according to Emerson, "There is no history; only biography"—with which opinion Allan Nevins tends to agree: "History is certainly from one point of view a compound of innumerable biographies." Our task here is to discover in how many ways biography is *like* history as well as in what ways it *differs from* history. The critics that follow consider the nature, function, and problems of biography as a separate art.

But since biography and history *are* in many ways allied, the questions asked about biography are similar to those asked about history: What have truth and fact to do with biography? What about the biographer's interpretation of the "facts" before him? Is biography a literary art? How does biography differ from fiction? There are many kinds of biography, but these questions are pertinent to all of them.

Sir Harold Nicolson
THE PRACTICE OF BIOGRAPHY

THE *Oxford English Dictionary* defines Biography as 'the history of the lives of individual men, as a branch of literature'. This excellent definition contains within itself the three principles that any serious biographer should observe. A biography must be 'history', in the sense that it must be accurate and depict a person in relation to his times. It must describe an 'individual', with all the gradations of human character, and not merely present a type of virtue or of vice. And it must be composed as 'a branch of literature', in that it must be written in grammatical English and with an adequate feeling for style.

A biography combining all these three principles can be classed as a 'pure' biography: a biography that violates any one of these principles, or combines them in incorrect proportions, must be classed as an 'impure' biography. A pure biography is written with no purpose other than that of conveying to the reader an authentic portrait of the individual whose life is being narrated. A biography is rendered impure when some extraneous purpose intrudes to distort the accuracy of presentation. [. . .]

The original cause of all biography was the desire to commemorate the illustrious dead. A leader dies: his tribe or family feel that some strength has passed from them: they seek to perpetuate his magic by a monument. [. . .] This commemorative instinct is bad for pure biography, since it leads the commemorator to concentrate solely upon the strength and virtue of his hero and to omit all weakness or shadow. Endemic, and sometimes epidemic, is this passion for commemoration; it has infected biography throughout the centuries. [. . .]

A second extraneous purpose is the didactic purpose. People have always been tempted to take the lives of individual men as examples of virtue, or as cautionary tales indicative of the ill-effects of self-indulgence or ambition. [. . .] The desire to teach or preach, the desire to establish examples, the desire to illustrate some moral, theological, political, economic or social theory—all these irrelevant intentions infect biography with strong, and sometimes subtle, doses of impurity. [. . .]

[At the other extreme,] the satirical attitude of the biographer towards his subject may [. . .] easily degenerate into false history and false psychology. [. . .]

Irony is [. . .] a dangerous tincture and one that should be applied only with a sable brush; when daubed by vigorous arms it becomes wearisome and even offensive. It is not merely that the reader is irritated by a biographer who implies in chapter after chapter that he is himself more enlightened, sensitive, or sincere than the hero whom he is describing. It is also that biography, if taken seriously, is an exacting task and not one that can be carried through with a sneer. The drudgery of collecting and checking material, the mechanical labour of completing a long book, require an effort more continuous than can be sustained by glimpses of self-satisfaction. The biographer must be constantly fortified by a fundamental respect, or affection, for the person whom he is describing; if all that he experiences is superficial contempt, his work will turn to ashes and his energy wilt and fail. No writer can persist for five hundred pages in being funny at the expense of someone who is dead.

There are other poisons, other temptations, to which this difficult art is liable. Biography is always a collaboration between the author and his subject; always there must be the reflection of one temperament in the mirror of another. The biographer should thus be careful not to permit his own personality to intrude too markedly upon the personality that he is describing; he should be wary of assigning his own opinions, prejudices or affections to the man or woman whose life he writes; he should take special pains to deal fairly with views which he does not share, or interests that bore him; his egoism should be muzzled and kept on a chain. He should constantly remind himself that it is not an autobiography that he is composing, but the life of someone else [. . .]

A further temptation that may afflict the affable biographer is that of adding to his narrative the colours of fiction or romance. He may seek to convey reality by introducing imaginary conversations, or to brighten his pages by inserting really beautiful passages of scenic description:

As their little cavalcade breasted the hill and emerged from the grove of umbrella pines (*pineus pinea*) that crowned its summit, the fair city lay before them, basking all amethyst in the fading light. The Palazzo Pubblico had already melted into the pink and azure shadows of the Piazza del Campo, but the Torre del Mangia soared upwards, straight as a tulip against the sunset sky. Galeazzo turned to his venerable companion. 'Messir', he said . . .

Such passages fail to convince the attentive reader, who is aware that umbrella pines are but few at Siena and that the company at the moment were travelling west to east. The imagination, as well as the self-assertiveness, of the author must be held in check.

Such then are the instincts, poisons and temptations that render biography impure. An undue desire to commemorate, a too earnest endeavour to teach or preach, a tendency to portray types rather than individuals, the temptation to enhance self-esteem by indulging in irony, the inability to describe selflessly, and the urge to slide into fiction or to indulge in fine writing;—all these are the pests and parasites that gnaw the leaves of purity.

Marchette Chute

GETTING AT THE TRUTH

TRUTH is a very large word. In the sense that it means the reality about a human being it is probably impossible for a biographer to achieve. In the sense that it means a reasonable presentation of all the available facts it is more nearly possible, but even this limited goal is harder to reach than it appears to be. A biographer needs to be both humble and cautious when he remembers the nature of the material he is working with, for a historical fact is rather like the flamingo that Alice in Wonderland tried to use as a croquet mallet. As soon as she got its neck nicely straightened out and was ready to hit the ball, it would turn and look at her with a puzzled expression, and any biographer knows that what is called a "fact" has a way of doing the same.

Here is a small example. When I was writing my biography, *Ben Jonson of Westminster*, I wanted to give a paragraph or two to Sir Philip Sidney, who had a great influence on Jonson. No one thinks of Sidney without thinking of chivalry, and to underline the point I intended to use a story that Sir Fulke Greville told of him. Sidney died of gangrene, from a musket shot that shattered his thigh, and Greville says that Sidney failed to put on his leg armor while preparing for battle because the marshal of the camp was not wearing leg armor, and Sidney was unwilling to do anything that would give him a special advantage.

The story is so characteristic both of Sidney himself and of the misplaced high-mindedness of late Renaissance chilvalry that I wanted to use it, and since Sir Fulke Greville was one of Sidney's closest friends the information seemed to be reliable enough. But it is always well to check each piece of information as thoroughly as possible and so I consulted another account of Sidney written by a contemporary, this time a doctor who knew the family fairly well. The doctor, Thomas Moffet, mentioned the episode but he said that Sidney left off his leg armor because he was in a hurry.

"Getting at the Truth" by Marchette Chute from *Saturday Review*, September 19, 1953. Reprinted by permission of the author and publishers.

The information was beginning to twist in my hand and could no longer be trusted. So I consulted still another contemporary who had mentioned the episode, to see which of the two he agreed with. This was Sir John Smythe, a military expert who brought out his book a few years after Sidney's death. Sir John was an old-fashioned conservative who advocated the use of heavy armor even on horse-back, and he deplored the current craze for leaving off leg protection, "the imitating of which . . . cost that noble and worthy gentleman Sir Philip Sidney his life."

So here I was with three entirely different reasons why Sidney left off his leg armor, all advanced by careful writers who were contemporaries of his. The flamingo had a legitimate reason for looking around with a puzzled expression.

The only thing to do in a case like this is to examine the point of view of the three men who are supplying the conflicting evidence. Sir Fulke Greville was trying to prove a thesis: that his beloved friend had an extremely chivalric nature. Sir John Smythe also was trying to prove a thesis: that the advocates of light arming followed a theory that could lead to disaster. Only the doctor, Thomas Moffet, was not trying to prove a thesis. He was not using his own explanation to reinforce some point he wanted to make. He did not want anything except to set down on paper what he believed to be the facts; and since we do not have Sidney's own explanation of why he did not put on leg armor, the chances are that Dr. Moffet is the safest man to trust.

For Moffet was without desire. Nothing can so quickly blur and distort the facts as desire—the wish to use the facts for some purpose of your own—and nothing can so surely destroy the truth. As soon as the witness wants to prove something he is no longer impartial and his evidence is no longer to be trusted. [. . .]

It might seem that there was an easy way for a biographer to avoid the use of this kind of prejudiced testimony. All he has to do is to construct his biography from evidence that cannot be tampered with—from parish records, legal documents, bills, accounts, court records, and so on. Out of these solid gray blocks of impersonal evidence it should surely be possible to construct a road that will lead straight to the truth and that will never bend itself to the misleading curve of personal desire.

This might be so if the only problem involved were the reliability of the material. But there is another kind of desire that is much more subtle, much more pervasive, and much more dangerous than the occasional distortions of fact that contemporary writers may have permitted themselves to make; and this kind of desire can destroy the truth of a biography even if every individual fact in it is as solid and as uncompromising as rock. Even if the road is built of the best and most reliable materials it can still curve away from the truth because of this other desire that threatens it: the desire of the biographer himself.

A biographer is not a court record or a legal document. He is a human being, writing about another human being, and his own temperament, his own point of view, and his own frame of reference are unconsciously imposed upon the man he is writing about. Even if the biographer [. . .] wants to write nothing but the literal truth, he is still handicapped by the fact that there is no such thing as a completely objective human being. . . .

It might seem that the ideal biographical system, if it could be achieved, would be to go through the years of research without feeling any kind of emotion. The biographer would be a kind of fact-finding machine and then suddenly, after his years of research, a kind of total vision would fall upon him and he would transcribe it in his best and most persuasive English for a waiting public. But research is fortunately not done by machinery, nor are visions likely to descend in that helpful manner. They are the product not only of many facts but also of much thinking, and it is only when the biographer begins to get emotional in his thinking that he ought to beware.

It is easy enough to make good resolutions in advance, but a biographer cannot altogether control his sense of excitement when the climax of his years of research draws near and he begins to see the pieces fall into place. Almost without his volition, A, B, and D fit together and start to form a pattern, and it is almost impossible for the biographer not to start searching for C. Something turns up that looks remarkably like C, and with a little trimming of the edges and the ignoring of one very slight discrepancy it will fill the place allotted for C magnificently.

It is at this point that the biographer ought to take a deep breath and sit on his hands until he has had time to calm down. He has no real, fundamental reason to believe that his discovery is C, except for the fact that he wants it to be. He is like a man looking for a missing piece in a difficult jigsaw puzzle, who has found one so nearly the right shape that he cannot resist the desire to jam it into place.

If the biographer had refused to be tempted by his supposed discovery of C and had gone on with his research, he might have found not only the connecting, illuminating fact he needed but much more besides. He is not going to look for it now. Desire has blocked the way. And by so much his biography will fall short of what might have been the truth.

It would not be accurate to say that a biographer should be wholly lacking in desire. Curiosity is a form of desire. So is the final wish to get the material down on paper in a form that will be fair to the reader's interest and worthy of the subject. But a subconscious desire to push the facts around is one of the most dangerous things a biographer can encounter, and all the more dangerous because it is so difficult to know when he is encountering it.

The reason Alice had so much trouble with her flamingo is that the average flamingo does not wish to be used as a croquet mallet. It has other purposes in view. The same thing is true of a fact, which can be just as self-willed as a flamingo and has its own kind of stubborn integrity. To try to force a series of facts into a previously desired arrangement is a form of misuse to which no self-respecting fact will willingly submit itself. The best and only way to treat it is to leave it alone and be willing to follow where it leads, rather than to press your own wishes upon it.

To put the whole thing into a single sentence: you will never succeed in getting at the truth if you think you know, ahead of time, what the truth ought to be.

Jacques Barzun

TRUTH IN BIOGRAPHY [1]

THE first principle of biography, whether it deal with a musician or a military man, is obviously, "by their fruits shall ye know them." It is the principle Lincoln used to confound Grant's enemies: if drinking whisky wins victories, let all the generals be given a pint of Scotch. But Grant was not a drunkard who happened to win battles. He was a military genius who happened to drink. Similarly, all our victims of biography are not idlers and profligates who were great artists on the side. They were artists whose characters were marred by adventitious elements precisely like certain other people that we all know. Daily and hourly to commit the fallacy of accident is the first great cause of defective biographical tradition, and it is an evil that amounts to far more than a mere personal "injustice" to Berlioz, Coleridge, or anybody else. It warps history, degrades art, and makes complacent humbugs of us all when we ought to be modest seekers after truth and grateful beholders of the genius of mankind.

Often, no doubt, it is because we seek a certain kind of truth that we become biographical vandals. In our eagerness to find the "cause" of individual achievements we pounce upon the nearest clue that suggests physical or psychological factors at work. Nearly all the so-called psycho-analytic criticism of the present day is of that sort. It uses the words "neurotic," "hysterical," "psychopathic" in the naïve belief that they are explanations. Unfortunately, these words not only do not explain but they are generally used ignorantly. [. . .]

Does it follow that we must simply record what we can of a man's life, shaking our head over its mystery, and letting the facts speak for themselves? Would this be more "scientific" than the pseudo-science of biographical psycho-analysis? Not a bit of it. The facts obviously do not speak for themselves. They remain dumb and meaningless until they are organized and interpreted. We must remember Sherlock Holmes [. . .] Watson sees everything that Holmes sees, but only Holmes understands. This means using not only creative ability but standards of judgement. So much is commonly agreed. Dispute begins when the standards are enunciated and applied.

In theory, the standard for judging a man's work ought to be derived from his own expressed or implied intentions. We must not blame the explorer for his bad grammar, nor be scornful, as some affect to be, because Berlioz did not engage in politics. Even within a man's professed limits, biographers can err—witness those delusive "summaries" in which it is said that Walt Whitman had not Wordsworth's natural piety, Keats' word magic, Shelley's idealism, or Emerson's conciseness. Why not add W. S. Gilbert's rhyming tricks and Tennyson's income? In a critical "life" we want to know what a man had and

From "Truth in Biography: Berlioz" by Jacques Barzun from *The University Review*, Kansas City, Volume 5, Number 4, Summer 1939. Reprinted by permission of the author and publishers.

1. Professor Barzun in this essay is discussing his biography of the composer Hector Berlioz.

was, not the endless might-have-beens
that the finite creature entirely missed.
[. . .]

But the task still remains of judging a man apart from his work and
of describing his conduct fairly, in its
trivial as in its significant aspects. It is
here that the biographer is most
tempted and consequently most fal-
lible. It is so easy to bring together a
striking instance, a curious detail, a
ludicrous act, and call the resulting
still-life a portrait. Besides, the melodramatic instinct loves to see in the
lift of an eyebrow at a crucial moment the key to human character. All
this is pure quackery. We are bound
to judge conduct by the social standards we accept; hence we must be
aware of what they are and state them
openly. At the same time we must
recognize that events are many-
faceted and that we are in honor
bound to judge a man by the prevailing tendency of his acts, not by a
single incident that we happen to
think amusing or derogatory.

Even when we have done our utmost to see and speak justly, we
should still remember that to put a
fluid and dynamic thing like life between the covers of a book—or as
publishers' slang funereally has it,
"between boards"—alters every time-
and-space relationship. A paragraph
represents a decade, or a love affair of
six months' duration; it settles a question of loyalty or ingratitude on the
basis of three documents and a good
hunch. The reader rarely suspects that
any links are missing, or worse yet,
that the chain of reasoning starts from
one accepted social standard and ends
with another as, for example, in the
assumption often made in discussing
the relations of Berlioz and Liszt, that
the friends of music must necessarily
like the music of their friends. [. . .]

When we have learned a man's
words (noting by the way that whole

modern nations use "awful" [. . .] to
describe an uncomfortable draft of
air upon the neck) we must likewise
persuade ourselves that the more sensitive an artist is, the greater will
slight differences seem to him, and,
usually, the wider will his range of
perceptions be. To us, a sense of proportion may well be the ability to see
things in an average, normal, institutional way; but we go to the man of
genius presumably because his sense of
proportion enables him to feel and
convey differently from us such differences as he alone perceives. At
times, indeed, he may liken the ocean
to a drop of water; but that is again
for the purpose of making us forget
our utilitarian scale and making us
adopt another, whose utility serves a
neglected part of our nature.

Rising from these particulars to our
final conclusion, we must assert what
no one questions in theory and everybody violates in practice, namely that
the complexity of life, taken both
quantitatively and qualitatively, is
greater than our documentary, chronological, and critical schemes allow
for. The clues and witnesses are, to
begin with, very numerous, taken as
brute facts by themselves. But they
are, even so, a vast oversimplification
of the past. There are available for
Berlioz's mature life an average of one
document a week. But huge as this
harvest of clues may seem, it is not
enough. The Ariadne's thread is missing. It is found in no letter, no archive,
no encyclopedia. It must be spun from
one's inner consciousness, at great risk
of error and on guard against cock-
sure superiority. Hence the need for
a priori sympathy, in the exact meaning of that term: *feeling with*.

"Feeling against" is sure falsification, for life is lived by everyone on
the assumption that it has meaning,
that he who lives it is a rational being,
honest, worthy, and human. The

genius has the added awareness of special gifts, and if he mentions them we must not take for boasting that which, if he concealed it, would convict him of hypocrisy. To put oneself in another's place is difficult; all the more so when the other man is one who visibly does not think and act like the grocer's boy around the corner. This is of course the pragmatic justification for not applying to genius the standards of morals, intelligence, and "normality" that would fit the grocer's boy. A multiple standard implies no weak snobbery, whereas the single standard surely betrays rigidity of mind and the urge to cavil masquerading as the critical spirit.

Thoreau: Four Critical Comments

In Part Two we have studied a number of critical statements about the chief types of literature (other than poetry and drama): the short story, the novel, the essay, and history and biography. In addition, we have examined a number of detailed analyses of the fiction (and the authors of that fiction) found in Part One. In our critical comments on nonfiction, however, we have not attempted to present comparable detailed analyses: by now your own critical tools should be sharp enough to enable you to dissect the nonfiction selections yourself. Still, one example of close critical analysis of nonfiction would not at this point be amiss; we have for this purpose chosen Thoreau and "Where I Lived, and What I Lived For." The selections that follow treat the man, the writer, and his works, especially his greatest work, *Walden*. Remember, also, E. B. White's tribute to Thoreau and *Walden* in Part One.

Ralph Waldo Emerson

THOREAU

HENRY DAVID THOREAU was the last male descendant of a French ancestor who came to this country from the Isle of Guernsey. His character exhibited occasional traits drawn from this blood, in singular combination with a very strong Saxon genius.

He was born in Concord, Massachusetts, on the 12th of July, 1817. He was graduated at Harvard College in 1837, but without any literary distinction. An iconoclast in literature, he seldom thanked colleges for their service to him, holding them in small esteem, whilst yet his debt to them was important. After leaving the University, he joined his brother in teaching a private school, which he soon renounced. His father was a manufacturer of lead-pencils, and Henry applied himself for a time to this craft, believing he could make a better pencil than was then in use. After completing his experiments, he exhibited his work to chemists and artists in Boston, and having obtained their certificates to its excellence and to its equality with the best London manufacture, he returned home contented. His friends congratulated him that he had now opened his way to fortune. But he replied, that he should never make another pencil. "Why should I? I would not do again what I have done once." He resumed his endless walks and miscellaneous studies, making every day some new acquaintance with Nature, though as yet never speaking of zoölogy or botany, since, though very studious of natural facts, he was incurious of technical and textual science.

At this time, a strong, healthy youth, fresh from college, whilst all his companions were choosing their profession, or eager to begin some lucrative employment, it was inevitable that his thoughts should be exercised on the same question, and it required rare decision to refuse all the accustomed paths and keep his solitary freedom at the cost of disappointing the natural expectations of his family and friends: all the more difficult that he had a perfect probity, was exact in securing his own independence, and in holding every man to the like duty. But Thoreau never faltered. He was a born protestant. He declined to give up his large ambition of knowledge and action for any narrow craft or profession, aiming at a much more comprehensive calling, the art of living well. If he slighted and defined the opinions of others, it was only that he was more intent to reconcile his practice with his own belief. Never idle or self-indulgent, he preferred, when he wanted money, earning it by some piece of manual labor agreeable to him, as building a boat or a fence, planting, grafting, surveying, or other short work, to any long engagements. With his hardy habits and few wants, his skill in wood-craft, and his powerful arithmetic, he was very competent to live in any part of the world. It would cost him less time to supply his wants than another. He was therefore secure of his leisure.

A natural skill [. . .] made him drift into the profession of land-surveyor. It had the advantage for him that it led him continually into new and secluded grounds, and helped his studies of Nature. His accuracy and skill in this work were readily appreciated, and he found all the employment he wanted.

He could easily solve the problems of the surveyor, but he was daily beset with graver questions, which he manfully confronted. He interrogated every custom, and wished to settle all his practice on an ideal foundation. He was a protestant *à l'outrance*, and few lives contain so many renunciations. He was bred to no profession; he never married; he lived alone; he never went to church; he never voted; he refused to pay a tax to the State; he ate no flesh, he drank no wine, he never knew the use of tobacco; and, though a naturalist, he used neither trap nor gun. He chose, wisely, no doubt, for himself, to be the bachelor of thought and Nature. He had no talent for wealth, and knew how to be poor without the least hint of squalor or inelegance. Perhaps he fell into his way of living without forecasting it much, but approved it with later wisdom. "I am often reminded," he wrote in his journal, "that, if I had bestowed on me the wealth of Crœsus, my aims must be still the same, and my means essentially the same." He had no temptations to fight against, —no appetites, no passions, no taste for elegant trifles. A fine house, dress, the manners and talk of highly cultivated people were all thrown away on him. He much preferred a good Indian, and considered these refinements as impediments to conversation, wishing to meet his companion on the simplest terms. He declined invitations to dinner-parties, because there each was in everyone's way, and he could not meet the individuals to any purpose. "They make their pride," he said, "in making their dinner cost much; I make my pride in making my dinner cost little." When asked at table what dish he preferred, he answered, "The nearest." He did not like the taste of wine, and never had a vice in his life. He said,—"I have a faint recollection of pleasure derived from smoking dried lily-stems, before I was a man. I had commonly a supply of these. I have never smoked anything more noxious."

He chose to be rich by making his wants few, and supplying them himself. In his travels, he used the railroad only to get over so much country as was unimportant to the present purpose, walking hundreds of miles, avoiding taverns, buying a lodging in farmers' and fishermen's houses, as cheaper, and more agreeable to him, and because there he could better find the men and the information he wanted.

There was somewhat military in his nature, not to be subdued, always manly and able, but rarely tender, as if he did not feel himself except in opposition. He wanted a fallacy to expose, a blunder to pillory, I may say required a little sense of victory, a roll of the drum, to call his powers into full exercise. It cost him nothing

to say No; indeed, he found it much easier than to say Yes. It seemed as if his first instinct on hearing a proposition was to controvert it, so impatient was he of the limitations of our daily thought. This habit, of course, is a little chilling to the social affections; and though the companion would in the end acquit him of any malice or untruth, yet it mars conversation. Hence, no equal companion stood in affectionate relations with one so pure and guileless. "I love Henry," said one of his friends, "but I cannot like him; and as for taking his arm, I should as soon think of taking the arm of an elm-tree."

Yet, hermit and stoic as he was, he was really fond of sympathy, and threw himself heartily and childlike into the company of young people whom he loved, and whom he delighted to entertain, as he only could, with the varied and endless anecdotes of his experiences by field and river. And he was always ready to lead a huckleberry-party or a search for chestnuts or grapes. Talking, one day, of a public discourse, Henry remarked, that whatever succeeded with the audience was bad. I said, "Who would not like to write something which all can read, like *Robinson Crusoe?* and who does not see with regret that his page is not solid with a right materialistic treatment, which delights everybody?" Henry objected, of course, and vaunted the better lectures which reached only a few persons. But, at supper, a young girl, understanding that he was to lecture at the Lyceum, sharply asked him, "whether his lecture would be a nice, interesting story, such as she wished to hear, or whether it was one of those old philosophical things that she did not care about." Henry turned to her, and bethought himself, and, I saw, was trying to believe that he had matter that might fit her and her brother, who were to sit up and go to the lecture, if it was a good one for them.

He was a speaker and actor of the truth,—born such,—and was ever running into dramatic situations from this cause. In any circumstance, it interested all bystanders to know what part Henry would take, and what he would say; and he did not disappoint expectation, but used an original judgment on each emergency. In 1845 he built himself a small framed house on the shores of Walden Pond, and lived there two years alone, a life of labor and study. This action was quite native and fit for him. No one who knew him would tax him with affectation. He was more unlike his neighbors in his thought than in his action. As soon as he had exhausted the advantages of that solitude, he abandoned it. In 1847, not approving some uses to which the public expenditure was applied, he refused to pay his town tax, and was put in jail. A friend paid the tax for him, and he was released. The like annoyance was threatened the next year. But, as his friends paid the tax, notwithstanding his protest, I believe he ceased to resist. No opposition or ridicule had any weight with him. He coldly and fully stated his opinion of the company. It was of no consequence, if everyone present held the opposite opinion. On one occasion he went to the University Library to procure some books. The librarian refused to lend them. Mr. Thoreau repaired to the President who stated to him the rules and usages, which permitted the loan of books to resident graduates, to clergymen who were alumni, and to some others resident within a circle of ten miles' radius from the College. Mr. Thoreau explained to the President that the railroad had destroyed the old scale of distances,—that the library was useless, yes, and President and College

useless, on the terms of his rules,—that the one benefit he owed to the College was its library,—that, at this moment, not only his want of books was imperative, but he wanted a large number of books, and assured him that he, Thoreau, and not the librarian, was the proper custodian of these. In short, the President found the petitioner so formidable, and the rules getting to look so ridiculous, that he ended by giving him a privilege which in his hands proved unlimited thereafter. [. . .]

It was said of Plotinus that he was ashamed of his body, and 'tis very likely he had good reason for it,—that his body was a bad servant, and he had not skill in dealing with the material world, as happens often to men of abstract intellect. But Mr. Thoreau was equipped with a most adapted and serviceable body. He was of short stature, firmly built, of light complexion, with strong, serious blue eyes, and a grave aspect,—his face covered in the late years with a becoming beard. His senses were acute, his frame well-knit and hardy, his hands strong and skillful in the use of tools. And there was a wonderful fitness of body and mind. He could pace sixteen rods more accurately than another man could measure them with rod and chain. He could find his path in the woods at night, he said, better by his feet than his eyes. He could estimate the weight of a calf or a pig, like a dealer. From a box containing a bushel or more of loose pencils, he could take up with his hands fast enough just a dozen pencils at every grasp. He was a good swimmer, runner, skater, boatman, and would probably outwalk most countrymen in a day's journey. And the relation of body to mind was still finer than we have indicated. He said he wanted every stride his legs made. The length of his walk uniformly made the length of his writing.

If shut up in the house, he did not write at all. [. . .]

Mr. Thoreau dedicated his genius with such entire love to the fields, hills, and waters of his native town, that he made them known and interesting to all reading Americans, and to people over the sea. The river on whose banks he was born and died he knew from its springs to its confluence with the Merrimack. He had made summer and winter observations on it for many years, and at every hour of the day and night. The result of the recent survey of the Water Commissioners appointed by the State of Massachusetts he had reached by his private experiments, several years earlier. Every fact which occurs in the bed, on the banks, or in the air over it; the fishes, and their spawning and nests, their manners, their food; the shad-flies which fill the air on a certain evening once a year, and which are snapped at by the fishes so ravenously that many of these die of repletion; the conical heaps of small stones on the river-shallows, one of which heaps will sometimes overfill a cart—these heaps the huge nests of small fishes; the birds which frequent the stream, heron, duck, sheldrake, loon, osprey; the snake, muskrat, otter, woodchuck, and fox, on the banks; the turtle, frog, hyla, and cricket, which make the banks vocal,—were all known to him, and, as it were, townsmen and fellow-creatures; so that he felt an absurdity or violence in any narrative of one of these by itself apart, and still more of its dimensions on an inch-rule, or in the exhibition of its skeleton, or the specimen of a squirrel or a bird in brandy. He liked to speak of the manners of the river, as itself a lawful creature, yet with exactness, and always to an observed fact. As he knew the river, so the ponds of this region. [. . .]

It was a pleasure and a privilege to walk with him. He knew the country like a fox or a bird, and passed through it as freely by paths of his own. He knew every track in the snow or on the ground, and what creature had taken this path before him. One must submit abjectly to such a guide, and the reward was great. Under his arm he carried an old music-book to press plants; in his pocket, his diary and pencil, a spy-glass for birds, microscope, jack-knife, and twine. He wore a straw hat, stout shoes, strong gray trousers, to brave shrub-oaks and smilax, and to climb a tree for a hawk's or a squirrel's nest. He waded into the pool for the water-plants, and his strong legs were no insignificant part of his armor. On the day I speak of he looked for the Menyanthes, detected it across the wide pool, and, on examination of the florets, decided that it had been in flower five days. He drew out of his breast-pocket his diary, and read the names of all the plants that should bloom on this day, whereof he kept account as a banker when his notes fall due. The Cypripedium not due till to-morrow. He thought, that, if waked up from a trance, in this swamp, he could tell by the plants what time of the year it was within two days. The redstart was flying about, and presently the fine grosbeaks, whose brilliant scarlet makes the rash gazer wipe his eye, and whose fine clear note Thoreau compared to that of a tanager which has got rid of its hoarseness. Presently he heard a note which he called that of the night-warbler, a bird he had never identified, had been in search of twelve years, which always, when he saw it, was in the act of diving down into a tree or bush, and which it was vain to seek; the only bird which sings indifferently by night and by day. I told him he must beware of finding and booking it, lest life should have nothing more to show him. He said, "What you seek in vain for, half your life, one day you come full upon, all the family at dinner. You seek it like a dream, and as soon as you find it you become its prey." [. . .]

Thoreau was sincerity itself, and might fortify the convictions of prophets in the ethical laws by his holy living. It was an affirmative experience which refused to be set aside. A truth-speaker he, capable of the most deep and strict conversation; a physician to the wounds of any soul; a friend, knowing not only the secret of friendship, but almost worshiped by those few persons who resorted to him as their confessor and prophet, and knew the deep value of his mind and great heart. He thought that without religion or devotion of some kind nothing great was ever accomplished: and he thought that the bigoted sectarian had better bear this in mind.

His virtues, of course, sometimes ran into extremes. It was easy to trace to the inexorable demand on all for exact truth that austerity which made this willing hermit more solitary even than he wished. Himself of a perfect probity, he required not less of others. He had a disgust at crime, and no worldly success would cover it. He detected paltering as readily in dignified and prosperous persons as in beggars, and with equal scorn. Such dangerous frankness was in his dealing that his admirers called him "that terrible Thoreau," as if he spoke when silent, and was still present when he had departed. I think the severity of his ideal interfered to deprive him of a healthy sufficiency of human society.

The habit of a realist to find things the reverse of their appearance inclined him to put every statement in a paradox. A certain habit of antagonism defaced his earlier writings,— a trick of rhetoric not quite outgrown in his later, of substituting for the obvious word and thought its diametrical opposite. He praised wild mountains and winter forests for their domestic air, in snow and ice he would find sultriness, and commended the wilderness for resembling Rome and Paris. "It was so dry, that you might call it wet."

The tendency to magnify the moment, to read all the laws of Nature in the one object or one combination under your eye, is of course comic to those who do not share the philosopher's perception of identity. To him there was no such thing as size. The pond was a small ocean; the Atlantic, a large Walden Pond. He referred every minute fact to cosmical laws. Though he meant to be just, he seemed haunted by a certain chronic assumption that the science of the day pretended completeness, and he had just found out that the *savans* had neglected to discriminate a particular botanical variety, had failed to describe the seeds or count the sepals. "That is to say," we replied, "the blockheads were not born in Concord; but who said they were? It was their unspeakable misfortune to be born in London, or Paris, or Rome; but, poor fellows, they did what they could, considering that they never saw Bateman's Pond, or Nine-Acre Corner, or Becky Stow's Swamp; besides, what were you sent into the world for, but to add this observation?" [. . .]

There is a flower known to botanists, one of the same genus with our summer plant called "Life-Everlasting," a *Gnaphalium* like that, which grows on the most inaccessible cliffs of the Tyrolese mountains, where the chamois dare hardly venture, and which the hunter, tempted by its beauty, and by his love (for it is immensely valued by the Swiss maidens), climbs the cliffs to gather, and is sometimes found dead at the foot, with the flower in his hand. It is called by botanists the *Gnaphalium leontopodium*, but by the Swiss *Edelweiss*, which signifies *Noble Purity*. Thoreau seemed to me living in the hope to gather this plant, which belonged to him of right. The scale on which his studies proceeded was so large as to require longevity, and we were the less prepared for his sudden disappearance. The country knows not yet, or in the least part, how great a son it has lost. It seems an injury that he should leave in the midst his broken task, which none else can finish,—a kind of indignity to so noble a soul that he should depart out of Nature before yet he has been really shown to his peers for what he is. But he, at least, is content. His soul was made for the noblest society; he had in a short life exhausted the capabilities of this world; wherever there is knowledge, wherever there is virtue, wherever there is beauty, he will find a home.

James Russell Lowell

AN EVALUATION OF THOREAU

WE HAVE just been renewing our recollection of Mr. Thoreau's writings, and have read through his six volumes in the order of their production. We shall try to give an adequate report of their impression upon us both as critic and as mere reader. He seems to us to have been a man with so high a conceit of himself that he accepted without questioning, and insisted on our accepting, his defects and weaknesses of character as virtues and powers peculiar to himself. Was he indolent, he finds none of the activities which attract or employ the rest of mankind worthy of him. Was he wanting in the qualities that make success, it is success that is contemptible, and not himself that lacks persistency and purpose. Was he poor, money was an unmixed evil. Did his life seem a selfish one, he condemns doing good as one of the weakest of superstitions. To be of use was with him the most killing bait of the wily tempter Uselessness. He had no faculty of generalization from outside of himself, or at least no experience which would supply the material of such, and he makes his own whim the law, his own range the horizon of the universe. He condemns a world, the hollowness of whose satisfactions he had never had the means of testing. [. . .] He had no artistic power such as controls a great work to the serene balance of completeness, but exquisite mechanical skill in the shaping of sentences and paragraphs, or (more rarely) short bits of verse for the expression of a detached thought, sentiment, or image. His works give one the feeling of a sky full of stars,—something impressive and exhilarating certainly, something high overhead and freckled thickly with spots of isolated brightness; but whether these have any mutual relation with each other, or have any concern with our mundane matters, is for the most part matter of conjecture, astrology as yet, and not astronomy.

It is curious, considering what Thoreau afterwards became, that he was not by nature an observer. He only saw the things he looked for, and was less poet than naturalist. Till he built his Walden shanty, he did not know that the hickory grew in Concord. Till he went to Maine, he had never seen phosphorescent wood, a phenomenon early familiar to most country boys. At forty he speaks of the seeding of the pine as a new discovery, though one should have thought that its golddust of blowing pollen might have earlier drawn his eye. Neither his attention nor his genius was of the spontaneous kind. He discovered nothing. He thought everything a discovery of his own, from moonlight to the planting of acorns and nuts by squirrels. This is a defect in his character, but one of his chief charms as a writer. Everything grows fresh under his hand. He delved in his mind and nature; he planted them with all manner of native and foreign seeds, and reaped assiduously. He was not merely solitary, he would be isolated, and succeeded at last in almost persuading himself that he was autochthonous. He valued everything in proportion as he fancied it to be exclusively his own. He complains in *Walden* that there is no one in Concord with whom he could talk of Oriental literature, though the man was living within two miles of his hut who had introduced him to it. This intellectual selfishness becomes sometimes almost painful in reading him. [. . .] Thoreau seems to have prized a lofty way of thinking (often we should be inclined to call it a remote one) not so much because it was good in itself as because he wished few to share it with him. It seems now and then as if he did not seek to lure others up "above our lower region of turmoil," but to leave his own name cut on the mountain peak as the first climber. This itch of originality infects his thought and style. To be misty is not to be mystic. He turns commonplaces end for end, and fancies it makes something new of them. As we walk down Park Street, our eye is caught by Dr. Windship's dumb-bells, one of which bears an inscription testifying that it is the heaviest ever put up at arm's length by any athlete; and in reading Mr. Thoreau's books we cannot help feeling as if he sometimes invited our attention to a particular sophism or paradox as the biggest yet maintained by any single writer. He seeks, at all risks, for perversity of thought [. . .] "A day," he says, "passed in the society of those Greek sages, such as described in the Banquet of Xenophon, would not be comparable with the dry wit of decayed cranberry-vines and the fresh Attic salt of the moss-beds." It is not so much the True that he loves as the Out-of-the-Way. As the Brazen Age shows itself in other men by exaggeration of phrase, so in him by extravagance of statement. He wishes always to trump your suit and to *ruff* when you least expect it. Do you love Nature because she is beautiful? He will find a better argument in her ugliness. Are you tired of the artificial man? He instantly dresses you up an ideal in a Penobscot Indian, and attributes to this creature of his otherwise-mindedness as peculiarities things that are common to all woodsmen, white or red, and this simply because he has not studied the pale-faced variety.

This notion of an absolute originality, as if one could have a patent-right in it, is an absurdity. A man cannot escape in thought, any more than he can in language, from the past and the present. As no one ever invents a word, and yet language somehow grows by general contribution and necessity, so it is with thought. Mr. Thoreau seems to us to insist in public on going back to flint and steel, when there is a matchbox in his pocket which he knows very well how to use at a pinch. Originality consists in power of digesting and assimilating thought, so that they become part of our life and substance. Montaigne, for example, is one of the most original of authors, though he helped himself to ideas in every direction. But they turn to blood and coloring in his style, and give a freshness of complexion that is forever charming. In Thoreau much seems yet to be foreign and unassimilated, showing itself in symptoms of indigestion. A preacher up of Nature, we now and then detect under the surly and stoic garb something of the sophist and the sentimentalizer. We are far from implying that this was conscious on his part. But it is much easier for a man to impose on himself when he measures only with himself. A greater familiarity with ordinary men would have done Thoreau good, by showing him how many fine qualities are common to the race. The radical vice of his theory of life was, that he confounded physical with spiritual remoteness from men. One is far enough withdrawn from his fellows if he keep himself clear of their weaknesses. He is not so truly withdrawn as exiled, if he refuse to share in their strength. It is a morbid self-consciousness that pronounces the world of men empty and worthless before trying it, the instinctive evasion of one who is sensible of some innate weakness, and retorts the accusation of it before any has made it but himself. To a healthy mind, the world is a constant challenge of opportunity.

Mr. Thoreau had not a healthy mind, or he would not have been so fond of prescribing. His whole life was a search for the doctor. [. . .]

Thoreau had no humor, and this implies that he was a sorry logician. Himself an artist in rhetoric, he confounds thought with style when he undertakes to speak of the latter. He was forever talking of getting away from the world, but he must be always near enough to it, nay, to the Concord corner of it, to feel the impression he makes there. [. . .] The dignity of man is an excellent thing, but therefore to hold one's self too sacred and precious is the reverse of excellent. There is something delightfully absurd in six volumes addressed to a world of such "vulgar fellows" as Thoreau affirmed his fellow-men to be. We once had a glimpse of a genuine solitary who spent his winters one hundred and fifty miles beyond all human communication, and there dwelt with his rifle as his only confidant. Compared with this, the shanty on Walden Pond has something the air, it must be confessed, of the Hermitage of La Chevrette.[1] [. . .] The natural man, like the singing birds, comes out of the forest as inevitably as the natural bear and the wildcat stick there. To seek to be natural implies a consciousness that forbids all naturalness forever. It is as easy—and no easier—to be natural in a *salon* as in a swamp, if one do not aim at it, for what we call unnaturalness always has its spring in a man's thinking too much about himself. "It is impossible," said Turgot, "for a vulgar man to be simple."

1. **Hermitage of La Chevrette**: a cottage built by Mme d'Epinay near her chateau of La Chevrette (in the valley of Montmorency, France) for the renowned French philosopher and writer, Jean Jacques Rousseau (1712–1778). The cottage was named the Hermitage.

Reginald Cook

INTERPRETATIONS OF THOREAU

Such a startling array of contradictory interpretations of Henry Thoreau has appeared that we inquire, even as Edwin Arlington Robinson inquired of the man Flammonde, "What was he, and what was he not?" He has been represented as a recluse—cold, humorless, inhuman; as a skulker; as a stoic; as a sentimentalist; as an Emersonian odd-jobber. To some he has appeared a frail, freakish, thin-blooded intellectual, gnarled as an oak, characteristically a New England Yankee in that he was a bundle of inhibitions. It is asserted that his life was a denial of life itself; that his soul-searching was merely a manifestation of latter-day Puritanism; that his skepticism and conscientiousness were negative rather than positive.

The representation of Thoreau as the devotee of a consecrated life has been the most persistent interpretation, and it cannot easily be ignored. Because he kept journals so assiduously over a period of twenty-five years, he has become for some the symbol of the New England sense of duty. True, he was sedulous in what he was doing, but the symbol does not reach deep enough. Why did he perform this duty?—not, what does he resemble?—is the real question to answer. Others have ascribed to Puritanism his sense of duty and his exaltation of principle. That he was partly a stoic, partly a mystic, who can deny? but the emphasis must be placed on partly. That he was a cold, humorless, inhuman hermit his relationship to his fellow men readily disproves. That his paradoxes are often irritating, and that his theorizing and assertions are sometimes impracticable is only too true. Many persons who otherwise might be predisposed to enjoy him are either annoyed or left simply cold by these qualities.

Thoreau's way of life and a careful reading of *Walden* attest that he did not skulk from the obligations of this world. His short life has a proportion which some critics either myopically miss or indifferently ignore. The classical humanist contends that Thoreau's actions represent a denial of life. But wasn't he an in-worldly man, not a worldly one? He turned to nature, which is not to abandon the world but only to prefer one aspect of experience to another—the natural for the factitious. That he turned inward and that he was self-absorbed are both apparent. He was introvertive. Unless introversion becomes anti-social, it is not to be deprecated. Extraversion, a counter-characteristic of the human personality, is also to be deprecated when it is socially aggressive.

His ascetic inclinations—his rice and water—represent to many a narrowing rather than an expanding standard of living. Beside Walt Whitman's exaggerated expansiveness—life "immense in passion, pulse, and power"—Thoreau's contracted diet appears thin-blooded, notional, faddish. Yet the effect his tonic and sanguine gospel has upon us is hardly contracting.

One may also feel about Thoreau, as Henry James did, that his genius was "a slim and crooked one," and that he was "imperfect, unfinished, in-

From the "Prefatory" to *Passage to Walden* by Reginald Cook. Reprinted by permission of Houghton Mifflin Company.

artistic," and "parochial." Or, one may regard him, as Hawthorne did, as a man in whose presence one felt ashamed of having any money or two coats to wear or a house to live in, since his own mode of life was "so unsparing a criticism on all other modes, such as the world approves." Some critics see only the twist in the fibre, the knot in the grain; others feel only the implied criticism of their private way of life. We acknowledge the crooked bent of his genius, but as for its slimness, who shall say? Perhaps in the sense that idealists rarely realize their ideals, and consequently fail to consummate perfection, he is "imperfect." But by what token is he "inartistic"? As for parochialism, he was aware of the problem. In a letter to Emerson, Thoreau wrote, "Concord's little arch does not span all our fate, nor is what transpires under it law for the universe." If Thoreau's experience appears circumscribed in horizon, nevertheless it is deep and strong. He did not range far and wide, but near and close. If he did not carry kingdoms in the shelter of his eye, he had at least pierced the surface to elemental essences, had glimpsed the world in a grain of Cochituate sand, heaven in a spiked orchis, held infinity in the cupped palm

of his muscular hands, and experienced eternity in an hour by his Walden doorstoop.

If, like the hunting hawk, he worked close to field and hedge, still he nested within hum of human voices. His "Indian life," as Hawthorne described it, was not lived in tepee, and its physical necessity—food —secured with bow and arrow. As a stream-follower and field-tramper, he was nature's eye-witness, and by his apprehension of the dramatic life within natural phenomena he excites our interest and shows us how the fields and woods and streams are also necessary sources of culture, which supplement schools, libraries, museums, churches, laboratories, concert halls, newspapers, and the political institutions of democracy. [. . .]

Thoreau is as near the Emersonian concept of Man Thinking as any writer of his or our time. The whole man stands back of the effort. What he sought was wholly sought. What he realized was wholly realized. When he says injunctively, "We must *live* all our *life*," he is reporting the singleness of purpose in his own effort. Because his writings embody acts of life, one must first see and feel what he lived in order to share his experience.

Henry Seidel Canby

THOREAU'S *WALDEN*

THE dominant idea of *Walden*, which is simple, has been abundantly misunderstood. Thoreau's problem is the poor student's (or artist's or scientist's) who wishes to study, investigate, create, in a society which

From *Thoreau* by Henry Seidel Canby. Reprinted by permission of Houghton Mifflin Company.

will not pay him enough for the proceeds of his labor, and is not interested in his brand of happiness. His solution is self-reliance, simplification of living, willingness to labor with the hands if necessary, resignation of everything not essential to his particular temperament, and a shrewd study of how he can provide for his sustenance with the least waste of time. Thoreau's own estimate of time needed was a month to six weeks out of a year.

This solution is worthless, however, unless it brings with it an expansion of every taste, interest, vocation, and avocation which is possible to the experimenter, wished for by him, and practicable in a life of disciplined simplicity. *Walden* calls for more life, not less. Nor is Thoreau's particular solution prescribed, like a reformer's panacea, to everyone, but only to the discontented who live lives of quiet desperation. "Strong and valiant natures, who . . . spend more lavishly than the richest, without ever impoverishing themselves . . . those who are well employed," can take care of themselves. He writes for that "most terribly impoverished class of all, who have accumulated dross, but know not how to use it," and "the mass of men who are discontented, and idly complaining of . . . their lot or of the times, when they might improve them." "I desire that there may be as many different persons in the world as possible; but I would have each one be very careful to find out and pursue *his own* way, and not his father's or his mother's or his neighbor's instead." The book is the story of how he, a poor scholar, and discontented, found *his way*, and how he enjoyed it. [. . .]

Walden was an artful tract, in the exact sense of that adjective. A true story is always the best argument, and this book was an autobiography. From the account of the hut and the bean field, with their statistics of cost and profit down to the last half cent, through the frank explanations of why he went to Walden and what he learned there, the outline of this book is straightforward narrative throughout. Nor does its story suffer in point because of the chapters about the friends who came to talk with him, or his neighbors in the woods, or the lake in its moods, or the books that he read, or the thoughts that he pondered through long winter evenings and in sunny musings. For these were all parts of his biography, and described the nature of the man who wrote, and the nature of his profitable happiness at Walden. These gave his escape from society and its pressure a meaning that could be estimated by the reader; made him feel that a man and not a theory wrote the book.

Yet much of the art of *Walden* inheres in its style. Thoreau's style in this book is most consistently at its best. Still rhetorical in the fashion of the early nineteenth century, [. . .] it is nevertheless able to recount in the tersest and most vigorous of American prose the simplest facts of daily experience, making them real, vivid, and significant. Yet it is able also to rise with the life of his imagination to magnificent poetic paragraphs. Or it can be epigrammatic, or humorous, or tender, or hard.

And thanks to his style, there is the unmistakable presence on every page of *Walden* of a personality, a man like a rock in his immovable principles, like an oak in his toughness, like a wild flower in his sensitiveness, like a woodchuck in his persistence, like a hawk in his flights. It is not always possible [. . .] to like Thoreau, but you can never escape from his personality, nor from admiring and respecting it. His egocentricity was justified, at least in literature, for it pervades this book as no lesser ego could have done. There is never a page which is not Thoreau's and no other's.

Walden is assuredly one of the great modern books, which is not to say that it is perfect. In spite of its doctrine of simplicity, the writing itself is never entirely simple. Its tone is of a satirically humorous detachment which is definitely literary and sometimes consciously rhetorical. This was a good level from which to descend into straightforward description or to rise into eloquence; yet it is an attitude, sometimes almost a pose, never for long allowed to relax. It is the attitude, pose if you please, which had become, and which was until our times the convention of the personal essay in the English tradition from the Augustans downwards. Nothing in such an essay can be said without due consideration of the effect upon the reader who is conscious all the time that he is reading, not mere statements, but literature. [. . .] There is a strain to write well in this book, which the modern reader, conditioned by journalism to familiar speaking, is sure to feel, though his own taste may prove to be more to blame than Thoreau. Like carefully prepared food, this style needs a slow and zestful consumption. Some modern readers also find too much detail, and particularly too much description in *Walden*. I did once, but on every re-reading my criticism diminishes. Thoreau would not be Thoreau without the details of his insatiable observing. [. . .] Thoreau went to Walden in pursuit of that eternal desire of ambitious youth, "to live deep and suck out all the marrow of life"—beans, hut, and simplifying were all a means to an end, a technique of experiment. He went on the trail of that sense of spiritual reality which all the Transcendentalists believed was a priceless possession of youth, and which had certainly been his posession. He hoped to reawaken his inner life, recover his lost "intimations of immortality," and he succeeded, as the book tells. Reality itself, whatever that was, he never found, but spent the rest of his life in the study of its tracks and trails in visible nature.

NOTES ON THE AUTHORS

GILBERT KEITH CHESTERTON (1874–1936), English poet, novelist, critic, and journalist, is best known as that rare phenomenon in the twentieth century, a true essayist. Moreover, he was an essayist who was extraordinarily skillful in combining charm of style, humor, and meaningfulness. Father Brown, the priest-detective, was one of his happiest creations; but of his many books those that are likely longest to survive are his various collections of essays, among which are *Heretics, Tremendous Trifles, All I Survey,* and *Avowals and Denials.* A compilation of some of the best of Chesterton's essays was published recently under the title *Selected Essays.*

JOSEPH CONRAD (1857–1924), originally Josef Teodor Konrad Korzeniowski, was born in the Ukraine of Polish parents. Orphaned early in his youth, Conrad joined first the French and later the British merchant marine. He spent seventeen years at sea, visiting the Far East, the Belgian Congo, and the South Atlantic. Conrad was naturalized a British subject in 1886 and published his first novel, *Almayer's Folly,* in 1894. He wrote of the Far East and the sea—novels like *Lord Jim* and *Victory,* and stories like "Youth," "Typhoon," and "The End of the Tether"—and also of politics and public affairs—*The Secret Agent, Nostromo,* "Gaspar Ruiz," "The Duel." Save for a visit to Poland in 1914 and a trip to the United States in 1923, Conrad spent the years following his retirement from the merchant marine in England. He and Henry James were acquainted and were mutually respectful of each other's work.

STEPHEN CRANE (1871–1900), novelist, short story writer, poet, and journalist, was born in Newark, New Jersey, and attended Lafayette College and Syracuse University, graduating from neither. He worked for the New York *Herald* and *Tribune* and was a correspondent for the *Journal* and the *World* during the Greco-Turkish and Spanish-American wars. Crane's masterpiece, *The Red Badge of Courage,* was written when he was twenty-one and proved to be a great success; his other important novel, *Maggie: A Girl of the Streets,* had been written in two days, when he was twenty. His short stories appeared in various volumes: *The Little Regiment and Other Episodes of the Civil War, The Open Boat and Other Tales of Adventure,* and *The Monster.*

BERNARD AUGUSTINE DE VOTO (1897–1956), novelist, historian, and literary critic, was born in Ogden, Utah, was graduated from Harvard College, and was in various periods a member of the Harvard English Department, an editor of *Harper's Magazine,* and the editor of the *Saturday Review of Literature.* De Voto's chief historical works are *The Year of Decision, Across the Wide Missouri,* and *The Course of Empire*—all on the subject of the development of the American West. He was also a leading authority on Mark Twain, and published two important books, *Mark Twain's America* and *Mark Twain at Work.*

LOREN COREY EISELEY (born 1907) was graduated from the University of Nebraska, has taught at various universities in the United States, and is now Chairman of the Department of Anthropology and the History of Science in the University of Pennsylvania. His works include *The Immense Journey*, from which comes the selection that appears in this anthology, *Darwin's Century*, *The Firmament of Time*, and *The Mind of Nature*.

RALPH WALDO EMERSON (1803–1882) was a contemporary of Thoreau, Hawthorne, and Melville, and a neighbor and friend of the former two. After graduating from Harvard College in 1821, forty years before Oliver Wendell Holmes, Jr., he studied for the ministry and became pastor for three years of the Second Unitarian Church of Boston. After resigning this position, he settled in Concord, north of Boston, and except for two trips to Europe and many lecture journeys around the United States, spent the rest of his life there.

Thoreau, fourteen years his junior, became Emerson's close friend and, at least to some degree, his disciple. Each man in his time was considered by the older generation to be a radical and by the younger generation to be an enormous stimulus to fresh and clear thinking. Emerson is best known as an essayist, lecturer (most of his lectures were later published as essays), and poet, but above all as a philosopher and a spokesman for transcendentalism, the doctrine that reality is essentially spiritual, that man's soul is divine and in harmony with nature.

Emerson kept a Journal—a depository for his thoughts rather than a diary—throughout his life. Published after his death, the *Journal* comprises ten stout volumes, and the student will find therein the beginnings of most of his lectures and essays.

WILLIAM FAULKNER (1897–1962) was born in Mississippi, the scene of most of his novels, and lived there, in Oxford, the seat of the University of Mississippi, all his life. During World War I, he was in France with the Canadian air force—it has been said he joined that service in order to avoid being labeled a Yankee—attended the University of Mississippi for a few terms on his return, and spent the rest of his life producing the novels and short stories that eventually, after many years, won him his enormous international reputation. He was awarded the 1949 Nobel prize for literature. His chief novels are *The Sound and the Fury; As I Lay Dying; Sanctuary; Light in August; Absalom, Absalom!* and *The Unvanquished*. His short stories were brought together in a single volume in 1950.

FRANCIS SCOTT KEY FITZGERALD (1896–1941) was born in St. Paul, Minnesota, went to the Newman School in Hackensack, New Jersey, and from there to Princeton, where he devoted much of his time to extracurricular activities, especially the dramatic productions of the Triangle Club. He left Princeton without graduating in 1917, during World War I, and joined the army. His first novel, *This Side of Paradise*, was published in 1920; its success encouraged him to give full time to writing from then on. Fitzgerald wrote many stories for popular magazines; spent much time in Europe; and toward the end of his life settled in Hollywood, where he wrote for the motion pictures. His two most important novels are generally considered to be *The Great Gatsby* and *Tender Is the Night*. His short stories were gathered together in *Flappers and Philosophers, Tales of the Jazz Age, All the Sad Young Men,* and *Taps at Reveille.*

EDWARD MORGAN FORSTER (born 1879) attended the Tonbridge School and King's College, Cambridge, of which he was made an honorary Fellow in 1946; he has resided at the College in recent years. In the period from 1905 to 1910, when he was in his late twenties and early thirties, his first four novels appeared, *Where Angels Fear to Tread, The Longest Journey, A Room with a View,* and *Howards End;* his fifth and last novel, *A Passage to India,* came fourteen years later, in 1924. Forster visited India in 1912 and in 1921, on both occasions as the guest of the Maharajah of the Indian state of Dewas Senior; during his second visit he was the Maharajah's private secretary. He was stationed in Egypt during World War I. His short stories appear in two volumes, *The Celestial Omnibus* and *The Eternal Moment,* and he is the author of, among other works, a widely influential critical study, *Aspects of the Novel,* two collections of essays, *Abinger Harvest* and *Two Cheers for Democracy,* and a biography of his great aunt, *Marianne Thornton.* An account of Forster's visits to India is found in *The Hill of Devi.*

HENRY WATSON FOWLER (1858–1933), the English lexicographer and grammarian, was educated at Oxford and for many years taught at Sedbergh School in Yorkshire. He produced two abridgments of the multivolume *Oxford English Dictionary* and compiled the famous *Dictionary of Modern English Usage,* first published in 1926.

WILLIAM GERALD GOLDING (born 1911) came from a long line of school-masters, and except for a five-year period of heavy action in the Royal Navy during World War II was himself a schoolmaster, at Bishop Wordsworth's School in Salisbury, England, from 1939 to 1961, when he retired in order to devote full time to his writing. Golding was visiting professor at Hollins College in Virginia in 1961–62; during that year he lectured on many campuses throughout the United States. He is the author of five novels, *Lord of the Flies, The Inheritors, Pincher Martin, Free Fall,* and *The Spire;* three or four short stories, including the one in this anthology and a long story entitled "Envoy Extraordinary"; and a play, *The Brass Butterfly.*

NATHANIEL HAWTHORNE (1804–1864) was born in Salem, Massachusetts, and attended Bowdoin College. For a time he lived in Concord, where he was a friend of Emerson and Thoreau; he was also a friend of Herman Melville. President Franklin Pierce appointed him U.S. consul at Liverpool (1853–57). His first novel was published in 1828, and his first collection of short stories, *Twice-Told Tales* (from which the selection in this anthology is taken), appeared in 1837. This latter work established his reputation. His famous novel, *The Scarlet Letter,* appeared in 1850. Among Hawthorne's many other volumes are *Mosses from an Old Manse, The House of The Seven Gables,* and *The Marble Faun.*

JOHN HAY (born 1915) was graduated from Harvard College, went into journalism, was on the magazine *Yank* during World War II, and is now Director of the Cape Cod Museum of Natural History at Brewster, Massachusetts. He is the author of *The Great Beach,* from which the selection that appears in this anthology is taken, and *Nature's Year*, among other works.

WILLIAM HAZLITT (1778–1830), English essayist and critic, was the son of a Unitarian minister who gave up any thought of entering the ministry himself in order to become a writer. A friend of Coleridge and Wordsworth, and of most of the other important figures of the English Romantic movement, Hazlitt became an influential critic and in his writings did much to determine the course and growth of the nineteenth-century English essay; Stevenson, for example, was greatly influenced by him. Noteworthy among his books are *The Characters of Shakespeare's Plays*, *Lectures on the English Poets*, *Table Talk*, and *The Spirit of the Age*.

ERNEST MILLER HEMINGWAY (1898–1961) was born in Oak Park, Illinois, and attended the public schools there; he played football and boxed and went on frequent hunting expeditions with his father, a physician. In World War I he was a volunteer with an American ambulance unit, and then served with the Italian Arditi and saw action on the Italian front, where he was wounded. After the war he became a newspaper correspondent, spending much of his time in Europe, and covering the Spanish Civil War and World War II. Hemingway, who was always greatly interested in sports, hunted in Africa and became an aficionado of the Spanish bullfight, about which he wrote in one of his nonfiction works, *Death in the Afternoon*. His major novels are *The Sun Also Rises*, *A Farewell to Arms*, *For Whom the Bell Tolls*, and *The Old Man and the Sea*. His many stories were gathered together in *Men Without Women*, *Winner Take Nothing*, and (with his only play) in *The Fifth Column and the First Forty-nine Stories*. The *Old Man and the Sea* won him the Pulitzer prize in 1953.

OLIVER WENDELL HOLMES, JR. (1841–1935), was the son of a famous father, the nineteenth-century American poet, essayist, novelist, and professor in the Harvard Medical School. The Holmeses were Bostonians, and young Holmes attended Harvard College, graduating in 1861 and serving for the next three years with the 20th Massachusetts volunteer regiment during the Civil War. He was wounded three times, and in 1864 was mustered out with the rank of captain. Two years later he was graduated from Harvard Law School and until 1881 practiced law in Boston. In 1882 he became a professor in the Law School and a justice of the Supreme Judicial Court of Massachusetts. In 1902, President Theodore Roosevelt appointed Holmes an associate justice of the United States Supreme Court, on which he served for thirty years; he is today considered to have been one of the great American jurists.

Holmes wrote a number of books on judicial matters, but the general reader is likely to find greater pleasure in his letters—those he wrote to his parents during the Civil War, and those he wrote in later life to two Britishers, Harold Laski and Frederick Pollock.

HENRY JAMES (1843–1916), novelist, short story writer, dramatist, essayist, and critic, was the brother of William James. He was educated largely by tutors and in private schools, although he did attend Harvard Law School for one year. James made a number of trips to Europe, with his family and by himself, in his youth; in 1876, when he was thirty-three, he resolved to move permanently to Europe, and after a year in Paris went to England where he resided for the rest of his life. Yet James never quite forgot America: again and again he took as his theme the impact of Europe on visiting Americans.

James was the writer par excellence. His whole life, his every thought, seems to have been devoted exclusively to his art. Author of dozens of novels, over a hundred short stories, many plays, and innumerable critical essays, he was nevertheless always a scrupulous artist, a man of high seriousness, completely devoted to his work. Among his more important books are *The American, The Portrait of a Lady, The Princess Casamassima, What Maisie Knew, The Turn of the Screw, The Wings of the Dove, The Ambassadors,* and *The Golden Bowl;* he also produced a critical biography of Hawthorne; his various pieces of literary criticism, mostly prefaces to his own novels, have been gathered together as *The Art of The Novel.*

WILLIAM JAMES (1842–1910), a member of one of America's most famous families, was the son of Henry James, the theologian and philosopher, and the brother of Henry James, the novelist. A student of painting both in Europe and America, James soon concluded that he did not have the talent to make a career in the arts worthwhile and enrolled in the Lawrence Scientific School of Harvard University and later in the Harvard Medical School, where he received his degree in 1869 and became an instructor in 1872. His work embraced the fields of biology, evolution, and psychology, but his interest was concentrated more and more on the last, and in 1877 he became an assistant professor of philosophy, there being no departments of psychology at the time. James is best known as one of the founders of pragmatism, a philosoph-

ical system that holds that ideas have value only in terms of their practical consequences. His chief works are *Principles of Psychology, The Will to Believe, The Varieties of Religious Experience,* and *Pragmatism.* Although inevitably drawn together because of their close family relationships, William and his brother Henry seldom agreed on questions of either philosophy or art.

JAMES AUGUSTINE ALOYSIUS JOYCE (1882–1941) was born and educated in Dublin, Ireland, but left his country—permanently, except for a very few visits—at the age of twenty-two and lived for the rest of his life on the continent. Joyce's impact on the modern novel has been immense, greater in its way than the impact made by James, yet whereas James wrote dozens of novels and more than a hundred stories, Joyce's output was relatively slim—one collection of stories, *Dubliners,* from which the selection in this anthology is taken, and three novels, the autobiographical *The Portrait of the Artist as a Young Man,* the highly experimental *Ulysses,* and the even more highly experimental *Finnegans Wake,* on which the author worked for seventeen years.

DAVID HERBERT LAWRENCE (1885–1930), the son of a miner, grew up in Nottinghamshire, England, attending the local high school and for a time teaching in the local elementary school. His first novel, *The White Peacock,* was published in 1911, and from that time on the flow of his works—novels, short stories, poetry, and books of travel—came steadily from the press. From 1919 on, he spent much of his time traveling, on the continent, in the Americas, and in Australia. His chief novels are *Sons and Lovers, The Rainbow,* and *Women in Love.* His many short stories appeared in *The Prussian Officer; England, My England; The Captain's Doll;* and other volumes. One of his most stimulating works is *Studies in Classic American Literature,* in which he presents provocative but often unconventional views of Franklin, Hawthorne, Melville, Whitman, Poe, and others.

CLIVE STAPLES LEWIS (1898–1963), British critic and novelist, was a professor of English Literature at Oxford University and later at Cambridge University. His chief works, both fiction and criticism, were on the subject of contemporary Christianity, but his literary criticism and his children's books are also of great interest. His science-fiction trilogy, *Out of the Silent Planet, Perelandra,* and *That Hideous Strength,* is an especial delight, albeit his dominant concern is with the subject of Christianity. Readers of this anthology who wish to follow further the extraordinary career of Screwtape should read Lewis's *The Screwtape Letters.*

WALTER LIPPMANN (born 1889) attended Harvard College, where he was, after graduation, assistant for a year to Professor Santayana and where he became acquainted with William James. Thereafter he became a journalist. During World War I he was for a time assistant to the Secretary of War and later a captain in the Military Intelligence Division; he attended the Peace Conference in 1919. After the War, Lippmann returned to journalism; he has for many years contributed a regular column of comment to the New York *Herald Tribune.* Lippmann, who has called himself a "connoisseur of public affairs," has through his books and columns been widely influential. Among his many works are *A Preface to Politics, Public Opinion, A Preface*

to Morals (from which the selection in this anthology is taken), and *The Good Society.*

HERMAN MELVILLE (1819–1891), because of his father's early death and the poverty of his family, went to sea at the age of twenty; for five years he was a hand on various ships, and for a period lived in the South Seas. He returned to America in 1844, and two years later his first book, *Typee,* was published. This and subsequent South Sea adventure tales were popular at the time; but when Melville's most important work, *Moby Dick,* appeared in 1851, his reputation had faded, and though he wrote many other novels and short stories, he never again was popular in his lifetime. Indeed, only within the last few years has his true stature as one of America's greatest writers been recognized.

Melville's friendship with Hawthorne, we judge from his letters (Hawthorne's letters to Melville have not survived), was a source of encouragement and inspiration. He became acquainted with Hawthorne when he resided at Pittsfield, Massachusetts, where, in the period from 1852 to 1856, he wrote the best of his short stories. Melville also wrote poetry; and late in his life he produced *Billy Budd,* which is second only to *Moby Dick* among his novels.

SAMUEL ELIOT MORISON (born 1887) is a Bostonian who graduated from Harvard College, received his doctorate there, taught there from 1914 on, and is the author of the official history of the University. During the period 1922–25 Morison was Harmsworth Professor of American History in Oxford University and wrote the *Oxford History of the United States.* In 1942 he received the Pulitzer prize for *Admiral of the Ocean Sea,* his biography of Columbus. This biography, and *Christopher Columbus, Mariner,* which is based on it and from which the selection in this anthology is taken, was the result of an unusual kind of research: Morison organized the Harvard Columbus Expedition, followed as closely as possible the track of Columbus' Third Voyage, and traced Columbus' earlier explorations in the West Indies. He felt, as he has said, that "what Columbus wanted was a sailor biographer, one who knew ships and sailing and who had visited, under sail, the islands and mainland that he discovered." In the same year, 1942, Morison was appointed historian of United States Naval Operations in World War II; that history has now been published in fourteen volumes, and its author is an Admiral of the United States Navy.

FRANK O'CONNOR (born 1903) is the pseudonym of Michael O'Donovan. He was educated in Cork, Ireland, and became a librarian there and, later, in Dublin. Now a resident of the United States, O'Connor is best known as a writer of short stories and as a critic of the novel and the theater. His account of his early years, a central portion of which work appears in this anthology, was published in 1961 with the title *An Only Child.*

GEORGE ORWELL (1903–1950), whose true name was Eric Blair, was born in India, the son of a member of the Anglo-Indian civil service. During the years 1922–27 he was a British policeman in Burma, where he became disillusioned about British imperialism; poor health and a desire to write, added to this conclusion, led him to return to Europe. His literary career began with *Down and Out in Paris and London* and *Burmese Days,* the latter of which bears comparison with *A Passage to India.* He was the author of many other books, both fiction and nonfiction, including collections of critical essays; his chief fame rests, however, on his two biting attacks on the totalitarian aspects of the world of the '30s and '40s, *Animal Farm* (1946) and *Nineteen Eighty-four* (1949).

KATHERINE ANNE PORTER (born 1890) is a Texan and a descendant of Daniel Boone. She has published four volumes of short stories, *Flowering Judas; Hacienda; Pale Horse, Pale Rider;* and *The Leaning Tower;* a book of criticism and personal reminiscence, *The Days Before;* and a novel, published in 1962, *Ship of Fools.* In 1965 her stories were brought together in *The Collected Stories of Katherine Anne Porter.* She is considered to be one of the most distinguished short story writers of the twentieth century.

BERTRAND ARTHUR WILLIAM RUSSELL (born 1872), the Third Earl Russell, is one of the preeminent mathematicians and philosophers of the twentieth century. He collaborated with A. N. Whitehead in writing *Principia Mathematica* (1900–13), and has in subsequent years written many works on mathematics, philosophy, education, sociology, and morals. He has been a socialist and a pacifist; he has taught in English and American universities; and he was awarded the Nobel prize in literature in 1950.

CARL SANDBURG (born 1878), the son of Swedish immigrants, spent his boyhood in Galesburg, Illinois, went off to the Spanish-American War (his life this far is brilliantly recounted in his autobiographical volume, *Always the Young Strangers*), and returned to Galesburg to work his way through Lombard College. He began to write in college, and after graduation, following a brief career in business, became a journalist, settling finally in

Chicago. Sandburg's first published poetry appeared in 1914 in *Poetry: A Magazine of Verse,* and his reputation was established in 1916 with the publication of *Chicago Poems.* Over the years he has published many volumes of verse. His *Complete Poems* appeared in 1950, and in 1951 he received the Pulitzer prize in poetry.

Although first and foremost a poet, a significant part of Sandburg's reputation stems from his being a biographer of Lincoln and a historian of the Civil War. In 1926 he published *Abraham Lincoln—The Prairie Years* in two volumes, and in 1939 *Abraham Lincoln—The War Years* in four volumes. He received the Pulitzer prize in history in 1940. The selection in this anthology comes from Volume II of *The War Years.*

GEORGE SANTAYANA (1863–1952) was born in Madrid, the son of Spanish parents; at the age of nine, however, he was taken to Boston (his mother had been previously married to an American). He was graduated from Harvard College, having studied there under William James, and from 1889 to 1912 was a member of the Department of Philosophy. His final years were spent in seclusion in an Italian convent.

Santayana, considered to be one of the leading twentieth-century philosophers, was the author of many works on esthetics, politics, and morals; he was also a poet and a novelist, and his three-volume autobiography, *Persons and Places, The Middle Span,* and *My Host the World,* is especially notable. The selection in this anthology comes from one of his later works, *Dominations and Powers.*

ROBERT LOUIS STEVENSON (1850–1894), Scottish poet, novelist, and essayist, was born and educated in Edinburgh, and at the age of twenty-five rejected

a career in the law to become a writer. He is best known for *Treasure Island, The Strange Case of Dr. Jekyll and Mr. Hyde,* and *Kidnapped,* for the essays gathered in *Virginibus Puerisque* and *Familiar Studies of Men and Books,* and for his travel books (Stevenson traveled in Europe, the United States, and the South Seas), *An Inland Voyage* and *Travels with a Donkey.* Stevenson considered himself to be, and was, a professional writer; of his work Henry James remarked, "It's a luxury, in this immoral age, to encounter someone who *does* write—who is really acquainted with that lovely art."

HENRY DAVID THOREAU (1817–1862) is closely identified with the small Massachusetts town of Concord, just north of Boston, and the home of Emerson, Hawthorne, and a surprising number of other famous nineteenth-century American writers and thinkers. Thoreau was born there, lived there most of his life, and died there. After graduating from Harvard in 1837, he taught school in Concord for three years; from that time forward, however, he never sought regular employment, and took satisfaction in supporting himself with occasional work as a skilled laborer, devoting most of his time to walking, thinking, and writing.

Thoreau's relationship with Emerson, almost a generation his senior, was very close; he lived during two different periods in Emerson's house, and, as Emerson's *Journal* indicates, they saw one another often throughout their lives. Thoreau was an even more severe critic of many phases of American life than Emerson, and what he said then, a century ago, seems even today, as E. B. White makes clear in his essay, to have bite and purpose. Yet Thoreau's love of nature is as significant a part of his writings as his criticism of American society. This is shown in *Walden*, from which the selection that appears in the anthology is taken. *Walden*, which was published in 1854, was Thoreau's chief work; but other of his books— *A Week on the Concord and Merrimack Rivers, The Maine Woods*, and *Cape Cod*—and his essays deserve close attention.

JAMES THURBER (1894–1961), who was born in Ohio and was graduated from Ohio State University, joined *The New Yorker* Magazine in 1927 and remained a member of its staff until his death. He was a colleague and friend there of E. B. White and collaborated with him on an early book. Thurber is as well known as a cartoonist as he is as a writer; indeed, the same subtle mixture of humor, irony, and seemingly painless yet withal lethal attack is found both in his drawings and in his essays and short stories. Some of the best of Thurber is to be found in *The Thurber Carnival, Thurber Country*, and *Lanterns and Lances*.

ARNOLD JOSEPH TOYNBEE (born 1889) is an English historian and philosopher of history. In his most important work, *A Study of History*, which appears in twelve volumes, he endeavors through close analysis to establish a recurring pattern in history. The selection that appears in this anthology is taken from Volume I of *A Study of History*.

JOHN HOYER UPDIKE (born 1932) was graduated from Harvard College in 1954, and has since then written extensively for *The New Yorker* and other magazines. His published volumes include two collections of poems, *The Carpentered Hen* and *Telephone Poles;* two collections of short stories, *The Same Door* and *Pigeon Feathers;* three novels, *The Poorhouse Fair, The Centaur*, and *Rabbit, Run;* and a collection of nonfiction, *Assorted Prose.*

EUDORA WELTY (born 1909) has been almost as closely connected with Mississippi—as residence and as the scene of her fiction—as was William Faulkner. She was educated at Mississippi State College for Women and at the University of Wisconsin. She is a distinguished amateur photographer, and she has lectured and taught at a number of American colleges. Like Katherine Anne Porter, her genius seems to find its most frequent expression in the short story. She has written only one short novel, *The Ponder Heart*, and two full novels, *The Robber Bridegroom* and *Delta Wedding;* her stories have appeared in *A Curtain of Green, The Wide Net, The Golden Apples*, and *The Bride of the Innisfallen.* Her first children's book, *The Shoe Bird*, was published 1964.

ELWYN BROOKS WHITE (born 1899) joined the staff of *The New Yorker* shortly after his graduation from Cornell University and has been there ever since, although he has also contributed to *Harper's* Magazine and although he has for some years, in the true Thoreauvian spirit, made his home in Maine. White is that rare creature on the contemporary literary scene, a true essayist, that is, a writer who has something to say and cares ·desperately how he says it, a writer in the tradition of Hazlitt and Stevenson, and a thinker who in at least some respects is in the tradition of Thoreau. The best of White's essays are found in *One Man's Meat, The Second Tree from the Corner*, and *Points of My Compass.*

AUTHOR INDEX

Arvin, Newton, 646

Barzun, Jacques, 777
Bates, H. E., 633
Brooks, Cleanth, 674

Canby, Henry Seidel, 789
Carr, E. H., 763
Chesterton, G. K., 460
Chute, Marchette, 774
Conrad, Joseph, 41
Cook, Reginald, 788
Crane, Stephen, 67, 665

Daiches, David, 613
Davis, Robert Gorham, 622
De Quincey, Thomas, 618
De Voto, Bernard, 556
Dichmann, Mary E., 648
Drew, Elizabeth, 608

Eble, Kenneth, 690
Edel, Leon, 703
Eiseley, Loren, 530
Emerson, Ralph Waldo, 429, 779

Faulkner, William, 131, 693, 697, 699
Fitzgerald, F. Scott, 114
Forster, E. M., 189, 610, 713
Fowler, H. W., 503

Golding, William, 176
Gordon, Caroline, 711
Gosse, Edmund, 605
Greene, Theodore Meyer, 607

Haugh, Robert F., 662
Havighurst, Walter, 638
Hawthorne, Nathaniel, 3
Hay, John, 537
Hazlitt, William, 472
Hemingway, Ernest, 143
Holmes, Oliver Wendell, Jr., 413

James, Henry, 20, 660
James, William, 480
Jones, William M., 709
Joyce, James, 87

Lawrence, D. H., 92

Lewis, C. S., 589
Lippmann, Walter, 576
Lowell, James Russell, 785
Lubbock, Percy, 723

Melville, Herman, 14
Miles, Josephine, 756
Mizener, Arthur, 683
Morison, Samuel Eliot, 543
Myers, Henry A., 615

Nevins, Allan, 767
Nicolson, Sir Harold, 772

O'Connor, Frank, 437
Orvis, Mary Burchard, 682
Orwell, George, 507

Porter, Katherine Anne, 108, 705

Rama Rau, Santha, 745
Russell, Bertrand, 523

Sandburg, Carl, 552
Santayana, George, 586
Smith, Alexander, 755
Stallman, Robert Wooster, 671
Stein, Jean, 693
Stevenson, Robert Louis, 466

Thoreau, Henry David, 448
Thurber, James, 519
Toynbee, Arnold, 580
Trilling, Lionel, 730
Tuchman, Barbara, 760

Updike, John, 183

Van Doren, Carl, 753

Warren, Robert Penn, 624, 674, 677
Wedgwood, C. V., 769
Welty, Eudora, 168, 642
White, E. B., 495
Wilde, Alan, 740

Young, Philip, 700

Zabel, Morton Dauwen, 655, 725

A 6
B 7
C 8
D 9
E 0
F 1
G 2
H 3
I 4
J 5

802